How To Write
And Get A Grant

by

Matthew Lesko

and

Mary Ann Martello

Researchers
Zsuzsa Beres; Giovina Taraschi
Melanie Coltan; Nancy Gibson
Mary Courtney Ore; Amy Hollingsworth
Allison Mays; Caroline Pharmer
Cindy Owens; Marcelle McCarthy
Bradley Sowash; Emily Subler;
Marty Brinkman, Laura Difore, Jennifer Maier

Production
Beth Meserve

Marketing
Kim McCoy

Support
Mercedes Sundeen

Cover
Ray Holland

Clip art used in this publication © Dynamic Graphics, Inc.; Totem Graphics; One Mile Up; Tech Pool; Image Club Graphics, Inc.; and Corel Corp.

FIRST EDITION

Library of Congress Cataloging-in-Publication date
    Lesko, Matthew
    Martello, Mary Ann

How To Write And Get A Grant

ISBN # 1-878346-64-4

Most books by Matthew Lesko are available at special quantity discounts for bulk purchases for sales promotions, premiums, fund-raising or educational use. Special books or book excerpts also can be created to fit specific needs.

For details, write Information USA, Special Markets, Attention: Kim McCoy, P.O. Box E, Kensington, MD 20895; or 1-800-797-7811, Marketing; {www.lesko.com}.

Other books available from Matthew Lesko:

Free Money To Change Your Life

Free Money To Change Your Life
     6-hour instructional audio cassette/CD

Lesko's Info-Power III

Government Giveaways for Entrepreneurs IV

Free Legal Help

Free Health Care

Gobs and Gobs of Free Stuff

Free Stuff For Busy Moms

Free Stuff For Women's Health, Fitness and Nutrition

Free College Money And Training For Women

Free Money And Help For Women Entrepreneurs

Free Money to Change Your Life CD-ROM

Free Money For Your Retirement

For ordering information on any of Matthew Lesko's publications, call 1-800-UNCLE-SAM, or contact his web site at www.lesko.com.

TABLE OF CONTENTS

MORE MONEY AND HELP FOR ENTREPRENEURS
FROM THE STATES 185

FREE SCHOLARSHIPS 793

Free Scholarships (continued)

FREE MONEY TO SEND YOUR CHILD TO PRIVATE KINDERGARTEN THRU HIGH SCHOOL

How To Write And Get A Grant

INTRODUCTION

Who would not love to get a grant? Everyone says that grants are so hard to get, but that is silly! Millions of people get grants every year, so why don't you? You don't get them because you have no idea where they are, and you don't know what to do when you find them! So, that is why I am here. I am going to tell you where all the grants are, what to do when you find them, and how to get them.

Next year, over three million people are going to get grants. I am sorry, not three million — 30 million! What the heck is a zero when it is government work? Thirty million people every year are getting grants and free money. That is why you should be getting one too. If you want to know about them, you have got to put in some effort.

I am going to tell you where these grants are, what to do when you find them, how to get them, and even how to write proposals.

Over $1.1 trillion in grants is given out every year. That is a trillion dollars! Do you know what a trillion is? No? Neither do I! Remember when Rockefeller was the vice president and running for president? Now, there was a guy throwing around a trillion. He probably knew what a trillion dollars was! But you and I don't know. A million dollars, a billion dollars, and now this is a trillion!

Look at this — about nine million new cars are sold every year at the average price of about $20,000. I did a little research and found out that comes to $180 billion worth of cars. So, if one trillion dollars is given out in grants each year, that is over six times the amount of all the new cars sold every year. That is a heck of a lot of money. That is why you have to know about grants.

Millions are spent every year on advertising and salesmen around the country are trying to get you to buy a car. We see ads for automobiles all over the place. Every time you turn on the TV, open a newspaper, a magazine or look at a billboard, you are likely to see an ad for an automobile. But there is never going to be advertising for grants. That is why, as a result, you have got to do the work. You are the one that is going to have to go out there and do something to find these grants. They are not going to come and hit you in the face by themselves.

Where the Grants Are

There are two major sources for grants. One source is foundations and non-profit organizations. These are those little funny people that love to give away money, like Bill Gates, who have foundations. There are literally thousands of people like him that give out money. And they give out collectively every year about $27 billion.

The government gives over a trillion dollars. If non-profit organizations and foundations are giving out $27 billion, and the government is giving over a trillion, we are talking about 40 or 50 times to one. So, the government gives out 40 times more money than all the foundations and non-profit organizations out there. These are your two sources for grants, the non-profit organizations and foundations, and the federal government. And remember, the federal government gives out 40 times more money! And that is what I know better than anyone.

Writing or Not Writing a Proposal

Half the federal budget is grants or other forms of free money that goes to individuals. There are two different kinds of grants. There are grants where you have to write a big proposal. You have to write some kind of paper, describing everything you are going to do. We will talk about how to get through that process later. There is no magic to doing a proposal; it is just a bigger bureaucratic hurdle to go through for you.

And there are other grants where you do not have to write a proposal. You just have to know about the program and fill out a page or two application to get the money. Technically this is a separate kind of grant. They are both free money in that you do not have to it pay back.

When you talk about grants, many people think of research scientists and filling out 500-page applications. We will talk about that too, but I am also going to tell you about the other kind where you just fill out a page or two, a short form, or a little government document and wow, you get a grant. There are also non-profit organizations that offer grants that do not require complicated forms.

Who Gets the Money

Who gets all this money? Well, it goes to people. Remember, 30 million people every year get this money. All kinds of organizations — non-profit organizations, government organizations — are giving out this money. I can categorize who gets grants. One category is people who have needs. People who might have trouble paying their bills. There are grants out there to help you to pay them.

If you have trouble paying a health bill, a heating bill or a phone bill, or just need extra money — (yes there is grant money for people who don't have a lot of money and just need extra money), there are two programs you should know exist. They are not major ones, but extremely important. Take out a pencil and paper, and write these down. I found out about these recently, and people should know about them. Even if you are not in the category yourself where you need this information or help, you may have relatives, friends, a senior citizen, or know someone who has a disability, who may benefit from this wonderful grant program. The program gives you $1,000 extra a year.

This is from the U.S. Department of Health and Human Services, and is money back to you. You can call the Department right now and get over $1,051 extra a year. There is an income limitation of around $15,000 for this program. If you are a senior, then you are probably not making that much. I have seen studies that show three million seniors are eligible for this program and do not apply. Also, people with disabilities are eligible. If this specific program is not for you, you should still know about it so you can help get this money for other people, their loved ones, or that little old lady down the street.

The way to find out about this program is to contact the U.S. Department of Health and Human Services. Actually, it is run through Medicare. It is {www.medicare.gov} on the web, or 800-MEDICARE. You are looking for the Medicare premium deductions, called the Qualified Medicare Beneficiaries Plan. There are a couple of names for it. The program gives Medicare Part B premiums back to people who need this kind of income, and many people are not applying for it.

There is another program that many people do not know exists through the Social Security system that gives you an extra $6,000 of spending money. This is called the Supplemental Security Income (SSI). If you have a problem with either of these programs, you can contact your congressman's or senator's office and they will help you learn more. These are important programs for people who are in need.

I want to make sure that more people know about these programs. When you learn this information, you not only help yourself getting grant money to do the things you want to do in life, but you help other people. That is what is so important. When you empower yourself with the information, help, and grant money available, (you can't spend

$1.1 trillion on yourself), you can start helping other people. Knowing about these two programs can help you help others.

97.5% Of Grants are From the Government

We are talking about $1.1 trillion. We have 40 to one government money, so non-profits and foundations give out less than 2.5%, and the rest is government money. The only program the government really advertises is the lottery program. That is why most people looking for money to do things they really want to do are going to play the Lotto, and that is a government program! They go and spend money at 7-Eleven to buy a lottery ticket hoping to get money from a government program. And what have you got, one in a million chance of getting that money? That is nonsense, isn't it?

One in a million chance for you to get money? The last time I looked, lotteries only gave out about $20 billion or so. We are talking about a trillion dollars a year from the government, and not one in a million chance. I will show you programs where two out of every three people who apply for the money get it.

Two out of every three people get money to start a business. A million people a year get money from the government to start or stay in a business. It is not one in a million like the lottery. It is one million people getting money for business each and every year!

The lottery is advertised so that is why we know about the program, and we are all standing in line trying to buy a Lotto ticket. But nobody knows about these other programs because THESE PROGRAMS ARE NOT BEING ADVERTISED! I am going to tell you about these programs and how to find them.

Grants Go To People Who Help Themselves and the Country

The biggest categories of people who get grants are people who want to solve problems. Do you have an idea? Do you want to solve a problem? Do you want to create jobs, or just get yourself a better job? These are people like you who want to do something in the world. They want to contribute to society, and that is how a lot of this money is used.

Want to get a better education? Want to create a business? Even though it sounds selfish, by helping yourself, you are helping society!

These grant programs fund real things that society wants and needs. Foundations and government offices have this money waiting to solve problems in society and provide things that society needs. Society needs more educated, energetic and problem-solving people. People that are going to create jobs. People that are going to create new inventions in their life. This money is there to help citizens do these kinds of things.

To me the lottery is welfare, because it is the only government program that encourages you to go sit on the beach. I do not want my taxes to pay for people to sit on the beach for the rest of their lives. I want people to get money in order to make themselves and the country better. If you are out there creating a better society, then that is a society I am living in too. So, then I will have better people around me, better tools, and a better and safer society. That is the purpose of these programs.

There are government grant programs that fund solutions to all kinds of strange problems. There are programs where they give money to teenagers to start a business. Other programs fund building a golf course or tennis court in your backyard. "Not enough tennis courts in people's backyards," does not sound like a big problem to me but for some reason, some bureaucrat thought there was. Actually, the politicians make the laws, and it is the bureaucrats that have to enforce and carry them out.

Programs that put tennis courts in the backyard are really for people in rural areas. Apparently we have a problem in our society where rural development is an issue because the farming society is not what it used to be. So, we have programs to give these ex-farmers money to go into the resort business. You can put a resort in your backyard where 40 acres of corn used to be.

You do not have to understand the reasons why these programs were instituted, but just know that they exist. These programs are there for you to do something in your life! What is important about this is that the programs are for the average Joe. I grew up in a little town called Wilkes Barre, Pennsylvania, and I used to think that anybody who got something from the government was either rich and took a congressman and senator to lunch, or real poor and on some kind of funny program that you were embarrassed to mention.

But that is not true. This money is for people who have the perseverance to go out and get it. The rich do it, the poor do it, and the middle class does it. If 30 million people are getting this money, they cannot all be rich because there are not 30 million rich people in this country. The money goes to people who know about it and go through the effort to get it.

I know a fellow named James Freericks, who got a half a million dollars from government grants to travel around the world! He was an ordinary kind of guy in his early thirties or so, and wound up with a half a million dollars by learning to use the system to travel around the globe.

I live and work in Maryland, and found that my state gives out grants to businesses all over the state. Actually, there is a company called Snyder Seed Company that got a $200,000 grant to work on rodent repellent made out of hot chili peppers. How would you like $200,000 to take your chili peppers and try to turn them into rodent repellant?

I do not know why the government does it. Maybe they are looking for better ideas. I am sure there is some rationale behind it, but mine is not to reason why. Mine is to tell you about these programs so more people apply for them. I hope to get a better group of people applying, so the government will have a better choice of who gets the money.

Tori Stewardson lives in Virginia, and got $15,000 as a 40-year old woman who never finished college. She found a government program that gave her a $15,000 grant to finish her college degree because she was suffering from low self-esteem. Now, would you ever think of calling the government and looking for the government's low self-esteem program? No!

We live in a society where the answers are all out there. I wear the question mark suits because I believe that we can get the answer to anything we want in life. The problem is, we do not know the right questions to ask, and that is what I am trying to help you to do, to show you what questions to ask.

Did you ever see that online brokerage company, Ameritrade advertised on TV? They are rich, making a lot of money. Well, they got a million dollar grant to open up an office in Annapolis. Would you ever think, "I will start a big business, and I have a lot of money but maybe I will see about some more free money!" Well, there it is.

I found a company in California called Beneficial Design who got $50,000 to develop a website on hiking trails. Are you a hiker? Wouldn't you love to spend the next year developing a website on hiking trails? This guy out in California found a program that gave him $50,000 to do that.

Speaking of hiking trails, I am looking for hiking boots because this summer I am taking part in a government program. I am going to Alaska with my family. My wife and I, and our two teenage boys, are flying to Alaska and are going to work on a government program doing an archaeological dig with Indians! How incredible is that? I would get bored sitting on the beach for two weeks. This is just one example of other types of programs that are out there for you.

Ritz Camera is another big company. They got a $75,000 grant for hiring new employees in Kansas. So, if you are a small business and are going to hire a new employee, find out about the grant money. If Ritz Camera is getting

$75,000, then maybe if you only hire one employee, you could get $2,000, but what the heck? That is free money in the bank for you.

Amazon.com received a $1.5 million grant because they decided to open up a distribution center in Kansas. Did you ever order books from Amazon? They have distribution centers all over the country.

What happens is the state government, the local government, the county government, and the city government are all trying to attract business to the area. So, they give big and small businesses special business incentives, and grant money to come and put the business there. If Amazon.com is cashing in on this, why shouldn't you?

Arlene Fink got $100,000 from the government to work on a better way of letting the elderly know they have a drinking problem! I don't understand it, but I guess there is a problem in the community that some seniors are drinking too much. So, she got $100,000 to develop pamphlets, as well as a program to do help them.

How about this? A woman up in Alaska got $200,000 to buy a fishing boat. Did you see *Perfect Storm*? I was thinking about that with these women fishermen. You can get a grant to be in the fishing business in Alaska.

Brett Stern, a fellow I know in New York state, got over $200,000 from the government to work on his invention — $200,000! He is a young boy, a couple of years out of college. He designed a sewing machine that puts together fabric that you do not have to sew. It works with synthetic fabric that will fuse together when it reaches a certain temperature. Throw away your sewing machines.

My dad had a garment factory in Wilkes Barre, Pennsylvania, and women used to sit there sewing all day. This way, they would not have to do it. The machine would just melt the material together.

Or how about this? Len Osbourne was a bouncer in Colorado, making $7 an hour in a nightclub. He was a big guy suited for this work but his career was not going anywhere. He went to the government and they gave him a $10,000 grant to take a computer course. He did not have a college degree. After he completed the 5-month computer course, he was able to get a job earning $50,000 a year with benefits.

He went from being a bouncer at $7 an hour, to making $50,00 a year with benefits on a grant from the government after five months. You are improving yourself and you are improving society, whether it is designing a new gizmo that will put fabric together, or getting a better job, or hiring employees. These programs are there to solve problems in our society, and that is the purpose of the grants.

Or, they are there to solve problems in your family. A woman by the name of Dorothy Heart from Texas called me, and said her daughter had a hospital bill of $40,000! The daughter was a single mom, struggling, and could not pay the bill. Hospitals always want their money now, as many are in financial trouble. Well, Dorothy found a program that gave her daughter the grant money so that she did not have to pay this hospital bill, $40,000! This kind of money is out there.

My Entire Family Gets Grants and I Make A Lot of Money

My wife runs a tutoring service in our neighborhood. We live in a neat community and a lot of the kids have trouble in grade school. Her tutoring service is all volunteers, and it has been going for about 5 years. She got a $4,000 grant from a local organization, and she did not have to fill out much paperwork at all.

That is exactly what I mean. My wife was trying to solve problems in the community and there are organizations that have money to invest in that issue. People who have money want to solve problems. It is a basic human instinct, but you have to know the system to get it and that is what I am trying to do here by showing you the ropes, and giving you the tools to find this kind of money.

As teenagers, my kids got a $10,000 grant. That is right, a $10,000 grant as teenagers. Now, you and I as adults are probably thinking, "Why the heck did they give them that? Why don't they give it to somebody worthwhile like me?" My boys were working on an anti-smoking program for kids, trying to get teens not to smoke. They found this money at the state level — $10,000. They did not line their pockets, but they learned a great deal from the process!

They got devices that you blow into and it shows how bad your lungs are affected by smoke. They went all around the county into the cafeterias during lunch hour and had kids blow into these machines. It is a great way for smokers and those living with smokers to visually see the affects on their lungs. It was very successful campaign. My boys learned a lot about getting grants, as well as solving problems in the community. This is what this country is about.

I talked to a guy in Washington, Raymond Whitfield. He is 68 years old, and he got $20,000 grant from the government to go back and get his master's degree. Twenty thousand dollars at 68 years old! So you old farts out there saying, "Nobody is going to give me money to do anything," nonsense! The government cannot discriminate. Raymond at 68 years old got $20,000 to do something he had always wanted to do, and you can too.

Ronald Olszewski of Alabama got a $500 grant to fix up his car. Did you ever think there were grants to fix up your car? Well, there are. You just have to know how to look, and look deep enough to find it. Sure, the car dealer is not going to say anything. There is not going to be a big sign at the car dealer saying, "Free grants. Come fix your car here."

How about a grant to buy a house? Sandie Dotson in Houston got $3,500 to cover closing costs to buy a new home. Three thousand five hundred dollars is not much towards a house, but for a lot of people, that will stop them from home ownership because they do not have the extra money for closing costs.

Or how about this? Linda Jacobs-Holcomb got a $5,000 grant for speech therapy for her child. Would you ever think that, "My child needs therapy, and I can't afford it," and that you could possibly get a grant of $5,000 for it? You can. You just have to know where to look. You have to go through the effort. You cannot knock on one door and expect to get $100,000 by next Tuesday. That one door is probably going to say no, and so you have got to go to the next door and then to the next door. You need to keep going until you get it. It is like getting a job. When you are job hunting, you do not go to one company and say, "Hey, are you hiring today?" If they say no, you do not go home and wait for them to change their mind. You go to the next door, and the next door and the next door. That is what you need to do.

The rich and famous use a lot of this free grant money. This is my biggest frustration in life. If I see the wealthy taking advantage of all these programs then people like you should be doing so too. If people like Ritz Camera, Amazon.com and Ameritrade are getting all this money, why don't you? These rich people hire someone to go and find this money for them. I was one of those guys. I would charge $100 an hour to find money programs for rich people. But what I found was that if a kid like me from Wilkes Barre can find this stuff, anyone can. I want to give you the tools to find it.

George W. Bush Got A $200,000 Grant For His Baseball Team

Just look at the people in the White House today. Do you know how George Bush became a millionaire? That is right, he is a millionaire now in addition to being the President. We all heard that he was more or less a ne'er do well, and was a mediocre student, just like me. The only real money he made was with his baseball team. He found $600,000 to invest in a baseball team in Texas and became the managing partner. As the head of the team, he got the government to give him $200 million to build a brand new baseball stadium.

What happens when you get $200 million for free to build a nice stadium for your team? The value of George's investment soared from $600,000 to about $12 million in a few years. He knew the system, and he got that government money to make him wealthy.

Dick Cheney was even better at it than George W. was. He got literally billions and billions of dollars in government money. He ran a Texas energy company called Halliburton. He got $1.5 billion from a government office called the Export-Import Bank that helped his business sell overseas. He also got another two or three **billion** dollars in contracts from the government. Government contracts are also money you do not have to pay back; you just have to do the work. This is another wonderful source of money.

The two people in the White House today are heroes to at least half of our society who voted for them, and they lived off government contracts and government grants. I am trying to get everybody to be aware of this. We have 30 million people a year who are cashing in on these things. You can, too. You could get grants to pay for your doctor bills, your telephone bills, your heating bills, your food bills — there are even grants around the country that if you have trouble paying for your mortgage, they pay it for you!

Grants To Pay Your Mortgage

That is right. If you lose your job, would you ever think of asking the government to pay your mortgage? Probably not, but there are programs like this. There are grants that pay for storm windows, automobile repairs, dance classes, childcare, prescription drugs — there are even grants to help you adopt a child. And there are even grants from organizations that are set aside just for grandmas!

Cheri Olssen in Nebraska got $4,500 to help pay for a truck to start a recycling business. Here is a woman who wanted to start a recycling business but was short on cash. She needed an extra four or five grand to buy a truck to start the business, and she got it. She said she did not need a grant writer and believes that anybody can do it. This is a little old lady out there in Nebraska who is telling you straight from her heart that she did not need a grant writer and that anybody can get a grant.

And the people running big organizations are not all the brightest crayons in the box. How many people have you worked for that were not very bright? I know I have worked for a bunch in my life. Nobody has any magic in this world. The magic is inside you. You have got to bring it out of yourself. You have got to go through the work and the perseverance to get it, and that is all it is. It is a matter of perseverance and focus, and I want to help you through the process.

I Have the Qualifications to Help You Get A Grant

Why should I be the one to give you the tools you need to get a grant? Because I have been doing this for a long time. I am 58 years old, so I am certainly old enough. I have been researching money programs for over 25 years. I am not aware of anyone in the country who has more credentials on this subject than me. But I am biased, so do not trust me.

I started a business back in 1975 that helped companies get money and information from Washington. I started in a one-bedroom apartment in Washington, DC, right near the famous Watergate, home to the break in that lead to Nixon's impeachment. Those of you who are old enough will know what I am talking about.

I had a little one-bedroom condominium and no money, and was doing research for fat cats. They would call me and want to know where they could get money to increase the size of their businesses. I would find the money programs and free information that they would use to make billion-dollar decisions. I went from me, a phone, a desk, and no money in a one-bedroom apartment to about 30 or 40 people down on K Street. And I did it in about 3 years.

After a while I got a little tired of helping the rich people. I grew up in a place called Wilkes Barre, Pennsylvania. I did not know anything about Washington. My clients made me smart. They would call and say things like, "We want to know where the money is." And I would go get it. I would do research on anything because I wanted desperately to get paid. I could not believe I was able find all this information, but then I started thinking that it was not really satisfying work. I found that these people would get this money with or without me. They could hire somebody else. If I charged $100 an hour, and was not around, they would hire some lawyer at $200 an hour to do the same kind of work I was doing.

Then I had a chance to write a book. There was an article written about me in *Parade* magazine back in the early '80s. I used to live off publicity then because I did not have any advertising money. A literary agent called me after seeing the Parade article and said, "You should write a book about what you know." I said, "Write a book, like a real book with New York publishers and everything?" He said, "Yeah!" I told him, "But I flunked English in college. I'm no writer. I couldn't write a book." He said. "That doesn't matter." And it is true — it did not matter. I wound up with two *New York Times* bestsellers. And since then, I have written over 100 books. Two of my books were awarded Best Reference Book of the Year by the American Library Association.

I wrote a syndicated column for the *New York Times*. That is right — the *New York Times*, this schmuck who flunked English in college. I thought you had to go to Harvard to write for the *New York Times*. I also wrote a column for years for *Good Housekeeping* magazine. I am living a life that I had no idea was possible. I thought someone else did all this stuff. But no — you do not need credentials to do anything in our society. Look at George Bush! He cannot even speak well, had terrible grades, and he is the president! So forget about credentials. Just go out and do your dream.

Since 1975 I have been working on how to get money, help, and information in this society. That is what these credentials show, and that is what I believe in, helping fat cats, poor cats, middle class cats, everybody. I have sold millions of books on this subject. I also know that people have a fascination with grants. That is why I want to tell you the ins and outs of getting a grant. The fat cats get the grants. I have gotten them for the fat cats. Other people have gotten them for the fat cats. But grants are for everybody, over one trillion dollars' worth.

You Can Do It Without Me and My Books

Companies like Procter & Gamble would call me and want to look for money programs. I didn't know where they were. I would just make 100 phone calls to find them. They were paying me $100 an hour, so I did not care how long it took. And I would eventually find them. You do not need my books. I believe the only thing you need is to believe that that stuff is there. If you believe it is there, you will go out and get it. It takes time, but in our society everybody is short on time. I hope what I am doing for you will cut down the time that it takes you to find this information. There is no magic in me. I am just digging ditches, finding the information that can benefit you. You could do it without my experience and learn it all yourself. It will just take you a little longer.

In most households it takes two busy people working to make ends meet in our society. It used to be that yuppies like me would go to the grocery store, buy food, bring it home and cook it. Now, because of the lack of time, I want go to the grocery store and get food that is already cooked, so it takes me less time. The service economy is big because we are all trying to save time. That is where the future of our society is. It is in selling services to each other that will save us time.

More Than Grant Money: Loans, Contracts and Venture Capital

I am going to tell you about grants. But as you go through this process and start looking for grants, you are going to come across other kinds of money. It is important to know about these and not dismiss these sources just because they are not grants. If you have a project you want to do, you may think that the only way you are going to get it done is if somebody gives you a chunk of free money to do it. There may be other alternatives that are just as good and will get the project done. Life is all about having an objective and figuring out the best way — maybe not the most perfect way, but a way to get it done.

We do not live in a society that is perfect. Nothing is perfect. Look at all the junk you and I buy. The important thing is getting it done. Keep your ears open for other kinds of money, because you are going to run into them and you may want to use them. You may be saying, to yourself, "I do not want anything to do with loans, because I do not want to be burdened with debt." Listen, if a loan is the only way that you are going to get the thing done, it is very important to do it. And by the way, the government has very interesting loans. The government has some loans you do not have to pay back! How do you like that? I don't know why they call them loans then, right? But they do!

I know a lady who got a loan for $30,000 to help her pay for a house. But if she stayed there for five or ten years, she did not have to pay it back. That is a nice loan, right? So, don't dismiss loans.

How about low interest loans? You may be saying, "I can't afford it," or, "I have bad credit. Nobody is going to give me a loan because I have bad credit." No! Actually many of these loans, particularly from non-profit and government organizations, are for people who cannot get loans anywhere else.

A lot of people are looking for grants because they say, "Nobody is going to lend me $100,000 to start my business or go to school because I have bad credit." Or, "I don't have collateral." You are thinking of banks, and these loans do not come from banks. The loans from non-profits and government organizations are really for people who cannot get loans anywhere else. You may be in that category. Keep your antenna open for any kind of money. You may run into loan programs while you are looking for a grant. Put that loan aside because maybe at the end of your search you may want to revert back to the loan because it is not such a bad deal after all. Or maybe you need $100,000 for a project and you only find $50,000 worth of grants. In cases like this, you can use a $50,000 loan to make up the difference.

Government contracts are another big source of cash. I spoke earlier of Dick Cheney getting two billion dollars worth of contracts. If you are a small business selling a service or product you may be saying to yourself, "If only I had $50,000, then I can go advertise my services so that everybody would know I am here and would come and buy my product. " It is easy to see how you would think that this would be the answer to your prayers.

You can do something better and safer. If you have advertising money, you really do not have any idea if your advertising is going to work. Like all those dot.com businesses that spent millions on Super Bowl ads only to go out of business. Instead, you can go to a government office that will help you get a $50,000 contract. That is exactly what you are in business to do — get work. And the government buys more of anything than anyone else in the world. One year the government even spent $30,000 on a freelance priest.

Once you learn to get one contract, then you can get another. And that could grow to Dick Cheney, where he got $2.3 billion of contracts. It is not like getting grants where you may only get one.

Another source of money that we are going to talk about is venture capital. It's like grants in that it's money you don't pay back. But it's like getting married. You get a partner. That is the bad side. But again, if you just want to get your project going, the important thing is to get it started. So what if you have a partner for a while. Learn the process and get the experience so that you do it the way you really want to do it next time.

Another source of money is a tax credit. Tax credits are very important. You are going to pay taxes, right? Well, the government has tax credits they give to do things, like hiring employees and training them, investing in certain industries or fixing up certain buildings.

Loan guarantees are another source. If you find a bank that says they will give you money but, " Do you have an rich uncle who can co-sign for you?" You are in luck because the government offers that service too.

Remember the important thing is that you are going to follow your dream, and you want to get it done, no matter what. It is taking your dream and doing it so you can go on to the next dream, because that one is going to be better!

Grants For Business

I get calls all the time telling us, "I want to start a business. I went down to the Small Business Administration and I asked them for grants. The person there said, 'There are no such things as grants for business. Have you been listening to that Lesko guy? He is just full of poppycock.'" The person at the Small Business Administration (SBA) is right; I am right and everybody is right. That is what is so neat about the world. We all have a piece of us that is right, and we all probably have a piece of us that is wrong.

It is true. I am a salesman so I can over-blow a story to get my point across. That is one of my faults and I understand that. They are right, because the Small Business Administration does not have grant money for businesses. People think that if they start a business and they are looking for money, that they should go to the Small Business Administration. I guess they are a great group, but that is really not the only place for a business to get money. You may or may not want to use them, and they do have a lot of programs. They are mostly loan programs. The Small Business Administration does not have grants, but that does not say that that is the only place for money. The Small Business Administration is a major source, true, but it is not everything. There are grants for businesses, but you have to look elsewhere.

One source of business grants is local and state governments. They can offer grants up to $500,000 if you start or expand a business in their area. If your company was hurt by imports, you can apply for grants up to $700,000. These grants are not from the Small Business Association. If you are in business and you want a grant, they are out there. It just takes effort to find them. And it is unlikely that the Small Business Administration even knows about these. It is impossible for any one person or office to know everything. I don't even know everything

Just think, there are three million people that work for the government. So, if you are going to go to one government office and ask them about all of the programs, they are not going to know everything. They barely know what is in their office!

There are only four of us that live in my house — my wife and my two kids. I do not even know what they are doing most of the time, and they live with me! So how the heck is a government employee going to know what every other government employee is doing? They cannot. That is why it takes effort on your part to find these things.

Grants For Paul Newman, Women and To Train Employees

Here is another grant program for business — $100,000 to sell your goods and products overseas! You know who used that once? Paul Newman. He saw me on a TV show in Connecticut. He called my office and all the ladies were so excited. He would not let us call him back, but he did call again. And as a result he found that government money to help sell his salad dressing overseas — $100,000.

There is a $5,000 grant for women who want to start businesses in North Dakota. Maybe they are just looking for women in North Dakota! You have no idea what is out there until you start looking. The Office of Economic Development in your state government is where you begin your search.

Found a way to save energy? There are grants that give you up to $425,000 as a business if you have a product that actually saves energy. Maybe it is a new Venetian blind that does not let in as much heat from your window. Maybe it is a new fuel-efficient carburetor. These are grants to develop your ideas into a big business.

Almost every business has employees, and almost every state now has grant money for you to train them. You can get $25,000 to upgrade the skills of your employees. If your employees do not know Excel, Access or some other computer program, go to your state government. Most every state in our country now has grant-training money to get your employees more efficient on the job, so we as a country can be more competitive. That is the name of the game. If your business is more competitive, then the country is more competitive, and we have a better society.

Or, is your business going to create new jobs. How about $10,000 for every job you create? State and local governments also give out grant money like this.

Or how about $30,000 to reduce wood waste? I am not sure what this is, but if you are manufacturing something out of wood, and you want to cut down on your waste, a $30,000 grant would be a welcome addition to help you accomplish this.

How about $100,000 just to develop a new product? There are state governments that want your business to grow by developing new products. If your business grows, then you hire new people and pay more taxes. So, they give out grants hoping they will get back the money in taxes when your business grows.

How about a $5,000 grant to travel overseas looking for business? Maybe you want to sell cowboy boots to France. American culture is big in Europe, and you can get a $5,000 grant (most of these are from the state government) to travel to France to find customers. The government wants you to sell goods and services overseas. That means more money, a bigger customer base for our products, and that means our economy will grow.

How about this? There are other states that will give you a $15,000 grant just to prepare a business plan to start a business in a small town. The government is very concerned that small towns are dying in this country. There is a lot of economic development help and incentives for people to start businesses in small towns. One state will give you $15,000 just to think about starting a business in a small town. How do you like that? You don't even have to start a business. You just have to think about it and do a business plan.

There are other states that will give you $10,000 for every new job you create. So, if you hire somebody for $20,000-30,000, the government will give you $10,000 in return. You get a one-third discount on that employee. That is an extra 10 grand in your pocket that you do not have to pay that employee.

If you hire somebody with a disability, there are programs that will give you $4,000. Or, if you have a disability and want to start a business, there are grants for your business start-up. They want to make you more productive, and will give you up to $15,000.

How about $100,000 to market your invention? Or how about this, there are some programs for businesses that get grants to work on better ideas. You can get up to a half million dollars. Then they have other programs to give you a $5,000 grant to work on the proposal to get a half million-dollar grant to work on your invention. Which means you can get a grant in order to get another grant!

Or how about a grant of $20,000 to start a daycare center in your business? Maybe you have a little recording studio and you start hiring people. All these people you hire have little kids at home and they want to be near them. Make your employees happy and get a grant from the government to put a daycare center in your business. Moms are happy because they can take a break, see the kid, and they are not anxious or worried about what the child's doing.

So, there are grants out there for businesses. It is just not going to be the obvious places, and they are not at the Small Business Administration. I often see that any time the government opens up an office to solve a problem and it stays there long enough, it almost becomes the last place to go, sort of like the Small Business Administration. They have been there to the end of time. They do good work, but you get caught up in the voicemail and bureaucracy.

If you want to start a business, start at your state and county economic development office. Did you ever see the environmental poster that says "Think global, act local?" It is the same way in getting money from the government. It is all federal and foundation money, but you want to start locally. Start by finding those local organizations that may be able to help you with your project. They are probably getting all their money from a federal or national office anyway.

A Government Contact is Money You Don't Have To Pay Back

Don' t forget government contracts. Maybe you have a service— a dog-walking service, a writing service, or you are a freelance artist. How are you going to sell your artwork as a freelance artist sitting in the middle of Iowa? You may be saying to yourself, "If I only had a $50,000 grant, I could sell my artwork." Here is another way. The government has offices that will get you freelance artwork contracts that you can to do right in Iowa on your kitchen table. You can be making $100,000 a year designing brochures for the Dept. of Agriculture.

All you need to be in business is a business card and maybe a few samples. You do not need a big office. You do not need staff. To be in business, you just have to say, "I'm in business."

Or, you can sell somebody else's products. If you think something is sellable, like my books, you can sell it. If you think the government should buy my books, I will sell them to you at a big discount, and you in turn can sell them at the regular price to the government, or to anyone else for that matter. You figure out who in the government buys my kind of books, hook up with a contract, and I will give you 40 percent or more of the sale. See? That is what I mean. And all you need is a business card and a phone, and you are in business.

I really believe that business is easy and very basic. I have an MBA in computer science, and was starting businesses back in the '70s. I had a computer software company back in the '70s that failed. I must have been the only person in the world who had a computer business that failed! I was starting businesses and failing back then, because I had an MBA. I was doing things they taught me in school, like getting business plans, proper accounting, the lawyers, the big office, the furniture, the power drapes, and the power business cards. And when my business failed, I looked around to see who the winners were. It was the people I bought the drapes from, the accountants, the lawyers, and anyone else I gave money to.

The third business I started, I said I do not need accountants. They are not critical to my success, particularly for a small business. The critical thing to your success is YOU and your time. If you are spending time at meetings picking out designer business cards or discussing tax strategies, you are wasting time because those decisions are not critical to your success. The critical thing to your success is getting the customer. Everything else in a business is detail. If you keep a checkbook, then you are an accountant. Money in, money out, and if you have none left, you are broke. That is all you have to know about accounting.

If you get an accountant, they are going to make it so complicated for you that you will need another accountant to understand what the accountant is doing. You do not have to do that. You just have to go and get customers. Concentrate all your time in getting customers. A business card and a phone is all you need. And the government will help you get customers.

I have a huge list of everybody who got a government contract last year. There are millions of businesses every year that are taking advantage of this opportunity. A lawn and tree service in Nebraska got $40,000 of gardening services from the government. Do you like to do gardening work? Why not get a $40,000 contract from the government to do gardening? Somebody's got to do those plants, and it might as well be you. All you need is a shovel or some tools to do it. Or, you can borrow the tools from the friend once you get the contract. Or you can get a contract, and with a contract in hand, any bank will lend you the money to purchase the tools.

Dell Computer Company, now they are no dummies. They sold almost a half a billion dollars of computers to the government last year. The government buys more of anything than anybody else in the world.

There is an organization right here in Washington that got almost $200,000 worth of writing services from the government. Writing! For all that nonsense and bull that comes out of Washington, somebody has got to put all that stuff on paper. The bureaucrats don't really do much themselves. They usually hire contractors to do all the real work.

Want to sell milk? The government recently spent $1 million for milk from a dairy farm in South Carolina.

Copying services is another item. One government office spent $186,000 for freelance copying services. So start looking for a cheap copying machine.

Do you like to make pasta? Last year the government bought $681,000 of macaroni from a company called Pasta USA in Spokane, Washington. You have to really like pasta to make that much of it. But look at all the dough it is bringing in.

I told you earlier that the government even spent $30,000 on a freelance priest. H. Ross Perot is a zillionaire because he found out how to get government contracts. He started his business in his home with $25,000 he got from his wife. Eventually he sold the business to General Motors for a zillion dollars. And when he left General Motors he started another business getting government contracts. It's like when they asked the famous bank robber, Willy Sutton, why he robbed banks, he said, "Because that is where the money is!"

My sister has a little art framing business. She gets about $300,000-400,000 worth of government contracts, just putting frames on artwork. That's a nice business. If you like framing go to the government. My sister's no dummy. I used to call her a dummy a lot when we were young, but she too knows where the real money is.

Government Venture Capital

Government contracts are important. If you have a business and are looking for grants, look for these too. The same holds true with venture capital. I did not know that the government even had venture capital. You probably got some office supplies from Staples. They got $1.5 million in venture capital from the government. That is money they did not have to pay back, but the government shares in the profits. Staples had to give up some of their business for the money, but what the heck? The important thing is to get it done. If it takes being in partnership with somebody, you do it.

Calloway Golf, maker of the famous Big Bertha drivers, got millions in venture money from the government. Their clubs swept the golf industry by storm. These are clubs that can cost $1,000.

Apple Computer and Federal Express also received venture capital money from the government to start their businesses. Intel, the largest manufacturer of computer chips got around $300,000 in the beginning from the government's venture capital.

Mother's Work, the maternity clothes stores for professional pregnant women got $500,000 in government venture capital to help start their business.

Free Cash In Tax Credits

When you are looking for business money, don't forget tax credits. There are business friendly tax credits for companies and for individuals at both the state and federal level.

You can get $2,500 for hiring certain employees in certain zip codes. That is right. Just because your employee is from a certain place, you can get real money in the form of a tax credit. How about $5,000 tax credit if you provide long-term care insurance for your employees? Or, a million dollar tax credit if you are going to expand your business? Or how about this — a $100,000 tax credit if you donate something to a non-profit organization? Or, if you hire somebody with a disability, you can get a $2,500 tax credit. Or, you can get a half a million-dollar tax credit if you invest in solar energy or you purchase an electric vehicle. So, maybe the next vehicle that you purchase for your business, get an electric vehicle.

Remember, all the money programs for your business may be grants. Grants are available and they are at the federal level, but they are more likely to be at the state or local level.

Also remember the venture capital, contracts, and tax credits. The most important thing is for you to get out there and just get the darn thing done!

You May Not Need As Much Money As You Think You Do

We think we want lots of money, right? "If I only had a million dollars, I could do this." "Oh, if I only had $10 million, I could do that." "If I had a half a million dollars, I could do this." When I see studies of businesses and why they went out of business, they all say, "Lack of adequate financing." That is a copout. Sure, if somebody threw lots of money at you, maybe you could stay around longer. But the real trick in life is how to do it with less money than you think you need. They are the kinds of people who are the survivors in our country. The survivors are not the ones that have millions and millions of dollars to do anything they want in life. With lots of money it is hard to create anything new. All you do is learn how to buy things.

We all yell at Congress because they seem to be throwing money at all the problems we have in our society and they always seem to want to spend more. We seem to do the same in our personal lives, right? We say to ourselves, "I can't go back to school because I don't have a lot of money." "I can't start a business because I don't have a lot of money." Gosh, we sound just like Congress when you have those kinds of feelings. You can do what you want to do in life and you just may not need as much money as you thought you did.

You can start a business nowadays with just a phone, a desk and a business card. How much money is that going to take? A hundred bucks? Fifty bucks? Twenty bucks? So, $200 and you are in business, and you go and get customers. That is it. If you don't have money, then think of another way to do it, or think of a way to do it with less money. There are other solutions. You are just not thinking. The biggest obstacle to success in life is our own mind.

When I started my business, I used to think the same thing. I would dream about all the things I could have been doing if I only had a lot of money. I started with a phone, a desk and a couple of thousand bucks. I used to put little one-inch ads in the *Wall Street Journal* because I was trying to sell research to businesses. In one-inch ads, I could not say a whole lot, but that was all I could afford. I got crazy people calling or writing letters in crayon on napkins and stuff like that.

Then I had a brainstorm. How do I get publicity without buying advertising? How can I get my name out to people without spending money? And that is what you see now. You see this idiot on TV, acting like a madman. I quickly found out that if you are an idiot and crazy, they will put you on TV! It does not matter what you say.

The way I did it was to publish a free newsletter. I said that if businesses wanted to know how to get free information for their business, subscribe to my free newsletter. And the *Wall Street Journal* wrote an article about my free newsletter, as did others.

Then I was getting legitimate inquiries on business stationery, like Citicorp Bank, who later became a client. They wrote for my free newsletter and wanted to know how to get free information so their business would be successful. I got a $3,000 contract from them. I figured out how to be in the *Wall Street Journal* for free. Now, if I had a million dollars, I would be spending more time writing a bigger ad because I would have an advertising agency, right? And if the next ad didn't work, I'd buy a bigger one, because I would have the money to say it louder.

But if you do not have money, you get smarter. You learn how to do it cheaper, and that is what you have to do to survive. Anybody can spend money, but can you get that business without spending the money? That is the key to success.

When I was going on TV and selling my books, I figured TV was pretty boring. I wondered who was watching? Most people have the TV on while they are doing something else. Then I thought, if I got on the *Today Show* and they said, "Next is Matthew Lesko to talk about the government," people are likely to say, "I don't want to know about the government." And they would likely go into the kitchen or bathroom and start doing something else.

My theory is, I have got to get you out of the bathroom. So, I go on TV and start jumping around and screaming. Then you come out of the bathroom and say, "What is that idiot talking about?" Now I have got your attention. Maybe I can teach you something. I used to be a professor, teaching computer science to adult students. They had been working all day and then would come to class. I knew if I could not keep them awake at night, I would never teach them anything! That is the same thing with TV. If I cannot keep you awake, I cannot teach you anything.

Then I saw the reason why they invited me back on TV shows. It was not because I sounded smart or I knew what I was saying. They wanted me because I acted like an idiot! This was entertainment. It was not what I said, but how I said it. And you know that when we see things, it is how people do things we remember and not really what they are saying. You have to play into that and use it. That is what I did.

You have to find out how to get customers with as little money as possible. Anybody can do it with a lot of money. That is why you should not stop your dream simply because you don't have all the money you thought you need. Find out how to do it with little money. Once you do, you will become smarter and stronger.

So many friends of mine, who had millions from venture capital companies, went out of business during the first downturn in society. And do you know why they went out of business? Because they only knew how to do it with a lot of money. When they did not have the money any more, they did not know how to survive.

I am going to be doing what I do for a long time because I can do it with no money or with lots of money. I don't care how much I have. I will find out how to get a customer with $0 in my bank account because that is the way I started. This is how you become a stronger individual. You become a stronger member of society. Anybody can spend money. You have to learn how to do it without the money.

This is true not only in business but also in all areas of society. It is easy to say, "I can't go back and get an advanced degree to better my family and myself, because I will need $300,000 to live in the style to which I have become accustomed." You are not going to grow unless you learn how to sacrifice for a few years. If you are in your thirties, forties or even fifties don't forget you are likely to live 40, 50 or 60 more years. I am going to be 60 soon and I figure I have at least 30 more years. You have got to think long-term.

$600,000 From a $16,000 Investment

A friend who works with me was once a welfare mom. She had four kids and was raising them by herself. The best job that she could get in those days was $25,000 to $30,000 a year. She knew that if she got an education she could better herself. It took her almost 10 years to get her undergraduate and graduate degree. Her first job after graduation earned her $50,000 a year.

She went from making $30,000 to $50,000 and it is not going to stop there. So what if she has $16,000 of college loans. It is stupid to go into debt to take a cruise, but not to invest in your education. It is always worth investing in yourself. It is your best chance of earning more money.

In the first year after graduation she made an extra $20,000. She will make at least $20,000 more each year for the rest of her life. And this is the result of only a $16,000 investment. In 30 years, she will make at least an extra $600,000. An investment of $16,000 turned into $600,000, just because she invested in that education. You will never get that at the bank, stock market or anywhere else.

Doing things with less money takes some imagination and some brain squeezing and stretching. You have to get out and try as many things as possible to see what works. You have to go and do things and have a belief that you can.

Maybe you can only get a grant for $10,000, but school is going to cost $20,000. You have to get out there and keep looking. Take another a step. Try it again, and again, and again.

Change the World Without Winning The Lottery

I was talking to a woman the other day who thinks she is going to get a great deal of money from a big Wall Street deal. She has an inside scoop on an IPO independent offering. This has turned her from a woman who never had a lot of money to a woman now dreaming of becoming a millionaire. She does not have a nickel of the money yet, but she has spent weeks dreaming about what she will do with all the money. Her kids are gone and she works hard at her job. She thinks she wants to use some of the money to help latchkey kids.

I asked why, and she said because her kids were latchkey kids. She was a single mom much of her life, raising her children. She now feels that those kids that do not have parents at home after school need more help, and she wants to do something for them. Instead of figuring out a way to work on the problem now, she believes that this goal can only be accomplished with a windfall of money.

When she was talking to me about it, she was crying. That is the neatest thing in life, to find something you are passionate about, that really moves you emotionally, so that you can put your whole heart and soul into it. That is what I do with my work, and I hope I can help people find things that they have passion for in life. That is when work is not work and you are doing what you want to do and love doing it. I have not worked in 30 years. I just do stuff that I love to do.

When she talked about this, she had so much passion. But then I said, "What are you going to do if you don't get the money?" She said, "Then I won't be able to do it." That is when I got angry. "What do you mean? You have found something that you have so much passion for, and you are only going to do it if you get a million dollars?" What a waste — what a waste of her, what a waste to society, what a waste for everyone. I said, "You can do it without a million dollars!" She told me that she did not know anything about doing it. And I said why don't you just go to the schools in your area and say, "Hey, can I use one of your classrooms after school?" Arrange volunteers to come in and help with the kids, all for free. Do it all on a volunteer basis.

She said, "Is that the way to do it?" I said, "I don't know the way to do it! I am just guessing. Maybe you go to the school board and talk to them. Who the heck knows?" She was trying to think of the perfect way to do it by sitting there in the restaurant guessing. You don't know! You have got to put your foot out the door and ask somebody, and then if that does not work you try something else. If that person tells you that you are stupid, you try something else until it is not so stupid any more.

The biggest problem is that you do not know until you take that first step. It is sort of like painting a canvas. I am not a painter so I really do not know what the heck I am saying. But I am sure that when artists paint or use any kind of art medium, they have only a vague idea of what they want to do. Once they have put the first brush stroke on the painting, something else comes to their mind. This brush stroke leads to another brush stroke, and this thing becomes different from their original idea. All our lives are that way. What you originally thought — you will go to school, get married, etc. —does not happen exactly, because something is in your way and changes your direction.

Yogi Berra said, "When you come to a fork in the road, take it." You do not know where you are going, but you have got to get out there and take that first step, in order to decide about the second. The more education we get in the country, the more we want to know what the last step is going to be before we even take the first step. We want to know what the bottom line is before we take the first step. You cannot. You have to take the first step and see what happens, and then take the next one.

It is so hypercritical when these bank people want business plans from you. They are not business plans; they are fairy tales. It is your best guess, but it is a guess. You thought through it, but that is never going to happen. As soon as you take your first step, as soon as you open that first day of business, everything changes. The environment changes every second, every day. By writing a business plan, you are sitting there in a cocoon saying what is going to happen.

I was reading the other day that when Einstein was a kid in school his father went to the headmaster to inquire about his prospects. Einstein had trouble reading, and did not even read at nine years old. Everybody thought he was mentally handicapped. His father asked the headmaster for advice on what kind of careers Einstein should pursue. Einstein's headmaster, the teacher who should know Einstein's intellectual ability better than anybody else said, "Don't worry. It doesn't matter what career he goes into, because he is going to be lousy at everything."

Einstein! His teacher told him he would be lousy at everything. What do experts know? They don't know. They are wrong most of the time. Weather reports? People spend gazillions of dollars and they cannot tell you if it is going to rain this afternoon. It is the best guess, but it is all we have got.

You know what is best for you. You have to get out there and take that first step. And there is a way to do it without having a gazillion dollars. Want to make a change in the world? You do not need a million dollars. You just have to start doing it. Find the stuff that you have passion for and you will not need as much money as you think you do!

Examples of starting a business with no money

I want to give you some examples of starting a business with no money. Last week I was in Detroit. The local NBC affiliate station pulled me in to act like a trained clown at the mall while they did cut-ins for the local promotion. At the mall every hour on the hour, I spoke to a couple of hundred people, gave out free books, answered their questions, and it was great fun. I did this for eight or 10 hours. People said, "Gosh, how could you do that all day long?" I love doing what I do. Actually, I got up at four o'clock in the morning, got on a plane, got to the mall in Detroit, worked all day, eight or ten hours, got on a plane coming back and got home at one or two o'clock in the morning. And I still had energy so I started working when I got home. That is the key. If you love what you are doing, you have got energy to do it all the time.

While I was at the mall in Detroit, people were asking me how to get money to start their businesses that they wanted to do. The more I heard about the businesses, I said, "Okay, you can go out and try to get a lot of money by looking for grants, loans or whatever. And remember I can personally identify about 100 to 150 grant programs for businesses, but a lot of business money is in the way of loans, venture capital, tax credits and contracts"

During this day I found a couple of good examples of how people could actually achieve their dream without even getting the money to do it. So many people wanted to be in the real estate business. They wanted to be real estate investors. "If I only had $100,000 I could go and buy property, fix it up and be this real estate entrepreneur." They have probably been watching infomercials late at night on TV, like mine.

Real Estate Tycoon With No Money Up Down Or Up Front

If you do not have the money, or if you do not want to spend all the time looking for the money, there are other options. To get in the real estate business, one of the ways to do this is to become a real estate information broker. I do not mean a real estate broker, but a real estate information broker. You could start a business that just gets information for people who want to buy and sell real estate. You are doing the legwork for them, and charge a fee because you work for people who have money and are looking for investments. By doing this, first of all, it costs no money to start that kind of business. With a phone, a desk and a business card, you are an information broker.

Now all you have to do is find the people who are looking to invest in real estate, and you work for them. You charge them by the hour — $25 an hour, $50 an hour, whatever the heck you can get away with to start a business. By doing that, you will learn more about that business than by going to school or even investing your own money. You are going to fail a lot in the beginning. That is what life is all about — failing and learning. So, this is a way to learn the business without failing with your own money. You fail with somebody else's money.

Also, by being an information broker your clients can eventually become your partners. You could manage their property for them for a piece of the action. There are all kinds of services you can provide. If you start a service business nowadays in this country, you are probably not going to go broke. The most important thing that people are trying to buy now is time. Nobody has time to do anything. So, if you have money to invest in real estate, you are probably lacking the time to find the properties to make those investments.

You can begin to sell your time and immediately be in the real estate business. Instead of waiting two to six months looking for the money you may or may not get, you can be in business by the end of the day.

No Money Down Beauty Salon

Here is another example. A lady came to me and said, "I want to get money to start a full-service salon and day spa where I would make money by renting out space in the spa to hairdressing people, manicurists and massage therapists, because that is how a lot of these businesses run." They make money by just leasing out the space and taking a piece of the profits.

I said, "Okay, that sounds like an interesting business." Personal care businesses are going to be growing in the future. We all want to take better care of ourselves, particularly as the baby boomers all grow older. An aging population means an increasing vanity factor. But I said, "Here is another way to do that business without money."

It seems to me that to do that business, you need a lot of money to either buy a building, or to lease space, lease the equipment, buy the equipment and all that. Then go out and find people to set up shop in your facility so that you make money together with them. It seems that the easy part of that business is buying a building or buying equipment. There are a lot of people who will be glad to take your money to invest in real estate or sell you equipment.

It seems the key to the business is finding people that will go into your shop and be contractors or partners for you. If that is the key for you and your business, it must be the key for every other beauty salon business. So, here is an opportunity that I would see in this kind of industry. If you did not find all the money you needed to start up that full-service beauty salon and day spa, you could be a talent broker for other beauty salons and day spas.

In other words, you can manage the problem of finding manicurists, hairdressers or massage therapists for beauty salons. All you need is a phone, a desk and a business card and you can start contacting existing beauty salons right now. Call them and say, "Hey, if you want to set up a manicurist in here, I will get the people. I will find them and manage them." And you do it all for a piece of the action.

If the manicurist is making $30,000 a year, I do not know how the arrangement works, but maybe the owner gets 50 percent and you get 10 percent — some kind of middleman fee. That was how it works with my agent who sells my books to people in New York. They get 15 percent of what I get, and all they do is make the deal. And that is what you could do. You could make the deal. You really take the headache from the owner of finding and managing people.

Maybe they are set up just for haircutting. Now they want to offer more services, but do not have the time or the energy to find and manage the people. That is what you could do, and do it for a fee. And again, all you need is a phone, a desk and a business card, and you are in business! There is always more than one way to skin a cat, or to make things happen.

Get Equipment For Your Business With No Money

Another guy came to me and said, "If I could get $100,000, I could start a van business immediately. There is so much money out there driving for the elderly." I guess Detroit is full of senior citizens. He works for another company now that provides this service, and said it is very easy to get contracts and all he needs is money to buy a van.

You can go out and search for the money. But I bet there is another way of doing this. If you can get a contract that easily than you can start a business right now. You go out and borrow, or rent someone else's van for the day, for the week, or whatever. There are a lot of people who will rent you vans. If you can go and get a little contract for $5,000 to shuttle people around, you can lease a van from somebody for a week or whatever the contract is worth until you build up some money to buy your own vans. If you know how to get that contract for that money, you are already in business. Anyone can get a van; the magic is getting the business.

If you knew somebody who wanted to buy 25 hours of recording facilities and you did not have one set up in your basement already, you could find one. I am sure somebody is sitting around the city with recording time that is not being used. You could make a deal. Maybe you will not make as much money as you would if you had your own recording studio, but you would not have to invest in your own studio and that is the way to learn the business.

If you keep learning how to get contracts for customers, eventually you will be able to afford your own recording studio. You might make more profit in the beginning because you will not be paying off your equipment. So, it is a way to be in the business without having to soak a lot of money into it. If you could find out how to get those contracts, whether it is for driving senior citizens or for getting recording business, then that is the key to success. When you have some money in the bank and some steady clients you can start investing in to your own equipment.

There was another fellow who came up to me and said that he was cleaning buildings at night but was a little smarter than the average cleaner-upper so he wanted to start his own business. He believed he needed a lot of money to do this. I said, "No, you don't. You don't need money. What you need is a broom, some cleaning equipment, and a vacuum cleaner." And he said, "I have to know how to get contracts and stuff like that." I said, "No, you just have to go out and ask for the business."

Go print business cards with Joe's Cleaning Service on them. Call on 50 small businesses and tell them, "If someone's cleaning your office now, I will clean it for 25 percent less." And you will, because you want that business. You will be working out of your basement so you will not have as big an overhead as an established business. You are probably doing it all yourself with just a few friends. You will be able to do it better and cheaper than anybody else. That is how you get a contract.

If you want to go to a big General Motors and do all of General Motors cleaning, sure, you need an organization. You will fill out 50 pages of contracts so all the people in suits feel safe. You probably need to get bonded because the suits get worried. And you say you don't know how to get bonded? Don't worry about it. Worry about it only if you have an opportunity to get big contract. You go after the small businesses where people have other concerns. I have somebody cleaning my offices now and pay them around $70 a week. They come in for a couple of hours and clean. I never asked them for anything. I just give them money. They look nice, work well and everyone is happy.

If you are doing business with big boys, you will need all that nonsense. Actually, when you get bigger, you could get that nonsense for free. Do you want to know how to get bonded or fill out a 50-page contract? Right in your area, there are government offices called Small Business Development Centers. It is not the SBA (Small Business Administration); this is a state office called Small Business Development Center that the SBA helps finance. They will sit down with you for free and help you do the contracts, and get you the free legal help to do it.

Or, if you want to get bonded and your bank will not help you, they have special programs in the government now to help you get bonded as a small business. But truthfully, you do not have to do anything complicated until the client says, "We won't do this unless you are bonded." Then you go out and figure it out. But don't sit there ahead of time thinking, "What happens if they ask me if I am bonded?" "What happens if they ask me, where's the official contract?"

Forget it! Go and get the business. If somebody says that you have to be bonded, then you figure out how to do it. That is the time when you really have to do it. Why waste all your time if you don't have to. Believe me, if you call on 50 small businesses, you will be lucky if one or two ask you for anything complicated. They just want their place cleaned. There are lots of opportunities out there, but they are not in the obvious places. You can always go to a lawyer before you start your business to talk about these concerns. But, if you do, believe me, they are going to scare the pants off of you. It's like talking to insurance salesman. They can always scare you in to paying for more insurance than you ever need. Why worry about being sued, if you don't even have any business, or money. When you get lots of money, then you can worry about those things.

Actually, my philosophy, too, is that you do not have to even file with the government. But you don't ignore the tax man. You never mess around with taxes. There is a tax form called a Schedule C, which lets your small business file taxes very easily. If you are starting a small business, particularly without any money like I am suggesting, it is going to take those bureaucrats three years to find you. Why waste your time? In three years, you may be out of business, and if you are not, fine. You will pay the $50 fine or whatever it is because you did not file on time. Big deal. And if you last three years, you are in good shape.

So, the most important thing is to conserve your energy and just keep looking for customers. That is the most critical part of doing any business.

How Do You Choose What You Really Want To Do?

How do you choose what you really want to do in life? I am trying to help you find grant money, and thinking gosh, you may not even know how you want to use the money! Or, you may not be sure that what you want the money for is the right thing for you. It took me a long time in my own life to find out what I should be doing in the world. But once I found it, I became one of the happiest people on earth.

Now, it is not easy, but you should be on a kind of quest. And if you have not already figured out what you should be doing in life, you should start working on it right now. Start today. Try to find out what you should really be doing in life, and start becoming the hero of your own movie. It is not going to be easy. Remember, heroes do not have an easy life. But the more you struggle, the greater the hero you become.

Think back to the movies that you have seen, or the books you read. *Great Deeds Done By Heroes* — remember? They do not make movies or write books about people who sit around and do nothing. They are always about people who do neat stuff, and you can be one of those, too! We all love heroes in stories. We respect them, and we wish there were more of them in the world. But most of us are content to sit on our butts, just getting by, doing nothing.

Fighting the Dragons

What really makes a hero is the fact that they struggle. They struggle to overcome challenges. Like in the books we read when we were kids. All the heroes were always slaying dragons that were put in the way of their quest. Well, there are not many dragons left roaming the modern day freeways, trying to stop you from fulfilling your dreams. But we do have our modern day equivalents, and all of us are going to face them when we go out to try to do the things we really want to do in life. Today's dragons are going to take the form of bureaucrats, who put insurmountable hurdles in front of our path, or roadblocks we put in our own minds.

It could also be information that leads you down blind alleys. Or, your dragons may be your friends, your loved ones, or even experts who are telling you why it is dumb to do the things that you are considering. To me, the biggest dragon of all that you will have to fight is you — your own laziness and your comfort with the status quo!

Love Is Helping You Do Whatever YOU Want To Do

Let me tell you a little aside about friends and loved ones. I believe that your loved ones could be your worst enemy. Loved ones want to protect you. They want you to be safe and not get hurt. They want you to get a job with the government, with a good pension.

Little do they know that not even jobs with the government are safe, and that you are only safe if you feel safe on the inside. I feel the only way to get safe in our society is to get an education and good training where your skills are in demand. If someone fires you, you can go across the street and get a better job than the one you have, or you start your own business. That way, because you are the boss, you are never going to get fired!

But in most families, it seems like your loved ones enjoy playing the role of being able to tell *you* what *you* should be doing with your life. But I believe true loved ones would help you do whatever you want to do with your life.

Love to me is helping someone fulfill their dreams, not trying to control their dreams. So, if someone is not really helping you do whatever you really want to do, I do not believe they really love you. Or, they do not know how to express love.

I was reading Aristotle and it was his philosophy too, that love is helping someone do whatever they want to do in life. Let us go back to the dragons. Comfort with the status quo is going to be your biggest dragon. You want to sit around and do nothing. Heroes do not sit around and do nothing. Just think if Martin Luther King would have been happy staying at home just preaching from the pulpit every Sunday and not going out and actually practicing what he preached; or if Mother Theresa would have been content just cleaning the parish rectory and left the caring of Calcutta's poor to some government program.

It's Hard Work To Be Different

It is going to be hard to do something different. It is going to be hard to change what you are already doing. Remember, as human beings we do not like change. I believe the only people who like change are busy cashiers or babies with wet diapers. The rest of us are going to be kicking and screaming before we make any changes in our life.

But one of the few things that I know for sure is that the only thing that is constant in our life now is change. Change is coming through our society like a freight train, so you have to change. If you do not, someone is going to come along and change you anyway, and they will do it their way and not your way.

No job is safe any more. Anything that you were successful at this year or last year, you are probably not going to be successful at next year because it is changing all the time. And if you are not going to change nowadays, you are not going to grow. A popular slogan in American culture has been, "Live Free or Die." But I think the slogan for America today is, "Change or Die."

How do you know what's the right thing to do?

How do you know if you are doing the right thing? Well, you really don't. We may be smart enough to sit down and think before we do anything — what is the bottom line going to be — before we start doing it. But you cannot know if it is the right thing. That is impossible. You may not know what you want to do, and that is okay. You cannot be exact. You have just got to go out and do it.

We really never know what the bottom line is until we get there. You cannot see the future, and neither can anyone else. The best we can do is guess. And as a result, we are going to be wrong most of the time anyway. Even the experts are wrong, like all those smart guys on Wall Street who invested big time in the high tech stocks in the '90s and wound up losing zillions of dollars. I was even one of them, and you would think I would know better because I have got an MBA! But I had no idea, either.

We are all guessing on what we are doing. It is sort of like Picasso. Everything in life leads from the last thing you do. You have to put one brush stroke out there and then see where that brush stroke leads. And that gives you another idea. You cannot sit in your room dreaming about what you are going to be doing five years from now. You have got to take that first step, look around, decide what it is like, then take the second step, look around and decide what that is like, and so on. That is what life is like. It is an art.

You'll Never Know Before You Get There

So, if you are not sure what the best path is, you are certainly not going to come up with the magic answer by simply thinking about it. You have to get out and start doing something. You cannot sit on your sofa and make decisions about things that you have no knowledge. You have to get out there and be in the middle of it to really understand what is going on.

You cannot possibly know exactly what you want to do until you are actually doing it. And that is okay, because even if you are not sure, the one thing you do know for sure is that you do not want to spend the rest of your life doing what you are currently doing. You have got to make a change, even though you do not know exactly what it is.

I believe that even though you have no idea what it is, you do know one thing. You know what it is not. So, the only way anything good has a chance of happening in your life is if you start moving away from something bad. Your obligation in life is to start taking that step away from it, no matter how little it is, so you can view the world from a different position. Then take another step and view the world from that position.

Plan For Accidents

Anything that I am doing now was by accident. I started out doing a variety of things, but when I got there, I saw it differently. Hey, that looks better over here — and I did it. The trick is to find what your art is, what you are the best at in life. I feel we are all artists, and that we all have something. It is our obligation to find out what makes us special.

As a youngster, I used to envy dancers, singers, painters, and people like that because I felt they had gifts that they had to share with the world, no matter what. They enjoyed doing their craft more than anything else. Work is probably the most boring part of life, and we spend most of our life doing it. I used to think, oh those lucky artists. They have something in them that makes them want to do their art every single day, whether they get paid for it or not. I was so frustrated that I did not have a talent that I could contribute, share with the world, and enjoy.

But later on, I found I was wrong. I do have a talent. I am an artist. It is not being a singer, a dancer or a painter. It is being a reference book publisher, compiler, and salesman. That is my art, and it took a long time to find it. But when I found it about 25 years ago, I have not worked a day since. That is the beauty of life. When you find your art, then you are not working any more.

I feel like Picasso, who just got up every day to do his art. He could not wait to create. I no longer live for vacations, fancy cars, or houses. I live for my work. My work is my art. I feel so spoiled that I found work that is really not work. Like Picasso, who would have to paint no matter how much his paintings sold for because he knew he had to paint, I feel the same way. I have got to do my work, no matter how much I get paid. Success or failure, I get up the next day and just do it because I love it more than anything else.

And the ironic thing is that I believe if you find your art, you will more likely get paid a lot more money than if you are not doing it. Why do you make more money when you find what you are special doing?

Once you start doing something you love, you want to do it no matter how much money you are making. And you are going to do it better than most people around you because you are thinking about it all the time. You are going to take it home at night. You see it as a challenging puzzle. That is how I see my work. I do not think about it just nine to five. It is running through my mind all the time. So, if my competitor is only thinking about it nine to five, I am outworking them and outthinking them because I am doing it all the time. And when you love what you are doing, that means it probably comes naturally to you, and it comes more naturally to you than others. You will not be forcing your body or your mind to do something that is unnatural.

When you are born to do a task, you are going to do it better than other people. Some people are born to hit a baseball and some are born to be counselors to young people. And if the values in our society suddenly take a big shift and we start paying counselors a lot more than baseball players, the baseball players should not change their careers to become counselors. They are lucky. They know they have to wake up in the morning and hit baseballs for life, and that is a wonderful feeling.

Another reason that you will probably get paid more if you pursue your art or try to find out what it is, is that you will stay there long enough to figure out how to make money at it. It does not take a whole lot of brainpower to do most things in the world. Look at the people that you have worked for in the past. I am sure they were not mental giants. Even look at the current president of the United States, George W. Bush. He was a C student who has trouble putting complete sentences together, and he is the leader of the Free World!

The longer you stay at something, the better you are going to get, and if you like being there, you are going to stay longer. You will see people come and go; the first sign of bad times, the weak are gone. The people who are doing it for the wrong reasons, for instance if they are just in it for the money, are going to be gone at the first downturn. And there are likely to be ups and downs in every activity, so when the weak ones leave and you stay, you become stronger. You are there through the good times and the bad times, getting stronger all the time. Then you will figure out how to make more money at it than anybody else. That is how success in life is always achieved, I believe. It takes desire, a lot of desire. And you will have that desire to stay there for the long haul and figure things out because you want to do your art more than anything else. You think that this is the most important thing for you to do in your life, and you cannot wait to jump out of bed in the morning and do these things. The neatest thing is that you will have something important to do forever.

Learn To Do 2 Things Well: Love and Work

I was reading a quote the other day. Sigmund Freud said, "There are only two things that a person should be able to do well in life — love and work." We are all still trying at love, right? So, we have got to keep trying at work, too.

Once you find your art, you are likely to see a bunch of other positive changes in your life. This is what happened to me, and I believe it is true for most people. Your work as an art gives you a higher reason for living. No, you are not going to become a god, but I do believe that you do get through life a lot easier when you have a mission that is bigger than you. And if you can find that mission, things will go a lot smoother. The little irritations in life will start to disappear.

When I used to work for other people, I used to get mad when I traveled. My boss would not let me fly first class or stay in a fancy hotel. That used to anger me somewhat. Maybe some other guy stayed at a fancier hotel. Once I started my own business, I stopped caring how I got anywhere. I just wanted to get there and do my work. I did not care if I went on a camel or if I stayed in a tent, and I am still like that.

The only reason I fly first class now is if I get a free upgrade. And to tell you the truth, that is happening more and more since I started wearing my question mark suit. Even if people have not seen me on TV, when they see the suit it makes people smile. It makes them happy, and the people at the ticket counter seem to love to do something nice for "the goofy guy in the question mark suit." Actually, wearing the suit has changed my life. People are nicer to me. I get better hotel rooms, better service at restaurants, and for the first time in my life, pretty girls actually come up and talk to me! Gosh, I wish I had the guts to wear this suit 30 years ago when I had a lot more hormones. The suit has also made me nicer. I cannot walk around like a grumpy old guy, overworked or traveling a lot, when everybody who looks at me is smiling and happy.

Also, another benefit when you find something you really love doing in life, is you also start feeling used, and this is wonderful! Being used is a good feeling. When you are being used, as much of yourself as you possibly can, that is what is really satisfying and healthy in life. We are all given minds and bodies to use, and to use them as much as we can. If we do not use them to our fullest, we remain a little empty in life. We all want to be satisfied that we are putting in a good day's work for a good day's pay. There is a wonderful satisfaction in playing your hardest, and that win or lose, you gave it all you have got. And by giving as much as you can to what you truly believe, is the most rewarding way to get this kind of satisfaction.

Another thing that happens is you feel useful, because you will be making the biggest contribution to the world that you ever can possibly imagine by finding what is special about you, developing it, and giving as much as you possibly can back to the world. That is so satisfying.

I do not believe that our mission in life is to see how big of a house we can get, a car or a vacation. I believe our mission in life is to see how much we can actually contribute to other people around us. How much can you give?

And by the way, here is a little aside. I believe giving is selfish. I feel that the greatest feeling in the world is giving something to somebody else. The problem is trying to find one deserving to give it to! It feels so wonderful to give.

When I was younger, I used to be proud. My in-laws would try to give me money or something, and I could not accept it. Now, I do not believe that, because by not accepting someone's gift, you are depriving that person of that wonderful feeling one gets by giving to someone they think is deserving. That is why I think giving is selfish. It makes the giver feel wonderful.

So, when you are able to find your art, and give it as much as you can to the world, you are giving all you possibly can back to society before you check out of here. And I truly believe that this is the way to go.

Isn't It A Lot Of Paperwork?

A lot of people say, "Hey, Lesko — isn't it a lot of paperwork to get money from the government or other places?" And the answer is yes, it could be. But who cares? Who cares if it takes you a night to fill out the paperwork, or a week, two weeks, a month, or if it is one page or 1,000 pages? Where else are you going to get $1,000 to do something, or $100,000— or a quarter of a million dollars?

What about the last week, the last month? What did you do that month? So many people say it makes them stop. It becomes an insurmountable hurdle. It is an excuse not to do something because they have to fill out some 20-page form. And that's not always true. There is a program, if you want to start a business that only has two pages to fill out, and you get $150,000. So, the paperwork should not stop you.

Sure, some of the complicated grant proposals may take 20 or 30 pages, and it could take you a couple of weeks to complete. But again, if you are getting $100,000 or a quarter of a million dollars to work on your invention, that is worth the effort. You have to do it. Remember, with every hurdle in life, you have to figure out a way over it, around it or through it. If you do not, you are out of the game, and you should not have started the game in the beginning.

How Long Does It Take To Get The Money?

How long does it take to get the money? Well, that is another question where the answer is, it depends. I know some micro-loan programs at the state level that say they guarantee an answer within two weeks. Other programs could take a few months. And there are other programs where they only give the money out once a year, so if you miss that cycle, you have got to wait until the next year. But again, just like the question on the amount of paperwork there is — who cares how long it takes?

There are some emergency funds that you can get very quickly, but most of the money that you want to use to change your life is not going to happen very quickly. You have to allow weeks or even months for this money. You may not even get approved the first time. You may do something wrong and have to file the form again. But again, who cares how long it takes?

I talked to this couple down in Florida who started a hairdressing salon and got $100,000 from the government to help them. They said it took them a few nights in front of the television filling out the forms. That was pretty neat. In a few nights, they got it done, and it was no problem at all. Is it going to take so long to get the money you are not going to apply? Nonsense! If that is your attitude, then do not do anything. Just sit home and be content with what you have now, because you never know how long it is going to take.

That should not stop you from doing anything. That is just another one of those hurdles that the bureaucrats are going to put in front of you to see if you are big enough to get through it, around it, or over it. These are little dragons that you have to slay to get to your quest, and your quest is getting that money or doing what you really want to do in life. And whether it takes a few extra days, a few extra weeks or even a few extra months, who cares? You have got the rest of your life to live. The important thing is that you are working on a mission to change the rest of your life!

Do You Have To Be Poor To Get Money?

Are there income requirements for this money? People ask me that question all the time. "Do I have to be rich?" "Do I have to be poor?" "Do I have to be on welfare?" "Do I have to be a millionaire, like Dick Cheney?" Again, like all the answers to these questions, it really depends. I estimate there are 15,000 money programs that give out money to people to do the things they want, and every program has a different requirement so I cannot really say. Some you do have to be rich, because they want to make sure that you pay some of that money back if it is a loan or a loan guarantee. Some programs you have to be poor, because they only give it to people in need, so you cannot have a high income.

But even for those programs where you have to be poor, listen to this — if you are a woman entrepreneur and want to get money for your business, the government considers you needy if you have $750,000 in the bank. You are almost a millionaire, and the government considers you needy.

Do not let that be a hurdle for you. You would be surprised at who the government thinks are needy. "I make too much money and I cannot get money to buy a house from the government." Nonsense. I have seen housing programs from the government where they consider you needy if your income is $85,000 a year. Can you believe that? Eighty-five thousand dollars a year and they consider you needy!

How about free prescription drugs? That is a favorite program of mine, and you can make $40-50,000 a year or more and get your prescription drugs for free. People believe, "Oh, I have to be destitute to do that." No, you just have to know about the program, and go through the bureaucratic hurdles to get it, but it is there. Actually, some of those programs for prescription drugs have no income requirements. You just have to say that you are having trouble paying for the drugs, and they give them to you.

Just think — rich people like George Bush and Dick Cheney got all that money for their careers and they certainly were not poor. I found a program just for grandmas to do what they really want to do in life. They can get up to $5,000 to work on their dreams.

Do you have to be rich? Do you have to be poor? Again, the real answer is it depends. You find the programs that fit you. For some business programs, you must not have a lot of money; other programs for business are just set aside for people who have no money.

It is the same way for housing. Some want you to have a lot of money, and others do not. Also some programs are just for people who cannot get money anywhere else. That is the important thing. A lot of government programs are really set up for people who cannot get money. So, if you are rich, have a friendly banker, or rich relatives, a lot of programs do not want to help you because you have another place to get it. Many of these programs are set up for people who cannot get money anywhere else.

I have a kid going to college, studying engineering, and I am paying almost nothing. I make good money, and I found government programs that will pay almost all of his college education. It is just amazing.

There are people that say, "I cannot get money to go back to school because I make too much money." You are just looking at the major programs. Any time you go and talk about anything, people usually talk about the general programs. The opportunities are in those nuggets that a lot of people do not know exist. So, if you talk to your college counselor about financial aid, they will tell you about the major programs. But the opportunities are in those non-major programs as well. They are the ones that take effort and work to find.

You have got to do the work, because the government is not going to come and hit you on the head to tell you about these programs. You have got to get out and find them yourself!

Getting Money To Buy Or Fix Up A House

Everybody seems to either want a bigger house, a first house, their third house, or fix up an existing house. Every year over 4 million people are getting government money for housing through dozens of programs that real estate brokers are likely to not know even exist!

There are three major levels of programs— the federal programs, state programs, and local programs with a couple of non-profits thrown in on top of that. Even if you do not have my books, you can go to your library and look up the federal programs. Or, you can call the U.S. Department of Housing and Urban Development. They will send you information about all the federal programs.

On the federal level, there are four areas: the U.S. Department of Housing and Urban Development, the U.S. Department of Agriculture for housing in smaller towns, the Veterans Administration (if you are a vet), and also the U.S. Department of Energy. They have programs to help make your house more energy-efficient. Collect all those and then go to your state capital.

Every state capital has what is called a Housing Commission. You can call your state capital information operator and say, "I am looking for the state housing commission." They will hook you up with an office there. You can have them send you information on their programs. Then you go to your city. Your city has a housing office and there will be programs in the city, and also the county. Actually, more action is happening at the county and local level than even at the state and federal level, particularly for new homebuyers and renters.

Houston has a program where they will give you $3,500 to help with down payment and closing costs. So many organizations, local municipalities, and state governments have money to get people into houses. If you buy a house, they think you will be a better member of society because you actually own a piece of it. You want to protect your home and you are going to work hard to pay the mortgage because you like having your own house.

Iowa has a program that gives you five percent of the mortgage in grant money to use for the down payment and closing costs. So, whatever your mortgage is, they will kick in five percent of your total mortgage and give you that as a grant.

In Minneapolis, you can get $4,000 at zero percent interest. Why do they sell zero percent interest? They do not want to charge you money. They are really not there to make money out of that money. They are there to make sure that you buy a house. You do not even have to pay back that $4,000 until you sell your house. In this society, any house by the time you buy it and sell it is going to go up in value at least $4,000 and that is where you get the money to pay the city.

Louisiana has a program where they give you $10,000 at zero percent interest, and no payments for 20 years. Even the car dealers do not say that. "Don't make a payment for next year." This is 20 years, zero percent interest, so it is wonderful money.

Los Angeles has a program where you can get two percent for closing costs. Whatever the value of the house is, they will give you two percent for closing costs, plus they will give you an extra $30,000 loan with no payments for 30 years. So, you are getting a grant, plus a loan for $30,000 that you do not have to pay back.

Missouri has a program. If you have $750 in your pocket, they will get you a house. That is all you need — $750. So go to your favorite uncle and get $750, and you are in business.

That is how this system works. Again, it takes effort. Remember when you call these housing authorities, you are not going to make one phone call and get a check in the mail for $100,000 for your home. Some are loans, and some are insured loans. There are grants out there and housing that needs rehab where you can get a good deal.

Houses For $1

The government has a program called Houses for a Dollar. The official name is the Urban Homesteading Act. These are rundown houses where if somebody does not pay their mortgage, the government gets that house. It sits and usually deteriorates. Eventually somebody says, "We better get rid of this eyesore," and they have some kind of lottery where for a dollar you buy a ticket. Maybe one in 10 people will get a house, and those are not bad odds. It is a wonderful deal. Then when you get the house, they will give you a low interest loan to fix it up. There are so many couples I know who found these kinds of homes. Isn't that remarkable? A house for a dollar!

I remember I was on a national TV program talking about that government program, the Urban Homesteading Act. They were forcing me to the wall, saying that, "We want to know a phone number where our audience can call." I had the main number in Washington for running the program, but what I did not know was that the program is really run by 170 offices around the country. I gave the main number of the office in Washington, and that whole office is just run by two people — the director of the program and the secretary. And they got 10,000 calls that day because I was on a national TV show. They got thousands and thousands of letters. They called me right away, complaining. When I do things like that, I say, "I will send somebody down and help answer your phones, mail or anything else you need." They usually back off, but I actually helped them. I answered a bunch of the mail, because if I caused the problem I feel the obligation to correct it.

When I do that to bureaucrats, they know they are in business to get the message out. They do not have a way as big as I do sometimes to get it out, and they really have to handle the volume. There are a lot of bureaucrats that do not like me too much, but on the other side I have got bureaucrats that call and say, "Hey, why don't you talk about my program? My program is more important than this program, and people should know about it."

I had a call from an office that gave money to people to start day care centers, and they could not give away all their money, and the year was running out. They called and asked me to talk about this money so people would come and apply for it. These poor bureaucrats could not make quota.

And that is what happens with all the bad publicity in the government offices, the best people do not apply, or the money does not get used well because not enough good people are applying.

If the bureaucrats have better people to choose from, then somebody's brother-in-law won't be hijacked off the street and the money shoved down their throat, which I am sure happens in these agencies. See, if the bureaucrat does not get rid of all their money this year, they will not get it next year.

Government Considers You Needy At $80,000 Per Year

Also on housing, remember that you do not have to be destitute to get money to buy or build a house with government money. For some of these programs as I mentioned earlier, you can be making over $80,000 a year and the government considers you needy, and that you need financial help to buy a house.

It sounds ridiculous but you cannot possibly know all the rules and all the regulations. I don't, and I have been doing this for 25 years. I am surprised every day.

I have found special money programs just to paint your house. Here is a program that I did not even know existed. The government will pay your mortgage! Who would ever think that the government would pay your mortgage?

Actually, they do it through non-profit organizations. If you have trouble paying your mortgage, have been in the house for a couple of years and lose your job, do not call the Credit Doctor.

The Government Will Pay Your Mortgage

The U.S. Department of Housing and Urban Development has set up non-profit organizations around the country that will help you with the mortgage. They will contact the bank, or wherever you owe that money, and work it out with them. Some of these people even have money to pay your mortgage five, six, or seven months while you are in between jobs. That is why I wear the question mark suit. Would you ever think of asking a government office to pay your mortgage? Well, it is there, and that is what is important.

If you are looking for your first house to buy, you may be able to take a free class from the government, and get up to $1,000 as a down payment because you took a the class. You take something for free and they give you free money because you did something for free. It is bizarre. What they are doing is trying to encourage, particularly first-time homebuyers, to be knowledgeable about what they are doing. That is why they entice people into taking this class. It is just a short course to learn about home buying and money management. Then they give you grant money towards a down payment. What a deal!

Again, my question mark suit — you do not know the questions to ask. The answers are easy. It is asking the right question that is hard.

$10,000 Grant To Fix Up Your Home

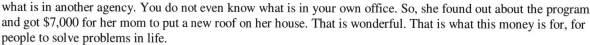

Here is a wonderful program I found for seniors to fix up a house. You can get up to $10,000 to fix up a house if you are over 62 years of age. A woman who works at the IRS came to see me when I was giving a speech at a local library, and asked me this question. Her mom lived in Pennsylvania and needed a new roof. Because she was a good daughter, she was going to pay for it.

I said, "Here, try this program." This is a woman who works in the government and has been there many, many years, and she did not even know about the program. It is impossible to know everything. You cannot know what is in another agency. You do not even know what is in your own office. So, she found out about the program and got $7,000 for her mom to put a new roof on her house. That is wonderful. That is what this money is for, for people to solve problems in life.

This is not welfare money. To me, the only real welfare money we have is the lottery. The lottery is welfare money because they want you to pay taxes. Play the lottery, and you are really giving more taxes to the government because all the lotteries are government programs. It is a way for them to collect taxes. Then they say, "You may win the lottery. You have one in a million chance of winning, and then you can go sit on the beach for the rest of your life."

What is more welfare than giving somebody money to go sit on the beach for the rest of their life? I do not want people to sit on the beach. I want them to be out there making society better for me, you and the rest of the world. That is what these programs are set up to do. It is for you to have a better life, make society better, get that education, improve the world, or to start that business we need.

$15,000 To Fix Up Your Home

Do you want to fix up your house? There is money to do that. Again, most of the fix-up money is not only at the federal level, but the state and local level as well. In Greensboro, you can get an $8,500 grant to fix your home from the city.

In Minneapolis, there is $15,000 at zero percent interest and no payments until you sell your house to fix it up. So, are you going to go to the bank and get $15,000 to put on that deck in the back, or do you go to the government and get zero percent interest which you do not have to pay it until you sell your house? What a deal!

How about Baton Rouge, Louisiana? Up to a $20,000 grant to fix up your home! How much will you have to work to make $20,000? Come to the bottom line. Maybe a third of it goes in taxes, so that means you have got to make $30,000 for you to get $20,000. That is maybe a whole year's income for most of us. And here is what you could get for free from the government to fix your home.

So housing help is at the federal, state, county, as well as city levels, and remember to get a list of all of the programs. The way to work with government agencies is to not call them and say what you want to do. You call them and get the information about what they have. When you get that, you take the literature home, read about the programs, and then call the bureaucrats back and tell them what they have. "Hey, you have this program here. I want to apply for it." That is how you deal with the bureaucracy. Get their paper, call them back, and tell them what they have.

Getting Money For College

There is lots of money out there for college. Actually, just in the government alone, there are 470 programs worth over $33 billion. Then you have the private sector, which has some money, but not a whole lot compared to the government sector. So, you are talking about $35 billion or so, just for students. That is every year.

The government level consists of federal, state and also some local money. But the two major areas are federal and state. You can get a four-year college degree, a junior college degree, graduate school, professional school, or just take a short course at a technical school. You can even get money to pay an artist to teach you at home. Education and training is hot in this country, and the government, the politicians and the think tanks all realize that for us to succeed as a society, more of us have to get better trained. It now takes brainpower to succeed.

I am 58-years old, and grew up mostly in the '50s and '60s, and went on to college. Those kids that went to work in the factories made a heck of a lot more money than I did when I got out of college, even four years later. At that time you could work for General Motors, a steel factory or in the transportation industry and make $50-100,000 a year, just with manual labor. They were wonderful jobs, and you only needed a high school education to get them.

But it is not that way any more. Those jobs have been shrinking in the last 20 or 30 years, and are going away in our society. All the manual labor jobs have gone overseas. We have just become eggheads, so all the jobs now require brainpower and not muscle power. So, you have got to have that education and training to get the brainpower to compete for good jobs in our society if you are going to succeed. And this is how our country is going to succeed. The bigger our brainpower, the better we will be able to compete internationally or globally. That is why it is important. You can never stop learning.

Going To College At 60

The programs I am going to talk about for education are for every age group. It does not matter how old you are. You can be 16 and going to college or attending training programs. Or, you could be 60 or 106! Remember, the government cannot discriminate with age. Actually, right now there is something like 350 universities and colleges around the country where you can go to school for free or next to nothing, just because you are 55 or 60. That is right. At 55 or 60, you can go back and take a computer course or a poetry course — or become a doctor or a lawyer! By the time you hit 60, living until you are 80 or 90 is going to be nothing. So you are a doctor for another 20 years, or a lawyer. Do the things you really want to do.

I even think retirement is a passe idea in our society. That is from the industrial age. You worked in a factory or manual labor all your life, and in your sixties you don't want to do that any more. You want to retire and sit on your butt somewhere. But now with brainpower, and particularly if you are doing the things you love to do, you want to stay contributing all your life. And you can do that.

It does not take manual labor. No matter how much energy you have, you still have to have that brain working. You could be teaching for the rest of your life. You could be counseling. You could be writing. You could be on the net if you want and contributing to our society, and doing it into your eighties or nineties.

I work with a college counselor now. This guy is 92 years old. He just came back from a national tour on his new book about colleges. The guy's terrific — 92 years old and still contributing. And I am paying him good money, and others are too.

You could be like that, but you have got to get that education and training. Find out where it is and get the money. You can get money at any age. Many people who are 35 or 40 are thinking about a new career. You started to become a lawyer and now you would rather be a French chef. Or, maybe you were a clerk typist or a legal secretary and now you want to become a lawyer. You can do those kinds of things in our society.

Actually, there are more people on the college campuses today over 35 than there are 18 and 19-year olds. That is a clue. If you are not thinking about it now, you should think about it soon.

See The Book I Copied From

When you look at federal programs, you can look at my book or the book I copied from in your library called the *Catalog of Federal Domestic Assistance*. Actually, my first *New York Times Bestseller* was from that book. I did not write a lick. This was 20 years ago. I found that at the Government Printing Office they had this book called the *Catalog of Federal Domestic Assistance*. I got so excited about it. Here was one book that had all the government programs to do anything.

So, what I did was I found a publisher in New York. Actually, I found an agent and a publisher in New York, and they gave me a few thousand dollars to write that book. I flunked English in college so I am not this big wordsmith. I got the Catalog from the Government Printing Office and I literally cut and pasted that book. Nothing in the government is copyrighted, so it was not plagiarism. I sent it to the people in New York and it was funny but they took a half a year or a year to edit this thing. The government just spent millions of dollars editing it. Those snobs in New York wanted to do it "their way."

When the book was published, I went on talk shows and it became a *New York Times Bestseller*. You can get better information than the experts themselves. Instead of buying it from my book, you can go right to the Catalog. Cut out the middleman, and get the best stuff.

If you do not think my book has the most up-to-date information, go there. You will see programs, and they are all in funny places. At the U.S. Department of Housing and Urban Development, you can get $15,000 for graduate students to study housing related topics. All the graduates complain that there is no money for graduate education, because they look at two or three major government programs and they forget about the others.

Do you want a job in law enforcement? There is a program in the Justice Department that is run through the state governments that will pay you for a four-year college degree in any area of law enforcement as long as you say that when you graduate you will work in law enforcement somewhere. If you want to become a cop, a lawyer, a DNA specialist and work on the OJ trial, anything at the federal or state level, you can get that money.

Or here is $5,000 to become a librarian from the Department of Education. That is right. The Department of Education — do you want to study library science? That is where it is.

Or, how about community planning? The Department of Housing and Urban Development has $11,000 for you to study community planning. See, it is all kinds of funny stuff.

How about $800 from the Department of Energy to attend a conference because you are an engineering student? Here is my idea. If you are an engineering student going to college up in the Northeast in the cold winter months, find a conference during winter break out in California. You get $800 to fly out there, attend a conference, and then you sit on the beach for the rest of the break and look at the girls. That is the way to use it.

How about $14,000 for a graduate degree in foreign languages? Or there is money at the Department of Defense to get your graduate degree in mathematics.

How about $2,500 for a degree in history from the National Endowment of the Humanities? Do you want to become a nurse, a nurse practitioner, or study child development or violence training? You can get up to $30,000 to do that from the Department of Health and Human Services.

Your State Has Money For College and Artists

There are all these programs in healthcare, criminal justice, or housing and they are all at the federal level. That is just one place you have got to look, because what you want to do next is go to the state level. You need to call your state office of higher education. Every state has one, and they will have a half a dozen to a dozen programs at the state level. That is one of the programs my engineering major son has gotten. He gets $3,000 as long as he says when he graduates he will work in engineering in the state of Maryland for a year. For every year they give him money, they want him to work for a year in the state. That sounds fair enough. He will probably wind up working in Maryland anyway, so it is a great deal.

In other states, you can get $1,000 towards your tuition if you join the Air National Guard or other weird things, like if you are a descendant of the Confederate Army and live in Florida, they give you $150. Or you could get $5,000 to study accounting at any university in New York. Or, receive $1,500 to become a music teacher in Tennessee. Go to the state level and they will send you a listing of the programs. Get the applications and fill them out. There is no magic to these things, and then you are on your way.

Also at the state level is money for artists. You could be a tap dancer, a choreographer, a singer, a storyteller, an arts teacher, a printmaker, a writer — even a poet. These are all at your state arts council. Every state government has an arts council, who give out up to $180 million every year. These are usually for short-term projects.

I actually talked to a piano player in Ohio. He is in one of my infomercials. He was a struggling piano player, and got money from the government to make his CD. He also gives concerts in the state and the government pays him.

If you are a performer you can travel overseas and perform. The U.S. Department of State will send your group to China, Japan or Yugoslavia or somewhere else to show them American art and music.

Go to your state capital and ask for the state office. It is usually called the state council for the arts. Get their programs. You could be a weaver and get $2,000 to work on your project. It is given out all the time.

Actually, if you are an artist, another neat thing is that the government buys art. You could be a freelance artist, drawing brochures for the EPA on your kitchen table, and getting government contracts, so that is another way to get paid for your art. They need more graphic design, so maybe you can make $50,000 creating pamphlets and information booklets.

A writer is the same way. Where are more words written anywhere else than in the government? All the government produces is words. If you are a writer or an editor, look at these government contracts and find out how you can get a piece of the action.

The other place for money for higher education is through non-profits. There are thousands and thousands of scholarships out there. They are real, and take effort. You could go on the web or to the library and find a lot about them. We even have them in our books.

What is the key to getting all this money? It is a numbers game. You are not going to go to the financial aid office and apply to one or two places, and expect to get everything you want. You are going to have to fill out 50 applications, maybe 100. Who cares? Once you fill out one or two, they are all the same anyway. That is how you get the money. The more applications you fill out, the better the chances you are going to have to get this money. You have heard about scholarships for people with two left ears or whose grandmother was in the Polish navy. That is all real, but you have to go out and search for it. There are already a lot of resources, organizations, and books that will help you identify these.

$8,000 To Train For A New Job

There is another source of money for education and training, and that is training money. There are a lot of training programs at the federal and state level. If you lose a job you could probably get $8,000 to go train to become a French chef or a computer network engineer. A guy called me, who was a bouncer in a club. He got $10,000 to become a computer network engineer. He went from $7 an hour to $50,000 a year. That kind of thing happens. A guy stopped me on the street and said, "Lesko, I got your book." They gave him $8,000 to take a course at George Washington University on how to become an event planner.

There is a lot of training money out there in our society because that is how you succeed in life, it seems. You have got to have those skills and the government is well aware of the need. The government has set up one-stop training information centers in every state, and in every county now, too. To start your quest for this money, the best place to start is your state government. Ask them about the one-stop training centers, and they can give you the local center. Go down, make an appointment and find out about the programs. They are not going to have every program, but they will know most of the programs.

There are 150 training programs, and the biggest problem is that you cannot go to the yellow pages to find out about any of them. That is the pity. The government does not advertise. You cannot look under "Training," or even "Government," to find them. You are going to have to do some work yourself, and the place to start is that one-stop training program in your state capital.

Also for women, every state capital has an office just for women. Call the governor's office and ask for the women's commission for your state. They will know about the training programs just for women. There are a lot of special organizations for women going back into the workforce, and there is special training money just for that situation. Women who want to get training in traditional men's jobs are eligible for special programs.

Women are a little bit more clever at all of this. Women know about the new society because they know they have to get the education, training or have their own business. That is why women start two out of every three businesses that are started today. That is why there are more women on college campuses now than there are men. They know what is happening in our society. The rest of us have to be aware of it, too, and get trained or get that education so that we can continue contributing for the rest of our lives!

Start Your Own Non-Profit

Maybe you want to start your own non-profit organization. That may be a reality for you. As you look around for grant money to change the world, you find out that a lot of it is for non-profit organizations. (See page 110, for the mechanics of starting your own non-profit)

Well, there are two ways of handling that issue. You can start your own non-profit organization, or another way to do it is to you find an existing non-profit organization with whom you can work. Are you looking for $100,000 to work with the elderly, youth or to improve the neighborhood, and the people giving out the money say you have to be a non-profit organization? You can go to your church, community college or any other non-profit organization and ask them to work with you if you give them a piece of the pie.

Usually what happens is that you can apply for this grant, and give the non-profit 10, 20 or 30 percent of the money for using their name and having a place to hang your hat. It is often called overhead. They get that to give you a desk there if you get the grant. You work out the deal with the non-profit that you only be there if you get the money. That is a normal relationship. Many of these non-profit organizations work that way. It is not difficult to try to talk them into doing this. It's a win/win situation.

The other alternative is that you start a non-profit yourself. There is no magic to this either. But like anything else in life, if you talk to an accountant or lawyers, they can complicate the heck out of everything and it can wind up costing you thousands. Or you can do it yourself for approximately $150.

There was a friend of mine who used to work with one of the big online companies, and he always wanted to start his own non-profit. He wanted to help kids, and was very active in veterans' organizations. Like me, he was a Vietnam vet. He thought, "What this country needs is not veterans who whine about how they were mistreated, but veterans who do something for the community." He went to an attorney and the attorney said, "Yeah, it will cost you $3,000 to become a non-profit organization." He said, "If I had $3,000 I would do something for the community, and not give it to some attorney to become a non-profit organization."

I was sitting in his office one day, opened up my book and said, "Here, call this office over at the IRS." The IRS has a special office that just helps people start non-profit organizations. And actually, they have a special office within that just for veterans' organizations. He called them and they sent him the paperwork. He had it all out on his dining room table and it took a couple of evenings to complete. He filled it all out, sent it in, and of course it was screwed up. The IRS sent it back to him and he made the changes. And with any question he had, he found he had a person at the IRS to call and straighten it out.

Just like taxes. You can worry the heck over it, or just give it your best shot and hope for the best. If you screw up enough, the government will tell you, and then you change it and send it back to them. It still beats paying a couple of grand to some attorney.

When he started his non-profit he raised $3,000 in his first fundraiser and gave it to the local Ronald McDonald's House in honor of veterans. See, that is what to do with money. Why give it to some attorney or an accountant to become a non-profit when you can take that same money and do something good with it? That is what a non-profit is in business to do, and that could be you.

The other hurdle is filing at the state government. Call the state capital operator, ask for the Secretary of State, and then ask them "How do I become a non-profit organization in the state?" That will cost you usually under $100 to become a non-profit and you can learn that system too. The important thing is that you did not let a hurdle like $3,000 for some attorney stop you from doing what you want to do, becoming your own non-profit.

And once you become a non-profit, the joy is not only finding the money that is out there for you, but it is fun taking advantage of all the other stuff for non-profit organizations. The government has programs where you could get volunteers to work for you for free. Action does that, Vista, and the White House even has a national service program that sends people to non-profit organizations to work for free. You could have free employees that are paid by the government to work for you.

Also, you could get free stuff, just because you are a non-profit organization. You know the drug confiscated limousines that the Justice Department gets from drug runners? Because you are non-profit, they could give it to you for free. Any surplus government property, you as a non-profit could get for free. And that is usually run through a state agency of surplus property. The federal government gives it to the state government, which in turn gives it to non-profit organizations. So, check out how to get free stuff or free property.

I know a woman down in Texas who got an entire air force base for free because she was going to set up a non-profit radio station. They had an air force base they were not using, so they gave it to this lady because she was a non-profit organization.

You want to do some volunteer work this summer? Go to your local homeless shelter or your local church. Learn about this system and how to get furniture for them for free from the government because they are a non-profit organization. But again, you have to know about the program in order to take advantage of it.

When a book is copyrighted, you have to send two copies to the Library of Congress. Actually, on my books I put a copyright on the title page but I don't send it to the Library of Congress. If people want to Xerox my book or copy it, you cannot really stop them and the copyright just keeps the honest people honest. The Library of Congress puts the good books on the shelf because people want to use them and get them for free. If they do not need the books, they give them away.

I got a call from the Library of Congress once. "Hey, Lesko — you didn't apply for a copyright, and it says it's copyrighted." I do this on all my books so I asked them why they were calling on this particular book. They told me that they were getting a lot of requests in the library for the book, and it wasn't in their collection. So when they found out it was copyrighted, they knew they could make me send them two copies for free under the law. That way they didn't have to buy one.

So, they got me. I had to send them a $35 application, plus two copies of the book because I put the copyright on the title page. But all the extra books the Library of Congress has they give away for free. Your grade school could have 1,000 free books sent to them. Work through your congressman's office to get this, and you can even use the books as a fundraiser. The free books are from the Exchange and Gift Division at the Library of Congress. Call up your congressman's office and they will provide the information for you.

Another thing available is art. The National Gallery of Art will send out free art to non-profits. How about getting a Jeep for your parade, a canon, a tank or the Blue Angels to come and fly over your parade? You can. Put in your request and they will do that for you.

How about if your women's group could get a top-gun pilot to come and speak at a meeting? You can get speakers because you are a non-profit organization, community group or an association of musicians. Want to know how to write off your summer vacation when you travel? Call the IRS and tell them your association's next meeting, and how you would like an agent to come and talk for free about how to write off your summer vacation. Because you are a non-profit, they will, and that is what is neat in this country. There are so many goodies out there for non-profit organizations if you know where to ask.

The Department of Energy has tools for schools. All the surplus equipment they have at the Department of Energy, such as scientific equipment, you can get for free if you are a school. For homeless shelters, there are certain surplus property programs set up just for people who run homeless shelters. Locate a homeless shelter or church in your community with whom you would like to work, and find out how to get the pastor a drug-confiscated limousine or a cigarette boat to run around the local lake.

More importantly, maybe you need a van. Maybe you need new furniture or used computers that are still very good and can be used. You could get equipment that is just a year or two old that is still very usable and worthwhile. You could get it for free because you are a non-profit organization. A lot of these grants are for non-profits, but do not let that stop you. You either work with the non-profit organization or you become your own non-profit organization and that is easy to do. You have just got to do it!

Develop An Info Tool Kit

Kaboom! Do you hear that? That is the information explosion. You have probably been hearing it for years now. Data, data everywhere and not a thought to think. We are living in this information society. There is more information now than in the history of mankind. Do you realize that in the last 30 years our society has created more information than in the previous 5,000? That is right. You know that. You have seen it. You have seen all the books, magazines and TV stations. Go on the web now and put in a keyword like "back pain," "grant money," or something like that, and you will get a million citations. That is how our society is now and you have to learn how to cope with this information explosion. That is what I want to talk about now.

I have been doing this for about 25 years. I have got an MBA in management information systems, and it was my dream to have some kind of business. I didn't care. I would have sold hotdogs in the park. Actually, back in the '70s, I even had a computer software company that went belly-up. I must have been the only person in the world that had a computer business that failed.

1973 Changed The World Of Information

After you have a lot of failures, what it seems like you do in this country is become a teacher or a consultant. Well, I became both. I became a professor in computer science at a local university, and then I became a consultant to Fortune 500 fat cats. By the way, the mid '70s was a crucial time in our society. Actually about 1973 was when the whole world changed. I really believe that.

Before 1973 whatever happened usually traveled along on a graph on a straight line. Organizations would plot sales for a couple of years and the path would normally continue. To keep things going along that path all you had to do was take care of what was going on inside of your organization.

Then 1973 changed our whole world, and the country has never been the same. We even fell behind countries like Japan and Germany. These people were beating our pants off until the '90s. So, we went through 20 or 30 years where we were not the best. Other people were better, and that is really because we did not know how to handle 1973.

Internal vs. External Information In Organizations

What happened in 1973? That was the time when people realized that information outside their organization was important. The oil embargo happened. We thought we had all the power in the world then all of a sudden, a few Arab states halfway across the world decided to yank up the price of oil and it crippled us. It devastated the whole economy because some little country decided to change their prices, and it brought us to our knees.

That was when we started to realize we could not just take care of what was inside our organization. We had to know what was outside of our organization, and that was how I started this company. Back in 1975, I started a business called Washington Researchers. I wanted to help organizations find out what was going on outside of their company, or outside of their organizations.

The accounting people ruled the companies — payroll, accounts receivable, manufacturing. That was what the executives had to know about in order to survive. Now, in 1973 they had to know more. They had to know what was going on outside of their organization. It was this external information that could hurt them more than the internal information.

The First Information Brokerage Business

That was why I set up a company that was going to get information. I was going to design an external management information system, and was going to get information for all these hotshot executives on what was going on outside of their organization. I said, "Hey, if you plotted and kept up to date on your markets you will succeed. I will prepare monthly reports on what is going on in your markets, and also your competitors."

Not only that, you had to know about legislation because Congress could pass a law and put you out of business. Or, what about the development of new technology that could help you? Gosh, is somebody going to have a new idea, or a new patent that will put you out of business? A good executive, I felt, had to monitor these four areas: markets, competition, legislation and technology.

I was going to go out and save the world, and convince organizations they needed this. I would do these reports every month. Well, it did not really work out that way. I could not convince anybody. Nobody had that kind of foresight. Everybody was fighting fire drills and did not want to get reports that would inundate them with paperwork. Really, they did not even understand me. These were fat cats of big corporations.

So, what I did was offer research. What do you want to know? I will get the information for you on anything you want. What happened was that these fat cats would call me and would want to know mostly about their competitors. They would want to know about getting into new businesses, or getting into new markets.

I started my business with just me, a phone and a desk. I had a little one-bedroom apartment here in Washington, DC, and I ran the whole business. I would be sitting in my underwear most of the time, waiting for the phone to ring. I just had two failing businesses and I was starting a business again. I think if I did not have those two failing businesses, I would not have anywhere near the success I have today. I would have some mediocre business that was just plugging along and getting by. But the failures were the best thing that happened to me.

My 2 Failures

I had a computer business that failed, and another little research company that failed. With an MBA, I would start a business like they taught me in business school. I would go out and get the accountants, the lawyers and the proper tax structure, the power furniture, the power business cards and the power drapes — all this stuff that I thought was necessary in order to succeed. When my companies went out of business, who won? The guy from whom I bought the drapes, the accountants and the lawyers were the winners. They got my money early, and I went out of business. I was SOL.

When I started my third business, I thought as an entrepreneur starting your own business, your most important resource is you. You are doing most everything, so you have to be very critical of how you spend your time. If you are having meetings about picking out drapes for your office, that is a waste of time. If you are having meetings with an accountant, figuring out the right tax structure, and you are not even making money yet, that is a waste of time. Who cares? You are going to pay taxes on what? Nothing.

Identify Your Critical Success Factors

I figured out that an entrepreneur had to focus on the critical success factors of the business. I believe the single critical success factor of any business is customers. If you do not have customers, you have got nothing! You have got zero, zilch, zip, nada. You have got to concentrate on getting customers. The rest will fall into place. If you can keep a checkbook, you are an accountant.

Now I have a big business. Every time I take it to accountants, I get so confused. I have to call them to find out what the heck I am doing. The more I keep to myself and just run it like my checkbook, I know what I am doing and how much money I have. So, I figure I am going to keep it simple and just concentrate on getting customers.

The other thing I learned from failure is that nobody cared if I failed. That was the big thing that used to stop me from doing anything. I used to worry that I was going to fail and people would point at me walking down the street. "Oh, there's Lesko, that failure." That big F on my forehead would be prominent to everyone else.

No One Cares If You Fail

But when I failed I found out that nobody really cared, even my friends and family. Superficially, maybe they cared for a few seconds or minutes, but we are all so involved in our own lives. We really do not care that much about other people. It makes interesting gossip, but they do not really care. That was what used to stop me from doing things — that fear of failure. Once I failed a couple of times and I saw that nobody really cared, that gave me courage. I could not wait to start another business because I felt that the worst that could happen is I fail, and I had already done that a couple of times.

Success Is Having Fun

So the third time I just said this time I am just going to start having fun. That was when it was different. That was when I tried to find out what was unique in me and bring that out so that I was different from everybody else. I was trying to be like everybody else in my other businesses because people were telling me, "This is the way to be successful," so I tried to do that. Than someone else would say, "This is the way to do it," and I would try to be like that.

Nonsense. What people want in this world is something different all the time, not something the same. We already have the same. So, I started trying to have fun, trying to be different, and that was when things started working. Even now, 20 years later after my first success, I still have to fight every day to find out what is unique about me and to keep having that fun. I know the successful part of it is when you are doing what is natural to you.

From 1 to 30 People In 3 Years

That was when it took off! I went from a one-bedroom apartment where my business was just me, a phone and a desk to where I had 30 or 35 people and a big office down on K Street in Washington, DC with all the other mucky-mucks down there trying to get money. And it all happened in about 3 years.

To tell you the truth, you got better service from me when I was in my bedroom. People used to call me, and I was the whole kit and caboodle. It was only me, and I think I charged $25 an hour back then. This was 20 years or so ago. I would work forever for that kind of money.

When I was on K Street, I would hire these people and charge $100 an hour, $200 an hour or whatever I could get, and I had people whose names I did not know working for my clients. It seems like you get diseconomies of scale as you grow bigger. You charge a higher price and give out a worse product. That is why I keep looking for little guys when I need to find some service— a person who owns it, operates it, does everything. If I went to some big company, I would get down to the 15th tier of some person who does not care. You can never find the people because nobody has their heart in it when they are working for somebody else.

Take Heart In Your Failure, Nixon Died A Hero

There are people in life that really should encourage you about failure, people like Richard Nixon. I will never forget when he was thrown out of the White House. Can you imagine anything worse in life than be thrown out of the White House? Could you imagine calling your mother up and saying, "Mom, they threw me out of the White House?" Nixon was thrown out of the White House, and somehow he redeems himself and dies a hero.

No matter what you do in life, you will never be worse than being thrown out of the White House. So do not worry about failure. When I started this business, I used to put little one-inch ads in the *Wall Street Journal*. I would say things like, "I can get research for you on any topic. Just call me." You cannot really tell your story in a one-inch ad, and that was the problem. I would get all kinds of weird stuff. People would write on napkins in crayon and it was a waste of money.

Little Money Leads To Big Creativity

Having little money is important. You have to be more creative. I took that little money I was using for one-inch ads in the *Wall Street Journal* and decided to come out with a free newsletter on how to get free information. I figured instead of a one-inch ad in the *Wall Street Journal*, if I could get the *Wall Street Journal* to write up about my free newsletter, then I would have the sanction of the *Wall Street Journal* saying, "This guy's a great researcher." I figured they would be more inclined to write up something that was free to their readers.

The hotshots in corporations were what I was after. I figured the *Wall Street Journal* was the place. I only knew about three or four things at the time, so I wrote them up in a four-page newsletter. On page four I put all the stuff that I could do. I am better, faster, cheaper and I will find anything — just call me.

Then these other organizations started writing about my newsletter — the *Wall Street Journal*, the business magazines. For the same price of a one-inch ad, I was able to do this little newsletter and send it out to the media, and they wanted to write about it because they have got to fill those pages with something that hopefully will help their readers. So, a free newsletter on finding free information sounded good, and that was when my phone never stopped ringing. That is what I do now.

It's Not What You Say It's How You Say It

Again, when I started doing consumer books, I found the same thing. You have got all these talk shows and they are not really talk shows. They are just vehicles for selling stuff. I would say, how do I get on talk shows? TV is really entertainment, so I figured out after I did one talk show that it is not what you say, but how you say it. That is what people buy on TV, how things are done.

When I went out there and showed all my energy, danced around and wore question mark suits, they wanted me on TV. They did not care what I said. They just wanted me there. I was on *Letterman* seven or eight times, *Larry King* about a dozen times. I had a beeper because they would use me when somebody cancelled. I remember I was in Chicago one day and Letterman called me. I think it was Christopher Walken who cancelled at the last minute. He had some film he hated and did not want to plug. If I can get seven minutes on national TV, that is worth tens of thousands of dollars.

I remember being on *Letterman* and thinking okay, I am here acting crazy, plugging my book, and then in the middle of my seven minutes I stop and somebody has a commercial for something for which they probably paid $40,000 or $50,000, maybe more for this one-minute commercial. I am getting seven minutes for free because I am acting like an idiot. So that is a lesson on how to use the system.

This business really taught me not only about that, but more importantly how to get information. When I started this business of getting information for business clients, anything they would ask I would do because I was hungry. I wanted to please them. I wanted to get paid, because the only way I got paid was if I got the information.

Mr. Potato Head

So, I was sitting there and I remember one of my first clients called me. It was a guy who was a friend of a friend who had a million dollars invested in a commodity on the New York Commodities Exchange called Maine Potatoes. I did not know anything about potatoes. I was a city kid. I remember when I came to Washington, a friend of mine had a country house and I went out there to see him for dinner. He sent me out in the backyard to find fresh potatoes for dinner. I was out there about 20 or 30 minutes. I finally came back and said, "I cannot find those potato trees.

Where the heck are they?" I had no idea potatoes grew under the ground. That was how much I knew about potatoes.

So, this potential client called me and he said he had all this money. He was a hotshot MBA from Wharton Business School, the University of Pennsylvania, and he knew that most of the people that invested in the market are really just trying to outguess the other idiots that are in the market. He figured if he had some basic information about the supply and demand of potatoes, he would have an edge on everybody else in this potatoes market.

Potatoes were going crazy at that time, and even the *Wall Street Journal* had front-page articles on the subject. What they normally sell for $15, were now selling for $100. People were making or losing fortunes every day in this thing.

So, he called me up on a Wednesday or Thursday and he said, "Lesko, if you can find in 24 hours what the basic supply and demand for Maine potatoes is, we have a deal because we want to make a trade by the end of the week." In those days I would say yes to anything. I did not know about Maine potatoes, but I only charged him if I got the information. So, we agreed on a couple of hundred bucks or whatever for me to get the information. I said yes and had no idea how much it would cost or how long it would take. But I had nothing else to do in those days. I would have worked for this guy for $25.

I would charge what I thought they would pay. That is why the more success you have, the more confident you are to charge more because they probably will pay it. I said okay, I will get the information in 24 hours. When you have a small business at home and you are waiting for clients, you hang around, watching soap operas, going to the kitchen and waiting for the phone to ring. The days can be real boring.

I Ran My Whole Business On One Book

So, now I had a real client. I used to run my whole business on one book called *The US Government Manual*. I knew nothing about Washington. I did not really know where stuff was, as I never used Washington that much. I would rely on the *US Government Manual* because it had a description of all the agencies.

You cannot find in your phonebook things like the Census Bureau. Nothing is listed by keyword. You cannot look under, "Census." You have to know the organizational structure. You have to know that the Census Bureau is part of the Department of Commerce, so you need to first look under the Department of Commerce in the blue pages, and then see under that a listing for the Census Bureau.

So, I picked up *The US Government Manual*. I looked in the index for potatoes. Nothing there. I thought, oh my gosh, what am I going to do? I turned to the table of contents, which had a listing in alphabetical order of all the major departments and agencies. The first agency right up at top was the U.S. Department of Agriculture. Hey, that sounds logical — agriculture, potatoes — so I called the U.S. Department of Agriculture.

I was trying to pretend that I was this big shot research company and needed this important information. I got on the phone and I said, "Hello, this is Mr. Lesko from Megabuck Research Company. I have a client who has to know about the basic supply and demand of Maine potatoes. Do you have someone there who could help me, sir?"

They said, "We have to put you on hold, Mr. Lesko." Like a good bureaucrat, they put me on hold. They came back and said, "Well, Mr. Lesko, we will have to switch you to Charlie Porter." I said, "Charlie Porter? Why are you switching me to Charlie Porter? Does this guy handle prank calls or something like that? I have got to know about the supply and demand of Maine potatoes in 24 hours for my important client."

He said, "Oh, no. He doesn't handle prank calls. Charlie Porter is our resident economist specializing in the supply and demand of Maine potatoes." I said, "Really? There is a guy there who just studies potatoes?" He said yes. Wonderful.

They switched me over to Mr. Porter and I hear, "Porter here." "Mr. Porter, this is Mr. Lesko and I am from Megabuck Research Company. I have got this client who needs to know the basic supply and demand of Maine potatoes in 24 hours. Could you help me out?"

He comes back with, "Yep, I think so." I am thinking in my mind, is this guy really going to help me? So, I start quizzing him a little bit about his background. "Mr. Porter, before I get into it, my client invests a lot of money and I would like to know a little bit about your background."

15 Years Of Studying Potatoes

So he starts telling me. He is a GS-17. For the last 15 or 16 years of his life he has been studying the supply and demand for potatoes. He has got a bachelor's in economics, and a master's in agricultural economics. He has spent 16 years and been making $70-80,000 a year just studying potatoes. I started smelling payday. Porter sounded like he could really help me.

I started getting excited. I said, "Well, Mr. Porter, we can do this. You sound great. How can I get this information?" He said, "Well, you could come down and see me, we could do it over the phone, or I could send you the material — any way you want to do it."

First of all, Mr. Porter did not sound real busy, and I certainly was not busy — this was my only client. So, I made an appointment to go see Charlie the first thing the next morning down at the Department of Agriculture. I was a cab ride away — actually, I rode my bicycle. Trying to find his office was a challenge. There are hundreds of little offices all over — north wing, south wing. I was 10 minutes late for our appointment because I got lost in the maze of all these offices around there.

I finally found his office, and opened the door. It was a little 12 by 12 room with a desk. Charlie was behind the desk. There was another chair in front of the desk, and then all around the walls were bookshelves. There were hundreds of books. I sat down on the chair in front of Charlie's desk, looking and glancing at these bookshelves all over, and I see that every book was about potatoes! I used to think maybe one book was written about potatoes, if you were lucky. Charlie had all these books about potatoes.

Charlie started going on about potatoes. I got there about 9:30 in the morning, and was there for over two and a half hours talking about potatoes. It was amazing. No matter what reference came up, he had a source for it. He would go into his drawers, into his files, and find graphs. He was telling me that he was also a potato statistician where he made potato models. When he said potato models, at first I was thinking of Mr. and Mrs. Potato Head. But no, these were statistical models that he designed that really forecast the supply and demand of Maine potatoes.

He would bring out graph paper, computer models that he generated, and he would put them on the window because he would want to show one graph over another graph. When these two lines crossed, it showed what was going to happen to supply and demand of Maine potatoes. It was just phenomenal.

We started talking about the potato problem in Europe. Everybody was worried. There was a potato shortage in Europe. He got on the phone, and a guy came in the office who was the European potato expert. He was telling us that the scare was just a false alarm because a boat came in just half-loaded with potatoes, or something like that. It was nothing with which to be concerned. It was amazing.

When I found Charlie Porter, the problem was not getting the information — the problem was getting out of his office! I had a feeling that he has been studying potatoes for the last 16 years of his life, and finally somebody asked him what he has been spending a lifetime studying.

His wife is sick of hearing about potatoes, right? Nobody in the government even knows he is there any more, and he just grinds away, studying. He loves potatoes. Who else is going to pay you $60-80,000 a year to study potatoes? Only the government, and that is where these people are.

Then he started showing me the statistics that come out every month from the Department of Agriculture, showing you the supply and demand of potatoes. It showed you how many potatoes were grown, how many potato chips were made, and even how many Pringles potato chips were made because they make them where they squish up all the potatoes, make them perfect and they spit them back out again in some machine. He said, "If you want to get this information every month for free from the government, go across the hall and talk to the potato statistician." There was a guy across the hall and all he did was count potatoes. I could not imagine this stuff.

So, I thanked Charlie after two and a half hours. I was kind of overloaded on potatoes at that time, but I thought that if I went across the hall and talked to the potato statistician, I could get these statistics every month. I could take the report from the government, put my name on it and sell it to my client every month for a revenue stream. What you are trying to do in business is find out how to get money regularly, and not just once in a while. So, that sounded like a good deal to me.

I went across the hall and there are these two big doors. It was like a whole gymnasium, full of people. Rows and rows of desks, and everybody was behind the desks with calculators. They even had the paper coming out of the calculators. It looked like spaghetti. What was amazing to me when I first came into the room was that they had nameplates, and the first name was Asparagus. I thought that was the guy's name, like Mr. Asparagus. But no, it was the name of their commodity. They had an expert, a statistician for every commodity. The first guy was asparagus and bananas; then celery and carrots. They went down the list.

So, I asked the first guy, where was the potato statistician? It was this huge room and looked like hundreds of people. He said, "You go down this row of people here, turn at the end over there, and you won't miss him because the guy way over in the corner is the potato statistician. It looked like one of those old movies of the insurance company.

I get to the end of the row and turn over to the corner, and there is another row there. I see a guy way at the end, and he was wonderful, too. He showed me how to read those statistics and made me smart so that I could then show my client.

I got home that afternoon, called my client, gave him all this stuff, and it was wonderful. That to me is what information is all about in our society. If you find somebody like that, a person who has spent his life studying something, you do not have to worry about information overload, because you have got somebody who read all that stuff.

Free Experts: The Key To Information Overload

I sat in that room with Charlie Porter who had read hundreds and hundreds of books on potatoes. I did not have to sit in the library and read all those books. I could ask Charlie, and he could tell me the one book to read. He could tell me what will be in the books next year because he is working on that research today.

That is the power of information in our society. That is how to cope with the information overload, and what I did for years and years, helping Fortune 500 clients. They would call me for anything. Procter and Gamble wanted to start a chain of pasta stores. Well, I found that the government has a pasta expert, who is some guy getting paid $80,000 a year just to study pasta. They would show me free market studies on pasta, what is hot and what is not, as well as what government money programs are available to start pasta stores.

Just think — if you go onto the web and put in "pasta," you are going to get a million citations. You do not know a good one from a bad one. That is why people are important. You find the experts, and the web may be good for that.

I remember doing a market study on Polish golf carts. Actually, my heritage is Czechoslovakian and that is pretty close to Poland, but gosh, I found a Polish golf cart expert in Washington that did a study on Polish golf carts that I got for free.

My brother was in a health food business. I found a free report on the health food industry for him, a market study that was something that could cost you millions of dollars.

I was doing a report for urinal screens. That is right — urinal screens! A client, a chemical company, was thinking about making urinal screens, and I found a government expert on urinal screens! When I was doing the study, the biggest selling brand for urinal screens was called Sweet Pee. How tacky a business is that? The second biggest selling brand was called Super Pee. My business was really answering thousands and thousands of requests like that from clients, and that was what made me smart. Your clients make you smart, no matter what business you are in because you want to please. You want to get the money or whatever it is, and you will do anything to do it. That is what stretches your imagination.

That is why when we get old, rich and comfortable, you are not stretching any more. The most important thing is change. Our society is changing. There are changes running through our society like a freight train, and the change started occurring back in 1973 because we had to know about our outside world. When you make decisions faster, you will get ahead of the game faster.

There Was Life Before Federal Express

Just think, it was not so long ago that Federal Express started. We did not have Federal Express 20 years ago. What was wrong with the mail? It wasn't fast enough, right? So we had Federal Express. Then after Federal Express, overnight was not fast enough, so we have fax machines to get it to you even faster. Email is doing that now, too, or your phone. You want to get information? We used to have phones only at home. Now we have mobile phones so we get information faster and make decisions faster.

All the indications around our society are that change is happening very fast, and you have to know how to deal with that change. There is more information now available in the world than ever before. I mentioned earlier that in the last 30 years we have created more information than in the past 5,000.

So, I believe as citizens, if you want to prosper in this society, want to get the money, information or help you need, you have to learn how to use the tools in our society. You have to understand what is good and bad about each of these tools. I look at the tools like this, and here is where we go for information in my mind. One is the computer. Two is the library and other things in the library — books, periodical stuff. The other thing is media. Then we have experts. We have paid experts and we have free experts. We have the government. We have the non-profit organizations. We have the telephone, which I think is still a very important tool for information, and your friends, which is another source of information.

Let us run through them again: computer, library, the media, paid experts, free experts, the government, non-profits, the telephone and your friends.

What Is Bad About Computers And The Internet

Now, the computer I gave you a little hint about before. What is good and bad about computers? Technology is always sold by sizzle. When computers first came out, they were selling personal computers like, "Boy, your kids are not going to go to college unless you have a computer. Life is going to pass you by unless you have a computer."

You can go on the computer and read 500 newspapers. Have you finished the morning newspaper on your front door? No. You do not have time to do that. What are you going to do with 500 newspapers? That is what I mean.

We get sucked up in technology and forget what is really good and bad about that technology. The salesmen sell us the sizzle. The key to buying technology is that the longer you wait, the better and cheaper it is.

Just think, the first piece of technology in our country that was for mass consumption was the automobile. The first automobiles were very expensive, just like the first computers or the first anything in technology. They were very complicated. To get around in this country, you jumped on a horse to get somewhere. Now these complicated automobiles with gas, clutches and all this kind of stuff would make you worry. There was no software for the automobiles — in other words, no roads. If you had a car and you did not have roads, you could not get anywhere. That was like having a computer without software, so it was very difficult.

Also, listen to this — horses were faster than the cars. So why did people buy those first automobiles? Because you had those high-tech junkies who wanted the first of everything. If you waited, until Henry Ford came along and made it cheap, mass-produced, and the infrastructure of the highway system was set up in our country and the cars became easier to use, then automobiles became a good buy.

It was the same way with computers. The first computers were almost like toys. People did not even write letters so they did not have to use word processors. Right now for a computer, the good parts are word-processing. Why you would have a typewriter nowadays is silly; but remember, we used to use typewriters way back when. We did not write that much, so why did we need a computer? You got sucked in anyway.

The other thing is that computers handle large amounts of data. That is what a computer does. They would show these things like, "Balance your checkbook by using a computer." If you did not balance your checkbook by hand, it would take you longer to put it into the computer and balance it. That is until we got the software sophisticated enough and easy enough like Quick Books. It really is easier now, but in the beginning it was not.

You have to evaluate what it is really good for, like the Internet and online databases. If you want to live in a cave and not do anything, that is fine. Most of the stuff on the Internet you could probably get somewhere else, but now it is becoming easier and easier. But in the beginning, it was not.

I bought one of the first PCs. It was almost $10,000. And that was in 1980 dollars. Then it got to about $5,000 and a $1,000 PC was unheard of. That is how much it costs today and they have all of the software. So, the longer you wait for something, the better it is. It was like that ten years ago with the first cell phones. I know people who paid thousands of dollars a month for their cell phones in the beginning, and now for $29.95 you have one. You waited, because that is what the economics of technology is. The longer you wait, the better it is, and the cheaper it will be.

Computers cause as many problems as they solve. You go on the Internet today and you put in a keyword like "money," "grants," or "back pain." You are going to get 5,000 citations. So now you have got a bigger problem than when you started. What are you going to do with 5,000 websites? You do not know a good website from a bad website. Maybe you say the first one is better. Why is that first one better? Do you know why that first one is probably first? Because that first person paid money to have his name come up first. That is the only reason that it is first, and that is how these websites work.

It causes many problems. You have to know when to use a computer as a good tool, and when it is not. To my mind, if you find a Charlie Porter, he knows all the websites. He knows the one website that is good and saves you that problem. That is how to use the computer and use another source to make sure that you have got the right place.

To me, even on the web, the best stuff is really coming from government or non-profit organizations, besides meeting friends and email. That is separate. But for actually getting information, it is those kinds of things. Also the web is wonderful for getting opinions from people, the forums and things like this. In other words, doctors used to have to wait to go to an annual meeting to find out something. Now, the smart doctors can find answers. They can just put it on a forum and get an answer, the same way you and I can. So, it increases the speed of our society because we get answers quicker. There are a lot of good things on the web and on the computer, but you have to know what is good and bad about it. It does not solve all your problems.

What Is Good About The Library

Also, we have another source — the library. Now, you are thinking, who is going to ever use the library? Well, nobody did much in the past, to tell you the truth. If you were not on the web you could go to your local library and probably get on the web there and they would help. I have been in this business 25 years, even before the web became popular. I used to think that because we live in an information society, the most important building in our community should be the library, right? But no, it is the video store or something like that. You never see big lines waiting to get into the library. You know why? Most libraries grew up handling books, periodicals, publications and things in print. To tell you the truth, things in print are about yesterday.

When I made my first book that became a *New York Times Bestseller*, I copied that whole book from a book that is published in the Government Printing Office. Nothing in the government is copyrighted so it was legal. It is plagiarism but plagiarism is not illegal. I took that, sent it to New York, and they messed around with it for six or eight months before it came out in the bookstore. So, if you got that book, it was out of date.

You could go to the Government Printing Office by the time the book came out and get a newer edition already. The publishing process is long and cumbersome. It is getting faster, and that is what the net is about, too, but when you are buying stuff in print, it is out of date. The answers are changing every day. It is so difficult to keep up. Most of us are looking for information about today and tomorrow. "Where do I get this money?" "What is the best job to get?" "What is the best investment?" These kinds of issues are about what is happening today in our society, not yesterday. Printed material is about yesterday.

It is the same with magazines. I used to write for *Good Housekeeping* magazine. They were two, three and four months from when I wrote the article and the article was printed. That is the problem. We, as consumers, are looking for information about today, when in fact the stuff in books, magazines, periodicals and things like that are about yesterday.

What is good about that, though, is that it is very important because it also finds you sources. If I wrote a book about information and it came out last year, I am probably still keeping up on that information, and keeping up about that topic. Printed material is good for history and also for finding out who the experts are in the field. That is why I go to the library a lot, to look for leads, to look for sources and things like that. We should honor those public libraries. What I want to do and what every library should have is a telephone. You could go there and they could help you find information on the telephone, and not just the web or books. The telephone is important, and we will get to that tool as we go on.

Actually, I worked in a public library for a while down in Orlando. It is one of the richest libraries in the world. I badmouth libraries all the time because they are not keeping up. I said I should put my money where my mouth is and find out from the inside. So, they let me work in this library in Orlando, Florida. It is a rich library because they get a percentage of all real estate taxes. Development was booming in Orlando. I worked there for a couple of weeks, every day helping at the reference desk or whatever. They were really good at solving people's problems concerning local information, like what movie schedules there were, who was your local congressman and things like that. They were terrific.

But to find out what the latest cure to back pain was, they would go to a book that was written a couple of years ago. Now you and I know, every day in the media we find out there is a new cure to this. Things are changing too quickly to find out the latest information if it is published in a book.

The Media Is Superficial

So, that is the library. We have covered computers, the Internet and the library. The media is another major source of information in our society. We have got to be really careful about using this media, because number one, the media is superficial. It is really not there to be an important source of information. Most all of it is headlines, not really checked for accuracy, and most of it is really a result of press releases. I have seen studies stating that 70 or 75 percent of everything that is in the media is coming from a press release.

There is a new study that talks about how estrogen replacement therapy really does not help with heart disease. For months, everybody believed it did. I am sure people knew that before, but it is somebody who did the study and sent a press release to the media about it. The media reads the press release and then they give you a one-minute sound bite. They do not give you the ifs, ands, buts or maybes because nobody has time. They know you will not listen to all the ifs, ands or buts.

The same thing happens if you see something on *CNN* about the growth of yogurt in this country. That is probably a result of a press release from the American Yogurt Council, who is trying to promote more yogurt in this country. They do a study, taking all the statistics from the yogurt council, who is biased. They show you how great yogurt is.

You are sitting there, "Oh, that is a good business opportunity to get into because *CNN* said so." No — *CNN* is taking it from somebody else who has a biased viewpoint and giving you one minute for it. So, you cannot really know the subject or depend on that and know the ifs, ands or buts.

Just think if you see a study that says eating broccoli cures cancer. You see these headlines all the time because that is a great headline and the media will grab onto that for sensationalism and try to make something of it. But if you go to your doctor and you say, "Hey, what about this," the doctor is not even going to know about it. They cannot keep up on all this stuff. It is impossible. That is why you have to have sources other than the media to get the ifs, ands or buts. I will show you later how you can find an expert, a Charlie Porter on broccoli and cancer — somebody who is studying that and not biased, and can get you the information. You can find out what you need to know, but you have to do some extra work.

Look in the media. Have you ever read in your local newspaper a story about something you know? Maybe you were at some event and then you read the story or you know the situation. What is going to happen is they are going to get the first paragraph right. The second paragraph is going to be a little off, and by the third paragraph, it is going to be like Disneyland! You will say, "Where the heck did they find that?" If that happens on something you know, think of what is going on with the stuff you read that you do not know. That is very important.

I was in Vietnam when Woodstock was going on. I did not really know about it. But my teenage kid wanted to go to Woodstock II and he could not get his yuppie friends to go with him. None of their parents would let them go because they were only 16 at the time. So, I went with him to Woodstock, and when I came back I read the stories about Woodstock II. They talked about the chaos, the fires and all this vandalism. That was true, but that was not the Woodstock I attended. When I was at Woodstock II, it was probably one of the most boring things I have ever seen. The kids were so nice. You had a quarter of a million young people. I was the oldest person there. I was in my mid-fifties and I was taking a survey of who was older than me. I saw this old guy walking around, and said, "Hey man, how old are you?" He stared me in the eye and then put up his fingers and started counting. He was a little drifty. Then he said, "Forty-seven." The guy looked like 116. I think he has been on drugs since the last Woodstock.

So, I was convinced that I was the oldest guy up there. But it was neat. These young people were so polite. A quarter of a million kids is like the 100th largest city in the United States. You know if you go to any large city, and you turn on the local news, you are going to see a fire, right? The local news is going to lead with a fire, some vandalism, a killing, a rape, whatever it is. But living in that city you will be oblivious to it. That may be going on, but that is not what the city's about.

At Woodstock II, that was what happened. I saw those fires. It was just going on. It was not even threatening, and I did not feel threatened. Maybe it was my age. When I was a teenager and went to a rock concert, you had all this machismo going on. You could not look at anybody cross-eyed, or fights would break out.

But at Woodstock II, everybody was so nice. I dress a little funny, even in casual clothes. People would comment and I would have some quick wit remark back, and then I would feel guilty because these people were really serious. We stayed right until the end, but all you saw in the media was that Woodstock II was terrible, fires, and gangsters.

Sure, there were 20, 30 or 40 people doing that, but you had 250,000 people who were nice, polite and having a great time. The media has to play up different things to make it news. Remember, news is something different. If they are showing you boring nice things, which is the norm, then that is not news. You have to get in your mind what news is all about. It is what is different, weird, and not the norm. Do not make any of your decisions based on what you see in the media. You have to go out and get other information before you make those important decisions.

Experts Are Wrong: They Can't Keep Up

The other tool is paid experts. If you need something, you go to a paid expert. You call me and want to know about information. I will charge you, as much as I can get. But like me, doctors, lawyers or whatever, most of what we know we learned in the first year in business. Everything I know now, the stories I am telling and the skills I have learned, I developed in the first year of business. I have spent the last 20 years putting different titles on it and saying it differently, trying to package it differently. I have got a business to run and I do not have time to learn any more.

A doctor is the same way. How much time does your doctor spend really learning that new cure to cancer? When was the last time that you spent more than three, four or five minutes with your doctor when he did not have his hand on the doorknob, waiting to go out the door? See, they do not have time any more. It is too tough.

Our society is so complicated now and changes so quickly that the so-called experts cannot keep up. It is impossible, so the experts do not really know. You talk about who is going to win the election before the election. Everybody is guessing. When these paid experts are getting money for something, they have less time to really study because now they are in the business of making money, and that is where their time is spent, making money and not learning, and getting as much leverage out of the little skills they do have.

In An Information Society: Free Is Better

Remember, you do not get what you pay for in our society. That is silly. Experts are there because they are convenient most of the time. You will see an ad for a lawyer. You will not see an ad for the free lawyer; they do not have the money to advertise. You will see ads for doctors nowadays; you will not see the ads for the free medical information because they do not have money to put the ad in the paper.

The bank will have ads about the money they have for sale. That is what banks do; they sell money. The government does not sell you money. They give it away for free, so they do not have ads for it. So, that is important.

To me, free experts are better. Where do the free experts hang out? They are not in clubs like the American Medical Association or the American Bar Association. That is why I could not make a whole lot of money selling research. I could not charge enough. When you sell services in this country, you really have to charge a lot of money. And the only way I feel that people get away with charging a lot of money are those that have good clubs and good unions, like the American Medical Association, the American Bar Association, the researcher's association — a big enough union that we could charge $300 an hour and really make a killing.

The free experts are out there. They are in two places: government and non-profit organizations. I believe — and I am biased so do not trust me a lot of times, either — the federal government and state government is the largest source of money, help and information in the world. I have made a career professing this, so again, I am very biased, but I believe it. Almost 35 percent of everything in our society is government. That is about what you pay in taxes. About a third of our income goes to government.

The government does not make stuff. It is not like General Motors, where it is making automobiles. It does not make products. It has two things: information and money. Information is in the form of paper or it is in the form of expertise. I actually went out and counted — in the federal government alone there are almost 700,000 experts, people like Charlie Porter, who are sitting there getting paid to study stuff, everything from broom handles to jelly beans.

Most people think of information in Washington as Pueblo, Colorado. I have made a living out of selling and using government information. I have done this almost my entire adult life, and I have never used Pueblo, Colorado. Pueblo, Colorado is just the tip of the iceberg.

Government Publishes Twice As Much As All Private Publishers

There is another organization in Washington called the National Technical Information Service. This is an organization that collects technical information from various agencies of the government. Every year, they publish 100,000 different titles. All of commercial publishing, all the New York publishers, every publisher in this country, all of them combined publish an average of 50,000 books a year. One little publisher in the government is publishing twice as much as all the private publishers in this country. That is what I mean about the power of information.

The government spends over $3 billion alone to do the census every 10 years, just to count people. We count a lot more than that, but $3 billion. Do you know how much $1 billion is? If you spent $1,000 every day since the day Christ was born, as of today, you would have not spent $1 billion. And we spend $3 billion on the census. We spend almost $2 trillion on the budget in the federal government. It is astounding. That is right, a third of everything.

A lot of people say, "Well, I want to ignore the government. I do not care what the government does as long as it stays away from me!" That is stupid. It is ignoring a third of our society. I live in Washington, DC. Hating the government is sort of like hating the freeways to get somewhere. You hate those freeways. But if I only have two days to get on the beach, am I going to take seven hours going on the small roads because I hate the freeways to get to the Jersey shore for the weekend? No. I am going to get on 95 because it is the fastest way I can use, even though I hate the freeways and they are boring.

That is the same way with the government. You may hate the government, but so many times it is going to be the fastest and best way to get anywhere. The other thing to remember is that you hear all the bad stuff about Washington because we have 6,000 reporters who are sitting at the National Press Building. Their job is to show you how the government screwed up today. You are going to look at the media and see stories about waste, fraud and abuse — "Hammers at the Defense Department for $50,000," or "Fraud at the Department of Housing and Urban Development," "Sex in the White House." Do you think sex is not going on anywhere else? You think that fraud is not going on anywhere else? No. It is just that we live in a society where all this is public.

But do not throw the baby out with the bathwater. There are a lot of tools that you could use that are there. Sure, all that stuff you read is true, but you can go to any organization and find the same. You say that everybody in the government is lazy and shiftless. In any big organization, most of the people are that way. Go to your bank or even the 7-Eleven. You get 20 percent of the people doing 80 percent of the work. That seems to be a basic law of physics in this country.

The government is so powerful. It has all these experts. Where else are you going to find these Charlie Porters or the grant money we are talking about to do anything? That is why the fat cats use this stuff. That is why it is not going to go away. I have been at this for 20-some years, through Republican administrations, Democrat administrations. Ronald Reagan said he was coming to town and he was going to cut the bureaucrats. The government grew under Ronald Reagan. That is the reality of it. It does not go away, no matter what they say. You have got to start learning how to use these things.

It does not solve every problem, but it is an important tool for you to start to use. If you could find an expert who spent their whole life studying a topic, they could tell you the one website to read. They could tell you the one book to read, or whatever it is. They could tell you what is going to be in the book or on the websites next month or next year because they are researching that today. That is what is fun, and what life is all about.

Non-profits organizations are another great source of information. Say you have a new idea for a teacup, and want to start a teacup business. You can go to Washington and find your Charlie Porter for teacups, plus you can contact a non-profit association that is an expert in this topic, the National Teacup Manufacturers Association. We are an extremely organized society.

How do you find these associations? There is a book in the library called *Gales Encyclopedia of Associations*. That is one book I wish I wrote. He has been selling that thing for 30 or 40 years. Every library and every big organization buys it because of the power that these associations have.

There is a Barbie doll association for people with Barbie dolls. If you want to invest in Barbie dolls, that is the place you should go first to find out about that investment. They are going to have some of the best information. It may be biased because they are pro-Barbie doll, but where else are you going to get it?

There is a bullfighting association. There is a green olive association. There is a bobsledding association. There is a hearing dog resource center association. Even a parents of murdered children association. Or how about this? A toilet seat manufacturers association. That is right. Remember my urinal screens? There is a urinal screen association, too.

I took a golf lesson this past week with my 16-year old kid who is a gorilla, about six foot two and about 185 pounds. He does not play that much, yet he hits a golf ball a mile.

After we had the lesson, the instructor told me he wanted to start a golf school and he did not know where to go. I said find the golf course manufacturers association, and learn what states and zip codes have the highest concentrations of new golf courses. Where are they building the most new golf courses in this country? That is where you probably want to start a school. You do not want to go where it is all mature market, where the schools and courses have been around forever. You want to go to a place where there are a lot of new players. They are the people who need lessons.

The Government Cured My Back Pain

Associations and the government are both web-oriented. But remember, a lot of the stuff on the web is going to be out of date. So don't stop after just checking their web site. You still have to rely on people. I had back pain about 20-some years ago, when I first started this business. I thought the back pain originated from the funny things they made me sleep on in the Navy. I was in the Navy for three years, two months and nine days, but who was counting?

I was going to my doctor, and he was telling me things like, "Oh Lesko, your back pain is not so bad. Everybody has back pain. Come back when we can operate." I would go to another doctor and he would tell me the same thing. "Try this." I go back, "No." "Well, try that." And that is a clue when they say, "Try this." You come back — "Try that." They are guessing.

I took some of my own medicine. I called the National Institutes of Health, and in about three or four phone calls I found this bureaucrat, who specializes in back pain. Here was a guy at the National Institutes of Health literally handing out millions of dollars in back pain research. He was telling me the results of research that were not even published yet. This was about 20-some years ago, and he said that 99 percent of back pain is caused by the way we lead our life. The tension ties the muscles, so it is really a lack of flexibility. He said the YMCA had a back pain course that had a 75 percent cure rate.

So, I went to Georgetown Road in Bethesda to the YMCA. I took a back pain course, and in a couple of sessions my back pain went away. I never have had it again. I just keep doing those exercises. I know friends who later had surgery and are still not cured. You can go to NIH today and get a copy of a report that shows half of back pain surgery is not worthwhile.

If you are arguing with your doctor and he says, "Let's do surgery. We will fix up that back for you," what do you say? You do not know. He has heard everything bad you could say about this, and you cannot argue with him. It is impossible.

"Well, Doctor — do I really need that surgery?" They will say some gobblety-gook you will not understand. But here is what you do. You go to the National Institute of Health. You get this free study that shows half of back pain surgeries that were performed were not worthwhile. You bring that study to your doctor, and put it on her desk. You say, "Hey, how am I different from the people in the study that had the operation and it was not worthwhile?" You have to make that doctor stretch her imagination. That is the only way you are going to get the best.

I feel that you could get better health advice for free than you can from the doctor because doctors cannot keep up on all the new developments. The answers are changing every day. But in a few phone calls, you can find somebody who spent a lifetime studying that topic. They are not out there to make money. They are out there to find the information, and get it out to people.

Remember Charlie Porter? When I found him, the problem was not getting the information. The problem was getting out of his office. You could do that for anything.

Get Better Legal Help Than A lawyer

Legal problems are another thing. You can look to the government to solve legal problems, too. We live in the biggest democracy in the world, right? And most of us feel that we cannot get any satisfaction because we cannot hire some high-priced lawyer. So, we walk around humble and hoping that nobody will get angry because we cannot hire an attorney to fight for us, right? Nonsense. We should all have access to legal help, and you can. If anybody messes you over in this country, you can get free legal help that is better than anything else you could find.

If you have a problem where your insurance company does not pay a claim, you could hire your attorney, your brother-in-law's attorney or whatever, and he will fight for you. You are going to be fighting the attorneys of the insurance company. Their attorneys do this day in and day out. They know all the loopholes. They know all the answers to any question you are going to ask. You cannot fight that way. All you are going to do is run up an attorney bill.

Here is what I think is better. The government has an office that will fight that insurance company for you. It is at your state capital, and called the Insurance Commissioner's Office. Every state capital regulates all the insurance companies doing business in their state. Their job is to investigate any complaint that you as a consumer have with that insurance company. What is neat about this is that they have to investigate even if you are wrong.

My kid had his car towed away from a department store because he parked there and he went away. It cost him $100 to get his car. He went to the government who came out, investigated the store, went over and talked to the guy, and got my kid's money back. Nobody knew it was my kid. He was 16 years old and was able to accomplish it. Now that is power.

I was so angry at an airline a couple of years ago because it made me late for my kid's soccer game. It was half my fault, but you know how you just want to blow off steam? So I wrote a letter to the government, complaining about the airline. I sent a copy to the airline. I got a $300 check in the mail from the airline as a peace offering. Remember, when the government calls the insurance company and complains, the government can put the insurance company out of business. If it is you and your lawyer, the worst they have to lose is to pay your claim eventually. But if they lose the argument with the government, the government can put them out of business. They have too much to lose to fight the government. It is cheaper for them to pay you off than to argue.

It is the same with me. I sell books in the mail. If our customer service screws up and you contact the U.S. Postal Service about me, I will get a letter from a postal inspector. I will call you personally, and will say, "Keep the books." I do not want to mess with the postal inspector.

When your dry cleaner screws up your question mark suit, or you bring in a sweater and when you bring it home it is the size of a potholder, that dry cleaner is regulated. You do not even have to call the government. You can just go back to the dry cleaner and say, "Hey, I am going to report you to the state licensing office." That small business dry cleaner could lose all his business, and he does not want that to happen. He will make amends, and do what you want.

The Government Has Salami Police

Think about your delicatessen. Do you know the government has salami police? If you go into a delicatessen, buy a pound of salami, bring it home and feel it is a little light, like maybe the deli owner had his thumb on the scale, you can call the Office of Weights and Measures in your state capital. Out come the salami police! They can investigate because you cannot mess with the scales.

The same thing can happen when you pump gas at a gas station. One day it costs you $10 to fill up, and the next day it costs you $15. Maybe they are messing with the pump. That is illegal.

You buy a cord of wood and maybe you do not know what a cord is. Later you find out you got cheated. They will come out and find that person who sold you that wood. You have got to know your rights. Everyone is regulated. When anybody messes you over — your bank, your insurance company, your real estate broker, your doctor, you can get the power back. You can find the office that regulates them, and they will investigate. You do not have to hire attorneys, as you can get it better for free.

I had a guy who owed me some money in a business deal down in Tennessee and he was not paying. So, what I did was call the state Attorney General's Office in Tennessee, and they contacted the business. This small business got a letter from the state Attorney General's Office. "What did you do to this guy in Maryland?" They rolled over and gave me the money. They do not want to mess with the Attorney General, as they can put them out of business. That is the power we all have as citizens of this country.

Another source that we use for information is our neighbors, or our friends. To me, that is so ridiculous. I live in a community that is really in the shadow of the National Institutes of Health. This is where the big research happens in the medical field.

I remember being at a party in my neighborhood, and this one neighbor asked the other neighbor, "Harry, I have hemorrhoids and I am thinking about having an operation. What did you do for your operation?" There he is, asking Harry for advice on his hemorrhoids when he could make a couple of calls and talk to an expert at the National Institutes of Health who spent the last 15 years of his life just studying hemorrhoid operations! You can find out what is good and bad about any hemorrhoid operation from that expert.

Why trust Harry? We have this feeling and maybe it is just a comfort level because somebody else went through it. How much research did Harry really do? You can get better information than Harry, and better information than your doctor.

You can get better legal help than from your lawyer. Maybe somebody made a pass at you at the Christmas party and you are a woman — or you are a guy, whatever. You are wondering if it is sexual harassment or not. What do you do? Do you hire an attorney at $200 an hour to see if it was sexual harassment? No. You can call an 800-number in the government and talk to somebody who wrote the sexual harassment laws. We have an office in the government and all they do is enforce it. If you have a case, they come out and sue the people for you.

I sell on Home Shopping, and one of the lawyers down at Home Shopping was telling me what I could or could not say because the Federal Trade Commission will yell at me. I just called the Federal Trade Commission and talked to the expert who writes these laws. I went back to Home Shopping and said, "Hey, you are full of bubkas. Here is what the Federal Trade Commission says, right from the horse's mouth." You can get better information than anybody in this country. You can get it for free, and it is available to you for the price of a phone call.

How You Treat People Determines Your Success

The problem is it takes a little effort to get it. Besides the web, books, the media, and all these other sources we mentioned, when you start trying to get experts, it is different. You have to learn how to think a little bit differently. The key to getting that kind of help is how you treat those people once you get them on the phone.

This is really the soul of what I am about, I think — how to treat people, how to get this information, how to use all the information sources in our society, and basically how to use people. That is one tool of technology we all know how to use. We all like people, and I think in the information explosion, they are even going to be more important. As you get more and more information, you have to know how to be able to go out and find the people who read all that kind of nonsense, who know what is good and bad about it, know the one website that is of value, know the one book that is going to have your answer. You do not have time to read a million citations on the web. You do not have time to read the 200 books that are written on that subject, because time is becoming very valuable. That is why how you treat people on the telephone, and these experts is an important tool for your survival in an information society, whether it is finding help, money, information or anything you need.

I developed what is called a "seven phone call rule." If you start looking for stuff using the phone, maybe you will find somebody who may be of help. If you are looking for grant money, they will send you one place. If it is not there, they will send you over to another. If it is not there, five calls later you may be back to the same person where you started. You get this bureaucratic runaround no matter what it is. That is going to happen.

1) *Introduce Yourself Cheerfully:*

You are finally going to get to the person who can help you after an average of seven phone calls. That is my theory. It takes you an average of seven phone calls to find whatever it is you want in this country. It may take 12, or maybe you can do it in one or two with some of my books, but an average of seven phone calls is what it takes.

What happens is that your pressure level builds because you get aggravated that you are not getting what you need and people could not help you. By the time you really get to the person who can help you, you are angry because you have been getting the bureaucratic runaround. You have been on hold and on voice mail for days. This person picks up the phone that can really help you, and what is in the back of your head is all this bad stuff that has happened to you over the last hour or two on the phone. So, that person picks up the phone and you start yelling, "Now listen, you lazy, shiftless bureaucrat. You better help me because my tax dollars pay your salary." Even if you do not say that in those words, it may come out that way. And when it does, you are not going to be the highlight of anybody's day.

Most of these free experts are on the government payroll or in non-profit organizations, and you are not paying them. So, if you are not paying them, their salary does not depend on how well they help you. They should help because we live in their society where we are trying to help each other, but it really does not work that way. So, you have got to use your personality to make them want to help you. The only thing you have is your personality because you are not going to send them a check or anything else.

In them, in all of us, is the need to want to help somebody else. But again, remember when I told you earlier how giving is very selfish and the problem is trying to find some deserving person? You have got to be this deserving person that they want to help. You are not going to do that by yelling and screaming the first words out of your mouth. The first things out of your mouth are so important. That sets the mood for the whole thing, so you have to be cheerful and nice so that they want to relax, sit back and talk to you.

If you do not create that feeling, remember they could hang up right after you say hello, and just not answer the phone after that. They will get paid the same, whether they answer the phone or not, or if they stay with you for a half hour on the phone. So, that is what you have to do. Somehow you, your personality and voice, have to make them want to spend time with you. You do that by carefully choosing your first words. Be very cheerful in the way you introduce yourself. Also, you have to be open and candid. You do not want to be sneaky. "You do not need to know who I am. I just need to know stuff." If you do not know what need, say, "I don't know." Or, "My boss is trying to get something." Or, "I am really just trying to find money to do a certain thing. What kinds of programs do you have? I really know nothing about this."

2) *Be Open and Candid:*

Do not pretend that you are something you not. You have to be open and candid about who you are and what you are doing. You want them to be open with you, and to tell you all about what is going on in their office, what kind of resources they have or what kind of money programs exist. Again, you have to create that feeling of openness by being candid.

3) *Be Optimistic:*

You have to believe in your mind that their office has the help or money you need. If you are not optimistic, and say, "You do not have any money for somebody who wants to open a golf course, do you? You do not have that kind of money, do you?" The easiest thing for them to do is say no. You are happy if they say no because you were looking for the "no" answer. Your implication and the way you phrased the question, they thought you were looking for a no, so they can please you by saying no. You go away, the problem goes away, and you are happy because you got what you expected.

But if you call and say, "Hey listen, I understand you may have this stuff. Are you sure you do not have it around here somewhere? " You have got to make these people stretch their minds, and that is important. Maybe it is across the hall, or maybe it is somewhere else. You have to be optimistic. Your optimism will make them stretch. You can make them think, "Where else can it be if it is not in my area? Maybe it is somewhere else. I have to find out about it for this person on the phone." That is what your optimism can do to these people.

4) *Be Humble and Courteous:*

That is obvious. You do not want to call and say, "I have been looking around for money for a long time now, and I know it is not around but I just want to make sure that you do not have any hiding somewhere." Nobody will want to talk to you. But if you portray yourself as in need of help, are polite, humble and courteous, that is important. Again, you create the atmosphere where they want to help you.

5) *Be Concise:*

Respect people's time. You want to be quick and to the point about what you are seeking. Showing respect for others is an important trait.

6) *Be Conversational:*

In addition to being concise, you want to talk about some other things. If you find the person is a baseball fan, you can talk about baseball. If you find out anything, like they are a Republican, you can mention being anxious for the Republicans to get the Senate back, or something like that. It is important because the more you talk about yourself or other things, the more you show your human side, and the more you show your human side, the harder it is for that person to flunk you. The person has the ability to pass or fail you in this test of getting money or information.

I do not know if you remember when you were in school. Actually, when I taught school, I saw it better. When I was a professor at college, I would have people come and talk to me after class. The smart kids really would not talk about the work; I taught computer science. They would sit in my office and show me pictures of their dog or their mother, and show their personal side. I would get to know them more as an individual. Then when we had the test, it was harder to flunk the person who I knew about their dog, their parents, and their relatives. The person I did not know in class and who had a failing grade, made it was so easy for me to give them an F.

It is the same way with getting information. Being conversational and talking about other things is important. Also, be complimentary. You do not want to say, "You have got a lousy job. You must be miserable. You do not really know much." If you call and say, "Somebody told me that you are the best person to talk to about how to get money to build a farm house," or something like that, or how to get money to travel overseas. We love to hear that we have the answers. When people say that to me, it goes to my head, and I am a nicer person. It is a natural thing.

7: *Return a Favor:*

If somebody gives you something nice, try to return the favor. I sent free books to a lot of sources that helped me. At least if you do not return the favor, at least send a thank you note to somebody who helps you. It takes you a minute, and it does not have to be in your word processor or your computer, but just a little handwritten note. These handwritten notes go a lot further in our professional life now than the computer ones.

Reader's Digest sends me letters with the name of my dog on it, and they are just computer-generated letters. But a handwritten note goes a long way. So, how you care for these people that can help you on the phone is really the key to your success at getting information. And it is important because all these information pools we talked about in society all have their value, and you have to know when to use and not use any of them, whether it is the computer, the library, the media, the experts, the government, non-profit organizations, your friends and the telephone. To me, one of the most important tools we have in our society for coping with this information explosion is the telephone, so do not forget to use the phone!

Other Grants And Freebies

You have been reading about how to get grants for your house, your business and your education. But there are other kinds of money out there. They are not particularly grants sometimes. They call them other things — maybe direct payments, financial help or even services that are worth more than the amount in grants that you could get.

These services and other things are probably even more valuable than the grant money because they are going to solve real problems in your life. The reason you are probably looking for a grant is because you are a little tight for money. I can show you how to get extra money by not paying for things you can get for free.

The first subject is healthcare. Everybody is going to have healthcare problems at some time in their life, and you should not only be thinking of yourself when you think about these programs.

This Book Is Out Of Date

And by the way, remember that everything gets out of date. If I give you a phone number, and you call and get some Chinese laundry, do not worry about it. The organization is still there. It is probably called something else or moved across the street. You may have to do a little work by contacting a government operator or the local information operator. Do not give up, as the program is still there.

These are all very valuable services. I think one of the important things in society is that we are really here to help other people, too. I am going to go over 20 or 30 items that you could really use, either for yourself, someone in your family, or for someone on your street. If you do not need these items right away, you will soon. We are all taking care of aging parents or grandparents, or little kids. Tonight you can begin telling others about the freebies I can things that I am going to show you now.

What gives me the most pleasure in life is that I am able to give somebody a phone number, just a phone number, that they can call to solve a problem. They will get a service for free that would have cost them thousands of dollars. Now they will not have to go and look for a $1,000 or a $2,000 grant for their life, because now they have got it for free, or get a problem solved they never thought could be solved. If you have a question, I will give you a phone number. I love telling people where to go!

Free Prescription Drugs

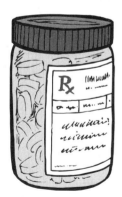

One of the greatest things I have found in healthcare is free prescription drugs. When I found this I thought they would put me on the cover of *TIME* magazine. Do you realize you could be making $40,000 or more in this country and get your prescription drugs for free?

It is actually run through the pharmaceutical companies. Every program is different. Some have income requirements and some have no income requirements, like Merck, the big pharmaceutical company. They have no income requirements at all to get free prescription drugs. All you have to say is you are having trouble paying for your prescription drug. And truthfully, most middle class people have trouble paying for prescription drugs. If you get a prescription now, it could be $100 or $200 a month. You could easily be spending $1,000 a year on some medication.

Medicare does not cover prescription drugs for seniors, so they are getting hit hardest. That is why all the politicians are saying, "We are going to start a program for seniors." Well, you do not have to wait that long. You can find out about it now. That is why it is a sin that the politicians and the media show these war stories about seniors eating dog food because they cannot pay for the prescription drugs. It perpetuates the myth that people cannot help themselves, but that is false. I will show you whom to call.

You can call the Pharmaceutical Research and Manufacturers of America at 1-800-PMA-INFO. They will send you a list of all the pharmaceutical companies that run these programs. Or, if you are online (which is how they prefer you view it) you can go to {www.phrma.org} and find the programs there. All you have to do is contact the manufacturer of the drug, tell them your circumstances, ask them about the requirements, and what usually happens is that you have to take a form to your doctor to sign. Your doctor has to sign this because they want to be friends with the doctor, not you. It is the doctor that prescribes the drugs. The doctor signs it and usually in two or three weeks you get the drugs sent to your doctor, and it is free.

I get wonderful phone calls from people all over saying, "Lesko, I took your advice and called. Sure, there is a little bit of paperwork, but now I am saving $100 a month, $200 a month, $300 a month, or thousands of dollars a year." It is not only for you, so look at it for everyone in your household. You have got your kids, your smoking patch, or Prozac. But you have to know about the program to take advantage of it. Put that phone number or put that website on the side and look into it for yourself and everybody else.

Free Healthcare For Kids

Here is free healthcare for kids. We have a program all around the country now that is called the CHIPS program. You can be making $40,000 a year or more and get free healthcare for your children. Maybe you are making $100,000 and do not need this, but you know somebody else that probably cannot afford healthcare. Make sure they know about this program. This could be worth at least $5,000 a year for them or you, and this is why people do not get healthcare in this country. It is too expensive.

To find out about CHIPS, just call up your State Department of Health in your state capital. Say you live in Pennsylvania. You call up Harrisburg and ask for the state capital operator. I think the area code in Harrisburg is 717. So, you find the area code; call 717 and the information operator, 555-1212. You ask for the state capital operator. They will give you another number to call. You call that number and say, "Hey, I want to talk to the information center at the State Department of Health for the state of Pennsylvania," or wherever you live. Then you call and say, "Hey, I want to know about the healthcare program for kids." You can also call toll-free 877-KIDS-NOW or check it out online at {www.insurekidsnow.gov}.

If they do not know about the program, then contact your local congressman or senator's office. They are the only ones in the system that have a motive to work for you. All the bureaucrats you are going to call get the same paycheck whether they work for you or not, whether they find you the stuff you need or not. But the congressman wants your vote. That is how they get paid. If they get more votes than anybody else, then they keep getting their paycheck. They will do that little favor for you because they know that their phone calls go on different colored pieces of paper.

When they call the government, it is different than you calling the government because they are the ones, the congressmen and senators, who give money to the bureaucrats to run their agencies. That is why these bureaucrats treat congressmen better than you or I.

$6,000 For A Senior or Disabled

Here is another thing that people do not know. Seniors or the disabled can get an extra $6,000 spending money. That is called Supplemental Security Income. Find out if you are eligible, but there is an income limit. Many seniors now are living on very little income. Their house is paid off. They are living on Social Security and maybe a little extra, and a lot of these things are not asset-based. You can call the Social Security Hot Line at 800-772-1213 and ask about Supplemental Security Income (SSI).

You are going to sit on hold, of course. If you call Microsoft, you are going to sit on hold forever. It is like that for everything. Nobody does customer service well. So, the government is not doing it well. I just called Microsoft, and was on hold for 30 minutes. They want to charge me $35 an hour, or $35 a problem, to solve a problem I have with their software. It is bizarre. You have got learn how to use the system. So, that is an extra $6,000 for seniors and people with disabilities.

Many Seniors Can Get $1,000 Now

Here is another freebie that seniors and people with disabilities do not even know exists. I have seen studies that show that three million people are eligible for this money and are not applying for it. It is worth over $1,000 a year. If you have seniors in your family, you could get this money for them. A lot of seniors are afraid of the system. They are not used to voice mail or how to deal with bureaucracies. So take a half hour out of your life, or an hour, whatever it takes, to get on the phone and find that program. It is part of Medicare.

The Social Security seniors are deducted a premium from their check to pay for Medicare Part B. At certain incomes, they do not have to have that deduction, and the government will repay that money to them. It is worth $1,000 a year. So, if you have a senior living on a fixed income of $12-15,000 a year, another $1,000 is serious money and you could get it for them. It is called the Qualified Medicare Beneficiaries Plan. To find out how to get this, call the Medicare Hot Line at 800-MEDICARE, or {www.medicare.gov}. What you are looking for is their free publication that describes these programs — "Guide to Health Insurance for People with Medicare." It shows how to get that deduction for Medicare Part B back for cash in your pocket.

The programs we just talked about can be easily worth $5,000 to $10,000 a year to your family. And I only talked about 4 items.

$2,500 To Adopt A Child

Or how about this — did you know you could get grants for adoptions? I know so many aging yuppies that are having trouble having kids so they look at adoption. Look for the grants for adoptions. You can get up to $2,500 or more to help you finance an adoption.

A good place to begin your search is with a couple of organizations. One is the National Adoption Information Clearinghouse and they are in Washington, DC. They will help you find the information. Also, use this clearinghouse for any kind of help you need for the adoption process, because the process is not easy. This information could be valuable to you or to someone you know who is considering adoption. That is the goal of my work. Not only do I educate somebody about something, but then they can educate somebody else. That is how we get more leverage on this information and more people get helped in society.

Two other organizations besides the National Adoption Information Clearinghouse are the National Adoption Center in Philadelphia and the National Council for Adoption in Washington DC. Call the information operator, get the phone numbers on these organizations, and call them. You can surf for them on the web and you will probably find the three organizations.

$6,000 Worth Of Free Speech Therapy

Here is a great program for anybody who has young kids in the house before they enter school. If they are having trouble with their speech, you can get up to $6,000 worth of free speech therapy, no matter what income level you are. You could be a millionaire and if your child is having trouble enunciating or you are concerned about their speech patterns, help is available. You need to go to your local school system, and tell them about it. Actually it starts for kids ages two or three years old. It is a wonderful service, but you have got to know about it to take advantage of it.

Like everything in life, people are not going to come over and bang you on the head to tell you about this stuff. You have got to go and find it for yourself. And even the experts won't know it exists. We interviewed doctors all over the country, and ninety-four percent of them did not even now about the free prescription drug program. That is why you cannot even trust the experts.

If your local school board does not know about it, call your congressman's office and tell them to contact the Office of Special Education Programs at the U.S. Department of Education. They will help you.

Free Alcohol And Drug Treatment

Here is an interesting item — free alcohol and drug treatment. There are so many substance abusers in this country now — alcohol and drugs, or other kinds of substances. I do not know the jargon that well, but I do know there is free treatment available. The free treatment is not always easy to find because there it is s complex array of places that are offer free treatment. But there is a lot of free treatment at the county level through non-profit organizations, and you may even have to go to another state or another locality to find this kind of help. But it is out there. It may just take a little effort.

There are two organizations that will help you find the free treatment. Do not forget that this is another service that you can use to help someone else. The National Drug and Treatment Routing Service is a special clearinghouse to help you find treatment. The phone number is 1-800-662-HELP. The clearinghouse is part of the National Institutes of Health and their website is {www.niaaa.nih.gov}.

The National Clearinghouse for Alcohol and Drug Abuse is another organization that can help. What is so neat about this country is that not only are there people to help you and give you things for free, but there are other people like this Clearinghouse that help you find the people giving you things for free. The number is 800-729-6686, and their website is {www.health.org}. This is for free alcohol and drug treatment. It could easily cost $5-10,000 for something like that.

See what I mean? Although you may not call them grants, all these free services like free prescription drugs, may be like having an extra $5,000 in your pocket. This is better than a grant.

Free Wheelchairs

How about free wheelchairs? Do you know somebody who needs a wheelchair? The American Cancer Society offers free wheelchairs, as well as the Easter Seals. Look in the phone book for the American Cancer Society and Easter Seals.

Free Mammograms

Free mammogram service is a wonderful program from the Centers for Disease Control out of Atlanta. The program is set up all over the country. Women 40 or 50 years old or more and making $40,000 can get free mammograms, free breast cancer treatment, and free cervical cancer treatment in every state of the country. You can call this number at the Centers for Disease Control, Division of Cancer Prevention: 770-488-4751. The program is also run through your state capital. You can call your state capital operator as I told you earlier, and ask for the State Department of Health. They should know about it. But again, remember that one bureaucrat does not know everything. If you get stuck, call the number above for the Centers for Disease Control.

Other places, such as the American Cancer Society or your local YMCA offer programs. You can also call the National Cancer Institute for any cancer problem. Their number is, 800-4CANCER. They are a wonderful clearinghouse and counseling service. I helped a friend who had breast cancer. When she called the hotline they were able to identify what stage of breast cancer she really had, and helped her identify the latest procedures for curing that stage of breast cancer. They also told her who were the best doctors in the area to perform that kind of procedure.

When you have a health problem, it is information that gives you the power. Usually the fear we have with health is the fear of the unknown. We may be sitting there with cancer or with whatever ailment we have, and do not know if we are going to die right now or live for 50 more years. We do not know what our chances are and we do not even know if the doctor really knows.

There is a way to get better information than your doctor. Earlier we talked about that and living in the information society. With 1-800-4CANCER, you can begin the search to get the best information and any aspect of cancer, including free videos on the effects of chemotherapy. As well are living longer, we are going to have more of these kinds of problems in our life and in lives of our loved ones.

Free Hospital Care

How about free hospital care? So many people go to the hospital and think they can pay for it. They find out later that the insurance company is not going to pay. There are hospitals around the country that have to treat you for free, whether or not you can pay the bill. This is not just emergency rooms, but this is the hospital itself. These are hospitals that got money under a program called the Hill Burton Act. Because they got this government money, they made a promise that they will treat a certain amount of people for free. To find the Hill Burton hospitals in your area call 800-638-0742, and they will give you a listing of hospitals.

This program also includes long-term care facilities. If Grandma wants to go to a nursing home and you know Medicaid will not pay for it because she makes too much or has too much assets, then check out Hill-Burton. This program is concerned more with a person's income rather than their assets. A lot of elderly do not make a lot of money day by day in income, but they have a lot of assets. So, you may be covered there.

By the way, most hospitals have other kinds of programs if they are not part of Hill Burton. At Johns Hopkins, this woman really had a serious cancer problem and her healthcare did not cover it. She had all these bills at Johns Hopkins, and they were sending out torpedoes from Detroit to try to get the money from this poor lady. I started making some calls for her.

See, people in need do not have the strength to fight for themselves. In the healthcare situation, you have to help other people when they have a problem. You have to sometimes be advocates for other people in the system.

I called the social workers over there and explained the problem, and they could not help. I called all the places I knew, and then I just started calling accounting at Johns Hopkins Hospital up in Baltimore, Maryland. I found this little accountant who found a program to pay this woman's bill. It was $8,000 or $9,000. I talked to her doctor up there; I talked to everybody. No one was helpful until I called deep enough in that bureaucracy at Johns Hopkins to get her bill covered, and it just took a phone call.

That is the power we have in our society. You do not have to take everything at face value. You have the power to change things. You have the power to change no to yes. You do, but it takes perseverance. I do not think no means no in our society any more, except in sexual harassment. It seems like in everything else, there are ways to change that no to a yes. I asked 50 people at Johns Hopkins, how can this woman not pay her bill? Oh, no, no, no! So, I found this little accountant who was able to change it to a yes, and you can do that, too, for other people.

Free Immunizations For Your Kids

How about free immunizations for your kids? This could be worth a couple of hundred bucks. Every kid needs to be protected from chickenpox, polio, diphtheria, mumps, whooping cough, German measles, tetanus, spinal meningitis, and Hepatitis-B. Just call the National Immunization Hot Line, 800-232-2522. Maybe you do not have a kid now, but you will run into somebody with a kid. Then you can say, "Hey, take this number for next time your kid needs an immunization shot." It is part of the Centers for Disease Control and their website is {www.cdc.gov/nip}.

50% Discount On Air Fare

How about this? Do you know you can get 50 percent off your airfare if you are going to visit a sick relative? When you call for a reservation and you have got to go see somebody who is sick, ask about bereavement and compassion fares. Call your airline of choice or find out how many airlines are going to your place that your sick friend or relative is. Then call each one of them and ask them about the bereavement and compassion fares. See how low you can go, because they can give you those deals of up to 50 percent discount.

So many think, "Oh, we just want to solve the problem, so we are getting on the next plane to go and help somebody." No — find out about the discount fares to visit a sick relative. That is a nice little freebie to have.

Insurance Coverage For Workers With A Disability

And do not forget that there is a new law. If you know somebody who has a disability and they are working with their disability, there is a law where they can get cheap health coverage under Medicaid. A 1997 law permits that. Here is a website to find out about it. It is called {www.bazelon.org}. The law is something your local state Department of Health should know.

Healthcare is outrageous. It is funny that so much of us live our life based upon our healthcare coverage. "I cannot take that job because it does not have healthcare." We are not using the best talents or the people in our society because they are making decision based on if they get healthcare or not. I do not think that is right, but that is another issue.

Free Taxies For Grandma

How about a taxi to get Mom to the doctor? If you are working and Mom calls and says, "I have a doctor's appointment today. Can you drive me to the doctor and back?" "Oh Mom, I can't. I've got meetings. My boss won't let me off to do that." What do you do? You can get a free taxi ride for Mom to go back and forth to the doctor. How do you find out about it? Again, you cannot look in the phone book under "Free Taxi." It is never going to be there. They are going to have all the four taxis that charge a lot of money.

Hotline To Help Your Grandparents

Call the Elder Care Hot Line. The government has set up as part of the Department of Health and Human Services an 800-number to help you with any kind of problem that you have with a senior, either a senior that is living near you or a senior who is living in another state. It is wonderful.

My mom wanted some legal advice. She lives in Florida and I called the Elder Care Hot Line. They hooked me up with somebody in Florida who gave her free legal help. She made an appointment, and in two days, she walked in and talked to this attorney for free about a legal problem. I could not get my attorney to act that fast, and she got it for free. The Elder Care Hot Line is at 800-677-1116. Keep that number handy.

Nursing Home Police

If mom is in a nursing home in Arizona, and you talk to her and find she is worried that they are not treating her well, then you can take some action. You call that hot line and find out who will come out and investigate Mom in her nursing home. The nursing home is regulated and you have the right to make sure that they are doing everything on the up and up. The government will send somebody out to make sure they are treating Mom right. That is the power you have, even though you are not in Arizona.

Free Health Insurance Counseling

You can find out about how to get free health insurance counseling. Health insurance is so complicated for seniors or for anybody, but now they have set up a special counseling service for seniors to help them choose the best healthcare. It is a free service.

You can hire a consultant and spend $100 an hour, or call an agent, and talk to someone who is biased. Or you can get the best experts in the world to help you make that kind of decision and get it for free. All these services are worth hundreds, thousands of dollars. They are better than money, because even if you got a grant for $5,000, you would not know about the free health insurance counseling, and would spend maybe $500 asking some expert and not get the best information. The government programs are not in business to sell you something, but they are in business to help you solve that problem.

$20,000 To Buy A Van Or Talking Computer

Do you know somebody who has a disability? There is money available out there to help them buy a van or a talking computer. More importantly, they also have free services that will send somebody to their house to evaluate what kind of new technology they could use to make their life better because of the disability. Maybe they do not walk as well any more, or are losing their eyesight.

Well, there is so much technology out there to help people with disabilities, and the government has set up an office called the Rehabilitation Engineering and Assistive Technology to help you find out what technology will help you live a better life. These are free consultants to help you. In addition a lot of states also have money, like low-interest loans and grant money, to help you buy this technology to make your life better. Some states even offer free loaner equipment.

You can find this two ways. The phone number in Virginia for the Rehabilitation Engineering and Assistive Technology is 703-424-6686, and the website is {www.resna.org}. They will direct you to your local office, which is usually in your state capital. They will work with you to find what you need.

Discounts On Dental Bills

A lot of people are looking for an inexpensive way to get braces for their kids. Kids, seniors and others are also looking for better way that they can afford. There are free dental services out there, too. Again, this could save you hundreds or even thousands of dollars. The services vary from location to location. Some are from the state Department of Health. Some are from local dental societies or from dental schools in the area. I used to go to the dental school at Georgetown University to get my teeth fixed. It was a fraction of what it would cost if I went to a private dentist. So, contact your local state Department of Health and start looking.

All this may take a little effort, but who cares if it takes 20 minutes on the phone if you are going to save $1,000 on a dental bill? It is going to take effort, but look at the money you save. Look at the help that is out there. That is what I mean when I say that a lot of this stuff is better than grants. If you are going to spend a couple of days trying to get a grant for $1,000 so you can have dental care, instead spend 20 minutes on the phone and try to find out how to get that dental care for free.

Emergency Rooms Have To Care For You

Also, remember if the emergency room is open, they have to care for you, whether you can afford to pay or not. You are legally responsible for the money, but they have to take care of you and not worry about the bill until after you are okay. Remember that. And if they do not treat you well, you can contact the U.S. government Centers for Medicare and Medicaid Services, and say you want them investigated.

That is how you get power in the system. If they say, "We can't treat you because you don't have insurance and we're afraid you won't pay," say, "I'm going to report you." Or, you do not have to be that mean about it. You can just say, "Well, I do not think you are treating me fairly, and I am going to contact the Centers for Medicare and Medicaid Services."

The hospitals are afraid of the Centers for Medicare and Medicaid Services. That is where they get all their Medicaid and Medicare money, and most hospitals are living off of government programs. The government pays for half the healthcare in this country. That is why it is strange when people say, "We can't have government financed healthcare," since half of it is financed already.

Free Care By The Best Doctors In The World

You can get healthcare by the best doctors in the world for free. Sam Donaldson, a gazillionaire, had his prostate surgery done for free from the government. Isn't that amazing? One of the richest people in our society has cancer and says, "Where should I get my cancer surgery done? I will go to the government and get it for free." And he did.

The average person would never think of that. The average person does not know about the program. The government gives $18 billion to doctors all over the country to treat conditions for free. Sam knew about it. Actually, I think he has beehives on his ranch out in Oklahoma or Texas, and he gets government money for his beehives. That's another government program.

Tom Brokaw of NBC News, even got money from the government to buy a radio station in North Dakota. See, the rich people use this stuff. But I think that there are more deserving people out there who should get this free cancer treatment rather than Sam Donaldson. But Sam knows about the program and got on the list. How do you find out about the program? It is done in Washington and all around the country.

So, there are a couple of places to look. One is that you can contact the Clinical Center, which is part of the National Institutes of Health. They have a hundreds of programs currently underway. So, if they are studying your condition, you can be treated for free because they need you. Some people say you are like a guinea pig, but again, it is the best doctors in the world, and in all medicine. Everybody is guessing, and here you get the best and the latest technology.

To find out about the program call 301-496-4891 or 800-411-1222. That is the Clinical Center, and you can ask about their clinical trials. What are they studying? Maybe you have headaches and they are studying the best treatments for your type of headaches.

I had a missing tooth and they were studying dental implants. I talked myself out of getting a free dental implant though, when I talked about it on *Larry King* and the office got 10,000 calls. They took me off the list.

Clinical trials are occurring all across the United States, not just at NIH. To keep track of them, there is a database where they can search to see who is doing research on your condition. It is called the Computer Retrieval and Information on Scientific Projects, and is from the Office of Reports and Analysis. Their number is 301-435-0656. They have a long website at NIH. It is {https://www-commons.cit.nih.gov/crisp}. They can run a database for you about who in the country is doing research.

To tell you the truth, the last time I talked with the people there, they were not the nicest people in the world. So, you may have to use your personality to get them to like you. But you do have a right to it, so hang in there. If they are mean to you, then call your congressman's office and tell them to call. Make sure they get this for you.

$5 For STD Tests

Here is something you may or may not be interested in. It is $5 for STD tests. These are sexually transmitted diseases. There is an STD Hot Line and they will show you where to get tested. If you are worried about any of this stuff with the AIDS crisis, then call, as they are very confidential and local. For only $5, there is no excuse. The hotline is 800-227-8922.

Free Research On Any Health Topic

How about free health information? As I mentioned earlier, I believe you can get free health information on any topic that is better than your doctor. Remember I found the expert at NIH, spending the last 13 years of his life studying back problems and was able to tell me results of research that was not even published yet.

Here are a couple of places to start to find this information. These are people who will do the research for you to find out who specializes in your condition or treatment. It is free research on any health topic. The first one is the National Health Information Center at 800-336-4797, or on the web at {www.health.gov/nhic}.

The government has one just for women now called the Women's National Health Information Center. It is part of the Centers for Disease Control and can be reached at 800-944-WOMEN or on the web at {www.4women.gov}. And also the National Institutes of Health has an information clearinghouse that will put you in contact with all of their information clearinghouses. NIH has information clearinghouses on everything they are studying, whether it is arthritis, cancer, bone diseases, headaches or anything. You can call their main number and they will put you through to the information clearinghouse. And remember, information clearinghouses are wonderful because they will do the research for you. They will find out who in our society specializes in the information that you want. It is like having your own librarian. Their number is 301-496-4000, and on the web at {www.nih.gov}.

Fight Your Insurance Company For Free

Also, you should be aware of how to fight the healthcare system. There are people out there who will fight for you if your insurance company does not pay a claim. Are you going to hire an attorney to fight that insurance company? Their attorneys are bigger than your attorney, and who knows what is going to happen. You are going to wind up with a big attorney bill.

Instead, you can call your state Insurance Commissioner's office and they will fight that health insurance company for you. I use it all the time. When a health insurance company says, "We are not going to cover you, Lesko," I just tell them, "You are not treating me fair and I am going to call the insurance commissioner." The office is located in your state capital, and again you can find this by contacting your state capital operator. They will investigate your insurance company. You can even be wrong, but they still have to investigate. So, use these to your heart's content. That is why they are there, and they are a way to get power back in the system. You do not have to hire an attorney.

Insurance companies are more afraid of the Insurance Commissioner than they are of you or your attorney. Remember, the worst they lose in arguing with your attorney is that they have to pay your claim. But when they argue with the Insurance Commissioner, the worst they lose is all their business, because the Insurance Commissioner could say, "Okay, you are a bad guy and we will not let you do business in our state." They do not want to mess with it.

Here is another advocacy group that could help you, too. This is a non-profit organization that will help you fight for your rights in the healthcare system. They are called the Center for Patient Advocacy. Located in McLean, Virginia, they can be reached at 800-846-7444, and on the web at {www.patientadvocacy.org}. Anytime you have a problem, try to find an advocacy group because they have learned the system and how best to fight it. It is like a lawyer who learns the system and fights the same cases over and over. They know the buttons to push, the way to make things happen. And these advocacy groups are usually free to you.

50% Discount On Your Phone Bill

Another incredible thing is that you can get a 50 percent discount on your phone bill. Are you having trouble paying your phone bill? The Federal Communications Commission is making phone companies give you a 50% discount. But the phone company is never going to say, "Hey, here is how to pay only half the price." They are not going to tell you that, so you need to find out for yourself.

Call your phone company and ask them about programs called Link Up America or Life Line program. There are two different programs from the Federal Communications Commission. If they do not know about the programs, find the Federal Communications Commission and ask them. Or again, just call your congressman and ask them to find out about it for you.

100% Discount On Eye Glasses

How about 100 percent discount on glasses? For a senior guy like me who is already in his late fifties, this is attractive. At Pearle Vision Centers if you are 50 years of age, they will give you a 50 percent discount either on your lenses or frames. You get 50 percent because you are in your fifties. If you are 60 years of age, you get a 60 percent discount. If you are 70 years of age, you get a 70 percent discount. This is at Pearle Vision. So, if you are 100, you get 100 percent discount.

What I find sometimes happens in these programs is that you will go into a Pearle Vision Center and they will not know about it. You may have to make them call headquarters. If everybody does not use it, nobody knows about it. It is not on the tip of their tongue. People come and go all the time, so tell them about it. Ask them to call corporate and find out about the program because it is a real program.

$7,000 Grant To Fix Up Your Home

Another program for seniors is that they can get $1,000 to $7,000 to fix up their home. The USDA, the U.S. Department of Agriculture runs this program. We talked about that earlier. Another program is through Community Connections. For more information and most housing programs call 800-998-9999.

Go To College For Free At 55

Do you realize that if you are 55 or older you can go back to school for free or next to nothing? Get Grandpa off the sofa. Instead of watching the weather channel all day or whatever he does, tell him that he can go to a local college and study poetry if he wants, or world history. He could even take courses in meteorology. Instead of just sitting there, complaining about the weather, he can go and study it. He will be more fun at Thanksgiving dinners that way, too.

Also, for people 55 or older there is free training. If you lose a job and are over 55, the U.S. Department of Labor has free training. In your state government, you have a state Department of Labor. Ask them about it. If they do not know about it, then go to U.S. Department of Labor in Washington DC, and look for the Division of Older Workers. If you are fifty and older, you are considered an older worker. I am 58 and I qualify for all these programs. So, if I do not sell any more books, I am going to be at the Division of Older Workers.

Free Hearing Aids

How about money to buy hearing aids? The Better Hearing Institute, 1-800-EAR-WELL, has money to help you buy hearing aids. If you know somebody, or you are someone who has trouble financing a hearing aid, there are money programs to assist you. Again, you do not have to get a grant. Here is money for you. On the web, it is {www.betterhearing.org}.

Free Eye Care

Free eye care — if you are over 65 you can get free eye care from the National Eye Care Project by the American Academy of Ophthalmology. Call 1-800-222-3937 and ask about the program. On the web, it is {www.eyenet.org}.

Get Paid As A Volunteer

Seniors can get paid to help in their community. If you are a senior, Grandma, Grandpa, yourself or the lady down the street who does not know what to do with her life, tell her about the National Senior Service Corps. Corps members become mentors, tutors, help in the community, schools, hospitals, and get paid for it. Do something in the community, and keep contributing. The National Senior Service Corps can be reached at 800-424-8867, and on the web at {www.cns.gov}.

Go On A Free Archeological Dig

You know what I am going to do this summer? I am going on a government program with my family. As I said before, I have got two teenage boys, who are now giants, 16 and 19. My wife, the two boys and I are going to Alaska on a free archaeological dig with the government. I always wanted to go on an archaeological dig. Sure, we have to pay to get there, but if you go to Outward Bound or some other place, they are going to charge you thousands of dollars for something like this. We are going with the best archeologist in the world and are actually working with Native Americans digging around for 500-year-old artifacts. Can you imagine the things we are going to learn? And learn as a family — that is what is so neat.

One year we went and restored historical buildings out in the wilderness in upstate Minnesota. These two programs are part of Passport in Time. Passport in Time is with the Department of Agriculture's Forest Service. The programs are located all over the country. They have a catalog they will send you and you can see all the stuff you can do anywhere in the country. But again, they do not advertise, so find it on the web, or just call the US Department of Agriculture locally and ask for Passport in Time. They can be reached at 800-281-9176 or on the web at {www.passportintime.com}. Get on their mailing list, get their catalog, and have a wonderful time.

After we did the first one in upstate Minnesota, one kid talked about marine biology. I said, "Let's do something in marine biology." I called the state of Maine and said, "Hey, I have got a family here. We want to volunteer and learn something about marine biology." I talked with the Natural Resource Division of the state of Maine. They did not know who I was. I just called out of the blue. See, if you treat people nicely, they start helping you. They found us some place that wanted to use us as volunteers in marine biology.

It was this wonderful museum on the coast of Maine where we went out and gathered specimens. We spent a whole week learning about marine biology. I know more about sea urchins and other sea life than I will ever use. It was an incredible experience, and it was all free. The best things in life are free, and all the best services in life are for free, but you just have to know where to go to get them, and that is what I love doing. I love telling people where to go!

Free Legal Help

We live in the greatest democracy in the world, and most of us walk around afraid that we will not get any justice because we cannot afford some hotshot attorney. But that is silly. You can get better legal help than you can from any lawyer if you learn how to use the system. That is the key.

Fight Insurance Companies Who Won't Pay Your Claim

Let's say your insurance company does not pay a claim, and you call that insurance company up in Hartford, Connecticut. You talk to some bureaucrat in this huge bureaucratic insurance company and they say, "Well buddy, did you see paragraph C, section B? We do not pay claims. We are the premium company. We just like collecting premiums." That is the way a lot of insurance companies work nowadays.

What is your recourse when something like that happens? Well, you know that Uncle So-and-so has a brother-in-law who is a lawyer. You call them and maybe they charge you, or maybe they give you the first hour free and then they charge you $100, $200, $300 an hour, whatever the heck they can charge.

But even if you have the money to afford a lawyer, you are probably not going to win against the insurance company. Their lawyers are better than anybody else's lawyers, because their lawyers do this 24 hours a day. That is all they do. And your brother-in-law, the attorney, how many cases like this does he really get? So, that is why you do not stand a chance against these companies who do it all the time. What happens, too, is that the company does not mind fighting with you because the worst that could happen is they have to pay the claim that they should have paid in the first place.

If you learn how to use the system, and the system is the government, you can call your state capital operator right now. If you are in Maryland, call Annapolis and ask for the state capital operator, and then ask them for the state Insurance Commissioner. Every state has a government-run office that regulates the insurance business in that state. That means that that a business has to comply with everything that the government says, and if they screw up, they are out of business. The Insurance Commissioner will investigate your claim whether you are right or wrong. You could be some idiot, completely wrong, but they will contact the insurance company.

The insurance companies do not want to mess with the government. First of all, the insurance company is a big bureaucracy, as is the government with whom they have to deal. For two big bureaucracies to talk to each other it costs them $5,000 just to exchange letters, correspondence and email. It becomes cheaper to pay you off with a couple of hundred bucks, a thousand bucks or whatever you are trying to get. That is why this is a wonderful tool.

My family and I have used this many times. When you contact the insurance company, all you have to say is, "I do not think I am being treated fairly, and I am going to contact the state Insurance Commissioner's office." That is usually enough for them to put you on hold, go in the back room, come back and start making other arrangements that are more pleasing to you.

When they start messing with the government, if they lose, they could lose their whole business. When your lawyer starts messing with their lawyer, the only thing they can lose is the amount of your original claim. Having the government on your side is like calling the same people who brought you Desert Storm to go out and hassle these people for you. These are the most powerful people in the world.

Fight Mail Order and Retail Companies

I sell books through the mail. If we screw up and do not send a refund or our office messes up your order, you could go through our customer service and try to get it settled. But you can contact the U.S. Postal Inspector, because you bought this book through the mail. They will contact us directly. When we get a letter from the Postal Inspector, I will call you personally! I will say to keep the book. I do not want to mess with the Postal Inspector because it will cost me too deal with them, and if I screw up somehow, they could put me out of business.

It is cheaper, easier, and better for me to just make you as happy as possible so that when they contact me I can say, "She's very happy. There's no problem there. Call her and see."

The way to get the upper hand in society is to find a government office that regulates the people who did you wrong.

Credit Card Problems

The problems we have are usually because some big corporation messed us over. For instance, let us look at your credit card bill. "I returned that merchandise and it is still on the bill." You call the bank and they say, "We called the store and they said you did not return it." You do not have to pay it, and that is why I love credit cards.

Call your state Banking Commissioner, as they are the ones who regulate the bank and the credit card industry. They will contact that credit card company for you, and that is how to get justice and satisfaction. There is a 600-pound gorilla now that is fighting for you. The credit card company will just shove the bill right back to the retailer, and it will be their problem and not yours any more.

Over 40 Is Age Discrimination

When I was about 50 I started looking into what things are available for senior citizens. I was trying to figure out when the government actually considers you a senior citizen. Do you know when it is? Forty years old! At 40 years old, the government considers you a senior. Do you know why? Because that is when the age discrimination law starts in our society. So, if you are in the workforce and are over 40, the government considers you an old guy or an old woman, and they will protect you.

If you are an over 40 person looking for a job and you feel they are only hiring younger people, that could be against the law. Or, maybe you got fired and find that the company kept all the young people. That too could be against the law. How do you find out?

Like in most things people say, "Well, I will go to an attorney." You know what? The attorney is going to charge you $100 or $200 an hour to go learn the law for you. Like doctors with medicine, it is hard for attorney's to keep up on all the changes in the law. The law changes every day.

So why pay for an attorney to go learn the current law for you when instead, you can call the government's Equal Employment Opportunity Commission and talk with an attorney who wrote the law, and they are free. If you have a case, they will come and sue the people for you and get you hundreds of thousands of dollars because you were discriminated against.

It is the same way in housing and in sexual harassment. If somebody makes a pass at you at the Christmas party and you are not sure if it is sexual harassment, find out. Do not call an attorney, but instead call the government. And if you do have a possible case, they will come and sue the people for you. Any legal problem you have, do not call attorneys who have to learn the law for you on your nickel. Call an attorney who wrote the law, and they are free.

Free Child Support Enforcement

There are so many ways to get justice, including child support. Do not forget that the government set up child support enforcement offices in every state. Only about half the women in this country who are owed child support get their full amount. That is only 50 percent. If you know somebody who is not getting all their payments or you are one, contact your state department of health and ask about the Child Support Enforcement Office. There is no income requirement. You could be a millionaire, still be owed child support, and they will go chase it down for you. They can go through the Social Security Administration records, the IRS, the Defense Department, the FBI, and the Veterans Administration. They have the authority to use all these databases now to find those deadbeat dads or deadbeat moms, whoever owes child support.

I found a neat organization in Toledo, Ohio, called the Association for Children for Enforcement and Support Locator. This is a clearinghouse that will help you get child support. They know the whole system and they advise you against hiring private people who try to collect the money for you and keep a percentage of it. You could get all of it yourself by going through the public sources. You can reach them at 800-537-7072 or on the web at {www.childsupport-aces.org}.

Muggers' Money

The government also has muggers' money. If you get mugged in this society, there is a crime victims assistance program where they have money, and can pay you for the days lost from work or some other expenditure. It is run through the Justice Department. If your local police department does not know about this, contact the U.S. Department of Justice and ask for the crime victims assistance program. It is a big pot of money out there.

Government Will Fight Your Lawyer, Your Doctor and Your Deli

Money is also set aside for lawyers that run off with your money, as they are regulated, too. Lawyers, doctors, dentists, accountants, every professional is regulated. If you have a lawyer that messes you over, you can contact your state capital. Contact the office that regulates the attorneys and file a complaint. What you need to do to get the attention of some professional is to contact their licensing board because they do not want a have bad letter on file, or to be investigated by their licensing board. How badly did they really mess you over? Even if you lose, it still looks bad for them.

It is the same way with your doctor's office. Go to the state licensing board and file a complaint. Get satisfaction. Make sure you get these people's attention. When you file a complaint or say you are going to go to the licensing board, you get their attention. That is when you get your phone call returned, and when you get your case reviewed. So, use these.

Every state capital now has a separate pot of money, so if for some reason your lawyer runs off with your money, they can reimburse you from this pot of money. It is nice to know that this kind of money is there, but what is amazing to me is that there is actually a pot of money. Lawyers run off with client's money so often that they have to set up a fund to cover it.

Even your delicatessen is regulated. If you go to your delicatessen and buy a pound of salami, and the salami seems a little light, like maybe the deli owner had his thumb on the scale, you can call the state capital and ask for the Office of Weights and Measures. They have salami police who come out and buy salami to see if they are messing with the scales. Every commercial scale is regulated, just like the pumps at the gas station. You fill up your gas tank and it costs you $15. You fill it up the next day and it is $20. Somebody may be messing with those pumps. Call the Office of Weights and Measures.

If you buy a cord of wood, and say, "Okay $200 for a cord of wood." But you do not even know what a cord is. Two weeks later, your neighbor says, "That is not a cord of wood. Here is how you measure a cord of wood, and you got screwed." What do you do? You call the Office of Weights and Measures, and they will go find the guy who sold you the wood. That is their job.

The same holds true with hospitals and nursing homes, as they too are all regulated. They get government money from Medicare, Medicaid or whatever, so they must follow certain rules and guidelines. If a hospital messes you over, just call the Department of Health and Human Services in Washington DC. Actually, they have regional offices, too, that will come out and investigate your hospital for cleanliness or treatment issues.

If your mom is in a nursing home down in Arizona, and says, "They are not treating me right. All the food was cold." Do you want to take care of Mom? You call the state capital in Phoenix and ask for the office that regulates nursing homes. They will go and check Mom's nursing home for you. All it costs you is a price of a phone call. You do not have to get on an airplane, go down to Arizona, and check it yourself.

Working Over 40 Hours Could Be Illegal

Are you working more than 40 hours a week and not getting paid time and a half? It could be illegal. How do you get that justice? The Department of Labor in your state capital will investigate your boss, and will do it anonymously. So, if you have any wage or overtime issues and things like that, it is the office of the Department of Labor in your state capital who can help.

Pension Police

Many retirees are worried about their pension, and think maybe they should be getting more. There are pension police — the Pension Benefit Guarantee Corporation in Washington DC. They will investigate that pension plan for you. Here is their 800-number — 800-400-7242, or on the web at {www.pbgc.gov}.

There Is Even IRS Police

And you know what? There are even people who will fight the IRS for you. If you get the runaround from the IRS or they are banging on your door, saying they are going to put a lock around your house for that 13 cents that you owe them from 1972, or they want hundreds of thousands of dollars from you and you cannot pay all that money, Congress has set up special offices that will fight the IRS for you. They are called tax advocate centers, and are wonderful. If you have an argument, they can go right into the computers, correct the information, stop you from getting that mail, and can be an advocate for you.

That is the way Congress set it up. Everyone in Congress believes the IRS has too much authority in this country, so they set up these offices for the taxpayer. It does not matter how rich or poor you are. They will work for you. Look in the blue pages of your phone book under U.S. Department of Treasury and ask for the tax advocate center. It cannot hurt to try. Why hire some attorney at $200 an hour when these people will do it for free!

More Free Money

We all want more money. Here I would like to talk about some little odds and ends that people often ask me when I go around the country. They are little things that I found out over the years. Don't forget, I have been doing this thing for 25 years.

One thing I found recently was that you can get $500 for turning in annoying telephone solicitors. Isn't that neat? There is a rule at the Federal Communications Commission, the FCC, that if one of these annoying people calls you, and you tell them not to call, but they still call you two more times within a 12-month period, you get $500 from them.

Or, if they call you with a prerecorded message to your home, that is against the law. You could get $500 for that. Or, if they call you before 8:00AM or after 9:00PM, that is another way for you to get the money. Or, if they send you an unsolicited fax, you get $500 from that.

And here is how to find out how to do this. You can call 888-CALL-FCC, or go to the web at {www.fcc.gov}. When telephone solicitors call me, I just yank their chain. I say, "I would like to talk to your supervisor, because six months ago I told your company that you cannot call me any more, and now under the U.S. Federal Communications Commission Rules, I am able to collect $500 from you." Just knowing the law gives you power over any of these people.

Also, if you owe people money and they are calling you at weird hours, there are laws against that, too. You do not have to put up with obnoxious people on the phone that are bugging you for money. How do you find out about the law? You do not hire an attorney. No, the Federal Trade Commission regulates the law. Call 877-FTC-HELP (toll-free) or on the web go to {www.ftc.gov}. They have free reports rules governing debt collection practices, and they also have some great free reports for credit issues.

You see the ads in the paper and on television for the Credit Doctor, who wants $500 from you to fix your credit. There is nothing they can do that you cannot do yourself. There is no magic to this. The Federal Trade Commission has free reports called, "Credit Repair," "Self-Help May Be the Best," "How to Dispute Credit Report Errors," or, "How to Deal with Credit Problems." These are all free, very easy and understandable to read, and are designed to help you deal with any credit problems you have.

I do not know if you have seen the ads for free credit counseling agencies. Be careful. Mostly they are non-profit organizations, trying to help. But one thing to consider is that the credit card companies may finance them. Anybody who is working with credit card companies will never tell you about your bankruptcy options. They want to make sure the credit card people get their money. Bankruptcy is a legal option in this country and is not reserved just for fat cats. If they do not talk about bankruptcy, you should go somewhere else. You can find out about credit repair and all these issues from the free reports from the Federal Trade Commission.

You can also go to your local county cooperative extension service. They are part of your county government and they too offer free credit counseling services. You can find them in the blue pages of your phone book under "County Government" and then "County Cooperative Extension Services." When you contact them, tell them you need help with credit problems. That is better than the people who will not tell you all the information you need to know.

Every community has a number of non-profit organizations that can be very helpful in times of need. If you are really stuck, or know somebody who is, these organizations can provide extra spending money, pay some necessary bills, or even help with medical problems.

There was a nanny in my neighborhood, who I met at my kid's school bus stop, and she needed prescription drugs. She actually needed an exam by a doctor in order to get the drugs but she could not afford the exam. I called around to doctors and nobody would help me. Then I called Catholic Charities and talked to a nun there. I explained the problem and within two days they got the examination for the woman. And you do not have to be a Catholic to get this help.

Community Action Agencies and the Salvation Army are also available to solve problems like this in the community. If you cannot find them, contact your local library and they will direct you. They are good places to check if you do not know where to go.

Another thing that could be very rewarding to know is unclaimed property. Mary Ann Martello, the woman who wrote this book with me, got on a website called {www.unclaimed.org} and found over $2,000 of unclaimed money for members of her family. She wrapped up the information as gifts and presented them as presents at Christmas. Being the bearer of good news is great fun.

This is a database of all the unclaimed property available from state governments. Say you moved into town 20 years ago and put down a deposit for the phone company. When you left town you probably forgot to collect your deposit. The money goes into the state government's unclaimed property program.

Or maybe your mom or your grandmother set up a $500 CD in the bank when you were born, and now, 30 years later, it is worth $10,000 and it is sitting in some bank in your old hometown. They do not come and look for you. They give that money to the state government and it sits there waiting for you to come and collect it. I remember years ago looking at California's listing of unclaimed property. They had money there for Bob Hope. You mean the state couldn't find him? Massachusetts had money for the Archbishop of Boston. There is literally billions and billions of dollars sitting in these unclaimed property places that you do not know.

If you are not online, go to your state capital and ask for the Office of the Secretary of State. They will be able to tell you where in that state they keep the unclaimed property.

Government auctions are another source of incredible bargains. A lot of people always want to know about government auctions. There are a couple of places to look for auctions, as each department handles things differently. The post office has auctions in about eight places in the country — Philadelphia, Atlanta, and a couple of places. I used to go to these auctions because they were fun to do. And for $100 I would get 500 stuffed animals, so I would have toys for my kids for the rest of their lives.

The post office also sells a lot of junk that is sold on late-night TV because if you refuse the shipment, the company often does not even want it back. It sits in the back of the post office waiting to be sold at these auctions. Or, it could be that sweater from Aunt Tilly in Seattle that you never received at Christmas time. It may be sitting in the back office of the post office, and once a month, they will have an auction to get rid of all that stuff. So, contact your local post office and they will tell you where all the auctions are. They also auction off jeeps, post office vans and other great stuff.

The U.S. Customs Service holds big time auctions that can include, jewelry, cars, or even saddles. These are items that are confiscated because they were entering the country illegally. They auction off furs, planes, boats, diamonds, and more. A private organization called EG&G in Fairfax, Virginia runs the auctions for the government. Their phone number is 703-273-7373, or on the web go to {www.treas.gov/auctions/customs} and find out about the auctions there. They are held all over the country and are fun. A lot of people I have met at the auctions just go to them on vacation. It is better than Disneyland for a lot of people.

What people often do is go to these auctions, get all this stuff, and then hold garage sales, selling it to make money. They buy it at one price, and then they sell it at flea markets for a higher price.

The Defense Department is loaded with stuff. They say that things they buy for $1, they sell for two cents. There is an office in Battle Creek, Michigan that runs their auctions. They can be reached at 800-GOVTBUY. On the web, it is {www.drms.com}, the Defense Reutilization Marketing Service. Great bargains on all kinds of things. I've talked to people that got cameras, vehicles, and clothing. Some Army/Navy surplus stores get all their stuff at these auctions which they then sell in their stores.

The IRS has unclaimed money, too — all those unclaimed refund checks. If you fill out your IRS form and you think you owe money but really you are due a refund, you may not be looking for a check. If you move in the meantime, the IRS check is not forwarded. It goes back to the IRS and waits for you to collect it. There is $62 million sitting there for people that do not know they are due a refund. Here is how to find out, 1-800-829-1040. It is worth it to just make a call and see.

Social Security has the same thing. Here is a number if you have an unclaimed social security check — 800-772-1213. If you are a veteran, here is where to find if you have a check sitting there, call 800-827-1000.

So, these are just other sources of more money. Check them out. Give them to other people to use. But most importantly, have fun!

Best Starting Places

I get so many questions. "Where do I start?" "Where do I go?" I cannot cover every possible situation. Even though you may have books of mine and there are thousands and thousands of sources, you are never going to have everything you want.

Here are two places that you could go when you do not know where to start. The first place is the Federal Information Center. This is an office set up by the government that will actually do for free what I charge lots of money to do. Their job is to find out who in the government could possibly solve your problem, has the information you need, or has the money you want. Remember, no one office is an end-all and be-all, but it is a good place to start. So, start here. The Federal Information Center can be reached at 866-FIRST-GOV (toll-free). Whether it is finding a passport, finding money to go to graduate school, or finding an expert on Maine potatoes, they will help you.

The other good starting point place is your state capital operator. They are located in your state government. Call the information operator in your state capital, and ask for the state capital operator. When you get the state capital operator say, "Hey, I am looking for _____." Toothpaste cleaner, or money to start an aircraft carrier or whatever the heck it is, let them work. They do this all the time, and they know where to get you started. So, the most important thing is that you have a place to start. When you get that place, you ask them. If they do not have the answer, you ask them where else to go. That is what I love doing. I love telling people where to go!

Closing

Thank you for reading this lengthy introduction. It was fun for me to have an opportunity to share what I've picked up in my 25 years of helping other get money and help.

If you're looking for me or my organization and you need more information, there are two ways to find me. My general 800-number is 1-800-UNCLESAM, and through that number you can find me or we will send you out literature. Or you can contact me on the web at {www.lesko.com}.

Remember, you can't get the magic that is in me. There is separate magic in you, and you have to make sure that you tap into your own magic and share it with the world.

Good luck to you.

Matthew Lesko
Author and Entrepreneur

Notes From Mary Ann

My name is Mary Ann Martello, and I've been co-authoring books with Matthew Lesko for years. If truth be told, Matthew comes up with the title and gets you to buy the book. I fill in the middle with resources that keeps you from returning it. It works out great. It has been a wonderful work experience for me. I get paid, plus I get lots of freebies. In fact, if you could see my house, and I am glad you cannot because it is such a mess, you would find drawers and drawers of coloring books, pamphlets, posters and pictures that I got for free. I found free prescription medications for my grandmother, job training for friends, college money for relatives and much more.

What I would like to do is show you the grant possibilities, and then you can take it from there. Grants come in many different shapes and sizes, from $2 million to expand your manufacturing business, down to $100 to pay your heating bill. I know we told you this before, but it is not going to be easy to get a grant. The bigger the grant, the more complicated the forms. But this does not mean that it is impossible to achieve. It just means that it will take some work.

What we discovered from grant recipients is that you need to talk to many different people to uncover grant programs. The way I have always approached research is that I believe that the information or resource I am seeking exists somewhere, and that I just need to talk with the right person.

We talk about the seven phone call rule a lot. We believe it will take seven phone calls to track down that right person. Sometimes it will take less when we are lucky. Unfortunately, there will be no blinking neon sign that says, "Free Money — Come and Get It." Anything worth doing will take some work, right? This is your chance to turn your dreams into reality, so let's go for it.

Finding the grant-making agency is a challenge. For instance, if you want a grant for a business, there are many different places to investigate. You can look at the federal and state governments for assistance, as well as even your county. That is what makes finding the grant a challenge. In addition, resources exist to help you get your ideas and paperwork in order.

The Book We Copy From

A good starting place for the federal money is the *Catalog of Federal and Domestic Assistance*. This manual has over 1,000 pages, providing information on federal funding programs. Your local library will usually have a copy of the publication. An easier way to search it is on the web at {www.cfda.gov}. You can search by keyword to find programs that may apply to you. Each listing provides information on who qualifies for the program, and a contact person for more information.

By writing, phoning or emailing these programs, you may find a winner. And if you do not qualify for their program, they may know of others. Through the catalog you can learn about hundreds of programs. Programs exist to help you start a business in a rural or depressed area, for women to get transportation contracts, and even for low-income people to start their own business.

For instance, inventors and researchers can qualify for the Small Business Innovation Research Program that provides small businesses the chance to explore the commercialization of their product. Past grant winners include businesses that designed a state-of-the-art wheelchair, seedless watermelon, herbal products, as well as others.

The U.S. Department of Energy's Inventions and Innovations Program provides grants to businesses that have an idea or an invention that will save energy. Winners include companies that made more efficient water heaters, solar energy, lighting and insulation.

I even saw where the Office of Environmental Education of the EPA gave a several thousand-dollar grant to a couple of puppeteers to create a play on recycling. Anything is possible. Just try and think of how your business plan or idea might match up with the government agency or office.

The Gateway to Grants From Non-Profits

Another good resource for uncovering federal government money programs is the website called the Non-Profit Gateway, on the web at {www.nonprofit.gov}. Now, you may be thinking that you are not a non-profit. So why should you check out this site? I am going to talk later about becoming a non-profit, but whether you are one now or not, this website is worth a look.

Non-Profit Gateway links you directly to every federal government department's and agency's grant sites. The grant sites outline all the grants available through the department or agency, contact people, eligibility, forms, past awardees and more. It eliminates the need to search each department's website to uncover grant opportunities. The website also provides a directory of the federal government and listings of information services and links. This will give you lots of starting places.

Many agencies have tips on completing proposals, sample forms and more. The purpose of all of this is to make applying for a grant easier and more understandable. What is nice about learning who got grants in the past is that you see what programs or projects were of interest and how much money they were awarded.

A little side note — in our surveys of people who purchased our book, we found that not everyone has access to the web. Check out your local library as many provide Internet access. There are also many free Internet access providers, such as Juno at {www.juno.com}. I did a search and found a site called Internet for Free, which lets you pick your state and area code, and you can find a free Internet access provider. They are at {www.internet4free.net}.

Each department within the federal government has an office called the Office of Small and Disadvantaged Business Utilization — a big name for a small office that is designed to help small businesses learn how to do business with that particularly department. But they also may be able to refer you to an office or bureau that handles your business interest. In addition, whether it is selling your product or providing your services, this office can get you started.

Contracts Can Be Better Than Grants

As Matthew always says, "A government contract is better than a grant," because your main objective is to do a business and provide a product or a service.

There are actually offices called Procurement Assistance Centers, whose job is to help small businesses get government contracts with any department bureau or office. These actually were started to help companies get Department of Defense contracts, but have now expanded to include the entire federal government. They are great resources, with offices located throughout the country. They can explain the bidding process, the resources available, and provide information in how the procurement system operates. They can even match your product or service with the appropriate agency, and then help you market your product. All you need now to do is start counting your money — not a bad deal.

Your state Department of Economic Development is located in your state capital. This office is designed to help businesses get started or expanded. They can answer all your questions and direct you to other appropriate offices within the state government for more specific business issues, such as licensing or registration. Many states offer special loan or grant programs, some more than others.

They also offer tax incentives, training assistance, and energy evaluations. If you need to get your employees up to speed on the latest computer technology, this office may be able to offer you money to cover the training, or help with reducing the cost.

Lots of Grants for Business

We uncovered several states that offer grants for recycling programs, alternative fuels, or even childcare centers. Iowa will give you $40,000 to recycle tires, and $10,000 to start a business if you have a disability. California has a $50,000 tax credit to start an onsite childcare facility. Minnesota will give you $4,000 for technical assistance to start your business, and Wisconsin has $30,000 to start a rural business. Maybe that bread and breakfast is really within your reach.

Tennessee, Michigan, Rhode Island and many other states want to give you money to train your employees. A majority of states will even give you a tax credit for each new job you create, or if you hire someone trying to get off welfare.

How does London, Paris or Rome sound? If you think overseas may be the ticket for your company, then there is money to attend tradeshows or other resources for exporting your product.

Cheri Olssen said she had a small recycling business where she bought and resold aluminum cans. She stumbled upon a grant offered by the Nebraska Department of Environmental Control. After she completed a simple application, she received a $4,500 grant for a flatbed gooseneck trailer and a truck. Check out your state to see what they can do for you today.

Another resource for money is venture capital. This is what is known as having a silent business partner. Join the likes of Staples, Intel, American Online and thousands of others who have used venture capital to start or expand their businesses.

The SBA licenses small business investment companies who in turn provide venture capital or start up financing for small businesses. You can check them out at the Small Business Administration website at {www.sba.gov}. There are also many different venture capital companies at the state level or in the private sector. Some venture companies' focus on a certain area of a state or the country, as well as have an area of expertise. It is worth investigating to see what money is out there for you.

Located at a more local level, there are sometimes agencies called Economic Development Councils or some other similar name. The mission of these councils is to stimulate the economy of a particular area, and often start up business assistance is included. Your local Chamber of Commerce, business organization or other associations may be able to direct you to those resources.

Free Consulting Help

If you need help writing your business plan and getting all your P's and Q's in order, then visit your local Small Business Development Center. These centers are located in a majority of counties throughout the United States, and are funded through both federal and state monies. The purpose of the centers is to help people write their business plan, and to begin searching for funding, if needed. They are experts in this field, and can help you organize your thoughts and complete a well thought out plan of action.

When Phillip Seahorn wanted to start his Internet marketing business, he went to one of these offices and said he got thousands of dollars worth of free business counseling, and even help with seeking funding for his venture. He had no idea that such an office of help existed and felt that his business would never be this far along without the assistance these people offered.

Having said all that, sometimes you actually need very little to start a business. Matthew started with a desk in his apartment and business cards. My own husband started a business working at night, using our computer in the den. A year later, he has an office and several employees. These offices will help you figure out what the minimum is that you need to get started, and you can grow with your business.

Foundations That Give You Support

I have talked a great deal about business grants, but I want to take a few minutes to discuss grants offered through foundations. If you cannot find what you need through the government, then you can turn to other sources for funds. Foundations made nearly $20 billion in charitable grants last year.

Before approaching foundations as your funding source, there are many issues to consider. Primarily, although there are always exceptions, these foundations provide grants to other non-profits, not to individuals, with some focus on a specific geographic area or interest. Probably the largest organization designed to help people learn about grants and grant writing is The Foundation Center. This is a non-profit center that gathers and disseminates information on foundations. They have an extensive collection of books, documents, reports and publications focused in the grants area, plus knowledgeable staff to assist users in locating information. They have five main offices scattered throughout the US, plus libraries in every state. In addition, they publish funding directories specific to certain fields, such as aging, arts, families, health, higher education and women.

They also offer grant writing classes and other courses to help you in your search. We found several Internet search engines that will help you find a non-profit organization that meets your needs. You can try {www.idealist.org} and {www.guidestar.org}. Guide Star actually has a searchable database of over 620,000 organizations.

Also, many corporations have foundations that support local projects. When I was trying to get sponsorship for a youth horse show, I found that the new professional hockey team in my town actually had a special office and monies to support just such events. Make sure that the foundation you are contacting matches with what you are trying to do. It will save time on your part and theirs.

I mentioned earlier about becoming a non-profit. A majority of foundations or organizations, and even government programs award grants only to non-profits. There are two avenues you can take. One, you can find a non-profit you can work with to apply for the grant, and then they can be a conduit for the money. Obviously, you need to work with an organization whose goals match with your cause, and who you feel you can trust.

Think of your current membership in various organizations and clubs. What about local service organizations or education institutions? You obviously now will be held accountable to both the grant making agency and the non-profit.

Start Your Own Non-Profit

The other avenue to take is to become a non-profit. It is not as difficult as you may imagine. I have a friend named Dan Meeks. He wanted to start a Vietnam vet service organization that would help troubled teens in the area. Dan did what most people would do — he went to a lawyer and was told it would take several thousand dollars to fill out the paperwork.

Since he knew us and had our books, he thought he should be able to apply by himself. He got the forms from the IRS and filled them out as best he could. Then he called the IRS and the guy actually walked him through the rest of the forms. He sent in a check for $150, which was the IRS filing fee and got his non-profit status without the lawyers' huge fees. Now Dan is able to seek funding from a variety of sources, and fulfill a dream that is important to him.

No More Starving Artists

Do you really need to be a starving artist or to suffer for your art? I do not think so. Heidi Hart, Doug Sharples, Bradley Sowash, David Sovlino, plus hundreds of other artists were able to take advantage of what their state arts councils had to offer in the way of grants.

When we talked with David Sovlino, he said that he followed a simple application process that was pretty straightforward, and then if he had any questions, the council was more than willing to give him a hand. Bradley Sowash had the same experience.

I know a choreographer that got a $10,000 fellowship designed to just free up her time to create new work. Many cities and counties have their own arts councils willing to assist those local artists in the creation and performance of their work. Search for those by contacting your city or county government, as well as your state arts and humanities organizations.

When I did a search for other grants for artists, I found many private arts organizations that offered help. Some provide travel money. Others provide financial assistance to artists in need. Many offer fellowships for artists who work in specific mediums, so that they can create free from external pressures.

Search on the web. Contact arts organizations. Check out arts publications, as well as talk to other artists to learn what is out there. Something that always has intrigued me is that a certain percentage of all federal and state building money must be spent on art. I think it would be interesting to take advantage of that opportunity.

When we searched for grants, we found specific ones for architects, sculptors, writers, vocalists, artists in their mature phase, $5,000 for comic book writers, and even $2,500 for artists who are emerging in their art form. There is something for everyone.

Even though the National Endowment for the Arts gives only limited money directly to individuals, their website links you to any government office that offers some type of arts or community grants, as well as to your state and local arts organization. I saw where there were grants for a sculpture garden, bike paths, and even a collection of oral histories.

Housing Grants

Wouldn't it be great to give Grandma $10,000 to repair her roof, or even get $6,000 for closing costs on your dream home? What about $2,000 for storm windows, or $700 to pay your electric bill?

I talked with the Chandlers who, even though they had some credit problems in the past were still able to get a $3,000 grant for closing costs to buy a new home. They talked about what a relief it was to get the grant, and how they never would have been able to come up with the money for the down payment without help. Sandy Dotson got $3,500 for her closing costs and said it was not hard to apply at all.

How did they get the money? They called around and talked with their local and state housing authorities. A majority of states offer grants or low interest loans to either first-time homebuyers or low-income residents. Just because you owned a home a while ago does not necessarily disqualify you from assistance. We learned that many states say that if you have not owned a home in three years, it means that you can still qualify for the first-time homeowner's help. It also may apply to those who are legally separated or divorced.

Many housing and community development agencies offer housing assistance and home repair programs. If you live in a small town, the U.S. Department of Agriculture's Rural Housing Service offers some grant and loan programs to buy, repair or build housing.

Even the U.S. Department of Housing and Urban Development has a housing repair program, and they offer counseling programs for those in danger of losing their homes. So, if you cannot pay your mortgage, they will help you work it out with your bank so you do not lose your home.

Your state energy office can direct you to heating and weatherization grants, and most utility companies can also offer to help with your bills. You do not need to be a professional grant writer to complete these simple forms. You just have to make a phone call to get the process started.

Grants for Education and Job Training

We sent out an email to people who bought our books and asked them to respond back if they got a grant. My mailbox overflowed with people that got grants to go to school. Ronald King gets money to go to school, plus a voucher for books and money to help with living expenses. Dennis Harwood gets $6,000 a year to go to auto mechanic school part-time at night. His goal is to double his salary. What is interesting is that his wife knew about the program, and once her husband went to school found that the phone kept ringing with other people asking her how he was able to do this. She just assumed everybody knew about the grant programs.

Karen Ladd is a stay-at-home mom with four kids. She wanted to finish her degree so that when her youngest goes to school, she can get a good job. She found out that you can get a federal grant to go to school, and that she can use the money to pay for her online courses she is taking to finish her accounting degree. She said she never would have been able to go to school without the money or the online classes. Many people, like Rebecca Lowers get money from both federal and state governments.

All states have a Department of Higher Education, and most offer some type of assistance programs for residents. You may be able to get grants if you are smart or if you are going into medical or teaching professions, or if you meet some income requirements. It varies state to state, so check it out. There are also millions of dollars worth of federal grant and loan programs. You can contact the U.S. Department of Education or talk with your school or potential university's financial aid office to learn more.

I see in many publications or some of the junk mail I get that companies offer to find scholarships for your kids' college tuition for a fee. My philosophy is that if someone is going to charge me money to do something, then I should be able to do it by myself for less.

A friend was going to spend $300 to have a company find scholarships for her. I went on the web, and by using a variety of search engines found her 30 scholarship programs that met her qualifications. There was no guarantee she would get them, but I did as much as that guy who was going to charge her $300 would do.

There are grants to study overseas, money to learn about history, anthropology, housing issues, hairstyling, gardening and more. There is even money for smart athletes to go to school. Many people have heard Matthew talk about a woman that got money to take computer courses, and that has to be one of the top calls we get in the office. People want to get their Microsoft certification, learn C++ or whatever the latest computer program is. This is not a once in a lifetime incident.

I talked with Len Osborne. Len was the bouncer making $7 an hour and was going to get laid off. He saw Matthew's book and called the state Department of Labor where he was living. He received $1,000 to live on, gas money to get to training, a computer to keep, money for books and took over $10,000 worth of classes so that he could become a Microsoft certified systems engineer. It quadrupled his salary to over $50,000 with benefits. Len says it absolutely works and literally turned his life around.

Ed Blakesley got the same thing when he was collecting unemployment. He says he will be able to make more money than ever before. Will Mosely and Samantha White also were able to get their computer courses paid.

Talk with your local Job Training Partnership Act Office, the Employment Services Office, or even your unemployment or workman's comp officer, if you have one. Most of our success stories people talk about how one person happened to know about a program, and how lucky they felt to get in.

Grants for Your Health

When my grandmother was getting treatment for cancer, the doctors prescribed her medication that was going to cost $200 a month. She was living on a fixed income and really could not afford the bill. The doctor and pharmacist were no help, but we happened to talk with a drug rep who was delivering sample products to a doctor's office. We learned that every drug company has a program to help people get the medications they need if they cannot afford them. It takes one phone call to the drug manufacturer and your doctor needs to sign a form. That is it.

My grandmother got her medications for free, and when we started talking about this program, we helped hundreds of others also take advantage of the service. Karen Moriarty gets $1,000 worth of free medications each year and learned about the program in one of our books. She cannot thank us enough. There are programs out there for health insurance for kids, cheap or free dental care, free mammograms, free hospitalizations and more. It may take a little digging, but these programs exist.

Copies of Grant Applications

I am going to give you two big tips that will help you actually win the grant. Once you have found a grant program that applies to you, if it is offered by a federal or a state agency, you can request a copy of a successful grant application. Most of the agencies have a listing of past awardees and you could submit a Freedom of Information Act request to get a copy of a specific completed application.

This takes a little time and will cost you about $20, but you get a chance to see what a winner looks like. It is very helpful to see how others submitted their proposals and really what a successful application package looks like.

The second tip applies to any grant program. Almost everyone we talked to said that they had many conversations with the grant-making agency. They asked hundreds of questions on how to complete the application and they always found the agencies helpful. Many agencies also let you submit a preliminary application, which they will comment on, and then return to you for completion.

A friend of mine who received a grant to make a CD said that the help the council gave him to complete his proposal was invaluable and made his application a grant winner, rather than a grant loser.

I know I have given you a lot of information and resources to check. It may seem overwhelming. What I find helpful is to make a list of all the possible places to check, even it may seem like a stretch. I always get the name of the person to whom I am talking and use my nicest telephone voice. It tends to make people want to be more helpful. I have had people dig through their desk to find old reports, or gone on hunts to find the right person who I need to talk to because I have treated them with kindness.

When All Else Fails

When all else fails and you are stumped, not knowing where to turn, remember that you have a Representative and Senators in Congress. These people are certainly running for re-election and would love your vote. They all have workers called case managers in their offices, whose job it is to cut through red tape for people, and try to solve constituent problems. If they help you, then you will be sure to tell your family and friends about it, and maybe next election they will win by a landslide.

I have given you as much as I can give you about grant hunting, so happy hunting and follow your dreams.

Mary Ann Martello
Author and Researcher

WRITING YOUR GRANT PROPOSAL

There are lots of places to look for help on the mechanics of grant writing. The library has books, government funding sources publish guidelines, organizations like the Foundation Center (www.fdncenter.org) and the Grantsmanship Center (www.tgci.com) have lots of useful information online, as well as publications you can purchase. A quick search on the Internet turned up 300,000 web sites that focus on grants writing!

But before you dive in, you need to ask yourself one question: Is it worth it? The instant answer is, "Of course!" You've already followed your heart instead of your wallet. But remember, you will be persuading someone to give you money, not telling them you have to have it. You'll need to marshal all your resources and be absolutely convinced that you are proposing an important project; otherwise, you'll feel as if you're begging and no one enjoys that. Have you asked yourself, are we the best people to do this job? Could we do a better job teaming up with some other, better-established organization and doing our project under their auspices? Is the service we are proposing needed? If we build it, would anybody come? Is there anybody with money out there who might be willing to back this project financially? What's in it for the organization that gives us the money?

If this is more soul searching than you had planned, you're not ready to start writing a grant proposal. Remember, flawless prose cannot conceal a weak proposal. The writing is easy compared to the thinking process that goes into planning a great project.

Every potential funder's expectations are different, but here are some general tips for how to prepare a convincing and successful grant proposal.

Proposal Writing Tips

Grants are a two-way transaction

In our hurry to explain how very much we need the money for an important project, it is easy to forget this vital fact: grants are a two-way transaction. Your organization gets much-needed funds, but what does the giver get in return? Frame your proposal, and the problem you're addressing, from the funder's perspective instead of your own. Don't devalue your own contribution to the community. What are you giving the funder? A better-educated workforce? A place to go after school that could cut down on the shoplifting and vandalism that is slowly destroying neighborhood businesses? A better image in the community?

Wal-Mart's charitable giving program (www.walmartfoundation.org) is a classic example of philanthropy that serves its stockholders as well as the communities where Wal-Mart does business. Wal-Mart has been accused of building its "big box" stores on the outskirts of small and medium size towns, where its lower prices and all-in-one-place convenience hasten the collapse of smaller, long-established local stores and empty the older downtowns. Wal-Mart's charitable giving for 1999, which totaled almost $164 million, is targeted, in part, to dissolve this image of the bully from out of town. The slogan on their web site makes the point succinctly: "Community Programs that work for Wal-Mart, SAM's Club and you. After all, we live here too." Funding decisions for charitable projects are made at the local level by store employees and most of the programs require Wal-Mart associates to volunteer in the fundraising process. When Wal-Mart does support national causes such as United Way, it insists that Wal-Mart's local contribution stays in the community where it was raised. Wal-Mart's generosity creates a better business climate for its stores as well as making a positive impact on the communities where it does business.

Do your homework

Before you put anything in writing, find out everything you can about the company, foundation or government agency you plan to ask for money. Read their printed application guidelines thoroughly. Read their annual reports, which will list grant recipients from previous years. Call previous grant recipients and get their take on working with the organization. Sometimes the granting organization will give you a copy of the form their evaluators use to "grade" the grant applications when they decide how to award the monies. These blank review sheets make a great checklist when it comes time for you to edit your draft proposal.

Cultivate a good relationship with the grant program officer

Most organizations giving grants have one or more employees responsible for collecting the applications and overseeing the process in which a panel of employees, experts, or other consultants decides which applicants will receive funds. Although job titles vary, this person is often called the program officer. Should you send this person a dozen long-stem roses the day after you submit your grant proposal? Absolutely not! Nevertheless, the program officer can be immensely helpful in furthering your success. Remember, reviewers want to see a stack of informative yet concise, appropriate proposals. Your best effort will make the program officer look better. Don't be afraid to ask program officers to clarify details. They will usually supply you with copies of winning proposals from previous years and some will even review your draft proposal and provide helpful comments if you give them plenty of time. There are a few cardinal rules, however; don't ask a question that is clearly answered in the guidelines, and don't expect any hand-holding if you've put off applying until the last minute.

Don't try to fit square pegs into round holes

Your priorities should match those of the organization you are applying to. For example, one local ice cream store was so besieged with requests for donations to everything from soccer clubs to Girl Scout troops to Sunday school picnics that the store finally announced that it would not consider requests for any money that did not contribute to education. Many organizations have very specific agendas, such as the environment, technology in schools, help for the elderly, or arts education, for example. Do some research before you ask.

Sometimes, what you need most is something nobody is interested in funding. Non-profits that have high-maintenance facilities, such as historical societies or theaters, have a notoriously difficult time getting the money for expensive but necessary upkeep, although lots of companies are willing to fund a specific event that gets their logo in front of the public. Before you begin asking corporate funders for money for a new roof, you should sit down with your organization's budget and make sure you have already sought grants for everything that is likely to be attractive to sponsors.

Consider starting small

If your group is the new kid on the block, you won't have the kind of track record that could reassure potential funders that you'll still be standing there, fiscally sound, at the end of the project. Although there are at least 90 kids in four different schools who desperately need the service you'll provide, your long-term success at funding such a program may depend upon successfully funding and completing a one-year "pilot program" at one school. If you have done a great job on the small scale test run, your credibility will be greater when you go back to ask for money to expand. (However, you may want to reconsider if you are applying to an organization that does not look kindly upon grant recipients returning to ask for money a second time.)

Companies love company

Most corporate givers and philanthropic organizations want to be associated with a group of "good citizen" companies. They probably will want to see their logos with a bunch of other sponsors'. To avoid a sort of chicken-and-egg cycle-we can't sponsor you until we know that other companies are willing to sponsor you-solicit non-monetary contributions first and share that information with potential funders. For instance, if you want money to develop a program that will encourage poor parents to read to their children, you could arrange for a local design firm to create the layout and a local printer to print the workbooks for free before you go to a corporation asking for dollars. Those donated services are essentially "matching gifts" that could be worth thousands of dollars. Submit your proposal to other potential funders as well as your most likely source. It's expected that you will do so and it shows that you are committed to your project. Do notify all potential funders that you are submitting the proposal to other sources.

Proof read, proof read, proof read

Wouldn't it be awful if your proposal was rejected because you added the figures wrong in the budget section? Or you didn't double-space the introduction according to the guidelines? Or you misspelled the foundation chairman's last name in the cover letter? Ask people unfamiliar with the project to read your prose to see if they understand what you're asking for. Make sure that any charts or graphs you use are not so complicated that it will take a reviewer 15 minutes just to decode them.

Write like a reporter

Put the most important elements at the beginning of each section and amplify in subsequent paragraphs. If a reviewer is only going to read the first paragraph of each section, what is the most essential information for her to have when she makes a decision? You can ask program officers about how much time reviewers have to read the applications and how many they are likely to receive. If you do the math and it looks as if your reviewer will be reading about three 30-page applications an hour, you'll want to get straight to the point in your application.

Don't forget to include an "evaluation" method

At the end of your project, funders will ask, "Was my money well spent?" You'll want to have hard data that demonstrates your success so that you'll have an even stronger proposal the next time you ask for money. If you need to pay a professional to evaluate your project, be sure to put that cost in your budget. A proposal without an effectively designed evaluation is like a science experiment without an explicit method for measuring results. The proposal and the experiment both flunk.

How much money should you ask for?

Don't give a low estimate because it will look as if you haven't planned realistically. Likewise, padding looks like waste and won't go over well. Most grant application guidelines are very specific about how to calculate costs. Also, don't ask a potential sponsor for $20,000 when their history suggests that they seldom give more than $5,000 per grant.

First impressions count, so do your best writing last

The first part of a proposal is almost always a summary or abstract, and you are sometimes limited to as little as 250 to 500 words. Don't write this until you have written everything else in the application. By this time you ought to be really focused and ready to drive home a few key points with a minimum of fluff. Remember, this might be the only section a reviewer reads so it better be good.

Be very specific about how the project will unfold

Be sure to tell what will happen in what sequence. You might want to draw up a timetable, which can make it easy for the evaluator to visualize the process. When you describe what paid or volunteer staff will be working on the project, don't forget to explain how you will free up time for a full-time employee who already has a full plate of responsibilities.

Tell your funders what will happen after the project

Funders will want to know that you have thought ahead to the time after your project is successfully completed. What sort of follow-up activities will take place? Will you need to seek more grant money or will you be able to carry on independently?

Back up any claims with hard facts

Chances are, the facts and figures you need are right in your own organization's records, or can be found by checking with state and local agencies. (This is all the more reason for your organization to keep accurate counts of attendance, volunteer hours, etc.) Use statistics to describe your community, your clientele, and the problem you plan to address. The following statement, written by the fictional, nonprofit Cornbelt Farm Families Association, uses easily obtained numbers to give the background for why it needs funds to offer more computer training classes for adults.

"Although our region of the Eastwest has prospered from the new technological services industries centered around Ourstate University Research Park, the small farm town of Cornbelt has suffered the double loss of declining agricultural produce prices and the closure of the Cleanfast vacuum factory, where at least one member of each of 500 Cornbelt farm families worked to provide a second income. Although the regional unemployment rate averages 5.5 percent, Cornbelt's hovers near 12 percent. Average per capita personal income for the region is $28,500, yet the annual income for Cornbelt Farm Families Association's clients averages $16,000. The drought of 1999 also hurt these families. Crop losses were an estimated $50 million for the Tri-County area.

"As conditions for farm families have worsened, the number of Cornbelt residents seeking computer training at Cornbelt Farm Families Association has increased by 30 percent, from 455 in 1998 to 650 in 2000."

Remember your manners

If you do receive a grant, write a thank you note. If you don't receive a grant, call and politely ask why. You might get answers that will provide you with the keys to writing a successful proposal next year. Some organizations will even provide you with copies of the evaluators' "grade cards," on request; these can provide a gold mine of constructive criticism.

What Information Should You Provide In Your Proposal?

Grant proposals can be short or long (some government-funded programs can easily run to 100 pages of documentation!) and the sections may have different titles, but the following list will give you an idea of the standard components of a proposal and the information they require.

The executive summary or abstract

In one page or less, this section must sum up everything to follow. The writing in this section should be so clear and compelling that the reviewer will want to find out more. If the executive summary is unclear the reviewer may well weed out your proposal without even reading the rest of the application. As noted previously, write this section last.

The statement of need or problem

This section tells why your project should be undertaken. You should set it up so that it leads naturally to the project description in the next section, which will describe how you want to address this need.

* Use accurate statistics that support your description of the problem.
* Demonstrate that your organization has a thorough understanding of the specific issue, along with the larger social issues that may be contributing factors.
* Show that the need or problem, as you have described it, can be at least partially solved.

The project description

This section tells what the grant will be used for. Subsections describe
* the objectives (what the results of the project will be);
* the methods for meeting those objectives;
* staffing (who will do what and how);
* how you will evaluate whether you are meeting your objectives.

The budget

This section contains an outline of projected expenses. Be sure to address each of the elements listed in the project description.

Organization information

This section conveys the information that demonstrates your organization's ability to carry out the project successfully. Without deluging the reader with facts and figures, you need to tell
* when your organization was founded;
* its mission statement (your proposal should be consistent with the mission);
* the services your organization provides and the audience it serves;
* how your organization is structured;
* expertise of key staff members.

Conclusion

Like a talented debater summing up at the end, you want to briefly reiterate your key points. This is the one place in the proposal where it's O.K. to get a little emotional. This might be the spot to share a pithy quote from a client whose life has been changed for the better by your services or an editorial from the local paper that supports your point.

TYPES OF ASSISTANCE AND GRANTS SOURCES
(or where you can find money)

Types of Assistance

You are on the money hunt, but exactly what are you shooting for? When you read grant guidelines or proposal information, you will find a great many new terms. Here are a few basic definitions to help you along.

Grants: Grants are generally considered a desirable form of financial assistance since they represent an outright award of funds and are not required to be repaid.

Project Grants: Grants provided for a fixed period for the development of a specific project or the delivery of specific services or products.

Loans: Since loans must be repaid, they are often viewed by applicants as less desirable than grants. However, with the reduction of federal funds available for grants and the increasing level of competition for such funds, loans are often the only form of assistance available.

Direct Loans: Loans given directly to the applicant for a specific period of time and are needed to be repaid with interest.

Guaranteed/Insured Loans: Programs in which the federal government makes an arrangement with a lender that protects the lender if the person fails to repay or defaults on a loan.

In-Kind Donation (Use of property, facilities, and equipment): Programs that provide the loan of or use of facilities, property, or materials.

Government Grants

Catalog of Federal Domestic Assistance

The best single resource for leads on federal funding programs is published by the federal government and is called the *Catalog of Federal Domestic Assistance*. This manual of more than 1,000 pages provides the most comprehensive information on federal funds, cross-indexed by agency, program type, applicant eligibility, and subject. The Catalog is available in many libraries, and describes federal government programs that provide funds or non-financial assistance to state and local governments, public agencies, organizations, institutions, and individuals. Included are the program's legislative authority, explanations of each program, types of assistance provided, restrictions, eligibility requirements, financial information, application and award procedures, information contacts, and related programs.

The Catalog and some of the other publications listed in this guide are also available as online databases. Such databases can be searched using personal computers with modems, or perhaps by arranging for a search to be conducted at a local library. While not all libraries offer online searching services, many larger public and research libraries do, generally for a fee. If a local library does not have online searching capabilities, library personnel may be able to direct interested parties to outside search services or consultants.

You can purchase a copy of the Catalog of Federal Domestic Assistance for $87 by contacting the Superintendent of Documents, U.S. Government Printing Office, P.O. Box 371954, Pittsburgh, PA 15250; 202-512-1800. You can also find the Catalog in many libraries and you can search it online at {www.cfda.gov}. In addition, you may purchase a copy of the Catalog on CD-ROM or on floppy diskette. The CD-ROM also contains the Federal Assistance Award Data System (FAADS) database. With this feature, you can check out a specific program to see who received the program funds in the past. This is an incredible feature, as it may help you tailor your proposal accordingly. You can search by program number, keyword, or location. The CD-ROM and diskette are available for $50 each by contacting the Federal Domestic Assistance Catalog Staff (MVS), 300 7th St., SW, Reporters Building, Room 101, Washington, DC 20407; 202-708-5126; Fax: 202-401-8233; {www.cfda.gov}. See "How To Read The Catalog of Federal Domestic Assistance" on page 94 and "Developing and Writing Federal Government Grant Proposals" on page 101.

Federal Register

Updated information on federal programs and grant awards appears in the daily *Federal Register*, also available from the Government Printing Office. Federal agencies are required to publish description of programs, guidelines, and eligibility requirements in the *Federal Register*. You can purchase a subscription for the Federal Register for $555 per year by contacting the Superintendent of Documents, U.S. Government Printing Office, Washington, DC 20402; 202-512-1800. You can also find the Federal Register in many libraries and you can view it online at {www.access.gpo.gov/nara/}.

Pre and Postaward Grants

In addition, House offices have access to two databases known as PREAward Grants and POSTaward Grants, available through the House Information Resources/Member Information Network System. (Senate offices have access to these databases via the Senate Library or Senate Reference Center.) These files include current grant availability data from the *Catalog of Federal Domestic Assistance* and the *Federal Register*, as well as reports from federal agencies about grants awarded during the latest four quarters. The databases are available only through congressional offices; requests for a search of these databases may be made through an individual Member of Congress. To contact your Representative, The United States House of Representatives, Washington, DC 20515; 202-224-3121; {www.house.gov}; and Your Senator, U.S. Senate, Washington, DC 20510; 202-224-3121; {www.senate.gov}.

Commerce Business Daily

The *Commerce Business Daily* (CBD) lists notices of proposed government procurement actions, contracts awards, sales of government property, and other procurement information. A new edition of the CBD is issued every business day. Each edition contains approximately 500-1,000 notices. Each notice appears in the CBD only once. All Federal procurement offices are required to announce proposed procurement actions over $25,000, and contract awards over$25,000, that are likely to result in the award of any subcontracts, in the CBD. You can purchase a subscription for the Commerce Business Daily for $275 per year by contacting the Superintendent of Documents, U.S. Government Printing Office, Washington, DC 20402; 202-512-1800. You can also find the CBD in many libraries and you can view it online at {http://cbdnet.gpo.gov}.

How To Read
The Catalog Of Federal Domestic Assistance

Program Number, Title, and Popular Name

Each program in the Catalog is preceded by a five-digit program identification number. The first two digits identify the Federal department or agency that administers the program, and the last three digits are assigned in numerical sequence. Thus, program number 10.500 is administered by the Department of Agriculture, 11.500 by the Department of Commerce, 12.500 by the Department of Defense, 93.500 by the Department of Health and Human Services, and so on. (In the numerical sequence of program numbers, some numbers do not appear due to program deletions or consolidations. To accommodate users' systems and records, the numbers are not reassigned to other programs but are reserved for the reinstated programs.)

Program Title:
The program title is the descriptive name given to a program. The popular name, which is less descriptive than the program title, is the name by which the program is commonly known. Not all programs have one.

Objectives:
This is a brief statement of what the program is intended to accomplish along with the goals toward which the program is directed.

Eligibility Requirements:

Applicant Eligibility
This section indicates who can apply to the Federal government for assistance and the criteria the potential applicant must satisfy. For example, individuals may be eligible for research grants, and the criteria to be satisfied may be that they have a professional or scientific degree, 3 years of research experience, and be a U.S. citizen. Universities, medical schools, hospitals, or State and local governments may also be eligible. Where State governments are eligible, the type of State agency will be indicated and the criteria that they must satisfy. Certain programs in the Catalog (e.g., the Pell Grant program that provides grants to students) involve intermediate levels of application processing, i.e., applications are transmitted through colleges or universities that are neither the direct applicant nor the ultimate beneficiary. For these programs, the criteria the intermediaries must satisfy are also indicated, along with intermediaries who are not eligible.

Beneficiary Eligibility
This section lists the ultimate beneficiaries of the program, the criteria they must satisfy, and who specifically is not eligible. The applicant and beneficiary will generally be the same for programs that provide assistance directly from a Federal agency. Financial assistance, however, that passes through State or local governments will have different applicants and beneficiaries since the assistance is transmitted to private sector beneficiaries who are not obligated to request or apply for the assistance.

Credentials/Documentation
This is a brief description of the credentials or documentation required prior to, or along with, an application for assistance. The eligibility factors that must be proven, certified, or established are indicated in this section. This section also indicates whether OMB Circular No. A-87 requirements, "Cost Principles Applicable to Grants and Contracts with State and Local Governments," are applicable. In cases in which specific Federal circulars or other regulatory requirements are not applicable to the program, disclaimer statements may be included referencing the requirements(s) from which the program is excluded.

Application And Award Process
Preapplication Coordination
This section indicates whether any prior coordination or approval is required with governmental or nongovernmental units prior to the submission of a formal application to the Federal funding agency. For example, programs may require: State agency approval prior to the submission of an application to a Federal agency; The submission of environmental impact information as required by the National Environmental Policy Act of 1969, or other types of requirements.

Application Procedure
This section discusses the basic procedural steps required by the Federal agency in the application process, beginning with the lowest level (e.g., State and local government units, institutions or organizations) and ending eventually with the Federal government. Each program indicates where applications are to be submitted. Numerous programs in the Catalog require the standard application forms in OMB Circular No. A-102. Other applications may be in the form of a written request to the funding agency stating the need for assistance and requesting available services, or a formal proposal prepared in response to an announcement in the Federal Register or the Commerce Business Daily. Also indicated in this section is guidance concerning the applicability of OMB Circular No. A-110, "Grants and Agreements with Institutions of Higher Education, Hospitals, and Other Nonprofit Organizations." When specific Federal circulars or other regulatory requirements are not applicable to the program, disclaimer statements may be included referencing the requirements(s) from which the program is excluded.

Award Procedure
This section lists the basic steps for awarding assistance, beginning with the organizational components of the Federal Agency that has final approval authority for the application and ending with the lowest level at which Federal resources are expended. Also indicated is whether assistance passes through the initial applicant for further distribution by intermediate level applicants to groups or individuals in the private sector. Accepted applications are evaluated by the headquarters, regional, local, or district office to determine the feasibility of the proposed project to include consistency with Federal and individual agency policies concerning its scope and purpose. Grant payments may be made by letter of credit, advance by Treasury check, or reimbursement by Treasury check. Awards may be made by the headquarters office directly to the applicant, an agency field office, a regional office, or by an authorized county office.

Deadlines
When available, this section indicates the deadlines for applications to the funding agency in terms of the date(s) or between what dates the application should be received. Reference is made to new applications, continuations, renewals, and supplementals. Application deadline information is indicated in the agency's program guidelines, or announced in the *Federal Register*. Where not available, applicants should contact the funding agency for deadline information.

Range of Approval or Disapproval Time
This section gives a representative range of time required for the application to be processed (in days or months) at the Federal level.

Appeals
In some cases, there are no provisions for appeal. Where applicable, this section discusses appeal procedures or allowable rework time for resubmissions. Appeal procedures vary with individual programs and are either listed in this section or are documented in the relevant Code of Federal Regulations (CFR).

Renewals
This section discusses whether renewals or extensions of applications are available and indicates the appropriate procedures. In some instances, renewal procedures may be the same as the application procedure, e.g. for projects of a non-continuing nature renewals will be treated as new, competing applications; for projects of an ongoing nature, renewals may be given annually.

Criteria for Selecting Proposals

This section indicates the criteria used by the Federal grantor agency to evaluate proposals and the criteria used to award funds for projects.

Examples of Funded Projects

This section indicates the different types of projects that have been funded in the past. Only projects funded under Project Grants or Direct Payments for Specified Use are listed here. The examples give potential applicants an idea of the projects that may be accepted for funding.

Range of Assistance Given

This section lists the representative range (smallest to largest) of the amount of financial assistance available. These figures are based on funds awarded in the past fiscal year and the current fiscal year to date. Also indicated is an approximate average amount of awards that were made in the past and current fiscal years.

Related Programs

This section lists programs in the Catalog that are closely related based on objectives and program uses. Applicants should also refer to these programs, as they may provide additional assistance in a related area of interest.

Program Accomplishments

This section briefly describes the accomplishments of the program using quantitative data, focusing on program output, results achieved, or services rendered during the past fiscal year, the current fiscal year, and projections for the next fiscal year.

Financial And Administrative Information

Federal Agency

The Federal agency is the Federal department, agency, commission, council, or instrumentality of the government, and the primary organizational sub-unit (the administering office) that has direct operational responsibility for managing a program.

Types of Assistance

This section indicates the form in which the assistance is transmitted from the Federal government and is initially received for use or distribution by the applicant. See also Types of Assistance.

Obligations

The dollar amounts listed in this section represent obligations for the past fiscal year, estimates for the current fiscal year, and estimates for the budget fiscal year as reported by the Federal agencies. In each succeeding edition of the Catalog, the dollar amounts are revised to reflect changes that may result from supplemental appropriations or amendments. Each program indicates what the obligation figures represent in terms of the type of assistance provided. Obligations for nonfinancial assistance programs indicate the administrative expenses involved in the operation of the program as an indication of the magnitude of the services being provided, or the items involved in obligations.

Budget Account Number

This 11-digit budget account identification code represents the account that funds a particular program. The code is consistent with the code given for the program area as specified in Appendix III of the Budget of the United States Government.

Authorization

This section lists the legal authority on which a program is based (acts, amendments to acts, Public Law numbers, titles, sections, Statute Codes, citations to the U.S. Code, Executive Orders, Presidential Reorganization Plans, and Memoranda from an agency head).

Regulations, Guidelines, and Literature
This section lists the title, number, and price of guidelines, handbooks, manuals, and other officially published information pertinent to a program. Code of Federal Regulations (CFR) citations are also listed.

Information Contacts

Regional or Local Office
This section lists the agency contact person, address, and phone number of the Federal Regional or Local Offices to

be contacted for detailed information regarding the program such as: current availability of funds and the likelihood of receiving assistance within a given period; preapplication and application forms required; whether a preapplication conference is recommended; assistance available in preparation of applications; whether funding decisions are made at the headquarters, regional, or local level; application renewal procedures (including continuations and supplementals) or appeal procedures for rejected applications; and recently published program guidelines and material. For many programs in the Catalog, this section suggests consulting Appendix IV for these offices.

Headquarters Office
This section lists names and addresses of the office at the headquarters level with direct operational responsibility for managing a program. A phone number is provided in cases in which a Regional or Local Office is not normally able to answer detailed inquiries about the program. Also listed is contact information for persons who can provide additional information. If the departmental or agency Internet site is known, it is shown as a link.

Assistance Considerations

Formula and Matching Requirements
This section indicates the formula and matching requirements prescribed in the allocation of funds or maintenance of effort requirements. A formula may be based on population, per capita income, and other statistical factors. Applicants are informed about any matching requirements to be met.

In general, the matching share represents that portion of the project costs not borne by the Federal government. Usually, a minimum percentage for matching share is prescribed by program legislation, and matching share requirements are included in the grant agreement. Attachment F of OMB Circular No. A-102 sets forth the criteria and procedures for matching requirements, including those made in cash or in-kind. Cash contributions represent the grantees' cash outlay, including the outlay of money contributed to the grantee by other public agencies, institutions, private organizations, or individuals. When authorized by Federal regulation, Federal funds received from other grants may be considered as the grantees' cash contribution. In-kind contributions represent the value of noncash contributions provided by the grantee, other public agencies and institutions, private organizations, or individuals. In-kind contributions may consist of charges for real property and equipment, and value of goods and services directly benefiting and specifically identifiable to the grant program. When authorized by Federal legislation, property purchased with Federal funds may be considered as grantees' in-kind contribution. Maintenance of effort (MOE) is a requirement contained in certain legislation, regulations, or administrative policies that a grantee must maintain a specified level of financial effort in a specific area to receive Federal grant funds, and that the Federal grant funds may be used only to supplement, not supplant the level of grantee funds. Programs that have MOE requirements and have total allocations over $100 million (current fiscal year) will have the following statement in this section: "This program has maintenance of effort (MOE) requirements, see funding agency for further details."

Length and Time Phasing of Assistance
This section indicates the time period during which the assistance is normally available, any restrictions on the time permitted to use the funds awarded, if any, and the timing of disbursement of the assistance, e.g. lump sum, annually, quarterly, or as a required.

Uses and Use Restrictions

This section describes the potential uses for the assistance provided to meet stated objectives, and the specific restrictions on the use of funds. The section cites one or more applications depending on the nature of a particular program. Since this section translates objectives into the uses of a program, users may develop a clearer understanding of the program's objectives.

Post Assistance Requirements

Reports

This section indicates whether program reports, expenditure reports, cash reports, or performance monitoring is required by the Federal funding agency, and specifies the time intervals (monthly, annually, etc.).

Audits

This section discusses audits required by the Federal agency. The procedures and requirements for State and local governments and nonprofit organizations and institutions are set forth in OMB Circular No. A-133.

These requirements pertain to awards made within the respective State's fiscal year - not the Federal fiscal year, as some State and local governments may use the calendar year or other variation of time span designated as the fiscal year period, rather than that commonly known as the Federal fiscally year (from October 1st through September 30th).

Records

This section indicates the record retention requirements and the type of records the Federal agency may require. Not included are the normally imposed requirements of the General Accounting Office.

Foundation Grants

If you can't find what you need through the government, then you can turn to other sources for funds. Private foundations are non-profit entities that are managed by a board of trustees and directors. When you think of these foundations, you usually think of the Ford or Rockefeller Foundations. These were established by wealthy families, and are designed to support a variety of humanitarian causes. They receive their monies from a principle fund or endowment. More than two-thirds of foundations are Family foundations that are influenced or managed by the founding donor or donor's family. Another type of foundation, called a Community Foundation, receives their monies from a variety of donors in a specific area and the focus is to support charitable activities in their area. In 1998, foundations made nearly $19.5 billion in charitable grants.

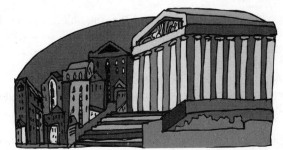

Before approaching these foundations as your funding source, there are many issues to consider. Primarily these foundations provide grants to other non-profits, not to individuals. Some foundations fund a specific focus area, such as the arts, children, or housing. Other considerations have to do with the geographic area. Foundations may fund projects nationally or internationally, but some only support projects in a particular state or region. It is generally a good to identify state or local foundations, as they may have a greater interest in local problems. Also, the type of support varies. Foundations may supply grants for scholarships, building funds, or seed money. Foundations often have specific funding cycles to consider and strict eligibility requirements. Planning ahead is the key.

As most of their funds go to non-profits, individual grant seekers may have difficulty receiving funds from private foundations. You must look carefully at the foundation's guidelines to see if you meet the requirements. Obviously, major foundations would be overwhelmed sifting through thousands of individual donor requests. In addition, there are strict regulations regarding record keeping and other financial issues that foundations must follow. Other non-profits are familiar with these and compliance is easier.

Find A Nonprofit To Work With

You may want to consider an affiliation with a tax-exempt organization. The organization would be the fiscal sponsor, which means that they would receive the grant funds, and then disperse them to your project. Think of your current membership in various organizations or clubs. What about local service organizations or educational institutions? Think of organizations that offer programs similar to yours or organizations that may gain some benefit by supporting yours. All of these are potential partners in your endeavor. Many organizations or community colleges would like the good public relations your project would generate. It is imperative that if you choose to affiliate with an organization, that the organization be a tax-exempt organization designated as such by the Internal Revenue Service. You should see that they have 501(c)3 status. The main purpose of establishing an affiliation is to open the doors to more funding opportunities. The tax exempt status will allow the organization to receive monies from foundations, as well as offer a tax deduction to those who donate to the organization. When you form an affiliation with an organization, there are several things to consider and that should be settled in some form of a letter of agreement.

- how long will this relationship last?
- who is responsible for the record keeping the funding organization will require?
- how much autonomy will you be allowed? Remember, your project will be a reflection on the affiliation organization, as well as on yourself.
- if your project involves music, writing, video, art, etc., who will own the copyright to these works?
- how will the financial arrangement be handled?
- what other types of support can they offer you?

The Foundation Center

The Foundation Center is a nonprofit organization which gathers and disseminates factual information on foundations. The Center's libraries in New York City, Atlanta, San Francisco, Cleveland, and Washington, DC, contain copies of foundations' tax returns, extensive collections of books, documents, and reports about the foundation field, and current files on the activities and programs of about 50,000 U.S. foundations, plus knowledgeable staff to assist users in locating appropriate information.

The Foundation Center also publishes funding directories specific to certain fields, such as: aging; arts and culture; children, youth, and families; health; higher education; international programs; libraries and information services; religion; women and girls; and elementary and secondary education.

In addition, the Center has established cooperating reference collections in each state, where Center publications and information on foundations in the immediate state or region can be consulted. A list of cooperating libraries housing these regional collections appears in most of the Center's publications.

It is a good idea to look for foundations close to home; they are more likely to have a greater interest in local problems than would larger foundations with a national focus. Foundation Center resources are a good starting point for identifying likely funding sources. The next step is to learn more about these foundations by obtaining copies of their annual reports and/or grants guidelines. Some may be available at the Foundation Center's cooperating libraries. Grantseekers will need to find out whether their projected proposals match the foundation's areas of interest and geographic guidelines, whether the proposal is within the foundation's budgetary constraints, and whether the foundation normally funds the type of project being considered. For further information, contact the Foundation Center, 79 Fifth Avenue, New York, NY 10003; 800-424-9836; 212-620-4230; {http://fdncenter.org}.

Developing and Writing Federal Government Grant Proposals

PART ONE:
Developing A Grant Proposal

Preparation

A successful grant proposal is one that is well prepared, thoughtfully planned, and concisely packaged. The potential applicant should become familiar with all of the pertinent program criteria related to the Catalog program from which assistance is sought. Refer to the information contact person listed in the Catalog program description before developing a proposal to obtain information such as whether funding is available, when applicable deadlines occur, and the process used by the grantor agency for accepting applications. Applicants should remember that the basic requirements, application forms, information, and procedures vary with the Federal agency making the grant award. Individuals without prior grant proposal writing experience may find it useful to attend a grantsmanship workshop. A workshop can amplify the basic information presented here. Applicants interested in additional readings on grantsmanship and proposal development should consult the references listed at the end of this section and explore other library resources.

Initial Proposal Development:
Developing Ideas for the Proposal

When developing an idea for a proposal it is important to determine if the idea has been considered in the applicant's locality or state. A careful check should be made with legislators and area government agencies and related public and private agencies which may currently have grant awards or contracts to do similar work. If a similar program already exists, the applicant may need to reconsider submitting the proposed project, particularly if duplication of effort is perceived. If significant differences or improvements in the proposed project's goals can be clearly established, it may be worthwhile to pursue Federal assistance.

Community Support

Community support for most proposals is essential. Once proposal summary is developed, look for individuals or groups representing academic, political, professional, and lay organizations that may be willing to support the proposal in writing. The type and caliber of community support is critical in the initial and subsequent review phases. Numerous letters of support can be persuasive to a grantor agency. Do not overlook support from local government agencies and public officials. Letters of endorsement detailing exact areas of project sanction and commitment are often requested as part of a proposal to a Federal agency. Several months may be required to develop letters of endorsement since something of value (e.g., buildings, staff, services) is sometimes negotiated between the parties involved. Many agencies require, in writing, affiliation agreements (a mutual agreement to share services between agencies) and building space commitments prior to either grant approval or award. A useful method of generating community support may be to hold meetings with the top decision makers in the community who would be concerned with the subject matter of the proposal. The forum for discussion may include a query into the merits of the proposal, development of a contract of support for the proposal, to generate data in support of the proposal, or development of a strategy to create proposal support from a large number of community groups.

Identification of a Funding Resource

A review of the Objectives and Uses and Use Restrictions sections of the Catalog program description can point out which programs might provide funding for an idea. Do not overlook the related programs as potential resources.

Both the applicant and the grantor agency should have the same interests, intentions, and needs, if a proposal is to be considered an acceptable candidate for finding.

Once a potential grantor agency is identified, call the contact telephone number identified in Information Contacts and ask for a grant application kit. Later, get to know some of the grantor agency personnel. Ask for suggestions, criticisms, and advice about the proposed project. In many cases, the more agency personnel know about the proposal, the better the chance of support and of an eventual favorable decision. Sometimes it is useful to send the proposal summary to a specific agency official in a separate cover letter, and ask for review and comment at the earliest possible convenience. Always check with the Federal agency to determine its preference if this approach is under consideration. If the review is unfavorable and differences cannot be resolved, ask the examining agency (official) to suggest another department or agency which may be interested in the proposal. A personal visit to the agency's regional office or headquarters is also important. A visit not only establishes face-to-face contact, but also may bring out some essential details about the proposal or help secure literature and references from the agency's library.

Federal agencies are required to report funding information as funds are approved, increased, or decreased among projects within a given State depending on the type of required reporting. Also, consider reviewing the Federal Budget for the current and budget fiscal years to determine proposed dollar amounts for particular budget functions. The applicant should carefully study the eligibility requirements for each Federal program under consideration (see the Applicant Eligibility section of the Catalog program description). The applicant may learn that he or she is required to provide services otherwise unintended such as a service to particular client groups, or involvement of specific institutions. It may necessitate the modification of the original concept in order for the project to be eligible for funding. Questions about eligibility should be discussed with the appropriate program officer. Deadlines for submitting applications are often not negotiable. They are usually associated with strict timetables for agency review. Some programs have more than one application deadline during the fiscal year. Applicants should plan proposal development around the established deadlines.

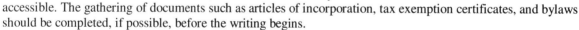

Getting Organized to Write the Proposal

Throughout the proposal writing stage keep a notebook handy to write down ideas. Periodically, try to connect ideas by reviewing the notebook. Never throw away written ideas during the grant writing stage. Maintain a file labeled "Ideas" or by some other convenient title and review the ideas from time to time. The file should be easily accessible. The gathering of documents such as articles of incorporation, tax exemption certificates, and bylaws should be completed, if possible, before the writing begins.

REVIEW

Criticism

At some point, perhaps after the first or second draft is completed, seek out a neutral third party to review the proposal working draft for continuity, clarity, and reasoning. Ask for constructive criticism at this point, rather than wait for the Federal grantor agency to volunteer this information during the review cycle. For example, has the writer made unsupported assumptions or used jargon or excessive language in the proposal?

Signature

Most proposals are made to institutions rather than individuals. Often signatures of chief administrative officials are required. Check to make sure they are included in the proposal where appropriate.

Neatness

Proposals should be typed, collated, copied, and packaged correctly and neatly (according to agency instructions, if any). Each package should be inspected to ensure uniformity from cover to cover. Binding may require either clamps or hard covers. Check with the Federal agency to determine its preference. A neat, organized, and attractive proposal package can leave a positive impression with the reader about the proposal contents.

Mailing

A cover letter should always accompany a proposal. Standard U.S. Postal Service requirements apply unless otherwise indicated by the Federal agency. Make sure there is time for the proposals to reach their destinations. Otherwise, special arrangements may be necessary. Always coordinate such arrangements with the Federal grantor agency project office (the agency which will ultimately have the responsibility for the project), the grant office (the agency which will coordinate the grant review), and the contract office (the agency responsible for disbursement and grant award notices), if necessary.

PART TWO:
Writing The Grant Proposal

The Basic Components of a Proposal

There are eight basic components to creating a solid proposal package:
- The proposal summary;
- Introduction of organization;
- The problem statement (or needs assessment);
- Project objectives;
- Project methods or design;
- Project evaluation;
- Future funding; and
- The project budget.

The following will provide an overview of these components.

The Proposal Summary:
Outline of Project Goals

The proposal summary outlines the proposed project and should appear at the beginning of the proposal. It could be in the form of a cover letter or a separate page, but should definitely be brief - no longer than two or three paragraphs. The summary would be most useful if it were prepared after the proposal has been developed in order to encompass all the key summary points necessary to communicate the objectives of the project. It is this document that becomes the cornerstone of your proposal, and the initial impression it gives will be critical to the success of your venture. In many cases, the summary will be the first part of the proposal package seen by agency officials and very possibly could be the only part of the package that is carefully reviewed before the decision is made to consider the project any further.

The applicant must select a fundable project that can be supported in view of the local need. Alternatives, in the absence of Federal support, should be pointed out. The influence of the project both during and after the project period should be explained. The consequences of the project as a result of funding should be highlighted.

Introduction: Presenting a Credible Applicant or Organization

The applicant should gather data about its organization from all available sources. Most proposals require a description of an applicant's organization to describe its past and present operations. Some features to consider are:
- A brief biography of board members and key staff members.
- The organization's goals, philosophy, track record with other grantors, and

- any success stories.

The data should be relevant to the goals of the Federal grantor agency and should establish the applicant's credibility.

The Problem Statement: Staffing the Purpose at Hand

The problem statement (or needs assessment) is a key element of a proposal that makes a clear, concise, and well supported statement of the problem to be addressed. The best way to collect information about the problem is to conduct and document both a formal and informal needs assessment for a program in the target or service area. The information provided should be both factual and directly related to the problem addressed by the proposal. Areas to document are:

- The purpose for developing the proposal.
- The beneficiaries - who are they and how will they benefit.
- The social and economic costs to be affected.
- The nature of the problem (provide as much hard evidence as possible).
- How the applicant organization came to realize the problem exists and what is currently being done about the problem.
- The remaining alternatives available when funding has been exhausted. Explain what will happen to the project and the impending implications. Most importantly, explain the specific manner through which problems might be solved. Review the resources needed, considering how they will be used and to what end.

> **There are eight basic components to creating a solid proposal package**

There is a considerable body of literature on the exact assessment techniques to be used. Any local, regional, or state government planning office, or local university offering course work in planning and evaluation techniques should be able to provide excellent background references. Types of data that may be collected include: historical, geographic, quantitative, factual, statistical, and philosophical information, as well as studies completed by colleges, and literature searches from public or university libraries. Local colleges or universities that have a department or section related to the proposal topic may help determine if there is interest in developing a student or faculty project to conduct a needs assessment. It may be helpful to include examples of the findings for highlighting in the proposal.

Project Objectives: Goals and Desired Outcome

Program objectives refer to specific activities in a proposal. It is necessary to identify all objectives related to the goals to be reached and the methods to be employed to achieve the stated objectives. Consider quantities or things measurable and refer to a problem statement and the outcome of proposed activities when developing a well stated objective. The figures used should be verifiable. Remember, if the proposal is funded, the stated objectives will probably be used to evaluate program progress, so be realistic. There is literature available to help identify and write program objectives.

Program Method and Program Design: A Plan of Action

The program design refers to how the project is expected to work and solve the stated problem. Sketch out the following:

- The activities to occur along with the related resources and staff needed to operate the project (inputs).
- A flow chart of the organizational features of the project. Describe how the parts interrelate, where personnel will be needed, and what they are expected to do. Identify the kinds of facilities, transportation, and support services required (throughputs).
- Explain what will be achieved through 1 and 2 above (outputs); i.e., plan for measurable results. Project staff may be required to produce evidence of program performance through an examination of stated objectives during either a site visit by the Federal grantor agency and or grant reviews which may involve peer review committees. It may be useful to devise a diagram of the program design. For example, draw a three column block. Each column is headed by one of the parts (inputs, throughputs, and outputs), and on

the left (next to the first column) specific program features should be identified (i.e., implementation, staffing, procurement, and systems development). In the grid, specify something about the program design, for example, assume the first column is labeled inputs, and the first row is labeled staff. On the grid, one might specify under inputs five nurses to operate a child care unit. The throughput might be to maintain charts, counsel the children, and set up a daily routine; outputs might be to discharge 25 healthy children per week. This type of procedure will help to conceptualize both the scope and detail of the project.

- Wherever possible, justify in the narrative the course of action taken. The most economical method should be used that does not compromise or sacrifice project quality. The financial expenses associated with performance of the project will later become points of negotiation with the Federal program staff. If everything is not carefully justified in writing in the proposal, after negotiation with the Federal grantor agencies, the approved project may resemble less of the original concept. Carefully consider the pressures of the proposed implementation, that is, the time and money needed to acquire each part of the plan. A Program Evaluation and Review Technique (PERT) chart could be useful and supportive in justifying some proposals. Highlight the innovative features of the proposal which could be could be considered distinct from other proposals under consideration.

- Whenever possible, use appendices to provide details, supplementary data, references, and information requiring in-depth analysis. These types of data, although supportive of the proposal, if included in the body of the design, could detract from its readability. Appendices provide the proposal reader with immediate access to details if and when clarification of an idea, sequence, or conclusion is required. Time tables, work plans, schedules, activities, methodologies, legal papers, personal vitae, letters of support, and endorsements are examples of appendices.

Evaluation: Product and Process Analysis

The evaluation component is two fold: (1) product evaluation; and (2) process evaluation. Product evaluation addresses results that can be attributed to the project, as well as the extent to which the project has satisfied its desired objectives. Process evaluation addresses how the project was conducted, in terms of consistency with the stated plan of action and the effectiveness of the various activities, within the plan.

Most Federal agencies now require some form of program evaluation among grantees. The requirements of the proposed project should be explored carefully. Evaluations may be conducted by an internal staff member, an evaluation firm or both. The applicant should state the amount of time needed to evaluate, how the feedback will be distributed among the proposed staff, and a schedule for review and comment for this type of communication. Evaluation designs may start at the beginning, middle, or end of a project, but the applicant should specify a start-up time. It is practical to submit an evaluation design at the start of a project for two reasons:

- Convincing evaluations require the collection of appropriate data before and during program operations; and,
- If the evaluation design cannot be prepared at the outset, then a critical review of the program design may be advisable.

Even if the evaluation design has to be revised as the project progresses, it is much easier and cheaper to modify a good design. If the problem is not well-defined and carefully analyzed for cause and effect relationships, then a good evaluation design may be difficult to achieve. Sometimes a pilot study is needed to begin the identification of facts and relationships. Often a thorough literature search may be sufficient.

Evaluation requires both coordination and agreement among program decision makers (if known). Above all, the Federal grantor agency's requirements should be highlighted in the evaluation design. Also, Federal grantor agencies may require specific evaluation techniques such as designated data formats (an existing information collection system) or they may offer financial inducements for voluntary participation in a national evaluation study. The applicant should ask specifically about these points. Also, consult the Criteria For Selecting Proposals section of the Catalog program description to determine the exact evaluation methods to be required for the program if funded.

Future Funding: Long-Term Project Planning
Describe a plan for continuation beyond the grant period, and/or the availability of other resources necessary to implement the grant. Discuss maintenance and future program funding if program is for construction activity. Account for other needed expenditures if program includes purchase of equipment.

The Proposal Budget: Planning the Budget
Funding levels in Federal assistance programs change yearly. It is useful to review the appropriations over the past several years to try to project future funding levels (see Financial Information section of the Catalog program description).

However, it is safer never to anticipate that the income from the grant will be the sole support for the project. This consideration should be given to the overall budget requirements, and in particular, to budget line items most subject to inflationary pressures. Restraint is important in determining inflationary cost projections (avoid padding budget line items), but attempt to anticipate possible future increases.

Some vulnerable budget areas are: utilities, rental of buildings and equipment, salary increases, food, telephones, insurance, and transportation. Budget adjustments are sometimes made after the grant award, but this can be a lengthy process. Be certain that implementation, continuation, and phase-down costs can be met. Consider costs associated with leases, evaluation systems, hard/soft match requirements, audits, development, implementation, and maintenance of information and accounting systems, and other long term financial commitments.

A well prepared budget justifies all expenses and is consistent with the proposal narrative. Some areas in need of an evaluation for consistency are:
- The salaries in the proposal in relation to those of the applicant organization should be similar;
- If new staff persons are being hired, additional space and equipment should be considered, as necessary;
- If the budget calls for an equipment purchase, it should be the type allowed by the grantor agency;
- If additional space is rented, the increase in insurance should be supported;
- If an indirect cost rate applies to the proposal, the division between direct and indirect costs should not be in conflict, and the aggregate budget totals should refer directly to the approved formula; and
- If matching costs are required, the contributions to the matching fund should be taken out of the budget unless otherwise specified in the application instructions.

It is very important to become familiar with Government-wide circular requirements. The Catalog identifies in the program description section (as information is provided from the agencies) the particular circulars applicable to a Federal program, and summarizes coordination of Executive Order 12372, "Intergovernmental Review of Programs" requirements in Appendix I [not available online]. The applicant should thoroughly review the appropriate circulars since they are essential in determining items such as cost principles and conforming with Government guidelines for Federal domestic assistance.

Guidelines And Literature
United States Government Manual
Superintendent of Documents
U.S. Government Printing Office
Washington, DC 20402

OMB Circular Nos. A-21, A-87, A-102, A-110, A-122, and A-133, and Executive Order 12372:
Publications Office
Office of Administration
Room-2200, 725 Seventeenth Street, NW
Washington DC 20503

Government Printing Office (GPO) Resources

The government documents identified above as available from the GPO can be requested (supply the necessary identifying information) by writing to:

Superintendent of Documents
Government Printing Office
Washington, DC 20402

Regional and Federal Depository Libraries

Regional libraries can arrange for copies of Government documents through an interlibrary loan. All Federal Depository Libraries will receive copies of the Catalog directly. A list of depository and regional libraries is available by writing:

Chief
Library Division
Superintendent of Documents, Stop SLL
Washington, DC 20402

How To Find Nonprofit Organizations

The Foundation Center is not the only resource for finding nonprofits. One unbelievably info packed location to find nonprofit organizations is Idealist, {www.idealist.org}. This site is maintained as a project of Action Without Borders, a self-described "global coalition of individuals and organizations working to build a world where all people can live free, dignified and productive lives." It is not associated with any specific nation or government.

Idealist has an enormous searchable database, including a list of 20,000 nonprofit and worldwide community organizations from 140 countries. The nonprofit groups run the gamut from children's relief services to the arts to environmental concerns to drug recovery programs. Also available at Idealist is a Nonprofit Career Center. Here you may search for a job in your chosen nonprofit field, look for fellowships in public service, obtain information regarding academic programs geared to students interested in nonprofit organizations as a career, and find many volunteer opportunities available both here and abroad. The career center also allows you to post an opportunity that your organization may have to fill.

In addition to the aforementioned information, Idealist has listings of many of the resources available to groups that maintain nonprofit status. Every imaginable business service is listed here including grant writing, insurance, accounting, video production, marketing, graphic design and public relations. For more information, contact Action Without Borders, 350 Fifth Ave., Suite 6614, New York, NY 10118; 212-843-3973; {www.idealist.org}.

Known as "The donor's guide to the charitable universe," GuideStar, {www.guidestar.org}, is a veritable Mecca of nonprofit information. Its searchable database has 620,000 (not a typo!) organizations listed for the United States. In addition to the plethora of listed nonprofits, GuideStar also offers help to those organizations, including how to file tax documents properly and successfully. GuideStar's website is maintained by a group called Philanthropic Research, Inc., (PRI) which serves to encourage all types of philanthropic work. Any group with nonprofit status can be listed at GuideStar free of charge. As with Idealist, GuideStar also offers a link to information regarding volunteering, jobs, careers, and how to make donations and give online. The Nonprofit HelpCenter is also available to help groups register online, so that they too, can be listed among the extensive group of GuideStar's database. Contact GuideStar, 427 Scotland St., Williamsburg, VA 23185; 757-229-4631.

The Foundation Center is an online "gateway to philanthropy on the World Wide Web." Along with a large database of philanthropic organizations, including links to funding groups and corporate and private foundations, there are links and information on how to write a proposal, how to establish a nonprofit organization, tax info and how to receive grants for individuals. There is also an extensive library, which has large excerpts from appropriate publications about nonprofits. Many of the books are available for sale online as well. Also available for purchase are CD-Roms and a huge selection of books and directories of nonprofits. Some of these directories are categorized by location, while others are listed by topic, such as Health, and the Arts. The list of resources is seemingly endless. A printable digest from The Foundation Center entitled Philanthropy News Digest is also accessible from this website and contains articles on a large variety of subjects relating to charitable works and organizations. There is also a large searchable database, The Foundation Directory Online, available by subscription, for $195.00 dollars annually. The directory is updated quarterly. You can search the Private Foundation Database by subject, keyword, or geographic area at {http://fdncenter.org/grantmaker/gws_corp/corp.html}. For further information, contact the Foundation Center, 79 Fifth Avenue, New York, NY 10003; 800-424-9836; 202-331-1400; {http://fdncenter.org}.

The Internet Nonprofit Center is operated by The Evergreen State Society located in Seattle, Washington. Their website has a Locator Search feature which provides the name and location of non-profits. Search at {www.nonprofits.org}. For more information, contact the Evergreen State Society, P.O. Box 20682, Seattle, WA 98102; 206-329-5640; {www.nonprofits.org}.

The Council on Foundations assists foundations to help them grow and work effectively. Their website {www.cof.org} has links to community foundations and to member foundations and corporate giving programs. For more information, contact Council on Foundations, 1828 L St., NW, Washington, DC 20036; 202-466-6512; {www.cof.org}.

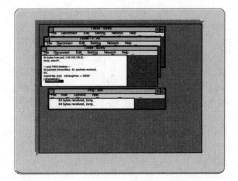

Here is your chance to use the IRS. The IRS has a database of over 1,000 tax-exempt organizations from which you can access a wealth of priceless information. You may access this database through the website. In order to understand the codes in these files, you will also have to download the Instructions Booklet, which is available on the same link. This information is also available on CD-ROM and includes more financial information per organization than the Internet data. Ask for the Statistics of Income (SOI) samples of Forms 990 and 990-EZ. Contact Internal Revenue Service, P.O. Box 2608, Washington, DC 20013; 202-874-0700; {www.irs.ustreas.gov/prod/ tax_states/index.html}.

In addition the Exempt Organizations Technical Division of the IRS publishes the Cumulative List of Organizations that includes a complete listing of names and addresses of exempt organizations. To order this subscription for $45 contact the Superintendent of Documents, U.S. Government Printing Office, Washington, DC 20402; 202-512-1800; {www.gpo.gov}. Don't forget to check with your state registration office for non-profits. See "How To Start Or Become A Nonprofit Organization" on page 110.

Corporate Grants

Within the past decade, as government funding on the federal, state, and local levels has declined, there has been a steady increase in grant seekers pursuing corporate support. Many corporations provide funds for local projects in areas where they have their headquarters or plants, or sponsor projects which somehow enhance their corporate image. Corporate foundations operate a little differently than private foundations, as they can often respond quicker to your requests and don't have the regulations that private foundations must follow. In addition, corporations will often also offer in-kind contributions, such as equipment, use of facilities, or expertise to assist you in your project. Information on corporate foundations and direct corporate giving is listed at the Foundation Center website at {http://fdncenter.org/grantmaker/gws_corp/corp.html}.

HOW TO START OR BECOME A NONPROFIT ORGANIZATION

Don't be Afraid...Read on!

Sound impossible? No way! Yes it can be bureaucratic and there's some red tape you'll have to wade through, but if you are a qualifying type of organization, getting nonprofit status is definitely the way to go, especially if you want to get grants from funding groups. Attaining nonprofit status for yourself as a group or organization may be critical in order to receive those grants that you are hoping will fund you, and it will only cost you a couple hundred dollars! Many grants are only available to nonprofits. So don't wince at the mention of what may sound like an overwhelming and daunting task. Dive in! It may be easier than you think.

First and foremost in establishing or creating a nonprofit is filing for Federal and state nonprofit tax status. Nonprofit status is not available to individuals, only to organizations, so your group must be incorporated or exist as an association or trust. To help you determine if your organization may qualify for tax-exempt status, or to find out what you will need to do in order to qualify, request Publication 557 from the local office of the Internal Revenue Service. This publication takes you step-by-step through the filing process, and contains instructions and checklists to help you provide all of the necessary information required to process your application the first time around. The fee to become exempt can be as low at $150! The IRS has even established a hotline at 877-829-5500 staffed with experts on completing the forms and can help you with any questions you may have. They can't make it any easier for you! You can also check out any questions you may have at {http://www.irs.ustreas.gov/plain/bus_info/eo/}.

Most organizations seeking tax-exempt status from the Federal government must use either; Form 1023, Application for Recognition of Exemption Under Section 501(c) (3) of the Internal Revenue Code; Form 1024, Application for Recognition of Exemption Under Section 501(a) or for Determination Under Section 120. The forms will ask you to provide the following information:

* A description of the purposes and activities of your organization
* Financial information, and if you have not yet begun operation, a proposed budget, along with a statement of assets and liabilities (if you have any)
* Information on how you intend to finance your activities, through fundraisers, grants, etc.

Another great feature available directly from the IRS is the Tax-Exempt Organization Tax Kit. Basically it's a packet that contains all the necessary forms for filing for exemption status, all informational publications and even forms for filing your tax return, the various versions of Form 990, Return of Organization Exempt from Income Tax. These publications are downloadable, grouped together at the IRS website, within the Tax-Exempt section. They are also available by calling 800-TAX-FORM, toll-free.

Critical when filing for tax-exempt status, obviously, is to have an organization that has a darned good reason for asking for exemption. The IRS has separated the classifications of acceptable organizations into ten groups within which your potential organization may fall, thus possibly qualifying for exemption.

* Charitable Organizations
    - Charitable
    - Religious
    - Educational
    - Scientific

    - Literary

* Social Welfare Organizations
    - Civic Leagues
    - Community Organizations

✳ Labor and Agricultural Organizations
- Labor Unions
- Farm Bureaus

✳ Social Clubs
- Hobby Clubs
- Country Clubs

✳ Business Leagues
- Trade Associations
- Chambers of Commerce
- Real Estate Boards

✳ Fraternal Societies
- Lodges and Similar Orders and Associations

✳ Veteran's Organizations
- Posts or organizations of past or present members of the Armed forces of the United States

✳ Employees' Associations
- Voluntary employees' benefit associations
- Local associations of employees

✳ Political Organizations
- Campaign committees
- Political parties
- Political action committees

✳ Other Tax-Exempt Organizations
- Miscellaneous qualifying organizations

The organization must also have an Employer Identification Number (EIN), be in the process of applying, or apply directly while applying for exemption status. Form SS-4, Application for Employer Identification Number, gives detailed instructions on obtaining an EIN over the phone. The form is downloadable from the IRS web site. Once you have your EIN enter it into your application for exemption form. Please note that the correct IRS contact information for all exempt organizations seeking an EIN is below.

Internal Revenue Service
Attn: Entity Control
Mail Stop 6271
P.O. Box 9941   801-620-7645 (not a toll-free number)
Ogden, UT 84201   {http://ftp.fedworld.gov/pub/irs-pdf/fss4.pdf}

The applications require detailed financial status. If it is a new organization, current financial statements must be provided along with projected budgets for the coming two years. Organizations in existence three years or more also must provide current information as well as detailed info from the last two years. Once you have submitted the necessary forms and fees, and all goes well, a ruling or determination letter should be on its way to you in no time.

To receive help and information directly from the IRS, contact your local office listed in the government pages of your telephone book or contact:

Exempt Organizations Technical Division
Internal Revenue Service
U.S. Department of Treasury
1111 Constitution Ave., NW, Room 6411   202-622-8100
Washington, DC 20224   {www.irs.gov}

Once you are granted tax-exempt status, you must move on to the task of filing new forms to account for your tax year. And careful, detailed accounting is a must. Filing your organization's Form 990, the IRS nonprofit tax return, requires some rigorous financial reporting. As a nonprofit organization, you must report carefully the following:

1. An object revenue & income statement, with particular categories specified (rental revenue),

2. A balance sheet, with particular categories specified like cash, accounts receivable, accounts payable (salaries, postage etc.),

3. A statement of functional expenses, in which all expenses are allocated to program services, fundraising, or operations,

4. A report of expenses segregated by individual program service (educational mailings, a seminar program),

5. A support schedule that details the organization's sources of revenue, with particular categories specified (charitable donations, membership fees, investment income).

Never fear! While it may sound confusing and tedious, there is hope! Luckily there is accounting software available to help you with your reporting. Sort of like Turbo Tax for nonprofits, these available software systems, if set up appropriately, can make your IRS reporting pretty easy. Thank goodness!

Although we do not recommend any particular accounting software, a simple internet search turned up a wealth of software systems. Here is a sampling of what we found:

- NfpAcounting.com, 2222 Dunhaven St., San Diego, CA 92110; 619-275-0907; {www.nfpaccounting.com}.

- CYMA Systems, 2330 W. University Dr., Suite 7, Tempe, AZ 85281; 800-292-2962; {www.cyma.com}.

- Araize, 130 Iowa Lane, Suite 102, Cary, NC 27511; 919-319-1770; {www.araize.com}.

- Automation Counselors, P.O. Box 3917, Frederick, MD 21705; 800-966-6725; {www.automationc.com}.

- SunGard Bi-Tech, 890 Fortress St., Chico, CA 95973; 530-891-5281; {www.bitech.com}.

- Fund EZ, 106 Corporate Park, White Plains, NY 10604; 914-696-0900; {www.fundez.com}.

- American Fundware, 1385 S. Colorado Blvd., Suite 400, Denver, CO 80222; 800-551-4458; {www.fundware.com}.

- MIP, 313 East Anderson Lane, Suite 120, Austin, TX 78752; 800-647-3863; {www.mip.com}.

There are many advantages to becoming a nonprofit organization. An obvious one is getting reduced rates on things like postage. But the United States Postal Service may not consider your group a nonprofit just because you have tax-exempt status. There are many rules, regulations and restrictions. For example, nonprofits must fall into categories somewhat like the IRS categories listed above, and then they must file Form 3624 in order to have their request processed. The acceptable categories are: religious, agricultural, educational, labor, scientific, veterans, philanthropic and fraternal. For more information, forms for application and all the Post Office rules, visit the USPS website, {www.usps.gov} and search the Postal Explorer, for "nonprofit."

Another thing that some nonprofits are able to do is set up lobbying groups. Again, there can be substantial red tape involved. You must file forms with the IRS and be of a particular nature to qualify. Basically, nonprofits may lobby if they are publicly funded in some way, educational or hospital medical research organizations, or organizations supporting government schools. Any group lobbying in any inappropriate way will not be permitted to do so. If it goes beyond the limits and lobbying is substantial, (this usually determined by proportion of moneys spent), the organization is likely to lose its Federal tax-exempt status.

State Registration

As with any filing of a tax application or return, when you send in something to the Federal government, you need to notify your state government as well. Although it is the IRS that gives you the authority to raise money as a tax-exempt organization, your state government will want to know about the proposed activities of your organization. Relevant information that your state will be interested in includes:

* The name and address of registrant
* The purpose of the nonprofit
* Any articles of incorporation
* The names and addresses of any board of directors

In existence is something known as the Unified Registration Statement, (URS) which serves as a kind of standard form that most of the states in the country accept as the ample documentation to register within said state as a nonprofit organization. The state will also want to know how much of a tax-exempt contribution you expect to attain over the course of a year. Some states have maximum amounts before you must register, while others have no minimum. Some states' fees are based upon the amount of contributions, and some are flat fees. The usual fee for filing this information with most states is minimal, usually from $30.00 to $50.00, with some states requiring no fee, and others going much higher. Contact the appropriate state corporation office, listed on page 129 to obtain the necessary forms, and see the state listings below for more specific state-by-state information. The state will also require an annual financial report, and most will accept a completed Federal IRS report.

Don't forget that state and Federal laws are not the only ones to which nonprofit organizations are subject. Governments of smaller jurisdictions, such as counties, cities, municipalities, small towns, and really any form of governmental authority, can and do implement laws that may be stricter or at least different than their superior governments. Such an authority may require organizations to register specifically within their jurisdiction, in addition to all other state and Federal registrations. Any soliciting organizations, no matter where they are based, that make charitable solicitations to residents of these jurisdictions, and don't adhere to the local law and its associated regulations, may be subject to legal action by that jurisdiction's governmental authority.

State Registration Requirements

Alabama
Office of the Attorney General
Consumer Affairs Section
11 South Union St.
Montgomery, AL 36130
334-242-7334

Registration Requirements
State form or URS
IRS Determination Letter
Articles of Incorporation or charitable organizational charter
$25 Registration fee

Organizations exempt from registration:
Educational institutions and their authorized and related foundations;
Religious organizations;
Political organizations;
Fraternal, patriotic, benevolent, social, educational, alumni, heath care foundation, historical and civil rights organizations, including fraternities and sororities;
Civic leagues and civic organizations, which solicit solely from their own membership;
Any charitable organization which does not intend to solicit and receive and does not actually receive contributions in excess of $25,000 during the fiscal year, provided all of its fundraising

functions are carried on by persons who are unpaid for their services;

Persons requesting any contributions collected for the relief of a specific named individual if all contributions do not exceed $10,000 and are turned over to the named beneficiary;

Any post, camp, chapter of a bona fide veteran's organization, or organization of volunteer firefighters, ambulance companies, or rescue squads and affiliates of those organizations, whose fundraising is done by unpaid volunteers

Annual Reporting Requirements
Due within 90 days of fiscal year end
Annual written report in required format
Annual $25 filing fee
IRS 990 or financial report
Registration renewal required annually on or before September 30th

Alaska

Attorney General
Alaska Department of Law
1031 W. 4th Ave., Suite. 200
Anchorage, AK 99501-1994
907-276-8554

Registration Requirements
State form -(URS not accepted)
IRS Form 990
Audit
Due September 1st

Organizations exempt from registration:
Religious organizations;

Charitable organizations that do not intend to or do not raise or receive contributions, excluding government grants, in excess of $5,000 during a fiscal year;

Organizations that do not receive contributions from more than ten (10) persons during a fiscal year if either, 1) all functions, including solicitation, are carried on by volunteers and/or, 2) an officer or member of the organization is not paid or does not otherwise receive all or part of the assets or income of the charitable organization

Annual Reporting Requirements
There are no annual reporting requirements once an organization is registered.

Arizona

Secretary of State
Charitable Organizations
1700 West Washington, 7th Floor
Phoenix, AZ 85007
602-542-6670

Registration Requirements
State Form A.R.S 44-6552 - (URS not accepted)
IRS Form 990

Organizations exempt from registration:
A charitable organization that is established and operated within Arizona exclusively for a charitable purpose and that has a board of directors that serves without remuneration, if the solicitations are conducted under any of the following conditions 1) by volunteers who receive no remuneration or 2) by bona fide paid employees or 3) at meetings or assemblies of the membership or with individual members;

Nonprofit hospitals and their foundations;

Nonprofit blood banks and their foundations;

Schools, colleges and universities, their associations and foundations;

Licensed public radio and TV stations that are raising monies for their own operations;

Solicitations solely from private foundations;

Political parties, candidates and campaign committees required to file financial information with election commissions or agencies;

Organizations soliciting contributions not exceeding $25,000;

Annual Reporting Requirements
State financial report form

Arkansas

Office of Attorney General
Consumer Protection Division
Fund Raiser Registration
323 Center St., #200
Little Rock, AR 72201-2610
501-682-6150

Registration Requirements
State Registration Form or URS
IRS Form 990, or
IRS Form 990-Ez and AR Attachment to IRS Form 990, or
Annual Report of Charitable Organization
IRS Determination letter
Copy of Irrevocable Consent for Service
No registration fee required

Organizations exempt from registration:
Nonprofits raising less than $25,000 per year with no
    paid staff or fundraisers;
Religious organizations;
Accredited educational institutions and parent-
    teacher associations associated with accredited
    institutions;
Governmental organizations -departments, branches
    or instrumentality of federal, state and local
    governments;
Nonprofit hospitals licensed in AR or any other state;
Political candidates and organization - any candidate
    for national, state, or local office or a political
    party or other committee required to file
    information with the Federal Election
    Commission or any other state election
    commission;

Annual Reporting Requirements
Due Date on or before May 15th or within 6 months
    after close of fiscal year
No annual filing fee
IRS 990 -EZ or annual report
Audit required for organizations with gross revenue
    in excess of $500,000

California

State of California
Office of Attorney General
Registry of Charitable Trusts
P.O. Box 903447
Sacramento, CA 94203-4470
916-445-2021
http://caag.state.ca.us/charities

Registration Requirements
State Form CT-1 or URS
Certificate/Articles of Incorporation
Bylaws
IRS Form 990
IRS Determination Letter

Organizations exempt from registration:
Religious corporations;
Religious organizations;
Government agencies;
Political committees;
Schools and hospitals

Annual Reporting Requirements
Due January 15th

Form RRF-1
$25 for organizations with assets or revenue
    exceeding $100,000 during fiscal year
IRS 990
Financial Report

Colorado

There is no registration requirement in Colorado at
    this time.

Connecticut

Office of Attorney General
Public Charities Unit
55 Elm St.
Hartford, CT 06106-1746
860-808-5030

Registration Requirements
State Form CPC-63 or URS
One-time filing fee of $20.00

Organizations exempt from registration:
Nonprofits normally receiving less than $25,000
    annually provided organization does not
    compensate any person primarily to conduct
    solicitations;
Religious corporations, institutions, and societies;
Parent-teacher associations or accredited educational
    institution;
Nonprofit hospitals licensed under laws of CT or
    another state;
Government units or instrumentalities of any state or
    the United States;

Organizations seeking an exemption must file Form
    CPC-54, "Claim of Exemption From
    Registration" (no fee required)

Annual Reporting Requirements
Due Date: Within 5 months of the fiscal year end
Form CPC-60, Annual Report Sheet
IRS Form 990
$25.00 filing fee
Audit if gross receipts (excluding government grants
    and fees) exceeds $100,000

Delaware

There is no registration requirement in Delaware at
    this time.

District of Columbia

Department of Consumer & Regulatory Affairs
941 N Capital St. NE, Room 7211
Washington, DC 20002-4259
202-442-4513

Registration Requirements

District form or URS
Certificate/Articles of Incorporation
Bylaws
IRS Form 990
IRS Determination Letter

Organizations exempt from registration:

Organizations receiving less than $1,500 in gross
total receipts in a calendar year, provided
individuals who are unpaid carry out all
functions, including fundraising;
Educational organizations raising money for
educational purposes;
Church or religious corporations or organizations
under the control of a church or religious
corporation;
The American Red Cross;
Organizations where solicitations are made
exclusively among the membership of the
soliciting agency

Please note that exempt organizations are required to
file a claim to that exemption.

Annual Reporting Requirements

Due April 15th
$25 filing fee
Financial report

Florida

Florida Department of Agriculture & Consumer
Services
407 S. Calhoun
Tallahassee, FL 32399-0800
850-922-2972

Registration Requirements

State form - (URS not accepted)
IRS Form 990 or financial report on state form
IRS Determination letter
Fees range from $10-$400

Organizations exempt from registration:

Anyone soliciting for a named individual, provided
all contributions collected without any
deductions are turned over to the beneficiary;

Charitable organizations, which limit solicitation of
contributions to the membership of the
organization

Annual Reporting Requirements

There is no reporting requirement after registration,
which must be renewed annually.

Georgia

Secretary of State
Securities and Business Regulation
Suite 802, West Tower
2 Martin Luther King Jr. Dr.
Atlanta, GA 30334
404-656-3920
www.sos.state.ga.us

Registration Requirements

State Form C100 or URS
IRS Form 990
IRS Determination Letter
$25 Registration fee
Audit if gross revenue over $1,000,000
Financial report reviewed by a CPA for organizations
with revenue between $500,000 and $1,000,000

Organization exempt from registration:

Nonprofit educational institutions;
Professional, business and trade associations that do
not solicit members or funds from the general
public;
Fraternal, civic, benevolent, patriotic and social
organizations if solicitations are carried on by
persons for their services and are confined to
their memberships;
Any solicitations for a named person where all
contributions are turned over to named person;
Charitable organizations whose total gross revenue is
less than $25,000
Any local or state organization of hunters, fishermen
and target shooters having tax-exempt status
Political parties, action committees and candidates
for federal or state office who are required to file
financial information to election commissions;
Publishers of commercial publications that solicit
advertisement and provide a percentage of
revenue for a charitable purpose

Please note that proof of exemption is required.

Annual Reporting Requirements

Due within one year of filing

$25 renewal/filing fee
IRS 990
Financial report required if proceeds are $500,000 or
more (CPA); independent CPA review required
for proceeds of$100,000 to $500,000
Audit required if revenue is over $1,000,000

Hawaii
There is no registration required in Hawaii at this
time.

Idaho
There is no registration required in Idaho at this time.

Illinois
Office of the Illinois Attorney General
Charitable Trust and Solicitations Bureau
100 West Randolph Street, 11th Floor
Chicago, IL 60601-3175
312-814-2595
www.ag.state.il.us/charityforms.html

Registration Requirements
State Form CO-1 or URS
Certificate/Articles of Incorporation
Bylaws
IRS Form 990
IRS Determination Letter
Audit if over $150,000 in gross revenue
$15 Registration fee
Financial report on state Form CO-2

Organizations exempt from registration:
Government agencies or subdivisions;
Educational institutions;
Religious organizations

Annual Reporting Requirements
Due within 6 months of close of fiscal year
$15 filing fee ($100 late fee if registration expires)
IRS 990
Financial report on state Form AG990-IL
Audit if revenue over is $150,000 or professional
fundraiser used

Indiana
There is no registration required in Indiana at this
time.

Iowa
There is no registration required in Iowa at this time.

Kansas
Secretary of State
First Floor, Memorial Hall
120 SW 10th Avenue
Topeka, KS 66612-1594
785-296-4564
www.kssos.org

Registration Requirements
State Form SC or URS
Certificate/Articles of Incorporation
IRS Form 990
IRS Determination Letter
Audit if contributions exceed $100,000.

Organizations exempt from registration:
Any religious corporation, trust or organization;
Accredited educational institutions or any of their
foundations;
Any other educational institution confining its
solicitation to the student body, alumni, faculty
and trustees;
Fraternal, social, alumni organizations and historical
societies when solicitation is confined to their
membership;
Any organization, which does not receive
contributions in excess of $10,000 per year

Annual Reporting Requirements
Due within 6 months of fiscal year end
$20 filing fee
IRS 990 (or financial report)
Audit if contributions exceed $100,000

Kentucky
Office of Attorney General
Consumer Protection Division
1024 Capital Center Dr.
Frankfort, KY 40602
502-696-5396

Registration Requirements
State form or URS
IRS Form 990

Organizations exempt from registration:
Organization soliciting contributions solely of its
members and their families;

Religious organizations soliciting funds for religious
purposes;
Accredited educational institutions soliciting
contributions from alumni, faculty, students and
families

Annual Reporting Requirements
Due within 4 1/2 months of fiscal year end
IRS 990, unless no 990 yet filed with the IRS

Louisiana
Dept. of Justice
Public Protection Division
One American Place
301 Main St., Suite 1250
Baton Rouge, LA 70801
225-342-7900

Registration Requirements
URS
IRS Determination letter
Certificate/Articles of Incorporation
Bylaws
Financial statement
Copies of Contracts with professional solicitors
List of all states where organization is registered
$25 Registration fee

Organizations exempt from registration:
Any charitable organization not utilizing the services
of professional fundraisers;
Religious organizations, including exempt from
federal income tax under IRS 501(c)(3), if not
primarily supported by funds solicited outside its
own membership or congregation; Educational
institutions recognized or approved by the
Louisiana Dept. of Education; Voluntary health
organizations organized under Louisiana or
federal law.

Annual Reporting Requirements
Due on the anniversary of annual registration
$25 renewal fee
IRS 990

Maine
Department of Prof. & Financial Regulation
Charitable Solicitation Registration
35 State House Station
Augusta, ME 04333-0007
207-624-8624

Registration Requirements
State of Maine Charitable Organization Registration
Form or URS
IRS Form 990
IRS Determination Letter
$50 Application fee, $100 registration fee (total:
$150)

Organizations exempt from registration:
Organizations that solicit primarily within their
membership and where members conduct
solicitation activities;
Organizations that do not receive contributions from
the public in excess of $10,000 or do not receive
contributions from more than 10 people during
the calendar year, if fundraising is carried on by
volunteers;
Educational institutions registered or approved by
Dept. of Education;
Hospitals that are nonprofit and charitable;
Persons soliciting contributions for the relief of any
individual specified by name at the time of the
solicitation where all contributions go directly to
said person for individual's use.

Organizations claiming exemptions must submit a
copy of form letter from IRS, any other
appropriate financial statements and a $10 fee.

Annual Reporting Requirements
Due by November 30th
Fee: $100, if more than $30,000 raised, then
additional $50 filing fee.
IRS 990
Financial Report may be submitted instead of IRS
990
Audit required if gross revenue is more than $30,000

Maryland
Office of the Secretary of State
Charitable Organizations Division
State House
Annapolis, MD 21401
410-974-5534

Registration Requirements
State Form COR-92 or URS
Certificate/Articles of Incorporation
Bylaws
IRS Form 990
IRS Determination Letter

Financial review (if revenue is between $100,000 and
   200,000)
Audit (if gross income from charitable contributions
   equals or exceeds $200,000)
Fee ranging from $50-$200

Organizations exempt from registration:
Religious organizations;
Organizations soliciting funds from their own
   memberships

Please note that organizations claiming exemption
   must provide evidence of its exemption.

Annual Reporting Requirements
Due within 6 months of fiscal year end
Fees range from $50-$200
IRS 990
Financial review (conducted by independent CPA if
   gross income from charitable contributions is
   greater than $100,000 but less than $200,000)
Audit (by an independent CPA if gross income from
   charitable contributions is greater than $200,000)

Massachusetts
The Commonwealth of Massachusetts
Office of Attorney General
Division of Public Charities
One Ashburton Place, Room 1413
Boston, MA 02108-1698
617-727-2200

Registration Requirements
State form Short Form- Schedule A-2 or URS
Certificate/Articles of Incorporation
Bylaws
$50 Registration fee

Organizations exempt from registration:
Religious;
The Red Cross and certain veteran's organizations

Annual Reporting Requirements
Due within 4 1/2 months of fiscal year end
Annual filing fees range from $35-250
IRS 990
Financial report - must use MA Form PC
Audit if revenue exceeds $250,000 (over $100,000
   and not more than $250,000, CPA review
   statement required)

Michigan
Department of Attorney General
Charitable Trust Section
P.O. Box 30214
Lansing, MI 48909
517-373-1152

Registration Requirements
State forms or URS
Certificate/Articles of Incorporation
Bylaws
IRS Form 990
IRS Determination Letter

Organization exempt from registration:
Religious organizations with tax-exempt status;
Educational institutions certified by the state board of
   education;
Veterans groups organized under federal law;
Licensed nonprofit hospitals and their foundations
   and auxiliaries

Please note that organizations seeking exemption
   must file a questionnaire before determination of
   exemption.

Annual Reporting Requirements
Due 30 days prior to registration expiration.
IRS 990
Financial Report.
Audit if revenue is over $250,000, financial review
   required if revenue is between $100,000 and
   $250,000

Minnesota
Office of Attorney General
Charities Unit, Suite 1200, NCL Tower
445 Minnesota St.
St. Paul, MN 55101-2130
651-296-6172
www.ag.state.mn.us

Registration Requirements
State registration form or URS
Certificate/Articles of Incorporation
IRS Form 990
IRS Determination Letter
$25 Registration fee

Organizations exempt from registration:
Organizations that do not employ paid staff of
   professional fundraisers and that do not receive
   or plan to receive more than $25,000 in one year;

Religious organizations exempt from filing IRS Form
    990;
Certain educational institutions;
Organizations limiting solicitations to persons who
    have a right to vote as a member;

Annual Reporting Requirements
Due within 6 months of close of fiscal year
Financial statement (Atty. Gen. Annual Report form)
IRS 990, 990-EZ, or 990-PF
Audit if revenue exceeds $350,000
$25 renewal fee

Mississippi
Mississippi Secretary of State
Charities Registration
P.O. Box 136
Jackson, MS 39205-0136
601-359-1633 or (toll free) 888-236-6167

Registration Requirements
State forms additional to URS- "Supplement to URS"
    including Annual Financial Reporting form
IRS Form 990
IRS Determination Letter
Certificate/Articles of Incorporation
Bylaws
$50.00 registration fee
Audit required if gross revenues over $100,000 (or
    over $25,000, if a professional fundraiser is
    used), or request for audits may occur on a case-
    by-case basis for registrants between $25,000
    and $100,000.

Organizations exempt from registration:
Accredited educational institutions;
Educational institutions that solicit solely from
    students, alumni, faculty, trustees and families;
Fraternal, patriotic, social, educational alumni
    organizations and historical societies when
    solicitation of contributions is made solely by
    their membership;
Any charitable organization that does not intend to
    solicit and receive and does not actually receive
    contributions in excess of $4,000 provided
    persons who are unpaid for such services carry
    on all fundraising functions

Organizations seeking exemption must file Form CE.

Annual Reporting Requirements
Reporting must be done on the URS and by doing so,
    renew registration and submit financial report
    simultaneously

Due at anniversary of original registration
$50.00 filing fee
IRS 990
Financial Report
Audit if gross revenues exceed $100,000 (or over
    $25,000, if a professional fundraiser is used).
    Audits may be requested on a case-by-case basis
    for registrants between $25,000-$100,000

Missouri
Missouri Attorney General
P.O. Box 899
Jefferson City, MO 65102-0899
573-751-1197

Registration Requirements
State registration Form 1-A or URS
Articles of Incorporation
IRS Form 990
IRS Determination Letter
$15 initial Registration fee, $50 thereafter

Organizations exempt from registration:
Religious organizations;
Educational institutions and their authorized and
    related foundations;
Fraternal organizations provided solicitations are
    limited to membership of such organizations;
Hospitals, provided fundraising not done by
    professional fundraiser;
All 501(c) 3, 501(c) 7 and 501(c)(8) organizations
    that have obtained and can document such status
    from the federal government

Annual Reporting Requirements
Due within 2 1/2 months of fiscal year end
$50 annual fee, after initial $15
IRS 990
Financial Report

Montana
There is no registration required in Montana at this
    time.

Nebraska
There is no registration required in Nebraska at this
    time.

Nevada
There is no registration required in Nevada at this
    time.

New Hampshire

Department of Justice
Charitable Trust Division
33 Capitol St.
Concord, NH 03301-6397
603-271-3591

Registration Requirements
State forms or URS
Conflict-of-interest policy
Certificate/Articles of Incorporation
Bylaws
IRS Form 990.
IRS Determination Letter
$25 Registration fee

Organizations exempt from registration:
Religious organizations

Annual Reporting Requirements
Due within 4 1/2 months of fiscal year end
Financial report on state Form NHCT-2A or
IRS 990 or
IRS 990-EZ or
IRS 990-PF

New Jersey

N.J. Division of Consumer Affairs
Charities Registration Section
124 Halsey Street, 7th Floor
P.O. Box 45021
Newark, NJ 07101
973-504-6215

Registration Requirements
State Form CRI-200, CRI-150I, CRI-300R or URS
Certificate/Articles of Incorporation
Bylaws
IRS Form 990
IRS Determination Letter

Organizations exempt from registration:
Religious organizations;
Educational institutions filing their curricula with the
    Dept. of Education

Annual Reporting Requirements
Due within 6 months of fiscal year end
Filing fees range from $0-$250
IRS 990

Financial report certified by authorized officer of
    organization if revenue under $100,000
Audit for revenue $100,000 and over

New Mexico

Office of Attorney General
Charitable Organization Registry
P.O. Drawer 1508
Santa Fe, NM 87504-1508
505-827-6693

Registration Requirements
State form or URS
Certificate/Articles of Incorporation
IRS Form 990
IRS Determination Letter
Audit if total revenue is in excess of $500,000

Organizations exempt from registration:
Any church or group organized for the purpose of
    worship, religious teaching, or other religious
    activity;
A school, college or other institution with a defined
    curriculum, student body and (faculty,
    conducting classes on a regular basis;
Charitable organizations that receive less than $2,500
    per year in contributions;
Local affiliates of statewide or national organizations
    for which all local fundraising expenses are paid
    by a registered parent organization

Annual Reporting Requirements
Due within 2 1/2 months of fiscal year
IRS 990
Financial Report may be submitted instead of 990
Audit if total revenue is in excess of $500,000

New York

Department of Law, Charities Bureau
120 Broadway 3rd Floor
New York, NY 10271
212-416-8400
www.oag.state.ny.us/charities

Registration Requirements:
State form CHAR410 or URS
Certificate/Articles of Incorporation
Bylaws
IRS Form 990
IRS Determination Letter

Audit if over $150,000 in revenues (CPA review if between 75,000-$150,000).
$25.00 Registration fee

Organizations exempt from registration

Religious agencies and organizations and charities operated, supervised, or controlled in connection with a charity organized under the Religious Corporations Law;

Educational institutions confining solicitations to student body, alumni, faculty and trustees and their families;

Fraternal, patriotic, social and alumni organizations and historical societies chartered by Board of Regents when soliciting memberships;

Organization receiving $25,000 or less and not paying professional fundraisers;

Local post, camp, chapter or county unit of a veteran's organization;

Educational institutions or libraries that file annual financial reports with Regents of University of State of New York or with an agency having similar jurisdiction in another state

Please note that even exempt organizations must submit Form CHAR006, which must be filed annually.

Annual Reporting Requirements

Due date 41/2 months after fiscal year end
Fees $10 or $25 depending on revenue generated
IRS 990
Financial Report - must be reviewed by CPA if revenue $75,000-$150,000.
Audit if revenue $150,000 and over

North Carolina

Department of Secretary of State
Division of Facility Services/
Solicitations Licensing Section
2 S. Salisbury St.
P.O. Box 29622
Raleigh, NC 27626-0622
919-807-2214

Registration Requirements

State form- (URS not accepted)
Certificate/Articles of Incorporation
Bylaws
IRS Form 990
IRS Determination Letter
Fees range from $0-$400

Organizations exempt from registration:

Any person that solicits for a religious organization;
Solicitations of charitable contributions by the federal, State or local governments or their agencies;

Any person who receives less than 25,000 in contributions in a calendar year and does not provide compensation to any officer, trustee, organizer, incorporator, fund-raiser or solicitor;

Any educational institution, the curriculum of which, in whole or in part, is registered, approved, or accredited by the Southern Assoc. of Colleges and Schools or an equivalent regional accrediting body, and any foundation or department having an established identity with any of these educational institutions;

Any licensed hospital and any foundation or department having established identity with that hospital if the governing board of the hospital, authorizes the solicitation and receives an accounting of the funds collected and expended;

Any noncommercial radio or television station;
A qualified community trust;
A bona fide volunteer fire department, rescue squad, or emergency medical service;
A YMCA or YWCA;
A nonprofit continuing-care facility

Annual Reporting Requirements

Due within 4 1/2 months of end of fiscal year
Fees range from $50-$200
IRS 990 or financial report

North Dakota

Secretary of State
State of North Dakota
600 E. Boulevard Ave., Dept. 108
Bismarck, ND 58505-0500
701-328-3665
800-352-0867 ext.83665
www.state.nd.us/sec

Registration Requirements

State Form SFN 11300, ($25 fee) and SFN 7974 ($10 fee) in addition to URS
State Articles of Incorporation for Nonprofit Form SFN 13003 ($30 fee)
IRS Form 990

Organizations exempt from registration:

A duly constituted religious organization, or any group affiliated with and forming an integral part of that organization that has tax-exempt status from the government of the United States;

Organizations soliciting funds for institutions of higher learning;

Private or public elementary or secondary school;

Charitable organizations using only volunteer unpaid fundraisers and soliciting funds for a political sub-division or other government entity or for a civic or community project with no contributions benefiting any individual;

Candidates for national, state and local elective office or political party or other committee required to file information with the federal or state election commission or similar agency

Annual Reporting Requirements

Due September 1st

$10 filing/renewal fee

Annual report /renewal application on required Form SFN 11302A

Ohio

Office of the Attorney General

Charitable Law Section

101 E. Town St., 4th Fl.

Columbus, OH 43215-5148

614-466-3180

www.ag.state.oh.us

Registration Requirements

State forms or URS

Certificate/Articles of Incorporation

Bylaws

IRS Form 990

IRS Determination Letter

Registration fees range from $0-$200

Organizations exempt from registration:

Any religious agencies and organizations, and charities, agencies, and organizations operated, supervised, or controlled by a religious organization;

Any educational institution, when solicitation of contributions is confined to alumni, faculty, trustees, or students and their families;

Any organization that does not receive gross revenue, excluding grants or awards from the government or a 501(c)(3) organization, in excess of $25,000 and does not compensate any person primarily to solicit;

Every person other than an individual, when solicitation of contributions for a charitable

purpose or on behalf of a charitable organization is confined to its members, present and former employees, or present and former trustees

Annual Reporting Requirements

Due within 4 1/2 months of fiscal year end

Fee: $50 -$200

IRS 990 or financial report (Attorney General's Form)

Oklahoma

Office of the Secretary of State

2300 N. Lincoln, Room 101

Oklahoma City, OK 73105-4897

405-521-3911

Registration Requirements

State form or URS

IRS Form 990

IRS Determination letter

Financial statement (SOS Form 0102)

$15 Registration fee

Organizations exempt from registration:

Organizations formed for religious purposes and other organizations directly operated, supervised, or controlled by a religious organization;

Educational institutions which have a faculty and regularly enrolled students, and offer courses of study leading to the granting of recognized degrees when solicitations of contributions are limited to students and their families, alumni, faculty, and trustees;

Fraternal organizations, when soliciting from their own members, and patriotic and civic organizations, when solicitations of contributions are confined to membership of said organization and managed by membership without paid solicitors;

Persons soliciting contributions for the relief of a named person where all contributions are turned over to named beneficiary;

Any organization, which collects from charitable solicitations less than $10,000/year

Annual Reporting Requirements

Due by March 31st or with annual registration renewal

Fee: $15

IRS 990

Financial report (state form required)

Oregon

Oregon Dept. of Justice
Charitable Activities
1515 SW 5th Ave. #410
Portland, OR 97201
503-229-5725
www.doj.state.or.us
Email: charitable.activities@doj.state.or.us

Registration Requirements
State registration Form RF-C or URS
IRS Determination letter
Certificate/Articles of Incorporation
Bylaws
No registration fees required

Organizations exempt from registration:
Cemetery corporations
Child-caring agencies regulated by the Department of
    Human Services
Foreign corporations or foundations making only
    grants or donations in the state of OR
Government agencies or sub-divisions
Post-secondary educational institutions holding no
    property in OR with individual solicitations
    confined to alumni
Religious organizations holding property solely for
    religious purposes

Annual Reporting Requirements
Due within 4 1/2 months of fiscal year end
Form CT-12, CT-12F, or CT-12S
Filing fees from $10.00-$200.00
IRS 990
Financial Report

Pennsylvania

Department of State
Bureau of Charitable Orgs.
124 Pine Street, Third Floor
P.O. Box 8723
Harrisburg, PA 17105
717-783-1720

Registration Requirements
State forms or URS
IRS Form 990
IRS Determination Letter
Audit required in certain cases
Certificate/Articles of Incorporation
Bylaws
Annual Registration Fees: ($15-$250)

Organizations exempt from registration:
Organizations of law enforcement personnel,
    firefighters, or other persons who protect public
    safety, not benefiting any person outside active
    membership of organization;
Religious institutions and separate groups or
    corporations that form an integral part that are
    tax exempt and primarily supported by fees
    charged for services rendered, government grants
    or contracts, or solicitations from their own
    memberships, congregations, or previous donors;
Accredited educational institutions and any
    associations, foundations and support groups that
    are directly responsible to educational
    institutions;
Hospitals subject to regulation by the Dept. of Health
    or Dept. of Public Welfare and any foundation,
    which is an integral part;
Nonprofit libraries that file an annual fiscal report
    with the state library system;
Senior citizen centers and nursing homes that are
    nonprofit, charitable and tax exempt, and have
    all fundraising activities carried out by
    volunteers;
Organizations raising $25,000 or less annually that
    do not compensate anyone;
Local post, camp, or chapter of any veterans'
    organization chartered under federal law and any
    service foundations recognized in their by-laws.

Annual Reporting Requirements
Due 135 days after end of fiscal year
Fee: $15-$250
IRS 990
Financial Report reviewed by CPA if contributions
    $25,000-$100,000
Audit if contributions $100,000 or more

Rhode Island

Department of Business Regulation
Securities Division,
233 Richmond St #232
Providence, RI 02903-4232
401-222-3048

Registration Requirements
State form or URS
IRS Form 990
Audit if annual gross budget exceeds $500,000
$75 Registration fee

Organizations exempt from registration:
Religious organizations;

Institutions indirectly affiliated with any religious organization that maintain and operate homes for the aged, orphans or unwed mothers;
Accredited educational institutions;
Organizations raising $25,000 or less in a calendar year, whose fundraising activities are carried on by volunteers;
Nonprofit hospitals;
Organizations soliciting contributions solely from their membership;
Public libraries;
Veteran's organizations and their auxiliaries;
Public art museums

Please note that organizations must file annually for exemptions.

Annual Reporting Requirements
Due on anniversary of registration
$75 filing/renewal fee
IRS 990
Financial Report
Audit if proceeds exceed $100,000

South Carolina
Office of the Secretary of State
Public Charities Section
P.O. Box 11350
Columbia, SC 29211
803-734-1790

Registration Requirement
State form or URS
IRS Determination letter
$50 Registration fee

Organizations exempt from registration:
Organizations expecting less than $20,000 in contributions, that have no paid staff, and have tax-exempt status;
Veteran's organizations chartered by Congress;
Membership organizations for which there are specific qualification for joining Other than paying dues)
Educational institutions
Political subdivisions of the state
Organizations established by persons requesting relief of an individual specified by name

Annual Reporting Requirements
Due within 4 1/2 months of fiscal year
$50 filing/renewal fee

IRS 990
Financial Report (may be submitted instead of 990)

South Dakota
There is no registration required in South Dakota at this time.

Tennessee
Secretary of State
Charitable Solicitations
James K. Polk Building, Suite 1700
Nashville, TN 37243-0308
615-741-2555

Registration Requirements
State forms SS-6001 or URS, and SS-6002
Certificate/Articles of Incorporation
Bylaws
IRS Form 990
IRS Determination Letter
Audit if gross revenue over $250,000

Organizations exempt from registration:
Churches;
Educational institutions, their booster clubs, parent organizations and affiliated groups;
Volunteer fire departments, rescue squads and local civil defense organizations;
Organizations raising less than $30,000 in gross contributions during their fiscal year

Annual Reporting Requirements
Due within 6 months of fiscal year end
Fees range from $100 -$300
IRS 990
Financial Report required when revenue is more than $100,000
Audit unless proceeds do not exceed $10,000

Texas
There is no registration required in Texas at this time.

Utah
Department of Commerce
Division of Consumer Protection
160 East 300 South
P.O. Box 146704

Salt Lake City, UT 84114-6704
801-530-6601
www.commerce.state.ut.us

Registration Requirements
State form- URS NOT accepted
$100.00 registration
Certificate/Articles of Incorporation
Bylaws
IRS Form 990
IRS Determination Letter
Audit
Renewal required annually on the 1st of January,
April, July, or October following the completion
of 12 months after initial registration

Organizations exempt from registration:
A solicitation that an organization conducts among its
own bona fide membership exclusively through
the voluntary efforts of other members or
officers of the organization;
A bona fide religious, ecclesiastical, or
denominational organization if 1) the solicitation
is for a church, missionary, religious or
humanitarian purpose and 2) the organization is a
physical place of worship where nonprofit
religious services and activities are regularly
conducted and carried on OR a bona fide
religious group that does not maintain a specific
place of worship, that is not subject to federal
income tax and not required to file an IRS Form
990 under any circumstance OR a separate group
or corporation that is an integral part of an
institution that is income tax exempt and is not
primarily supported by funs solicited outside its
own membership or congregation;
A broadcast media owned or operated by an
educational institution or governmental entity;
Any school or institution of higher learning
accredited by the state or club, parent, teacher,
student organization within and authorized by
the school in support of the operation and
activities of the school;
A volunteer fire department, rescue squad or local
civil defense organization whose financial
oversight is under the control of a local
governmental entity.

Annual Reporting Requirements
Due quarterly during year one 30 days after end of
quarter
Due 30 days after end of fiscal year thereafter
Financial report or IRS 990

Vermont
There is no registration required in Vermont at this
time.

Virginia
Commonwealth of Virginia
Dept. of Agriculture and Consumer Services
Division of Consumer Affairs
P.O. Box 1163
Richmond, VA 23218
804-786-2042
www.state.va.us/~vdacs/vdacs.htm

Registration Requirements
State Form 102 or URS
Certificate/Articles of Incorporation
Bylaws
IRS Form 990 or audit
IRS Determination Letter
$100 Registration fee

Organizations exempt from registration:
Any accredited educational institutions or related
foundations, and any other educational
institution confining its solicitation of
contributions to its student body, alumni, faculty
and trustees, and their families;
Persons requesting contributions for the relief of any
individual specified by name at the time of
solicitation when all contributions are turned
over directly to named beneficiary;
Charitable organizations that do not intend, in a
calendar year or the three preceding years, to
receive contributions from the public in excess of
$5,000, and all of whose functions are carried
out by volunteers;
Organizations that solicit only within the membership
of the organization;
Organizations that have no office within the
Commonwealth and solicit within the state,
solely by means of telephone, telegraph, direct
mail or advertising in national media and have a
registered chapter, branch or affiliate within the
Commonwealth;
Tax-exempt health care institutions licensed by their
state Dept. of Health or Mental Health and any
supporting organizations;
Civic organizations such as a local service club,
veterans' post, fraternal society or association,
volunteer fire or rescue group, or local civic
league or association operated exclusively for
educational or charitable purposes for the benefit

of the community Organizations seeking exemption must file "Forms 100A-100H" as applicable.

Labor unions, associations and organizations with tax-exempt status;

Agencies designated by the Virginia Department for the Aging as area agencies on aging;

Nonprofit debt counseling agencies

Please note that exempt organizations must file appropriate forms and a $10 filing fee.

Annual Reporting Requirements

State Form 102
Due within 4 1/2 months of fiscal year end
Registration renewal fee: $30 - $325
IRS 990,990-PF, 990-EZ or certified annual audit or certified treasurer's report where proceeds are less than $25,000
Current list of officers, directors, trustees, and principal salaried staff members
Current copies of contracts with paid fund-raising organizations
Certificate/Articles of Incorporation or amendments to those documents not previously filed;
Bylaws or amendments to that document not previously filed;
IRS Determination letter

Washington

Office of Secretary of State
Charities Program
P.O. Box 40234
505 E. Union
Olympia, WA 98504-0234
800-332-4483
360-753-0863
Email: charities@secstate.wa.gov

Registration Requirements

State form or URS
IRS Form 990
IRS Determination letter
$20 Registration fee

Organizations seeking exemption must file an exemption form.

Annual Reporting Requirements

Due within 4 1/2 months of fiscal year end
$10 filing/renewal fee
IRS 990
Financial Report

West Virginia

Secretary of State
State Capitol, Room 157-K
Charleston, WV 25305
304-558-6000

Registration Requirements

State form - (URS not accepted)
IRS Form 990
IRS Determination letter
Fees range from $15-50
Audit if contributions exceed $10,000

Organizations exempt from registration:

Educational institutions, the curriculums of which in whole or in part are registered or approved by the state board of education, either directly or by acceptance of accreditation by an accrediting body and any auxiliary associations, foundations and support groups which are directly responsible to any such educational institutions;

Persons requesting contributions for the relief of any individual specified at the time of solicitation when all of the contributions collected without any deduction are turned over to the named beneficiary;

Hospitals, which are nonprofit;

Organizations which solicit only within the membership of the organization by members thereof: provided that the term "membership" shall not include those persons who are granted membership upon making a contribution as the result of solicitation;

Churches, synagogues, associations or conventions of churches, religious orders or religious organizations that are an integral part of a church, which qualifies as tax exempt under 501(c)(3);

Organizations sponsoring single fund-raising events for a named charitable organization;

Organizations such as local youth athletic organizations, community service clubs, fraternal organizations, volunteer fireman or auxiliaries are exempt if they do not employ a professional solicitor or fund-raiser or do not intend to solicit or receive contributions in excess of $10,000 during the calendar year.

Annual Reporting Requirements

There is no annual reporting requirement other than registration renewal.

Wisconsin

Department of Regulation & Licensing
Charitable Organizations
1400 E. Washington Ave.
P.O. Box 8935
Madison, WI 53708-8935
608-266-5511, ext. 441
Email: dorl@drl.state.wi.us

Registration Requirements
State forms or URS
Certificate/Articles of Incorporation
Bylaws
IRS Form 990
IRS Determination Letter
Audit if contributions exceed $100,000
$15 Registration fee

Organizations exempt from registration:
Candidate for national, state or local office or a
    political party or other committee or group
    required to file financial information with the
    federal elections commission; Organizations that
do not raise or receive contributions in excess of
    $5,000;
Fraternal, benevolent, patriotic or social
    organizations that solicit contributions solely
    from their membership;
Veteran's organizations;
Nonprofit postsecondary educational institutions;
Organizations soliciting contributions for relief of a
    named individual if all contributions are given to
    the named individual

Annual Reporting Requirements
Due August 1st
$15 filing/renewal fee
IRS 990
Financial Report if contributions from exceed $5,000
    organizations must file either
Audit if charitable contributions exceed $100,000

Wyoming
There is no registration required in Wyoming at this
    time.

State Corporation Divisions

Alabama

Division of Corporation, Secretary of State, 4121 Carmichael Road, Montgomery, AL 36106 or P.O. Box 5616, Montgomery, AL 36103-5616, 334-242-5324, Fax: 334-242-4993; {www.sos.state.al.us}. Selected Publications: Guide to Incorporation. Phone Information: 334-242-5324. Office is not completely computerized yet, but can do word search or partial name search by officer, incorporator, or serving agent. Copies of documents on File: Available by written request for $1 per page plus $5 for certified copies. Can provide information over the phone at no cost. Mailing Labels: No. Magnetic Tape: No. Microfiche: No. New Corporate Listings: No. Custom Searches: Can do word or partial name search. Printout of search results by mail is free. Online Access: Yes. Number of active corporations on File: Figures Not Available

Alaska

State of Alaska, Division of Banking, Securities and Corporation, Corporation Section, P.O. Box 110808, Juneau, AK 99811-0808, 907-465-2530, Fax: 907-465-3257; {www.commerce.state.ak.us}. Selected Publications: None. Phone information: 907-465-2530. Copies of Documents on File: Complete corporate record (Articles of Incorporation, annual report, amendments, etc.) Cost $30, certified copies add $5, list of officers and directors cost $1, Certificate of Status cost $10. Mailing Labels: No. Magnetic tape: no, only diskettes. Copy of complete master file excluding officers and directors is priced at $100. Monthly supplements are an additional $10. Microfiche: No, only disk and email. New corporate listings: yes. Custom Searches: yes. Online Access: Yes. Number of active corporations on file: 25,172.

Arizona

Arizona Corporations Division, Records Division, Secretary of State, 1200 W. Washington, Phoenix, AZ 85007 or P.O. Box 6019, Phoenix, AZ 85005, 602-542-3026, Fax: 602-542-4100; {www.cc.state. az.us}. Selected Publications: Sample packet with forms and statutes mailed for $8. Guideline booklets will be available soon. Phone Information : 602-542-3026. Copies of Documents on File: Cost 50 cents per page, $5 for certified copies. Mailing Labels: No. Magnetic Tape: Master File $400, issued monthly. Requester must supply blank tape. Microfiche: All corporations statewide $75. New Corporate Listing: Monthly Listing of New Domestic Companies for

$200 plus $200 for new foreign listings. Custom searches: Yes, request in writing or in person. Can search by company name, agent name or officer name. Online Access. There is a charge for filing online. Contact business connection for forms 602-280-1480. Available through Information America, Dunn and Bradstreet and other commercial services. Number of corporations on file: 100,000

Arkansas

Secretary of State, Corporations Division, State Capitol Building, Room 058, Little Rock, AR 72201, 501-682-5151, Fax: 501-682-3437; {http:\\sos.state. ar.us}. Selected Publications: None. Phone Information: 501-682-5151. Copies of Documents on file: Call 501-371-3431 for copies at 50 cents per page plus $5 for certified copies. Domestic companies $50, Foreign companies $300. Mailing labels: No. Magnetic Tape: Master file 2 cents per name. Microfiche: No. New corporate Listing: Statistics only. Custom Searches. Categories include foreign, domestic, profit, and non-profit corporations. Cost: 2 cents per name, 50 cents per page. Online Access: Yes. Number of active corporations on file: 1,000,000

California

Corporations, Supervisor of Records, Secretary of State, 1500 11th Street, CA 95814-5701, 916-653-6814, {www.ss.ca.gov}. Selected Publications: Corporations Checklist Booklet. Request must be in writing and cost is $5. Phone Information: 916-653-6814. Copies of Documents on File: Articles of Incorporation: cost is $1 for first page, 50 cents for each additional page plus $5 for certified copies, Certificate of status $6, Statement of officers $5 and $10 for certified copies (written requests only). You must pay in advance or send blank check not to exceed $20. Send requests to secretary of state, Attention RIC unit. Mailing Labels: No. Magnetic Tape: Yes, Master copy $17,600 annually. Call 916-653-8905 for information. Hard copy $14,000.13. Microfiche: No. Custom Searches: Computer generated listing of Active Stock ($17,030), Active Non-Stock ($422). Active Non-Stock by Classification $150 per list. Management Services Division, Information Systems Section, 1230 J Street, Suite 242, Sacramento, CA 95814. All orders must be submitted in writing. Basic cost of magnetic tape copy is $1.02 per 1,000 names. Basic cost of same run, for custom search, printed on paper, is $4.13 per

1,000 names. $150 minimum is applied to both. Online Access: Yes. Number of Corporations on File: 2,000,000.

Colorado

Corporate Division, Secretary of State, 1560 Broadway, Suite 200, Denver, CO 80202, 303-894-2251, Fax: 303-894-2251; {www.sos.state.co.us}. Selected Publications: Corporate Guide. Copies of Documents on File: Cost is 50 cents per page, plus $10 for certification. Mailing Labels: No. Magnetic Tape: Available for $500 for complete set of five. Tapes must be purchased individually. Categories: Foreign and Domestic. Microfiche: available at $1 a sheet (includes Summary of Master Computer File, must be purchased in its entirety). New Corporate Listings: Reporting Service costs $200 a year. Weekly list of New Corporations. Written requests only. Custom searches: Yes. Categories: Foreign and Domestic available on a cost recovery basis. The minimum fee is $50. Online Access: Available. Fee is $300 for 3 months or $1,000 per year. Number of Corporations on File: 235,000.

Connecticut

Office of Secretary of State, Division of Corporations, 30 Trinity Street, Hartford, CT 06106; Fax: 860-509-6068; {www.state.ct.us/sots}. Selected Publications: None, but to get a copy of Connecticut General Statutes, call 860-509-6190. Phone Information: 860-509-6001. Copies of Documents on File: Fees are $20 regardless of number of pages, $25 for certified. Written requests only. Mailing Labels: No. Magnetic Tape: Copy of master database of corporations $300. Requester must provide tapes. Microfiche: No. New Corporate Listing: No. Custom Searches: No. Online Access: Yes. Number of Corporations on File: over 200,000

Delaware

Delaware Department of State, Division of Corporations, Secretary of State, P.O. Box 898, Dover, DE 19903, 302-739-3073, Fax: 302-739-3812; {www.state.de.us\ corp}. Selected Publications: Incorporating in Delaware. Phone Information: 302-739-3073. Copies of Documents on File: (for domestic only) Available at $1 per page $20 for certification. Short forms $20 and $100 for long forms of good standing. Certificate of incorporation $50 minimum, amendment certificate $100 minimum, change of registered agents $75. Requests may be faxed to 302-739-3812, but written requests are preferred. Requests must be paid for in advance,

add county fee and send a check. Call for number of pages. Documents filed prior to 1983 are not on computer and must be requested in writing. They offer same day or 24-hour expedited services to file or retrieve certified documents. Same day request completed and released by 5pm, when requested by 2pm. Additional fee is $20. Mailing Labels: No. Magnetic Tape: No. Microfiche: No. New Corporate Listings: No. Custom Searches: Yes, domestic corporations only. Number of Active Corporation on File 397,829.

District of Columbia

Corporations Division, Consumer and Regulatory Affairs, 941 N. Capitol NE, 1st Floor, Washington, DC 20002, 202-442-4430, Fax: 202-442-4523; {www.dcra.org}. Selected Publications: Guideline and Instruction Sheet for Profit, Non-Profit, Foreign, or Domestic. Phone Information: 202-442-9453. Copies of Documents on File: Available for $25 each (all copies certified). Mailing Labels: Will be available in near future. Profit and non-profit lists updated quarterly. Magnetic Tape: No. Microfiche: No. New Corporate Listings No. Custom Searches: Computer searches on registered agents are available. Online Access: Yes. Number of Active Corporations on File: 50,000.

Florida

Division of Corporations, Secretary of State, PO Box 6327, Tallahassee, FL 32314, 850-487-6000, Fax: 850-487-6012; {www.sunbiz.org}. Selected Publications: Copy of the Law Chapter 607 (corporate law). Forms included. (Publications on laws of non-profit corporations and limited partnerships also available.) Phone Information: 904-488-9000. Limit of up to 3 inquiries per call. $10 charge to receive hard copy of microfiche on the corporations, no charge for faxing copies. Copy of Documents on File: Available at $1 per page if you do it yourself. Written requests must be paid for in advance: $1 for non-certified annual report; $10 for plain copy of complete file; $8.75 per 8 pages and $1 each additional, for any certified document including complete file. Microfiche: Yes. Contact Frank Reinhart or Ed Bagnell at Anacomp, 850-488-1486. Magnetic Tape: No. New Corporate Listings: No. Custom Searches: 850-488-1486. Online Access: Available through on CompuServe, 800-848-8199, address written request to Attn: Public Access, division of Corporations, 904-487-6866. Ask for a CompuServe intro-pak. Charge for connect time online is $24 per hour, plus $12.50 per hour additional corporate access fee. Both are prorated by time used. CompuServe can be contacted directly at South eastern Information Systems, P.O. Box 6867, Tallahassee, FL 32314, Attn: Keith Meyer, 904-656-4500. As of February, 1992, Anacomp will handle. Contact Eileen Self, 904-487-6073 for service. Number of active Corporations on File: 691,000.

Georgia

Division of Business Services and Regulation, Secretary of State, Suite 315, West Tower #2, Martin Luther King Drive, SE, Atlanta, GA 30334, 404-656-2185, Fax: 404-651-9059; {www.sos.state.ga.us}. Selected Publications: None, but information package on how to file sent upon request. Phone Information: 404-656-2817. Copies of Documents on File: Available for a minimum of $10 and all copies certified. Bills will be sent for orders over $10. Mailing Labels: No. Magnetic Tape: No. Microfiche: No. New Corporate Listings: through Georgia Net at 404-651-8692. Cost is $1,000 for a one time listing, if you want to receive a monthly or weekly update, cost is $600. Lists are on magnetic tape. Custom Searches: No. Online Access: Yes Number of Active Corporations on File: 350,000

Hawaii

Business Registration Division, Department of Commerce and Consumer Affairs, 1010 Richards Street, PO Box 40, Honolulu, HI 96810, 808-586-2744, Fax: 808-586-2733; {www.state.hi.us/dcca/breg-seu/}. Selected Publications: None. Phone Information: 808-586-2727. Copies of Documents on File: Available at 25 cents per page, plus $10 per page for certified copies. Expedited service available for $10 fee plus 25 cents per sheet, plus $1 per page. Mailing Labels: No. Magnetic Tape: No. Microfiche: No. New Corporate Listing: Weekly printout available but only for walk-ins. Custom Searches: No. Online Access: Yes. Downloading information from database available through FYI at 808-586-1919. Number of Active Corporations on File: 45,000

Idaho

Corporate Division, Secretary of State, Room 203, Statehouse, Boise, ID 83720, 208-334-2300, Fax: 208-334-2847; {www.idsos.state.id.us}. Selected Publications: Idaho Corporation Law. Phone Information: 208-334-2300. Copies of Documents on File: Available at 25 cents per page, $2 for certified copies. Mailing Labels: Very flexible and may be combined with custom search. Fee is $10 for computer base, 25 cents for first 100 pages, 10 cents for next 500 pages and 5 cents per page thereafter.

Magnetic Tape: available for $20 per tape if you supply the tape. They will supply diskette for additional $10. Microfiche: Available for $10, 50 cents for each additional copy of same. Custom Searches: Yes. You supply the tapes or they will supply them at cost. New Corporate Listing: No, but published weekly in The Idaho Business Review. Online Access: Available though Data Share program. Call computer department 208-334-5354. Number of Active Corporations on File 200,000.

Illinois

Corporations Division, Centennial Building, Room 328, Springfield, IL 62756, 217-782-6961, Fax: 217-782-4528; {www.sos.state.il.us}. Selected Publications: Guide for Organizing (Domestic, Non-Profit, or Foreign). Phone Information: 217-782-7880. Copies of Documents on File: available at $5 per page up to first 10 pages; 50 cents for each page thereafter. Mailing Labels: No. Magnetic Tape: yes. Categories: Domestic and Foreign cost $1,500; Not-for-Profit cost $1,500. You must supply tape. Microfiche: Available for $171. New Corporate Listings: Daily list of newly formed corporations costs $185 per year; Monthly List priced at $105 per year. Contact Sharon, 217-782-4104 for more information. Custom Searches: No. Other: Certified List of Domestic and Foreign Corporations (Address of Resident Agent included) costs $38 for two volume set. Online Access: Yes.

Indiana

Office of Corporation, Secretary of State, E018, 302 West Washington Street, Indianapolis, IN 46204, 317-232-6582, Fax: 800-726-8000; {www.state.in.us/sos}. Selected Publications: Guide Book. Request by calling 800-726-8000. Phone Information: 317-232-6576. Copies of Documents on File: Available at $1 per page and $15 to certify. May pay in advance or be billed. Mailing Labels: No. Magnetic Tape: No. Microfiche: No. New Corporate Listings: Daily Listing is published monthly for $20 a month. Custom Searches: No. Online Access: Available: Yes. Number of Active Corporations on file: 200,000.

Iowa

Corporate Division, Secretary of State, Hoover State Office Building, Des Moines, IA 50319, 515-281-5204, Fax: 515-242-6566; {www.sos.state.ia.us}. Selected Publications: Iowa Profit Corporations. Phone Information 515-281-5204. Copies of Documents on File: available at $1 per page; certified copies cost $5. Mailing Labels: No. Magnetic Tape: No. Master file is available on CD-Rom for $200. Microfiche: No. New Corporate Listings: No. Custom Searches: Yes. Searches by name of corporation or partial name. Online Access: Available through Dial Up Program. Contact Sheryl Allen 515-281-5247. Cost is $175 per year, plus telephone charges. Number of Active Corporations on File: 200,000.

Kansas

Corporate Division, Secretary of State, Capitol Building, Second Floor, 300 SW 10th Avenue, Topeka, KS 66612-1594, 785-296-7456, Fax: 785-296-4570; {www.kssos.org}. Selected Publications: None. Will send out forms with instruction sheets. Phone Information: 785-296-4564. Copies of Documents on File: Available at 50 cents per page plus $7.50. Certificate of Good Standing $7.50, Letter of Good Standing $5, Written Record Search $5. Magnetic Tape: Yes. Master file is available. Microfiche: No. Other: New Corporate Listings: No. Custom Searches: Yes, but they cannot search for. Online Access: Available through Info Network Kansas, 785-296-5143. Number of Active Corporations on File: 66,000.

Kentucky

Corporate Division, Secretary of State, Room 154, Capitol Building, 700 Capitol Avenue, PO Box 718, Frankfort, KY 40601, 502-564-2848, Fax: 502-564-4075; {www.sos.state.ky.us}. Selected Publications: None. Phone Information: 502-564-2848. Copies of Documents on File: Call 502-564-7330 to obtain number of copies in advance. Cost is 50 cents per page; $5 for certified copies. Computer screen print out is $1. Mailing label: No. Magnetic Tape: No. CD Rom available for free and they can send it to you for free. Microfiche: No. New Corporate Listings: available for $50 a month. Custom Searches: Yes, partial name search. Online Access: Yes. Number of Active Corporations on File: 400,000.

Louisiana

Corporate Division, Secretary of State, 3851 Essen Lane, Baton Rouge, LA 70809, 225-925-4704, Fax: 225-925-4410; {www.sec.state.la.us}. Selected Publications: Corporate Law Book ($10). Phone Information: 225-925-4704. Copies of Documents on File: Available starting at $10 for certified articles only. Cost for complete file, including amendments is $20. Mailing Label: No. Magnetic Tape: No. Microfiche: No. New Corporate Listing: Weekly

Newsletter at no charge. Requester must supply self addressed stamped envelope. Custom Searches: Yes, can search by agents and individual names. Online Access: Dial Up Access, 225-922-1475. Cost is $360 per year. Number of Active Corporations on File: 120,000.

Maine

Information and Report Section, Bureau of Corporations, Secretary of State, 101 State House Station, Augusta, ME 04333-0101, 207-287-4195, Fax: 207-287-5874; {www.state.me.us/sos/cec/}. Selected Publications: None at this time. Phone Information: 207-287-4195. Copies of Documents on File: Available for $2 per page, plus $5 for certified copies. Mailing Labels: No. Magnetic tape: No. Microfiche: No. New Corporate Listings: Monthly Corporations Listing costs $10. Send written request to Audrey Dingley or call 207-287-4188. Custom Searches: Yes, by corporation name. Online Access: Yes. Number of Active Corporations on File 46,000.

Maryland

Corporate Charter Division, Department of Assessments and Taxation, 301 W. Preston Street, Baltimore, Maryland 21201, 410-767-1330, Fax: 410-333-5873; {www.dat.state.md.us\bfsd}. Selected Publications: Information Guides for Filing and other issues are available. Phone Information: 410-225-1330. Copies of Documents on File: Available for $1 per page, plus $6 for certified copies. There is a $20 expediting fee. Certificate of good standing $6, Articles of Incorporation $20. Mailing Labels: No. Magnetic Tape: available on 6 tapes for $75 each. Contact Dale Brown of Specprint in Timonium, 410-561-9600. Microfiche: No. New Corporate Listings: Monthly corporate Computer Printout costs $25 a month. Custom Searches. Yes. They can search for names, agents, principal offices, and documents filed by the corporation. Online Access: Yes. Number of Active Corporations on File: 300,000.

Massachusetts

Corporate Division, Secretary of State, 1 Ashburton Place, Boston, MA 02108, 617-727-9640; {www.state.ma.us/sec/cor}. Selected Publications: Compendium of Corporate Law ($15). Phone Information: 617-727-9640. Copies of Documents on File: available for 20 cents per page, $12 for certified copies. Mailing Labels: No. Magnetic Tape: Cost is $300 for copy of master file and record layout. Requester must supply tapes. Microfiche: No. New Corporate Listings: Semi-monthly Filings cost $15;

Quarterly Filings cost $50; bi-weekly printout cost $15. Custom Searches: available on a cost recovery basis. Online Access: Direct Access program. Cost is $149 annually. Connect time is 40 cents per minute. Number of Corporations on File: 375,000.

Michigan
Corporation Division, Corporation and Securities Bureau, Michigan Department of Commerce, PO Box 30054, 6546 Mercantile, Lansing, MI 48909, 517-334-6302, Fax: 517-334-8048; {www.cis. state.mi.us/bcs/corp/}. Selected Publications: None. Phone Information: 517-334-6311. Call 517-334-6905 for automated form request line. Copies of Documents on File: available at a minimum of $6 for 6 pages or less, $1 for each page thereafter. Certified copies cost $10. (Request a price list.) Mailing Labels: No. Magnetic Tape: No. Microfiche: Available for $145. New Corporate Listings: Monthly Listing ranges at about $100 per month (each month is priced differently). Custom Searches: No. Online Access: Available through KnowX (www.knowx.com), a division of Information America, 800-235-4008. You can pay for these online searches by credit card or prepaid account. Price varies. To view all records of a corporation, $15. Other prices range from $1 to $6. Number of Corporations on File: 251,000.

Minnesota
Corporate Division, Secretary of State, 180 State Office Building, 100 Constitution Avenue, St. Paul, MN 55155, 651-296-2803; {www.sos.state.mn.us}. Selected Publications: Guide to Starting a Business in Minnesota. Phone Information: 651-296-2803. Copies of Documents on File: Available for $3 per copy, $8 for certified copies. Request copies by sending a letter, indicating your address or fax number. Mailing Labels: No. Magnetic Tape: Yes, on 9 tapes for $11,250 annually and $710 per month. Microfiche: No. New Corporate Listings: Daily Log costs 25 cents per page. Custom Searches: Available on a cost recovery basis. Categories same as for mailing labels. Online Access: Yes. Number of Corporations on File: 194,500

Mississippi
Office of Corporations, Secretary of State, PO Box 136, Jackson, MS 39205, 601-359-1350, Fax: 601-359-1499; or street address: 202 N. Congress, Suite 601, Jackson, MS 39205; {www.sos.state.ms.us}. Selected Publications: None. Phone Information: 601-359-1627. Copies of Documents on File: $1 per page plus $10 for certified copies. Mailing Labels:

No. Magnetic tape: No. Microfiche: No. New Corporate Listings: No. Custom Searches: Available to limited extent. Printout costs $2 per page. Online Access: Yes. Number of Active Corporations on File: 80,000.

Missouri
Corporate Division, Secretary of State, 600 W. Main and 208 State Capitol, PO Box 778, Jefferson City, MO 65102, 573-751-4936, Fax: 573-751-5841; {http://mosl.sos.state.mo.us}. Selected Publications: Corporation Handbook (free). Phone Information: 573-751-4153. Copies of Documents on File: available at 50 cents per page plus $10 for certified copies. Mailing Labels: No. Magnetic Tape: No. Microfiche: No. New Corporate Listings: not usually, but can be set up on special request. Custom Searches: Yes, on website. Online Access: Yes. Number of active Corporations on File: 192,000.

Montana
Corporate Division, Secretary of State, Capitol Station, Helena, MT 59620, 406-444-3665, Fax: 406-444-3976; {www.state.mt.us\sos}. Selected Publications: None. Phone Information: 406-444-3665. Copies of Documents on File: available for 50 cents per page; $3 for certification. Prepaid accounts are available for obtaining certificates and other information. Mailing Labels: No. Magnetic Tape: No. Microfiche: No. New Corporate Listings: No. Custom Searches: No but can search by name of corporation only. Online access: Yes. Number of Active Corporations on File: 33,000

Nebraska
Corporate Division, Secretary of State, State Capitol, Lincoln, NE 68509, 402-471-4079, Fax: 402-471-3666; {www.nol.org\home\SOS}. Selected Publications: None. Phone Information: 402-471-4079. Copies of Documents on File: Available for $1 per page, $10 for certified copies. Fax your requests and they will bill you, or request over the phone. Mailing Labels: No, but database is available on floppy or CD-Rom. Magnetic Tape: Contact Nebraska Online at 800-747-8177. Microfiche: No. New Corporate Listings: also available through Nebraska Online. Custom Searches: No: Online Access: Yes. Number of Active Corporations on File: 50,000.

Nevada
Office of Corporations, Secretary of State, Capitol Complex, Carson City, NV 89710, 702-684-5708, Fax: 702-684-5725; {www.sos.state.nv.us}. Selected

Publications: Guidelines. Phone Information: Corporate Status call 900-535-3355, $3.50 per call. Copies of Documents on File: available for $1 per page, $10 for certified copies. Prepayment required (they will not send a bill). Mailing Labels: No. Magnetic Tape: Copy of master file available, 702-684-5715. Corporations takes 2 tapes which requester supplies. Cost per tape is $25. Microfiche: No. New Corporate Listings: Monthly Listing of New Corporations costs $20 a month. Custom Searches: yes. Cost determined at time of request. Other: A listing of corporations on file, the "Alpha Listing", which includes names of active and inactive corporations can be fully downloaded for $100. Available on reel tape only. Contact Timothy Horgon. Online access: Yes. Number of active Corporations on File: 60,000.

New Hampshire
Corporate Division, Secretary of State, State House, Room 204, Concord, NH 03301, 603-271-3244. Selected Publications: None. Phone Information: 603-271-3246. Copies of Documents on File: Available for $1 per page, plus $5 for certified copies, and $25 expedited services. Annual report can be faxed to you for $10. Mailing Labels: No. Magnetic Tape: No. Microfiche: Complete listing of all registrations. No breakdown by type of entity (updated monthly). Annual Subscription costs $200. New Corporate Listings: Monthly Subscriber List costs $25 plus postage. Custom Searches: No. Online Access: No. Number of Active Corporations on File: 33,000.

New Jersey
Commercial Recording Division, Secretary of State, 820 Bear Tavern Road, West Trenton, NJ 08628, (Mailing address: CN 308), 609-530-6400, Fax: 609-530-6433; {http:\\accessnet.state.nj.us}. Selected Publications: Corporate Filing Packet. Phone Information: General Information call 609-530-6400; Forms call 609-292-0013; Expedite Service call 609-984-7107. There is a charge for standard information, $15 look-up fee for each verbal or fax request plus $10 expedited service fee. User may pay with Visa, Master Card or Discover. Requests may be sent by Fax at 609-530-6433. Copies of Documents on File: available for $1 per page plus $25 for certified copies (except for LLCs and Non-Profit corporations, which cost $15 to certify). Mailing Labels: No. Magnetic Tape: No. Microfiche: No. New Corporate Listings: No. Custom Searches: Yes. Each request is reviewed on individual basis. Requester is billed for computer

time. Online Access: Yes. Number of Active Corporations on File: 436,314.

New Mexico
State Corporation Commission, PO Drawer 1269, Santa Fe, NM 87504-1269, 505-827-4502, Fax: 505-827-4502; {www.nmprc.state.nm.us}. Selected Publications: None. Phone Information: 505-827-4504. Copies of documents on File: Available for $1 per page, minimum $10, plus additional $25 for certified copies. Mailing Labels: No. Magnetic Tape: No. Microfiche: No. New Corporate Listings. Yes. Monthly listings available. Requester must send manila self-addressed envelope, with postage worth $1.70 each, for as many listings as you would like. Online Access: Custom Searches: Yes, call their information line, 505-827-4509. They provide free printouts of certificates of good standing, officers and agent names. Number of Active Corporations on File: Over 100,000.

New York
New York State, Department of State, Division of Corporations, 41 State Street, Albany, NY 12231, 518-474-0050; {http:\\www.dos.state.ny.us\corp\ corpwww.html}. Copies of Documents on File: Available for $5 per document, $10 for certified copies. Call 900-835-2677 to obtain information on a filed corporation or status of a corporation. To receive copies of documents on file, send in a letter of request. Mailing Labels: No. Magnetic Tape: No. Microfiche: No. New Corporate Listing: Report of Corporations is printed daily and mailed out every other day. It is available in the Daily Report through subscription only, for $125 per year, $75 for 6 months or $40 for 3 months. Online Access: Yes. Number of Corporations on File: 1,200,000.

North Carolina
Division of Corporation, Secretary of State, 300 N. Salisbury Street, Raleigh, NC 27603-5909, 919-733-4201, Fax: 919-733-1837; {www.state.nc.us/ secstate}. Selected publications: North Carolina Business Corporation Guidelines, North Carolina's Non-Profit Corporation Handbook. Phone Information 919-733-4201. Copies of Documents on File: available for $1 per page, $5 for certified copies. You can leave a message with your requests by calling 888-246-7630. Mailing Labels: No. Magnetic Tape: Available on cost recovery basis. To make a request write Bonnie Elek. Categories: All active corporations, foreign, domestic, non-profit, and profit. Microfiche: No. New Corporate Listings:

Available for $20 per month and issued in hard copy only. Custom Searches: Yes. Categories: Type of Corporation, Professional Corporations, Insurance Corporations, Banks, and Savings and Loans. Online Access: Available. Number of Active Corporations on File: 400,000.

North Dakota

Corporation Division, Secretary of State, Capitol Building, 600 E. Boulevard Ave., Bismarck, ND 58505, 701-328-2900, Fax: 701-328-2992; {www.state.nd.us/sec}. Selected Publications:. Phone Information: 701-328-2900. Copies of Documents on File: $5, $25 for certified copies, $1 additional for every four pages. Written or phone requests accepted. Fax on demand service will send you the forms you need, 701-328-0120. Mailing Labels: No. Magnetic Tape: No. Microfiche No. New Corporate Listings: Monthly Corporation list costs $35-$37 per month. Custom Searches: No. Online Access: Yes. Number of Active Corporations on File: 22,500.

Ohio

Corporation Division, Secretary of State, 30 East Broad Street, 14th Floor, Columbus, OH 43266-0418, 614-466-4980, Fax: 614-466-3899. Selected Publications: Corporate Checklist. Phone Information: Corporate Status call 614-466-3910; Name Availability call 614-466-0590. Copies of Documents on File: contact 614-466-1776. Available for $1 per page, $5 for certified copies. Mailing Labels: No. Magnetic Tape: available for $125 for 6,250 corporation names, thereafter the cost is 2 cents per corporate name with a maximum of 25,000 names. Microfiche: No. New Corporate Listing: List is updated daily. $48 flat fee, plus 5 cents a page and 3 cents a line. Depends on how recent or old a list you would like. Custom Searches: Yes. Categories: location (county), Foreign, Domestic, Profit, Non-Profit. Online Access: No. Number of Active Corporations on File: 400,000.

Oklahoma

Corporations, Secretary of State, 101 State Capitol Building, Oklahoma City, OK 73105, 405-521-3911, Fax: 405-521-3771; {www.state.ok.us/~sos}. Selected Publications: Forms and Procedures to Incorporate. Phone Information: 900-555-2424 for record search. Charge is $3 per call. Copies of Documents on File: available for $1 per page, $10 for certified copies. Mailing Labels: No Magnetic Tape: $500 per tape. Requester must supply 3490 type cartridges. Contact Vicky Mitchell, 405-521-3257.

Microfiche: No. New Corporate Listings: Hard Copy costs $150 a month, with Amendments it is $250 a month plus postage. Custom Searches: Yes, date of incorporation and registered agent information is provided. Online Access: Yes. Number of Corporations on File: 224,159.

Oregon

Corporation Division, Secretary of State, 255 Capitol St., NE, Suite 151, Salem, OR 97310-1327, 503-986-2200, Fax: 503-986-2346; {www.sos.state.or.us/corporation/corp/hp.html}. Selected Publications: None. Phone Information: 503-986-2200. Copies of Documents on File: Available for $5 for all documents in a corporation's file except annual report. Annual reports are an additional $5. Certification fee is $15. Business Registry on diskette or email is $15 per month or $150 per year. Mailing Labels: No. Magnetic Tape: Complete master file costs $200. Requester must provide tape. Microfiche: No. New Corporate Listings: Statistical Report of New Corporations is available for $15 per monthly issue. $150 per year. Custom Searches: Yes, minimum charge is $50. Online Access: Yes. Mead Data, Information America and Dunn and Bradstreet also have database. Number of Active Corporations on File: 73,000.

Pennsylvania

Corporation Bureau, 308 N. Office Building, Harrisburg, PA 17120, 717-787-1057, Fax: 717-783-2244; {www.dos.state.pa.us/corp.htm}. Selected Publications: Corporate Guide. Phone Information: 717-787-1057. Copies of Documents on File: Available for $2 per page, $12 search fee, $28 for certified copies. Mailing Labels: No. Magnetic Tape: Copy of master file available for $3500 startup fee. Monthly, you will be charged $48.12 for each tape received. This is the only way to receive the master file. It is not currently on disk or CD-Rom. Microfiche: No. New Corporate Listings: County or area listing available for cents per name. Custom Searches: Yes. Categories: Non-Profit, Domestic, Foreign county location, Limited partnerships, Fictitious name, Trademarks, Foreign Non-profits, Cooperatives, Professional Corporations cents per name. Online Access: Online Searches will be available in the future. Available from Information America at 404-892-1800; Prentice-Hall, Legal and Financial Services at 518-458-8111; or Mead Data Central at 513-865-6800. Number of Corporations on File: 616,000.

Rhode Island

Corporations Division, Secretary of State, 100 North Main Street, Providence, RI 02903, 401-222-3040, Fax: 401-222-1309; {www.state.ri.us}. Selected Publications: Instruction sheet, The Rhode Island Law Manual (Free). Phone Information: 401-222-3040. Staff will look up two corporations per call. Copies of Documents on File: Available for 50 cents per page, $5 for certified sheet. Mailing Labels: No. Magnetic Tape: Yes, master file is available. Microfiche: No. New Corporate Listings: Not usually provided. New corporate listings are published weekly in The Providence Journal, Sunday Business Section. Send a letter requesting weekly printouts. Custom Searches: No. Online Access: Yes. Number of Active Corporations on File: 90,000.

South Carolina

Division of Corporation, Secretary of State, PO Box 11350, Columbia, SC 29211, 803-734-2158, Fax: 803-734-2164. Selected Publication: None. Phone Information: 803-734-2158. Copies of Documents on File: available for $1 for first page, 50 cents thereafter. $3 for certified copies. Mailing Labels: No. Magnetic Tape: No. Microfiche: No. New corporate Listing: Yes. Custom Searches: No. Online Access: Yes. Number of Active Corporations on File: 250,000.

South Dakota

Corporate Division, Secretary of State, 500 East Capitol, Pierre, SD 57501, 605-773-4845; Fax: 605-773-4550; {www.state.sd.us/sos/sos.htm}. Selected Publications: None. Phone Information: 605-773-4845. Copies of Documents on File: Available for 50 cents per page plus $5 for certification. Mailing Labels: No. Magnetic Tape: No. Microfiche: No. New Corporate Listings: No. Custom Searches: No. Online Access: No. Number of Active Corporations on File: 30,000.

Tennessee

Office of Secretary of State, Services Division, Suite 1800, James K. Polk Building, Nashville, TN 37243-0306, 615-741-2286, Fax: 615-741-7310; {www.state.tn.us/sos/}. Selected Publications: None. Phone Information: 615-741-2286. Copies of Documents on File: All available information on a corporation is available for $20. Mailing Labels No. Magnetic Tape: Yes. Categories: All Corporations on file, Foreign, Domestic Profit, Non-Profit, Banks, Credit Unions, Cooperative Associations. Charge of an additional $2 for each tape supplied. Cost, done on a cost recovery basis, is determined at time of request. Contact Mr. Thompson at 615-741-0584. Microfiche: No. New Corporate Listings: Monthly New Corporation Listing on a cost recovery basis of 25 cents per page, 8 names per page. Call 615-741-1111. Custom Searches: Yes. Online Access: Yes. Number of Active Corporations on File: 100,000.

Texas

Corporation Section, Statute Filing Division, Secretary of State, PO Box 13697, Austin, TX 78711, 512-463-5586, Fax: 512-463-5709; {www.sos.state.tx.us}. Selected Publications: Filing Guide to Corporations. Phone Information: 512-463-5555. Copies of Documents on File: Available for $35; for names and all filings of corporations. Certification is $10 plus $1 for each additional page. $5 for express services. Business entity information, excluding individual names is $3 per call, 10 cents for each page after 20 pages. Mailing Labels: No. Magnetic Tape: No. Microfiche: Names of officers and directors available. Cost determined at time of request. New Corporate Listings: Weekly Charter Update costs $27.50 per week. Custom Searches: No. Online Access: Available through Information America 404-892-1800. Number of Active Corporations on File: Not Available.

Utah

Corporations and UCC, Division of Business Regulations, P.O. Box 45801, 160 East 300 South Street, Second Floor, Salt Lake City, UT 84145-0801, 801-530-4849, Fax: 801-530-6111 or 801-530-6438; {www.commerce.state.ut.us}. Selected Publications: Doing Business in Utah; A Guide to Business Information (available online). Phone Information: 801-530-4849. Copies of Documents on File: Available for 30 cents a page plus $10 for certified copies. Mailing Labels: No. Magnetic Tape: No. Microfiche: No. New Corporate Listing: Updated every ten days. You can obtain by calling their information line. Custom Searches: Yes. Cost includes printing charge of 30 cents per page. Online Access: Available through Datashare. Call 801-538-3440. It gives you access to their database online. You need to obtain a log in name and password by signing up. Number of Active Corporations on File: 40,000.

Vermont

Corporate Division, Secretary of State, 109 State Street, Montpelier, VT 05609-1104, 802-828-2386, Fax: 802-828-2853; {www.sec.state.vt.us}. Selected

Publications: None. Phone Information: 802-828-2386. Copies of Documents on File: Available for $1 per page, $5 for certified copies. Send the $5 certification fee in advance. They will bill you for the copies. Mailing Labels: No. Magnetic Tape: No. Microfiche: No. Corporate Listings: Yes. Monthly New Corporations an Trade names on diskette cost $6 plus 1 cent per name. Total cost is never more than $15. Out-of-State Corporations, $50 for complete list. Custom Searches: Yes. Categories: Foreign, Domestic, Non-profits, by date of registration. Cost is 1 cent per name plus $6 to run list. Online Access: Yes. Number of Active Corporation on File: 24,000.

Virginia

Clerk of Commission, State Corporation Commission, Secretary of State, 1330 East Main Street 23219, 804-371-9733, Fax: 804-371-9654; {www.state.va.us/scc}. Selected Publications: Business Registration Guide. Phone Information: 804-371-9733. Copies of Documents on File. Available for $1 per page, $3 for certified copies. Mailing Labels: No. Magnetic Tape: Yes. They provide you tapes for $1,000 a month and you do not have to provide blank tapes. Microfiche: No. New Corporate Listings: No. Custom Searches: Yes. Online Access: Available through Direct Access. You will dial into their database for free to obtain the information you need. Call 804-371-9733 to ask for a password. Number of Active Corporations on File: 160,000.

Washington

Corporate Division, Secretary of State, 2nd Floor Republic Bldg., 505 Union Ave. Mail Stop PM-21, Olympia, WA 98504, 360-753-7115, Fax: 360-586-5629; {www.secstate.wa.gov}. Selected Publications: None. Phone Information: 360-753-7115. Copies of Documents on File: Fees are $1 for the first page and 20 cents thereafter. Certification is $10. Mailing Labels: No Magnetic Tape: No. Microfiche: Cost is $10 a month. New Corporate Listings: No. Custom Searches: No. Online Access: Yes. Number of Active Corporations on File: 145,000.

West Virginia

Corporate Division, Secretary of State, Room 139 West, State Capitol, Charleston, WV 25305, 304-

558-8000, Fax: 304-558-9000. Selected Publications: None. Phone Information: 304-558-8000. Copies of Documents on File: Available for 50 cents per page, $10 for certified copies. Mailing Labels: No. Magnetic Tape: No. Microfiche: No. New Corporate Listing: Monthly Report costs $5 a month or $50 per year. Custom Searches: yes. Cost is $1 for first hour and $5 for every hour thereafter, prorated. Online Access: No. Number of Active Corporations on File: 39,000.

Wisconsin

Corporate Division, Secretary of State, PO Box 7846, Madison, WI 53707; Street address: 345 West Washington Avenue, 3rd Floor, Madison, WI 53703, 608-266-3590, Fax: 608-267-6813; {www.wdfi.org}. Selected Publications: Chapter 180 Statutes Book ($4). Phone Information: 608-266-3590. Copies of Documents on File: For simple copy request must be in writing. Fee is $2. Requests for certified copies may be phoned in. Fee is $5. Mailing Labels: No. Magnetic Tape: No. Microfiche: Yes. Monthly new Corporations costs $12 per month. New Corporate Listing: Yes (see Microfiche entry). Minimum cost is $10 per week. Custom Searches: Yes. Online Access: yes. Number of Active Corporations on File: 130,708.

Wyoming

Corporate Division, Secretary of State, State of Wyoming, Capitol Building, Cheyenne, WY 82002, 307-777-7311; Fax: 307-777-5339; {http:\\soswy.state.wy.us}. Selected Publications: Wyoming Business Corporation Act (available free on website). Phone Information: 307-777-7311. Copies of Documents on File: available for 50 cents for first 10 pages then 15 cents per page, $3 for certified copies. Mailing Labels: No. Magnetic Tape: No. Microfiche: No. New corporate Listings: yes: $300/yr for monthly listing of both foreign and domestic corporations, or $150 each. Custom Searches: Yes: Categories: Foreign, Domestic, Statutory trust, Non-profit and Profit, Limited Partnership, Limited Liability, Trade names and Trademarks. Listing of all active profit corporations can be purchased for $25 on diskette. They can email it to you at no cost. Contact Jeanie Sawyer, 307-777-5334. Online Access: Yes. Number of Active Corporations on File: 33,000.

MORE HELP IN FINDING A GRANT

No one source can be a complete guide to finding a grant, including ours, so we wanted to include other resources you can use in your search. There are publications, experts, and even classes you can take to assist you in making your dreams come true.

As we stated earlier, The Foundation Center is a nonprofit organization which gathers and disseminates factual information on foundations. The Center's libraries in New York City, Atlanta, San Francisco, Cleveland, and Washington, DC, contain copies of foundations' tax returns, extensive collections of books, documents, and reports about the foundation field, and current files on the activities and programs of about 50,000 U.S. foundations, plus knowledgeable staff to assist users in locating appropriate information.

The Foundation Center also publishes funding directories specific to certain fields, such as: aging; arts and culture; children, youth, and families; health; higher education; international programs; libraries and information services; religion; women and girls; and elementary and secondary education.

In addition, the Center has established cooperating reference collections in each state, where Center publications and information on foundations in the immediate state or region can be consulted. A list of cooperating libraries housing these regional collections appears below. The Center also offers classes and seminars on a variety of topics, including proposal writing, basics of seeking a grant, and "how to" classes on the use of the resources and website. For further information, contact the Foundation Center, 79 Fifth Avenue, New York, NY 10003; 800-424-9836; 212-620-4230; {http://fdncenter.org}.

Foundation Center Reference Collections

The Foundation Center
2nd Floor, 79 Fifth Ave.
New York, NY 10003
212-620-4230

The Foundation Center
312 Sutter St., Room 312
San Francisco, CA 94108
415-397-0902

The Foundation Center
1001 Connecticut Ave., NW
Washington, DC 20036
202-331-1400

The Foundation Center
Kent H. Smith Library
1422 Euclid, Suite 1356
Cleveland, OH 44115
216-861-1933

The Foundation Center
Suite 150
Grand Lobby
Hurt Building
50 Hurt Plaza
Atlanta, GA 30303
404-880-0094

Cooperating Collections

Alabama
Birmingham Public Library
Government Documents
2100 Park Place
Birmingham, AL 35203
205-226-3620

Huntsville Public Library
915 Monroe St.
Huntsville, AL 35801
256-532-5940

University of South Alabama
Library Building
Mobile, AL 36688
334-460-7025

Auburn University at Montgomery Library
7300 University Dr.
Montgomery, AL 36124
334-244-3200

Alaska
University of Alaska at Anchorage
Library
3211 Providence Dr.
Anchorage, AK 99508
907-786-1847

Juneau Public Library
Reference
2929 Marine Way
Juneau, AK 99801
907-586-5267

Arizona
Phoenix Public Library
Information Services Department
1221 N. Central
Phoenix, AZ 85004
602-262-4636

Tucson Pima Library
101 N. Stone Ave.
Tucson, AZ 87501
520-791-4010

Arkansas
Western Community College
Borham Library
5210 Grand Ave.

Ft. Smith, AR 72913
501-788-7200

Central Arkansas Library System
100 Rock St.
Little Rock, AR 72201
501-918-3000

Pine Bluff-Jefferson County Library System
200 E. Eighth
Pine Bluff, AR 71601
870-534-2159

California
Humboldt Area Foundation
P.O. Box 99
Bayside, CA 95524
707-442-2993

Ventura County Community Foundation
Resource Center for Nonprofit Organizations
1317 Del Norte Rd., Suite 150
Camarillo, CA 93010
805-988-0196

Fresno Regional Foundation
Nonprofit Advancement Center
1999 Tuolumne St., Suite 650
Fresno, CA 93720
559-498-3929

Center for Nonprofit Management in Southern
California
Nonprofit Resource Library
315 West 9th St., Suite 1100
Los Angeles, CA 90015
213-623-7080

Flintridge Foundation
Philanthropy Resource Library
1040 Lincoln Ave., Suite 100
Pasadena, CA 91103
626-449-0839

Grant and Resource Center of Northern
California
Building C, Suite A
2280 Benton Dr.
Redding, CA 96003
530-244-1219

Los Angeles Public Library
West Valley Regional Branch Library
19036 Van Owen St.
Reseda, CA 91335
818-345-4393

Riverside Public Library
3581 Mission Inn Ave.
Riverside, CA 92501
909-782-5202

Nonprofit Resource Center
Sacramento Public Library
828 I St., 2nd Floor
Sacramento, CA 95814
916-264-2772

San Diego Foundation
Funding Information Center
1420 Kettner Blvd.
Suite 500
San Diego, CA 92101
619-239-8815

Nonprofit Development Center
Library
1922 The Alameda
Suite 212
San Jose, CA 95126
408-248-9505

Peninsula Community Foundation
Peninsula Nonprofit Center
1700 S. El Camino Real, R201
San Mateo, CA 94402
650-358-9392

Los Angeles Public Library
San Pedro Regional Branch
9131 S. Gaffey St.
San Pedro, CA 90731
310-548-7779

Volunteer Center of Greater Orange County
Nonprofit Management Assistance Center
1901 E. 4th St., Suite 100
Santa Ana, CA 92705
714-953-5757

Santa Barbara Public Library
40 E. Anapamu St.
Santa Barbara, CA 93101
805-564-5633

Santa Monica Public Library
1343 Sixth St.
Santa Monica, CA 90401
31-545-0831

Seaside Branch Library
550 Harcourt St.
Seaside, CA 93955
408-899-8131

Sonora Area Foundation
20100 Cedar Rd., N
Sonora, CA 95370
209-533-2596

Colorado
El Pomar Nonprofit Resource Library
1661 Mesa Ave.
Colorado Springs, CO 80906
719-577-7000

Denver Public Library
General Reference
10 West 14th Parkway
Denver, CO 80204
303-640-6200

Connecticut
Danbury Public Library
170 Main St.
Danbury, CT 06810
203-797-4527

Greenwich Library
101 West Putnam Ave.
Greenwich, CT 06830
203-622-7900

Hartford Public Library
500 Main St.
Hartford, CT 06103
80-543-8656

New Haven Free Public Library
Reference Department
133 Elm St.
New Haven, CT 06510
203-946-8130

Delaware
University of Delaware
Hugh Morris Library
Newark, DE 19717
302-831-2432

Florida
Volusia County Library
City Island
105 E. Magnolia Ave.
Daytona Beach, FL 32114
904-257-6036

Nova Southeastern University
Einstein Library
3301 College Ave.
Fort Lauderdale, FL 33314
954-262-4601

Indian River Community College
Learning Resources Center
3209 Virginia Ave.
Fort Pierce, FL 34981
561-462-4757

Jacksonville Public Libraries
Grants Resource Center
122 N. Ocean St.
Jacksonville, FL 32202
904-630-2665

Miami-Dade Public Library
Humanities/Social Science
101 W. Flagler St.
Miami, FL 33130
305-375-5575

Orange County Library System
Social Sciences Department
101 E. Central Blvd.
Orlando, FL 32801
407-425-4694

Selby Public Library
Reference
1331 First St.
Sarasota, FL 34236
941-316-1181

Tampa-Hillsborough County Public Library
900 N. Ashley Dr.
Tampa, FL 33602
813-273-3652

Community Foundation of Palm Beach and Martin
Counties
324 Datura St., Suite 340
West Palm Beach, FL 33401
561-659-6800

Georgia
Atlanta-Fulton Public Library
Foundation Collection- Ivan Allen Department
1 Margaret Mitchell Square
Atlanta, GA 30303
404-730-1900

United Way of Georgia
Community Resource Center
277 Martin Luther King Jr. Blvd., Suite 301
Macon, GA 31201
912-745-4732

Savannah State University
Asa Gordon Library
P.O. Box 20394
Savannah, GA 31404
912-356-2185

Thomas County Public Library
201 N. Madison St.
Thomasville, GA 31792
912-225-5252

Hawaii
University of Hawaii
Hamilton Library
2550 The Mall
Honolulu, HI 96822
808-956-7214

Hawaii Community Foundation Funding Resource
Library
900 Fort St., Suite 1300
Honolulu, HI 96813
808-537-6333

Idaho
Boise Public Library
715 S. Capitol Blvd.
Boise, ID 83702
208-384-4024

Caldwell Public Library
1010 Dearborn St.
Caldwell, ID 83605
208-459-3242

Illinois
Donors Forum of Chicago
208 South LaSalle, Suite 735
Chicago, IL 60604
312-578-0175

Evanston Public Library
1703 Orrington Ave.
Evanston, IL 60201
847-866-0305

Rock Island Public Library
401 19th St.
Rock Island, IL 61201
309-788-7627

University of Illinois at Springfield
Brookens Library
Shepherd Rd.
Springfield, IL 62794
217-206-6633

Indiana
Evansville-Vanderburgh County Public Library
22 Southeast Fifth St.
Evansville, IN 47708
812-428-8200

Allen County Public Library
900 Webster St.
Ft. Wayne, IN 46802
219-421-1200

Indianapolis-Marion County Public Library
Social Sciences
40 E. St. Clair
Indianapolis, IN 46206
317-269-1733

Vigo County Public Library
1 Library Square
Terre Haute, IN 47807
812-232-1113

Iowa
Cedar Rapids Public Library
Foundation Center Collection
500 First St., SE
Cedar Rapids, IA 52401
319-398-5123

Southwestern Community College
Learning Resource Center
1501 W. Townline Rd.
Creston, IA 50801
515-782-7081

Public Library of Des Moines
100 Locust

Des Moines, IA 50309
515-283-4152

Sioux City Public Library
529 Pierce St.
Sioux City, IA 51101
712-252-5669

Kansas
Dodge City Public Library
1001 2nd Ave.
Dodge City, KS 67801
316-225-0248

Topeka and Shawnee County Public Library
1515 SW 10th Ave.
Topeka, KS 66604
785-233-2040

Wichita Public Library
223 S. Main St.
Wichita, KS 67202
316-261-8500

Kentucky
Western Kentucky University
Helm-Cravens Library
Bowling Green, KY 42101
502-745-6125

Lexington Public Library
140 E. Main St.
Lexington, KY 40507
606-574-1611

Louisiana
East Baton Rouge Parish Library
Centroplex Branch Grants Collection
120 St. Louis
Baton Rouge, LA 70802
225-389-4967

Beauregard Parish Library
205 S. Washington Ave.
De Ridder, LA 70634
318-463-6217

Ouachita Parish Public Library
1800 Stubbs Ave.
Monroe, LA 71201
318-327-1490

New Orleans Public Library
Business and Sciences Division

219 Loyola Ave.
New Orleans, LA 70140
504-596-2580

Shreve Memorial Library
424 Texas St.
Shreveport, LA 71120
318-226-5894

Maine
Maine Grants Information Center
University of Southern Maine Library
314 Forrest Ave.
Portland, ME 04104
207-780-5029

Maryland
Enoch Pratt Free Library
Social Science and History
400 Cathedral St.
Baltimore, MD 21201
410-396-5430

Massachusetts
Associated Grantmakers of Massachusetts
294 Washington St., Suite 840
Boston, MA 02108
617-426-2606

Boston Public Library
Social Science Reference
700 Boylston St.
Boston, MA 02117
617-536-5400

Western Massachusetts Funding Resource Center
65 Elliot St.
Springfield, MA 01101
413-732-3175

Worcester Public Library
Grants Resource Center
Salem Square
Worcester, MA 01608
508-799-1655

Michigan
Alpena County Library
211 N. First St.
Alpena, MI 49707
517-356-6188

University of Michigan- Ann Arbor
Graduate Library

Reference and Research Services Department
Ann Arbor, MI 48109
313-764-9373

Willard Public Library
Nonprofit and Funding Resource Collections
7 W. Van Buren St.
Battle Creek, MI 49017
616-968-8166

Henry Ford Centennial Library
Adult Services
16301 Michigan Ave.
Dearborn, MI 48124
313-943-2330

Wayne State University
Purdy/Kresge Library
5265 Cass Ave.
Detroit, MI 48202
313-577-6424

Michigan State University Libraries
Social Sciences/ Humanities
Main Library
East Lansing, MI 48824
517-353-8818

Farmington Community Library
32737 West 12 Mile Rd.
Farmington Hills, MI 48334
248-553-0300

University of Michigan- Flint
Library
Flint, MI 48502
810-762-3408

Grand Rapids Public Library
Business Department- 3rd Floor
60 Library Plaza NE
Grand Rapids, MI 49503
616-456-3600

Michigan Technological University
Van Pelt Library
1400 Townsend Dr.
Houghton, MI 49931
906-487-2507

Maud Preston Palenske Memorial Library
500 Market St.
Saint Joseph, MI 49085
616-983-7167

Northwestern Michigan College
Mark and Helen Osterin Library
1701 E. Front St.
Traverse City, MI 49684
616-922-1060

Minnesota
Duluth Public Library
520 W. Superior St.
Duluth, MN 55802
218-732-3802

Southwest State University
University Library
North Highway 23
Marshall, MN 56253
507-537-6176

Minneapolis Public Library
Sociology Department
300 Nicolleg Mall
Minneapolis, MN 55401
612-630-6300

Rochester Public Library
101 2nd St., SE
Rochester, MN 55904
507-285-8002

St. Paul Public Library
90 W. Fourth St.
St. Paul, MN 55102
651-266-7000

Mississippi
Jackson/Hinds Library System
300 N. State St.
Jackson, MS 39201
601-968-5803

Missouri
Clearinghouse for Midcontinent Foundations
University of Missouri
5110 Cherry, Suite 310
Kansas City, MO 64110
816-235-1176

Kansas City Public Library
311 E. 12th St.
Kansas City, MO 64106
816-01-3541

Metropolitan Association for Philanthropy, Inc.
211 North Broadway, Suite 1200

St. Louis, MO 63102
314-621-6220

Springfield-Greene County Library
397 E. Central
Springfield, MO 65802
417-837-5000

Montana
Montana State University- Billings
Library- Special Collections
1500 North 30th St.
Billings, MT 59101
406-657-1662

Bozeman Public Library
220 E. Lamme
Bozeman, MT 59715
406-582-2402

Montana State Library
Library Services
1515 E. 6th Ave.
Helena, MT 59620
406-444-3004

University of Montana
Maureen and Mike Mansfield Library
Missoula, MT 59812
406-243-6800

Nebraska
University of Nebraska- Lincoln
Love Library
14th and R Sts.
Lincoln, NE 68588
402-472-2848

W. Dale Clark Library
Social Sciences Department
215 S. 15th St.
Omaha, NE 68102
402-444-4826

Nevada
Clark County Library
1401 E. Flamingo
Las Vegas, NV 89119
702-733-3642

Washoe County Library
301 S. Center St.
Reno, NV 89505
775-785-4190

New Hampshire
Concord Public Library
45 Green St.
Concord, NH 03301
603-225-8670

Plymouth State College
Herbert H. Lamson Library
Plymouth, NY 03264
603-535-2258

New Jersey
Cumberland County Library
800 E. Commerce St.
Bridgeton, NJ 08302
609-453-2210

Free Public Library of Elizabeth
11 S. Broad St.
Elizabeth, NJ 07202
908-354-6060

County College of Morris
Learning Resource Center
214 Center Grove Rd.
Randolph, NJ 07869
973-328-5296

New Jersey State Library
Governmental Reference Services
185 W. State St.
Trenton, NJ 08625
609-292-6220

New Mexico
Albuquerque Community Foundation
3301 Menaul NE, Suite 30
Albuquerque, NM 87176
505-883-6240

New Mexico State Library
Information Services
1209 Camino Carlos Rey
Santa Fe, NM 87505
505-476-9714

New York
New York State Library
Humanities Reference
Cultural Education Center, 6th Floor
Empire State Plaza
Albany, NY 12230
518-474-5355

Suffolk Cooperative Library System
627 N. Sunrise Service Rd.
Bellport, NY 11713
516-286-1600

New York Public Library
Bronx Reference Center
2556 Bainbridge Ave.
Bronx, NY 10458
718-579-4257

The Nonprofit Connection, Inc.
One Hanson Place- Room 2504
Brooklyn, NY 12243
718-230-3200

Brooklyn Public Library
Social Sciences/Philosophy Division
Grand Army Plaza
Brooklyn, NY 11238
718-230-2122

Buffalo and Erie County Public Library
Business, Science and Technology Department
1 Lafayette Square
Buffalo, NY 14203
716-858-7097

Huntington Public Library
338 Main St.
Huntington, NY 11743
516-427-5165

Queens Borough Public Library
Social Sciences Division
89-11 Merrick Blvd.
Jamaica, NY 11432
718-990-0700

Levittown Public Library
1 Bluegrass Lane
Levittown, NY 11756
516-731-5728

New York Public Library
Countee Cullen Branch Library
104 W. 136th St.
New York, NY 10030
212-491-2070

Adriance Memorial Library
Special Services Department
93 Market St.

Poughkeepsie, NY 12601
914-485-3445

Rochester Public Library
Social Sciences
115 South Ave.
Rochester, NY 14604
716-428-8128

Onondago County Public Library
447 S. Salina St.
Syracuse, NY 13202
315-435-1900

Utica Public Library
303 Genessee St.
Utica, NY 13501
315-735-2279

White Plains Public Library
100 Martine Ave.
White Plains, NY 10601
914-422-1480

North Carolina
Community Foundation of Western
  North Carolina
Learning Resources Center
16 Biltmore Ave., Suite 201
P.O. Box 1888
Asheville, NC 28802
704-254-4960

The Duke Endowment
100 N. Tryon St., Suite 3500
Charlotte, NC 28202
704-376-0291

Durham County Public Library
301 North Roxboro
Durham, NC 27702
919-560-0110

State Library of North Carolina
Government and Business Services
Archives Bldg.
109 E. Jones St.
Raleigh, NC 27601
919-733-4488

Forsyth County Public Library
660 W. 5th St.
Winston Salem, NC 27101
336-727-2680

North Dakota
Bismarck Public Library
515 N. Fifth St.
Bismarck, ND 58501
701-222-6410

Fargo Public Library
102 N. 3rd St.
Fargo, ND 58102
701-241-1491

Ohio
Stark County District Library
Humanities
715 Market Ave. N
Canton, OH 44702
330-452-0665

Public Library of Cincinnati and
Hamilton County
Grants Resource Center
800 Vine St.
Library Square
Cincinnati, OH 45202
513-369-6000

Columbus Metropolitan Library
Business and Technology
96 S. Grant Ave.
Columbus, OH 43215
614-645-2590

Dayton and Montgomery County Public Library
Grants Resource Center
215 E. Third St.
Dayton, OH 45402
937-227-9500 ext. 211

Mansfield/Richland County Public Library
42 W. 3rd St.
Mansfield, OH 44902
419-521-3110

Toledo-Lucas County Public Library
Social Sciences Department
325 Michigan St.
Toledo, OH 43624
419-259-5245

Public Library of Youngstown and
Mahoning County
305 Wick Ave.
Youngstown, OH 44503
330-744-8636

Muskingum County Library
220 N. 5th St.
Zanesville, OH 43701
614-453-0391

Oklahoma
Oklahoma City University
Dulaney Browne Library
2501 N. Blackwelder
Oklahoma City, OK 73106
405-521-5822

Tulsa City- County Library
400 Civic Center
Tulsa, OK 74103
918-596-7940

Oregon
Oregon Institute of Technology
Library
3201 Campus Dr.
Klamath Falls, OR 97601
541-885-1780

Pacific Non-Profit Network
Grantsmanship Resource Library
33 N. Central, Suite 211
Medford, OR 97501
503-779-6044

Multnomah County Library
Government Documents
801 SW Tenth Ave.
Portland, OR 97205
503-248-5123

Oregon State Library
State Library Building
Salem, OR 97310
503-378-4277

Pennsylvania
Northampton Community College
Learning Resources Center
3835 Green Pond Rd.
Bethlehem, PA 18017
610-861-5360

Erie County Library System
160 East Front St.
Erie, PA 16507
814-451-6927

Dauphin County Library System
Central Library

101 Walnut St.
Harrisburg, PA 17101
717-234-4976

Lancaster County Public Library
125 N. Duke St.
Lancaster, PA 17602
717-394-2651

Free Library of Philadelphia
Regional Foundation Center
Logan Square
Philadelphia, PA 19103
215-686-5423

Carnegie Library of Pittsburgh
Foundation Collection
4400 Forbes Ave.
Pittsburgh, PA 15213
412-622-1917

Pocono Northeast Development Fund
James Pettinger Memorial Library
1151 Oak St.
Pittston, PA 18640
570-655-5581

Reading Public Library
100 South Fifth St.
Reading, PA 19475
610-655-6355

Martin Library
159 Market St.
York, PA 17401
717-846-5300

Rhode Island
Providence Public Library
225 Washington St.
Providence, RI 02906
401-455-8088

South Carolina
Anderson County Library
202 East Greenville St.
Anderson, SC 29621
864-260-4500

Charleston County Library
68 Calhoun St.
Charleston, SC 29401
843-805-6950

South Carolina State Library
1500 Senate St.
Columbia, SC 29211
803-734-8666

Community Foundation of Greater Greenville
27 Cleveland St., Suite 101
P.O. Box 6909
Greenville, SC 29606
864-233-5925

South Dakota
South Dakota State Library
800 Governors Dr.
Pierre, SD 57501
605-773-5070
800-592-1841 (SD only)

Dakota State University
Nonprofit Grants Assistance
132 S. Dakota Ave.
Sioux Falls, SD 57103
605-367-5380

Siouxland Libraries
201 N. Main Ave.
Sioux Falls, SD 57104
605-367-7081

Tennessee
Knox County Public Library
500 W. Church Ave.
Knoxville, TN 37902
423-544-5750

Memphis and Shelby County Public Library
1850 Peabody Ave.
Memphis, TN 38104
901-725-8877

Nashville Public Library
Business Information Division
225 Polk Ave.
Nashville, TN 37203
615-862-5842

Texas
Nonprofit Resource Center
Funding Information Library
500 N. Chestnut, Suite 1511
P.O. Box 3322
Abilene, TX 79604
915-677-8166

Amarillo Area Foundation
700 First National Place
801 S. Fillmore
Amarillo, TX 79101
806-376-4521

Hogg Foundation for Mental Health
3001 Lake Austin Blvd.
Austin, TX 78703
512-471-5041

Beaumont Public Library
801 Pearl St.
Beaumont, TX 77704
409-838-6606

Corpus Christi Public Library
Funding Information Center
805 Comanche St.
Reference Department
Corpus Christi, TX 78501
361-880-7000

Dallas Public Library
Urban Information
1515 Young St.
Dallas, TX 75201
213-670-1487

Center for Volunteerism and Nonprofit Management
1918 Texas Ave.
El Paso, TX 79901
915-532-5377

Southwest Border Nonprofit Resource Center
Nonprofit Resource Center
1201 W. University Dr.
Edinburgh, TX 78539
956-316-2610

Funding Information Center of Fort Worth
329 S. Henderson
Ft. Worth, TX 76104
817-334-0228

Houston Public Library
Bibliographic Information Center
500 McKinney
Houston, TX 77002
713-236-1313

Nonprofit Management and Volunteer Center
Laredo Public Library

1120 East Carlton Rd.
Laredo, TX 78041
956-795-2400

Longview Public Library
222 W. Cotton St.
Longview, TX 75601
903-237-1352

Lubbock Area Foundation, Inc.
1655 Main St., Suite 209
Lubbock, TX 79401
806-762-8061

Nonprofit Resource Center of Texas
111 Soledad, Suite 200
San Antonio, TX 78205
210-2274333

Waco-Mclennan County Library
1717 Austin Ave.
Waco, TX 76701
254-750-5975

North Texas Center for Nonprofit Management
624 Indiana, Suite 307
Wichita Falls, TX 76301
940-322-4961

Utah
Salt Lake City Public Library
209 East 500 South
Salt Lake City, UT 84111
801-524-8200

Vermont
Vermont Department of Libraries
Reference and Law Information Services
109 State St.
Montpelier, VT 05609
802-828-3261

Virginia
Hampton Public Library
4207 Victoria Blvd.
Hampton, VA 23669
757-727-1312

Richmond Public Library
Business, Science and Technology
101 East Franklin St.
Richmond, VA 23219
804-780-8223

Roanoke City Public Library System
706 S. Jefferson
Roanoke, VA 24016
540-853-2477

Washington
Mid-Columbia Library
405 South Dayton
Kennewick, WA 99336
509-586-3156

Seattle Public Library
Fundraising Resource Center
100 Fourth Ave.
Seattle, WA 98104
206-386-4620

Spokane Public Library
Funding Information Center
West 811 Main Ave.
Spokane, WA 99201
509-626-5347

United Way of Pierce County
Center for Nonprofit Development
1501 Pacific Ave., Suite 400
P.O. Box 2215
Tacoma, WA 98401
206-272-4263

Greater Wenatchee Community Foundation at the
Wenatchee Public Library
310 Douglas St.
Wenatchee, WA 98807
509-662-5021

West Virginia
Kanawha County Public Library
123 Capitol St.
Charleston, WV 25301
304-343-4646

Wisconsin
University of Wisconsin- Madison
Memorial Library
Grants Information Center
728 State St.
Madison, WI 53706
608-262-3242

Marquette University Memorial Library
Funding Information Center
1415 W. Wisconsin Ave.

Milwaukee, WI 53201
414-288-1515

University of Wisconsin- Stevens Point
Library- Foundation Collection
900 Reserve St.
Stevens Point, WI 54481
715-346-4204

Wyoming
Natrona County Public Library
307 E. 2nd St.
Casper, WY 82601
307-237-4935

Laramie County Community College
Instructional Resource Center
1400 E. College Dr.

Cheyenne, WY 82007
307-778-1206

Campbell County Public Library
2101 4-J Rd.
Gillette, WY 82718
307-687-0115

Teton County Library
125 Virginia Lane
Jackson, WY 83001
307-733-2164

Rock Springs Library
400 C St.
Rock Springs, WY 82901
307-352-6667

(Library list courtesy of The Foundation Center)

Foundation Center Publications

(Remember that many of these publications are located in your library or in the state foundation libraries listed above. For further information, contact the Foundation Center, 79 Fifth Avenue, New York, NY 10003; 800-424-9836; 212-620-4230; {http://fdncenter.org}.)

✱ *Foundation Directory* ($215): Provides a description of over 10,000 large American foundations having at least $3 million in assets or $200,000 in annual giving. Each entry includes factual and financial data, statement of purpose and activities, and grant application procedures; indexed by fields of interest, names of donors, trustees, and administrators, and by state and city.

✱ *The Foundation Directory, Part 2* ($185): provides information on 8,700 private and community foundations making grants of $50,000-$200,000 annually and holding assets of less than $3,000,000. This is a guide to smaller but significant grantmakers whose giving often supports local organizations. Over 83% of the entries include geographic limitation statements showing preferences for giving within specific cities or states. The directory provides lists of sample grants whenever available, to provide concrete indications of the foundation's fields of interest, geographic preferences, and range of giving.

✱ *Foundation Grants Index* ($165): Describes over 97,000 grants awarded by approximately 1,000 foundations within the previous year or two. This is a selective listing, useful for identifying potential funding sources based on previously awarded foundation grants. The main listing of grants is arranged by major subject fields with the grants listed alphabetically by state. A typical grant record includes the name and location of the recipient, the amount awarded, the date authorized and a description of the grant. Grant descriptions are succinct but descriptive, for example: "To promote community involvement in ground water protection in Ohio." Includes a detailed subject index.

✱ *Foundation Grants to Individuals* ($65): While the majority of foundations in the United States limit their grants to nonprofit organizations, this publication gives information on funds available to individuals from approximately 3,800 foundations. Emphasis is placed on educational and scholarship awards. Six indexes help users target prospective grants by subject area, types of support, geographic area, sponsoring company (for employee restricted awards), educational institutions, and foundation name. Bibliography included.

✱ *Guide to U.S. Foundations, Their Trustees, Officers, and Donors* ($215): Lists over 50,000 private, corporate, operating, and community foundations, including thousands of smaller ones not described in other sources. These smaller foundations are especially important as local sources of funding. Overall arrangement is by state, with foundations listed from largest to smallest in terms of grants awarded. For each foundation, the Guide gives the foundation's address, telephone number (when available), financial summary, list of officers, trustees and donors, geographic limitation, and (when available) contact person.

✱ *The Foundation 1000* ($295): Provides data on the 1,000 largest U.S. foundations, including names of officers and staff to contact, current program interests, and names of nonprofit organizations which have already received grants for similar projects. Indexed by subject field, foundation name, type of support, and geographic location.

✱ *Corporate Foundation Profiles* ($155): Detailed profiles of over 207 of the largest corporate foundations, those that give at least $1.2 million annually. Includes address, contact person, purpose, and statement on limitations in giving, application guidelines, key officials, and sponsoring company profile. Subject, type of support, and geographic area indexes are included.

✱ *National Directory of Corporate Giving* ($195): Comprehensive descriptions of over 1,900 corporate foundations plus 1,000 direct giving programs. Alphabetically arranged by company name with a general description of the company and its activities and a description of the company's direct giving program and/or foundation for each entry. Indexed by corporation, officers, donors, trustees, geographic areas, types of support, subject, and types of business.

Other Interesting Publications:

National Directory Of Corporate Public Affairs. New York, Columbia Books, 2000. 1277 p. ($109): This directory identifies the key people in the corporate public affairs profession. The first section is arranged by companies, an alphabetical list of almost 2,000 companies of varied sizes with public affairs programs. It includes corporate headquarters, and (where they exist) Washington, DC, area offices; political action committees; foundation or corporate giving programs; and corporate publications. Key facts and figures on corporate philanthropic activity and political action committee involvement are also summarized. Also included is a list of each company's public affairs personnel, and the office in which they are located. The second section of the book is an alphabetical list of approximately 16,000 individuals in the public affairs field.

Annual Register of Grant Support 2001: A Directory of Funding Sources. New Providence, NJ, R. R. Bowker. Annual. ($210): Descriptions of over 3,000 government and private programs, arranged by broad fields of interest, which give purpose, types of awards, eligibility requirements, financial data, application, and deadline information. Access is provided by subject, organization, geographic, and personnel indexes.

Directory of Research Grants 2000. Phoenix, Oryx Press. Annual. ($159.50): Concise descriptions of nearly 6,000 research programs that offer nonrepayable funding for projects in medicine, the physical and social sciences, education, the arts, and humanities. Grant programs are listed in alphabetical order, followed by three indexes: subject, sponsoring organization, and program type.

Internet Resources

The dynamic nature of the Internet means that information resources appear and disappear without warning. The sources listed below were chosen because the organizations which provide the home pages are stable, committed to the sharing of grant information on the Internet.

It is possible to find additional Internet resources by using different World Wide Web search engines, such as AltaVista (www.altavista.com), InfoSeek (www.infoseek.com), Yahoo (www.yahoo.com), Lycos (www.lycos.com), Hotbot (www.hotbot.com), Excite (www.excite.com), Metacrawler (www.metacrawler.com), and others. When searching for grants or funding resources, combine a subject of interest (e.g., education or small business) with terms such as:

- grants
- financial aid or financial assistance
- charities or charity
- foundations
- fund raising or fundraising

Current and updated information on Internet grants sources can also be found in newspapers and such periodicals as Internet World, Internet User, Yahoo Internet Life, and The Net, which may be available at a local public, university, or research library.

National Technical Information Service (NTIS) {www.ntis.gov}: An official resource for U.S. scientific, technical, engineering, and business-related information. Whether you are a research scientist, corporate librarian, or government engineer, NTIS can help you through its mission as the central source for U.S. government scientific, technical, and business information. You can conduct detailed subject searches through the NTIS Government Research Center's online databases or lookup any of the 400,000 documents in their collection.

GRANTSNet: {www.os.dhhs.gov/progorg/grantsnet/}: GrantsNet is a tool for finding and exchanging information about the U.S. Department of Health and Human Services (HHS) and selected other Federal grant programs. It is part of the much-publicized national movement toward providing government resources to the general public in a more accessible and meaningful manner. HHS has approximately 300 grant programs, most of which are administered in a decentralized manner by several agencies, and they do not have a single publication that describes all the grant programs. This site provides links to grant resources and other assistance for grantseekers.

FEDIX (Federal Information Exchange): {www.sciencewise.com/fedix/}: FEDIX is a free outreach tool that provides grant information to educational and research organizations, as well as others, from participating federal agencies. You can select one of the agencies and search for funding opportunities. You can also search for foundation and corporate grants from this site.

Council on Foundations: {www.cof.org}: The Council on Foundations is a nonprofit association of grantmaking foundations and corporations. For those interested in starting a foundation, the COF is a great resource. It explains what a foundation is, the different types of foundations, as well as the steps you need to take in establishing one. There are also helpful links, resources, workshops, and conferences.

The Internet Nonprofit Center: {www.nonprofits.org}: The Internet Nonprofit Center provides a wealth of information about nonprofits. An extensive topic list is posted in their Library section, and they have links and other resources as well.

NonProfit Gateway: {www.nonprofit.gov}: This incredible website is the federal government's attempt to help nonprofits access programs. There are links to departments and agencies that have programs of interest to nonprofits. You can learn about services and resources for nonprofits, general governmental information, and much more. Past grant recipients are often listed in the links. You can search the *Catalog of Federal Domestic Assistance,* and learn more about the various rules and regulations.

OVER 150 GOVERNMENT GRANTS FOR YOUR BUSINESS

One of the biggest frustrations we hear is from people looking for FREE MONEY from the government for their business. By free money, they usually mean grants or other programs where they don't have to pay back the money they receive. Many people will contact the Small Business Administration asking about free money programs and will be told that there is no such thing. Well, they are right and wrong. They are right, because the Small Business Administration does not offer grants. They specialize in loans and loan guarantees. But, they are wrong because there are dozens of other government organizations that do offer grants to businesses.

The real good stuff in life is never the most plentiful and always takes extra effort and sometimes ingenuity to uncover it.

A recent survey showed that approximately 33% of the top 500 fastest growing small businesses in the U.S. started with less than $10,000. It doesn't take much money to start a business in today's information age and service economy. We're no longer in the manufacturing age, when you needed a lot of money to start a business because you needed to buy an expensive plant and costly equipment. Today, many businesses are started with nothing more than a phone, a desk and business cards.

When people are looking for money to start a business, the first place that comes to mind is the Small Business Administration (SBA). Although they do not give out grants, they do offer a wide array of low-interest loans and loan guarantees. The SBA also has a variety of programs to provide technical assistance to entrepreneurs starting or expanding their businesses.

Just because the SBA does not give out grants, doesn't mean that grants do not exist. The Federal and state governments give out thousands of grants each year, but you have to do a little digging to uncover them. Here are some starting places to help you on your search.

As described earlier (see Government Grants), the Catalog of Federal Domestic Assistance is the best single resource for leads on federal funding programs. This manual of more than 1,000 pages provides the most comprehensive information on federal funds, cross-indexed by agency, program type, applicant eligibility, and subject. The Catalog is available in many libraries or online at {www.cfda.gov}, and describes federal government programs that provide funds or non-financial assistance to state and local governments, public agencies, organizations, institutions, and individuals. Included are the program's legislative authority, explanations of each program, types of assistance provided, restrictions, eligibility requirements, financial information, application and award procedures, information contacts, and related programs. The number and program title in parentheses refer to the Catalog.

$1 Billion To Work On Ideas

The Small Business Innovation Research (SBIR) Program is a highly competitive program that encourages small businesses to explore their technological potential and provides the incentive to profit from its commercialization. Each year, ten federal departments and agencies are required to reserve a portion of their research and development funds to award to small businesses. SBIR funds the critical start-up and development stages and it encourages the commercialization of the technology, product, or service. There are three phases to the program: start-up, development, and marketplace.

To learn more about how to apply and about the various agencies involved, contact Office of Technology, U.S. Small Business Administration, 409 Third St., SW, Washington, DC 20416; 202-205-6450; {www.sba.gov/SBIR}.

Technology Assistance

The Small Business Technology Transfer (STTR) Program is a highly competitive program that reserves a specific percentage of federal research and development funding for awarding to small business and nonprofit research institution partners. Small business has long been where innovation and innovators thrive, and nonprofit research laboratories are instrumental in developing high-tech innovations. STTR combines the strengths of both entities by introducing entrepreneurial skills to hi-tech research efforts. There are specific requirements that must be met.

To learn more about how to apply and the various agencies involved, contact Office of Technology, U.S. Small Business Administration, 409 Third St., SW, Washington, DC 20416; 202-205-6450; {www.sba.gov/SBIR}.

Invention Assistance

Do you have a plan to develop a company based on your energy-saving invention or innovation? Have you been searching for financial and technical support to bring your idea to market? The U.S. Department of Energy's Inventions and Innovation Program can help.

This program provides financial assistance for establishing technical performance and conducting early development of innovative ideas and inventions. Ideas that have a significant energy savings impact and future commercial market potential are chosen for financial support through a competitive solicitation process. In addition to financial assistance, this program offers technical guidance and commercialization support to successful applicants.

For more information, contact U.S. Department of Energy, Golden Field Office, Inventions and Innovation Program, 1617 Cole Blvd., 17-3, Golden, CO 80401; 303-275-4744; {www.oit.doe.gov/inventions}.

Hurt By Imports?

The Economic Development Administration of the U.S. Department of Commerce funds the Trade Adjustment Assistance Program. If your company is affected by import competition, you may file a petition for certification of impact. If your firm is certified, you may then apply for technical assistance in diagnosing your problems, and assessing your opportunities. Once approved, your firm can apply for technical assistance to implement the recovery strategy. The average grant is for over $700,000. For more information, contact Economic Development Administration, U.S. Department of Commerce, 14th and Constitution Ave., NW, Room 7804, Washington, DC 20230; 202-482-5081; {www.doc.gov/eda}.

$50,000,000 For Air Service

The Airline Deregulation Act gave airlines almost total freedom to determine which markets to serve domestically and what fares to charge for that service. The Essential Air Service Program was put into place to guarantee that small communities that were served by certificated air carriers before deregulation maintain a minimal level of scheduled air service.

The Department of Transportation currently subsidizes commuter airlines to serve approximately 100 rural communities across the country that otherwise would not receive any scheduled air service. For more information, contact Office of Aviation Analysis, Office of the Assistant Secretary, U.S. Department of Transportation, 400 7th St., SW, Washington, DC 20590; 202-366-1053; {http://ostpxweb.dot.gov/aviation}.

Sell Overseas

The Foreign Market Development Cooperator Program is designed to develop, maintain, and expand long-term export markets for U.S. agricultural products. The program has fostered a trade promotion partnership between the U.S. Department of Agriculture (USDA) and U.S. agricultural producers and processors who are represented by nonprofit commodity or trade associations called cooperators.

The USDA and the cooperators pool their technical and financial resources to conduct market development activities outside the United States. Trade organizations compete for funds on the basis of the following allocation criteria: past export performance, past demand expansion performance, future demand expansion goals, and contribution levels. Projects include market research, trade servicing and more.

For more information, contact the Foreign Agriculture Service, Marketing Operations Staff, Stop Code 1042, U.S. Department of Agriculture, Washington, DC 20250; 202-720-4327; {www.fas.usda.gov/mos/programs/fmd.html}.

Advanced Technology Money

Not-yet-possible technologies are the domain of the National Institute of Standards and Technology's Advanced Technology Program (ATP).

The ATP is a unique partnership between government and private industry to accelerate the development of high-risk technologies that promise significant commercial payoffs and widespread benefits for the economy. ATP projects focus on the technology needs of the U.S. industry. The ATP does not fund product development. It supports enabling technologies that are essential to the development of new products, processes, and services across diverse application areas. There are strict cost-sharing rules and peer-review competitions.

For more information on how to apply for funding, contact Advanced Technology Program, National Institute of Standards and Technology, A407 Administration Building, Gaithersburg, MD 20899; 800-ATP-FUND (287-3863); {www.atp.nist.gov}.

$425,000 To Save Energy

The U.S. Department of Energy sponsors an innovative, cost-sharing program to promote energy efficiency, clean production, and economic competitiveness in industry. The grant program, known as NICE3 (National Industrial Competitiveness through Energy, Environment, and Economics), provides funding to state and industry partnerships for projects that develop and demonstrate advances in energy efficiency and clean production technologies. The overall goal of NICE3 is to improve industry energy efficiency, reduce industry's costs, and promote clean production.

Grants support innovative technology deployment that can significantly conserve energy and energy-intensive feedstocks, reduce industrial wastes, prevent pollution, and improve industrial cost competitiveness. For more information, contact U.S. Department of Energy, Office of Industrial Technologies, Golden Field Office, 1617 Cole Blvd., 17-3, Golden, CO 80401; 303-275-4728; {www.oit.doe.gov/nice3}.

Venture Capital

The Small Business Investment Company (SBIC) programs are privately organized and privately managed investment firms that are licensed by the Small Business Administration. With their own capital and with funds borrowed at favorable rates through the federal government, SBICs provide venture capital to small independent businesses, both new and already established.

A major incentive for the SBICs to invest in small businesses is the chance to share in the success of the small business if it grows and prospers. Small businesses qualifying for assistance from the SBIC program are able to receive equity capital, long-term loans, and expert management assistance. For more information on SBICs or for a Directory of Small Business Investment Companies, contact Investment Division, U.S. Small Business Administration, 409 Third St., SW, Washington, DC 20416; 202-205-6510; {www.sba.gov/INV}.

$100,000 to $300,000
in Massachusetts Venture Capital

The Venture Capital Fund provides debt and, occasionally, equity financing to established businesses to enable them to expand or retain employment for local residents. Financing is provided for firms that are unable to meet all of their capital needs in the traditional markets. Funds are available for working capital, expansion, or acquisition costs. The preferred investment range is $100,000 to $300,000 with the Community Development Fund Corporation providing up to one third of the total financing. Interest rates are fixed for the term of the loan.

Grants To North Dakota Women

The North Dakota Women's Business Program was designed to provide counseling and technical assistance for women entrepreneurs, as well as administer the women's incentive grant program. This office can certify women-owned businesses for federal and state contracting purposes and more.

Contact North Dakota Women's Business Program, 418 East Broadway, Suite 25, Bismarck, ND 58501; 701-328-5855; {www.growingnd.com}.

For more information, contact Massachusetts Office of Business Development, One Ashburton Place, Room 2101, Boston, MA 02108; 617-727-3206; 800-5-CAPITAL; {www.state.ma.us/mobd/venture.htm}.

80% Discount on Energy Consultants

Today, businesses need innovative ways to cut costs, and one way to cut costs is to conserve energy. Companies that are energy efficient have more money for capital improvements, wages, and jobs. The Massachusetts Division of Energy Resources (EAS), through its Energy Advisor Service provides the technical assistance companies need to cut energy costs. EAS utilizes engineers from the private sector who provide flexible and comprehensive energy efficient analyses of manufacturing processes and facilities. The service is customized to meet the needs of individual companies. EAS is partly subsided through federal dollars so customers only pay approximately 12% of the overall cost. For more information, contact Massachusetts Office of Business Development, One Ashburton Place, Room 2101, Boston, MA 02108; 617-727-3206; 800-5-CAPITAL; {www.magnet.state.ma.us/mobd/energy.htm}.

Grants To Train Employees

The Set-Aside for Economic Development is designed to provide matching job training funds to companies that are either relocating to Rhode Island or expanding present operations in the state. The funds are used for the training of new employees through either customized training programs or on the job training. The Set-Aside may also be used to upgrade and/or retrain existing employees in order to develop increased business and long term employment.

For more information, contact Rhode Island Economic Development Corporation, One West Exchange St., Providence, RI 02903; 401-222-2890; {www.riedc.com/growth/jobs/job_programs.htm}.

$25,000 To Upgrade Employees Skills

The Competitiveness Improvement Program allows an employer to upgrade the skills of existing employees, thus improving the productivity of the business. The program awards matching grants of up to $25,000 per company through a competitive proposal process. Businesses are urged to work through trade associations and local colleges and universities to increase the effectiveness of the training programs. For more information, contact Rhode Island Economic Development Corporation, One West Exchange St., Providence, RI 02903; 401-222-2890; {www.riedc.com/growth/jobs/ job_programs.htm}.

$5,000 To Learn New Technology

Rapid changes require rapid and effective responses. To meet your organizational needs, the Rhode Island Economic Development Corporation can afford you the opportunity to increase your overall productivity. The intent of the Project Upgrade funds is to upgrade skills of currently employed workers who are being impacted by technological or organizational changes in the workplace. A maximum $5,000 Project Upgrade grant can be obligated to each eligible company. For more information, contact Rhode Island Economic Development Corporation, One West Exchange St., Providence, RI 02903; 401-222-2890; {www.riedc.com/growth/jobs/job_programs.htm}.

$500,000 Venture Capital From New York

High tech entrepreneurs, companies with technologies ready for market, and leading-edge enterprises each have different needs for investment capital. New York State has the seed and growth capital that will enable your high tech business to grow. The Small Business Technology Investment Fund Program (STBIF) is a source of early-stage debt and equity funding for high tech companies. Initial investments can come to as much as $300,000 and later stage investments can go up to $500,000. New York State is banking on a strong high tech future.

For more information, contact Empire State Development/Small Business Technology Investment Fund, 30 S. Pearl St., 6th Floor, Albany, NY 12245; 518-292-5134; {www.empire.state.ny.us}.

Convert Gas Vehicles to Alternative Fuels

In an effort to improve Pennsylvania air quality and reduce the consumption of imported oil, the Office of Pollution Prevention and Compliance Assistance developed the Alternative Fuels Incentive Grant Fund. Money can be used to increase the use of alternative fuel vehicles and develop a refueling infrastructure in Pennsylvania. Applicants may request a grant to cover a percentage of their costs to convert an existing gasoline vehicle that meets certain age and mileage restrictions to operate on alternative fuel, as well to purchase and install a refueling or recharging facility.

For more information, contact Department of Environment Protection, Office of Pollution Prevention and Compliance Assistance, 400 Market St., 15th Floor, RCSOB, P.O. Box 8772, Harrisburg, PA 17105; 717-772-8912; {www.dep.state.pa.us/dep/deputate/airwaste/ aq/afv/afvafig1.htm}.

MONEY FOR JOB TRAINING

Pennsylvanian companies can take advantage of the Opportunity Grant Program. This Program provides grant funds to create or preserve jobs within the Commonwealth. Funds may be used for job training, infrastructure improvements, land and building improvements, machinery and equipment, working capital and environmental assessment and redemption. A 4 to 1 private to public match is required.

For more information, contact Department of Community and Economic Development, 494 Forum Bldg., Harrisburg, PA 17120; 727-787-7120; 800-379-7448; {www.dced.state.pa.us/PA_Exec/DCED/business/f.opportunity.htm}.

Keep Jobs In Pennsylvania

The Customized Job Training Program provides grants to businesses in need of training assistance for new hires, retraining efforts, and upgrading employees in an effort to retain and create jobs in Pennsylvania. Grants are available of up to 100% of the eligible costs for new job creations; 70% for job retention; and 25% for upgrade training. Money can be used for instructional costs, supplies, consumable materials, contracted services, and relevant travel costs for instructors. For more information, contact Department of Community and Economic Development, 494 Forum Bldg., Harrisburg, PA 17120; 717-787-7120; 800-379-7448; {www.dced.state.pa.us/PA_Exec/DCED/business/3-ch-work.htm}.

Clean Up Assistance

Pennsylvania companies involved in the reuse of former industrial land may be eligible for the Industrial Sites Reuse Program. Grants and low interest loan financing are provided to perform environmental site assessment and remediation work at former industrial sites. This program provides grants and loans of up to $200,000 for environmental assessment and up to $1 million for remediation. A 25% match is required for grant and loan projects. The interest rate for loans is 2%. For more information, contact Department of Community and Economic Development, 494 Forum Bldg., Harrisburg, PA 17120; 717-787-7120; 800-379-7448; {www.dced.state.pa.us/PA_Exec/DCED/business/f.isrp.htm}.

Pollution Control Grants From Virginia

The Virginia Department of Environmental Quality has partnered with others to offer $10,000 pollution prevention grants. The Pollution Prevention Grants Program is designed to encourage the implementation of pollution prevention techniques in businesses and governments throughout Virginia. It is an effort to support industrially significant pollution prevention programs that reduce the production waste and to help contribute to the bottom line of Virginia's manufacturers and businesses.

For more information, contact Virginia Department of Environmental Quality, 629 E. Main St., Richmond, VA 23219; 804-698-4545; 800-592-5482; {www.deq.state.va.us/p2}.

Agriculture Marketing Grants

North Dakota agricultural products or by-products can get a helping hand from the Agricultural Products Utilization Commission. Funds are available for the development or implementation of a sound marketing plan for the promotion of these products. The products should be new to the area of should be an expansion of a use or uses of existing products.

For more information on requirements, contact North Dakota Agricultural Products Utilization Commission, 1833 East Bismarck Expressway, Bismarck, ND 58505; 701-328-5350; {www.growingnd.com/brochure.html}.

$150,000 to $2 Million
in Delaware Venture Capital

Venture capital is needed for both technology-based and non-technology oriented companies to get them up and running. In order to help these companies grow, the State of Delaware has joined as a partner in three venture capital funds. Each one funds businesses at various stages of development, but their investment focus varies.

For more information on the funds, contact Delaware Economic Development Office, 99 Kings Highway, Dover, DE 19901; 302-739-4271; {www.state.de.us/dedo/resources/index.htm}. (follow links)

Money For Development And
Marketing In Delaware

Companies based in Delaware may be eligible for the Delaware Innovation Fund that "provides financial and technical assistance to businesses which have the potential to launch innovative products and processes into national markets, to create new jobs, and to make a significant contribution to the economic diversity and the technology base of Delaware's communities." Money can be used to establish patents, develop business plans, and begin the commercialization process. A match is required for investments, but sweat equity is considered.

For more information, contact Delaware Innovation Fund, 100 West 10th St., Suite 413, Wilmington, DE 19801; 302-777-1616; {www.state.de.us/dedo/finance/innovatn.htm}.

$5,000 To Train Employees In Tennessee

The Tennessee Department of Labor operates a grant program for companies desiring to upgrade their employee safety programs. The goal of this program is to fund the education and training of employees in safe employment practices and to promote the development of employer-sponsored health and safety programs in the employer's own business.

For more information, contact Tennessee Department of Labor, Occupational Safety and Health Grant Program, Gateway Plaza 2nd Floor, 710 James Robertson Parkway, Nashville, TN 37243; 800-332-2667; 615-741-2582; {www.state.tn.us/ecd/smbus/ichpt6.htm}.

$3 Million To Growing Tennessee Businesses

Commerce Capital LP is a Small Business Investment Company that has equity funds for rapidly growing small business operating capital needs in the Tennessee Valley. These investments are made in both debt and equity financing for companies in health care, manufacturing, environmental services, communications and information systems. For more information, contact TVA Economic Development, 400 W. Summit Hill Dr., Knoxville, TN 37902; 423-632-3405; {www.state.tn.us/ecd/rg_ch5.htm}.

$50,000 For
Delaware Inventors

The Small Business Innovation Research (SBIR) grant program is a federal government program designed to encourage small business to explore their technological potential and provides the incentive to profit from its commercialization. SBIR funds the critical start-up and development stages. Phase I provides awards up to $100,000 for six months support for the exploration of technical merit or feasibility of an idea or technology. Delaware businesses that receive Phase I support are eligible for a bridge grant of up to $50,000 if they submit a Phase II proposal. For more information, contact Delaware Economic Development Office, 99 Kings Highway, Dover, DE 19901; 302-739-4271; {www.state.de.us/dedo/resources/index.htm}. (follow links)

Venture Capital for Low-Income Entrepreneurs

Maryland's Equity Participation Investment Program provides investments in technology-based businesses and business acquisitions that will be owned 70% or more by disabled, socially, or economically disadvantaged persons. The amount of money available ranges from $100,000 to $3 million and can be used to purchase machinery and equipment, inventory, working capital, real estate acquisitions, and more.

For more information, contact Maryland Department of Business and Economic Development, Division of Marketing, 217 E. Redwood St., Baltimore, MD 21202; 410-767-6555; 800-811-0051; {www.mdbusiness.state.md.us}. (follow links)

Money To Train Kentucky Employees

The Bluegrass State Skills Corporation (BSSC) works with business and industry and Kentucky's educational institutions to establish a program of skills training. The BSSC provides funding support for the training of workers of Kentucky's new and expanding industries, and for skills upgrade and occupational upgrade training of workers of existing industries. There is a matching funds requirement. For more grant information, contact Bluegrass State Skills Corporation, Capital Plaza Tower, 21st Floor, 500 Mero St., Frankfort, KY 40601; 502-564-2021; {www.thinkkentucky.com/bssc}.

$250,000 To Train Ohio Employees

The Ohio Industrial Training Program is designed to provide financial assistance and resources for customized training involving employees of new and expanding Ohio manufacturing businesses. Financial assistance is on a reimbursement basis for a portion of training expenses incurred, including instructor costs, materials, special needs, and more. For more information, contact Ohio Industrial Training Program, Ohio Department of Development, 77 South High St., 28th Floor, Columbus, OH 43215; 614-466-4155; {www.resourceohio.com/fr_work.html }.

Money To Recycle Tires

The Ohio Department of Development has loans and grants available to scrap tire recyclers who locate or expand in Ohio and who demonstrate that they will create new/reuse scrap tire products. $2 million is available for qualifying loans and grants. For more information, contact Economic Development Division, Ohio Department of Development, 77 S. High St., P.O. Box 1001, Columbus, OH 43215; 614-644-8201; {www.resourceohio.com}.

$10,000 For Alternative Fuel In Indiana

The Alternative Energy Systems Program provides grants to businesses to fund eligible alternative-fuel technologies and infrastructure development. Eligible technologies include alternative fuels, landfill methane outreach, agricultural applications, geothermal heat pumps, wood waste boilers, and solar repair and service. The maximum amount available per project is $10,000 and matching funds are required. Contact Indiana Department of Commerce, Energy Policy Division, Alternative Energy Program, One North Capital, Suite 700, Indianapolis, IN 46204; 317-232-8940; {www.state.in.us/doc/energy/transportation.html}.

Grants and Help For Ohio Business

The Business Development Account 412 helps Ohio businesses prosper through technical assistance programs and customized assistance resources. It provides assistance with up-to-date information on sites, buildings, labor, markets, taxes, and financing. It helps companies seek state, local, or private financing and coordinates tax incentive programs and assists companies' infrastructure needs.

For more information, contact Office of Business Development, Ohio Department of Development, 77 South High St., 28th Floor, Columbus, OH 43215; 614-466-4155; {www.resourceohio.com}.

$30,000 to Reduce Wood Waste

The North Carolina Division of Pollution Prevention and Environmental Assistance set a goal to reduce solid waste by 40 percent. They have created the Organics Waste Recycling Grant which funds projects up to $30,000, with a 25% match from the business, to help in meeting that goal. Projects that reduce the flow of organic wastes to landfills or incinerators, or that stimulate market demand for recycled organic wastes are eligible for this project.

For more information, contact North Carolina Division of Pollution Prevention and Environmental Assistance, 1639 Mail Service Center, Raleigh, NC 27699; 919-715-6524; {www.p2pays.org/financial/trust/ index.htm}.

Grants To Improve Energy Efficiency

The National Industrial Competitiveness Through Energy, Environment and Economics Grant is a federal grant with possible state matching money to improve energy efficiency, promote a cleaner production process and improve the competitiveness of industry. Those eligible include manufacturers in industrial glass, metals, chemicals, forest products, petroleum, steel, and aluminum. The maximum grant is $400,000 and a 55% match is required. Contact Indiana Department of Commerce, Energy Policy Division, Alternative Energy Program, One North Capital, Suite 700, Indianapolis, IN 46204; 317-232-8940; {www.state.in.us/doc/energy/industrial.html}.

$5,000 To Go Overseas

The Trade Show Assistance Program provides financial assistance to Indiana manufacturers by reimbursing a portion of the costs incurred while exhibiting their products at overseas trade shows. Reimbursement includes 100% of exhibit space rental or $5,000 whichever is less. Eligible companies may use this program one time per fiscal year and may not use the grant for the same show in two consecutive years. Applicants must be ready to export, have available manufacturing capacity for export and have basic export knowledge. For more information, contact Indiana Department of Commerce, International Trade Division, One North Capital, Suite 700, Indianapolis, IN 46204; 317-232-8845; {www.state.in.us/doc/trade/tsap.html}.

$1.6 For Illinois Job Training

The Industrial Training Program (ITP) assists companies in meeting their employee training needs. There are two ways employers can access state training funds available through ITP. One way is for individual employers to apply for grant funds to assist with training the employees. The second way is through the Multi-Company Training Project that allows companies with common employee training needs to join together. For more information, contact Office of Industrial Training, Department of Commerce and Community Affairs, 620 Adams St., Springfield, IL 62701; 217-785-6284; {www.commerce.state.il.us/workforce/ITP/ITP_home.htm}.

Use Recycled Materials

The Market Development Program provides funding assistance in the form of loans and grants for the purchase or conversion of equipment to manufacture products from recycled products, and procurement and end-use testing of recycled content products. For more information, contact Resource Development Section, Bureau of Energy and Recycling, Illinois Department of Commerce and Community Affairs, 620 Adams St., Springfield, IL 62701; 217-785-2006; {www.commerce.state.il.us/resource_efficiency/ Recycling/RecycleProgramOverview.htm}.

Used Tire Grants

The Used Tire Recovery Unit's mission is to develop self-sustaining markets for used and waste tires. The program offers funding in the form of grants and loans for projects which reuse, recycle, or recover energy from used tires. For more information, contact Used Tire Recovery Unit, Bureau of Energy and Recycling, Illinois Department of Commerce and Community Affairs, 620 Adams St., Springfield, IL 62701; 217-785-3999; {www.commerce.state.il.us/resource_efficiency/Recycling/RecycleProgramOverview.htm}.

Grants to Recycle Solid Waste

The mission of the Recycling Industry Modernization (RIM) Program is to divert materials from the solid waste stream and improve the competitiveness of Illinois manufacturing firms, through modernization. RIM projects increase the use of recycled materials and/or promote solid waste source reduction. Grants are available to fund modernization assessments and implementation projects.

For more information, contact Bureau of Energy and Recycling, Illinois Department of Commerce and Community Affairs, 620 Adams St., Springfield, IL 62701; 217-785-2638; {www.commerce.state.il.us/resource_efficiency/ Recycling/ RecycleProgramOverview.htm}.

$1,000 Job Training Grants

The Economic Development Job Training program is a major feature of Michigan's economic development incentive package. While the employer matches 25% of the state assistance, under this program employers customize training programs to meet their needs; training funds are channeled through Michigan's expansive educational network; and grants average $500- $1,000 per employee. For more information, contact Michigan Economic Development Corporation, 201 N. Washington Square, Lansing, MI 48913; 517-373-9808; {www.michigan.org}.

Grants For Environmental Cleanup In Wisconsin

Brownfields are potential business sites, but currently pose a danger due to environmental problems. The Brownfields Grant Program provides grants to persons or businesses for environmental remediation activities where the owner is unknown, cannot be located, or cannot meet the cleanup costs. For more information, contact the Department of Commerce, 201 W. Washington Ave., Madison, WI 53707; 608-266-3494; 800-HELP-BUS; {www.commerce.state.wi.us/ CD/CD-bfi.html#Brownfields Grant Initiative}.

$10,000 For Every New Job Created

The goal of the Vocational Rehabilitation Economic Development Partnership is to increase employment opportunities for Division of Vocational Rehabilitation (DVR) clients by providing equipment grants, technical assistance grants, customized technical assistance and other assistance to companies that will hire persons with disabilities.

Companies interested in applying should contact Wisconsin Department of Commerce, Bureau of Minority Business Development, Job Creation Program, 101 W. Pleasant St., Suite 100A, Milwaukee, WI 53212; 414-220-5360; {www.commerce.state.wi. us/MT/MT-FAX-0817.html}.

Recycle Wisconsin

The Recycling Early Planning Grant Program encourages the creation and expansion of businesses that will undertake the production of goods from recycled materials, or increase the use of recycled materials. Funds may be issued for up to 75% of eligible project costs to a maximum of $15,000.

For more information, contact the Department of Commerce, 201 W. Washington Ave., Madison, WI 53707; 608-267-9548; 800-HELP-BUS; {www.commerce.state.wi.us/MT/MT-FAX-0818.html}.

Get 50% of Training Costs

The Customized Labor Training Fund provides training grants to businesses that are implementing new technology or production processes. The goal is to help Wisconsin manufacturers maintain a workforce that is on the cutting edge of technological innovation. The program can provide up to 50% of the cost of customized training that is not available from the Wisconsin Technical College System. For more information, contact the Department of Commerce, 201 W. Washington Ave., Madison, WI 53707; 608-266-1018; 800-HELP-BUS; {www.commerce.state.wi.us/MT/MT-FAX-0802.html}.

$30,000 To Start A Rural Business

The Rural Economic Development Program Early Planning Grant Program's goal is to stimulate the start up and expansion of small businesses in communities throughout Wisconsin. The program provides grants to rural entrepreneurs and small businesses so that they may obtain the professional services necessary to determine the feasibility of a proposed start-up or expansion. It makes individual awards up to $15,000 for feasibility studies and other professional assistance to rural businesses with fewer than 50 employees.

For more information, contact the Department of Commerce, 201 W. Washington Ave., Madison, WI 53707; 608-266-1018; 800-HELP-BUS; {www.commerce.state.wi.us/MT/MT-FAX-0809.html}.

Minority Enterprise Grants

The Minority Business Early Planning Grant Program offers individual grants for planning and managerial assistance to minority entrepreneurs and business owners. Grants are to be used to hire professional consultants for feasibility studies, business and management planning, marketing assistance and planning, and/or financial statements and loan packaging. Grants are up to $15,000 with a 25% match being required.

For more information, contact the Department of Commerce, 201 W. Washington Ave., Madison, WI 53707; 608-267-9550; 800-HELP-BUS; {www.commerce.state.wi.us/ MT/MT-FAX-0808.html}.

Grants for Recycling Businesses

The Recycling Market Development Board, attached to the Wisconsin Department of Commerce, identifies markets for recycled materials, and awards loans and grants to companies and organizations committed to manufacturing products from recycled materials. For more information, contact the Department of Commerce, 201 W. Washington Ave., Madison, WI 53707; 608-2667-9548; 800-HELP-BUS; {www.commerce.state.wi.us/RB/RB-Organization.html}.

Wood Utilization Grants

The Lake States Wood Utilization Grant Program awards up to $100,000 to universities, private and federal laboratories, and forest products industry businesses located in Wisconsin to develop value-added products from manufacturing by-products and other wood waste; to provide economical solutions to environmental protection; or to improve the use of available timber resources. Applicants must provide 25% of the project cost in cash or in-kind. For more information, contact the Department of Commerce, 201 W. Washington Ave., Madison, WI 53707; 608-266-1018; 800-HELP-BUS; {www.commerce.state.wi.us}.

$4,000 For Technical Assistance

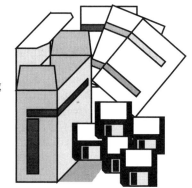

The Microenterprise Assistance Grants help start-up entrepreneurs and expanding businesses receive technical assistance and, in some cases, financial support through selected nonprofit business development organizations. Technical assistance may include assisting business owners in evaluating their abilities and/or needs of their business; making knowledgeable choices about their business operations; developing new management or operations skills; and underwriting expenses related to the implementation of their business plans.

For more information, contact Minnesota Department of Trade and Economic Development, 500 Metro Square, 121 7th Place East, St. Paul, MN 55101; 651-297-1170; 800-657-3858; {www.dted.state.mn.us}.

Recycle Missouri

The Missouri Market Development Program assists recycling throughout Missouri by focusing economic development efforts on businesses and projects that use materials recovered from solid waste in manufacturing operations and other end-uses. They can help identify what financial and business development assistance is available to you through a variety of resources and connect you with collection systems, processors, and manufacturers using recovered materials. Maximum amount of financial assistance is $75,000.

For more information, contact Missouri Market Development Program, Environmental Improvement and Energy Resources Authority, P.O. Box 744, Jefferson City, MO 65102; 573-526-0744; {www.ecodev.state.mo.us/cd/finance/programs/ momarket.htm}.

Grants To Train Arkansas Employees

The primary purpose of the Existing Workforce Training Program (EWTP) is to provide financial assistance to Arkansas manufacturing industries for upgrading the skills of their existing workforce. EWTP will pay a portion of the costs of the approved training program. Financial assistance will range from 20 percent to 70 percent depending upon a series of scoring criteria.

To learn more, contact the Arkansas Department of Economic Development, 1 State Capitol Mall, Little Rock, AR 72201; 501-682-7323; {www.work-ed.state.ar.us/ind_coord.html}.

Smart Texas Jobs

Smart Jobs is a business incentive program designed to help Texas companies become more competitive. Smart Jobs provides grants to employers for customized training. The employer decides what training is needed for the work force and who will provide the training. There is an employer match component. For more information, contact Texas Department of Economic Development, Smart Jobs Fund, P.O. Box 12728; Austin, TX 78711; 800-888-0511; {www.tded.state. tx.us/smartjobs/}.

Quality Oklahoma Jobs

The innovative Oklahoma Quality Jobs Program allows qualifying businesses that are creating new quality jobs to receive a special incentive to locate or expand in Oklahoma. The program provides quarterly cash payments of up to 5 percent of new taxable payroll directly to a qualifying company, for up to ten years. There are requirements such as payroll amount, health insurance coverage, workweek, and more. For more information, contact Office of Business Recruitment, Oklahoma Department of Commerce, P.O. Box 26980, Oklahoma City, OK 73126; 800-588-5959; 415-815-5213; {www.odoc.state.ok.us}.

Money For Small Businesses

The Oklahoma Small Employer Quality Jobs Program allows qualifying small businesses that are creating a minimum of ten new direct jobs within one year of the date of application to receive a special incentive to locate or expand in Oklahoma. The program provides annual cash payments of 5% of taxable payroll for new employees to a qualifying company for up to five years. There are requirements that must be met including health insurance coverage, hours worked, and more. For more information, contact Office of Business Recruitment, Oklahoma Department of Commerce, P.O. Box 26980, Oklahoma City, OK 73126; 800-588-5959; 405-815-5213; {www.odoc.state.ok.us}.

Iowa Job Training

The Iowa Industrial New Jobs Training Program provides funds to train new employees of eligible Iowa businesses. Eligible businesses may be new to Iowa, expanding their Iowa work force, or relocating to the state. Employees qualifying for training services must be in a newly created position and pay Iowa withholding tax. Job training services are defined as any training needed to enhance the performance of a business' new employees. Services include vocational and skill assessment testing, adult basic education, job-related training, cost of company, college, or contracted trainer or training services, and more.

The program is administered and operated by Iowa's 15 community colleges. Each college works with eligible businesses to assess training needs, determine funds availability, and provide training. For more information, contact Iowa Department of Economic Development, Workforce Development, 200 East Grand Ave., Des Moines, IA 50309; 515-242-4878; {www.state.ia.us/ided}.

Forgivable Loans For Training

The Community Economic Betterment Account program provides financial assistance to businesses creating new job opportunities or retaining existing jobs. Assistance may be provided to encourage new business start-ups, expansion or retention of existing businesses, or recruitment of out-of-state businesses into Iowa. Assistance may be in the form of loans and/or forgivable loans.

For more information, contact Iowa Department of Economic Development, Workforce Development, 200 East Grand Ave., Des Moines, IA 50309; 515-242-4878; {www.smart.state.ia.us/financial.htm}.

New Skills Development

The Iowa Innovative Skills Development Program promotes the development of new, creative and innovative approaches that address Iowa's current and future work force needs. Program services are prioritized in support of projects that concentrate on skill development for new or emerging technologies as well as enhancement of technological skills for our current work force. Allowable program costs include purchase or development of training curricula and materials, cost of assessment, recruitment, outreach, tuition, vocational and skill assessment, adult basic education, and more.

For more information, contact Iowa Department of Economic Development, Workforce Development, 200 East Grand Ave., Des Moines, IA 50309; 515-242-4878; {www.state.ia.us/ided}.

Business Network

The Iowa Community College Business Network Training Project consists of five or more businesses located in two or more community college districts with at least two community colleges sponsoring the training project. A community college business network training project is eligible for up to $50,000 in program assistance per participating community college. A 25% cash match from the participating businesses is required for consortia projects costing $45,000 or more. Projects costing less than $45,000 do not require a cash match.

For more information, contact Iowa Department of Economic Development, Workforce Development, 200 East Grand Ave., Des Moines, IA 50309; 515-242-4878; {www.state.ia.us/government/ided/workforce/IJTP.htm}.

Entrepreneurs With Disabilities

The Entrepreneurs With Disabilities Program provides technical and/or financial assistance to qualified individuals with disabilities seeking self-sufficiency by establishing, maintaining, expanding, or acquiring a small business. Program services include technical assistance such as business plan development, accounting, legal services, and financial assistance for the purpose of purchasing business equipment, supplies, inventory, rent and more. Financial assistance shall not exceed $15,000. For more information, contact Iowa Department of Economic Development, Workforce Development, 200 East Grand Ave., Des Moines, IA 50309; 515-242-4878; {www.smart.state.ia.us/financial.htm}.

Money For Iowa Entrepreneurs

The Entrepreneurial Ventures Assistance program provides financial and technical assistance to start-up and early-stage companies. The eligible business must be located in Iowa and in an industry sector offering the greatest start-up and growth potential for the state. To qualify, applicants must have completed or be participating in an entrepreneurial training program. An initial investment of up to $20,000 may be awarded for product development, working capital, purchase of machinery and equipment, and for other qualifying business expenses. Funds may be used to finance up to 50% of total project costs. For more information, contact Iowa Department of Economic Development, Workforce Development, 200 East Grand Ave., Des Moines, IA 50309; 515-242-4878; {www.smart.state.ia.us/financial.htm}.

Kansas
Job Training Grants

The High Performance Incentive Program promotes the establishment and expansion of high performance industry in the state. The program provides incentives to qualified firms to provide training to employees to upgrade existing employee job skills and offers a sales tax exemption and substantial tax credits in connection with capital investment.

For more information, contact High Performance Incentive Program, Business Development Division, Kansas Department of Commerce and Housing, 700 SW Harrison, 13th Floor, Topeka, KS 66603; 785-296-5298; {www.kansascommerce.com}.

Venture Capital For Kansas Businesses

The Innovation and Commercialization Corporations (ICCs) seek entrepreneurs and scientists who are in need of help, to aid in commercializing high-tech products in the development stage. The ICCs aid clients in preparing quality business plans to attract venture capital as well as assistance in preparing competitive ARMF proposals. ICCs help client corporations find affordable business incubator space nearby, so that they can take clients "on-board" and provide constant support. The ICCs also each operate a pre-seed capital fund, which empowers start-up businesses to commercialize new technology. The type of aid available differs slightly between the three corporations. For more information, contact one of the following:

- Kansas Innovation Corporation, 1617 St. Andrews Dr., Lawrence, KS 66047; 785-832-2110; {www.kic.com}.

- Mid-America Commercialization Corp., 1500 Hayes Dr., Manhattan, KS 66502, 785-532-3900; {www.ksu.edu/tech.transfer/macc/macc.htm}.

- Wichita Technology Corporation, 1845 N. Fairmont, NIAR Bldg., Wichita, KS 67260; 316-978-3690; {www. wichitatechnology.com}.

Grants For Businesses In Rural Kansas

The Rural Economic Development Loan and Grant Program provides zero-interest loans and grants to projects with the purpose of promoting rural economic development and job creation. For more information, contact Kansas Electric Power Cooperative, Inc., P.O. Box 4877, Topeka, KS 66604; 785-273-7010; {www.kepco.org}.

Kansas Venture Capital

Instituted to increase the availability of risk capital in Kansas, the venture capital and seed capital programs make use of income tax credits to encourage investment in venture and seed capital pools as a source of early stage financing for small businesses. Businesses demonstrating strong growth potential but lacking the financial strength to obtain conventional financing are the most likely candidates for risk capital funding.

The Business Development Division has in operation and continues to develop a network of venture capital resources to assist qualified small businesses in locating potential sources of venture capital financing. Contact Business Development Division, Kansas Department of Commerce and Housing, 700 SW Harrison, Suite 1300, Topeka, KS 66603-3712; 785-296-5298; {www.kansascommerce.com}.

$3,500 For Trade Shows

The Kansas Trade Show Assistance Program provides Kansas companies with financial assistance to target new markets. Companies who receive approval can be reimbursed for up to 50% of the show related expenses to attend trade shows.

To apply, contact Trade Development Division, Kansas Department of Commerce and Housing, 700 SW Harrison St., Suite 1300, Topeka, KS 66603; 785-296-4027; {www.kansascommerce.com}.

$1,000 For Your Kansas Invention

The Invention Development Assistance program is designed to help inventors in the beginning stages with marketing their inventions to increase market-driven products and processes that can be commercialized in Kansas. Assistance is limited to matching grants of up to $1,000 per invention.

For more information, contact Kansas Technology Enterprise Corporation, 112 W. 6th, Suite 400, Topeka, KS 66603; 785-296-5272; {www.ktec.com}.

$5,000 To Prepare Grant Proposals

The Small Business Innovation Research (SBIR) Matching Grants assist businesses in preparing federal SBIR/STTR grant proposals and to increase the number and quality being submitted by Kansas small businesses that will meet the research and development needs of the federal government. Reimbursement assistance is up to $5,000 in preparing a quality proposal, review of the draft proposal prior to submission, and assistance in locating resources.

For more information, contact Kansas Technology Enterprise Corporation, 112 W. 6th, Suite 400, Topeka, KS 66603; 785-296-3686; {www.ktec.com}.

New Mexico Job Training

The New Mexico Industrial Development Training Program provides funds for classroom or on-the-job training to prepare New Mexico residents for employment. Training may be tailored to the needs of the business and is usually provided in one of three ways: classroom in nature and provided by a public education institution facility; training conducted at the business facility; and on-the-job and/or classroom training. Trainees must be guaranteed full-time employment upon successful completion of training. Trainees wages are reimbursed to the company at 50% during hours of training.

For more information, contact New Mexico Economic Development Department, Development Division, 1100 St. Francis Dr., Santa Fe, NM 87503; 505-827-0323; {www.edd.state.nm.us/SERVICES/TRAINING/index.html}.

Washington Job Skills

The Job Skills Program brings together employers or industries who have specific training needs with educational institutions that can provide customized employee training. Through matching grants, the Job Skills Program funds industry-education partnerships in which customized training materials are developed and short-term, job-specific training is delivered.

For more information, contact Workforce Training and Education Coordinating Board, Building 17 Airdustrial Park, Olympia, WA 98504; 360-753-5662; {www.wa.gov/wtb/index.html}.

Oregon Venture Capital

Equity-based capital is available for Oregon businesses through the Oregon Resource and Technology Development Fund. Areas of focus include: biological and biomedical services, high technology, and natural resource industries. Funds are available to eligible companies for seed capital, applied research, and technical information. For more information, contact Oregon Resource and Technology Development Fund, 4370 NE Halsey, Suite 233, Portland, OR 97213; 503-417-2165.

Child Care Money

Alaska offers the Child Care Grant program that provides a small business subsidy for child care centers and licensed homes. Grantees must use the money for the long-term benefit of the child care facility and the children in care. Most child care facilities use these funds for staff salaries and benefits, goods relating to health, safety and nutrition, and age appropriate equipment, supplies and activities for the children.

For more information, contact Child Care Programs Coordinator, Division of Community and Rural Development, Department of Community and Regional Affairs, 333 West Fourth Ave., Suite 220, Anchorage, AK 99501; 907-269-4529; {www.comregaf.state.ak.us/dcrd_ccg.htm}.

$25,000 To Develop
Business Plans And Patents

The Delaware Innovation Fund provides financial and technical assistance to Delaware-based business that have the potential to launch innovative products and processes into national markets, to create new jobs, and to make a contribution to the economic diversity of Delaware. Demonstration Funding provides $25,000 to aid in establishing patents, business plans, and proof of concept issues. Commercialization Funding goes up to $250,000 to be used to begin the commercialization process of early-stage businesses.

For more information, contact Delaware Innovation Fund, 100 W. 10th St., Suite 413, Wilmington, DE 19801; 302-777-1616; {www.delawareinnovationfund.com}.

Train Colorado Employees

The Colorado FIRST Program is to encourage quality economic development by providing training assistance as an incentive for the location of new or expanding firms in Colorado. Companies can utilize innovative approaches to training. Training programs are not designed to assist companies with normal, on-going training requirements. Companies should provide a health plan for their employees.

To learn more, contact Office of Business Development, 162 Broadway, Suite 1710, Denver, CO 80202; 303-892-3840; {www.state.co.us/gov_dir/obd/facts/jobtrnprog.htm}.

Utah's Short Term Intensive Training Grants Cover New Employees

Utah's Short Term Intensive Training (STIT) Grant programs are customized and designed to meet full-time job openings. Programs are usually less than one year in length and are designed to meet the specific training needs of a company. Although employees must pay tuition to participate, STIT can provide qualified employees from which a company can hire. STIT gives the option of training at 50-70% discount of normal training costs. For more information, contact Department of Community and Economic Development, 324 South State St., Suite 500, Salt Lake City, UT 84111; 801-538-8700; {www.dced.state.ut.us/NATIONAL/incentiv.htm}.

$100,000 To Move Your Business To Utah

The State of Utah has an Industrial Assistance Fund that can be used for relocation costs. This incentive loan can be repaid as Utah jobs created. For more information about eligibility and requirements, contact Department of Community and Economic Development, 324 South State St., Suite 500, Salt Lake City, UT 84111; 801-538-8700; {www.dced.state.ut.us/NATIONAL/incentiv.htm}.

Grants to Dairy Farmers Whose Milk Is Contaminated Because of Pesticides
(10.053 Dairy Indemnity Program)

The Dairy Indemnity Program is designed to protect dairy farmers and manufacturers of dairy products who through no fault of their own, are directed to remove their milk or dairy products from commercial markets because of contamination from pesticides which have been approved for use by the federal government. Dairy farmers can also be indemnified because of contamination with chemicals or toxic substances, nuclear radiation or fallout. Types of assistance: direct payments with unrestricted use. Estimate of annual funds available: Direct payments: $650,000. Contact: U.S. Department of Agriculture, Farm Service Agency, 1400 Independence Ave., SW, Washington, DC 20250-0512; 202-720-7641.

Grants to Sell Food Related Products Overseas
(10.601 Market Access Program)

The Market Access Program was created to encourage the development, maintenance, and expansion of commercial export markets for U.S. agricultural commodities through cost-share assistance to eligible trade organizations that implement a foreign market development program. Priority for assistance is provided for agricultural commodities or products in the case of an unfair trade practice. Funding of the program is accomplished through the issuance by the Commodity Credit Corporation (CCC) of a dollar check to reimburse participants for activities authorized by a specific project agreement. Types of assistance: direct payments for specified use (cooperative agreements). Estimate of annual funds available: Direct payments: $90,000,000. Contact:

Grants to Producers of Corn, Sorghum, Barley, Oats, and Rye
(10.055 Production Flexibility Payments for Contract Commodities)

The objective of this grant program is to support farming certainty and flexibility while ensuring continued compliance with farm conservation and wetland protection requirements. Estimate of annual funds available: Contract Payments: $5,042,431,000. Contact: Philip W. Sronce, U.S. Department of Agriculture, Farm Service Agency, Economic and Policy Analysis Staff, Stop 0532, 1400 Independence Ave. SW, Washington, DC 20250-0532; 202-720-4418.

Deputy Administrator, Commodity and Marketing Programs, Foreign Agricultural Service, U.S. Department of Agriculture, Washington DC 20250; 202-720-4761.

Money to Local Communities Near National Forests to Help Businesses Grow or Expand
(10.670 National Forest-Dependent Rural Communities)

This program provides accelerated assistance to communities faced with acute economic problems associated with federal or private sector land management decisions and policies or that are located in or near a national forest and are economically dependent upon forest resources. Aid is extended to these communities to help them to diversify their economic base and to improve the economic, social, and environmental well-being of rural areas. Types of assistance: project grants; direct loans; use of property, facilities, and equipment; training. Estimate of annual funds available: $5,200,000. Contact: Deputy Chief, State and Private Forestry, Forest Service, U.S. Department of Agriculture, P.O. Box 96090, Washington, DC 20090-6090; 202-205-1657.

Grants to Nonprofits to Lend Money to New Businesses
(10.769 Rural Development Grants)

Rural Development Grants facilitate the development of small and emerging private business, industry, and related employment for improving the economy in rural communities. Types of assistance: project grants. Estimate of annual funds available: Grants: $40,300,000. Contact: Director, Specialty Lenders Division, Rural Business-Cooperative Service, U.S. Department of Agriculture, Washington, DC 20250-3222; 202-720-1400.

Grants and Loans to Telephone Companies That Then Provide Financing to Small Businesses
(10.854 Rural Economic Development Loans and Grants)

These loans and grants are designed to promote rural economic development and job creation projects, including funding for project feasibility studies, start-up costs, incubator projects, and other reasonable expenses for the purpose of fostering rural development. Types of assistance: direct loans; project grants. Estimate of annual funds available: Loans: $15,000,000; Grants: $11,000,000. (Note: Grants to establish Revolving Loan Fund Programs.) Contact: Director, Specialty Lenders Division, Rural Business-Cooperative Service, U.S. Department of Agriculture, Washington, DC 20250; 202-720-1400.

Free Plants to Nurseries
(10.905 Plant Materials for Conservation)

The Plant Materials for Conservation Program is designed to assemble, evaluate, select, release, and introduce into commerce, and promote the use of new and improved plant materials for soil, water, and related resource conservation and environmental improvement programs. To develop technology for land management and restoration with plant materials. To transfer technology on plant materials. Types of assistance: provision of specialized services. Estimate of annual funds available: Salaries and expenses: $8,745,000. Contact: Deputy Chief For Science and Technology, Natural Resources Conservation Service, U.S. Department of Agriculture, P.O. Box 2890, Washington, DC 20013; 202-720-4630.

GRANTS TO COMMUNITIES THAT PROVIDE MONEY AND HELP TO SMALL BUSINESS INCUBATORS

(11.300 Economic Development Grants for Public Works and Infrastructure Development)

Economic Development Grants for Public Works and Infrastructure Development promote long-term economic development and assist in the construction of public works and development facilities needed to initiate and encourage the creation or retention of permanent jobs in the private sector in areas experiencing substantial economic distress. Types of assistance: project grants. Estimate of annual funds available: Grants: $191,178,000. Contact: David L. McIlwain, Director, Public Works Division, Economic Development Administration, Room H7326, Herbert C. Hoover Building, U.S. Department of Commerce, Washington, DC 20230; 202-482-5265.

Grants to Communities That Help Finance New or Old Businesses Due to New Military Base Closings

(11.307 Special Economic Development and Adjustment Assistance Program-Sudden and Severe Economic Dislocation (SSED) and Long-Term Economic Deterioration (LTED))

This program is to assist state and local areas develop and/or implement strategies designed to address structural economic adjustment problems resulting from sudden and severe economic dislocation such as plant closings, military base closures and defense contract cutbacks, and natural disasters (SSED), or from long-term economic deterioration in the area's economy (LTED). Types of assistance: project grants. Estimate of annual funds available: Grants: $129,929,000 (includes funds for economic adjustment, defense adjustment, disaster recovery and trade impacted areas). Contact: David F. Witschi, Director, Economic Adjustment Division, Economic Development Administration, Room H7327, Herbert C. Hoover Building, U.S. Department of Commerce, Washington DC 20230; 202-482-2659.

Grants to Fishermen Hurt by Oil and Gas Drilling on the Outer Continental Shelf

(11.408 Fishermen's Contingency Fund)

The Fishermen's Contingency Fund compensates U.S. commercial fishermen for damage/loss of fishing gear and 50 percent of resulting economic loss due to oil and gas related activities in any area of the Outer Continental Shelf. Types of assistance: direct payments with unrestricted use. Estimate of annual funds available: Direct payments: $500,000. Contact: Chief, Financial Services Division, National Marine Fisheries Service, 1315 East West Highway, Silver Spring, MD 20910; 301-713-2396.

Grants to Develop New Technologies For Your Business

(11.612 Advanced Technology Program)

The Advanced Technology Program works in partnership with industry to foster the development and broad dissemination of challenging, high-risk technologies that offer the potential for significant, broad-based economic benefits for the nation. Types of assistance: project grants (cooperative agreements). Estimate of annual funds available: Cooperative Agreements: $209,931,000. Contact: Dr. Lura Powell, Director, Advanced Technology Program, National Institute of Standards and Technology, Gaithersburg, MD 20899; 301-975-5187; E-mail: {lura.powell@nist.gov}. To receive application kits, call ATP customer service staff 1-800-ATP-FUND.

GRANTS FOR MARINE RESEARCH
(11.417 Sea Grant Support)

Grants for Marine Research support the establishment and operation of major university centers for marine resources research, education, and training and to support marine advisory services. Some individual efforts in these same areas also receive funding. Types of assistance: Project grants. Estimate of annual funds available: $48,950,000. Contact: National Sea Grant College Program, National Oceanic and Atmospheric Administration, 1315 East-West Highway, Silver Spring, MD 20910; 301-713-2448.

Grants to Organizations That Help Minorities Start Their Own Businesses
(11.800 Minority Business Development Centers)

Minority Business Development Centers provide business development services for a minimal fee to minority firms and individuals interested in entering, expanding, or improving their efforts in the marketplace. Minority business development center operators provide a wide range of services to clients, from initial consultations to the identification and resolution of specific business problems. Types of assistance: project grants. Estimate of annual funds available: Grants: $9,600,000. Contact: Mr. Paul R. Webber, Acting Deputy Director, Room 5087, Minority Business Development Agency, U.S. Department of Commerce, 14th and Constitution Avenue, NW, Washington, DC 20230; 202-482-6022.

Grants to Organizations That Help American Indians Start Their Own Businesses
(11.801 Native American Program)

The Native American program was created to provide business development service to American Indians interested in entering, expanding, or improving their efforts in the marketplace. To help American Indian business development centers and American Indian business consultants to provide a wide range of services to American Indian clients, from initial consultation to the identification and resolution of specific business problems. Types of assistance: project grants. Estimate of annual funds available: Grants: $1,701,500. Contact: Mr. Joseph Hardy, Business Development, Specialist for the Office of Operations, Room 5079, Minority Business Development Agency, U.S. Department of Commerce, 14th and Constitution Ave., NW, Washington, DC 20230; 202-482-6022.

Grants to Help Minority Businesses Enter New Markets
(11.802 Minority Business Development)

The resource development activity provides for the indirect business assistance programs conducted by MBDA. These programs encourage minority business development by identifying and developing private markets and capital sources; expanding business information and business services through trade associations; promoting and supporting the mobilization of resources of federal agencies and state and local governments at the local level; and assisting minorities in entering new and growing markets. Types of assistance: project grants (cooperative agreements). Estimate of annual funds available: Cooperative Agreements/Contracts: $1,721,730. Contact: Mr. Paul R. Webber, Acting Deputy Director, Room 5055, Minority Business Development Agency, U.S. Department of Commerce, 14th and Constitution Avenue, NW, Washington, DC 20230; 202-482-6022.

Grants to Organizations That Will Help You Sell to the Department of Defense

(12.002 Procurement Technical Assistance For Business Firms)

Procurement Technical Assistance grants increase assistance by the DoD for eligible entities furnishing PTA to business entities, and to assist eligible entities in the payment of the costs of establishing and carrying out new Procurement Technical Assistance (PTA) Programs and maintaining existing PTA Programs. Types of assistance: Cooperative agreements. Estimate of annual funds available: Cooperative Agreements: $12,000,000. Contact: Defense Logistics Agency, Office of Small and Disadvantaged Business Utilization (DDAS), 8725 John J. Kingman Rd., Suite 2533, Ft. Belvoir, VA 22060-6221; 703-767-1650.

GRANTS FOR HOUSING RESEARCH

(14.506 General Research and Technology Activity)

General Research and Technology Activity grants carry out research, demonstration and program evaluation and monitoring projects of high priority and pre-selected by the Department of improve the operations of the Department's programs. Types of assistance: Project grants. Estimate of annual funds available: $50,100,000. Contact: Assistant Secretary for Policy Development and Research, Department of Housing and Urban Development, 451 7th St., SW, Washington, DC 20410; 202-708-1796.

Grants to Small Coal Mine Operators to Clean Up Their Mess

(15.250 Regulation of Surface Coal Mining and Surface Effects of Underground Coal Mining)

The objective of this program is to protect society and the environment from the adverse effects of surface coal mining operations consistent with assuring the coal supply essential to the Nation's energy requirements. Types of assistance: project grants; direct payments for specified use. Estimate of annual funds available: $50,656,000. (Includes all cooperative agreements and State Grants except SOAP grants.) Small Operator Assistance: $1,500,000. Contact: Chief, Division of Regulatory Support, Office of Surface Mining Reclamation and Enforcement, U.S. Department of the Interior, 1951 Constitution Ave., NW, Washington, DC 20240; 202-208-2651.

EMERGENCY HOUSING GRANTS

(14.231 Emergency Shelter Grants Program)

The program is designed to help improve the quality of emergency shelters and transitional housing for the homeless, to make available additional shelters, to meet the costs of operating shelters, to provide essential social services to homeless individuals, and to help prevent homelessness. Types of assistance: Formula grants. Estimate of annual funds available: $150,000,000. Contact: Office of Special Needs Assistance Programs, Department of Housing and Urban Development, Room 7266, Washington, DC 20410; 202-708-4300.

GRANTS TO ASIAN ELEPHANTS

(15.621 Asian Elephant Conservation)

The Asian Elephant Conservation grant is to provide financial assistance to any organization or individual responsible for Asian elephant conservation, and any organization or individual with experience in Asian elephant conservation, for approved elephant conservation projects to support research, conservation, management and protection of Asian elephants. Types of assistance: Project grants. Estimate of annual funds available: $970,000. Contact: U.S. Fish and Wildlife Service, U.S. Department of Interior, Office of International Affairs, 4401 N. Fairfax Dr., Room 730, Arlington, VA 22203; 703-358-1754.

GRANTS FOR PROTECTION OF
IMMIGRATION RIGHTS
(16.110 Education and Enforcement of the Antidiscrimination Provision
of the Immigration and Nationality Act)

This program was created to educate employers and workers about their rights and responsibilities under the Immigration and Nationality Act in order to prevent employment discrimination based on citizenship status or national origin. Types of assistance: Project grants. Estimate of annual funds available: $5,065,000. Contact: Outreach Coordinator, Office of Special Counsel, Civil Rights Division, Department of Justice, P.O. Box 27728, Washington, DC 20038; 202-616-5594.

Money to Fishermen Who Have Their Boats
Seized by a Foreign Government
(19.204 Fishermen's Guaranty Fund)

The Fishermen's Guaranty Fund provides for reimbursement of losses incurred as a result of the seizure of a U.S. commercial fishing vessel by a foreign country on the basis of rights or claims in territorial waters or on the high seas which are not recognized by the United States. Effective November 28, 1990, the United States acknowledges the authority of coastal states to manage highly migratory species, thus reducing the basis for valid claims under the Fishermen's Protective Act. Types of assistance: insurance. Estimate of annual funds available: Reimbursement of Losses: $500,000. Contact: Mr. Stetson Tinkham, Office of Marine Conservation, Bureau of Oceans and International Environmental and Scientific Affairs, Room 5806, U.S. Department of State, Washington, DC 20520-7818; 202-647-3941, Fax: 202-736-7350.

GRANTS TO BUILD AN
AIRPORT
(20.106 Airport Improvement Program)

The Airport Improvement Program assists sponsors, owners, or operators of public-use airports in the development of a nationwide system of airports adequate to meet the needs of civil aeronautics. Types of assistance: project grants; advisory services and counseling. Estimate of annual funds available: Grants: $1,600,000,000. Contact: Federal Aviation Administration, Office of Airport Planning and Programming, Airports Financial Assistance Division, APP-500, 800 Independence Avenue, SW, Washington, DC 20591; 202-267-3831.

GRANTS TO BUS COMPANIES
(20.509 Public Transportation for Nonurbanized Areas)

Public Transportation Grants for Nonurbanized Areas improve, initiate, or continue public service in nonurbanized areas by providing financial assistance for the operating and administrative expenses and for the acquisition, construction, and improvement of facilities and equipment. Also to provide technical assistance for rural transportation providers. Types of assistance: formula grants. Estimate of annual funds available: Grants: $203,164,311. Contact: Federal Transit Administration, Office of Grants Management, Office of Capital and Formula Assistance, 400 Seventh Street, SW, Washington, DC 20590; 202-366-2053.

GRANTS TO BECOME A WOMEN-OWNED TRANSPORTATION RELATED COMPANY
(20.511 Human Resource Programs)

Human Resource Programs provide financial assistance for national, regional and local initiatives that address human resource needs as they apply to public transportation activities. Such programs may include but are not limited to employment training programs; outreach programs to increase minority and female employment in public transportation activities; research on public transportation manpower and training needs; and training and assistance for minority business opportunities. This description is applicable only to projects awarded directly by the Federal Transit Administration (FTA) under the authority of Section 5314(a), the National component of the Transit Planning and Research Program. Types of assistance: project grants (cooperative agreements); dissemination of technical information. Estimate of annual funds available: Grants, Cooperative Agreements: $1,189,000. Contact: Director, Office of Civil Rights, Federal Transit Administration, U.S. Department of Transportation, 400 Seventh Street, SW, Room 7412, Washington, DC 20590; 202-366-4018.

Grants to U.S. Shipping Companies That Have to Pay Their Employees Higher Salaries Than Foreign Shipping Companies
(20.804 Operating Differential Subsidies)

Operating Differential Subsidies promote development and maintenance of the U.S. Merchant Marine by granting financial aid to equalize cost of operating a U.S. flag ship with cost of operating a competitive foreign flag ship. Types of assistance: direct payments for specified use. Estimate of annual funds available: $51,030,000 in 1998. Contact: Edmond J. Fitzgerald, Director, Office of Subsidy and Insurance, Maritime Administration, U.S. Department of Transportation, 400 Seventh Street, SW, Washington, DC 20590; 202-366-2400.

Money for Airlines to Fly to Small Towns and Make a Profit
(20.901 Payments for Essential Air Services)

The Payments for Essential Air Services Program is designed to assure that air transportation is provided to eligible communities by subsidizing air carriers when necessary to provide service. Types of assistance: direct payments for specified use. Estimate of annual funds available: Direct payments to air carriers: $50,000,000. Contact: Director, Office of Aviation Analysis, X-50, U.S. Department of Transportation, 400 Seventh Street, SW, Washington, DC 20590; 202-366-1030.

GRANTS TO WOMEN-OWNED BUSINESSES TO HELP GET CONTRACTS FROM THE DEPARTMENT OF TRANSPORTATION
(20.903 Support Mechanisms for Disadvantaged Businesses)

The objective of this program is to develop support mechanisms, including liaison and assistance programs, that will provide outreach and technical assistance to small disadvantaged business enterprises (DBEs) to successfully compete on transportation-related contracts. Recipients will provide a communications link between the Department of Transportation; its grantees, recipients, contractors, subcontractors; and minority, women-owned and disadvantaged business enterprises (DBEs) in order to increase their participation in existing DOT programs and DOT funded projects. Types of assistance: project grants (cooperative agreements). Estimate of annual funds available: Cooperative Agreements: $1,100,000. Contact: Office of Small and Disadvantaged Business Utilization, S-40, Office of the Secretary, 400 Seventh Street, SW, Washington, DC 20590; 800-532-1169.

Grants to Help Learn About Computers
(47.070 Computer and Information Science and Engineering)

Computer and Information Science and Engineering grants support research improving the fundamental understanding of computer and information processing, to enhance the training and education of scientists and engineers who contribute to and exploit that understanding, to enhance the personnel pool for these fields, to provide access to very advanced computing and networking capabilities, and to provide the information intensive knowledge underlying selected national initiatives. Types of assistance: Project Grants. Estimate of annual funds available: $422,530,000. Contact: Computer and Information Science and Engineering, National Science Foundation, 4201 Wilson Blvd., Arlington, VA 22230; 703-306-1900.

Grants to Provide Technical Assistance to Businesses
(59.007 Management and Technical Assistance for Socially and Economically Disadvantaged Businesses)

This grant program was created to provide management and technical assistance and access to capital and other forms of financial assistance and business training and counseling through qualified individuals, public or private organizations to 8(a) certified firms and other existing or potential businesses which are economically and socially disadvantaged; businesses operating in areas of high unemployment or low income; firms owned by low-income persons; or participants in activities authorized by Sections 7(I), 7(j), and 8(a) of the Small Business Act. Types of assistance: Project grants. Estimate of annual funds available: $5,000,000. Contact: Associate Administrator for Minority Enterprise Development, 409 Third St., SW, Washington, DC 20416; 202-205-6410.

Help for Contractors and Others to Get Bonded to Obtain Contracts
(59.016 Bond Guarantees for Surety Companies)

This program guarantees surety bonds issued by commercial surety companies for small contractors unable to obtain a bond without a guarantee. Guarantees are for up to 90 percent of the total amount of bond. Types of assistance: insurance (guaranteed surety bonds). Estimate of annual funds available: Guaranteed Surety Bonds: $1,672,000,000. Contact: Assistant Administrator Robert J. Moffitt, Office of Surety Guarantees, Small Business Administration, 409 3rd Street, SW, Washington, DC 20416; 202-205-6540.

Grants to Local Organizations That Help Women Start Their Own Businesses
(59.043 Women's Business Ownership Assistance)

The Women's Business Ownership Assistance program funds non-profit economic development organizations to assist, through training and counseling, small business concerns owned and controlled by women, and to remove, in so far as possible, the discriminatory barriers that are encountered by women in accessing capital and promoting their businesses. Types of assistance: project grants (cooperative agreements or contracts). Estimate of annual funds available: Cooperative Agreements: $9,000,000. Contact: Harriet Fredman, Office of Women's Business Ownership, Small Business Administration, 409 3rd Street, SW, Washington, DC 20416; 202-205-6673.

Grants to Local Organizations That Help Veterans Start Their Own Businesses
(59.044 Veterans Entrepreneurial Training and Counseling)

The objective of this grant program is to design, develop, administer, and evaluate an entrepreneurial and procurement training and counseling program for U.S. veterans. Types of assistance: project grants (cooperative agreements). Estimate of annual funds available: Grants: $600,000. Contact: William Truitt, Office of Veteran Affairs, Small Business Administration, 6th Floor, 409 3rd Street, SW, Washington, DC 20416; 202-205-6773.

GRANTS TO VA HOMELESS PROVIDERS
(64.024 VA Homeless Providers Grant and Per Diem Program)

These grants assist public and nonprofit private entities in establishing new programs and service centers to furnish supportive services and supportive housing for homeless veterans through grants that may be used to acquire, renovate or alter facilities, and to provide per diem payments, or in-kind assistance in lieu of per diem payments, to eligible entities which established programs after November 10, 1992 that provide supportive services and supportive housing for homeless veterans. Types of assistance: project grants. Estimate of annual funds available: $31,653,000. Contact: VA Homeless Providers Grant and Per Diem Program, Mental Health Strategic Healthcare Group (116E), Department of Veterans Affairs, 810 Vermont Ave., NW, Washington, DC 20420; 202-273-8966.

Money for Disabled Veterans to Start New Businesses
(64.116 Vocational Rehabilitation for Disabled Veterans)

The Vocational Rehabilitation for Disabled Veterans grant program provides all services and assistance necessary to enable service-disabled veterans and service persons hospitalized or receiving outpatient medical care services or treatment for a service-connected disability pending discharge to get and keep a suitable job. When employment is not reasonably feasible, the program can provide the needed services and assistance to help the individual learn skills to achieve maximum independence in daily living. Types of assistance: direct payments with unrestricted use; direct payments for specified use; direct loans; advisory services and counseling. Estimate of annual funds available: Direct payments: $403,206,000; Loan advances: $2,531,000. Contact: Veterans Benefits Administration, Vocational Rehabilitation and Counseling Service (28), U.S. Department of Veterans Affairs, Washington, DC 20420; 202-273-7419.

Help for Retired Military to Start a Business
(64.123 Vocational Training for Certain Veterans Receiving VA Pension)

These vocational training grants assist new pension recipients to resume and maintain gainful employment by providing vocational training and other services. Types of assistance: direct payments for specified use; advisory services and counseling. Estimate of annual funds available: Direct Payments: $23,000. Contact: Veterans Benefits Administration, Vocational Rehabilitation and Counseling Service (28), U.S. Department of Veterans Affairs, Washington, DC 20420; 202-273-7419.

INSURANCE AGAINST YOUR BUSINESS IN ANOTHER COUNTRY BEING HURT BY FOREIGN POLITICS
(70.003 Foreign Investment Insurance)

Foreign Investment Insurance is used to insure investments of eligible U.S. investors in developing countries and emerging markets, against the political risks of inconvertibility, expropriation, and political violence. Special programs include insuring contractors and exporters against arbitrary drawings of letters of credit posted as bid, performance or advance payment guaranties, energy exploration and development, and leasing operations. Types of assistance: insurance. Estimate of annual funds available: Insurance Issued: $6,000,000,000. Contact: Information Officer, Overseas Private Investment Corporation, 1100 New York Ave., NW, Washington, DC 20527; 202-336-8799, Fax: 202-336-8700; E-mail: {OPIC@opic.gov}, {www.opic.gov.}

Money to Work on an Energy-Related Invention
(81.036 Energy-Related Inventions)

The Energy-Related Inventions program is designed to encourage innovation in developing non-nuclear energy technology by providing assistance to individual and small business companies in the development of promising energy-related inventions. Types of assistance: project grants; use of property, facilities, and equipment; advisory services and counseling; dissemination of technical information. Estimate of annual funds available: Grants: $2,900,000. Contact: Sandra Glatt, Office of Industrial Technologies (EE-23), U.S. Department of Energy, 1000 Independence Ave., SW, Washington, DC 20585; 202-586-3987.

Grants for Science Research
(81.049 Office of Science Financial Assistance Program)

The Office of Science Financial Assistance Program provides financial support for fundamental research, training and related activities in the basic sciences and advanced technology concepts and assessments in fields related to energy. Types of assistance: Project grants. Estimate of annual funds available: $515,000,000. Contact: Grants and Contracts Division, Office of Science, SC-64, Department of Energy, 19901 Germantown Rd., Germantown, MD 20874; 301-903-5212.

Grants for Biomass Energy Technologies
(81.079 Regional Biomass Energy Programs)

Regional Biomass Energy Programs build State and municipal capacity for accelerating biomass technology deployment, in partnership with industry; and provide assistance in outreach, public education, and behavior modification activities. To conduct a balanced, long-term demonstration of biomass technologies tailored to specific regions of the country for feedstock production, conversion technologies, and municipal solid waste. Grants will be offered to develop and transfer technology to various regions of the continental United States. Types of assistance: Project Grants. Estimate of annual funds available: $3,500,000. Contact: Office of Fuels Development, Regional Biomass Energy Program, EE-31, Department of Energy, Washington, DC 20585; 202-586-9815.

Grants to Local Organizations That Help Women and Minorities Get Department of Energy Contracts

(81.082 Management and Technical Assistance for Minority Business Enterprises)

The objectives of this grant program are: (1) To support increased participation of minority, and women-owned and operated business enterprises (MBE's); (2) to develop energy-related minority business assistance programs and public/private partnerships to provide technical assistance to MBE's; (3) to transfer applicable technology from national federal laboratories to MBE's; and (4) to increase the Department of Energy's (DOE) high technology research and development contracting activities. Types of assistance: advisory services and counseling. Estimate of annual funds available: Contracts and Grants: $542,000. Contact: Sterling Nichols, Office of Economic Impact and Diversity, U.S. Department of Energy, ED-1, Forrestal Building, Room 5B-110, Washington, DC 20585; 202-586-8698.

Grants to Develop Energy Saving Products

(81.086 Conservation Research and Development)

This grant program was created to conduct a balanced long-term research effort in the areas of buildings, industry, and transportation. Grants will be offered to develop and transfer to the non-federal sector various energy conservation technologies. Types of assistance: project grants. Estimate of annual funds available: Grants: not separately identified. (Note: Discretionary funds for grants are not specifically contained in the President's request for Energy Conservation Programs. However, the Department does issue grants if found to be appropriate as a result of unsolicited proposals that clearly are consistent with program objectives and are appropriate as grants in lieu of other contractual methods. Unsolicited proposals have received grants totaling approximately $2,000,000 to $2,500,000 over the past 5 years.)

Contact: Energy Efficiency and Renewable Energy Programmatic Offices:
• Office of Building Technology, State and Community Programs, Lynda Dancy, 202-586-2300
• Office of Transportation Technologies, Nancy Blackwell, 202-586-6715
• Office of Industrial Technologies, Beatrice Cunningham, 202-586-0098
• Office of Utility Technologies, Gloria Elliott, 202-586-4142

Grants to Work on Solar Energy Products

(81.087 Renewable Energy Research and Development)

Renewable Energy Research and Development grants are used to conduct balanced research and development efforts in the following energy technologies; solar buildings, photovoltaics, solar thermal, biomass, alcohol fuels, urban waste, wind, and geothermal. Grants will be offered to develop and transfer to the nonfederal sector various renewable energy technologies. Types of assistance: project grants. Estimate of annual funds available: Grants: not separately identified. (Note: Discretionary funds for grants are not specifically contained in the President's request for Renewable Energy Research and Development Programs. However, the Department does issue grants if found to be appropriate as a result of unsolicited proposals that clearly are consistent with program objectives and are appropriate as grants in lieu of other contractual methods. Unsolicited proposals have received grants totaling approximately $1,500,000 to $2,000,000 over the past 5 years.)

Contact: Energy Efficiency and Renewable Energy Programmatic Offices:
• Office of Building Technology, State and Community Programs, Lynda Dancy, 202-586-2300

- Residential, Commercial and Institutional Buildings, Regina Washington, 202-586-1660
- Office of Industrial Technologies, Beatrice Cunningham, 202-586-0098
- Office of Transportation Technologies, Nancy Blackwell, 202-586-6715
- Office of Utility Technologies, Gloria Elliott, 202-586-4142

Grants to Develop Uses of Fossil Fuels
(81.089 Fossil Energy Research and Development)

The mission of the Fossil Energy (FE) Research and Development program is to promote the development and use of environmentally and economically superior technologies for supply, conversion, delivery and utilization of fossil fuels. These activities will involve cooperation with industry, DOE Laboratories, universities, and states. Success in this mission will benefit the Nation through lower energy costs, reduced environmental impact, increased technology exports, and reduced dependence on insecure energy sources. Types of assistance: project grants; project grants (cooperative agreements). Estimate of annual funds available: Grants and cooperative agreements: $7,500,000. Contact: Mary J. Roland, Fossil Energy Program, FE-122, U.S. Department of Energy, Germantown, MD 20545; 301-903-3514.

grants for health research
(81.108 Epidemiology and Other Health Studies Financial Assistance Program)

This financial assistance program provides financial support for research, education, conferences, communication and other activities relating to the health of Department of Energy workers, as well as other populations potentially exposed to health hazards associated with energy production, transmission, and use. Types of assistance: Project grants. Estimate of annual funds available: $1,200,000. Contact: Office of Epidemiologic Studies, Department of Energy, Mail Stop EH-62/270CC, Germantown, MD 20874; 301-903-3721.

Grants to Businesses That Employ People with Disabilities
(84.234 Projects with Industry)

Projects with Industry grants create and expand job and career opportunities for individuals with disabilities in the competitive labor market, to provide appropriate placement resources by engaging private industry in training and placement. Types of assistance: project grants; project grants (cooperative agreements). Estimate of annual funds available: Grants: $22,071,000. (Note: This amount may change upon enactment of the Rehabilitation Act.) Contact: Ms. Martha Muskie, Rehabilitation Services Administration, U.S. Department of Education, 600 Independence Ave., Washington, DC 20202; 202-205-7320.

Grants for International Peace
(91.001 International Peace and Conflict Management)

Grants for International Peace provide support for education and training, research, and public information on international peace and conflict resolution. Types of assistance: project grants. Estimate of annual funds available: $1,900,000. Contact: United States Institute of Peace, 1200 17th St., NW, Suite 200, Washington, DC 20036.

Grants for International Peace Articles

(91.002 International Peace and Conflict Management - Articles and Manuscripts)

This grant program provides support for education and training, research and public information on international peace and conflict resolution and on themes and topics identified by the institute. Types of assistance: project grants. Estimate of annual funds available: $1,000,000. Contact: Office of Public Affairs, United States Institute of Peace, 1200 17th St., NW, Suite 200, Washington, DC 20036.

Grants for Nursing Research

(93.361 Nursing Research)

The National Institute of Nursing Research supports clinical and basic research to establish a scientific basis for the care of individuals across the life span- from management of patients during illness and recovery to the reduction of risks for disease and disability and the promotion of healthy lifestyles. Types of assistance: Project grants. Estimate of annual funds available: $5,498,000. Contact: National Institute of Nursing Research, National Institutes of Health, Building 45, Room 3AN12, 45 Center Drive, MSC 6300, Bethesda, MD 20892; 301-594-6869.

Grants for Family Violence Prevention

(93.592 Family Violence Prevention and Services/ Grants for Bettered Women's Shelters-Discretionary Grants)

This grant program was created to fund a wide range of discretionary activities for the purpose of preventing family violence; protecting victims and their dependents; improving the design, delivery, and coordination of services to address family violence; gathering information on the incidence of family violence; and increasing knowledge and understanding of the issue through research, demonstration, and evaluation projects. Types of assistance: Project grants. Estimate of annual funds available: $10,230,000. Contact: Office of Community Services, Administration for Children and Families, 370 L'Enfant Promenade, SW, Washington, DC 20447; 202-401-5529.

Grants for Agricultural Safety Research

(93.956 Agricultural Health and Safety Programs)

Agricultural Health and Safety Programs address the research, education, and intervention activities that are unique to agriculture by establishing centers for agricultural research, education, and disease and injury prevention. Types of assistance: Project grants. Estimate of annual funds available: $7,962,408. Contact: Grants Management Branch, Procurement and Grants Office, Centers for Disease Control and Prevention, 2920 Brandywine Rd., Atlanta, GA 30341; 770-488-2710.

MORE MONEY AND HELP FOR ENTREPRENEURS FROM THE STATES

Who Can Use State Money?

All states require that funds be used solely by state residents. But that shouldn't limit you to exploring possibilities only in the state in which you currently reside. If you reside in Maine, but Massachusetts agrees to give you $100,000 to start your own business, it would be worth your while to consider moving to Massachusetts. Shop around for the best deal.

Types Of State Money And Help Available

Each state has different kinds and amounts of money and assistance programs available, but these sources of financial and counseling help are constantly being changed. What may not be available this year may very well be available next. Therefore, in the course of your exploration, you might want to check in with the people who operate the business "hotlines" to discover if anything new has been added to the states' offerings.

Described below are the major kinds of programs that are offered by most of the states.

Information

Hotlines or One-Stop Shops are available in many states through a toll-free number that hooks you up with someone who will either tell you what you need to know or refer you to someone who can. These hotlines are invaluable -- offering information on everything from business permit regulations to obscure financing programs. Most states also offer some kind of booklet that tells you to how to start-up a business in that state. Ask for it. It will probably be free.

Small Business Advocates operate in all fifty states and are part of a national organization (the National Association of State Small Business Advocates) devoted to helping small business people function efficiently with their state governments. They are a good source for help in cutting through bureaucratic red tape.

Funding Programs

Free Money can come in the form of grants, and works the same as free money from the federal government. You do not have to pay it back.

Loans from state governments work in the same way as those from the federal government -- they are given directly to entrepreneurs. Loans are usually at interest rates below the rates charged at commercial institutions and are also set aside for those companies, which have trouble getting a loan elsewhere. This makes them an ideal source for riskier kinds of ventures.

Loan Guarantees are similar to those offered by the federal government. For this program, the state government will go to the bank with you and co-sign your loan. This, too, is ideal for high-risk ventures that normally would not get a loan.

Interest Subsidies On Loans is a unique concept not used by the federal government. In this case, the state will subsidize the interest rate you are charged by a bank. For example, if the bank gives you a loan for $50,000 at 10 percent per year interest, your interest payments will be $5,000 per year. With an interest subsidy you might have to pay only $2,500 since the state will pay the other half. This is like getting the loan at 5 percent instead of 10 percent.

Industrial Revenue Bonds Or General Obligation Bonds are a type of financing that can be used to purchase only fixed assets, such as a factory or equipment. In the case of Industrial Revenue Bonds the state will raise money from the

general public to buy your equipment. Because the state acts as the middleman, the people who lend you the money do not have to pay federal taxes on the interest they charge you. As a result, you get the money cheaper because they get a tax break. If the state issues General Obligation Bonds to buy your equipment, the arrangement will be similar to that for an Industrial Revenue Bond except that the state promises to repay the loan if you cannot.

Matching Grants supplement and abet federal grant programs. These kinds of grants could make an under-capitalized project go forward. Awards usually hinge on the usefulness of the project to its surrounding locality.

Loans To Agricultural Businesses are offered in states with large rural, farming populations. They are available solely to farmers and/or agribusiness entrepreneurs.

Loans To Exporters are available in some states as a kind of gap financing to cover the expenses involved in fulfilling a contract.

Energy Conservation Loans are made to small businesses to finance the installation of energy-saving equipment or devices.

Special Regional Loans are ear-marked for specific areas in a state that may have been hard hit economically or suffer from under-development. If you live in one of these regions, you may be eligible for special funds.

High Tech Loans help fledgling companies develop or introduce new products into the marketplace.

Loans To Inventors help the entrepreneur develop or market new products.

Local Government Loans are used for start-up and expansion of businesses within the designated locality.

Childcare Facilities Loans help businesses establish on-site daycare facilities.

Loans To Women And/Or Minorities are available in almost every state from funds specifically reserved for economically disadvantaged groups.

Many federally funded programs are administered by state governments. Among them are the following programs:

The SBA 7(A) Guaranteed and *Direct Loan* program can guarantee up to 90 percent of a loan made through a private lender (up to $750,000), or make direct loans of up to $150,000.

The SBA 504 establishes Certified Development Companies whose debentures are guaranteed by the SBA. Equity participation of the borrower must be at least 10 percent, private financing 60 percent and CDC participation at a maximum of 40 percent, up to $750,000.

Small Business Innovative Research Grants (SBIR) award between $20,000 to $50,000 to entrepreneurs to support six months of research on a technical innovation. They are then eligible for up to $500,000 to develop the innovation.

Small Business Investment Companies (SBIC) license, regulate and provide financial assistance in the form of equity financing, long-term loans, and management services.

Community Development Block Grants are available to cities and counties for the commercial rehabilitation of existing buildings or structures used for business, commercial, or industrial purposes. Grants of up to $500,000 can be made.

Every $15,000 of grant funds invested must create at least one full-time job, and at least 51 percent of the jobs created must be for low and moderate income families.

Farmers Home Administration (FmHA) Emergency Disaster Loans are available in counties where natural disaster has substantially affected farming, ranching or aquaculture production.

FmHA Farm Loan Guarantees are made to family farmers and ranchers to enable them to obtain funds from private lenders. Funds must be used for farm ownership, improvements, and operating purposes.

FmHA Farm Operating Loans to meet operating expenses, finance recreational and nonagricultural enterprises, to add to family income, and to pay for mandated safety and pollution control changes are available at variable interest rates. Limits are $200,000 for an insured farm operating loan and $400,000 for a guaranteed loan.

FmHA Farm Ownership Loans can be used for a wide range of farm improvement projects. Limits are $200,000 for an insured loan and $300,000 for a guaranteed loan.

FmHA Soil And Water Loans must be used by individual farmers and ranchers to develop, conserve, and properly use their land and water resources and to help abate pollution. Interest rates are variable; each loan must be secured by real estate.

FmHA Youth Project Loans enable young people to borrow for income-producing projects sponsored by a school or 4H club.

Assistance Programs

Management Training is offered by many states in subjects ranging from bookkeeping to energy conservation.

Business Consulting is offered on almost any subject. Small Business Development Centers are the best source for this kind of assistance.

Market Studies to help you sell your goods or services within or outside the state are offered by many states. They all also have State Data Centers which not only collect demographic and other information about markets within the state, but also have access to federal data which can pinpoint national markets. Many states also provide the services of graduate business students at local universities to do the legwork and analysis for you.

Business Site Selection is done by specialists in every state who will identify the best place to locate a business.

Licensing, Regulation, And Permits information is available from most states through "one-stop shop" centers by calling a toll-free number. There you'll get help in finding your way through the confusion of registering a new business.

Employee Training Programs offer on-site training and continuing education opportunities.

Research And Development assistance for entrepreneurs is a form of assistance that is rapidly increasing as more and more states try to attract high technology-related companies. Many states are even setting up clearing houses so that small businesses can have one place to turn to find expertise throughout a statewide university system.

Procurement Programs have been established in some states to help you sell products to state, federal, and local governments.

Export Assistance is offered to identify overseas markets. Some states even have overseas offices to drum up business prospects for you.

Assistance In Finding Funding is offered in every state, particularly through regional Small Business Development Centers. They will not only identify funding sources in the state and federal governments but will also lead you through the complicated application process.

Special Help For Minorities And Women is available in almost every state to help boost the participation of women and minorities in small business ventures. They offer special funding programs and, often, one-on-one counseling to assure a start-up success.

Venture Capital Networking is achieved through computer databases that hook up entrepreneurs and venture capitalists. This service is usually free of charge. In fact, the demand for small business investment opportunities is so great that some states require the investor to pay to be listed.

Inventors Associations have been established to encourage and assist inventors in developing and patenting their products.

Annual Governors' Conferences give small business people the chance to air their problems with representatives from state agencies and the legislature.

Small Business Development Centers (SBDCs), funded jointly by the federal and state governments, are usually associated with the state university system. SBDCs are a godsend to small business people. They will not only help you figure out if your business project is feasible, but also help you draw up a sensible business plan, apply for funding, and check in with you frequency once your business is up and running to make sure it stays that way.

Tourism programs are prominent in states whose revenues are heavily dependent on the tourist trade. They are specifically aimed at businesses in the tourist industries.

Small Business Institutes at local colleges use senior level business students as consultants to help develop business plans or plan expansions.

Technology Assistance Centers help high tech companies and entrepreneurs establish new businesses and plan business expansions.

On-Site Energy Audits are offered free of charge by many states to help control energy costs and improve energy efficiency for small businesses. Some states also conduct workshops to encourage energy conservation measures.

Minority Business Development Centers offer a wide range of services from initial counseling on how to start a business to more complex issues of planning and growth.

Business Information Centers (BICs) provide the latest in high-tech hardware, software, and telecommunications to help small businesses get started. BIC is a place where business owners and aspiring business owners can go to use hardware/software, hard copy books, and publications to plan their business, expand an existing business, or venture into new business areas. Also, on-site counseling is available.

Alabama

Alabama Development Office
401 Adams Avenue
Montgomery, AL 36104-4340
800-248-0033
334-242-0400
Fax: 334-242-0415
www.ado.state.al.us

Alabama Department of Revenue
P.O. Box 327001
Montgomery, AL 36132-7001
334-242-1170
www.ador.state.al.us

Business Assistance

Alabama Development Office: A one-stop source for business support and incentives that will tailor programs to meet individual companies' needs.

Economic Development Partnership of Alabama: A private, not-for-profit organization of Alabama businesses and industries dedicated to assisting business development in Alabama. Its Business Information division manages databases with information on the state, including available buildings and sites. Contact: Economic Development Partnership of Alabama, 500 Beacon parkway W, Birmingham, AL 35209; 800-252-5453, {www.edpa.org}.

Alabama Technology Network: The Alabama Technology Network is a nonprofit organization that links the University of Alabama System, Auburn University, the Economic Development Partnership of Alabama, and selected two-year colleges in a coordinated effort to improve economic development opportunities in the state through technical assistance, workforce training and technology transfer. Field engineers are based in ten regions throughout Alabama and offer a wide range of technical expertise to help Alabama manufacturers improve their global competitiveness. They provide a variety of services, which include: providing on-site technical consultations, conducting detailed needs assessments, outlining potential solutions, providing technical assistance to solve problems, and identifying external service providers as needed. Contact the Technology Network directly via the Internet {www.atn.org}, or through Alabama Industrial Development Training.

Alabama Small Business Consortium: The Alabama Small Business Development Consortium (ASBDC), hosted by the University of Alabama at Birmingham, provides managerial and technical consulting assistance and training at no cost to current and potential small business persons statewide. This service is offered through 10 Small Business Development Centers, the Alabama International Trade Center, the Alabama Technology Assistance Program, and the Alabama Small Business Procurement System. Contact ASBDC via the Internet at {www.asbdc.org} or at Alabama Small Business Development Consortium, Office of the State Director, University of Alabama at Birmingham, 2800 Milan Ct., Birmingham, AL 35211; 205-943-6750.

Procurement Technical Assistance Program: This program run by the Alabama Small Business Development Consortium assists small businesses by notifying businesses of bidding opportunities on government contracts, counseling businesses on the procurement process and marketing products and services to the government, training business owners at procurement workshops and providing networking opportunities.

Department of Agriculture and Industry: Supplies both information and technical support to farmers, businesses and consumers. Contact: Department of Agriculture and Industry, P.O. Box 3336, Montgomery, AL 36109; 334-240-7171; {www.agri-ind.state.al.us}.

Alabama Industrial Development Training: Offers recruiting, assessing and training potential employees; developing and producing training materials, and locating facilities; and, delivering customized services. Contact: Alabama Industrial Development and Training, One Technology Court, Montgomery, AL 36116; 334-242-4158; {www.aidt.edu}.

Alabama's Answers: Comprehensive handbook on doing business in Alabama, available from the Alabama Development Office.

Business Financing

Industrial Revenue Bonds: Financing available for land, buildings and equipment.
Economic Development Loan Program: Loans for the purchase of land, buildings, machinery and equipment for new and expanding businesses.
Revolving Loan Funds: Gap financing for land, buildings, equipment, renovation and working capital for companies creating jobs.
Business Loan Guarantee Program: Provides funding for the acquisitions of fixed assets or working capital for companies creating or retaining jobs in economically distressed areas.
Venture Capital Funds: Small companies may receive equity capital and long-term loans.
Local and Regional Development Organizations: More than 100 throughout the state assist in securing loan assistance.
Section 108 Loan Guarantee: Provides communities with an efficient source of financing for economic development and large-scale physical development projects.
Tennessee Valley Authority's Economic Development Loan Fund: Multi-million dollar revolving loan program that provides financing for new industrial plants, plant expansions, plant retention, and infrastructure development such as speculative industrial buildings and industrial parks.
Alabama Plan for Linked Deposits: This program, which is run by the State Treasurer's Office, allows the Treasurer to make deposits in state banks on which the banks pay 2% below the normal interest rate paid to the state for its funds. The reduction in the interest rate paid by the bank must be passed on to the borrower on loans qualifying for this program. This pass-along amounts to a 2% subsidy on the borrower's interest rates for two years.
USDA Rural Development: Community and business programs for areas with populations of less than 50,000 include Business and Industry Guaranteed Loans up to $25 million and Direct Loans up to $10 million, Rural Business Enterprise Grants, and Rural Economic Development Zero Interest Loans.

Tax Incentives

Alabama is the only state to allow the deduction of all federal income taxes paid.
No inventory tax for businesses.
Corporate income tax limited to 6.5 percent.
Income Tax Capital Credit: If a business entity invests in a qualifying project that meets certain requirements and is approved by the Alabama Department of Revenue, the company may receive an annual credit against its income tax liability generated from the qualifying project. The capital credit is equivalent to 5% of the capital costs of the qualifying project, and can be utilized for a period of 20 years beginning during the year the project is placed in service.
Net Operating Loss Carryforward: Corporate income tax law provides for a 15-year carryforward of net operating losses. In computing net income, a corporation is allowed a deduction for the sum of the net operating losses which are carried forward. Each net operating loss may be carried forward and deducted only during the 15 consecutive year period immediately following the year in which it arose.

Enterprise Zone Credit

Pollution Control Equipment Deduction: All amounts invested in pollution control equipment/materials acquired or constructed in Alabama primarily for the control, reduction, or elimination of air or water pollution are deducted directly from the income apportioned to Alabama.
Enterprise Zone Credit: The corporate income tax enterprise zone credit is offered to help encourage economic growth to areas in Alabama that are considered economically depressed. To qualify for this credit, a business must meet detailed requirements concerning site location and employee qualifications.
Educational Tax Credit: An employer could qualify to receive a credit of 20% of the actual cost of an employer sponsored educational program that enhances basic skills of employees up to and including the twelfth grade functional level.

Foreign Corporation Deduction for Manufacturing Facilities: Alabama law contains several provisions to allow foreign corporations to significantly reduce or almost eliminate their corporate franchise tax liability.

Assessed Value fixed by Alabama Constitution: Amendment 373 of the Constitution provides that business property will be assessed at 20% of its fair market value. That is, for property with a fair market value of $1,000,000, the assessed value would be $200,000 ($1,000,000 x 20%). The combined state and local millage rate would then be applied to the assessed value.

Low Millage Rates: Section 214 of the Constitution limits the state millage rate on both real and personal property to 6.5 mills. This rate is equivalent to a tax of $6.50 for every $1000 of assessed value. However, both cities and counties may levy millage rates in addition to the state's 6.5 mills. These local rates vary but the average rate for any one locality is 43 mills, including the state's 6.5 mills. For business property with a fair market value of $1,000,000 the average property tax would be only $8,600 ($1,000,000 x 20% x .043).

Tax Incentive Reform Act: Allows qualified industries to receive abatements of non-educational ad valorem taxes for new businesses locating to Alabama, and for expansions of existing facilities in Alabama.

Tax Incentive Reform Act

Inventory and Raw Materials Exemption: All stocks of goods, wares, and merchandise held for resale, as well as raw materials, are statutorily exempt from ad valorem taxes.

Raw Materials, Finished Goods, and Inventory Exemptions: All raw materials, finished goods, and stocks of goods, wares, and merchandise held for resale are statutorily exempt from property taxes.

Corporate Shares Tax Deductions: Domestic corporations (incorporated in Alabama) are responsible for the payment of corporate shares tax. This tax is actually an ad valorem tax on the assessed value of capital stock of the corporation. The shares tax is calculated like any other ad valorem tax. There are several deductions from the value of shares that can be considered as tax incentives for Alabama domestic corporations.

Deduction For Investing In New And Existing Manufacturing Facilities: Business entities making a new investment in a new or existing manufacturing facility in Alabama may deduct the amount invested from their Alabama net worth.

Exports

International Trade Center: Services offered include foreign market research, strategic planning and consulting, implementation recommendations, training seminars and general information. Contact: Alabama International Trade Center, University of Alabama, Box 870396, Tuscaloosa, AL 35287; 205-348-7621.

Alabama Development Office: Offers trade promotion services to Alabama manufacturers, including:
- Participation in overseas catalog shows, trade shows, and trade missions
- Opportunities to meet one-on-one with foreign buyers visiting Alabama
- Listing in the *Alabama International Trade Directory*, a publication that is disseminated worldwide
- *Public/Private Grant Program*: Designed to assist Alabama companies in expanding export activities through participation in foreign trade shows and missions
- *Representative Offices*: Germany, Japan, South Korea, and the Middle East

Women and Minorities

Office of Minority Business Enterprise: Assists minorities in achieving effective and equitable participation in the American free enterprise system and in overcoming social and economic disadvantages that have limited their participation in the past. Management and technical assistance is provided to minority firms on request. Contact: Office of Minority Business Enterprise, 401 Adams Ave., Montgomery, AL 36130; 334-242-2224; 800-447-4191.

Alaska

Alaska Department of Community and Economic Development
P.O. Box 110809
Juneau, AK 98111-0809
907-465-2017
800-478-LOAN
Fax: 907-465-3767
www.dced.state.ak.us

Alaska Industrial Development and Export Authority
813 West Northern Lights Blvd.
Anchorage, AK 99503
907-269-3000
Fax: 907-269-3044
www.aidea.org

Business Assistance

Division of Community and Business Development: This division of the Alaska Department of Community and Economic Development serves as a commercial liaison for the state and for private sector businesses. The office provides promotion and development of resource markets to promote Alaska as a desirable location for business investment opportunities and to assist in test marketing of resource products; assistance to new and existing Alaskan businesses and industry through business counseling, Alaska Product Preference, and Made in Alaska product identification; and economic and business information.

Alaska Product Preference, Forest Product Preference, and The Alaska Recycled Product Preference Programs: These programs provide incentives for Alaska businesses responding to bids or proposals for state contracts by giving preferential consideration. The Alaska Product Preference Program and the Alaska Forest Product Preference Program can provide a cost preference of up to 7%, while the Recycled Product Preference Program offers a 5% preference.

For these programs, contact Department of Community and Economic Development, Division of Community and Business Development, 550 W. 7th Ave., Suite 1770, Anchorage, AK 99501-3510; 907-269-8108; Fax: 907-269-8125; {www.dced.state.ak.us/econdev/prodpref.htm#AlaskaProductPreference}.

Buy Alaska: The Buy Alaska Program's mission is to assist businesses, consumers, and government entities in finding competitive Alaskan sources for goods and services with the goal of keeping more dollars in Alaska. The Buy Alaska Program offers the free service of researching buying needs and "matching" buyers with sellers. Businesses and consumers seeking to buy competitively-priced goods and services can get help from Buy Alaska in identifying local Alaskan vendors and providers from which to make their purchases. For these programs, contact Buy Alaska, University of Alaska, Small Business Development Center, 430 W. 7th Avenue, Suite 110, Anchorage, AK 99501; 907-274-7232; 800-478-7232; {www.alaskanet.com/buyalaska}.

Alaska Export Assistance Center: This branch of the U.S. Department of Commerce champions the interests of Alaskan companies around the world, particularly small and medium-sized firms. Primary focus is on the Russian Far East and countries of the Pacific Rim. Contact Alaska Export Assistance Center, 550 W. 7th Ave., Suite 1770, Anchorage, AK 99501; 907-271-6237; Fax: 907-271-6242; {www.alaska.net/~export}.

Alaska Economic Development Resource Guide: This publication is available for #7. It describes more than 100 assistance programs for Alaskan individuals and businesses. It is also available free in electronic form at {www.comregaf.state.ak.us/EDRG/EDRG.htm}. For a print copy, send your check to Department of Community and Regional Affairs, Municipal and Regional Assistance Division, Research & Analysis Section, P.O. Box 112100, Juneau, AK 99811; 907-465-4750.

Business Financing

Sustainable Development Program: The program's primary function is to provide (grant) seed money to entities that propose viable sustainable development projects that are community based and supported. The program is not intended to fund pure research. The maximum funding available for any one project is $50,000. But, it's anticipated that most applicants will receive less, thereby allowing the program to fund between six to twelve sustainable development projects. This program is not intended to provide the sole or majority funding of a project. The program will continue funding projects for as long as money is available.

Alaska Science and Technology Foundation Grants (ASTF): Major individual grants of over $2,000 and group grants are both available under this program. Projects that provide economic development, direct benefits and utilize end user participation are considered ideal. ASTF typically requires a financial match equal to the amount they contribute and technology projects that develop a product or process are required to repay ASTF funds through revenue, license fees or profit from sales of the product. For this program, contact Alaska Science and Technology Foundation, 4500 Diplomacy Drive, Suite 515, Anchorage, AK 99506; 907-272-4333; {pprc.pnl.gov/pprc/rfp/astf.html}.

Alaska Growth Capital: This is a commercial financial institution, licensed and regulated by the State of Alaska. It is not regulated as a bank, but rather as a Business and Industrial Development Corporation (BIDCO). BIDCOs do not accept deposits and do not provide consumer lending. BIDCOs focus exclusively on financing businesses. For more information, contact Alaska Growth Capital, 2121 Abbot Road, Suite 101, Anchorage, AK 99507; 907-349-4904; 888-315-4904; {www.akgrowth.com}.

Power Project Fund: Provides loans to local utilities, local governments or independent power producers for the development or upgrade of electric power facilities, including conservation, bulk fuel storage and waste energy conservation, or potable water supply projects. Loan term is related to the life of the project. For more information, contact Department of Community and Regional Affairs, Division of Energy, 333 West 4th Avenue, Suite 220, Anchorage, AK 99501-2341; 907-269-4625.

The Polaris Fund: The purpose of the Polaris Fund is to finance young companies with potential to achieve profitable sales by providing equity capital. Ideal companies should have an experienced management team, an innovative, distinctive product with a $100-$500 million growing market and a well-defined channel for sales. Polaris investments are usually in the $100,000 to $500,000 range, and favor companies that align Polaris closely with management. For more information, contact Jim Yarmon, c/o Yarmon Investments, 840 K Street, #201, Anchorage, AK 99501; 907-276-4466.

Business Incentive Program: Under this program companies will be reimbursed (rather than be paid up front) for designated portions of relocation costs, site development costs, special employee training not covered by other programs, and special analysis of sites in Alaska. The program was passed into law in April 1998 and is limited to $3 million annually. Contact: Bill Paulick, Division of Trade & Development, P.O. Box 110804, Juneau, AK 99811-0804; 907-465-3961; {E-mail: Bill_Paulick@commerce.state.ak.us}.

Small Business Economic Development Revolving Loan Fund: This program was established in 1987 in conjunction with the U.S. Department of Commerce, Economic Development Administration (EDA). The purpose of the program is to provide private sector employment in the areas designated by EDA. The maximum loan amount is $300,000. Applicants are required to obtain additional private, non-public financing of approximately twice the amount requested. The interest rate of prime minus 4 points is set by the Loan Administration Board consisting of three members from the existing divisional loan committee and two members from the private sector. The board is responsible for setting loan policy and for making all major loan decisions. For more information, contact Alaska Department of Community and Economic Development, Division of Investments, P.O. Box 34159, Juneau, AK 99803; 907-465-2510; 800-478-LOAN; {www.dced.state.ak.us/investments}.

Commercial Fishing Revolving Loan Fund: Commercial fishing loans are available for various purposes at prime plus two percent (up to a maximum of 10.5%) for a 15-year term. All loans must be secured by adequate collateral. Contact: Alaska Department of Community and Economic Development, Division of Investments, P.O. Box 34159, Juneau, AK 99803; 907-465-2510; 800-478-LOAN; {www.dced.state.ak.us/investments}.

Alaska Industrial Development and Export Authority: AIDEA is a public corporation of the State of Alaska, constituting a political subdivision under the laws of the state. It was created by the Alaska Legislature to "promote, develop and advance the general prosperity and economic welfare of the people of Alaska, to relieve problems of unemployment, and to create additional employment". AIDEA accomplishes this through its credit and development finance programs. It does not provide grants.

Development Finance: Alaska Industrial Development and Export Authority (AIDEA) may own and operate projects that provide infrastructure support for resource development and bring economic benefits to Alaska. To qualify a project must be endorsed by the local government where the project will be sited and be economically feasible.

Loan Participation Program: This AIDEA program provides long-term financing to Alaska businesses for new or existing projects or for the refinancing of existing loans. AIDEA is not a direct lender, but through the Loan Participation Program, AIDEA purchases a portion of a loan that is sponsored and originated by an eligible financial institution. In most cases, the interest rate on the AIDEA portion of the loan is slightly lower than the rate on the bank's portion. The term of the AIDEA portion of the loan can also exceed the term of the bank portion. This can result in lower scheduled payments for the borrower. AIDEA provides fully amortizing, long term financing, up to 15 years for personal property or 25 years for real property, based on a maximum loan to value of 75%.

The Rural Development Initiative Fund (RDIF): This loan program is targeted to create employment opportunities to Alaskan communities of 5,000 or less by providing small, basic industries with business capital. Individuals may borrow up to $100,000 with two or more borrowers eligible for up to $200,000. AIDEA can guarantee a portion of the RDIF loan retained by the originating financial institution. RDIF is administered by the Department of Community and Regional Affairs.

For these programs, contact: Alaska Industrial Development and Export Authority, 480 West Tudor, Anchorage, AK 99503; 907-269-3000; Fax: 907-269-3044; {www.alaska.net/~aidea}.

Fisheries Enhancement Loan Program: Loans may be made for planning, construction, and operation of fish hatchery facilities, including preconstruction activities necessary to obtain a permit, construction activities to build the hatchery facility, and costs to operate the facility. The maximum loan term is 30 years. No repayment of the principal is required for an initial period of six to ten years; no interest on the principal shall accrue during that period. Contact Alaska Department of Community and Economic Development, Division of Investments, P.O. Box 34159, Juneau, AK 99803; 907-465-2510; 800-478-LOAN; {www.dced.state.ak.us/investments}.

Alaska Science and Technology Grants: The Alaska Science and Technology Foundation awards grants that further its purpose of promoting and enhancing, "through basic and applied research and the development and commercialization of technology, economic development and technological innovation in Alaska; public health; telecommunications; and the sustained growth and development of Alaskan scientific and engineering capabilities." Contact Sharon Fisher, Outreach Administrator, 794 University Avenue, Suite 102, Fairbanks, AK 99709; 907-452-1624, Fax: 907-452-1625; {www.astf.org}.

- Major Individual Grants focus on either knowledge projects, designed to develop and distribute new knowledge to Alaskans; or technology projects, which focus on the development and commercialization of technology.
- Small grants are comprised of the same features of those found in major grants but the overall financial assistance does not exceed $20,000.
- Group projects are categorized by possessing many participants aimed at restructuring an industry or launching a major new product.
- Small Business Innovation Research SBIR Bridging Grants assist in bridging the period from the completion of one phase of an SBIR grant to the beginning of the next.

Tax Incentives

Work Opportunity Tax Credit (WOTC): Offers employers tax credits as an incentive to hire people from seven target groups including Alaska Temporary Assistance Program (ATAP) and Aid for Families with Dependent Children (AFDC) recipients, food stamp recipients, veterans, vocational rehabilitation recipients, ex-felons, and high risk youth. The credit amount is 40% of up to $6,000 in qualified first year wages with a maximum credit of $2,400.

Welfare-to-Work Tax Credit (W2W): The W2W tax credit is available for hiring long-term ATAP and AFDC clients. The W2W tax credit is 35% of the first $10,000 in wages paid the first year, and 50% of the first $10,000 paid for the second year. The maximum tax credit is $3,500 the first year and $5,000 the second year for a total of $8,500.

For information on these programs, contact Alaska Employment Service, WOTC Coordinator, P.O. Box 25509, Juneau, AK 99802; 907-465-5925; {www.state.ak.us/local/akpages/LABOR/offices/win_of.htm}.

Exploration Incentive: Up to $20 million in qualifying costs can be credited against future state corporate income tax, mining license tax and production royalties. Geophysical and geochemical surveys, trenching, bulk sampling, drilling, metallurgical testing and underground exploration are included as qualifying costs. Unused credit can be retained for 15 years and may be assigned to successors in interest. For more information, contact Department of Natural Resources, Division of Mining, 3601 C Street, Suite 884, Anchorage, AK 99503; 907-269-8600; {www.dnr.state.ak.us}.

Depreciable Property: 18% of the federal income tax credit for investment in specified depreciable property can be applied to Alaska state corporate income tax. Each tax year, as the property is put into use in the state, up to $20 million of qualified investments may be claimed with the exception of the unlimited credit allowed on pollution control facilities. Contact: Alaska Department of Revenue, Income & Excise Audit Division, P.O. Box 110420, Juneau, AK 99811-0420; 907-465-2320; {www.revenue.state.ak.us/index.htm}.

Exports

Division of Trade and Development: Trade representatives help to promote Alaska products and services by providing information and access to markets, acting as liaisons between domestic and foreign markets, and promoting investment in Alaska's natural resources. Contact: Division of Trade & Development, 3601 C Street, Suite 700, Anchorage AK 99503; 907-269-8121; {www.commerce.state.ak.us/trade/econ/prodpref.htm}.

Alaska Industrial Development Export Authority (AIDEA): AIDEA assists businesses through two programs:
1. *Loan Participation*: New or existing projects can receive long term financing or the refinancing of existing loans. Eligible projects include commercial facilities such as office buildings, warehouses, retail establishments, hotels, and manufacturing facilities. AIDEA participation may total up to 80% of a commercial lending institution loan with a maximum of $10 million.
2. *Business and Export Assistance*: This loan guarantee program provides financial institutions with up to an 80% guarantee on the principal of a loan. AIDEA's added support can make project financing, refinancing, and working capital guarantees up to $1 million available to borrowers who might not otherwise find commercial financing.

Accelerated Amortization Program: Under this program, AIDEA may allow the financial institution to amortize its portion of the loan using an accelerated amortization schedule if the project can support the increased debt service, and if the shortened schedule is necessary for the bank's participation. Borrowers may obtain such financing for manufacturing facilities, real estate and equipment under the Loan Participation Program.

Arizona

Department of Commerce
3800 N. Central, Suite 1650
Phoenix, AZ 85012
602-280-1480
800-542-5684
Fax: 620-280-1339
www.commerce.state.az.us/

Business Assistance

Arizona Business Connection: A resource center for information, referrals and advice for every stage of small business development. Representatives are available to answer questions and provide a free custom packet.

Small Business Advocate: Works with chambers of commerce and other groups to develop policies and programs that will address fundamental statewide issues of concern to all small businesses.

- Develops customized packets of information and licenses required for small business start-up, expansion, and relocation.
- Provides the booklet *Entrepreneur's Encyclopedia* which includes an extensive directory and resources for referrals and networking opportunities.
- Provides coordination and publicity for programs and services that assist minority and women business owners, and assists state agencies in certification of minority and women owned businesses.
- Conducts seminars to help local companies procure goods and services from qualified firms.
- Assists entrepreneurs in resolving matters involving state government offices.
- The High Technology Division aids and assists the growth of high technology companies in Arizona.

The Community Planning Staff: Provides technical assistance on development-related issues, such as community-strategic planning, land-use planning, design review, zoning and infrastructure development, and financing. Provides direct assistance to rural communities in organizing an economic development program or effort, and evaluating community resources. Provides assistance with downtown revitalization projects. Provides support for rural community tourism development efforts. This program helps organizations responsible for retention and expansion develop a program to retain and encourage expansion of existing businesses. The program places significant emphasis on creating a business environment for stable, successful companies. It also provides resources to aid in the design and implementation of a locally defined and community-based Business Retention and Expansion program. It provides assistance with designing, implementing and monitoring cost-effective energy conservation projects in residential, commercial and industrial buildings throughout the state.

Arizona's Work Force Recruitment and Job Training Program: Provides job training assistance to businesses creating net new jobs in Arizona. The program is designed to provide companies with a well equipped work force while ensuring maximum leverage of state and federal training funds.

Business Financing

Commerce & Economic Development Commission (CEDC): The CEDC is appointed by the governor to advise and coordinate economic development policy for the state of Arizona. The Commission administers the CEDC Fund that provides financial assistance to support the state's economic development efforts.

Job Training Grants: provide financial assistance to companies creating new jobs in Arizona. Funds can be used to offset costs associated with developing and implementing a job training plan specific to the company. Typically it funds between $300 and $1,000 per net new job created..

Private Activity Bonds: can be used for the construction of industrial and manufacturing facilities and the purchase of equipment.

Tax Incentives

Corporate income tax is levied for all firms at 6.69 percent. The minimum filing amount is $50. In general, Arizona:

- Has no corporate franchise tax
- Business inventories are exempt from property tax
- Levies no state income tax on dividends from controlled subsidiaries in other states (parent companies).
- Adopted a "water's edge" limitation to combine worldwide corporate income
- Has a five-year accelerated depreciation schedule for assessing valuation of class three and class four personal property.
- Provides for a 10 percent income tax credit on purchase price of real and personal property used to control or prevent pollution
- Exempts chemicals used directly as part of an integrated system in manufacturing, mining, research and development, and certain other activities from transaction privilege and use tax.
- Exempts machinery or equipment used directly in manufacturing, processing, fabricating, job printing, refining or metallurgical operations from both transaction privilege and use tax
- Exempts machinery or equipment used in research and development from transaction privilege and use tax.

Defense Restructuring Program: Since 1993, Arizona has had a program to assist defense contractors in maintaining the maximum share of contracts with the U.S. Department of Defense and to support conversion to non-defense production. Benefits include:

- A tax credit against corporate income taxes for up to 40 percent of the real and personal property taxes paid. The credit is based on the number of jobs retained or created.
- Corporate and individual tax credits for increases in net employment above an established baseline. Credits for each new employee can total $7,500 over five years.
- Depreciation or amortization for costs of capital investments may be subtracted from Arizona gross income in one-half of the time period allowed under the Internal Revenue code.

Military Reuse Zone: The Arizona Legislature designated the former Williams Air Force Base, now known as Williams Gateway Airport, as a Military Reuse one. Companies locating within this zone will have their personal property classified as class 8, representing an 80 percent property tax saving, for five years. In addition, there is a transaction privilege tax exemption for many types of construction that is performed for an eligible company located in a military reuse zone.

Research and Development Income Tax Credit: This is a state income tax credit for qualified research and development done in Arizona. This includes research conducted at a state university and funded by the company. The maximum credit is $100,000 in year one, $250,000 in year two, $400,000 in year three, and $500,000 in year four and subsequent years. The program allows a 15-year carry-forward.

Pollution Control Tax Credit: Provides a 10 percent income tax credit on real or personal property used to control or prevent pollution.

Accelerated Depreciation: Provides an aggressive depreciation schedule to encourage new capital investment and reduce personal property tax liability.

The Enterprise Zones Program: Arizona's Enterprise Zone Program offers a state income tax credit up to $3,000 over a three-year period. It also offers property tax reclassification for eligible companies meeting employment and industry requirements. Benefits are based on net new job creation, employment of economically disadvantaged or dislocated workers and location in an enterprise zone.

Exports

The Arizona Department of Commerce provides export counseling, access to federal documents assisting with market research, contact facilitation, access to Arizona State offices in several foreign cities, publications including *Arizona International Business Resource Guide.*

Women and Minorities

Minority/Women-Owned Business Enterprises Office: Acts as a resource and advocate for women and minority small businesses. Services include: a statewide directory of women/minority-owned businesses, Professional Women's conference sponsorship, newsletter containing calendar of events and relevant articles, marketing to state agencies and businesses, and certification seminars.

Arkansas

Arkansas Department of Economic Development
One Capitol Mall
Little Rock, AR 72201
800-ARKANSAS
Fax: 501-682-7341
www.1-800-arkansas.com

Business Assistance

EXISTING WORKFORCE TRAINING PROGRAM

Existing Workforce Training Program (EWTP): Provides financial assistance to Arkansas manufacturing industries for upgrading the skills of their existing workforce. Secondary objectives are to build the capacity within their state-supported institutions to supply the ongoing training needs of Arkansas industries and to increase industry participation in the state's School-to-Work initiative. {www.seark.org/AEWDC/ewtp.htm}

ScrapMatch: A program designed to help Arkansas manufacturers find markets for their industrial scrap materials, thereby lowering the cost of doing business. ScrapMatch uses an electronic data management system to match industrial waste generators with secondary material markets. {www.1-800-arkansas.com/ematch/}

Industrial Waste Minimization Program and Resource Recovery: Reduction, reuse, and recycling of industrial waste is the Industrial Waste Minimization Program's focus. By-product and surplus asset marketing assistance are also provided. The program provides on-site waste reduction audits and technical assistance to industry. {www.adeq.state.ar.us/}

Environmental Permitting Services: The Arkansas Department of Environmental Quality works in a pro-business manner with companies looking to locate or expand operations in Arkansas. The agency recognizes the need for business growth in Arkansas while maintaining their state's positive environmental quality. Contact: Arkansas Department of Environmental Quality, 8001 National Dr., Little Rock, AR 72219; 501-682-0821; {www.adeq.state.ar.us/}

Customized Training Incentive Program: Provides intensive pre-employment training for Arkansas workers to meet the increasing technical employment needs of the state's new and expanding businesses. Additionally, financial assistance to manufacturing industries for upgrading the skills of their existing workforce is also available. {www.work-ed.state.ar.us/listcoord.html}

Business Financing

Bond Guaranty Programs: For companies that have a financial history but are unable to sell industrial revenue bonds to the public, the Arkansas Department of Economic Development (ADED) can assure bond holders of repayment by guaranteeing up to $4 million of a bond issue. The state's guaranty allows the bonds to be sold at a higher credit rating, therefore lowering the effective interest rate for the company. The ADED charges a 5% fee for guaranteeing issues of this type.

Arkansas Capital Corporation: A privately-owned, nonprofit organization established in 1957 to serve as an alternative source of financing for companies in Arkansas. Its main goal is to improve the economic climate in the state by providing long-term, fixed-rate loans to Arkansas companies. As a preferred lender for the Small Business Administration, ACC makes loans to existing operations and business start-ups for everything from new construction and equipment to working capital. ACC loans may be used in combination with bank loans, municipal bond issues, or other sources of financing. Contact: Arkansas Capital Corporation, 225 S. Pulaski St., Little Rock, AR 72201; 501-374-9247; {www.arcapital.com}.

ASTA Investment Fund: The Arkansas Science and Technology Authority (ASTA) administers a special Investment Fund of $2.8 million which can provide seed capital for new and developing technology-based companies through loans, royalty agreements, and limited stock purchases. Contact: Arkansas Science and Technology Authority, 100 Main St., Suite 450, Little Rock, AR 72201; 501-324-9006.

Economic Development District Revolving Funds: Several planning and development districts in Arkansas have revolving loan funds for economic development purposes. The loans are limited to $100,000 per business, must involve specific levels of job creation, and must be matched by a bank loan.

Create Rebate Program: Companies hiring specified net new full-time permanent employees within 24 months after completion of an approved expansion and/or new location project can be eligible to receive a financial incentive to be used for a specific purpose. This incentive ranges from 3.9% to 5% in areas with an unemployment rate in excess of 10%, or more than 3% above the state's average unemployment rate for the preceding calendar year.

Industrial Revenue Bonds: Provide manufacturers with below-market financing. Interest on tax exempt issues is normally 80% of prime, but this may vary depending on terms of the issue. For real estate loans, 15 years is the most common term. The primary goal of this financing program is to enable manufacturers to purchase land, buildings, and equipment to expand their operations.

Tax Incentives

Arkansas Economic Development Act (AEDA): To utilize the AEDA program, companies must sign a financial agreement prior to construction outlining the terms of the incentives and stipulations. There are two basic incentives provided: A state corporate income tax credit up to 100% of the total amount of annual debt service paid to the lender financing a project; Refund of sales and use taxes on construction materials, machinery, and equipment associated with a project during the period specified by the financial agreement.

Advantage Arkansas Program: A job tax credit program for qualifying new and expanding companies which provides corporate income tax credits and sales and use tax refunds to companies locating or expanding in Arkansas.

Income Tax Credit: Advantage Arkansas provides a credit on income tax equal to the average hourly wage of each new worker times 100, with a $3,000 cap per employee. The multiplier increases from 100 to 400 when a business locates in a county that had an unemployment rate equal to or in excess of 150 percent of the state's average unemployment rate for the previous calendar year; there is a $6,000 cap per employee in these counties. Employees must be Arkansas taxpayers to qualify for the credit. The income tax credit begins in the year in which the new employees are hired. Any unused portion of the credit may be applied against income tax for the succeeding nine years.

InvestArk Tax Credit: Available to industries established in Arkansas for 2 years or longer investing $5 million or more in plant or equipment. A credit against the manufacturer's state sales and use tax liability of 7% of the total project cost, not to exceed 50% of the total sales and use tax liability in a single year, is allowed.

Free Port Law: No tax on goods in transit or raw materials and finished goods destined for out-of-state sales; no sales tax on manufacturing equipment, pollution control facilities, or raw materials; no property tax on textile mills.

Day Care Facility Incentive Program: Companies can receive a sales and use tax refund on the initial cost of construction materials and furnishings purchased to build and equip an approved child care facility. Additionally, a corporate income tax credit of 3.9% of the total annual payroll of the workers employed exclusively to provide childcare service, or a $5,000 income tax credit for the first year the business provides its employees with a day care facility is also available.

Tourism Development: Provides state sales tax credits up to 10% of approved project costs for the creation or expansion of eligible tourist attractions exceeding $500,000, and 25% of project costs exceeding $1,000,000.

Recycling Equipment Tax Credit: Allows taxpayers to receive a tax credit for the purchase of equipment used exclusively for reduction, reuse, or recycling of solid waste material for commercial purposes, whether or not for profit, and the cost of installation of such equipment by outside contractors. The amount of the credit shall equal 30% of the cost of eligible equipment and installation costs.

Motion Picture Incentive Act: Qualifying motion picture production companies spending in excess of $500,000 within six months, or $1 million within 12 months may receive a refund of state sales and use taxes paid on qualified expenditures incurred in conjunction with a film, telefilm, music video, documentary, episodic television show, or commercial advertisement.

Biotechnology Development and Training Act: Offers three different income tax credits to taxpayers furthering biotechnical business development. The first credit is a 5% income tax credit applied to costs to build and equip eligible biotechnical facilities. The second credit allows a 30% income tax credit both for eligible employee training costs and for contract with state-supported institutions for higher education to conduct qualified cooperative research projects. The third credit allows an income tax credit for qualified research in biotechnology, including but not limited to the cost of purchasing, licensing, developing, or protecting intellectual property. This credit is equal to 20% of the amount the cost of qualified research exceeds the cost of such resource in the base year.

Enterprise Zone Program: Corporate income tax credits and sales tax refund.

Sales and Use Tax Refunds: Advantage Arkansas participants are eligible for a refund of sales and use taxes for building materials and taxable equipment connected with the eligible project. To receive refunds, a local resolution must be passed and an application approved by the Arkansas Department of Economic Development.

Exports

The *Arkansas Department of Economic Development's (ADED)* international offices assist Arkansas companies in exporting their products and services by arranging personalized meetings with potential distributors, sales representatives or end users in the countries targeted for ADED's export promotion efforts. In addition to this service, they also offer the following:

- Market research
- Assisting companies exhibiting in international trade fairs
- Planning and coordinating trade missions
- Obtaining trade leads
- Representing and/or advising companies on export transactions
- Accompanying company representatives on export sales trips
- Promoting companies in meetings with prospective buyers

California

California Technology, Trade and Commerce Agency
801 K St., Suite 1700
Sacramento, CA 95814
916-322-1394
800-303-6600
http://commerce.ca.gov

California's business resources are many and varied with many local and regional programs. The following is not all-inclusive:

Business Assistance

Office of Small Business: Offers workshops, seminars, individual counseling, and publications for those interested in small businesses. They have information and expertise in dealing with state, federal, and local agencies.

Business Financing

The Loan Guarantee Program: Assists small businesses that cannot qualify for bank loans. Normally, 80% of the loan amount, with the guaranteed portion of the loan not exceeding $350,000 is offered.

Energy Technology Export Program: The California Energy Commission assists California companies through several energy export programs. For more information, contact California Energy Commission, Energy Technology Export Program, 1516 Ninth St., MS-45, Sacramento, CA 95814; 916-654-4528; {www.energy.ca.gov}.

Fishing Vessel: Direct loans to finance commercial fishing vessel equipment and modifications that result in fuel savings. Loans are from $10,000 to $25,000.

Hazardous Waste: Direct loans to finance equipment or a production practice that reduces waste or lessens hazardous properties. The minimum loan is $20,000. The maximum loan is $150,000.

Bond Guarantees: Access to surety bonds that allow greater participation by small and emerging contractors in state public works contracts. Maximum is $350,000 liability per contract.

Small Corporate Offering Registration Network: Raise up to $1 million each year by issuing shares directly to investors through a state-registered public offering.

Sudden and Severe Economic Dislocation (SSED): The California Technology, Trade and Commerce Agency provides gap financing to businesses in areas of the state affected by plant and military base closures, defense downsizing, industry layoffs, presidentially declared disasters and other economic problems which have contributed to job loss in California.

Old Growth Diversification Revolving Loan Fund: The California Technology, Trade and Commerce Agency provides low cost capital to businesses that create jobs in targeted timber-dependent areas. Businesses may borrow from $25,000 to $100,000 at a reduced interest rate to purchase machinery and equipment or for working capital.

The California Capital Access Program: The California Pollution Control Financing Authority (CPCFA) provides a form of loan portfolio insurance which provides up to 100% coverage on certain loan defaults, encouraging banks and other financial institutions to make loans to small businesses that fall just outside of most banks' conventional underwriting standards. The maximum loan amount is $2.5 million. The maximum premium CPCFA will pay is $100,000 (per loan). Contact: California Pollution Control Financing Authority, Attention: SBAF Program Manager, 915 Capitol Mall, Room 466, Sacramento, CA 95814; 916-654-5610.

California Industrial Development Financing Advisory Commission (CEDFAC): The Treasurer's office assists California manufacturing businesses in funding capital expenditures for acquisitions or expansions. Allows a business to borrow funds at competitive rates through the issuance of tax-exempt bonds enhanced by a letter of credit. The maximum face amount of an IDB bond issue is $10 million per applicant per public jurisdiction. Contact: California Industrial Development Financing Advisory Commission, 915 Capitol Mall, Sacramento, CA 95814; 916-653-3843.

Financing for Child Care Facilities: Facility financing through direct loans or loan guarantees are available for licensed child care centers and licensed family day care homes serving more than six children. Each facility and project must primarily serve children from low income families; and create or preserve child care spaces.

California Technology Investment Partnership (CalTIP): The CalTIP matching grant program facilitates the creation of new high-tech businesses in California by helping small high-tech companies bring produt to market. The program works by funding business assistance services through the Regional Technology Alliances, and by directing financial aid to small- and medium-sized California companies. CalTIP grants provide up to $250,000 in targeted support to California companies that are already receiving federal funds. For more information, contact California Technology, Trade & Commerce Agency, Division of Science, Technology & Innovation, 801 K Street, Suite 1926, Sacramento, CA 95819; 96-322-6419; {http://commerce.ca.gov/dsti}.

Tax Incentives

Manufacturers operating in California are eligible for a 6% manufacturers' investment credit (MIC). This credit is generally unlimited.

Provides "new" or start up companies the option of a 5% partial sales or use tax exemption on all qualifying manufacturing property purchased or leased generally during the company's first three years of operation.

Research and development tax credits allow companies to receive a credit of 12% for qualifying research expenses (research done in-house) and 24% for basic research payments (payments to an outside company), making it the highest in the nation.

Net Operating Loss Carryover: Allows businesses that experience a loss for the year to carry this loss forward to the next year in order to offset income in the following year.

Enterprise Zone Program: Encourages business development in 39 designated areas through numerous special zone incentives.

Local Agency Military Base Recovery Area: Designations which are similar to enterprise zones allowing communities to extend the aforementioned California tax credits to companies locating in a LAMBRA zone.

Child Care Tax Credit: For employers who pay or incur costs for the start up of a child care program or construction of an on-site child care facility are eligible for a credit against state income taxes equal to 30% of its costs, up to a maximum of $50,000 in one year. Excess credits may be carried over to succeeding years.

Joint Strike Fighter Income Tax Credits: California recently created two entirely new income tax credits for businesses involved in the Joint Strike Fighter Program. They are 1) a hiring wage credit and 2) a property credit. These credits apply to taxpayers under initial contract or subcontract to manufacture property for ultimate use in a Joint Strike Fighter. The credits are available for taxable years beginning on or after January 1, 2001, and before January 1, 2006.

Exports

International Trade and Investment: Acts as a catalyst to create jobs in California through vigorous and sustained promotion of exports to global markets and foreign investment into the Golden State. They have offices in California and ten foreign locations. They offer promotion of California products and companies abroad through the Office of Export Development, current information on foreign market opportunities, the Special American Business Internship Training Program, and assistance with attracting foreign investment through the California Office of Foreign Investment. They also provide exporting financial assistance for going global through several economic development programs provided by the California Export Finance Office, a division of California's Trade and Commerce Agency. The maximum guarantee amount is $750,000. That is 90% of an $833,000 loan.

Women and Minorities

Child Care and Development Facilities Loan Guarantee Fund and Child Care and Development Facilities Direct Loan Fund: Together, these funds support the California Child Care Facilities Finance Program. The Department of Housing and Community Development will deposit $3.1 million from the Child Care and Development Facilities Loan Guarantee Fund into the Small Business Expansion Fund. Corporations can issue guarantees against this fund as long as the transaction adheres to the following HCD rules: The loan must be used for creating new child care spaces or preserving spaces that would otherwise be lost; the projects must fit into the HCD priority categories. A direct loan may not exceed 20% of the total project cost if the same facility is also utilizing a guaranteed loan. In no case can a direct loan exceed 50% of the project cost. Home-based child care will be financed by non-profit microlenders. Both small businesses and non-profit organizations will be eligible for either guarantees and/or direct loans.

Colorado

Office of Economic Development and International Trade
1625 Broadway, Suite 1710
Denver, CO 80202
303-892-3840
Fax: 303-892-3848
TDD: 800-659-2656
www.state.co.us

Colorado Housing and Finance Authority
1981 Blake Street
Denver, CO 80202-1272
303-297-2432
800-877-CHFA (2432)
www.colohfa.org

Business Assistance

Office of Economic Development: The Office of Economic Development (OED) works with companies starting, expanding or relocating in Colorado. OED offers a wide range of services to assist new and existing businesses of every size.

Marketing Colorado: Marketing activities are conducted nationwide to promote sectors of the Colorado economy which are growing and provide high quality jobs. Marketing activities include attendance at selected trade shows, company visits, cooperative marketing with local enterprise zones and community economic development councils and industry research. *Colorado Facts* is published annually by OBD and includes statistics and comparisons of key indicators to evaluate Colorado's economic climate and to provide information of special interest to the business community.

Job Training: Colorado First and Existing Industries Job Training Programs assists employers with customized job training. Assistance is provided to new and existing businesses to retrain workers and improve their workplace skills. The goal of the Colorado First program is to assist companies in training employees to fill newly created full-time permanent quality jobs.

Colorado Business Assistance Center: Acting as the first point of contact for the Colorado Small Business Development Center Network, the Colorado Business Assistance Center (BAC) is a one-stop shop for new and existing business owners for information regarding all their federal, state and local licensing requirements. The BAC provides referrals to other state assistance programs including counseling at the 20 local Small Business Development Centers around the state. The BAC distributes the *Colorado Business Resource Guide*, a comprehensive guide to starting and operating a business in Colorado. Business owners can obtain many of the federal, state and local forms necessary for registering a business. Contact Colorado Business Assistance Center, 2745 Welton St., Denver, CO 80205; 303-592-5920; 800-333-7798.

Business Financing

Revolving Loan Fund Programs (RLFs): Administered locally in 16 geographic regions covering the rural areas of the state. RLFs have considerable flexibility to make small loans of two or three thousand dollars up to $100,000. Applicants can be existing or startup businesses.

Larger Business Loans: Between $100,000 and $250,000 are provided by OBD through the Community Development Block Grant Business Loans Program when the local government is willing to assume the risk on the loan in order to create or retain jobs. Larger loans may be considered on a case by case basis.

Economic Development Commission: Will provide interest rate write-downs, low interest rate loans or subsidies to companies interested in relocating to or expanding in Colorado.

Private Activity Bonds (PABs): Provide a tax-exempt financing vehicle for facilities and equipment used in the manufacture or production of tangible personal property.

ACCESS Program: A first mortgage program for small businesses acquiring land, buildings, and equipment which generally requires 10% equity on the part of the borrower. CHFA may participate with a local lender or may directly originate the first mortgage while SBA provides a second mortgage generally resulting in a 90% loan to value. Through the ACCESS loan program, the small business will receive a fixed interest rate on all or a large portion of the first mortgage.

Business & Industry Loan Program: Targeted to for profit or not for profit businesses located in communities with populations under 50,000. The loan may be used to finance real estate, equipment, and machinery. The loan offers a fixed rate on fully amortized terms of 3 to 25 years and is partially guaranteed by Rural Business Cooperative Service, a division of the U.S. Department of Agriculture. The minimum equity requirement is 10% with maximum loan amount of up to $5,000,000. Business in the startup phase must contribute a minimum of 20%.

Nonprofit Real Estate Loan Program: Provides loans for real estate purchases for nonprofit organizations. Loans have a fixed rate and are made directly by CHFA.

QAL Program: Provides land, equipment, and machinery financing to farm and ranch operations. The financing is made available through local banks in participation with Rural Business-Cooperative Service (RBS), formerly Farmer's Home Administration. Loans are made at below market interest rates for terms up to 25 years.

Quality Investment Capital (QIC) Program: A small business loan program that provides long term fixed rate financing for real estate, equipment, and working capital. Refinancing of existing debt can be considered. These loans are guaranteed by the Small Business Administration and are fully amortizing.

RENEW Colorado: Provides financing to businesses which include waste diversion or recycling activities in their operations. The funds may be used to purchase equipment, real estate, or as working capital. Loan terms can extend up to 30 years, and interest rates will be fixed at below-market.

Tax Incentives

Investment Tax Credits: The Colorado Tax Equity Act, signed into law during the 1987 legislative session, reinstates the Colorado Investment Tax Credit, up to $1,000 per year, for tax years beginning on or after January 1, 1998, based on 10% of what the Federal Investment Tax Credit would have been had such credit not been restricted by the Tax Reform Act of 1986. Excess credits may be carried forward up to three years.

Enterprise Zone Tax Credits: Enterprise Zones are geographic areas designated to promote economic development. Sixteen such zones have been designated in Colorado. They cover most rural areas of the state with the exception of the ski area/resort counties. There are also urban zones designated to attract investment and jobs to selected areas. Enterprise Zones offer the following advantages to businesses locating or expanding within their boundaries:

- A $500 credit for each new full-time employee working within the Zone.
- Double job tax credit for agricultural processing.
- $200 job tax credit for employer health insurance.
- Local government incentives.
- 3% investment tax credit for businesses making investments in equipment used exclusively in an Enterprise Zone.
- Exemption from state sales and use taxes for manufacturing equipment.
- Income tax credit of up to 3% for expenditures on research and development activities (as defined in federal tax laws) in an Enterprise Zone.
- A credit of 25% of qualified expenditures up to $50,000 to rehabilitate buildings which are at least 20 years old which have been vacant at least two years.
- A 25% tax credit for private contributions to local zone administrators for qualifying projects or programs within zones.
- A 10% tax credit for employer expenditures for qualified job training and school-to-work programs.

Sales Tax Exemptions: For purchases over $500 on machinery and machine tools purchased for use in manufacturing; Purchases of electricity, coal, gas, or fuel oil for use in processing, manufacturing, and all industrial uses; Sale of tangible personal property for testing, modification, inspection, or similar types of activities in Colorado; Interstate long distance telephone charges.

Local Governments: May provide incentive payments or property tax credits based on the amount of increased property taxes for qualifying new business activity in their jurisdictions.

Exports

Colorado International Trade Office (ITO): Responsible for assisting Colorado companies with all aspects of exporting, including counseling, protocol, leading trade missions, and conducting trade shows abroad. By promoting Colorado exports and attracting foreign investment, the ITO helps to build Colorado's identity as an international business center, encouraging foreign buyers to look to Colorado for products and services. The ITO is open to the public and most services are rendered at no cost.

Women and Minorities

Women's Business Office: Strives to keep the women entrepreneurs of Colorado informed about pertinent issues through all modes of communication.

Office of Economic Development Minority Business Office: Acts as a clearinghouse to disseminate information to the minority business community. Promotes economic development for minority businesses in cooperation with the state economic development activities. Establishes networks between majority and minority business sectors. Promotes minority participation in state procurement. Assists Colorado in achieving its Minority Procurement Goals of 17%. Works with the Minority Business Advisory Council and the minority community in promoting minority business development.

Connecticut

State of Connecticut Department of Economic and Community Development
505 Hudson Street
Hartford, CT 06106-7107
860-270-8000
www.state.ct.us/ecd/

Connecticut Economic Resource Center, Inc.
805 Brook Street, Building #4
Rocky Hill, CT 06067-3405
860-571-7136
800-392-2122
www.cerc.com

Business Assistance

The Department of Economic and Community Development: The state agency responsible for promoting economic growth. DECD develops strategies and programs to attract and retain businesses and jobs, revitalize neighborhoods and communities, ensure quality housing, and foster appropriate development in Connecticut's cities and towns. DECD partners with utility/telecommunications companies and other state agencies to operate the Connecticut Economic Resource Center a private, nonprofit corporation that serves as a comprehensive source of information about Connecticut businesses and economic development professionals. Two free publications, *Starting a Business? Start With Our Help*, and *Help Is Here* are available from CERC by calling 800-392-2122.

One Stop Centers: Authorized to enable businesses to obtain many necessary permits and licenses in one location.

Connecticut Economic Resource Center (CERC): A non-profit private-sector organization formed and managed through a unique partnership of utility/telecommunication companies and state government. The CERC coordinates Connecticut's business-to-business marketing and recruitment efforts on behalf of the state. As a one-stop gateway to the state's programs and services for business, the CERC helps businesses obtain quick and accurate information in the areas of financing, export assistance, licensing, manufacturing programs, job training, utility, telecommunications and real estate help, all at no cost.

Business Resource Index: The Connecticut Economic Resource Center's website {www.cerc.com}offers a large and comprehensive database of programs and services for businesses. The database contains information from the public and private sectors on federal, state and local levels including license and permit information. The *Business Resource Index* is divided into three major sections, each of which can be searched individually or collectively. The sections include *Resources By Agency*, *Licensing*, and *Helpful Fact Sheets*. Available business resources are often divided by city or region. Listings are extensive. To illustrate, a search with the keyword "Small Business" yielded 119 documents including loans, technical assistance, consulting services, grants, and economic development assistance among others. As an example, the Entrepreneurial Loan Program offers loans up to $100,000 insured by the Connecticut Development Authority, for the benefit of start-up and early stage business anywhere in Connecticut. The website also features a real estate search engine enabling the user to input parameters such as size of building and desired location to aid with business site selection.

Technology Extension Program: Provides direct technical assistance to small and mid-sized manufacturing firms.

Institute for Industrial and Engineering Technology: Offers assistance with process improvement, technical training, procurement, human resources, business incubators, and others.

SiteFinder: A comprehensive computer database of available commercial and industrial properties.

Demographic and Economic Analysis: Services include industry profiles, competitive intelligence, regional analysis, survey research, bench marking and evaluation.

Business Financing

Connecticut Development Authority: Works to ensure that Connecticut businesses have access to capital to accelerate business formation and expansion and to create and retain jobs. The CDA works with private section lending and business professionals to provide loan guarantees and direct loans for working capital, equipment and real estate. The CDA offers the following financing programs:

Entrepreneurial Loan Program: Provides up to $100,000 in start-up and expansion financing. 75% of past loans were made to women and minority owners.

URBANK: Loans up to $500,000 for any small business enterprise in targeted communities that are unable to obtain conventional financing.

Business Loans: Up to $10 million for medium size enterprises.

Junior Participation Loans: Up to $5 million to assist the lender in meeting the company's total borrowing requirements.

Inducement Loans: Up to $10 million at below market interest rates restricted to significant competitive business retention or recruitment.

Industrial Revenue Bonds: Low rate, tax exempt financing for manufacturers, utilities, certain non-profits and others.

Job Training Finance Program: Pays up to 25% of the cost of improving skills of manufacturing workers.

Custom Job Training Program: Department of Labor will pay up to 50% for eligible training expenses.

For all the above loan programs, contact Connecticut Development Authority, 999 West St., Rocky Hill, CT 06067; 860-258-7800; {www.state.ct.us/cda}..

Manufacturing Assistance Fund: Program includes loans, defense diversification project funding, tax credits and funding for new machinery and equipment.

Naugatuck Valley Loan Fund: Fund can be used to purchase land or buildings, construction, renovation, rehabilitation, and/or the purchase and installation of machinery and equipment. Maximum loan is $200,000.

Connecticut Programs Fund: Program provides venture capital, including minority-focused venture capital, mezzanine financing and funds for restructuring.

For the above loan programs, contact Department of Economic and Community Development, 249 Thomaston Ave., Waterbury, CT 06702; 203-596-8862.

Community Economic Development Fund: Provides financing for a wide range of projects in certain targeted investment and public investment communities throughout the state.

Regional Revolving Loan Funds: Provide supplemental financing to stimulate job growth and business activity.

Community-Based Development Organizations: Local economic development organizations offering financing on varying conditions and terms.

For the above loan programs, contact Community Economic Development Fund, 50-G Weston St., Hartford, CT 06120; 800-656-4613; 860-249-3800.

Connecticut Innovations: The state's corporation dedicated to technology development, making risk capital investment in high technology companies throughout the state. They offer a wide range of support from research assistance to financing for product development and marketing. Connecticut Innovations offers the following financing programs:

Product Development and Product Marketing Financing: Typical investments range from $50,000 to $1 million and the company must be able to raise matching funds.

Yankee Ingenuity Initiative Funding: Provides funding for collaborative research between Connecticut businesses and Connecticut colleges and universities.

The Biotechnology Facilities Fund: A $30 million fund to support the expansion of biotechnology laboratory space in Connecticut. Funding may be offered in the form of lease or loan guarantee and/or direct investments.

Renewable Energy Fund: Promotes investment in renewable energy resources, e.g. fuel cells, landfill gas, and tidal, wind and solar power.

Connecticut Technology Partnership: Invests $50,000 to $500,000 in Connecticut businesses pursuing funding through federal research and development programs such as the Small Business Innovations Research (SBIR) program and the Advanced Technology program (ATP).

For more information regarding the loan programs listed above, contact Connecticut Innovations, Inc., 999 West Street, Rocky Hill, CT 06067; 860-563-5851; {www.ctinnovations.com}.

Connecticut Venture Group (CVG): A voluntary professional association that is committed to connecting leading venture investment professionals with high growth emerging companies. CVG promotes capital formation through networking, leading edge informational seminars, an annual Crossroads Venture Fair and other events throughout the year. Contact Connecticut Venture Group, 1895-B Post Road, Fairfield, CT 06430; 203-256-5955; {www.ct-venture.org}.

Tax Incentives

Corporate Tax Credits:
- 50% for financial institutions constructing new facilities and adding new employees
- 5% annual credit for fixed capital investment in tangible personal property
- 5% annual credit for investments in human capital, employee training, childcare, and donations to higher education for technology training
- 10% credit for increased investment in machinery and equipment for companies with 250 or fewer full-time permanent employees
- 5% credit for companies with 251 to 800 full time permanent employees in the state
- Research and development credits from 1% to 6% research and development expenditures
- 100% credit for property taxes paid on data processing hardware, peripheral equipment and software
- 25% credit for an increase in grant to institutions of higher learning for R&D related to technology advancement
- 100% credit for investment over 10 years in an investment fund creating insurance related facilities and jobs
- 100% credit for SBA loan guarantee fees paid by companies with less than $5 million in gross receipts
- Other credits for low-income housing, contributions to neighborhood assistance programs, and alternative employee transportation

Corporate Business Tax Exemptions:
- All insurance companies (Connecticut incorporated and non-Connecticut incorporated)
- Corporate income, insurance premiums and sales and use taxes for certain banks, insurers and investment companies located in the Hartford Financial Services Export Zone that conduct all business with non-US persons
- Capital gains from the sale of protected open space or class I or II water company land to the state or certain entities
- Non-US corporations whose sole activities in Connecticut are trading stocks, securities or commodities for their own account

Corporate Sales Tax Exemptions:
- 100% on machinery used in the manufacture of finished products or in the biotechnology industry and materials, tools, and fuel used in the manufacture or fabrication of finished products or in the biotechnology industry. 50% on machinery, tools, fuels and equipment that may not meet the requirements for the 100% exemption
- 100% on computer and data processing services beginning July 1, 2002. Declining 1% annually from current 3%
- 100% on repair, replacement and component parts for manufacturing machinery
- 100% calibration services, registration and compliance services related to ISO 9000 and personnel training services offered by colleges or universities
- 100% on vehicles powered by alternative fuels, vehicle conversion equipment and alternative fuel filling station equipment
- 100% on fuel and electric power used in manufacturing or to heat a manufacturing facility, provided that a 75% usage test is met
- 100% of the cost of services related to creating and maintaining a website

- 100% of the cost of aircraft, repairs, parts and services on aircraft exceeding 6,000 pounds maximum takeoff weight
- 100% on safety apparel worn by employees
- 100% on goods purchased inside or outside Connecticut for use outside Connecticut provided all conditions are met

Real and Personal Property Tax Exemptions
- 100% for 5 years on newly acquired and installed machinery and equipment eligible for 5-7 year depreciation
- 100% for inventories
- 30% to 100% from the increased assessment for personal property for manufacturers and 20% to 50% for eligible real property improvements can be offered by towns for 2 to 7 years, depending on the investment amount
- 100% for unbundled software and machinery and equipment that will be exempt once installed and used
- 100% for 5 years on new commercial motor vehicles weighing over 26,000 pounds that are used to transport freight for hire and on all new commercial vehicles weighing over 55,000 pounds

Other Tax Incentives
- Connecticut's corporation business tax rate is 7.5%. There is no tax on Subchapter S companies.
- Passive investment companies that hold loans secured by real property are not subject to corporation business tax
- Financial service companies are allowed a single factor apportionment method based on customer location
- Net operating loses can be carried forward 20 years for losses incurred on or after January 1, 2000

Exports

Access International: Program designed to put businesses in touch with resources to support exporting efforts including consultants, suppliers, services and support.

Women and Minorities

Procurement Program: Set-Aside Program requires state agencies and political subdivisions to set aside 25% of their budget for construction, housing rehabilitation and the purchasing of supplies. These services are awarded to certified small business contractors, minority businesses, enterprises, non-profit corporations and individuals with a disability. 25% of this amount is to be awarded to certified minority owned firms.

Minority Supplier Development Council: A non-profit organization whose mission is to foster business relationships between corporations and certified minority businesses. Services include training seminars, matchmaking activities, bid notifications, networking functions and a large trade expo.

For these programs, contact Minority and Small Business Contractors Set-Aside Program, Department of Economic and Community Development, 505 Hudson St., Hartford, CT 06106, Attn: Set Aside Unit; 860-270-8025; {www.state.ct.us/ecd/setaside}.

Delaware

Delaware Economic Development Office
99 Kings Highway
Dover, DE 19901
302-739-4271
www.state.de.us/dedo/

Business Assistance

Delaware Economic Development Office: Offers referrals to appropriate state agencies and other organizations. Free tabloid, *Small Business Start-Up Guide* is available. Provides support for new businesses and coordinates the efforts of organizations statewide that assist small businesses.

Workforce Development Section: Works to ensure the availability of a skilled, multilevel workforce for new and existing Delaware businesses. Helps employers obtain, upgrade and retain suitable workers, by helping Delawareans gain the education and training to get and keep quality jobs and steady employment.

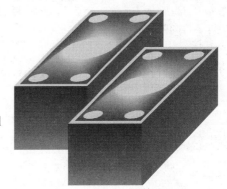

Blue Collar Training Fund Program: When the labor market cannot respond to an employer's needs, or when additional skills are necessary because of a particular business situation, the Delaware Economic Development Office has access to recognized educational resources, which can provide skill training tailored to a company's specifications. Training contracts may be arranged with colleges, vocational schools, specialized training centers, and independent agencies that provide business, industrial, and service-related instruction. Workforce Development also supports in-house, on the job training. The Blue Collar Training Fund is created by a .15% assessment of the unemployment insurance tax paid on the first $8,500 of employee wages. Throughout the fiscal year, DEDO receives 25% of the receipts generated by this assessment. This fund is used to help Delaware businesses provide customized training programs to upgrade and/or retrain their employees, provide financial assistance to full or part time employees (Workforce Development grant) and to help the Office of State Personnel provide career ladder training for state employees (State Employees Job Training Program).

Governor's Workforce Development Grant: This program grants tuition reimbursement for small companies unable to provide tuition assistance and for part time workers who don't quality for tuition assistance through their employers.

Business Research Section: Collects, analyzes and distributes statistical data on the state's economy and business climate and develops research regarding the economic vitality of the State of Delaware

Delaware Tourism Office: Assists the tourism industry.

The State Data Center: Provides economic and demographic data for Delaware.

Business Calendar: Maintained by the Delaware State Chamber of Commerce (DSCC), it is the state's central location for listing business-related events.

Advanced Technology Centers (ATCs): Public/private partnerships designed to bolster Delaware's technology base and to create and retain quality high-tech jobs. The State of Delaware has committed $11 million to date in grants to establish five Centers. Funding for the program comes from the state's 21st Century Fund. Amounts are not available without a specific inquiry. For more information, contact Delaware Economic Development Office, 820 French St., Wilmington, DE 19801; 302-577-8477.

Green Industries Initiative: Targets specific businesses for receipt of financial and technical assistance to further the goals of Governor Castle's Executive Order #82 and Delaware's Pollution Prevention Program. The State of Delaware provides corporate income tax credits and/or gross receipts tax reductions for existing Delaware firms and those choosing Delaware as a location for new operations. The type of financial assistance is dependent upon the category under which assistance is requested.

Business Financing

Industrial Revenue Bonds: Statewide financial assistance to new or expanding businesses through the issuance of bonds (IRBs). The maximum for IRBs issued annually in Delaware is $150 million.

Economic Development Loan Program: Assists Delaware businesses to finance projects when 100% financing cannot be obtained through a bank. The program does require 70% bank financing. The remaining 30% is financed through the program up to a maximum of $450,000. In most cases the interest rate for monies loaned through the Economic Development Loan Program is 60% of the prime lending interest rate.

The Delaware Access Program: Designed to give banks a flexible and extremely non-bureaucratic tool to make business loans that are somewhat riskier than a conventional bank loan, in a manner consistent with safety and soundness. It is designed to use a small amount of public resources to generate a large amount of private bank financing, thus providing access to bank financing for many Delaware businesses that might otherwise not be able to obtain such access. The program sets minimum and maximum limits for the borrower's payment. At a minimum, it must be at least 1-1/2% of the loan amount. The maximum is 3-1/2% . (The premium payment, and other up-front expenses, may be financed as part of the loan.)

Small Business Innovation Research (SBIR): Bridge grant assistance to encourage Delaware businesses to participate in the federal Small Business Innovation Research (SBIR) grant program. The SBIR program requires that 1.25% of all federal research dollars be made available to small businesses. Phase I awardees are granted up to $100,000 by the federal government.

The Delaware Innovation Fund: Assists in the initial capitalization of pre-seed and seed stage enterprises within the State of Delaware. The Fund provides financial and technical assistance to Delaware based businesses which have the potential to launch innovative products and processes into national markets, to create new jobs, and to make a significant contribution to the economic diversity and the technology base of Delaware's communities.

- ***Demonstration Funding***: Limited one-time availability, provides $10,000 to $25,000 to aid in establishing patents, business plans and proof of concept issues.
- ***Commercialization Funding***: Ranging from $25,000 to $250,000, this funding is used to begin the commercialization process of early-stage businesses and may be available in multiple years.

Venture Capital Funds: Three funds — Anthem Capital, L.P., Triad Investors Corporation, and Blue Rock Capital — have the ability to fund a variety of seed stage, early stage, and later stage companies in both technology-related and non-technology fields. The investment focus of each fund varies. Investments can range from $150,000 for seed stage companies up to $2,000,000 or more for later stage companies.

City of Wilmington: Projects located within the city limits of Wilmington may also apply for financing through the Wilmington Economic Development Corporation (WEDCO). Financing programs offered include SBA Section 504 Loans, Revolving Loan Funds, and other special purpose financing. Contact: Wilmington Economic Development Corporation, 605A Market St., Wilmington, DE 19801; 302-571-9088.

Sussex County: Operates an Industrial Revenue Bond program with a cap of $15 million each year for industrial projects in the County. Project review requires a letter of commitment for placement of the bond before a project recommendation is made by the Industrial Revenue Bond Review Committee to Sussex County Council (political jurisdiction). The Industrial Revenue Bond process may require as little as five weeks from inception to bond closing. Contact: Sussex County Office of Economic Development, P.O. Box 589, 9 S. Dupont Hwy., Georgetown, DE 19947; 302-855-7770.

Tax Incentives

Bank Franchise Tax Credits: For taxable years beginning after December 31, 1996, credits against bank franchise taxes are available to qualifying firms. Credits are $400 per year for each new qualifying employee in excess of 50 new employees and are for a period of ten years.

Export Trading Company Exemption: Delaware exporters who qualify as an Export Trading Company can receive exemption from Delaware income and mercantile taxes.

Targeted Area Tax Incentives: Firms which qualify for targeted industry credits and are located in one of the targeted areas, qualify for corporate income tax credits of $650 for each new employee and $650 for each new $100,000 investment.

Retention and Expansion Tax Credits: Corporate income tax credits and gross receipts tax reductions are available to qualifying manufacturers and wholesalers planning new facilities or large expansions. The maximum annual credit cannot exceed $500,000. Gross receipts tax reductions are limited to a maximum total credit of $500,000 over the ten-year life.

Green Industries Tax Credits: Manufacturers that reduce their chemical waste, as reported under the Toxics Release Inventory, by 20% or their other wastes by 50%, are granted a $400 corporate income tax credit for each 10% reduction.

Public Utility Tax Rebates for Industrial Users: Industrial firms meeting the criteria for targeted industries tax credits are eligible for a rebate of 50% of the Public Utilities Tax imposed on new or increased consumption of gas and electricity for five years.

Property Tax Incentives: The cities of Wilmington, Newark, Dover and the counties of New Castle and Kent offer a variety of property tax incentives for new construction, renovation, and property improvements. Amounts vary.

Exports

The International Trade Section: A one-stop resource for exporter assistance and international trade information in Delaware. Contact the International Trade Section, Delaware Economic Development Office, 820 French St., Carvel State Office Bldg., 10th Floor, Wilmington, DE 19801; 302-577-8477.

District of Columbia

Office of the Deputy Mayor for Planning and Economic Development
441 4th St., NW, Suite 1140
Washington, DC 20001
202-727-6365
www.dcbiz.dc.gov

Business Assistance

Welcome To Washington D.C. Online: A useful website with links to
   business & finance opportunities in the district. {www.dcbiz.dc.gov}
Transferable Development Rights: Permits businesses to purchase the right
   to develop at higher densities in designated TDR "receiving zones."
Contact Local Business Development, 441 4th St., NW, Suite 970N,
Washington, DC 20001; 202-724-1385.

Business Location Assistance:
   D.C. Chamber of Commerce, 1301 Pennsylvania Ave., NW, Suite 309,
   Washington, DC 20004; 202-347-7201; {www.dcchamber.org};
   D.C. Building Industry Association, 5100 Wisconsin Ave., NW, Suite
   301, Washington, DC 20016; 202-966-8665;
   {www.reji.com/associations/dcbia}.

DC Marketing Center: A public/private partnership between the District of Columbia's Office of the Deputy Mayor
   for Planning and Economic Development and six other key District stakeholders – the DC Chamber of
   Commerce, Potomac Electric & Power Company (PEPCO), the DC Building Industry Association, Verizon,
   FannieMae, and GEICO Insurance. DC Business Connections, part of the DC Marketing Center, is the District
   of Columbia's business retention program, designed as an economic development customer service tool for the
   business community. Through DC Business Connections, participation Washington-based companies have the
   opportunity to establish a unique communication forum with the Government of the District of Columbia to
   address important issues associated with conducting business in the District. Contact Washington, DC
   Marketing Center, 1710 H Street, NW, 11th Floor, Washington, DC 20006; 202-347-7201.

Business Financing

Enterprise Zone: Eligible for up to $15 million per business in tax exempt bonds for businesses within an Enterprise
   Zone; $20,000 of additional expensing of business equipment.
Bond Financing and General Information: Contact D.C. Revenue Bond Program, 441 4th St., NW, Suite 360,
   Washington, DC 20001; 202-727-6055; 202-727-2778; {www.dccfo.com/dcbons.htm}.

Tax Incentives

Enterprise Zones: Consists of 65 census tracts with 20% and higher poverty rate. Benefits include:
   - *Tax-Exempt Bond Financing*: Up to 15 million.
   - *Federal Capital Gains Exemption*: Requires 80% of the business' total gross income be derived from a
     business or trade conducted within the enterprise zone.
   - *Employment Tax Credit*: Up to $3,000 for each employee at the EZ facility who is also a D.C. resident.
   - *Special Expensing Allowance*: $20,000 available for business equipment and depreciable property
     purchase by EZ businesses.
Public Schools Tax Credit: Available for contributions to school rehabilitation and repair, the provision of school
   equipment, materials and teacher training and the advancement of innovative K-12 programs.

Work Opportunity Tax Credits: $2,400 first time work opportunity tax credit for each worker in the first year of employment.
Welfare-To-Work Tax Credit: $8,500 welfare to work one-time tax credit for employees certified by D.C. DOES.

Exports

The DC Office of International Business: OIB was created to support the District of Columbia's development and expansion of local business through international trade and joint-venture partnerships, and to attract outside investment to the District of Columbia. Programs offered include:
- *International Trade Counseling and Technical Program*: OIB offers counseling and assistance on all aspects of international business to firms, organizations and residents of the District of Columbia.
- *Resource Center for International Trade Information*: Offers country market profiles, current export licensing regulations, information on trade and financing, a comprehensive database of trade resources and a directory of Washington-based international firms.
- *Trade and Investment Program*: Offers a database of local, small and medium sized businesses, using criteria and categories useful for the analysis of the local market; match making potential for local small business, and investment needs; facilitates trade and investment leads; identifies overseas markets for local goods and services; supports trade and investment missions; hosts foreign buying delegations; works in tandem with its sister agencies in devising strategies and marketing activities to attract foreign investment and business entities to the District of Columbia; establishes regular and close relationships with the diplomatic community, chambers of commerce and other regional and state agencies to identify export and investment opportunities for local and area businesses.
- *OIB Seminar Series*: Provides hands-on training through an eight week course designed to provide concise, nuts-and-bolts instructions on how to conduct import, export, and joint venture transactions. Topics cover every aspect of international trade with emphasis on small business involvement. Upon successful completion of the course, participants receive a "Certificate of Achievement."
- *OIB Internship Program*: OIB offers a high school and college internship program that provides local youth with on-the-job training, skill development and an orientation to international trade.

Women and Minorities

Minority Business Opportunity Commission: Promotes equal opportunity in all aspects of District life and fosters minority business development through:
- *Business Marketing Directory*: listing of Local, Small, Disadvantaged and Minority Business Enterprises.
- *Minority Business Certification Program*
- *Technical Assistance Program*: Aids minority business enterprises through workshops, contracting conferences, referrals and the MBOC Directory to bid and compete on District Government contracts.
- *Bonding Assistance Program*: Establishes a financial assurance pool to serve as limited collateral for surety bonds on public construction projects awarded by the DC government.

For these programs, contact D.C. Department of Human Rights and Local Business Development, DC Department of Human Rights and Minority Business Development, 441 4th Street, NW, Suite 970, Washington, DC 20001; 202-724-1385; Fax: 202-724-3786.

Florida

Florida Economic Development Council
502 East Jefferson Street
Tallahassee, FL 32301
805-222-3000
Fax: 850-222-3019

Enterprise Florida
390 North Orange Avenue, Suite 1300
Orlando, FL 32801
407-316-4600
Fax: 407-316-4599
www.floridabusiness.com

Business Assistance

Enterprise Florida: Offers information and referral services for current and potential small business owners. Also serves as ombudsman to small businesses to help resolve problems being experienced with state agencies. They sponsor workshops and business forums and an annual Small Business Development Workshop that brings together local, state, and federal agency representatives. Offers two exceptionally detailed publications; each is available for purchase for $4.95 plus $2 shipping and handling. Call 407-316-4600 to order *Florida Small Business, The 2000-2001 Guide to Starting & Growing a Small Business*, or *Business Florida, Florida's Guide to Business Opportunities*.

Innovation and Commercialization Centers: Sponsored by Enterprise Florida, Technology Development Corporation provides services and assistance designed to help entrepreneurs and emerging technology-based companies grow, launch new products and succeed in the marketplace. Services include business planning, market development, technology access, commercialization assistance, financial expertise and additional services.

- *Vendor Bid System*: An online computer service allowing searches for state bids that fit a particular business.
- *Quick Response Training*: Up to 18 months of employee training for businesses that produce exportable goods or services, create new jobs and employ Florida workers who require customized entry-level skills training.
- *Info-bid*: Helps businesses locate bid opportunities to sell to federal, state and local government agencies, as well as some commercial firms.
- *Expedited Permitting Assistance*: State and local permit streamlining procedures are available to assist businesses in obtaining necessary permits and approvals in a quick, efficient and predictable manner.

Business Financing

Enterprise Bonds: Tax-exempt Industrial Development Bonds (IDBs). These bonds provide a cost-effective means for qualified manufacturers, processors and nonprofit organizations to access public and private bond markets, particularly for small fixed asset investment projects with limited access to those markets. Minimum loan size is $500,000. Maximum loan size is $2,000,000 unless a larger amount is strongly supported by local economic development officials.

The Economic Development Transportation Fund: Commonly referred to as the "Road Fund," provides funding to units of local government for the elimination of transportation problems that adversely impact a specific company's location or expansion decision. Up to $2,000,000 may be provided to a local government to implement the improvements.

Florida Energy Loan Program: Provides low interest loans for energy conservation measures (ECM) to encourage eligible Florida businesses to reduce energy consumption while increasing energy efficiency. Maximum to $75,000; Minimum of $1,500.

The Florida Recycling Loan Program: Provides funding for machinery and equipment for manufacturing, processing, or conversion systems utilizing materials which have been or will be recycled; collection systems are not eligible. Direct Loans — Maximum to $200,000; minimum of $20,000. Maximum amount for leveraged loans will be $200,000, or 40% of total eligible costs, whichever is less.

Florida Export Finance Corporation: Makes available pre- and post-shipment working capital to small and medium size Florida exporters. Programs include state-supported direct loans and guarantees as well as packaging services that provide access to EXIM Bank and SBA export finance and working capital guaranty programs. Direct loans for the lesser of 90% of the product cost or $50,000. Loan guarantees for the lesser of 90% of a loan provided by a lender or $500,000. No minimum size.

Community Development Corporation Support and Assistance Program: Provides funds to local community development corporations, which in turn make loans to private businesses for the establishment of new businesses; provide financial assistance to existing businesses; or purchase equity interest in businesses located within a service area.

Rural Revolving Loan Program: Designed to provide gap funding for economic development projects in rural counties. Loan size to $200,000 or 10% of the project being assisted, whichever is less.

Florida Venture Finance Directory: Acts as a "wholesaler" in providing information to assist in the guidance of financing searches, Capital Development developed and published *The Florida Venture Finance Directory*. The *Directory* serves as an effective tool for economic development organizations (primary distributors) to assist local businesses in their fund raising efforts.

Venture Capital Network Development: Financial support, within budget limitations, is provided to a limited number of venture capital conferences at which Florida entrepreneurs have opportunity to present their ventures to members of the venture capital community. Enterprise Florida also is specifically interested in supporting initiatives leading to increased participation of private individual investors in Florida business ventures.

The Technology Investment Fund: Makes co-investments with Florida companies in promising technology-related projects with near-term commercial potential. Investments fall within a range of $25,000 to $250,000, depending upon the project's scope, commercial potential, matching funds, leveraged funds, the number and quality of other proposals received and the amount of funding requested in the highest ranked proposals.

Cypress Equity Fund: A $35.5 million venture capital "fund of funds" organized to facilitate investment in the venture capital asset class by Florida financial institutions, and to provide a platform to showcase Florida to the national venture capital community.

Quick Response Training Program: This program provides grant funding for customized training to new or expanding businesses. The program is flexible and structured to respond quickly to meet business training objectives. A local training provider – community college, area technical center or university – is selected and available to assist in the application process and program development or delivery. If the business has a training program in place, a state training provider will supervise and manage the training program and serve as the fiscal agent for the grant funds. Reimbursable training expenses include instructors'/trainers' salaries, curriculum development, textbooks/manuals, and materials/supplies.

Economic Development Transportation Fund: This grant program provides up to $2 million to local governments for the construction or improvement of transportation infrastructure needed to accommodate new or expanding industry.

Tax Incentives

No corporate income tax on limited partnerships, individuals, estates, and private trusts.

No state personal income tax.

No inventory or goods tax.

No collected or assessed property tax at the state level.

No sales tax on "Boiler Fuels" used at a fixed Florida location in an industrial manufacturing, processing, production or compounding process.

No sales and use tax on goods manufactured or produced in the state for resale for export outside the state.

The Qualified Target Industry Tax Refund Program: This program provides an inducement for target industry to locate new facilities in Florida or to expand existing facilities in Florida. The program provides tax refunds of $3,000 per new job created. The incentive is increased to $6,000 per job if the company locates in a rural county or an Enterprise Zone. Higher awards are available to companies paying very high wages. To quality for the

"QTI" program, a company must create at least 10 new jobs (or a 10% increase for expanding Florida companies), pay an average of at least 115% of area wages, have a significant positive impact on the community and have local support.

Enterprise Zone Program: Offers financial incentives to businesses to encourage private investment as well as employment opportunities for residents of 30 designated Enterprise Zones. Tax incentives are available to all types of businesses located within a designated zone which employ zone residents, rehabilitate real property or purchase business equipment to be used in the zone. Tax credits, sales tax exemptions and refunds are also available.

Sales and Use Tax Exemptions:

- Silicon technology-based industry transactions involving manufacturing or research equipment.
- Purchases of machinery and equipment used by a new or expanding Florida business to manufacture, produce, or process tangible personal property for sale.
- Labor, parts and materials used in repair of and incorporated into machinery and equipment that qualify for sales tax exemption upon purchase (phased in over four years, 50% exempt on July 1, 2000).
- Aircraft parts, modification, maintenance and repair, sale or lease of qualified aircraft.
- Commercial space activity-launch vehicles, payloads and fuel, machinery and equipment for production of items used exclusively at Spaceport Florida.
- Labor component of research and development expenditures.

Exports

Enterprise Florida offers on-staff multi-language capabilities and are prepared to help businesses open and operate companies in Florida or to engage in trade. A sophisticated and experienced network of financial, trade, transportation, and commercial services, including freight forwarders and the largest number of customs brokers and insurers in the United States, supports the global marketing efforts of the state's business community. A statewide network of world trade centers, bi-national chambers of commerce, and international business associations also can assist companies wishing to explore international business opportunities.

Women and Minorities

Minority Business Development Centers: Offers existing and potential minority entrepreneurs a wide range of free services, from initial counseling on how to start a business to the more complex issues of planning and growth.

Minority Business Advocacy and Assistance Office: Responsible for certifying minority business enterprises to do business with state agencies.

Office of Minority Business Development: Develops statewide initiative to help minority and women-owned businesses prosper in Florida and the global marketplace. Advocates for minority economic development and provides assistance to minority businesses and organizations. Contact: Office of Minority Business Development, 2801 Ponce de Leon Blvd., Suite 700, Coral Gables, FL 33134; 305-569-2654.

Black Business Investment Board: Oversees the state's investment in black business investment corporations, which provide technical assistance and loans to black-owned businesses. For more information, contact Florida Black Business Investment Board, 1711 S. Gadsen St., Tallahassee, Fl 32301; 850-487-4850.

Black Business Investment Corporations: Provides loans, loan guarantees, joint ventures, limited partnerships or any combination thereof. For more information, contact Florida Black Business Investment Board, 1711 S. Gadsen St., Tallahassee, Fl 32301; 850-487-4850.

Black Business Venture Corporation: A vehicle for initiating business acquisitions and engaging in real estate development. Serves a twofold purpose: to provide real and/or commercial office space for Black businesses; and to address the larger community needs such as local employment and retail centers.

Florida Contractors' Cooperative Surety Bond Support and Management Development Program: Assists the African American contractor in developing a relationship with a surety company that is equipped to meet long-term bonding needs of the business.

Georgia

Office of Economic Development
60 Executive Park South, NE
Atlanta, GA 30329-2231
404-679-4940
Fax: 800-736-1155
www.dca.state.ga.us

Business Assistance

Georgia Department of Community Affairs (DCA): Responsible for state administration of many incentive programs as well as providing technical assistance in the area of economic development to local governments, development authorities, and private for-profit entities. Provides information on financing programs and other services offered by the state government.

DCA maintains a highly skilled and extremely dedicated graphics and editorial staff to ensure that the information it gathers is effectively digested and promptly disseminated. Some of the department's many publications include:

1. *Small Business Resource Guide*: Manual for small business owners with useful instruction, organization addresses and telephone numbers and resources.
2. *Georgia's Communities-Planning, Growing, Achieving*: Publication contains information about various federal, state, and local financing programs that benefit businesses located in Georgia.
3. *Economic Development Financing Packet*
4. *Regional Development Center Listing*: List of Georgia's 16 RDCs with addresses and telephone numbers.

One-Stop Environmental Permitting: Georgia offers one-stop environmental permitting through its Department of Natural Resources, Environmental Protection Division. The state has the full authority of the U.S. Environmental Protection Agency (EPA) to issue permits that meet Federal standards, thus allowing a single permit to meet all requirements.

Emissions Credit Banking and Trading System: Companies can buy, sell or trade credits received for reducing the amount of pollutants it emits beyond those required by Federal regulations. These credits can be used at a later time to offset requirements on pollution created by the company's new growth, or could be sold or traded to another company.

Industrial Revenue Bonds: Taxable and tax-exempt industrial revenue bond financing is available through the state or local development authorities at competitive, below-prime rates.

Supplier Choice Power: Georgia companies with electricity demands of 900 kilowatts or higher may choose among competing suppliers, taking advantage of a competitive market. This cost-saving option has been available to Georgia consumers long before deregulation of the industry was even contemplated.

Georgia Secretary of State: First Stop Business Information Center provides the small business owner and the prospective entrepreneur with a central point of information and contacts for state regulatory requirements for opening a business. Contact: Georgia Secretary of State, 214 State Capitol, Atlanta, GA 30334; 404-656-2881; Fax: 404-656-0513; {www.sos.state.ga.us}.

Quick Start: The state of Georgia's training program for new and expanding business and industries. Administered by the Georgia Department of Technical and Adult Education, it is among the state's primary incentives for the recruitment of new jobs into Georgia. Unlike many states which only provide training grants, Quick Start directly provides a full range of high quality customized training services at no cost to client companies. These services cover not only job specific skills but also automation, productivity enhancement, and human resource development training. Examples of these concepts include Statistical Process Control, Programmable Logic Controller, and Team Skills Training. In addition to manufacturing operations, Quick Start also provides comprehensive training for office operations such as corporate headquarters, billing and remittance centers, and telecommunications operations such as customer service centers. Since its inception in 1967, Quick Start has trained over 294,000 employees for over 2,850 Georgia companies. Contact Georgia Department of Technical and Adult Education, 1800 Century Place, Suite 300, Atlanta, GA 30345; 404-679-2922; {www.dtae.tec.ga.us/quickstart}.

The Intellectual Capital Partnership Program (ICAPP): The programs of ICAPP provide one-stop entry to the intellectual capital of the University of Georgia, which includes its educational programs, faculty expertise, research and development facilities. For more information, contact ICAPP at 706-542-3521; {www.icapp.org/about}.

Business Financing

The Entrepreneurial Development Loan Fund (EDLF): A loan program to facilitate economic development, particularly in targeted Atlanta Project cluster areas by making credit available to small businesses located within those areas, particularly businesses owned by minorities and women. Typically, loans range from a low of $25,000 to a maximum of $100,000; however, smaller amounts and larger amounts may be considered.

Lead Safe Homes Demonstration Program: Exists for the purpose of reducing lead-based paint hazards in approximately 475 homes occupied by low and moderate income persons. There is no set amount that each applicant can receive.

Appalachian Regional Commission (ARC): An economic development program providing matching grant funds to eligible applicants for projects that will benefit the entire 35-county area of Appalachian Georgia.

Appalachian Region Business Development Revolving Loan Fund: A $2.2 million pool that can be used in the Appalachian Region for loans to projects that create or save jobs. The maximum loan amount is $200,000 per qualifying business, or 50% of total project cost, whichever is less. There is no maximum project cost and no minimum loan amount.

The Business Improvement Loan Fund (BILF) Program: Designed to encourage the revitalization of targeted business districts in Atlanta, and to support commercial/ industrial development in other eligible areas. Direct loans and loan participation up to $50,000 are available to businesses that are not able to obtain a market rate loan.

The Phoenix Fund: A program created to assist small and medium-sized businesses providing loan amounts from $10,000-$100,000 for construction or renovation of privately-owned commercial buildings, equipment purchases needed to operate a business, and, in some cases, working capital. Contact: Atlanta Development Authority, 86 Pryor St., SW, Atlanta, GA 30303; 404-880-4100; {www.atlantada.com}.

Atlanta Export Assistance Center: Provides marketing assistance, a resource center and financial assistance. The professional counseling services provided by EAC counselors are free of charge. Most market research and trade information is furnished at no cost to the client. Contact: Export Assistance Center, 285 Peachtree Center Ave., Suite 200, Atlanta, GA 30303; 404-657-1964.

The Georgia Procurement Assistance Center: Assists firms in their efforts to do business with the federal government. The Center helps firms solicit bids and locate procurement opportunities with the Department of Defense and area military facilities seeking certain goods and services. Although assistance is given upon request to any firm, the majority of clients are small and disadvantaged businesses. Contact Georgia Tech Economic Development Institute, 208 O'Keefe Bldg., Atlanta, GA 30332; 404-894-6121.

Surety Bond Guarantee Program: Enables small contractors to obtain the surety bonds necessary to compete for government and non-government contracts.

Coastal Venture Investment Forum (VIF): Designed to promote the development of promising businesses located within the coastal region of Georgia. VIF assists by reviewing business plans to determine if private investment is warranted. For further information, contact Coastal Venture Investment Forum, P.O. Box 10844, Savannah, GA 31412, or Bureau of Business Research & Economic Development, Georgia Southern University, 912-681-0213, {www2.gasou.edu/VIR}.

Tax Incentives

Research and Development Tax Credit: Companies are eligible for a tax credit on research expenses for research conducted within Georgia for any business or headquarters of any such business engaged in manufacturing, warehousing and distribution, processing, telecommunications, tourism, and research and development industries. The credit is 10% of the additional research expense over the base amount and may be carried forward ten years, but may not exceed 50% of the business' net tax liability in any one year.

Small Business Growth Companies Tax Credit: Tax credit is granted for any business or headquarters of any such business engaged in manufacturing, warehousing and distribution, processing, telecommunications, tourism, and research and development industries having a state net taxable income which is 20% or more above that of the preceding year if its net taxable income in each of the two preceding years was also 20% or more. The credit applies to companies whose total tax liability does not exceed $1.5 million.

Georgia Employment Tax Credit Program: A tax credit on Georgia income taxes for eligible businesses that create new jobs in counties or "less-developed" census tract areas.

Job Tax Credit: Companies engaged in manufacturing, warehousing and distribution, processing, telecommunications, tourism or research and development that create 25 or more jobs may receive between a $500 and $2,500-per-job tax credit. Companies that locate in industrial enterprise zones are required to create 10 new jobs to be eligible for this tax credit.

Investment Tax Credit: Taxpayers operating an existing manufacturing or telecommunications facility or telecommunications support facility in Georgia for three years may obtain a 1% credit against their income tax liability when they invest $50,000. That credit increases to 3% for recycling, pollution control and defense conversion activities.

Optional Investment Tax Credit: Taxpayers qualifying for the investment tax credit may choose an optional investment tax credit with the following threshold criteria: Designated Minimum % Tax Area Investment Credit: Tier 1: $5 million 10%; Tier 2, $10 million 8%; Tier 3 or Tier 4, $20 million 6%. The credit may be claimed for 10 years, provided the qualifying property remains in service throughout that period. A taxpayer must choose either the regular or optional investment tax credit. Once this election is made, it is irrevocable.

Industrial Enterprise Zones: The City of Atlanta, as authorized under a special provision of Georgia law, has designated two industrial parks as industrial enterprise zones. Companies in both the Atlanta and Southside industrial parks receive 100% freeport on all three classes of inventory and may receive real property tax reduction for up to 25 years. All buildings constructed in these enterprise zones are exempted from local property taxes at levels that begin at 100%. These exemptions decrease in increments of 20% every five years. New businesses in both parks are eligible for a $2,500-per job tax credit for a payroll of ten or more persons.

The Atlanta Empowerment Zone: Businesses which locate in the federally designated City of Atlanta Empowerment Zone and employ residents from this zone are eligible for various federal and state tax incentives, job training benefits and other assistance. A local executive board decides and manages the allocation of federal funds that are channeled through the State of Georgia.

Commercial Enterprise Zone: City of Atlanta offers a commercial enterprise zone designation for office employers applying in portions of the city including the central business district. Substantial property tax relief is possible.

Retraining Tax Credit: This credit allows some employers to claim certain costs of retraining employees to use new equipment, new technology, or new operating systems. The credit can be worth 50% of the direct costs of retraining full-time employees up to $500 per employee per approved retraining program per year. The credit cannot be more than 50% of the taxpayer's total state income tax liability for a tax year. Credits claimed but not used may be carried forward for 10 years.

Child Care Credits: Employers who provide or sponsor child care for employees are eligible for a tax credit of up to 75% of the employers' direct costs. The credit cannot be more than 50% of the taxpayer's total state income tax liability for that taxable year. Any credit claimed but not used in any taxable year may be carried forward for five years from the close of the taxable year in which the cost of the operation was incurred. In addition, employers who purchase qualified child care property will receive a credit totaling 100% of the cost of such property. These two child care credits can be combined.

Research & Development Tax Credit: A tax credit is allowed for research expenses for research conducted within Georgia for any business or headquarters of any such business engaged in manufacturing, warehousing and distribution, processing, telecommunications, tourism, or research and development industries.

Small Business Growth Companies Tax: A tax credit is granted for any business or headquarters or any such business engaged in manufacturing, warehousing and distribution, processing, telecommunications, tourism, or research and development industries having a state net taxable income which is 20% or more above that of the preceding year if its net taxable income in each of the two preceding years was also 20% or more.

Ports Activity Job Tax & Investment Credits: Businesses or the headquarters of any such businesses engaged in manufacturing, warehousing and distribution, processing, telecommunications, tourism, or research and development that increase their port traffic tonnage through Georgia ports by more than 10% over their 1997 base year port traffic, or by more than 10% over 75 net tons, five containers or 10 20-foot equivalent units (TEU's) during the previous 12-month period are qualified for increased job tax credits or investment tax credits.

Headquarters Tax: Companies establishing their headquarters or relocating their headquarters to Georgia may be entitled to a tax credit if certain criteria are met. The credit may be taken against Georgia income tax liability and a company's withholding taxes. Credits may be carried forward for 10 years.

The Georgia Tax Credit for Adult Basic Skills Education: Designed to encourage businesses to provide or sponsor basic skills education programs for their employees. Business enterprises may benefit by providing or sponsoring for their employees basic education skills that enhance reading, writing, or mathematical skills up to and including the 12th grade level.

State Tax Exemptions:

Manufacturing Machinery and Computer Sales Tax Exemption: Provides for an exemption from the sales and use tax for 1) machinery used directly in the manufacture of tangible personal property when the machinery is bought to replace or upgrade machinery in a manufacturing plant presently existing in the state and machinery components which are purchased to upgrade machinery used directly in the manufacture of tangible personal property in a manufacturing plant; 2) machinery used directly in the manufacture of tangible personal property when the machinery is incorporated as additional machinery for the first time into a manufacturing plant presently existing in this state; 3) machinery which is used directly in the manufacture of tangible personal property when the machinery is incorporated for the first time into a new manufacturing plant located in this state; 4) machinery used directly in the remanufacture of aircraft engines, parts, and components on a factory basis.

Primary Materials Handling Sales Tax Exemption: Purchases of primary material handling equipment and racking systems which are used directly for the storage, handling, and moving of tangible personal property in a new or expanding warehouse or distribution facility when such new facility or expansion is valued at $5 million or more and does not have greater than 15% retail sales are exempt from sales and use taxes.

Electricity Exemption: Electricity purchased that interacts directly with a product being manufactured is exempt from sales taxes when the total cost of the electricity exceeds 50% of the cost of all materials used, including electricity, in making the product.

For further information on sales tax exemptions, contact Georgia Department of Revenue, Room 310, 270 Washington Street, Atlanta, GA 30334; 404-656-4060.

Exports

The *Atlanta Export Assistance Center* offers the following resources: Marketing Assistance, Resource Center, Financial Assistance, The Atlanta Export Assistance Center combines the export promotion and finance resources of the following eight agencies: U.S. Department of Commerce, U.S. Small Business Administration, The Georgia Department of Agriculture, The Georgia Department of Industry, Trade & Tourism, The Georgia Housing and Finance Authority, Georgia's Institute of Technology's Center for International Standards and Quality, and the Service Corps of Retired Executives.

The *Atlanta Region* houses consulates, trade offices, and Chambers of Commerce for 44 countries. These organizations provide assistance with foreign exporting, importing and investing.

International Trade Data Network (ITDN): A not-for-profit data multiplier, GDITT provides the business community with the timely, detailed market intelligence needed to be competitive in the global arena.

For these programs, contact Atlanta Regional Export Assistance Center, 285 Peachtree Center Avenue,, Suite 200, Atlanta, GA 30303; 404-657-1900; Fax: 404-657-1970.

Women and Minorities

The Atlanta Women's Business Center: A major new resource for women who want to start a business or for those who already operate a business. The center offers assistance with various aspects of business operations including cash flow and profit margin projections. The center has a well organized information section stocked with computers, manuals, books and audio and videotapes on various business topics. Counselors from the SBA's Atlanta SCORE Chapter are available to women entrepreneurs. Workshops and seminars are offered throughout the year and cover such topics as the basics of starting a business, developing a business plan, marketing, sources of business capital, and technology as a business tool. For more information, contact the Center at 404-965-3983, {www.onlinewbc.org}.

Georgia Minority Subcontractors Tax Credit: Provides for an income tax adjustment on the State Tax Return, to any company which subcontracts with a minority-owned firm to furnish goods, property or services to the State of Georgia. The law allows a corporation, partnership, or individual, in computing Georgia taxable income, to subtract from federal taxable income or federal adjusted gross income, 10% of the amount of qualified payments to minority subcontractors. For more information, contact Small and Minority Business Program, 200 Piedmont Ave., Suite 1304, West Floyd Bldg., Atlanta, GA 30334; 404-656-6315; 800-495-0053.

Atlanta Economic Development Corporation (AEDC): Provides financial and technical assistance to small minority and female owned businesses to expand and/or relocate in the city. In cooperation with local financial institutions and government agencies, it provides a variety of financial aids for business development projects that have corresponding public benefits.

Minority Small Business Resource Organizations: These organizations provide a variety of technical counseling and financial assistance to minority small businesses:

1. *Atlanta Business League*, PO Box 92363, Atlanta, GA 30314; 404-584-8126
2. *Atlanta Public Schools*, Contract Compliance Office, 1631 LaFrance Street, NE, Atlanta, GA 30307;404-371-7129
3. *Business Development Center – NAACP*, 2034 Metropolitan Parkway, SW, Atlanta, GA 30315; 404-768-5755
4. *Department of Commerce*, Minority Business Development Agency (MBDA), Summit Building, Room 1715, 401 West Peachtree Street, NW, Atlanta, GA 30308; 404-730-3300
5. *Small Business Administration*, Minority Small Business Division, 1720 Peachtree Road, NW, Suite 606, Atlanta, GA 30309; 404-347-7416.

Hawaii

Department of Business, Economic Development and Tourism
P.O. Box 2359
Honolulu, HI 96804
No. 1 Capitol District Bldg.
250 S. Hotel Street
Honolulu, HI 96813
808-586-2593
Fax: 808-586-2589
www.state.hi.us/dbedt

Business Assistance

Business Resource Center: Assists both new and existing businesses with information on government permit and license requirements, government procurement, sources of alternative financing, marketing, preparing a business plan, and available entrepreneurship training programs. Access to statistical, economic and marketing information, as well as information and services available from other government sources. Contact Business Resource Center, Department of Business, Economic Development and Tourism, No. 1 Capitol District Bldg., 250 S. Hotel St., 4th Floor, EWA Wing, Honolulu, HI 96813; 808-586-2423.
Small Business Information Service: Responsible for providing referrals and information on government licenses, permits and procurement, funding source, and entrepreneurship training.
Business Services Division: Helps new and existing businesses with direct business loans, community development projects, information programs, licensing and permit information and referral, and business advocacy.
Business Action Center: Provides Hawaii's entrepreneurs with the information, business forms, licenses and permits they need to make their small business dreams a reality. Contact: Business Action Center, State Department of Business, Economic Development and Tourism, 1130 N. Nimitz Hwy., Suite A-254, Honolulu, HI 96817; 808-586-2545.
Financial Assistance Branch: Administers loan programs.
Business Resource Center: Accurate timely statistical and economic information for Hawaii. Access to information and services available from other government sources in the State of Hawaii, nationally and internationally. 15,000 titles relating to business, government and economic development in the State of Hawaii with an emphasis on statistical information.
Pacific Business Center Program University of Hawaii at Manoa: The Pacific Business Center matches faculty, students, and facilities at the University of Hawaii at Manoa with requests for assistance from businesses and community development organizations in Hawaii and the U.S. territories in the Pacific Islands. Consultation with program staff is free of charge, and after that clients may be assessed a modest consulting fee to pay faculty and students working on individual projects. Contact: Pacific Business Center, College of Business Administration, University of Hawaii at Manoa, 2404 Maile Way, 4th Floor, Honolulu, HI 96822; 808-956-6286.
University of Hawaii Office of Technology Transfer & Economic Development (OTTED) works to involve the University of Hawaii system in economic development support activities for the state. OTTED is responsible for patenting and licensing technologies developed at the University, for funding University-based R&D projects and the development of unique computer applications, and for matching University-based technical, educational and business development resources with the needs of the community.
Hawaii Island Economic Development Board: HIEDB's mission is to facilitate federal resource programs and implement appropriate economic development projects. HIEDB provides valuable information and contacts for area businesses and industries, as well as key liaison to federal, state, county and private sector resources in financing, business planning, permitting, legal advice and other business services. Contact Hawaii Island Economic Development Board, Box 103-281, Hilo, HI 96720; 808-966-5416; Fax: 808-966-6792.

Employment and Training Fund Program: Business-specific training, upgrade training, new occupational skills training, management skills training, and other similar activities are available to both employers and individuals.

High Technology Development Corporation: Promotes the growth of commercial high-technology industry and assists in promoting hi-tech products and software. Contact High Technology Development Corporation, 2800 Woodlawn Dr., Suite 10, Honolulu, HI 96822; 888-677-4292; {www.hawaii.htdc.org}.

Pacific Business Center: The Center matches faculty, students and facilities at the University of Hawaii with requests for assistance from businesses and community development organizations in Hawaii and the Pacific Islands. Initial free consultation, after which modest fees may be assessed. 808-956-6285.

Business Financing

Innovation Loan Program: Controls loans up to $100,000 to start-up companies with innovative projects.

Hawaii Department Of Agriculture Loan Programs:
1. The Agricultural Loan Program is intended to provide financing to "Qualified Farmers" and "New Farmers" engaged in agricultural production of food, feed and fiber. Loans can be made to qualifying sole proprietorships, corporations, partnerships and cooperatives. In addition, qualifying corporations and cooperatives can obtain funding for enterprises engaged in marketing, purchasing, processing and for those who provide certain farm business services.
2. Aquaculture Loan Program: Aquaculture means the production of aquatic plant and animal life in a controlled salt, brackish, or freshwater environment situated on real property. Loans can be made to "Qualified Aquaculturists" organized as sole proprietorships, corporations, cooperatives and partnerships.

For these, contact Department of Agriculture, Agricultural Loan Division, P.O. Box 22159, Honolulu, HI 96823; 808-973-9460; 808-468-4644, ext. 39460; {www.hawaiiag.org}.

Hawaii Small Business Innovation Research Grant Program: Its purpose is to expand science and technology-based economic development in Hawaii, increase revenues and quality job opportunities in the State.
1. Federal SBIR Program: Phase I awards determine the feasibility of a new technology and are valued up to $100,000. Phase II awards are a continuation of successful Phase I efforts. Phase II awards typically involve developing a prototype and are valued up to $750,000
2. Hawaii SBIR Matching Grant Program: To encourage Hawaii companies to participate in the program, the High Technology Development Corporation provides a matching grant of up to $25,000 to Hawaii companies that receive Phase I awards

The Rural Economic Transition Assistance: Hawaii (RETA-H) Program provides a limited "window of opportunity" to existing and potential entrepreneurs who would like to take part in the transition of Hawaii's agricultural economy from sugar caned-based monoculture to diversified agriculture and are willing to support the Program's goals. Any individuals, especially displaced sugar workers, and community and agricultural associations with an entrepreneurial spirit, are invited to determine if their ideas are eligible for RETA-H funds. These funds are only available for establishing or expanding businesses which produce, process and/or service agricultural products where funds will ultimately go to establishing former sugar workers as business owners and which will speed the transition toward a diversified agriculture in Hawaii. Most grants are in the range of $50,000 - $200,000.

Hawaii Strategic Development Corporation (HSDC) is a state agency created in 1990 to promote economic development and diversification in conjunction with private enterprise. HSDC has established four venture funds, some of which have new funds in formation. Keo Kea Hawaii is typical of the four funds, which are:
- Keo Kea Hawaii LP (KKH) is a Hawaii Based venture capital limited partnership that invests in start-up, emerging and established companies located in the state of Hawaii with an emphasis on high technology. KKH will purchase up to a maximum of 50% of the limited partnership units offered by each Venture Company, while the other units are purchased by third parties who are not directly involved with the Venture Partnership or the project, nor otherwise directly affiliated with the Venture Partnership or its general partner(s). KKH's maximum commitment is $50,000 per investment and may assist in identifying other investment partners when requested.
- HMS Investments, L. P.
- Hawaii Venture Fund, L. P.
- Tangent Growth Hawaii, L. P.: Mezzanine and Later Stage Fund

Contact: Hawaii Strategic Development Corporation, No. 1 Capitol District Building, 250 South Hotel Street, Suite 503, P.O. Box 2359, Honolulu, HI 96804; 808-587-3829; Fax: 808-587-3832; {www.htdc.org}.

Hawaii Department of Business, Economic Development and Tourism: This department offers two loan programs:

- ***Hawaii Capital Loan Program***: Provides loans to small businesses in amounts up to $1,000,000. Generally these loans must be secured and interest rates are pegged to the prime rate.
- ***Hawaii Innovation Loan Program***: Loans up to $100,000 to Hawaii start-up companies with innovative projects.

Call DBEDT at 808-856-2577 for more information about either program.

Tax Incentives

Hawaii has only two levels of government taxation: state and local.

No personal property tax.

No tax on inventories, furniture, equipment or machinery.

Credit against taxes paid on the purchase of capital goods, machinery, and equipment.

No state tax on goods manufactured for export.

No stock transfer tax: All security exchange transactions are exempt from general excise tax, as an incentive to financial institutions.

No unincorporated business tax.

Banks and financial institutions pay only one business tax.

Manufactured products or those produced for export are exempt from the general excise tax, including custom computer software.

Manufacturers, wholesalers, processors, millers, refiners, packer and canners are taxed on 0.5% of gross proceeds.

Insurance solicitors and agents are taxed at .15 percent.

Contractors are taxed 4% of gross proceeds. All sales of retails goods and services are taxed at 4% of gross income.

Purchase of depreciable and tangible property is allowed with a refundable tax credit against excise and use taxes.

General excise tax exemptions are in effect for air pollution control facilities, certain scientific contracts with the United State, ships used in international trade and commerce, sugar and pineapple manufacturers, and sales of tangible personal property to the federal government.

Enterprise Zones (EZ) Program: A joint state-county effort intended to stimulate--via tax and other incentives-- certain types of business activity, job preservation, and job creation in areas where they are most appropriate or most needed. Incentives include 100% exemption from the General Excise Tax (GET) and Use Tax every year. Contractors are also exempt from GET on construction done within an EZ for an EZ-qualified business. An 80% reduction of state income tax the first year. (This reduction goes down 10% each year for 6 more years.) An additional income tax reduction equal to 80% of annual Unemployment Insurance premiums the first year. (This reduction goes down 10% each year for 6 more years.)

Tax Incentives For Technology Companies:

- Investment in a technology business earns an income tax credit equal to 10% of the investment, up to a maximum of $500,000.
- Increasing research activities also qualifies for a tax credit, equivalent to an additional 2.5% of expenses over the base amount.
- No targeted taxes on Internet commerce. Recognizing the growing importance of e-commerce, the Hawaii Internet Tax Freedom Act specifically prohibits discriminatory taxes aimed directly at the Internet.
- Stock options held in high tech businesses are exempt from capital gains or income tax. Increasingly, stock options are part of the compensation package for high tech companies. The Hawaii exemption even allows tock options gained outside the state to be exempt.
- Royalty income from the sale of licensing of intellectual property is exempt from both general excise tax and income tax. Hawaii wants to encourage creativity and invention, especially for companies such as software developers, which derive most of their income from royalties on copyrights.
- Leveling the Tax Playing Field: General excise tax (GET) exemptions are provided for those Hawaii-based contractors and service businesses which perform a service or fulfill a contract outside Hawaii. The aim is to help Hawaii tech businesses compete with out of state contractors and service providers. Exported services and contracting are now treated in the same way as tangible personal property exports: both are exempt from the GET.

Exports

U.S. Department of Commerce-Commercial Service (Honolulu District office): The trade specialist at the Honolulu District office assists U.S. companies seeking to expand into export markets. The Honolulu District office provides companies with trade leads, foreign market research, and information on trade events, seminars, and conferences.

Foreign Trade Zones: Ports designated for duty-free entry of goods. Merchandise may be stored, displayed, or used for manufacturing within the zone and re-exported without duties being paid. Contact: Foreign Trade Zone #9, 521 Ala Moana, Pier 2, Honolulu, HI 96813; 808-586-2507.

Local Chambers of Commerce: Provide exporters with copies of and instructions for completing a general Certificate of Origin. This certificate is a notarized statement authenticating the country of origin of an export good.

Consulate Generals in Hawaii: Various consulate generals in Hawaii offer limited trade counseling and a few have trade libraries.

Thai Trade Representative Office: Focuses primarily on the promotion of Thailand products in Hawaii.

Women and Minorities

The Honolulu Minority Business Development Center: The objectives of the Honolulu Minority Business Development Center are to 1) promote the creation and/or expansion of viable and competitive minority-owned businesses, 2) increase contracting opportunities from public and private sources for minority-owned businesses, and 3) provide management and technical assistance to qualified minority individuals and firms in the areas of planning, finance, construction assistance, and general management to improve the overall performance, profit, and net worth of minority firms.

Alu Like, Inc.: Alu Like provides technical and/or consultant services to existing native Hawaiian-owned businesses, prospective Hawaiian entrepreneurs, and community economic enterprise development. These services are available through Alu Like's five island multi-service centers or its state office in Honolulu. Contact Alu Like-Oahu Business Development Center, 1120 Maunakea Street, Suite 271, Honolulu, HI 96817; 808-542-1225; {www.alulike.org}.

Idaho

Idaho Department of Commerce
700 West State Street
P.O. Box 83720
Boise, ID 83720-0093
208-334-2470
Fax: 208-334-2631
www.idoc.state.id.us/pages/businesspage.html

Business Assistance

Economic Development Division: This office can provide information and expertise in dealing with state, federal, and local agencies. They also have information on financing programs and other services offered by the state government.

Starting a Business in Idaho: A free publication with information on how to plan a business as well as contacts for state agencies and other helpful organizations, is available from the Department of Commerce.

Idaho Small Business Solutions Website: This site will help you find your way through the requirements of government agencies that regulate businesses in the state of Idaho. {www.idahobizhelp.org}.

Idaho Small Business Development Center: The Idaho SBDC offers a wide variety of services to small businesses throughout the state. Among them are Business Formation and Expansion, and Consulting/Counseling, Business Plans, Business Sale/Dissolution Assistance, Demographic and Economic Data, Market Research, SBIR (Small Business Innovation Research) Grants, Speakers Bureaus, Training (Business. Contact Idaho Small Business Development Center, Boise State University, 1910 University Drive, Boise, ID 83725; 208-426-1640; 800-225-3815; Fax: 208-426-3877.

Idaho Business Network (IBN): Operated by the Idaho Department of Commerce to help Idaho companies bid on federal, state and large corporation contracts. Any Idaho company may join the Idaho Business Network for $25 per year. For additional information or to sign up for IBN services, call 208-334-2470.

- *Opportunity Notices*: Every day bid notices on federal, state and private contracts are entered into the Idaho Business Network computer. These bidding opportunities are matched with the capabilities of Idaho businesses participating in the IBN. When a match occurs the client company is notified with a printed or e-mail version "opportunity notice" alerting them to the opportunity and providing information needed to obtain the bid package.

- *Military and Federal Standards*: Federal bid packages often reference military and federal specifications by name or number without providing the actual documents. The Idaho Business Network maintains a CD-ROM library of all military and federal standards and specifications. Printed copies of required specifications and standards are provided at no charge to businesses participating in the IBN.

- *Federal Acquisition Regulations (F.A.R.)*: Contains the rules and regulations used by federal agencies to purchase products and services. Bid packages often refer to F.A.R. clauses by name or number without providing the text of the document. The IBN maintains the F.A.R. on CD-ROM, and provides printed copies of needed clauses to participating companies at no charge.

- *Trade Missions*: All IBN clients are welcome to attend periodic trade missions to visit large corporations, military sites, and other government agencies. Businesses attending the trade missions have the opportunity to meet with buyers to market their products and services.

- *Workshops and Seminars*: The IBN holds workshops statewide on topics such as selling to Mountain Home Air Force Base, selling to the INEEL, how to package for the military, quality assurance, etc.

- *The Governor's Business Opportunity Conference*: Annually, the IBN hosts the Governor's Business Opportunity Conference with over 60 large private corporations and government agencies sending buyers to meet with representatives of Idaho businesses. Concurrent training workshops are also held during the conference on a wide range of topics, such as introduction to procurement and marketing strategies for small businesses.
- *Electronic Bulletin Board*: Provides computer and modem access to all bid notices obtained by the IBN for the most current ten days.
- *CAGE Code*: All companies wishing to do business with the U.S. Department of Defense must have an identification number known as a Commercial and Government Entity Code, or CAGE Code. Companies applying for a CAGE Code must be sponsored by a government agency. The Idaho Business Network provides CAGE Code application forms and sponsors participating Idaho business applications
- *New Industry Training Program*: Provides customized job training for new and expanding industries.
- *Work Force Training*: Funds are available to provide skilled workers for specific economic opportunities and industrial expansion initiatives.

IDA-ORE: A charitable nonprofit development company created for the benefit of communities located in 10 southwestern Idaho and 2 eastern Oregon counties. IDA-ORE has four general missions which enable the organization to enrich the communities in the areas of services to older Americans, workforce development, economic and community development planning, business development services and development finance. Contact IDA-ORE Planning and Development, 10624 Executive Drive, Boise, ID 83713; 208-322-7033; Fax: 208-322-3569; {www.ida-ore.com}.

Business Financing

Revenue Allocation Finance Areas: Any city in Idaho can have established urban renewal areas. New facilities located within designated revenue allocation area boundaries may qualify for tax exempt bonds. Tax revenues from increases in property value within the urban renewal area are dedicated to servicing the bonds. Also known as Tax Increment Financing, these funds can be used to pay for infrastructure development costs of a project.

Industrial Revenue Bonds: Idaho cities and counties are able to form public corporations for the purpose of issuing industrial revenue bonds (IRBs). The IRB program provides for loans of up to $10 million, at tax-exempt interest rates, to finance the improvement or purchase of land, buildings, and machinery or equipment used in manufacturing, production, processing, or assembly.

Rural Economic and Community Development Administration: Offers guarantees up to 90% of loans between $500,000 and $10 million made to small businesses located in areas not within the boundaries of a city of 50,000 or more. Loan proceeds can be used for the purchase, development or improvement of land, buildings and equipment, or a start-up and working capital.

IDA-ORE Reinvestment Loan Fund (RLF): This lending tool was developed to assist both small business start-ups and healthy, growing businesses that are unable to qualify for conventional bank financing. IDA-ORE, working in partnership with local private lenders, helps businesses qualify for financing for economic expansion and job creation. Typically, a job must be created or retained for each $10,000 in financing provided by IDA-ORE in the loan structure. The RLF is available to assist with most legitimate business needs. The RLF generally will not support the refinance of existing debt. A healthy, growing business should expect to contribute at least 10% of the project costs (start-ups somewhat more). The private lender will generally contribute up to 57% of project costs and IDA-ORE should contribute about 33% (up to $150,000).

The IDA-ORE MicroEnterprise Loan: This loan program is designed to provide short-term, fixed rate financing for smaller loans. These loans are available to start-ups and established growing small businesses. Businesses are generally eligible if loan proceeds are for business development purposes and existing businesses have average annual sales for the previous 3 years which do not exceed $5 million and employees fewer than 100 people, including affiliates.

Tax Incentives

Idaho's Investment Tax Credit: Equal to 3% of qualified investment (not to exceed more than 45% of a given year's tax liability) and may be carried forward for seven years.

Nonbusiness-Related Contributions: Corporations are allowed credit for certain nonbusiness-related contributions, e.g., education and rehabilitation. Net operating loss carrybacks are limited to $100,000 per tax year. The $100,000 loss limit may be carried back three years and if it is not absorbed by the income in those three years, the rest of the loss may be carried forward 15 years. Instead of carrying a loss back, a taxpayer may choose to carry the loss forward for up to 15 years or until it has been completely absorbed.

Property Tax Exemptions: Include inventories, livestock, stored property in transit, pollution control facilities, household belongings, clothing, and properly licensed motor or recreational vehicles. Statewide, tax rates vary generally from 0.8 to 2.8 percent, with an average of 1.7 percent.

Excluded from a 5% sales tax: Utilities, motor fuels (which are taxed separately), and tangible personal property used for production activities involved in manufacturing, farming, processing, mining, and fabricating.

Mining Claims: Non-patented mining claims are exempt from property taxation.

For more information, contact the Idaho State Tax Commission, P.O. Box 36, Boise, ID 83722-0410; 800-972-7660; {www2.state.id.us/tax}.

Exports

The Idaho Department of Commerce's Division of International Business: Provides a variety of services and assistance to all Idaho firms interested in doing business overseas, with special programs for small- and medium-sized firms.

Idaho International Business Development Center (IIBDC): Seeks to coordinate efforts statewide to promote Idaho in the global marketplace. The division, in partnership with the Boise Branch Office of the U.S. Department of Commerce, maintains regular contact with importers, distributors, wholesalers, and retailers in foreign countries and can supply market data and information on foreign packaging, labeling requirements, language barriers, consumer preferences, and other trade factors.

Idaho Department of Agriculture: Offers a broad range of assistance to Idaho companies which export Idaho agricultural commodities and processed and specialty food products. The Department of Agriculture sponsors many special agricultural trade events and participates with the Department of Commerce in joint seminars, workshops, and trade shows.

Women's Business Center: A public/private partnership with the Small Business Administration, US Bank as a founding partner, and First Security Bank as a contributing sponsor. The Center is designed to assist women who are considering starting a business or who already own one and need to gain additional skills and support. The Center provides training, counseling, and mentoring services to clients through staff and volunteers. The Center focuses on the specific needs of women entrepreneurs. Contact Women's Business Center, 1021 Manitou, P.O. Box 6700, Boise, ID 83707-0700; 208-336-5464; Fax: 208-426-5281; {www.wemswbc.org}.

Hispanic Business Association (HBA): An all-volunteer organization created to promote advancement of Hispanic professionals by expanding educational and business opportunities for the Hispanic population of southwest Idaho, eastern Oregon, and the Northwest. Scholarships, internships, trade shows, and business loans are some of the opportunities for members. Contact Hispanic Business Association, 904 E. Chicago St., Caldwell, ID 83605; 208-455-9659.

Illinois

Department of Commerce and Community Affairs
620 E. Adams
Springfield, IL 62602
217-782-7500
Fax: 217-524-3701
www.commerce.state.il.us

100 West Randolph St.
Suite 3-400
Chicago, IL 60601
312-814-7179
Fax: 312-814-2370

First Stop Business Center of Illinois
620 E. Adams, Third Floor
Springfiled, IL 62701
800-252-2923 (in state)
877-221-4403

Business Assistance

Department of Commerce and Community Affairs: Provides information, assistance and advocacy to facilitate and advance the economic development process in partnership with Illinois' communities, businesses, and their network of public and private sector providers.

Small Business Division: Responsible for an environment that supports small business success resulting in increased employment opportunities and prosperous communities throughout Illinois. Provides advocacy, business assistance, training and information resources to help entrepreneurs, small companies and their partners enhance their competitiveness in a global economy. Serves customers through a dynamic, integrated small business assistance delivery system that matches the diversity of their customers' current and future needs.

Business Association Directory: Includes organization mission, location and member information.

Workforce Development & Manufacturing Technology Assistance: Provides programs to assist manufacturers to improve employee job skills and manufacturing efficiency. Labor-Management programs are also available.

First Stop Business Information Center: Provides individuals with comprehensive information on state business permits and licenses, business startup assistance, regulatory guidance, demographic and census data. Guides them through permitting, licensing and regulatory processes. Phone: 800-252-2923.

Procurement Technical Assistance Centers (PTAC): Provide one-on-one counseling, technical information, marketing assistance and training to existing Illinois businesses that are interested in selling their products and/or services to local, state or federal government agencies. The services are offered through PTACs located at community colleges, universities, chambers of commerce and business development organizations.

Small Business Innovation Research Centers (SBIRC): Provide counseling, technical information and training to Illinois entrepreneurs and small businesses interested in pursuing research and development opportunities available to them through various federal and state programs. These programs provide small businesses with a means of developing new and marketable technologies and innovations and also for enhancing existing products and services.

Business Financing

Participation Loan Program, Development Corporation Participation Loan Program, Minority, Women and Disabled Participation Loan Program: Through these loan participation programs, the Illinois Department of Commerce and Community Affairs (DCCA) helps small businesses obtain financing through Illinois banks, development corporations, and lending institutions for business start-up, expansion, modernization and competitiveness improvement. Generally, the Department may provide subordinated small business loans up to 25% of the total amount of a project, but not less than $10,000 or more than $750,000.

Title IX Revolving Loan Fund: Provides low-cost supplemental financing to small and medium-sized manufacturers located in areas declared eligible for assistance. Proceeds may be used for the acquisition of land, buildings, machinery and equipment, building construction or renovations, and leasehold improvements.

Rural Development Loan Program: Assists businesses in communities with populations less than 25,000. Proceeds may be used to purchase land, construct or renovate buildings and purchase machinery and equipment.

Farm Development Authority Programs: 85% guarantee for loans by local lenders; up to $300,000 for farm owners. Proceeds may be used for land acquisition, building construction and improvements and the purchase of machinery and equipment.

State Treasurer's Economic Program: Provides companies with access to affordable capital to expand their operations and retain or create jobs in the state. For each permanent full-time job that is created or retained, the Treasurer can deposit $25,000 at well below market rates into the borrower's financial institution. That institution will then lend the money at below prevailing interest rates to the borrower.

Enterprise Zone Financing Program: Designed to encourage businesses to locate within an Illinois Enterprise Zone. DCCA may participate in an eligible loan for no less than $10,000, nor more than $750,000. In no case shall the amount of DCCA's subordinated participation exceed 25% of the total project. Ineligible uses of funds are debt refinancing and contingency funding.

Development Corporation Participation Loan Program: Provides financial assistance through a Development Corporation to small businesses that provide jobs to workers in the region served by the Development Corporation. The state will participate in loans up to 2% of the total amount of a project but not less than $10,000 nor more than $750,000.

Capital Access Program (CAP): Designed to encourage lending institutions to make loans to businesses that do not qualify for conventional financing. CAP is based on a portfolio insurance concept where the borrower and DCCA each contribute a percentage of the loan amount into a reserve fund located at the lender's bank. This reserve fund enables the financial institution to make loans beyond its conventional risk threshold and is available to draw upon to recover losses on loans made under the program.

Capital Access Program

Technology Venture Investment Program (TVIP): Provides investment capital for young or growing Illinois businesses in cooperation with private investment companies or investors. Program investments will be used for businesses seeking funding for any new process, technique, product or technical device commercially exploitable by Illinois businesses in fields such as health care and biomedical products, information and telecommunications, computing and electronic equipment, manufacturing technology, materials, transportation and aerospace, geoscience, financial and service industries, and agriculture and biotechnology. Program funds shall be used for such costs including, but not limited to, research and development costs, acquisition of assets, working capital, purchase or lease of machinery and/or equipment, and the acquisition and/or improvement or rehabilitation of land and buildings.

Affordable Financing of Public Infrastructure Program: Provides financial assistance to or on behalf of local governments, public entities, medical facilities and public health clinics.

Community Services Block Grant Loan Program: Provides long-term, fixed-rate financing to new or expanding businesses that create jobs and employment opportunities for low-income individuals.

Industrial Training Program: Assists companies in training new workers or upgrading the skills of their existing workers. Grants may be awarded to individual companies, multi-company efforts and intermediary organizations offering multi-company training.

Prairie State 2000 Programs: Businesses that need to retrain employees may utilize these funds. Loans are available to cover 100% of direct training costs. Grants covering 50% of those costs are also available. {www.state.il.us/ps2000}

Industrial Revenue Bonds: IDFA issues tax-exempt bonds on behalf of manufacturing companies to finance the acquisition of fixed assets such as land, buildings and equipment. Proceeds may also be used for new construction or renovation.

Illinois Large Business Development Program (LBDP): Provides incentive financing to encourage large out of state companies to locate in Illinois or existing large companies to undertake substantial job expansion or retention projects. Funds available through the program can be used by large businesses (500 or more employees) for typical business activities, including financing the purchase of land and buildings, construction or renovation of fixed assets, and site preparation. LBDP funds are targeted to extraordinary economic development opportunities, that is, projects that will result in substantial private investment and the creation and/or retention of 300 or more jobs.

Tax Incentives

Retirement income is not taxed.

Enterprise Zones: Incentives for businesses within a designated Enterprise Zone include:
- Sales tax exemption on building materials to be used in an Enterprise Zone.
- Sales tax exemption on purchases of tangible personal property to be used in the manufacturing or
- Assembly process or in the operation of a pollution control facility within an Enterprise Zone.
- Tax exemption on gas, electricity and the Illinois Commerce Commission's administrative charge is available to business located in Enterprise Zones.
- Tax credit of 0.5% is allowed a taxpayer who invest in qualified property in a Zone.
- Dividend Income Deduction for individual, corporations, trust, and estates are not taxed on dividend income from corporation doing substantially all their business in a Zone.
- Jobs tax credit allows a business a $500 credit on Illinois income tax for each job created in the Zone for which a certified eligible worker is hired.
- Financial institutions are not taxed on the interest received on loans for development within a Zone.
- Businesses may deduct double the value of a cash or in-kind contribution to an approved project of a designated Zone organization form taxable income.

Corporate Income Tax: Corporate income is taxed at 7.3% which includes a 4.8% state income tax and a 2.5% personal property replacement tax.

Incentives include:
- The 2.5% replacement tax may be deducted from the 4.8% state income tax.
- After 2000, apportionment will be based on sales alone.

Tax Credits include:
- 0.5% credit for investment in mining, manufacturing or retailing, plus an additional 0.5% if employment increases over 1%; a 1/6% training expense tax credit; and a 6.5% Research and Development credit.
- There are no local corporate income taxes in Illinois.

Sales Tax Exemptions: Purchases of manufacturing machinery as well as replacement parts and computers used to control manufacturing machinery; purchases of farm machinery; pollution controls, building materials to be used in an Enterprise Zone; and materials consumed in the manufacturing process in Enterprise Zones. Purchases or manufacturing machinery receive a credit equal to 50% of what the taxes would have been if the manufacturing machinery was taxable, making it possible for the manufacturers to use this credit to offset any other sales tax liability they incur. Food and drugs are taxed at the reduced rate of 1%.

Property Tax Exemptions: All property other than real estate is exempt from the property tax. Taxing bodies within Enterprise Zones may abate property taxes without a dollar limit for the life of the zone.

Illinois EDGE Program: Intended to help level the playing field between Illinois and its neighboring Midwestern states when competing for the location of large job creation projects. As a tax credit, the EDGE program allows a firm to reduce the costs of doing business in Illinois when compared with similar costs in other states where it could have located its operation. The credits would be available to the firm for up to a total of 10 years for each project. While each annual tax credit amount cannot be larger than the firm's state income tax liability (the income tax credits would not be refundable), the credit can be carried forward for up to five years. Each firm receiving competitive credits would have to maintain the jobs created and/or retained along with the capital investment concurrent with the period in which it claims the credits.

Tax Increment Financing (TIF): A tool Illinois lawmakers gave local governments more than 20 years ago to help local governments restore their most rundown areas or jumpstart economically sluggish parts of town. With this tool, financially strapped local governments can make needed improvements, such as new roads or new sewers, and provide incentives to attract businesses or help existing businesses expand, without tapping into general funds or raising taxes. For more information about TIFs and which Illinois communities use them, contact the Illinois Tax Increment Association {www.illinois-tif.com}.

Exports

International Trade Centers/NAFTA Opportunity Centers (ITC/NOC): Provide information, counseling and training to existing, new-to-export Illinois companies interested in pursuing international trade opportunities. The NOCs provide specialized assistance to those firms seeking to take advantage of the trade opportunities in Mexico and Canada made possible by the North American Free Trade Agreement.

Foreign Trade Zones: Offering low-cost production and warehousing facilities for imported and export-bound products.

Women and Minorities

Business Enterprise Program for Minorities, Females, and Persons with Disabilities (BEP): Promotes the economic development of businesses owned by minorities, females, and persons with disabilities.
The Business Enterprise for Minorities, Females, and Persons with Disabilities Act is designed to encourage state agencies to purchase needed goods and services from businesses owned and controlled by members of minority groups, women, and/or persons with disabilities.

Surety Bond Guaranty Program: Designed to provide Illinois' small, minority and women contractors technical assistance, help them receive experience in the industry and assist in obtaining bid, performance and payment bonds for government, public utility and private contracts.

Minority, Women and Disabled Participation Loan Program: (See Business Financing above) Additional information: The Minority, Women and Disabled Participation Loan Program guidelines differ, in that the program funding may not exceed 50% of the project, subject to a maximum of $50,000.

Indiana

Indiana Department of Commerce
One North Capitol, Suite 700
Indianapolis, IN 46204
317-232-8888
800-463-8081
317-233-5123 Fax
www.ai.org/bdev/index.html

Business Assistance

Indiana Department of Commerce: This office can provide information and expertise in dealing with state, federal, and local agencies. They also have information on financing programs and other services offered by the state government.

Technical & Marketing Assistance

Quality Initiative: Provides quality-awareness education, assessments and information to companies attempting to implement or improve quality-management programs.

Energy Policy Division Services: A wide range of assistance in energy efficiency, alternative energy and recycling market development programs.

Enterprise Advisory Group: Counsels emerging and mature businesses.

International Trade Services: Assistance to Indiana companies in export development in order to increase the sale of Indiana products worldwide.

Office of Regulatory Ombudsman: Acts as a mediator, expediter and problem-solver in areas affecting business.

Trade Show Assistance Program (TSAP): Provides reimbursement for a portion of the costs incurred while companies exhibit their products at overseas trade shows.

Employee Training Program: Provides financial assistance to new and expanding companies committed to training their workers. Eligible companies can receive reimbursement up to $200,000 or up to 50% of eligible training costs. Indiana will also continue this commitment to training by welcoming companies back after two years to apply for more funds to retrain employees.

Resources

Indiana Development Finance Authority (IDFA): Helps Indiana businesses obtain financial assistance through loan guaranty programs, tax-exempt private activity bonds for industrial development, Ex-Im Bank loan guarantees, insurance and direct loans for export products and flexible lending through case reserve accounts. Contact: Indiana Development Finance Authority, One N. Capitol, Suite 320, Indianapolis, IN 46204; 317-233-4332; {www.state.in.us/idfa}.

Indiana Small Business Development (ISBD) Corporation: Offers conferences and workshops, one-on-one counseling and up-to-date information on new market opportunities. The ISBD Corp. also identifies contracting opportunities with the government, assists growth-oriented companies in approaching new market opportunities and serves as a statewide advocate for contracting and marketing with Indiana's women- and minority-owned businesses. Contact: Indiana Small Business Development Corp., One N. Capitol, Suite 1275, Indianapolis, IN 46204; 317-264-2820; 888-ISBD-244; {www.isbdcorp.org}.

Indiana Economic Development Association (IEDA): Provides continuity to a statewide community development effort. The organization has two objectives: (1) to utilize the knowledge and resources of the association to make economic development activities in the state more effective, and (2) to cooperate and interact with all state and local organizations engaged in promoting the economic welfare of Indiana. Contact: Indiana Economic Development Association, One N. Capitol, Indianapolis, IN 46204; 317-573-2900; {www.ieda.org}.

Business Financing

Loans

Product Development/Commercialization Funding: Provides loans for businesses in need of financing to support research and development projects, or to support commercialization of new technology. Loan amounts vary.

Capital Access Program (CAP): Helps financial institutions lend money to Indiana businesses that don't qualify for loans under conventional lending policies. CAP loans may be of any amount

Certified Development Companies (CDC): Long-term, fixed-rate financing for a business's fixed-asset needs. CDC provides up to 40% of the cost with a commercial bank financing 50% of the total cost. The CDC portion is limited to $750,000. Minimum project cost is $125,000. Contact: Indiana Statewide Certified Development Corp., 8440 Woodfield Crossing, Suite 315, Indianapolis, IN 46240; 317-469-6166.

Hoosier Development Fund: Loans for small to medium-sized businesses. Loans range from $250,000 to several million dollars.

Indiana Community Business Credit Corporation (ICBCC): Loans for small to medium-sized businesses that exceed banks' customary limits. Loan amounts range from $100,000 to $750,000, and must be at least matched by a participating lender. Minimum project is $200,000. Contact Indiana Community Business Credit Corp., 8440 Woodfield Crossing, Suite 315, Indianapolis, IN 46240; 317-469-9704.

Industrial Development Infrastructure Program (IDIP): Supplemental financing for infrastructure projects in support of job creation/retention for low- to moderate-income persons. Amounts determined based on project needs. The program is designed to supplement local funding sources.

Industrial Development Loan Fund: Revolving loans for industrial growth. Loans up to $1 million are available.

Industrial Energy Efficiency Fund: The Energy Policy Division provides loans for improving energy efficiency in industrial processes. The maximum amount available per applicant is $250,000 or 50% of the total eligible project costs, whichever is less.

Loan Guaranty Programs: Financing for land or building acquisition or improvements, structures, machinery, equipment, facilities and working capital.

Product Development/Commercialization Funding: Loans for research and development or to support commercialization of new technology. Loan amounts are determined by the Business Modernization and Technology Corporation (BMT) and the business. Leveraging of outside funds is encouraged in the loan consideration.

Recycling Promotion and Assistance Fund: Loans to enhance the development of markets for recyclable materials.

Small Business Investment Company Program: Long-term and/or venture capital for small firms.

Strategic Development Fund (SDF): Loans or grants for not-for-profits and cities, towns and counties whose purpose is to promote industrial/business development. Generally $100,000 to $500,000, but can vary depending on the particular SBIC.

Trade Finance Program Financing: Assistance for companies exporting internationally. Amounts: Varies with programs.

Grants

Industrial Energy Efficiency Audits: The Energy Policy Division provides grant to manufacturers to study energy use in their facilities and recommend ways to reduce energy use and energy costs. Maximum amount available per applicant is $5,000.

Alternative Energy Systems Program: The Energy Policy Division offers grants to businesses to fund eligible alternative-fuel technologies and infrastructure development. The maximum amount available per project is $10,000.

Community Development Action Grant (CDAG): Grants to help organizations whose missions include economic development to expand administrative capacity and program development by offsetting miscellaneous expenses. In the case of organizations serving at least two counties, the amount of the grant may not exceed one dollar for every one dollar raised by the organization. The maximum grant award for organizations serving two or more counties may not exceed $75,000. Contact: Community Development Division, Indiana Department of Commerce, One N. Capitol, Suite 600, Indianapolis, IN 46204; 317-232-8911; 800-824-2476.

Industrial Development Grant Fund: Grants for non-profits and local units of government for off-site infrastructure projects in support of new business development. The grant amount is determined based on project needs. However, the program is designed to supplement local funding sources

National Industrial Competitiveness Through Energy, Environment and Economics Grant: The Energy Policy Division has information about Federal grants, with possible state matching funds, to improve energy efficiency, promote a cleaner production process and improve the competitiveness of industry. The maximum amount of federal grant available per applicant is $400,000.

Strategic Development Fund (SDF): Grants or loans for not-for-profits and cities, towns and counties whose purpose is to promote industrial/business development. Grant or loan funds may not exceed 50% of the cost of the project. The maximum grant amount is $250,000. The maximum grant and loan combination may not exceed $500,000.

Tire Recycling Market Development Program: The Energy Policy Division has grants to businesses involved in the production of a product that uses scrap tires as a feedstock. Recycled Tire Product Marketing grants up to $20,000. Recycled Tire Product Procurement grants up to $40,000.

Scrap Tire Market Development Research and Prototype Grant Program: Provides grant to support research on new products or machinery for handling scrap tire recycling. Grant range from $5,000 to $50,000.

Tire-Derived Fuel Testing Grant Program: Provides grants to develop fuel uses for scrap tires. Amount based on project needs.

Trade Show Assistance Program (TSAP): Provides reimbursement for a portion of the costs incurred while companies exhibit their products at overseas trade shows. Reimbursement includes 100% of exhibit space rental or $5,000, whichever is less.

Training 2000: Grants for reimbursement of eligible training costs. Up to 50% of eligible training costs. Awards for retraining have a maximum ceiling of $200,000. For companies seeking to become QS-9000 certified, up to 75% of QS-9000 related costs may be reimbursed.

Bonds

Tax-Exempt Bonds: Provide fixed-asset financing at competitive rates. Limits vary according to the type of project. Most manufacturing facilities are limited to $10 million. Contact: Indiana Development Finance Authority, One N. Capitol, Suite 320, Indianapolis, IN 46204; 317-233-4332.

Tax Increment Financing (TIF): Allows use of TIF revenues for purpose of developing an area. Amounts: Depends on the new property taxes generated as a result of development in the TIF allocation area.

Small Bond Program: Manufacturing companies and certain not-for-profit organizations with financing needs of $1 million or less may qualify for the IDFA's Small Bond Program. The program offers reduced time frames, reduced fees and less paperwork to qualifying companies. Smaller companies may find it easier to access the tax-exempt market with the IDFA's Small Bond Program, where participating banks purchase and hold the bonds. The Small Bond Program also features an agricultural tax-exempt bond to assist first time farmers in financing certain capital assets. Up to $250,000 is available per farmer, and the IDFA has made up to $10 million in Volume Cap available per year for Agricultural Bonds. The IDFA can also issue pooled or stand alone child care bonds to assist licensed Indiana child care providers in financing long term capital debt less expensively.

The following programs are offered by the Indiana Small Business Development Corporation, a not-for-profit organization that serves as an economic development resource to enhance the growth and expansion of Indiana companies, to include women and minorities in the federal, state, and commercial sectors of the economy. It is the only entity with a statewide focus for growth-oriented small business. Most services are provided free.

- The ***Government Marketing Assistance Group*** exists to help Indiana businesses market their products and services to the federal , state and local governments. GMAG's Government Marketing Specialists will help you identify opportunities and understand the process from start to finish, so you can compete for a share of this business.

- ***NxLeveL*** will help potential and existing entrepreneurs learn the skills needed to create and strengthen successful business ventures. Unlike other business education programs, NxLeveL addresses the special needs of entrepreneurs by providing a practical, hands-on approach to developing a small business-whether just starting out or ready to grow.

- ***Electronic Commerce and Computer Counseling*** includes instruction in electronic commerce/electronic data interchange (EC/EDI), guidance for selecting software and service providers, demonstrations of electronic commerce technologies, Internet training, online bulletin boards, computer needs assessment, software evaluation and selection guidance, industrial information systems assessment.

- *The Small Business Incubator Program* performs two important tasks within Indiana communities. Incubators foster local community development and nurture emerging businesses through startup periods.
- *Financial Assistance*: The ISBD Corp provides support for local programs for financial assistance and business growth. These include the Enterprise Development Fund (EDF), and the Microloan Program.
- *Microloan Program*: Leverages local investment dollars through a financing pool. This allows for smaller, high risk loans. A small business can borrow up to $25,000 from locally managed funds and take advantage of the management and technical assistance.

Tax Incentives

Indiana Corporate Income Tax: Taxpayers eligible for state corporate income tax credits apply the value first against gross tax liability, then against corporate adjusted gross tax liability and finally against supplemental net liability. Some credits may be applied against future tax liabilities if the amount of current credit exceeds taxes due.

College and University Contribution Credit: A credit for contributions to Indiana colleges and universities. Limited to the lesser of: (a) $1,000; (b) 50% of the contribution; or (c) 10% of the adjusted gross income tax.

Neighborhood Assistance Credit: Credit to corporate or individual taxpayers contributing to neighborhood organizations or who engage in activities to upgrade disadvantaged areas. Up to 50% of the amount invested, not to exceed $25,000 in any taxable year.

Drug and Alcohol Abuse Credit: Maximum credit is $6,250 for corporations with more than 1,000 employees, and $3,750 for corporations with fewer than 1,000 employees.

Research Expense Credit: Credit to any corporate taxpayer entitled to the Federal Research Expense Credit who incurs qualified Indiana research expenses.

Teacher Summer Employment Credit: Credit to persons who hire a public school teacher during the summer in a position that is relevant to a teaching-shortage area in which the teacher is certified. Limited to the lesser of: (a) $2,500; or (b) 50% of the compensation paid.

Enterprise Zone Employment Expense Credit: A taxpayer who conducts business in an enterprise zone is entitled to a maximum credit of $1,500 for each employee who is an enterprise zone resident and who is employed primarily by the taxpayer.

Enterprise Zone Loan Interest Credit: A credit equal to 5% of the lender interest income from qualified loans made in an enterprise zone.

Enterprise Zone Investment Cost Credit: Credit to individual taxpayers against state tax liability equal to a percentage times the price of qualified investment in an enterprise zone business.

Industrial Recovery Tax Credit: Credit for qualifying investments to rehabilitate vacant industrial facilities ("dinosaurs") that are at least 20 years old and at least 300,000 square feet in size.

Personal Computer Tax Credit: Credit for donations of computer units to the "Buddy-Up with Education Program." A credit of $125 per computer unit is allowed.

Twenty-First Century Scholars Program Support Fund Credit: Credit for contributions to the fund. A maximum credit of the lesser of (a) $1,000; (b) 50% of the contribution made; or (c) 10% of the adjusted gross income tax is available.

Maternity Home Credit: Credit for maternity-home owners who provide a temporary residence for a pregnant woman (women).

Prison Credit: Credit for investments in Indiana prisons to create jobs for prisoners. The amount is limited to 50% of the inventory in a qualified project plus 25% of the wages paid to the inmates. The maximum credit a taxpayer may claim is $100,000 per year.

Property Tax Abatement: Property tax abatement in Indiana is authorized under Indiana Code 6-1.1-12.1 in the form of deductions from assessed valuation. Any property owner in a locally designated Economic Revitalization Area (ERA) who makes improvements to the real property or installs new manufacturing equipment is eligible for property tax abatement. Land does not qualify for abatement. Used manufacturing equipment can also qualify as long as such equipment is new to the state of Indiana. Equipment not used in direct production, such as office equipment, does not qualify for abatement.

Real-Property Abatement Calculation: Real-property abatement is a declining percentage of the increase in assessed value of the improvement based on one of the three following time periods and percentages as determined by the local governing body.

Enterprise Zones: The purpose of the enterprise zone program in the state of Indiana is to stimulate local community and business redevelopment in distressed areas. An enterprise zone may consist of up to three contiguous square miles. There are 18 enterprise zones in Indiana. In order to stimulate reinvestment and create jobs within the zones, businesses located within an enterprise zone are eligible for certain tax benefits. These tax benefits include:

- A credit equal to 100% of property-tax liability on inventory.
- Exemption from Indiana Gross Income Tax on the increase in receipts from the base year.
- State Investment Cost Credit (up to 30% of purchase price) for individuals purchasing an ownership interest in an enterprise zone business.
- State Loan Interest Credit on lender interest income (5%) from qualified loans made in an enterprise zone.
- State Employment Expense Credit based on wages paid to qualified zone-resident employees. The credit is the lesser of 10% of the increase in wages paid over the base year, or $1,500 per qualified employee.
- Tax deduction to qualified zone-resident employees equal to the lesser of 50% of their adjusted gross income or $7,500.

Interstate Inventory Tax Exemption: Indiana has a modest inventory tax with a number of deductions available, including the Interstate Inventory Tax Exemption. Finished goods awaiting shipment to out-of-state destinations are usually exempt from the inventory tax. In most instances, a taxpayer may determine the exemption by applying the percentage of that location's total shipments, which went out of state during the previous year.

Industrial Recovery Site (Dinosaur Building): Much like the dinosaurs, many large buildings that were once used for mills, foundries and large manufacturers are obsolete for today's new production methods and technologies. Because of this, these buildings now stand vacant. This program offers special tax benefits to offset the cost of adaptive reuse. Tax benefits are available for 10 years from date of project approval and include the following:

Investment Tax Credit: A credit against the cost of remodeling, repair or betterment of the building or complex of buildings.

Local Option Inventory Tax Credit: A municipality or county has the option of awarding an Inventory Tax Credit to tenants of "dinosaur" buildings.

Maritime Opportunity District: A geographical territory designated at Indiana ports by the Indiana Port Commission. Companies located in a designated district are eligible for tax benefits through the authority of the commission.

Tax Increment Financing (TIF): provides for the temporary allocation to redevelopment or economic districts of increased tax proceeds in an allocation area generated by increases in assessed value. Thus, TIF permits cities, towns or counties to use increased tax revenues stimulated by redevelopment or economic development to pay for the capital improvements needed to induce the redevelopment or economic development. Bond amounts are determined by the size of the project and the amount of the increment available.

Economic Development for a Growing Economy (EDGE): Provides tax credits based on payroll. Individual income tax withholdings for the company's employees can be credited against the company's corporate income tax. Excess withholdings shall be refunded to the company.

For more information on taxes, contact the Indiana Department of Commerce or the Indiana Department of Revenue, 100 N. Senate Ave., Room N-105, Indianapolis, IN 46204; 317-232-2240; {www.state.in.us/dor}.

Exports

International Trade Services Program: The driving force behind the International Trade Services Program is a group of individuals whose job title is international trade specialist. Many of these people have lived and worked overseas and are proficient with foreign languages. They understand the cultural differences that must be overcome for successful exporting. And they are dedicated to helping Indiana companies -- at no cost -- in the following areas: export assistance, export documentation, foreign buyer visits to Indiana, overseas trade show identification, financial assistance, attendance at overseas trade shows, enrollment of employees in export-related classes/seminars, developing international markets, identification and selection of foreign agents, representatives and distributors, representation of companies at foreign trade shows, provision of economic and political information on other nations.

The Trade Finance Program (TFP): Provides Indiana manufacturers with the tools for export finance. On behalf of Indiana manufacturers and lending institutions, trained representatives at the Indiana Department of Commerce process applications Ex-Im Bank guarantees, loans and export credit insurance. The TFP helps exporters face the challenges of expanding their existing market by becoming more competitive in terms of price, performance, service and delivery by enabling Indiana's exporters to: get paid upon shipment, offer extended credit terms to minimize risk, offer foreign buyers better payment terms.

Available programs

- 90% working-capital loan guarantees, and may be used to purchase finished products, materials, services and labor to produce goods for export.
- Medium- & long-term export guarantees and loans.
- Guarantees provide repayment protection. Loans provide competitive, fixed-rate financing for U.S. export sales.
- Export credit insurance: Protects exporters against political and commercial risk.

Trade Show Assistance Program: Helps small and medium-sized companies realize their full export potential by participating in international trade shows and exhibitions. Financial assistance is available for qualified Indiana exporters who need a little help getting to their trade show of choice. The program also reimburses firms up to $5,000 for booth rental costs at overseas trade shows.

Foreign Trade Zones: Offer great financial incentives for conducting import/export business in the state.

Foreign Trade Zone or Free Trade Zone: An enclosed, secure area that is located outside U.S. Customs territory. A company located within a Foreign Trade Zone does not pay duties or personal property taxes on goods stored within the zone. Foreign and domestic goods may enter a zone to be stored, processed, distributed, manufactured, assembled or exhibited. Benefits to companies located in a Foreign Trade Zone include the following:

- Duty is deferred on imported goods admitted to the zone, thus improving cash flow for the company.
- No U.S. duty is assessed when exporting goods from the zone.
- Processing goods within the zone can eliminate or lower tariffs.
- Duties can be avoided on defective or damaged goods by inspecting and testing imported goods within a zone.
- Savings may be realized in transport insurance.
- Inventory stored in a Foreign Trade Zone is exempt from local property tax.

Contact International Trade Division, Indiana Department of Commerce, One North Capitol, Suite 700, Indianapolis, IN 46204; 317-233-3762.

Women and Minorities

LYNX: A privately owned company established to link capital to minority business opportunities. The fund provides subordinated debt to minority-owned businesses in Marion and surrounding counties. Capital can be provided in the form of equity or debt. Minimum project amount is $75,000. Contact Cambridge Capital Management Corporation, 8440 Woodfield Crossing, Suite 315, Indianapolis, IN 46240; 317-469-3925.

Women and Minorities in Business Group (WMBG): Eligibility: Indiana businesses owned by women and/or minorities. Services/Uses: Counsels emerging and mature businesses. Client needs are determined, evaluated and advised at no cost. Services include: workshops and seminars, direct counseling, information clearinghouse and referral source, general information, including statistics regarding women- and minority-owned businesses, administers Minority Outreach Resource Executive (MORE) Program in six regions. Contact Indiana Small Business Development Corporation (ISBD Corp.), One N. Capital Ave., Suite 1275, Indianapolis, IN 46204; 317-264-2820; 888-ISDB-244; {www.isbdcorp.org/index.htm}.

Minority Outreach Resource Executives (MORE): Extension of WMBG services in Gary, South Bend, Fort Wayne, Indianapolis, Evansville and Jeffersonville. Contact: Indiana Small Business Development Corporation (ISBD Corp.), One N. Capital Ave., Suite 1275, Indianapolis, IN 46204; 317-264-2820; 888-ISDB-244; {www.isbdcorp.org/index.htm}.

Iowa

Department of Economic Development
200 East Grand Ave.
Des Moines, IA 50309-1827
515-242-4700
800-245-IOWA
Fax: 515-242-4809
TTY: 800-735-2942
www.state.ia.us/ided
www.smart.state.ia.us

Business Assistance

Workforce Development Fund: Programs under this fund provide training for new and existing employees and include: Jobs Training, Business Network Training, Targeted Industries Training, Innovative Skills Development.

Professional Site Location/Expansion Services, Resources, and Confidential Consultation for Growing Companies: Provides expanding companies with many valuable and unique services, with the end goal of streamlining the site location process. Iowa Department of Economic Development (IDED) confidential services include:

- Working on a confidential basis with companies to determine expansion project needs
- Providing data and information on available buildings, sites and communities
- Coordinating community/site visits
- Packaging appropriate financial assistance and job training programs
- Serving as a liaison with state environmental permitting officials

Center for Industrial Research and Service: Assists companies with management, production, marketing, engineering, finance, and technology problems and/or contact with resource people, organizations, and agencies that can help provide solutions, and operates as an industrial arm of University Extension, Iowa State University. Contact: Center for Industrial Research and Service, ISU Research Park, 2501 N. Loop Park, Suite 500, Ames, IA 50010; 515-294-3420; {www.ciras.iast.edu}.

Cooperative Services: Provides free technical assistance to help rural residents form new cooperative ventures and improve operations of existing cooperatives. Contact: USDA-Rural Development, 873 Federal Bldg., 210 Walnut St., Des Moines, IA 50309; 515-284-4714.

Manufacturing Technology Center: A resource for small and mid-sized manufacturers. Helps identify problems and resources, conducts formal needs assessments, and develops strategic plans. Also assists with modernizing facilities, upgrading processes, and improving work force capabilities through the use of effective training and skill development. Contact: Iowa Manufacturing Technology Center, Advanced Technology Center, Building 3E, 2006 S. Ankeny Blvd., Ankeny, IA 50021; 515-965-7125; {www.iowamtc.org}.

Regulatory Assistance Programs: Provide assistance with environmental permitting, regulations, and compliance with the EPA Clean Air Act.

University of Northern Iowa/Market Development Program: Provides customized market research, analysis, and strategic planning services to existing businesses, primarily manufacturers. Contact: University of Northern Iowa, College of Business Administration, The Business Building, Suite 5, Cedar Falls, IA 50614; 319-273-2886.

Virtual Management Assistance Program: Maintains and monitors a comprehensive, confidential, database system designed to act as a clearinghouse to foster business-to-business connections by connecting entrepreneurs with prospective management consultants and/or strategic alliance partners.

Smart State: Iowa's Smart State website {www.smart.state.ia.us} provides information from manyu public agencies and private organizations in an exceptionally easy to access format. Much of this information is also available in the *Business Resource Workbook*, a free publication from the Department of Economic Development Entrepreneurial Services Team. Call 800-532-1216 to request a copy.

Iowa Procurement Outreach Center (IPOC): Assists Iowa businesses in competing for federal, state and local government contracts. Contact IPOC, Center for Industrial Research and Service, 2272 Howe Hall, Suite 2620, Ames, IA 50011; 515-294-4483; {www.ciras.iastate.edu}.

Iowa State University Research Park Corporation: An office space environment where new and established companies can access ISU technology. Contact ISU Research park, 2501 Loop Drive, Suite 600, Ames, IA 50010; 515-296-PARK; {www.isupark.org}.

John Pappajohn Entrepreneurial Centers: These centers help entrepreneurs in all stages of business planning and development. They are located at the University of Iowa {www.biz.uiowa.edu/entrep}, Iowa State University (www.isupjcenter.org), University of Northern Iowa (www.jpec.org), North Iowa Area Community College {www.niacc.com/pappajohn}, and Drake University {www.disc.drake.edu/pappajohn}.

Small Business Ombudsman: Helps find solutions in conflicts between small business persons and State of Iowa governmental agencies. Contact Small Business Ombudsman, Iowa Citizen's Aide/Ombudsman, 215 East 7th Street, Capitol Complex, Des Moines, IA 50319; 515-381-3592, 888-IA-OMBUD; Email: {ombud@legia.state.ia.us}.

Business Assistance Services for Entrepreneurs (BASE): Provides training, information and technical assistance to individuals with disabilities interested in starting or expanding a small business in Iowa. Contact Business Assistance Services for Entrepreneurs (BASE), W118 Oakdale Hall, Oakdale Research Campus, Iowa City, IA 52242; 515-684-8983; {www.baseiowa.org}.

Business Financing

New Jobs Training Program: Provides training funds for companies creating new jobs, including assistance with screening, skills assessment, testing and custom-designed training and other training programs. Companies can be reimbursed up to 50% of new employees' salaries and fringe benefits during the training period.

Community Economic Betterment Account (CEBA): Provides financial assistance to companies that create new employment opportunities and/or retain existing jobs, and make new capital investment in Iowa. The amount of funding is based, in part, on the number of jobs to be created/retained. Funds are provided in the form of loans and forgivable loans. The CEBA program can provide assistance up to $1 million. As an alternative, non-traditional, short-term float loans or interim loans greater than $1 million may be available. The funding level for start-up companies varied depending upon employee wage rates. Assistance through CEBA's "Venture Project" component is provided as an "equity-like" investment, with a maximum award of $100,000.

Economic Development Set-Aside Program (EDSA): Provides financial assistance to companies that create new employment opportunities and/or retain existing jobs, and make new capital investment in Iowa. The amount of funding is based, in part, on the number of jobs to be created/retained. Funds are provided in the form of loans and forgivable loans. The EDSA program can provide assistance up to $500,000.

Entrepreneurs with Disabilities Program: Provides technical and financial assistance to individuals with disabilities who are seeking self-sufficiency by establishing, maintaining, expanding, or acquiring a small business.

Self Employment Loan Program: Offers low-interest loans to low-income entrepreneurs of new or expanding small businesses. Maximum amount is $10,000 with a 5% simple interest rate.

Value-Added Products and Processes Financial Assistance Program (VAAPFAP): Seeks to increase the innovative utilization of Iowa's agricultural commodities. It accomplishes this by investing in the development of new agri-products and new processing technologies. The program includes two components:
- Innovative Products and Processes encourages the processing of agricultural commodities into higher-value products not commonly produced in Iowa, or utilizing a process not commonly used in Iowa to produce new and innovative products from agricultural commodities.
- Renewable Fuels and Co-Products encourages the production of renewable fuels, such as soy diesel and ethanol, and co-products for livestock feed.
  Any single project may apply for up to $900,000 in assistance. Financial assistance is provided in the form of loans and forgivable loans. Generally, assistance of $100,000 or less is provided as a forgivable loan, while larger awards are usually a combination of loans and forgivable loans, with the forgivable portion decreasing as the award size increases.

Small Business Loan Program and Economic Development Loan Program: Provides financing to new and expanding businesses through the sale of tax-exempt bonds. The maximum loan is $10 million.

Link Investments for Tomorrow (LIFT): Assists with rural small business transfer, and horticulture and alternative agricultural crops. Contact: Treasurer of State's Office, Capitol Bldg., 1st Floor, Des Moines, IA 50309; 515-281-3287.

USDA Business and Industrial Loan Guarantee Program: Provides guarantees on loans up to $10 million or more made by private lenders for start-up or expansion purposes to for-profit or non-profit businesses or investors of any size.

Venture Network of Iowa (VNI): A statewide forum via the Iowa Communications Network in which Iowa Entrepreneurs, investors and business advisors interact, network and find financial and intellectual capital. Contact VNI, Iowa Department of Economic Development, 200 E. Grand Ave., Des Moines, IA 50309; 515-242-4750, 800-532-1216; {www.state.ia.us/sbro/vni.htm}.

TecTERRA Food Capital Fund: Provides equity for Iowa food processors and biotechnology companies with growth potential, especially those offering ownership opportunities and other benefits to Iowa agricultural producers. Contact The Cybus Capital Group, 520 Walnut Street, Suite 500, Des Moines, IA 50309; 515-246-8558.

Tax Incentives

Iowa Corporate Income Tax: Iowa's single factor, non-unitary tax is based only on the percentage of total sales income within the state. An Iowa manufacturer selling all its products outside Iowa would pay no Iowa corporate income tax. Iowa allows 50% deductibility of federal taxes from Iowa corporate income tax. Iowa corporate income tax may be reduced or eliminated by the New Jobs Tax Credit and Research and Development Tax Credit.

New Jobs Tax Credit: Businesses entering into an agreement under the state's training program, and which increase their workforce by at least 10 percent, may quality for this credit to its Iowa corporate income tax. This credit is equal to 6 percent of the state unemployment insurance taxable wage base. The credit for 2000 is $1,038 per new employee. The tax credit can be carried forward up to 10 years.

Research Activities Tax Credit: A credit for increasing research activities is 6.5 percent of the company's apportioned share of qualifying research expenditures in Iowa. A company must meet the qualifications of the federal research activities credit in order to be eligible for the credit on the Iowa return.

No Sales or Use Tax on Manufacturing Machinery and Equipment: The purchase of industrial machinery and equipment, and computers assessed as real property and used for manufacturing or used to process data by insurance companies, financial institutions, or certain commercial enterprises, is exempt from Iowa sales or use tax. No sales tax is due on purchases or electricity or natural gas used directly in the manufacturing process.

No Property Tax on New Industrial Machinery and Equipment: Manufacturing machinery and equipment, as well as computers used to process data by insurance companies and financial institutions installed and first assessed on or after January 1, 1995, is exempt from property tax.

Pollution Control or Recycling Property Tax Exemption: Pollution control and recycling equipment may be eligible for a property tax exemption. Improvements to real property that are primarily used to control pollution of air or water, or primarily used for recycling, may qualify. An application must be filed for exemption.

Local Tax Abatement: Iowa law allows cities and counties to abate local property taxes for value-added to industrial real estate.

Tax Increment Financing: City councils or county boards of supervisors may use the property taxes resulting from the increase in taxable valuation due to construction of new industrial or commercial facilities to provide economic development incentives to a business or industry. Tax Increment Financing may be used to pay the cost of public improvements and utilities which will serve the new private development, to finance direct grants or loans to a company, or to provide the local match for federal or state economic development assistance programs.

No Personal Property (Inventory) Tax: Personal property is not assessed for tax purposes. In Iowa, personal property includes corporate inventories of salable goods, raw materials and goods in process.

New Jobs and Income Program: The Iowa New Jobs and Income Program provides a package of tax credits and exemptions to businesses making a capital investment of at least $10.38 million and creating 50 or more jobs meeting wage and benefit targets.

Assistive Device Tax Credit: Iowa small businesses can reduce their taxes by buying or renting products or equipment, or by making physical changes to the workplace to help employees with disabilities get or keep a job. To qualify for the Assistive Device Tax Credit, a business must be located in Iowa and employ 14 or fewer full time employees OR have $3 million dollars or less in gross annual receipts. The credit applies to expenditures made on or after January 1, 2000, and equals one-half of the first $5,000 in qualifying expenses each tax year. Excess credits can be refunded or carried over to the next tax year.

Exports

Export Trade Assistance Program: Promotes international trade though financial assistance for increased participation in overseas trade shows and trade missions.

Women and Minorities

Targeted Small Business Financial Assistance Program (TSBFAP): Designed to assist in the creation and expansion of Iowa small businesses that have an annual gross sales of $3 million and are at least 51% owned, operated and managed by women, minorities or persons with a disability. The business must be certified as a "Targeted Small Business" by the Iowa Department of Inspections and Appeals before applying for or receiving TSB funds. Awards may be obtained in one of the following forms of assistance:
- Low-interest loans - Loans of up to $25,000 may be provided at interest rates of 0-5 percent, to be repaid in monthly installments over a five- to seven-year period. The first installment can be deferred for three months for a start-up business and one month for an existing business.
- Loan guarantees are available up to $40,000. Loan guarantees can cover up to 75% of a loan obtained from a bank or other conventional lender. The interest rate is at the discretion of the lender.
- In limited cases, equity grants - to be used to leverage other financing (SBA or conventional) - are available in amounts of up to $25,000.
- TSB funds may be used to purchase equipment, acquire inventory, provide operating capital or to leverage additional funding.

Self-Employment Loan Program (SELP): This program is designed to assist in the creation and expansion of businesses owned, operated and managed by women, minorities, or persons with a disability. To qualify for a SELP loan, applicants must have an annualized family income that does not exceed current income guidelines for the program. An applicant is automatically eligible for SELP if he or she is receiving Family Investment Plan (FIP) assistance or other general assistance such as disability benefits. The applicant can also qualify for SELP funds if determined eligible under the Job Training Partnership Act, or is certified as having a disability under standards established by the Iowa Department of Education, Division of Vocational Rehabilitation Services. SELP loans of up to $10,000 are available. The interest rate is 5 percent, and the loan is to be repaid in monthly installments over a five-year period. The first installment can be deferred for three months for a start-up business and one month for an existing business.

Entrepreneurs With Disabilities (EWD): Helps qualified individuals with disabilities establish, acquire, maintain or expand a small business by providing technical and financial assistance. To be eligible for the program, applicants must be active clients of the Iowa Department of Education Division of Vocational Rehabilitation Services or the Iowa Department for the Blind. Technical Assistance grants of up to $10,000 may be used to pay for any specific business-related consulting service such as developing a feasibility study or business plan, or accounting and legal services. Financial Assistance grants of up to $10,000 may be used to purchase equipment, supplies, rent or other start-up, expansion or acquisition costs identified in an approved business plan. Total financial assistance provided to an individual may not exceed 50% (maximum of $10,000) of the financial package. EWD financial assistance must be fully matched by funding from other sources.

Institute of Social and Economic Development: Focuses on minorities, women, persons with disabilities and low-income individuals. Encourages self-sufficiency through the growth of small business and self-employment opportunities, and provides services for any person who wants to start or expand a business employing up to five employees, including the owner(s). Contact Institute of Social and Economic Development, 1901 Broadway, Suite 313, Iowa City, IA 52240; 319-338-2331, 800-888-ISED; Fax: 319-338-5824.

Kansas

Department of Commerce and Housing
700 SW Harrison Street, Suite 1300
Topeka, KS 66603-3712
785-296-5298
Fax: 785-296-3490
TTY: 785-296-3487
www.kansascommerce.com

Business Assistance

First-Stop Clearinghouse: A one-stop Clearinghouse for general information. It also provides the necessary state applications required by agencies which license, regulate and tax business, and furnishes information about starting or expanding a business.

From the Land of Kansas Trademark Program: Offers marketing opportunities for Kansas produced food, arts, crafts, and plants.

Agricultural Value Added Center: Identifies new technologies and assists companies in commercialization efforts. Both food/feed and industrial related projects are potential candidates for assistance.

Kansas Match: Promotes economic growth in the state by matching Kansas manufacturers who are currently buying products from outside Kansas with Kansas suppliers of those same products. The benefit to the buyer includes reductions in freight, warehousing, and communication costs.

Business First: Drawing from the existing KDOC&H business retention and expansion instrument, this new survey software program assists communities of any size in establishing a customized local retention and expansion program.

Business Retention & Expansion Program: Offered to Kansas communities and counties who wish to sustain existing industry, support its modernization and competitiveness, foster its expansion and provide an environment that encourages new industry creation and recruitment. The Department works with community leaders and volunteers to conduct on-site surveys of local businesses. The information gathered is then analyzed and the results are used to solve immediate short-term problems, as well as to develop long-term local retention and expansion strategies.

Partnership Fund: Provides financial assistance to Kansas cities and counties by making low-interest loans for infrastructure projects needed to encourage and assist in the creation of new jobs either through the relocation of new businesses or the expansion of existing businesses.

Industrial Training Program (KIT): Provides training assistance primarily to manufacturing, distribution and regional or national service firms in the process of adding five or more new jobs to a new or existing Kansas facility. KIT will pay the negotiated cost of pre-employment, on-the-job and classroom training expenses that include instructor salaries, travel expenses, minor equipment, training aids, supplies and materials, and curriculum planning and development.

Industrial Retraining Program (KIR): Provides retraining assistance to employees of restructuring industries who are likely to be displaced because of obsolete or inadequate job skills and knowledge.

Publications

The Kansas Department of Commerce & Housing (KDOC&H) distributes a variety of publications to help Kansas residents, businesses and visitors find the information needed about their state. Here are a few:

Data Book: The information found in the *Data Book* gives a good idea of what Kansas has to offer new and expanding businesses. The book is filled with information about the Kansas economy, labor and workforce training. It briefly describes taxes and incentives for new and expanding businesses. It also includes sections on finance, technology and education, markets and transportation, and the environment.

The Kansas Aerospace Directory: A complete resource for aircraft production, parts, equipment, research and development, etc. *Directory* includes a wide range of aviation products and companies.

Kansas Agribusiness Directory: A complete resource for agriculture-related business, the *Kansas Agribusiness Directory* offers assistance in contacting any firm or business as well as finding specialized products or services.

Steps to Success: A Guide to Starting a Business in Kansas: Created to give entrepreneurs and small business owners all the information needed on licenses, forms, rules and regulations required by State agencies. It discusses the aspects of business development including finance, incentives and taxation. Plus, it has referrals to programs such as Small Business Development Centers, development companies, the Kansas Technology Enterprise Corporation, Inc. and the Small Business Administration.

Business Financing

Venture Capital & Seed Capital Programs: Instituted to increase the availability of risk capital in Kansas. These programs make use of income tax credits to encourage investment in venture and seed capital pools as a source of early stage financing for small businesses. Businesses demonstrating strong growth potential but lacking the financial strength to obtain conventional financing are the most likely candidates for risk capital funding. The Business Development Division has in operation and continues to develop a network of venture capital resources to assist qualified small businesses in locating potential sources of venture capital financing.

Economic Opportunity Initiatives Fund (KEOIF): A funding mechanism to address the creation/retention of jobs presented by unique opportunities or emergencies. The fund has a higher level of flexibility than do many of the other state financing programs and allows the State to participate as a funding source when other options have been exhausted.

> **INVESTMENTS IN MAJOR PROJECTS AND COMPREHENSIVE TRAINING (IMPACT)**

Existing Industry Expansion Program (KEIEP): Performance based, with a focus on the expansion/ retention of jobs that are associated with the activities of existing firms.

Investments In Major Projects And Comprehensive Training (IMPACT): A funding mechanism designed to respond to the training and capital requirements of major business expansions and locations in the state. SKILL (State of Kansas Investments in Lifelong Learning) funds may be used to pay for expenses related to training a new work force. MPI (Major Project Investment) funds may be used for other expenses related to the project such as the purchase or relocation of equipment, labor recruitment, or building costs. Individual bond size may not exceed 90% of the withholding taxes received from the new jobs over a 10-year period.

Network of Certified Development Companies: Provides financial packaging services to businesses, utilizing state, Small Business Administration, and private financial sources. The state provides supplemental funding to these organizations in recognition of the service they provide.

Private Activity Bonds (PABs): Tax-exempt bonds (IRBs) for facility and equipment financing for qualifying manufacturers and processors. The reduced financing costs generated through these bonds are passed through to the company.

Training Equipment Grants: Provide area technical schools and community colleges an opportunity to acquire instructional equipment to train or retrain Kansas workers.

Tax Incentives

Enterprise Zone Act: Establishes a non-metropolitan regional business incentive program and provides for business expansion and development incentives on a statewide basis. Businesses throughout the state may be eligible for 1) a Sales Tax Exemption on the personal property, materials, and services associated with the project; 2) a Job Creation Tax Credit; and 3) an Investment Tax Credit. Tax credits may be used to offset up to 100% of the business' annual Kansas income tax liability. Unused credits may be carried forward indefinitely.

High Performance Incentive Program (HPIP): Provides incentives to qualified companies which make significant investment in employee training and pay higher than average wages. Incentives include 1) a Sales Tax

Exemption; 2) a potentially substantial Training Tax Credit; 3) a generous Investment Tax Credit; and 4) priority consideration for other business assistance programs. Tax credits may be used to offset 100% of the business' annual Kansas income tax liability. Unused credits may be carried forward and must be used within a 10-year time frame.

Tax Exemptions In Connection With The Usage Of Industrial Revenue Bonds: Property financed with the proceeds of an IRB issue can be exempt from property taxation for a period of 10 years. In addition, the cost of building materials and permanently installed equipment are exempt from state and local taxes.

Property Tax Exemptions: Can be made available by the governing body of a city or county for up to ten years. The exemptions apply to land, building, machinery and equipment for new or expanding businesses.

Sales Tax Exemption On Manufacturing Machinery & Equipment: Manufacturing machinery and equipment used directly and primarily for the purposes of manufacturing, assembling, processing, finishing, storing, warehousing, or distributing articles of tangible personal property intended for resale are exempt from sales tax.

Research & Development Tax Credits: May be claimed at 6.5% of the amount which exceeds the business' average R&D expenditures during the preceding three years. A maximum of 25% of the total credits may be used in any given year and unused credits may be carried forward indefinitely.

Child Day Care Tax Credits: Available to businesses that pay for, or provide, child day care services to their employees. The credit is 30% of the annual cost of providing the service, not to exceed $30,000 total credit. A credit of up to 50%, not to exceed $45,000, may be earned during the first year on the costs of establishing a child day care facility. Multiple taxpayers may work together to establish such a facility.

Venture Capital Tax Credit: Designed to encourage cash investments in certified Kansas venture capital companies. Tax credit is equal to 25% of the taxpayer's cash investment in a venture capital firm in the year in which the investment is made.

Local Seed Capital Pool Tax: Designed to encourage cash investments in certified local seed capital pools. Credit is equal to 25% of the taxpayer's cash investment.

Job Expansion And Investment Tax Credit Act Of 1976: Allows an income tax credit for a period of 10 years, up to 50% of a business' Kansas income tax liability. The Job Expansion Tax Credit is $100 for each qualified business facility employee. The Investment Tax Credit is $100 for each $100,000 in qualified investment.

Economic Development Tax Abatement Assistance Program: Provides technical application assistance as well as consulting services to companies and communities applying for economic development and/or industrial revenue bond (IRB) tax exemptions. The Assistance Program serves as liaison between the applicant and the Board of Tax Appeals to ensure quality service and enhance approval success.

Exports

Export Loan Guarantee Program: Allows financial institutions to provide working capital loans to help Kansas companies pay for costs associated with an export transaction. The guarantee protects the financial institution against exporter non-performance risk. In addition to significantly reducing a lender's risk on an export loan, expertise available through the Kansas Export Finance Program can assist a lender in the area of international trade.

Kansas Export Financing Program: Allows the state to enter into agreements with Kansas exporters and financial institutions, and other public and private agencies to provide guarantees, insurance, reinsurance, and coinsurance for commercial pre-export and post-export credit risks.

Kansas Trade Show Assistance Program: Allows a Kansas company to receive a reimbursement of up to 50% of their international trade show expenses to a maximum of $3,500 per show and $7,000 per state fiscal year.

Foreign Trade Zones: Provide a duty-free and quota-free entry point for foreign goods into specific areas under customs' supervision for an unlimited period of time.

Kansas International Trade Resource Directory: A complete resource for anyone needing assistance in exporting goods to foreign countries and to other states. The guide offers a comprehensive listing of government agencies.

It lists the state's six regent universities and the international trade services and information provided by each. It also lists international law firms, bankers, consultants and freight forwarders/ customhouse brokers. Also, it lists foreign consulates, U.S. Embassies, international telephone country and city codes, metric conversion tables and a complete glossary of terms used in international trade.

Women and Minorities

Office of Minority & Women Business Development: Promotes and assists in the development of minority-owned and women-owned businesses in Kansas. The program provides assistance in procurement and contracting, financing resources, business planning, and identification of business opportunities. A directory of minority-owned and women-owned businesses in Kansas is published annually.

Single Source Certification Program: Responsible for certifying minority-and-women-owned businesses as small disadvantaged businesses for non-highway related firms.

Kentucky

Kentucky Cabinet for Economic Development
2300 Capital Plaza Tower
500 Mero Street
Frankfort, KY 40601
502-564-7670
800-626-2930
www.thinkkentucky.com

Business Assistance

Kentucky Cabinet for Economic Development: The Cabinet is the
primary state agency responsible for creating new jobs and new
investment in the state.

- Job Recruitment, Placement And Training: Provides a package of
  time-and cost-saving employee recruiting and placement services
  to Kentucky employers, at no cost to either employers or
  employees.
- Industrial Location Assistance: Provides a comprehensive
  package of assistance to large manufacturing, services, and
  administrative facilities, both before and after their location in
  Kentucky.

Business Information Clearinghouse: Provides new and existing businesses a centralized information source on
business regulations, licenses, permits, and other business assistance programs. Call 800-626-2250.

Business Financing

Kentucky Economic Development Finance Authority (KEDFA): Provides business loans to supplement other
financing. KEDFA provides loan funds at below market interest rates. The loans are available for fixed asset
financing (land, buildings, and equipment) for business startup, locations, and expansions that create new jobs
in Kentucky or have a significant impact on the economic growth of a community. The loans must be used to
finance projects in agribusiness, tourism, industrial ventures, or the service industry. KEDFA may participate
in the financing of qualified projects with a secured loan for up to $10,000 per new job created, not to exceed
25% of a project's fixed asset cost. The maximum loan amount is $500,000 and the minimum is $25,000.
Small businesses with projects of less than $100,000 may receive loans on fixed assets for up to 45% of the
project costs if enough jobs are created. Interest rates are fixed for the life of the loan, and are determined by
the length of the loan term.

Commonwealth Small Business Development Corporation (CSBDC): Works with state and local economic
development organizations, banks, and the SBA to achieve community economic development through job
creation and retention by providing long-term fixed asset financing to small business concerns. The CSBDC
can lend a maximum of 40% of project cost or $750,000 per project (in certain circumstances $1,000,000).

Linked Deposit Program: Provides loans up to $50,000 for small business and agribusiness. Credit decisions are
the responsibility of the lender making the loan. The state will purchase certificates of deposit from
participating lenders through the State Investment Commission, at the New York Prime interest rate less four
percent, but never less than 2%.

Local Financial Assistance: Several local governments and area development districts offer loans and other
financial incentives for economic development projects. The levels and terms of financial assistance provided
generally are negotiable, and are based upon the availability of funds, jobs created, economic viability of the
project, and other locally determined criteria.

Bluegrass State Skills Corporation (BSSC): An independent dejure corporation within the Cabinet for Economic
Development, provides grants for customized skills training of workers for new, expanding and existing
industries in Kentucky.

Industrial Revenue Bonds (IRB): Can be used to finance manufacturing projects and their warehousing areas, major transportation and communication facilities, most health care facilities, and mineral extraction and processing projects.

Utility Incentive Rates: Electric and gas utility companies regulated by the Kentucky Public Service Commission (excluding municipal systems) can offer economic incentive rates for certain large industrial and commercial customers.

Kentucky Investment Fund (Venture Capital): Encourages venture capital investment by certifying privately operated venture funds, thereby entitling their investors to tax credits equal to 0% of their capital contributions to the fund.

Kentucky Tourism Development Act: Provides financial incentives to qualifying tourism projects. Tourism projects are defined as a cultural or historical site, recreation or entertainment facility, or area of natural phenomenon or scenic beauty.

Local Government Economic Development Fund: Grants are made to eligible counties for specific project that enable the counties to provide infrastructure to incoming and expanding business and industry.

Job Development Incentive Grant Program: Grants are made to eligible counties from their coal severance accounts for the purpose of encouraging job development. The grant amount cannot exceed $5,000 per job created.

Tax Incentives

Kentucky Industrial Development Act (KIDA): Investments in new and expanding manufacturing projects may qualify for tax credits. Companies that create at least 15 new full-time jobs and invest at least $100,000 in

projects approved under KIDA may receive state income tax credits for up to 100% of annual debt service costs (principal and interest) for up to 10 years on land, buildings, site development, building fixtures and equipment used in a project, or the company may collect a job assessment fee of 3% of the gross wages of each employee whose job is created by the approved project and who is subject to Kentucky income taxes.

Kentucky Rural Economic Development Act (KREDA): Larger tax credits are available for new and expanding manufacturing projects that create at least 15 new full time jobs in counties with unemployment rates higher than the state average in each of the five preceding calendar years and invest at least $100,000.

Kentucky Jobs Development Act (KJDA): Service and technology related companies that invest in new and expanded non-manufacturing, non-retail projects that provide at least 75% of their services to users located outside of Kentucky, and that create new jobs for at least 25 full-time Kentucky residents may qualify for tax credits.

Kentucky Industrial Revitalization Act (KIRA): Investments in the rehabilitation of manufacturing operations that are in imminent danger of permanently closing or that have closed temporarily may qualify for tax credits. Companies that save or create 25 jobs in projects approved under KIRA may receive state income tax credits and job assessment fees for up to 10 years limited to 50% of the costs of the rehabilitation or construction of buildings and the reoutfitting or purchasing of machinery and equipment.

Other Income Tax Credit:
- A credit of $100 is allowed for each unemployed person hired for at least 180 consecutive days.
- Credits are allowed for up to 50% of the installed costs of equipment used exclusively to recycle or compost business or consumer wastes (excluding secondary and demolition wastes) and machinery used exclusively to manufacture products substantially from recycled waste materials.
- A credit is allowed for up to 4.5% of the value of Kentucky coal (excluding transportation costs) used for industrial heating or processing.

Kentucky Enterprise Zone Program: State and local tax incentives are offered to businesses located or locating in zones, and some regulations are eased to make development in the area more attractive. A zone remains in effect for 20 years after the date of designation.

Tourism Sales Tax Credit: Approved new or expanding tourism attractions will be eligible for a sales tax credit against sales tax generated by visitors to the attraction.

Property Tax Exemptions: Manufacturing machinery, pollution control facilities, raw materials and work in process, tangible personal property in foreign trade zones.

Favorable Tax Treatments: Available for finished goods in a transit status, private leasehold interest in property owned and financed by a governmental unit through industrial revenue bonds.

Sales Tax Exemptions: Machinery for new and expanded industry, raw materials, supplies used directly in manufacturing, industrial tools, energy and energy-producing fuels used in manufacturing, industrial processing, mining or refining, pollution control equipment and facilities, fee processor or contract manufacturers that do not take title to the tangible personal property that is incorporated into a manufactured product for raw materials, supplies and industrial tools directly used in the manufacturing process, containers, packaging and wrapping materials, equipment used to collect, separate, compress, bale, shred or handle waste materials for recycling, customized computer programs, gross receipts from the sales of newspaper inserts or catalogs purchased for storage, use, or other consumption outside this state, motor fuels for highway use, motor vehicles, trailers, and semi-trailers registered for highway use, locomotives, rolling stock, supplies, and fuels used by railroad in interstate commerce, air carriers, parts and supplies used for interstate passenger or freight services, marine vessels, and supplies, farm machinery, livestock, feed, seed, fertilizer, motion picture production companies.

Exports

Kentucky International Trade Office: The Office offers the following services:
- Export Consulting
- Export Marketing
- Education and Training
- Overseas Offices
- International Trade Directory
- Kentucky Export Guide

Louisiana

Department of Economic Development
P.O. Box 94185
Baton Rouge, LA 70804
225-342-6000
225-342-5388
www.lded.state.la.us

Economically Disadvantaged Business Development Division: Division was created to assist businesses owned by economically disadvantaged individuals. It offers Development Assistance Program where a preliminary assessment analysis of a business is conducted; Mentor-Protégé Program; Recognition Program; Small Business Bonding Program; and more. Contact: Division for Economically Disadvantaged Business Development, 339 Florida Blvd., Suite 212, P.O. Box 44153, Baton Rouge, LA 70804; 225-342-5373.

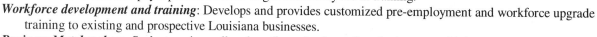

Quality jobs: Provides an annual refundable credit of up to 5% of payroll for a period of up to 10 years for qualifying companies.

Cost-free training: Louisiana's QuickStart Training Program utilizes the state's vocational-technical institutes to provide cost-free pre-employment training customized to a company's requirements. The Jobs Training Partnership Act Program can help a company find trainees and will also pay a portion of their wages while they are in training.

Workforce development and training: Develops and provides customized pre-employment and workforce upgrade training to existing and prospective Louisiana businesses.

Business Matchmakers: Seeks to pair small and medium-sized suppliers in the state with larger companies which are currently making purchases out of state.

Small Business Loan Program: Provides loan guarantees and participations to banks in order to facilitate capital accessibility for businesses. Guarantees may range up to 75% of the loan amount, not to exceed a maximum of $1.5 million. Loan participations of up to 40% are also available. Applicants must have a business plan and a bank that is willing to fund the loan.

Business Linked Deposit Program: Provides for a 1% to 4% interest rate reduction on a maximum of $200,000 for a maximum of 2 to 5 years on term loans that are funded by banks to Louisiana businesses. Job creation, statistical area employment, and cash flow requirements for underwriting are all criteria, which will effect the percentage and term of the linked deposit.

Micro Loan Program: Provides loan guarantees and participations to banks that fund loans ranging from $5,000 to $50,000 to Louisiana small businesses.

Contract Loan Program: Intended to provide a loan participation and guarantee to a bank for government contract loans. These loans are intended to help businesses finance working capital for contracts with local, state, or federal government agencies. Loans may range from $5000 to $1,000,000 and must be for terms of one year or less.

Exim Bank City/State Program: LEDC has a relationship with the U.S. Export-Import Bank in Washington, DC Under this program, LEDC facilitates export working capital loans for small Louisiana businesses.

Venture Capital Match Program: Provides for a match investment for Louisiana venture capital funds. The fund must have at least $5 million of private investment for which LEDC may provide $5 million.

Venture Capital Co-Investment Program: Provides for a co-investment in a Louisiana business of up to 1/4 of the round of investment, but not more than $500,000, with any qualified venture capital fund with at least $7.5 million in private capital. The venture capital fund may be from outside of Louisiana.

BIDCO Investment Program: Provides for a match or co-investment in certified BIDCOs. BIDCOs are state-chartered, non-depository alternative financing sources for small businesses. BIDCOs frequently provide equity and subordinated debt financing to new and growing companies, as well as to companies requiring turnaround assistance. A BIDCO must have at least $2 million in private capital. LEDC may match the investment $1.00 for $2.00 of private capital up to $2.5 million. Co-investments are considered on a project by project basis and cannot exceed 33% of the total investment.

Specialty BIDCO Investment Program: Provides for a match or co-investment in certified Specialty BIDCOs. Specialty BIDCOs are BIDCOs established with a particular focus on assisting disadvantaged businesses and businesses located in impoverished and economically disadvantaged areas. The BIDCO must have at least $250,000 in private capital. LEDC may match the investment $1.00 for every $1.00 of private capital up to $2.5 million. Co-investments are considered on a project by project basis and cannot exceed 50% of the total investment.

Small Business Bonding Assistance Program: The primary goal of this program is to aid certified Economically Disadvantaged Businesses (EDBs) in acquiring quality bid, performance, and payment bonds at reasonable rates from surety companies. EDBs receive help reaching required bonding capacity for specific projects. Contractors often do not reach these levels on their own due to balance sheet deficiencies and a lack of adequate managerial and technical skills. After certification by the Division and accreditation by LCAI, contractors are eligible to receive bond guarantee assistance to be used as collateral when seeking bonds. The Division will issue a letter of credit to the surety for an amount up to 25% of the base contract amount or $200,000.

Economic Development Award: Provides financial incentives in the form of linked deposit loans, loan guarantees and grants to industrial or business development projects that promote economic development and that require state assistance for basic infrastructure development.

All of the above financing programs are available through Louisiana Economic Development Corporation, P.O. Box 44153, Baton Rouge, LA 70804; 225-342-5675.

Tax Incentives

Industrial property tax exemption: Exempts any manufacturing establishment entering Louisiana or any manufacturing establishment expanding its existing Louisiana facility from state, parish, and local property taxes for a period of up to ten years.

Enterprise zone: Provides a tax credit of $2,500 for each net new job created in specially designated areas. Also provides for a rebate of state sales/use taxes on building materials and operating equipment. Local sales/use taxes may also be rebated. Credits can be used to satisfy state corporate income and franchise tax obligations.

Restoration tax abatement: Encourages restoration of buildings in special districts by abating Ad Valorem taxes on improvements to the structure for up to ten years

Inventory tax credit: Provides tax credits against state corporate income and franchise tax obligations for the full amount of inventory taxes paid. When credits are in excess of tax obligations, a cash refund is made.

Exports

Freeport law: Cargoes in transit are exempt from taxation as long as they are kept intact within their smallest original shipping container. Most manufacturers can bring raw materials into the state without paying taxes on them until they are placed in the manufacturing process.

Foreign trade zones: Louisiana's six Foreign Trade Zones (FTZ) make it possible to import materials and components into the U.S. without paying duties until they enter the U.S. market. Goods shipped out of the country from FTZs are duty-free. Contact: International Trade Division, 101 France St., Baton Rouge, LA 70802; 225-342-4320.

Women and Minorities

Minority Venture Capital Match Program: Provides for a match investment for qualified minority venture capital funds. The fund must have at least $250,000 of private investment for which LEDC may invest $1.00 for every $2.00 of private capital up to $5 million.

Maine

Office of Business Development
Department of Economic and Community Development
59 State House Station
Augusta, ME 04333
207-287-3153
Fax: 207-287-5701
TTY: 207-287-2656
www.econdevmaine.com

Business Assistance

Small Business Energy Conservation Program: This program provides small businesses with free energy audits, conservation recommendations and low-interest loans for the purpose of energy conservation.

Business Answers: Maine's toll-free business information hotline provides rapid responses to questions about doing business in Maine. Call 800-872-3838.

One-Stop Business License Center: This central clearinghouse for state regulatory information helps simplify the process of complying with state business regulations. Callers may request business license and permit applications, as well as information on state regulations.

Business Answers/Small Business Advocate: Serves as a central clearinghouse of information regarding business assistance programs and services available to state businesses. Also helps small businesses resolve problems they may be experiencing with state regulatory agencies.

Maine Products Marketing Program: Provides marketing assistance to producers of Maine-made consumer goods. Members of the program promote their message of Maine quality through the use of product tags and labels, literature and package design, which carry the unified theme, "Maine Made America's Best." The program also publishes the "Maine Made" Buyer's Guide, which is sent to more than 25,000 wholesale buyers.

Apprenticeship Program: Maine's Apprenticeship Program provides customized training and instruction so workers can obtain professional credentials. Many of Maine's larger firms have taken advantage of this innovative workforce development program, which will underwrite 50% of apprenticeship-related tuition for new and existing employees. For more information contact Kenneth L. Hardt, Maine Apprenticeship Program, Maine Department of Labor, 55 State House Station, Augusta, ME 04333-0055; 207-624-6390; Fax: 207-624-6499; E-mail: {k.skip.hardt@state.me.us}.

School-to-Work Initiatives: This public-private partnership is designed to provide Maine industry with a competitive workforce. The program employs three strategies to train Maine youth. These include:

- Maine Career Advantage: a nationally recognized two-year combination of business internship and integrated academics, including one free year at the technical college level.
- Registered Pre-Apprenticeship: four years of employer-driven high school academics, coupled with two summers of on-the-job training. This culminates in permanent employment and a Registered Apprenticeship upon high school graduation.
- Tech Prep: sequential, industry-driven academic and technical training beginning in eleventh grade and progressing through completion of Certificate, Associate and/or Bachelor Degrees.

For more information contact Susan Brown, Center for Career Development, Maine Technical College System, SMVTC, Fort Road, South Portland, ME 04106; 207-767-5210 ext. 111; Fax: 207-767-5210; E-mail: {susan@ccd.mtcs.tec.me.us}; {www.mtcs.net}.

Maine Quality Centers Program. This is an economic development initiative of the Maine Technical College System, which provides new and expanding businesses with a trained and ready workforce. New or expanding firms creating at least eight new full-time jobs with benefits may be eligible to receive state financing for 100% of pre-hire classroom training. For a packet of information and application contact Michael M. Aube, Director,

Maine Quality Centers, Maine Technical College System, 323 State Street, Augusta, ME 04330; 207-287-1070; Fax: 207-287-1037; E-mail: {MMAube@syst.mtcs.tec.me.us}; {www.mtcs.tec.me.us}.

Governor's Training Initiative: This program reimburses training costs when they are required for business expansion, retention or unique upgrading issues. Businesses that meet eligibility requirements may receive reimbursements for on-the-job training, competitive retooling, specialized recruitment, workplace literacy, high-performance skills or customized technical training. For an application contact Bureau of Employment Services, Maine Department of Labor, 16 State House Station, Augusta, ME 04333-0016; 207-624-6490; 888-457-8883; Fax: 207-624-6499; E-mail: {caroline.p.morgan@state.me.us}; {www.mainecareercenter.com}.

Safety Education and Training: At no cost to a company, Maine's Bureau of Labor Standards provides customized health and safety training, site evaluation and technical support. Priority is given to small and mid-sized employers and large employers with documented health and safety problems. For more information contact Alan Hinsey, Director, Bureau of Labor Standards, Maine Department of Labor, 45 State House Station, Augusta, ME 04333-0045; 207-624-6400; Fax: 207-624-6449; E-mail: {alan.c.hinsey@state.me.us}.

Business Financing

The Finance Authority of Maine (FAME) is Maine's business finance agency. FAME supports start-up and expanding businesses by working closely with Maine banks to improve access to capital. FAME offers a wide array of programs, ranging from traditional loan guarantees for small and large businesses to tax credits for investments in dynamic manufacturing or export-related firms. FAME has also established taxable and tax-exempt bond financing programs that provide loans to creditworthy firms at very favorable rates and terms.

- ***The Commercial Loan Insurance Program***: This program provides large business borrowers, who would otherwise have problems securing conventional loans, with access to capital. FAME can insure up to 90% of a commercial loan, not to exceed $7 million, for most types of business projects. There is a $2.5-million limitation on recreational projects; additional limitations and restrictions apply.

- ***Major Business Expansion Program***: Any business proposing to expand or locate in Maine and whose borrowing needs fall in the $5,000,000 to $25,000,000 range is eligible for tax-exempt or taxable bond financing for up to 100% of project's cost.

- ***Economic Recovery Loan Program***: Designed as a supplemental financial resource to help small businesses access the capital required to become more productive and more competitive. Maximum request is $200,000 for businesses seeking last-resort financial assistance.

- ***Agricultural Marketing Loan Fund Program***: Helps natural resource based industries by providing a source of subordinated debt for eligible projects and borrowers. Maximum loan size is $25,000 for any person or organization in the business of growing or harvesting plants, raising animals, growing or obtaining plant or animal byproducts, aquaculture or engaged in the producing, processing, storing, packaging or marketing of a product from such business.

- ***Small Enterprise Growth Program***: Provides financing for small companies that demonstrate a potential for high growth and public benefit. Financing is limited to a maximum of $150,000 per loan and borrower must be engaged in at least one of the following: Marine Science, Biotechnology, Manufacturing, Exporting, Software Development, Environmental Sciences, Value Added Natural Resource and/or other enterprises that the Board determines will further the purposes and intent of the program.

- ***Marine Technology Investment Fund***: Provides investment in businesses with technology that can lead to product or process innovation. Targets funding for the next step required to bring a promising idea from the bench to commercialization.

- ***Tax Increment Financing (TIF) Districts***: Municipalities can use Tax Increment Financing as an economic development incentive within their community. The program enables a municipality to designate a TIF District in which new or expanding businesses can receive financial support based on the new property tax revenues generated by their project. The municipality may choose to fund a portion of the project improvements or to return a percentage of the tax revenues to the company to offset the costs of development.

- *Business Assistance Program*: Provides a grant to a local government to either loan or grant up to $400,000 to businesses to finance fixed assets including capital equipment, commercial or industrial buildings, fixtures or property improvements.
- *Development Fund Loan Program*: Can provide up to $200,000 or gap financing for up to 40% of a business' development activities.
- *Investment Banking Service*: FAME helps borrowers seeking large amounts of capital for major commercial projects find and secure financing alternatives.
- *Occupational Safety Loan Program*: In cooperation with the Maine Department of Labor, FAME administers a program to provide direct loans to businesses making workplace safety improvements.
- *Plus l Computer Loan Program*: This program provides lenders with loan insurance on an expedited basis for small businesses that need to borrow money to acquire and install computer equipment and software.
- *Rapid Response Guarantee*: FAME's Rapid Response Guarantee provides lenders with loan insurance on an expedited basis for small business loans that meet certain minimum credit standards.
- *Regional Economic Development Revolving Loan Program*: This program distributes $10 million to community, regional or statewide public-sector or non-profit entities that, in turn, loan the funds to eligible small business borrowers.
- *Small Business and Veterans' Small Business Loan Insurance Program*: This program is designed to help small businesses that cannot obtain conventional commercial financing. FAME can insure up to 90% of a small business loan, to a maximum insurance exposure of $1 million. If the borrower is an eligible wartime veteran, the authority may insure up to 100% of a loan of $75,000 or less, and up to 90% of a loan up to a maximum exposure of $1.1 million.
- *Small Enterprise Growth Fund*: This program was created to provide Maine entrepreneurs with access to "patient" sources of venture capital. The Fund targets the needs of entrepreneurs with financial requirements of between $10,000 and $300,000.
- *Bond Financing Programs*: FAME, using its authority to issue taxable and tax-exempt bonds, provides reduced-rate financing to large projects. Under the SMART-E Bond Programs, FAME issues tax-exempt bonds for manufacturing projects, which must meet eligibility requirements established under the Internal Revenue Code. The SMART Bond Program and Major Business Expansion Program offer reduced interest rates by using FAME's guarantee authority to put the strength of the State of Maine's credit rating behind financing for larger projects.

For information on the above programs, contact Finance Authority of Maine, 83 Western Ave., P.O. Box 949, Augusta, ME 04332; 207-623-3263; {www.famemaine.com}.

Tax Incentives

Business Equipment Property Tax Reimbursement Program: Program reimbursed, for up to 12 years, all local property taxes paid on eligible business property.

Employee-Assisted Day Care Credit: Provides an income tax credit of up to $5,000. The credit is limited to the lesser of $5,000, 20% of the cost incurred or $100 for each child of an employee enrolled on a full-time basis or for each full-time equivalent throughout the tax year.

Employer Provided Long-term Care Benefits Credit: Provides an income tax credit equal to the lesser of $5,000, 20% of the cost incurred or $100 per employee covered by a long-term care policy as part of a benefits package.

Employment Tax Increment Financing (ETIF): This program returns between 30 and 50% of new employees' income withholding tax to companies who add new workers. To qualify, employees must be paid a wage equal to or above the per capita wage in their labor market area, and be provided group health insurance and access to an ERISA qualified retirement program. The company must also demonstrate that ETIF funding is an essential component of the expansion project's financing.

High-Technology Investment Tax Credit: Offers businesses engaged in high-tech activities that purchase and use eligible equipment a credit amount equal to the adjusted basis of equipment place in service less any lease payments received during the taxable year.

Jobs and Investment Tax Credit: This program helps businesses with an income tax credit on equipment and facilities that generate new jobs. The program provides a 10% credit against Maine income taxes for investment in most types of personal property that generates at least 100 new jobs within two years, as long as the investment is at least $5 million for the taxable year. The credit amount is tied to the federal investment tax credit and is limited to $500,000 per year with carry-forwards available for seven years.

Research and Development Tax Credit: Maine's R&D tax credit provides an income tax credit for qualifying research and development activities. The program is based on definitions within the Internal Revenue Code; therefore, Maine's Bureau of Taxation recommends a careful study of Section 41 of the Code. In general, qualified research expenses include in-house and contract research related to discovering information that is technological in nature and is intended for use in developing a new or improved business.

Custom Computer Programming Sales Tax Credit Program: Exempts from sales tax the purchase of custom computer programming.

Biotechnology Sales Tax Exemption: Exempts sales tax of purchase of machinery, equipment, instruments and supplies used by any biotechnology company directly and primarily in a biotechnology application.

Manufacturing Sales Tax Exemptions: Sales of machinery and equipment used by any manufacturing company directly and primarily in the production of tangible personal property is eligible for a sales tax exemption.

Partial Clean Fuel Vehicle Sales Tax Exemption: Businesses that sell clean fuel vehicles to the general public are eligible for an exemption amount based on a portion of the sales or lease price of a clean fuel vehicle.

Research and Development Sales Tax Exemption: Sales of machinery and equipment used by the purchaser directly and exclusively in research and development by any business is eligible for a sales tax exemption.

Fuel and Electricity Sales Tax Exemption: Program exempts any business from sales tax 95% of the sales price of all fuel and electricity purchased for use at the manufacturing facility.

Business Property Tax Reimbursement Program: Maine reimburses what companies pay in local property taxes on facilities built after April 1, 1995. Taxes on this property may be reimbursed by the state for a maximum of 12 years. The definition of qualified business property for this program is broad and specified by law.

Maine Seed Capital Tax Credit Program: FAME authorizes state income tax credits to investors in an amount equal to 30% of the cash equity they provide to eligible Maine businesses.

For more information, contact Maine Revenue Services, 24 State House Station, Augusta, ME 04333; 207-287-2336.

Exports

Maine offers businesses and organizations international assistance through the Maine International Trade Center. The Trade Center's mission is to expand Maine's economy through increased international trade in goods and services and related activities such as:

- Trade missions
- Training programs in international trade
- Conferences, such as a major Trade Day event
- Publications, including the Trade Center newsletter
- Special member-only programs and one-on-one counseling and technical service assistance
- Comprehensive international library resources

For more information on the Maine International Trade Center, including membership information, contact Perry Newman, Trade Director, Maine International Trade Center, 511 Congress Street, Portland, ME 04101; 207-541-7400; Fax: 207-541-7420; E-mail: {newman@ mitc.com}; {www.mitc.com}.

Export Financing Services: Working Capital Insurance from FAME provides additional security to lenders and encourages greater lending activity for international business ventures. Export Credit Umbrella Insurance, provided by the Export-Import Bank of the United States (Eximbank) and administered by FAME, reduces international credit risk and allows an exporter to offer credit terms to foreign buyers in a competitive market.

Maryland

Department of Business and Economic Development
217 East Redwood St.
Baltimore, MD 21202
410-767-6300
800-541-8549
Fax: 410-333-6792
TDD/TTY: 410-333-6926
www.mdbusiness.state.md.us

Business Assistance

Department of Business and Economic Development (DBED):
This office can provide information and expertise in dealing with state, federal, and local agencies. They also have information on financing programs and other services offered by the state government.

Workforce Resources: Maryland offers several training and grants for training programs to meet a variety of workforce needs. The following are two of their many programs:
1. Maryland Job Service: Provides recruitment and screening services based on the specifications of a company at no costs. It maintains a state/ nationwide data bank of job seekers and acts as the state's labor exchange agent to match qualified workers with available employment opportunities.
   Industrial Training Program: Provides incentive grants for the development and training of new employees in firms locating or expanding their workforce in Maryland. MITP reimburses companies for up to 100% of the direct costs associated with training programs customized to the work process.
2. Partnership for Workforce Quality: Targets training grants to manufacturing firms with 500 or fewer employees to upgrade skills for new technologies.

Regional Response Resources: Coordinates services designed to improve the quality, productivity and competitiveness of a business and help develop new and innovative products and processes.

Engineering Assistance: Provides a gateway for companies to access the expertise of the University of Maryland faculty, staff and resource of the University's Engineering Resource center.

Technology Support: Helps companies diversify into new markets. In addition, the office: provides technical assistance to firms seeking to commercialize new technologies; facilitates collaboration between businesses and universities and federal laboratories; and oversees the Strategic Assistance Fund, which provides matching funds to support the cost of private sector consultants to aid in both strategic plan development and new market strategies.

Regulatory and Permitting Assistance: The Office of Business Advocacy assists businesses in navigating through the processes and regulations of local, state and federal government. The Office provides ombudsman service to businesses and acts an information source and liaison on behalf of the business community.

Business Financing

Investment Financing Programs: Provide for direct investment in technology-driven Maryland-based companies through three programs. All three provide a novel alternative to grants, direct loans or credit enhancements available through other State financing programs. All three involve the use of private sector capital, including venture capital, on a co-investment basis, and while having an underlying economic development agenda, are capital gains and return-on-investment driven.

Challenge Investment Program: Provides emerging or early "seed" stage, technology-driven companies with a capital formation capability of $100,000 through a direct investment of $50,000 from the Challenge Program, which facilitates a required 1:1, $50,000 co-investor match. A return on investment is potentially achieved through a repayment of up to $100,000 over a ten year period for DBED's original $50,000 investment, based on a contingent stream of royalty payments. The contingency is based in turn on the achievement of certain revenue and capital structure thresholds by the company during that time period. The Challenge Program invests $500,000 annually, in two "rounds" of five $50,000 investments, about six months apart.

Enterprise Investment Fund: An investment financing tool that enables DBED to make direct equity investments in "second -stage" technology driven companies located in the state. Investments range from $150,000 to $250,000 per entity. Investment decisions are based on the potential for return on investment, as well as the promotion of broad-based economic development and job creation initiatives.

Day Care Special Loan Fund: Direct loans up to $10,000 for minor renovations and upgrades to meet standards.

Maryland Venture Capital Trust: Administered by DBED through the Division of Financing Programs and the Investment Financing Group. As a "Fund of Funds", the trust has invested a total of $19,100,000 directly in eight separate, private sector venture capital funds. The source of this funding from the State, from the Maryland Retirement System, and from the Baltimore Retirement System. In the aggregate, these eight venture capital funds seek to make direct investments of at least $19,100,000 on a pro-rata basis, in Maryland-based, technology-driven companies. The Enterprise Investment Fund will work closely with these eight venture capital funds in attempting to facilitate its co-investment requirements.

Community Financing Group (CFG): Consists of programs that support the effort of local jurisdictions to create jobs and enhance their communities. These innovative programs have been very successful in revitalizing downtown areas, creating attractive business areas, developing industrial sites, creating attractive business locations, and in general, improving the State's industrial and commercial base.

The Four CFG programs include the Maryland Industrial Land ACT (MILA), the Maryland Industrial and Commercial Redevelopment Fund (MICRF), the Community Development Block Grant for Economic Development (CDBG-ED), and the Economic Development Opportunities Program Fund (Sunny Day). Each has unique attributes that allow effective and timely support of the needs and priorities of Maryland's local jurisdictions.

- **Maryland Industrial Land ACT (MILA)**: MILA loans provide a financial resource in cases where the need to develop industrial sites is not fully met by the private sector. Loans are made to counties or municipalities at below market interest rates and are secured by the full faith and credit of the borrowing government. The Act authorizes loans for acquisition of industrial land, development of industrial parks, improvement to infrastructure of potential industrial sites, construction of shell buildings for industrial use, installation of utilities, and rehabilitation of existing buildings for business incubators.

- **Maryland Industrial & Commercial Redevelopment Fund (MICRF)**: MICRF financing is intended to encourage private investment to facilitate industrial and commercial development or redevelopment. Loans are made to counties or municipalities who can then re-loan the proceeds to an eligible end user.

- **Sunny Day Fund**: Created to allow the State to take advantage of extraordinary economic development opportunities where assistance from other sources are constrained by program design, timing or available resources. The fund has been an extremely valuable tool in both business retention and recruiting. Maryland has taken advantage of opportunities with rapid and creative proposals that have assisted in the establishment of several high-profile private sector enterprises, including prized technology and research companies.

Maryland Industrial Development Financing Authority (MIDFA): Available to industrial/commercial businesses except certain retail establishments. Normal project range is $35,000 to $5 million. Insured up to lower of 80% of loan or $1 million. The amount of insurance varies with each loan and is determined after discussing the lender's needs. Typically, MIDFA insures from 20% to 50% of the loan.

Tax Exempt Program: Available to manufacturers or 501(c)(3) non-profit organizations. Normal project range is $1 million to $10 million. May insure up to 100% of bond. Normal policy: financing not to exceed 90% or real estate value or 75% of equipment cost. The actual amount of insurance generally varies with each project.

Taxable Bond Program: Available to industrial/ commercial businesses with certain exceptions. Normal project range is $1 million or more. Insurance level varies with each project but is limited to $5 million. May be insured up to 100% of bond amount. Approved Uses of Funds: To finance fixed assets.

Seafood & Aquaculture Loan Fund: Available to individuals or businesses involved in seafood processing or aquaculture. Normal Project Range: $20,000 to $800,000. Maximum Program Participation: The lesser of $250,000 or 80% of the total investment needed.

Energy Financing: Eligible applicants are businesses seeking to conserve energy, to co-generate energy, to produce fuels and other energy sources, and to recycle material. Normal Project Range: $800,000 to $160 million. Maximum Program Participation: 80% to 90% of value not exceeding 100% of cost.

Contract Financing Program: Eligible applicants are businesses owned 70% or more by socially and economically disadvantaged persons. Normal Project Range: Up to $500,000. Maximum Program Participation: Direct up to $500,000. Loan guarantee up to 90% not to exceed a maximum participation of $500,000. Approved Uses of Funds: Working capital required to begin, continue and complete government or public utility contracts. Acquisition of machinery or equipment to perform contracts. Interest Rates: For guaranteed loans, maximum rate is prime plus 2%. For direct loans, maximum is 15%.

Long Term Guaranty Program: Eligible applicants are businesses owned 70% or more by socially and economically disadvantaged persons. Must have 18 successive months of experience in the trade or business for which financing is sought. Normal Project Range: $50,000 to $1 million. Maximum Program Participation: Loan guarantees may not exceed the lesser of 80% of the loan or $600,000.

Surety Bond Program: Eligible applicants are independently owned small businesses generally employing fewer than 500 full-time employees or those with gross annual sales of less than $50 million. Normal Project Range: Guaranty Program - None. Direct Bonding Program - Up to $750,000. Maximum Program Participation: Guaranty Program - Guarantees up to 90% of face value of the bond not to exceed a total exposure of $900,000. Direct Bonding Program - Can directly issue bonds not to exceed $750,000. Approved Uses of Funds: Guaranty Program - Guarantees reimbursement of losses on a bid, payment or performance bond required in connection with projects where the majority of funds are from government or a regulated public utility. Direct Bonding Program - Issues bid, payment or performance bonds on projects where the majority of funds are from government or a regulated public utility.

Equity Participation Investment Program - Technology Component & Business Acquisition Component: Eligible applicants are technology based businesses and business acquisitions which will be owned 70% or more by disabled, socially or economically disadvantaged persons. Normal Project Range: $100,000 to $3 million. Maximum Program Participation: The lesser of $250,000 or 80% of the total investment needed.

Equity Participation Investment Program - Franchise Component: Eligible applicants are franchises that are or will be owned 70% or more by disabled, socially or economically disadvantaged persons. Must have at least 10% of total project cost in owner's equity. Normal Project Range: $50,000 to $1.5 million. Maximum Program Participation: Equity investments or loans up to 45% of initial investment or $100,000, whichever is less.

Challenge Investment Program: Eligible applicants are technology-driven companies, with principal activity located in Maryland; applicants must have complete business plan as a minimum requirement. Size of Investment: $50,000.

Enterprise Investment Program: Eligible applicants are technology-driven companies, with principal activity located in Maryland; applicants must have complete business plan as a minimum requirement. Size of Investment: $150,000 to $250,000.

Defense Adjustment Loan Fund (DALF): The primary purposes of this program are: (1) to stimulate and support the development of defense and non-defense enterprises in Maryland that have the potential to create employment in areas hurt by defense downsizing; and (2) to support the diversification of Maryland defense companies. On average, DALF intends to create or retain one job for every $35,000 loaned. The fund will lend capital to companies with growth potential for working capital, product development, technology commercialization, or manufacturing modernization. Preference will be given to loans that will catalyze investment or loans from other sources. Loans as small as $25,000 are permitted, but it is expected that loans will average $100,000 to $250,000. Committed funds may be released by DALF against the achievement of specified milestones.

Neighborhood Business Development Program (NBDP): Initiative to help stimulate Maryland's established, older communities, NBDP provides flexible, gap financing (up to 50% of total project cost) for many small businesses starting up or expanding in targeted urban, suburban or rural revitalization areas throughout the State. Terms and conditions are established on an individual basis. Financing ranging from $25,000 to $500,000, up to 50% of total project cost, where other funds clearly are unavailable. Contact Maryland Department of Housing and Community Development, Neighborhood Business Development Program, Revitalization Center, 1201 W. Pratt Street, Suite D, Baltimore, MD 21223; 410-514-7288; Fax: 410-685-8270; {www.dhcd.state.md.us}.

Tax Incentives

No unitary tax on profits.
No income tax on foreign dividends.
No gross receipts tax on manufacturers.
No corporate franchise tax.
No separate school taxes.

Job Creation Tax Credits: ncome tax credits granted to businesses for the creation of jobs. Credit granted will be the lesser of $1,000 or 2 1/2% of a year's wages for each qualifying permanent job.

Employment of Individual with Disabilities Tax Credit: Includes tax credits for wages paid and for child care or transportation expenses for qualifying individuals with disabilities.

Employment Opportunity Tax Credit: Includes credits for wages and child care or transportation expenses for qualifying employees who were recipients of state benefits from the "Aid to Families with Dependent Children" program immediately prior to employment.

Neighborhood and Community Assistance Program Tax Credit: Provides tax credits for business contributions to approved, non-profit Neighborhood and Community Assistance Programs.

Property Tax Exemptions and Credits: Maryland does not impose a personal property tax on business. For those jurisdictions that do tax personal property, exemptions and credits available include the following: machinery, equipment, materials and supplies use in manufacturing or research; manufacturing inventory; commercial inventory for warehousing and distribution; custom computer software.

Enterprise Zones Tax Credits:
1. Property Tax Credits: Ten year credit against local property taxes on a portion of real property improvements. Credit is 80% the first five years, and decreases 10% annually thereafter to 30% in the tenth and last year.
2. Income Tax Credits: One to three year credits for wages paid to new employees in the zone. The general credit is a one-time $500 credit per new workers. For economically disadvantaged employees, the credit increases to a total of $3,000 per worker distributed over three years.
3. Priority access to Maryland's financing programs.

Empowerment Zone Incentives: Firms locating in the federally designated Empowerment Zone in Baltimore, one of six in the nation, may be eligible for state enterprise zone incentives including: income tax credits for job creation; property tax credits for real property improvements. Businesses in the Zone may also qualify for potential federal incentives such as: wage tax credits; increased depreciation on equipment; tax exempt bond financing; employment development incentives.

Brownfields Tax Incentives: The counties, Baltimore City or incorporated municipalities may elect to grant a five-year credit equal to 50% of real property taxes attributable to the increase in the assessment resulting from cleanup and improvement of a qualified Brownfields site. The Brownfields real property credit may be expanded as follows: localities may grant an additional credit of up to 20%; localities may extend the credit by an additional five years if the site is in a state-designated enterprise zone; a credit will also apply against state real property taxes for the same percentage and duration.

Sales Tax Exemptions: The following are major business-oriented exemptions from the Maryland Sales and Use tax. Local jurisdictions do not impose a sales tax:
1. Sales of capital manufacturing machinery and equipment, including equipment used for testing finished products; assembling, processing or refining; in the generation of electricity; or used to produce or repair production equipment.

2. Sales of noncapitalized manufacturing machinery and equipment; safety and quality control equipment use on a production activity site; and equipment used to move a finished product on the production site.
3. Sales of tangible personal property consumed directly in manufacturing, testing of finished products, assembling, processing or refining, or in the generation of electricity.
4. Sales of fuels used in manufacturing, except those used to cool, heat and light the manufacturing facility.
5. Sales for resale and sales of tangible personal property to be incorporated in other tangible personal property manufactured for resale. In addition, there is an exemption for sales of computer programs reproduced for sale or incorporated in whole or in part into another computer program intended for sale.
6. Sales of customized computer software.
7. Sales of equipment and equipment used or consumed in research and development, to include testing of finished products.
8. Sales of aircraft, vessels, railroad rolling stock, and motor vehicles used principally in the movement of passengers or freight in interstate and foreign commerce.
9. Sales of certain end-item testing equipment used to perform a contract for the U.S. Department of Defense and transferred to the federal government.

Exports

Trade Financing Program: Eligible applicants are industrial/ commercial businesses which are engaged in the export and import of goods through Maryland ports and airport as well as service providers to the overseas market. Normal Project Range: $10,000 to $5 million. Maximum Program Participation: Insured up to lower of 90% of obligation or $1 million for export financing and 80% for all others. The actual amount of insurance generally varies with each transaction.

The State of Maryland's Office of International Business (OIB): Offers export assistance to small and medium-sized Maryland firms with internationally competitive products and services. OIB's international trade professionals provide Maryland companies with access to international market intelligence, targeted trade activities, financial assistance and high-level introductions to potential customers.

*   ***Exporter's Hotline & Referral Service***: OIB marketing specialists deliver basic trade information to companies in all stages of the export process. The Exporter's Hotline handles inquiries concerning the exporting process, assistance offered to Maryland firms by international trade service providers, and data on Maryland's international business activity. The hotline's number is 410-767-6564.

Export Assistance Network: An alliance of international business assistance centers, was developed by the State of Maryland to facilitate the transition of small and medium-sized companies to the global marketplace. The Network gives Maryland businesses convenient access to foreign market reports, profiles of the top industries for export, trade leads and contacts, travel information, trade statistics, and other information needed for entering the global market. The five centers are:
★ World Trade Resource Center, Baltimore; 410-576-0022
★ Eastern Shore Export Assistance Center, Salisbury; 410-548-5353
★ Southern Maryland Export Assistance Center, La Plata; 301-934-2251
★ Suburban Maryland Export Assistance Center, Rockville; 301-217-2345
★ Western Maryland Export Assistance Center, Cumberland; 301-777-5867

Maryland's Trade Finance Program: Offers up to $1 million in loan insurance per borrower for export and import financing. The trade finance office also provides access to the export financing and foreign credit insurance programs of the United States Export-Import Bank and the Overseas Private Investment Corporation.

Sister State Relationships: Promotes business, educational and cultural exchanges between Maryland and regions in Asia, Europe and Latin America. This program, which is managed through alliances with the World Trade Center Institute and the Maryland Business Center China, facilitates high-level international contacts, meetings with visiting delegations and networking with Maryland's international executives. Maryland has active sister state relationships in Belgium, China, Japan, Korea, Poland and Russia.

Foreign Offices & Representatives: Network of foreign offices and representatives provide exporters with in-country resources and expertise around the globe. These foreign offices in China, Japan, the Netherlands and Taiwan -- and representatives in Argentina, Brazil, Chile, Israel and Mexico -- deliver support in the following areas: agent/distributor searches and business appointments; credit reports, competitor analysis and regulatory information; marketing and logistical support at trade shows; market research and analysis.

Export Credit Program: Businesses conducting substantial economic activity in Maryland may submit proposals to receive export offset credits accrued from state purchases.

Publications

- *Trade Secrets: The Export Answer Book*: This guide contains over 100 answers to the most commonly asked questions concerning international trade; provides contact information for export experts; and describes more than 300 current publications, software programs and other international trade resources. The book, produced by the Maryland Small Business Development Center, is distributed for free to Maryland businesses through the State's Export Assistance Network.

- *World View*: A collaborative effort of the State's international office and other international service providers, the World View newsletter covers exporting issues, events and other topics of interest to Maryland's international executives. *World View* is published bimonthly by the Office of International Business and distributed for free.

Women and Minorities

Day Care Facilities Guarantee Fund: Eligible applicants are individuals or business entities involved in the development or expansion of day care facilities for infants and children, the elderly, and disabled persons of all ages. Normal Project Range: Up to $1 million. Maximum Program Participation: Loan guarantee up to 80%.

Child Care Facilities Direct Loan Fund: Eligible applicants are individuals, business entities involved in the development of day care facilities for children, either center-based or home-based. Normal Project Range: Minimum $15,000. Maximum Program Participation: Maximum of 50% of fixed assets.

Child Care Special Loan Fund: Eligible applicants are individuals, business entities for expanding or improving child care facilities, meeting state and local licensing requirements and improving the quality of care. Normal Project Range: $1,000 to $10,000. Maximum Program Participation: Direct loans up to $10,000.

Massachusetts

Massachusetts Office of Business Development
10 Park Plaza, 3rd Floor
Boston, MA 02116
617-973-8600
800-5-CAPITAL
Fax: 617-973-8797
www.state.ma.us/mobd

Business Assistance

Massachusetts Office of Business Development (MOBD): Through five regional offices, they will advise and counsel businesses and individuals in utilizing federal, state, and local finance programs established to help businesses with their capital formation needs.

Entrepreneurial Group: Provides funding, oversight, and, in some cases, the operation of a number of entrepreneurial training programs designed to help dislocated workers start their own businesses or consulting practices.

Achieving the Competitive Advantage Program: An intensive 10-week course designed to introduce entrepreneurs to strategic skills, methods, and models that are critical in planning and implementing a successful business plan. The classes provide training in the areas of business management, technology and financing, as well as such concepts as strategic partnerships, quality assurance and motivational vision.

One-Stop Business Centers: Offers a streamlined approach to economic development assistance. Offices located throughout the state are staffed with professionals who know about Massachusetts' programs and opportunities for businesses throughout the state's diverse regions.

Massachusetts Site Finder Service: Offers confidential, statewide searches for industrial land or buildings to fit defined specifications for expanding businesses. MOBD can also provide up-to-date Community Profiles of communities being considered as a business location. Information provided includes the local tax structure, local permitting requirements, and a demographic profile of area residents. For more information, contact Massachusetts Alliance for Economic Development, 800 Boylston St., Suite 1700, Boston, MA 02199; 617-247-7800; 800-872-8773; {www.massecon.com}.

Economic Development Incentive Program (EDIP): To stimulate economic development in distressed areas, attract new businesses, and encourage existing businesses to expand in Massachusetts.

Business Finance Specialists: Assists companies with financing targeted to urban and economically disadvantaged areas through the Community Development Finance Corporation and other public funds.

One-Stop Permitting Program: For all construction-related, state-issued permits. Project Managers act as advocates, assisting with identifying all required permits and moving the application through the entire process.

Massachusetts Energy Advisor Service: Helps companies identify energy efficiency opportunities in facilities and manufacturing processes. The University of Massachusetts and the Corporation for Business, Work, and Learning provide a similar service focusing on smaller and medium-sized manufacturing plants.

Economic Development Programs: Designed to encourage businesses to expand their operations, to move into the state, or to address specific utility needs. Within a year, businesses will be able to shop around for electricity, thereby creating competition among electric providers. This new opportunity will position Massachusetts in a more competitive environment regarding utility costs and will bring about lower commercial and industrial rates.

Business Consulting and Municipal Loan Pools: Professional staff are available at the municipal level who can offer business and technical assistance, as well as valuable insights on the local business climate and available local resources. Some municipalities also administer loan pools that can provide businesses with low-interest financing.

Massachusetts Manufacturing Partnership (MMP): Helps plan and implement a strategy for increased competitiveness, whether by adopting new production technologies and management techniques, finding new markets, or training a work force. Industry led regional offices are staffed by Field Agents who will work with a company to create the best combination of assistance.

The Commonwealth has resources to assist smaller and medium-sized manufacturers to stay competitive and to ensure that their work force has the skills necessary to be re-employed. Through the Corporation for Business, Work, and Learning, the Commonwealth provides training and job search services to unemployed workers, and offers consulting services and a loan fund/loan guarantee program for turnarounds.

The New England Suppliers Institute (NESI): Helps manufacturing companies become better suppliers to their larger customers by assisting them to develop quality business relationships, implement continuous improvement strategies, achieve supplier certification, and enhance company-wide work force and management skills.

Massachusetts Manufacturing Network Program: Provides technical assistance and funding to help them leverage resources, share information, and accomplish tasks that they could not do on their own.

Office of Defense Adjustment Strategy: Provides information about federal and state defense conversion programs. MOBD experts can discuss how defense companies wishing to diversify into new commercial markets may be eligible for federal grants.

Environmental Agency has an Office of Technical Assistance that has helped many firms replace or reduce the use of toxic substances in production, increasing productivity while lowering treatment and disposal costs. Massachusetts' Energy Advisor Service helps companies reduce pollution related to energy use while cutting their consumption and cost of energy. The Industrial Extension Service has expertise in helping firms make greater use of recycled materials.

Starting a Business in Massachusetts: A comprehensive guide for business owners available from MOBD.

Business Financing

The Capital Access Program (CAP): Designed to assist small businesses throughout the Commonwealth in obtaining loans to start, expand or continue operating profitably. The program is designed to gain access to capital where none currently exists. The state provides "cash collateral" guarantees for banks willing to make loans to smaller, "less bankable" businesses. Any person or business authorized to do business in Massachusetts may borrow through CAP. There are no minimum loan amounts.

The Emerging Technology Fund (ETF): A useful tool for economic growth for technology based companies. Targeting the fields of biotechnology, advanced materials, electronics, medical, telecommunications and environmental technologies, the fund provides companies in these industries with a greater opportunity to obtain debt financing. Loans can be guaranteed for tenant build-out, construction or expansion of facilities and equipment purchased for up to $1.5 million or 50% of the aggregate debt, whichever is less. Loans are also provided for hard asset-owned facilities and equipment, with a maximum amount of $2.5 million or 33 1/3% of the aggregate debt, whichever is less.

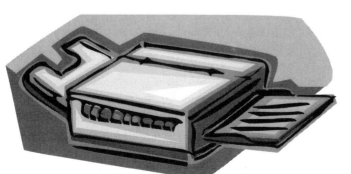

Equipment Lease/Purchase Program: The tax-exempt lease/purchase program provides manufacturers, non-profit institutions and environmental enterprises with a low-cost alternative for financing $300,000 or more in new equipment needs. By enabling leasing companies to furnish below-market, tax-exempt interest rates, the program offers companies sizable cost savings. Offers fixed interest rates approximately 70% of traditional leasing rates. 100% financing is available. Institutions must qualify as a 501(c)(3), not-for-profit entity and be located in Massachusetts. Potential borrowers include educational institutions, cultural institutions, long term care facilities, and other non-profits.

Tax-Exempt Industrial Development Bonds: Companies can borrow money via a tax-exempt Industrial Development Bond (IDB) to provide the lowest possible borrowing rates. Funds for an IDB can be used to purchase land, buildings and new equipment as well as to construct or renovate buildings. Based on the proposed project, the purchase of a new site, any new equipment needs and renovation or construction of facilities could be financed through an IDB. Should the project require a more flexible financing structure, the Massachusetts Development Finance Agency can work with the particular company to structure a taxable bond. Project size ranges from approximately $1.5 million to a federally imposed maximum of $10 million.

Tax Incentives

Investment Tax Credit: Massachusetts gives businesses a 3% Investment Tax Credit against the corporate excise tax for the construction of manufacturing facilities. The credit also applies to the purchase or lease of equipment. It is available to companies involved in manufacturing, research and development, agriculture or commercial fishing.

R&D Tax Credit: Massachusetts has permanent 10% and 15% R&D tax credits with a fifteen-year or indefinite carry-forward provision for companies investing in research and development. Companies are allowed to compute defense and non-defense R&D separately. This constitutes one of the highest R&D tax credits in the nation.

Economic Opportunity Areas: Qualified businesses operating within one of 36 Economic Target Areas are eligible for tax and financing incentives: A 5% Investment Tax Credit for all businesses, not just manufacturing; A 10% Abandoned Building Tax Deduction (at least 75% vacant for at least 24 months); Local Property Tax Benefits (Special Tax Assessment or Tax Increment Financing); Priority status for state capital funding.

Economic Target Areas (ETA) are designated throughout Massachusetts. Within ETAs, Economic Opportunity Areas of particular economic need and priority are further defined. Businesses that undertake certified projects within Economic Opportunity Areas can qualify for additional investment incentives: 5% Investment Tax Credit for Certified Projects, 10% Abandoned Building Tax Deduction within designated areas, Municipal Tax Benefits (Tax Increment Financing or Special Assessments on Property Values), Priority for state capital funding.

Tax Increment Financing: Businesses may also benefit from the substantial property tax savings offered through Tax Increment Financing (TIF). TIF enables municipalities to enter into agreements with private companies to determine a baseline property value level at which taxes will be levied for a specified number of years.

Exports

Massachusetts Export Center: One-stop resource for international business. The Export Center is a cooperative effort of the Massachusetts Office of International Trade and Investment, the Massachusetts Port Authority, the Massachusetts Small Business Development Center, Mass Development and the Massachusetts Office of Business Development. Offers:

- One-on-one Export Counseling
- Export Workshops, Training Programs and Conferences
- Overseas Market Research, Statistics and Trade Leads
- International Marketing Activities, including Trade Missions and Exhibitions
- Network of International Offices
- Meetings with International Business Delegations
- Export Financing
- International Business Resource Library
- Bimonthly Newsletter on International Trade Opportunities

Contact the Massachusetts Export Center, Fish Pier West, Bldg., II, Boston, MA 02210; 617-478-4133; {www.state.ma.us/export}.

Assistance is also provided through the ***Massachusetts Trade Office.*** This office's home page provides information on upcoming trade missions and lists events and seminars about doing business in the global market. Contact Massachusetts Trade Office, State Transportation Bldg., 10 Park Plaza, Boston, MA 02116; 617-367-1830; {www.state.ma.us/moiti}.

Women and Minorities

State Office of Minority and Women Business Assistance (SOMWBA): Certifies companies as minority or women-owned or controlled, and publishes a directory listing of verified firms. SOMWBA provides management and technical assistance seminars and workshops for minority and women entrepreneurs on a wide variety of business topics.

Minority Business Financing: A MOBD Business Finance Specialist can guide a company to several targeted financing programs including the Community Development Finance Corporation's Urban Initiative Fund, the Economic Development Fund and others.

Michigan

Michigan Economic Development Corporation
201 North Washington Square
Victor Office Center, 4th Floor
Lansing, MI 48913
517-373-9808
Fax: 517-335-0198
http://medc.michigan.org

Business Assistance

Michigan Business Ombudsman: Serves as a "one-stop" center for business permits. Acts as a mediator in resolving regulatory disputes between business and the various state departments and also provides consultation and referral services.

Michigan Works! is the state's workforce development resource agency. Offers workforce development services at 25 locations.

MiProSite: Lists more than 2,600 sites that can be searched based on client criteria for industrial site locations.

Economic Development Jobs Training: Provides financial assistance to companies that need to train or retrain workers to meet marketplace needs. Grant average: $2,000 per employee.

Business and Economic Services Team: Provides a broad variety of business and economic services to employers, entrepreneurs, and to those seeking to do business with the State of Michigan, which enable businesses to keep pace with civil rights and equal employment opportunity legal standards.

Customer Assistance: Provides a centralized intake unit in which economic development and workforce customers obtain services quickly and efficiently, and where individuals can receive information about starting a business in Michigan.

Economic Development Corporations: Provides a flexible tool to assist in job creation at the local level by acquiring, developing, and maintaining land, buildings, machinery, furnishings, and equipment necessary to complete a project plan.

Michigan Business Development: Assists existing companies with a wide array of business services that are customized to meet the specific needs of the business.

Michigan Business Strategies 2000: Provides affordable high quality management consulting services for small businesses seeking to position themselves for long-term growth. Businesses can receive expert consulting services in areas such as accounting, marketing, information systems, financial management, and internal operations.

Certified Industrial Park Program: Industrial park developers and communities have used this identification as a marketing tool to show prospective clients that they are prepared to accept the new client without delay. For more information, contact Michigan Economic Developers Association, P.O. Box 15096, Lansing, MI 48901; 517-241-0011.

Child Care Clearinghouse: Employers and organizations needing general information on employer-sponsored child care can obtain a resource kit which includes a series of fact sheets on topics related to workplace child care and information about a variety of tax issues. For more information, contact Michigan Child Care Clearinghouse, 201 N. Washington Square, Lansing, MI 48913; 517-373-9808; 800-377-2097.

Michigan Technical Assistance Center Network: Assists companies with government contracting and exporting.

Research Services: Detailed information concerning Michigan's economy and business climate. Information is also available regarding various industrial sectors critical to Michigan.

Employee Ownership Program: Provides information, technical assistance, and financing to enhance the establishment of employee-owned companies and Employee Stock Ownership Plans.

Business Financing

Alternative Investments Division: Invests in businesses with strong management that show a substantially above-average potential for growth, profitability, and equity appreciation. A typical initial investment is $5,000,000 and up. Contact: Michigan Department of Treasury, Alternative Investments Division, P.O. Box 15128, Lansing, MI 48901; 517-373-4330.

Capital Access Program: An extremely flexible and non-bureaucratic program designed to assist banks in making business loans that are somewhat riskier than conventional bank loans. The program utilizes a special loss reserve to assist banks in covering losses from a portfolio of loans that a bank makes under the program. The program is very broad based and can be used to finance most types of Michigan businesses. Due to premium payments that range from 3% to 7% of the amount borrowed [which are made to help fund the special loss reserve], loans under the program are generally more expensive than conventional bank loans. The key point is that, through the program, banks can provide access to bank financing for many businesses that otherwise might not qualify. Although there are no loan size limits, the average loan is approximately $53,000.

Business and Industrial Development Corporations (BIDCOs): Many sound businesses are unable to obtain growth capital because their finances are considered too risky for conventional bank lending, yet they cannot provide the high rates of return required by venture capitalists. BIDCOs are a new type of private institution designed to fill this growth capital gap. BIDCOs offer an array of financing options that can be structured flexibly to suit the needs of individual companies. In addition, they can provide management assistance to help businesses grow. As a privately owned and operated corporation, each BIDCO establishes its own criteria for the kinds of businesses it will finance and for the types of loans and investments it will make. BIDCOs do not normally finance start ups.

POLLUTION CONTROL LOANS

Industrial Development Revenue Bond Program (IDRB): Tax-exempt bonds issued on behalf of the borrower by the Michigan Strategic Fund and purchased by private investors. These loans can be made for manufacturing and not-for-profit corporation projects and solid waste facilities. Bond proceeds can only be used to acquire land, building and equipment. Working capital and inventory are not eligible for this type of financing. These bonds are generally used when financing of $1 million and higher is required.

Pollution Control Loans: Intended to provide loan guarantees to eligible small businesses for the financing of the planning, design, or installation of a pollution control facility. This facility must prevent, reduce, abate, or control any form of pollution, including recycling. SBA can guarantee up to $1,000,000 for Pollution Control Loans to eligible businesses. The 7(a) Program interest rates and maturities apply and are negotiated with the lender.

Equipment and Real Property Purchases: Municipal Bonds provide streamlined tax-exempt, fixed interest rate financing well suited to equipment purchases. For more information, contact Michigan Municipal Bond Authority, Treasury Bldg., 3rd Floor, 430 West Allegan, Lansing, MI 48922; 517-373-1728.

Freight Economic Development Project Loans/Grants: Provides financial assistance to non-transportation companies which promote the development or expansion of new business and industries, by financing freight transportation infrastructure improvements needed to operate a new venture. For more information, contact

Michigan Department of Transportation, Bureau of Urban and Public Transportation, Freight Services and Safety Division, 425 W. Ottawa, P.O. Box 30050, Lansing, MI 48909; 517-373-6494.

Industrial Development Revenue Bonds (IRBs): Provides healthy, profitable firms locating or expanding in Michigan with capital cost savings stemming from the difference between taxable and tax exempt interest rates. Maximum size of bonds is limited to: $1,000,000 free of any restriction on capital expenditures, or $10,000,000 subject to certain conditions.

Private Rail Loans: Privately owned railroad companies may receive capital loans up to 30% of the total project cost to improve or expand the privately owned infrastructure. For more information, contact Michigan Department of Transportation, Bureau of Urban and Public Transportation, Freight Services and Safety Division, P.O. Box 30050, Lansing, MI 48909; 517-373-6494.

Taxable Bond Program: Provides small and medium sized companies access to public capital markets normally available to larger companies.

Venture Capital Fund: Provides venture capital to growth-oriented firms ranging from $3 - $10 million.

Tax Incentives

Enterprise Zones: The program allows a designated community to provide a business and property tax abatement reducing property taxes approximately 50% on all new investment.

Tax-Free Renaissance Zones: 11 regions of the state designated as virtually tax free for any business or resident presently in or moving to a zone. The zones are designed to spur new jobs and investment. Each Renaissance Zone can be comprised of up to six smaller zones (sub zones) which are located throughout the community to give businesses more options on where to locate.

MEGA Jobs Tax Credit: Companies engaged in manufacturing, research and development, wholesale and trade, or office operations that are financially sound and that have financially sound proposed plans, are eligible to receive a tax credit against the Michigan Single Business Tax for a new location or expansion project and/or the amount of personal income tax attributable to new jobs being created.

Property Tax Abatements: Can be granted by the state and by local units of government. They reduce property tax on buildings, machinery and equipment by 50% for new facilities, 100% for existing.

Air Pollution Control Systems Tax Exemptions for Installation: Relieves a company of sales tax, property tax, and use taxes for air pollution control equipment.

Economic Growth Authority: Awards credits against the Single Business Tax to eligible companies for up to 20 years to promote high quality economic growth and job creation that otherwise would not occur without this program.

Registered Apprenticeship Tax Credit: Makes available a tax credit of up to $2,000 annually per apprentice to employers who, through registered apprenticeships, train young people while they are still in high school.

Work Opportunity Tax Credit: The tax credit is 35% of the first $6,000 in wages paid during the first year of employment for each eligible employee.

Exports

Export Working Capital Program (EWCP): The EWCP was designed to provide short-term working capital to exporters. It is a combined effort of the SBA and the Export-Import Bank. The two agencies have joined their working capital programs to offer a unified approach to the government's support of export financing.

International Trade Loan (ITL): This program provides short- and long-term financing to small businesses involved in exporting, as well as businesses adversely affected by import competition. The SBA can guarantee up to $1.25 million for a combination of fixed-asset financing and working capital. Loans for facilities or equipment can have maturities of up to 25 years. The working capital portion of a loan has a maximum maturity of three years. Interest rates are negotiated with the lender and can be up to 2.25% over the prime rate.

Export/Foreign Direct Investment Program: Promotes the export of Michigan-produced goods and services and attract investment in Michigan by foreign-based companies.

Women and Minorities

Minority And Women's Prequalification Loan and the Women's Pre-Qualification Loan Program: Use intermediaries to assist prospective minority and women borrowers in developing viable loan application packages and securing loans. The women's program uses only nonprofit organizations as intermediaries; the minority program uses for-profit intermediaries as well.

The Women Business Owner Advocacy Unit: Provides information to women business owners regarding government contracting, financing, legislation, and other business issues. It is establishing a statewide network to facilitate the sharing of information, resources, and business expertise, and more. Contact Women's Business Owner Advocate, Michigan Jobs Commission, 201 N. Washington Square, 1st Floor, Lansing, MI 48913; 517-335-1835; Fax: 517-373-9143.

Disadvantaged Business Enterprise Certification: Insures that firms owned and controlled by disadvantaged individuals, minorities, and women participate in federal-aid contracts and grant entered into and administered by MDOT.

Small Business Group: Promotes job creation and retention in small firms by fostering communication, coordination partnerships between the Michigan Jobs Commission and those public and private sector groups and organizations which advocate for and/or provide services to small companies and minority, women, and handicapped-owned businesses.

Minnesota

Department of Trade and Economic Development (MTED)
500 Metro Square Blvd.
121 7th Place East
St. Paul, MN 55101-2146
651-296-5657
800-657-3858
www.dted.state.mn.us

Business Assistance

Minnesota Small Business Assistance Office: Provides accurate, timely, and comprehensive information and assistance to businesses in all areas of start-up, operation, and expansion. They can also provide referrals to other state agencies.

Business Development and Site Location Services: For businesses interested in expanding or relocating to a Minnesota site, it serves as a bridge between government and the resources that businesses are seeking. Business Development Specialists act as liaisons between businesses and state and local government to access financial and technical resources. The program also serves as an important information source, providing businesses with data on topics ranging from the availability of buildings and property or the labor supply in a particular location, to transportation or tax comparisons. The one-on-one nature of this program provides businesses with assistance throughout every phase of their expansion or location projects.

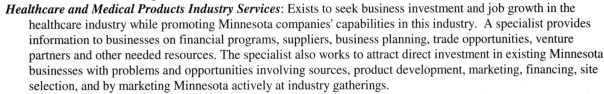

Computer and Electrical Components Industry Services: Exists to foster the growth of jobs, revenues, and investment in Minnesota's computer and electrical components industries. A specialist provides technical review of projects, coordination of statistical analysis, overview of prospect proposals, participation in development efforts with industry associations and other agencies.

Healthcare and Medical Products Industry Services: Exists to seek business investment and job growth in the healthcare industry while promoting Minnesota companies' capabilities in this industry. A specialist provides information to businesses on financial programs, suppliers, business planning, trade opportunities, venture partners and other needed resources. The specialist also works to attract direct investment in existing Minnesota businesses with problems and opportunities involving sources, product development, marketing, financing, site selection, and by marketing Minnesota actively at industry gatherings.

Printing and Publishing Industry Services: Exists to foster the growth of jobs, revenues, and investment in Minnesota's printing and publishing industry. A specialist provides information on resources, markets, technologies, buildings and sites, transportation, and other issues, both in response to inquiries and by marketing Minnesota actively at industry gatherings.

Wood Products, Plastics, and Composites Industry Services: Exists to foster the growth of jobs and added value in Minnesota's wood processing and related businesses and to attract new industry consistent with environmental protection. A specialist represents the industry and the Department of Trade and Economic Development by reviewing projects, organizing statistical data, participating in development efforts with Department of Natural Resources, University of Minnesota, Minnesota Technology, Inc., National Resources Research Institute and other agencies, and by helping to coordinate demonstration projects like model homes. This position has evolved from a primary focus on wood products, to a wider interest in plastics and composite materials that are more frequently used in conjunction with wood.

A Guide to Starting a Business in Minnesota: Provides a current discussion of many of the major issues faced by persons planning to start a new business in Minnesota, including forms or organizations, business name filing, business licenses and permits, business plans, financing, employers' issues, business taxes and small business resources.

Business Financing

Minnesota Investment Fund: To create new and retain the highest quality jobs possible on a state wide basis with a focus on industrial manufacturing and technology related industries; to increase the local and state tax base and improve the economic vitality for all Minnesota citizens. Grants are awarded to local units of government who make loans to assist new expanding businesses. Maximum available: $500,000. Only one grant per state fiscal year can be awarded to a government unit.

Minnesota Job Skills Partnership Board: Awards grants for cooperative education and training projects between businesses and educational institutions.

Small Business Development Loan Program: Provides loans to industrial, manufacturing or agricultural processing businesses for land acquisition, building construction or renovation, machinery and equipment. Maximum available: $500,000 minimum up to a maximum of $6 million.

Rural Challenge Grant Program: Provides job opportunities for low-income individuals, encourage private investment, and promote economic development in rural areas of the state. The Business and Community Development Division has a partnership with each of six regional organizations to provide low-interest loans to new or expanding businesses in rural Minnesota. Eligible projects: Up to 50% of start-up or expansion costs, including property acquisition, site improvements, new construction, building renovation, purchase of machinery and equipment, and working capital. Maximum available: $100,000. Most loans will be smaller due to the high demand for funds compared with the funds available.

Tourism Loan Program: Exists to provide low-interest financing to existing tourism-related businesses providing overnight lodging. Additionally, the program assists with the development of business plans. Businesses with feasible business plans qualify to receive financing for up to half of all eligible costs. Business owners meet with DTED staff to determine project eligibility and receive counseling. Direct loans, or participation loans in cooperation with financial institutions, can be made for up to 50% of total project cost. The maximum state loan may not exceed 50% of the total project cost, or $65,000, whichever is less. Maximum available Septic System Loans: Participation Loans - State funds are used in conjunction with loaned funds from financial institutions. Loans for septic system replacement or upgrade are eligible for an additional $65,000. Direct Loans - Only septic system projects of under $10,000 may receive a direct loan. The borrower must fund 50% of the project with private financing. The maximum direct loan is $5,000.

Certified Community Development Corporation: Certified CDCs may apply for grant funds for several purposes: 1) specific economic development projects within a designated area, 2) dissemination of information about, or taking application for, programs operated by DTED, or 3) developing the internal organizational capacity to engage in economic development activities.

Capital Access Program: To encourage loans from private lending institutions to businesses, particularly small-and medium sized-businesses, to foster economic development. When loans are enrolled in the program by participating lending institutions, the lender obtains additional financial protection through a special fund created by the lender, borrower and the State. The lender and borrower contribute between 3% and 7% of the loan to the fund. The amount of funds contributed by the borrower/lender must be equal; however, the funds contributed by the bank may be recovered from the borrower as additional fees or through interest rates. If the amount of all enrolled loans is less than $2,000,000, the State contribution will be 150% of the borrower/lender contribution. The borrower/lender contribution can be financed as part of the loan.

Contamination Cleanup/Investigation Grant Program: The Department of Trade and Economic Development can award grants towards contamination investigations and the development of a Response Action Plan (RAP) or for the cleanup of contamination on sites which will be redeveloped. The contamination investigation grants will allow smaller, outstate communities to access sites believed to be contaminated which are typically not addressed due to limited financial resources. The Contamination Cleanup grants address the growing need for uncontaminated, developable land. In both cases, grants are awarded to those sites where there is serious, imminent private or public development potential.

Minnesota Pathways Program: Act as a catalyst between business and education in developing cooperative training projects that provide training, new jobs and career paths for individuals making the transition from public assistance to the workforce. Grants are awarded to educational institutions with businesses as partners. Maximum available: $200,000 of Pathway funds per grant can be awarded for a project.

Underground Petroleum Tank Replacement Program: Exists to provide low interest financing to small gasoline retailers for the replacement of an underground petroleum tank. Business owners submit an application on the approved form along with supporting documentation including third party cost estimates from a certified installer, prior year federal tax return, schedule of existing debt and proof of gasoline volume sold in the last calendar year. Loans can only be made to businesses that demonstrate an ability to pay the loan from business cash flow. The maximum loan in $10,000.

Exports

Minnesota Trade Office: Acts as an advocate for Minnesota businesses pursuing international markets and to promote, assist and enhance foreign direct investments that contribute to the growth of Minnesota's economy. Services provided for Minnesota companies include information on trade shows and trade missions; education and training; and financial assistance programs for Minnesota companies.

Services for International Companies: Resources, services and direct counseling for all companies interested in international trade.

Minnesota World Trade Center Corporation: An international business resource for Minnesota and the upper Midwest.

Minnesota Export Finance Authority: Assists with the financing of exports through four focus areas: working capital guarantees for purchase orders, receivable insurance for foreign buyers, ExIm bank, and agency liaison.

Women and Minorities

Microenterprise Assistance Grants: To assist Minnesota's small entrepreneurs successfully startup or expand their businesses and to support job creation in the state. Any type of business is eligible to receive assistance, especially nontraditional entrepreneurs such as women, members of minority, low-income individuals or persons currently on or recently removed from welfare assistance who are seeking work. Startup entrepreneurs and expanding businesses receive technical assistance and, in some cases, financial support through selected nonprofit business development organizations. Businesses are eligible for up to $4,000 of technical assistance through this program. Participating organizations are reimbursed by DTED for up to half of this amount for approved expenses they incur on behalf of the grant recipient. The participating organization provides the other matching amount.

Minnesota Job Skills Partnership Program: Acts as a catalyst between business and education in developing cooperative training projects that provide training for new jobs or retraining of existing employees. Grants are awarded to educational institutions with businesses as partners. Preference will be given to non-profit institutions, which serve economically disadvantaged people, minorities, or those who are victims of economic dislocation and to businesses located in rural areas. Maximum available: $400,000 of Partnership funds per grant can be awarded for a project.

Urban Initiative Loan Program: Exists to assist minority owned and operated businesses and others that will create jobs in low-income areas of the Twin Cities. Urban Initiative Board enters into partnerships with local nonprofit organizations, which provide loans and technical assistance to start-up and expanding businesses. Project must demonstrate potential to create jobs for low-income people, must be unable to obtain sufficient capital from traditional private lenders, and must be able to demonstrate the potential to succeed. Eligible projects: Start-up and expansion costs, including normal business expenses such as machinery and equipment, inventory and receivables, working capital, new construction, renovation, and site acquisition. Financing of existing debt is not permitted. Micro-enterprises, including retail businesses, may apply for up to $10,000 in state funds. Maximum available: The maximum total loan available through the Urban Initiative Program is $300,000. The state may contribute 50% of the loan up to $150,000.

Mississippi

Mississippi Development Authority
P.O. Box 849
Jackson, MS 39205-0849
601-359-3449
800-340-3323
Fax: 601-359-2832
www.decd.state.ms.us

Business Assistance

Mississippi Development Authority: This office can provide information and expertise in dealing with state, federal, and local agencies. They also have information on financing programs and other services offered by the state government.
- *Training*: Customized industrial training programs provided through the State Department of Education. Job Training Partnership Act assistance provided through the Mississippi Department of Economic and Community Development.
- *Site Finding*: The Mississippi Resource Center in Jackson offers an interactive video for site viewing and detailed data on video, computer disk, or hard copy for later study.
- *One-stop environmental permitting*.

Business Financing

Loan Guarantee Program: Provides guarantees to private lenders on loans made to small businesses allowing a small business to obtain a loan that may not otherwise be possible without the guarantee protection. The maximum guarantee is 75% of the total loan or $375,000, whichever is less.

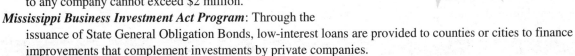

Industrial Development Revenue Bond Program: Reduces the interest costs of financing projects for companies through the issuance of both taxable and tax-exempt bonds. Additionally, ad valorem and sales tax exemptions are granted in conjunction with this type of public financing. There is a $10 million cap.

Small Enterprise Development Program: Provides funds for manufacturing and processing companies to finance fixed assets. Although a company may qualify for more than one loan under this program, the aggregate amount loaned to any company cannot exceed $2 million.

Mississippi Business Investment Act Program: Through the issuance of State General Obligation Bonds, low-interest loans are provided to counties or cities to finance improvements that complement investments by private companies.

Airport Revitalization Revolving Loan Program: Funds from the issuance of state bonds provide loans to airport authorities for the construction and/or improvement of airport facilities. Maximum loan amount is $500,000.

Port Revitalization Revolving Loan Program: Designed to make loans to port authorities for improvement of port facilities. Maximum is $500,000.

Agribusiness Enterprise Loan Program: Designed to encourage the extension of conventional financing by lending institutions by providing interest-free loans to agribusinesses. Maximum loan is 20% of the total project cost or

$200,000, whichever is less. Proceeds may be used to finance buildings and equipment and for costs associated with the purchase of land.

Small Business Assistance Program: Established for the purpose of providing funds to establish revolving loan funds to assist in financing small businesses. Maximum is $100,000.

Energy Investment Program: Provides financial assistance to individuals, partnerships or corporations making energy conserving capital improvements or designing and developing energy conservation processes. This program offers low-interest loans of up to $300,000.

Local Industrial Development Revenue Bonds: Local political entities have the authority to issue tax-exempt and taxable industrial development revenue bonds to finance new or expanding industrial enterprises up to 100% of total project costs.

General Obligation Bonds: Local political entities have the authority to issue general obligation bonds for the purpose of acquiring sites and constructing facilities for lease to new or expanding industries.

Tax Incentives

Jobs Tax Credit: Provides a five-year tax credit to the company's state income tax bill for each new job created by a new or expanding business. Amounts: $2,000 per new job for less developed counties, $1,000 per new job for moderately developed counties, and $500 per new job for developed counties.

R&D Jobs Tax Credit: Provides a five-year credit of $500 per year for each net new R&D job created by new or expanding businesses.

Headquarter Jobs Tax Credit: Provides a five-year tax credit of $500 per year for each net new job created by the transfer of a national or regional headquarters to Mississippi.

Child/Dependent Care Income Tax Credit: An income tax credit of 50% of qualified expenses is offered to any employer providing child/dependent care for employees during working hours.

Basic Skills Training Tax Credit: Provides a tax credit to new or existing businesses that pay for certain basic skills training or retaining for their employees. Credit is equal to 25% of qualified expenses of the training.

Rural Economic Development Credits: Companies financing projects through the Small Enterprise Development or Industrial Revenue Bond Program may be eligible to receive credits on corporate income taxes.

Mississippi State Port Income Tax Credit: Provides an income tax credit to taxpayers who utilize the port facilities at state, county, and municipal ports in Mississippi. The taxpayer receives a credit in an amount equal to certain charges paid by the taxpayer of export cargo.

County Property Tax Exemptions: For new or expanding manufacturers, certain properties may be exempted from county property taxes, except school taxes, for up to ten years at the local option.

Local authorities may grant a fee in lieu of taxes, including school taxes, on projects over $100 million.

Free Port Warehouse Law: Exempts finished goods from property taxes, including school taxes.

No state property tax except school taxes.

Sales Tax Exemptions: No sales tax on purchases of raw materials, processing chemicals, or packaging materials. No sales tax on direct purchases of construction materials, machinery, and equipment for businesses that are financed through certain bonds or located in less developed counties.

Partial Sales Tax: 50% sales tax exemptions for purchases of construction materials, machinery and equipment in moderately developed and developed counties. A 1 1/2% sales tax on machinery and parts used directly in manufacturing and on industrial electricity, natural gas, and fuels.

Exports

Foreign Trade Zones (FTZ): A safe area where goods can be landed, stored, processed, and transhipped--all without incurring custom duties (import tax). Foreign trade zones can provide customers with manufacturing, assembling, packaging, and display facilities, all free of duties. They are considered outside the customs territory of the United States in reference to many factors relating to international trade.

Women and Minorities

Minority Business Enterprise Division (MBED): Provides assistance to businesses in those categories. The division acts as principal advocate on behalf of minority- and women-owned business enterprises and promotes legislation that will help them operate more effectively. Developing funding sources, including state funding, bonding resources, federal and local funds, and others is among the major aims of MBED. But identifying funding sources represents only one aspect of MBED's service to Mississippi's women- and minority-owned firms. The division also attempts to put those businesses in touch with potential customers; MBED maintains an outreach program designed to include them in contracting of goods and services and procurement of contracts. A regional and statewide network of workshops, seminars, and trade shows continually provide training to stimulate the role of entrepreneurship in Mississippi's economic development.

Minority Surety Bond Guaranty Program: Program enables minority contractors, not meeting the surety industry's standard underwriting criteria, to obtain bid and performance bonds on contracts with state agencies and political subdivisions. Maximum bond guarantee is 75% of contract bond amount, or $112,500, whichever is less.

Minority Business Enterprise Loan Program: Designed to provide loans to socially and economically disadvantaged minority-or women-owned small businesses. Loan proceeds may be used for all project costs associated with the establishment or expansion of a minority business, including the purchase of fixed assets or inventory or to provide working capital. The minimum loan is $2,000 and the maximum loan is $25,000. MBFC may fund up to 100% of a total project.

Missouri

Department of Economic Development (DED)
Truman Building, Room 720
P.O. Box 118
Jefferson City, MO 65102-0118
573-751-4962
800-523-1434
Fax: 573-526-2416
www.ecodev.state.mo.us

Business Assistance

First Stop Shop: Serves to link business owners and state government and provides information on state rules, regulations, licenses, and permits.

Business Assistance Center: Provides information and technical assistance to start-up and existing businesses on available state and federal programs. Offers several useful publications. Contact: 888-751-2863.

University Outreach and Extension: Programs to help citizens apply university research knowledge to solve individual and community problems. Working with business owners and managers on a one-to-one basis, B&I specialists help entrepreneurs identify problem areas and find solutions.

Workforce Development System: Integrates previously fragmented employment and training programs into a comprehensive workforce development system. Services benefit both job seekers and employers through One-Stop Career Centers. Contact Workforce Development Transition Team, P.O. Box 1928, Jefferson City, MO 65102-1928; 573-751-7039; Fax: 573-751-0147.

Small Business Incubators: Buildings that have been divided into units of space, which are then leased to new small businesses. In addition to low-cost physical space, incubators can help clients with access to necessary office machines, reception and secretarial services, furniture, conference rooms and technical expertise in business management.

Innovation Centers: Provide a wide range of management and technical assistance to businesses. These centers are familiar with up-to-date business management and technology innovations and help businesses apply these innovations to help increase profits.

Mid-America Trade Adjustment Assistance Center: Available to small and medium-sized manufacturers who have been hurt by foreign competition. Helps firms analyze their strengths and weaknesses, develop a strategy to offset foreign competition, pay for implementing this strategy with federal cost-share fund.

Regional Planning Commissions: Services provided include business assistance, development, education, job training programs, loan preparation request, community assistance, airport planning, environmental assessments, grant administration and writing, hazardous waste planning, housing programs, legislative activities, local emergency planning, research, rural assistance, solid waste management, transportation planning, water and sewer planning, workshop development.

Business Financing

Action Fund Program: The program provides a subordinate loan to certain types of for-profit companies that need funds for start-up or expansion and have exhausted other sources. The projected growth of the company, economic impact, the risk of failure, and the quality of management are critical factors for approval. DED must determine that the borrower has exhausted other funding sources and only the least amount needed to complete the project may be provided. In any event, an Action Fund Loan would be limited to the lower of: $750,000 per project; 30% of the total project cost; or $20,000 per new full-time year-round job.

Brownfield Redevelopment Program: The purpose of this program is to provide financial incentives for the redevelopment of commercial/industrial sites owned by a governmental agency that have been abandoned for at least three years due to contamination caused by hazardous substances. The program provides state tax credits for eligible remediation costs. DED may provide a loan or guarantee for other project costs, or a grant for public infrastructure. Also, tax credits may be provided to businesses that create jobs at the facility. The program provides Missouri state income tax credits for up to 100% of remediation costs. Guaranteed loans or direct loans to an owner or operator of the property are limited to $1 million. Grants to public entities are also available up to $100,000 or 50% for feasibility studies or other due diligence costs. Grants can also be issued up to $1 million for the improvement of public infrastructure for the project. The total of grants, loans or guarantees cannot exceed $1 million per project.

CDBG Loan Guarantee Program: The purpose of this program is to provide "gap" financing for new or expanding businesses that cannot access complete funding for a project. "Gap" financing means other sources of financing (including bank loans and owner equity) have been maximized, and a gap exists in the total project cost. The Department of Economic Development (DED) will guarantee 50% to 80% of the principal balance (after liquidation of assets) of a loan made by a financial institution. DED must determine that the borrower has exhausted other funding sources and only the least amount needed to complete the project may be provided. The maximum funding available is based on the lower of: $400,000 per project or $20,000 per new full-time permanent job created or retained. Approval is based on the good character of the owners, sufficient cash flow, adequate management and reasonable collateral.

Certified Capital Companies (CAPCO): Purpose is to induce private investment into new or growing Missouri small businesses, which will result in the creation of new jobs and investment. DED has initiated the formation of private venture capital firms (CAPCOs). These firms have certain requirements to make equity investments in eligible businesses in Missouri. The amount a CAPCO may invest in one Missouri business depends on various factors, however the maximum amount is 15% of the CAPCO's certified capital. Funding decisions are made by each CAPCO based on their evaluation of the return on investment relative to the risk. CAPCO funds may be used for equity investments, unsecured loans or hybrid investments in eligible businesses. Typically, venture capitalists require a projected 25-40% annual ROI, depending on the risk.

Economic Development Administration Revolving Loan Funds: Designed to provide gap financing for start-up as well as existing business and industry in rural areas. The Revolving Loan Funds are administered by various agencies throughout the state and are available in cooperation with area financial institutions.

Industrial Development Bonds (IDBs): Developed by the US Congress and the Missouri General Assembly to facilitate the financing of business projects. The interest received by the bondholders may be exempt from federal and state income taxes, if the project is eligible.

Missouri Market Development Program: Financial assistance is targeted toward developing and expanding manufacturing capacity in the state by assisting businesses with the development, purchase and installation of specialized equipment needed to convert manufacturing facilities to utilize recovered materials. The maximum amount of financial assistance for any one project is $75,000.

Neighborhood Improvement Districts Program: General obligation bonds are issued to finance public improvements requested by benefiting property owners. The bonds are paid by special assessments to the property owners. The project should realistically be in excess of $150,000 due to the financing costs. The outstanding bonds cannot exceed 10% of the city or county's assessed valuation.

Urban Enterprise Loan Fund (UEL): A micro lending instrument established by the State of Missouri, Department of Economic Development and administered in Kansas City by the downtown Minority Development

Corporation and in St. Louis by the St. Louis Development Corporation. The program is designed to assist Missouri residents with the creation, expansion, and retention of micro-enterprises. Eligible enterprises must be located - or aspire to locate- within the Federally designated Enhanced Enterprise Community and the State Enterprise Zone. One job must be created for every $20,000 in Urban Enterprise Loan proceeds invested. Loans from the State fund range from a minimum of $10,000 up to a maximum of $100,000. The Urban Enterprise Loan Fund also has a matching funds requirement and new job creation criteria.

Missouri First: The State Treasurer has reserved a portion of available linked deposit funds for small businesses. State funds are deposited with participating lending institutions at up to 3% below the one-year Treasury Bill rate, with the lender passing on this interest savings to the small business borrower. A company must have less than 25 employees, be headquartered in Missouri, and be operating for profit. Small Business MISSOURI FIRST Linked Deposit loans are available for working capital. The maximum loan amount is $100,000. Contact State Treasurer's Office, P.O. Box 210, Jefferson City, MO 65102-0210; 800-662-8257.

Market Development Loans for Recovered Materials: The Environmental Improvement and Energy Resources Authority funds activities that promote the development of markets for recovered materials. Loans of up to $75,000 are available to companies for equipment used in the production or manufacture of products made from recovered materials. After three years, if all contract obligations are met, the loan is forgiven and repayment is not required. Contact: Environmental Improvement and Energy Resources Authority, P.O. Box 744, Jefferson City, MO 65102; 573-526-5555.

Financial Aid for Beginning Farmers: Beginning farmers can receive federally tax-exempt loans from commercial lenders at rates 20 to 30% below conventional rates through this program. A qualified borrower can borrow up to $250,000 to buy agricultural land, farm buildings, farm equipment and breeding livestock in Missouri. The borrower must be a Missouri resident, at least 18 years old and whose chief occupation must be farming or ranching after the loan is closed. The borrower's net worth must not exceed $150,000, and he or she must have adequate working capital and experience in the type of farming operation for which the loan is sought. A beginning farmer is one who has not previously owned more than 15% of the medium-sized farm in their county. Land cannot be purchased from a relative. For more information, contact Missouri Agricultural and Small Business Development Authority, Beginning Farmer Program, P.O. Box 630, Jefferson City, MO 65102; 573-751-2129.

Small Corporation Offering Registration (SCOR): Missouri's Small Corporate Offering Registration (SCOR) provides a process for entrepreneurs to register their securities. The SCOR process has been designed by state securities regulators to make it easier and less expensive for small companies to raise needed capital from Missouri residents. All securities registered through this process need to complete form U-7 available from the Secretary of State's Office. For more information, contact Securities Division, Secretary of State's Office, P.O. Box 1276, Jefferson City, MO 65102; 573-751-4136.

Working Capital, St. Louis: Working Capital is a micro-lending program which identifies small business people in the St. Louis area and makes available to them the commercial credit and business support which enables them to expand their business. Working Capital utilizes a peer-lending technique. At required monthly meetings borrowers receive continuing assistance in the marketing of their goods or services. The maximum first-time loan is $500 payable in four to six months; subsequent loans can have increased amounts (up to $5,000) and longer duration. Working Capital gives priority to individuals already in business to minimize loan risk; will consider applications from start-ups. Contact Working Capital, 3830 Washington, St. Louis, MO 63108; 314-531-4546.

Economic Council of St. Louis County: Services include Business Development Fund (BDF), Metropolitan St. Louis Loan Program, Minority/ Disadvantaged Contractor Loan Guarantee, Recycling Market Development Loan Program, SBA 504 Loan Program and Minority & Women's Prequalified Loan Program. Economic Council of St. Louis County, 121 South Meramec St., St. Louis, MO 63105; 314-889-7663.

St. Charles County Economic Development Council: Program assists eligible companies with fixed asset and working capital needs; acts as the certified development company which packages SBA 504 loans. Contact St. Charles County Economic Development Council, 5988 Midrivers Mall Dr., St. Charles, MO 63304; 314-441-6880.

St. Louis Development Corporation:

1. St. Louis City Revolving Loan Fund: Provides direct, low interest, subordinated loans for working capital, machinery and equipment, purchasing land and buildings, renovation and constructing facilities and leasehold improvements. Business must be located in the City of St. Louis and be licensed to do business in the City. Must create one full-time job for every $10,000 of funds. Loans can provide up to 1/3 of the project cost to a maximum loan amount of $150,000.

2. St. Louis Urban Enterprise Loan, St. Louis Development Corporation: Provides loans to businesses located within the Enterprise Community area or the Enterprise Zone within the City of St. Louis. Eligible borrowers must be for profit businesses with current employment of less than 100. Eligible program activities will include fixed asset or working capital needs. Eligible projects must retain existing or create new jobs (one job created for every $20,000 of funding). The UEL can lend up to 50% of the project costs to a maximum loan amount of $100,000.

3. LDC Micro Loan Program, St. Louis Development Corporation: Microloans are available to start-up companies or businesses less than one year old located within the City of St. Louis; one job, other than the owner's, must be created. Successful applicants must demonstrate a viable business plans and the inability to secure bank financing. Companies must show the ability to start or grow the business with a maximum loan amount of $25,000. Loans may be used to cover start-up costs, working capital and purchase of machinery and equipment.

Contact St. Louis Development Corporation, 1015 Locust St., #1200, St. Louis, MO 63101; 314-622-3400.

First Step Program, Kansas City: The First Step Fund (FSF) offers training in business basics such as record keeping, budgeting and marketing; assistance in completing a feasibility study for a business; opportunity to apply for loans of up to $2,500; and ongoing support group. FSF participants must be residents of Jackson, Clay or Platte counties in Missouri and must meet federal guidelines for low to moderate income. During a 10-week business training program, students work on a feasibility study for the proposed business. Potential borrowers receive continuing education at monthly meetings. Participants review each others' feasibility studies and approve loans. The maximum loan amount for first-time borrowers is $2,500 and $5,000 for second-time borrowers. Contact First Step Fund, 1080 Washington St., Kansas City, MO 64105; 816-474-5111, ext. 247; Fax: 816-472-4207.

Kansas City's Urban Enterprise Loan Fund, Kansas City: Fund is designed to assist with the creation, expansion and retention of small businesses located, or aspiring to locate, within the federally designated Enhanced Enterprise Community and the State Enterprise Zone. Eligible applicants include any Missouri resident with a for-profit business with gross annual revenues of less than $250,000 and less than 100 employees. Loan amounts can range from $10,000 to $100,000; matching funds are required as well as new job creation (minimum of one job per $20,000 borrowed). Contact First Business Bank, 800 West 47th St., Kansas City, MO 64112; 816-561-1000.

Community Development Corporation of Kansas City: Provides microloan business assistance to small businesses located in a five-county area; assists entrepreneurs whose credit needs are $25,000 and under. Contact Community Development Corporation of Kansas City, 2420 E. Linwood Blvd., Kansas City, MO 64109; 816-924-5800; Fax: 816-921-3350.

Thomas Hill Enterprise Center, Macon: The Thomas Hill Enterprise Center established a Revolving Loan Fund (RLF) to fill financing gaps not covered by conventional lenders. While certain restrictions exist, the RLF is designed to provide financing for businesses which cannot obtain adequate funds from conventional sources. Contact: Thomas Hill Enterprise Center, 1709 Prospect Dr., Suite B, Macon, MO 63552; 660-385-6550; 800-470-8625.

In$Dent Small Business Support: Peer lending program designed to assist low income residents of Dent County attain economic self-sufficiency by helping them start and/or maintain profitable businesses. All borrowers complete an approved business management training program and must be a member of a peer lending group. Loans will not be for more than $1,000 for any one group member. After the initial loan is repaid, members can apply for larger loans up to $2,000; each loan thereafter will have a ceiling of twice the previous loan, up to a maximum of $10,000. Contact: Bryan Adcock, Child and Family Development Specialist, 112 E. 5th St., Jucicial Building, Suite 4, Salem, MO 65560; 573-729-3196.

CDBG Industrial Infrastructure Grant: This program assists local governments in the development of public infrastructure that allows industries to locate new facilities, expand existing facilities or prevent the relocation or closing of a facility. The use of this program is based on the local government exhausting their available resources. DED has targeted a 20% match by the community base upon the availability of unencumbered city or county funds.

Tax Incentives

Small Business Investment "Capital" Tax Credit: The state of Missouri, through the Small Business Investment Capital Tax Credit Program offers a 40% tax credit to eligible investors in qualified businesses. Eligible investors may not be principle owners in the business. Only unsecured investments are considered eligible. All businesses wishing to participate in the program must make application to the Department of Economic Development prior to accepting investments for which tax credits are to be issued.

Business Facility Tax Credit Program: State income tax credits are provided to the business based on the number of new jobs and amount of new investment created at the qualifying facility. The credits are provided each tax year for up to ten years after the project commences operations. The tax credits are earned each tax period for up to 10 years. The formula to earn the tax credits is based on:

- $100 (or $75 for a new MO company) for each new job created at the project.
- $100 (or $75 for a new MO company) per $100,000 of the new capital investment at the project.

Capital Tax Credit Program: The investors of an approved business will receive a 40% state income tax credit on the amount of their equity investment or, in the case of a qualified investment in a Missouri small business in a distressed community, may receive a 60% state income tax credit. The percentage of stock purchased by the investors is negotiated with the business. The minimum amount of tax credits allowed per investor is $1,500 ($3,750 investment). The maximum amount of tax credits allowed per investor is $100,000 ($250,000 investment).

Community Bank 50% Tax Credit: The purpose of this program is to induce investment into Community Banks, which then invest in new or growing businesses or real estate development, resulting in an expansion of the tax base, elimination of blight, reduction of reliance on public assistance and the creation of jobs. A contributor may obtain state tax credits based on 50% of investments or contributions in a Community Bank. The Community Bank then makes equity investments or loans to a business, or investment in real estate development within a target area. No more than $750,000 can be invested or loaned by the Community Bank for any one business (including any affiliated or subsidiary of the business) or real estate development.

Enterprise Zone Tax Benefits: State income tax credits are provided to the business based on the number of new jobs and amount of new investment created at the qualifying facility. The business may earn credits based on the facility's new jobs and investment, the number of zone residents and "special" employees hired and trained for the facility.

Historic Tax Credit: The program provides state tax credits for 25% of eligible costs and expenses of the rehabilitation of an approved historic structure.

Infrastructure Tax Credit Program

- ***Missouri Development Finance Board (MDFB):*** Provides state tax credits to a contributor based on 50% of the contribution. The contributed funds are granted to a public entity to finance infrastructure needed to facilitate an approved project. Eligible contributors receive a tax credit of 50% of the contribution against Chapter 143 (excluding certain withholding taxes), 147, and 148 taxes. Contributions may be eligible for federal tax deductions also.

- *Distressed Communities Tax Credit Program*: Based on demographic requirements. Some entire cities qualify, and some areas qualify based on census block group demographics. The total maximum credit for all businesses already located within distressed communities shall be $750,000 for each calendar year.
- *Research Expense Tax Credit Program*: Purpose of the Research Expense Tax Credit Program is to induce existing businesses to increase their research efforts in Missouri by offering a tax credit. The amount of qualified research expenses for which tax credits shall apply, may not exceed 200% of the taxpayer's average qualified research expenses incurred during the three-year period immediately prior to the tax period the credits are being claimed. The aggregate of all tax credits authorized shall not exceed $10 million in any taxable year.
- *Seed Capital Tax Credit Program*: Purpose is to stimulate investment in new or young Missouri companies to fund the research, development and subsequent precommercialization phases of new, innovative products or services. Any person who makes a qualified contribution to a qualified fund shall be entitled to receive a tax credit equal to 50% of the amount of their contribution. This credit may be used to satisfy the state tax liability due within the year of the qualified investment, or in any of the ten tax years thereafter.
- *Small Business Incubator*: The purpose of the Small Business Incubator Tax Credit Program is to generate private funds to be used to establish a "protective business environment" (incubator) in which a number of small businesses can collectively operate to foster growth and development during their start-up period. The minimum tax credit is $1,500 per contributor. The maximum tax credit is $50,000 per contributor if made to a single incubator and $100,000 per contributor if made to multiple incubators. There is no maximum if the contribution is made to the Incubator Fund. The overall maximum amount of tax credits that can be issued under this program in any one calendar year is $500,000.
- *Tax Increment Financing Program*: A method to invent redevelopment of a project that otherwise would not occur. TIF redirects an approved portion of certain local taxes caused by the project to reduce project costs. The amount and length of the increment is negotiated by the TIF Commission based on the least amount to cause the project to occur. The "increment" may be up to 100% of the increased amount of real property taxes and 50% of local sales, utility and (in St. Louis and Kansas City) earnings taxed for a period of up to 23 years, as approved by the municipality.
- *Transportation Development Tax Credit Program*: A company (or individual) may be provided a state income tax credit for up to 50% of a contribution to a public entity for eligible activities. The project is needed to facilitate a business project or is a community development/public infrastructure improvement.
- *Wine and Grape Production*: To assist vineyards and wine producers with the purchase of needed equipment and materials by granting tax credits. A grape grower or wine producer is allowed a 25% state income tax credit on the amount of the purchase price of all new equipment and materials used directly in the growing of grapes or the production of wine in the state.

Exports

Missouri Office Of International Marketing: Services include: International Consulting Service, Competitive Analysis Reports, Trade Show Reports, Trade Exhibitions, Catalog Shows, Missouri International Office Assistance, Foreign Company Background Checks, Rep-Find Service, International Travel Program, Marketing Program, Trade Opportunity Program, Foreign Trade Missions, Strategic Alliance Program, Export Finance Assistance, Made In Missouri Catalogs, Missouri Export Directory, Recognition Program.

Missouri's Export Finance Program: Missouri companies that need financial assistance exporting to foreign markets can use programs of the Export and Import Bank of the United States(Ex-Im Bank) and the Small Business Administration (SBA) through a joint project that provides local access for Missouri businesses. There are primarily two programs available, Working Capital Loan Guarantees and Export Credit Insurance. These programs are designed to help small and medium-sized businesses that have exporting potential but need funds or risk insurance to produce and market goods or services for export.

Export Credit Insurance: The state of Missouri offers assistance in obtaining export credit insurance through the Export/Import Bank of the US to take the risk out of selling to customers overseas. The Missouri program, which insures both commercial and political risks, guarantees an exporter that once his goods are shipped, he will be paid. Insured receivables can enhance an exporter's ability to obtain export financing and allow an exporter to offer more attractive credit terms to foreign buyers. For more information contact Missouri Export Finance Program, P.O. Box 118, Jefferson City, MO 65102-0118; 573-751-4855.

Women and Minorities

Missouri Women's Council: To help Missouri women achieve economic self-sufficiency by supporting education, training, and leadership opportunities. Each year the Missouri Women's Council reviews pilot program proposals across the state and selects projects to fund which promote training, employment, and support Missouri women in the work place.

Workplace Readiness for Women: This particular program provides skills for employment in manufacturing industries for women living in Camden, Laclede, and Pulaski Counties. Training includes classroom instruction, one-on-one instruction and tutoring, computer training and work experience assignments with private employers who agree to provide the necessary supervision and work experience to assist participants with skills development and transition into employment in the manufacturing industry. For more information on this program, please contact Trish Rogers, Central Ozarks Private Industry Council, 1202 Forum Drive, Rolla, MO 65401; 800-638-1401 ext. 153; Fax: 573-634-1865.

Workforce Preparation for Women: This program is currently served in two Missouri locations; Mineral Area College in Park Hills and Jefferson College in Hillsboro. These programs focus on self-esteem, foundation skills and competencies as identified by an assessment process, and a workforce preparation plan developed by each student. Experts from education, business, and industry serve as speakers and consultants for the training sessions. Furthermore, the program matches each student with a mentor. For more information on this program, please contact Dr. Nancy Wegge, Consortium Director, Jefferson College, Hillsboro, MO 63050; 573-431-1951; Fax: 573-431-9397.

Capital for Entrepreneurs, Kansas City: Seed capital fund divided into three separate funds of $1 million each: Fund for Women, Fund for Hispanics, and Fund for African-Americans. Contact: Capital for Entrepreneurs, 4747 Troost Ave., Kansas City, MO 64110; 816-561-4646; Fax: 816-756-1530.

Office of Minority Business (OMB): Charged with the responsibility of identifying and developing support systems that assist the minority business community in gaining a foothold in the mainstream of Missouri's economy. This responsibility entails counseling minority small businesses on business start-up, retention, expansion, financing, and procurement; also including but not limited to providing ready access to information regarding current legislation and regulations that affects minority business. The staff of the Office of Minority Business can provide assistance with; administering technical and financial assistance programs; providing new and small businesses with management expertise; business development information; tying minority firms to national and global markets; connecting minority firms to the labor market; accessing research and technology; and other customized assistance.

Montana

Department of Commerce
1424 Ninth Ave.
P.O. Box 200505
Helena, MT 59620-0505
406-444-3814
800-221-8015 (in MT)
Fax: 406-444-1872
http://commerce.state.mt.us

Business Assistance

Economic Development Division: Offers a variety of programs aimed at assisting start-up and existing businesses with the technical and financial assistance necessary for their success. Works closely with other department divisions, state agencies, and federal and private programs, as well as local development groups, chambers and similar organizations.

Business Location Assistance: Provides prompt referrals of prospective expanding or relocating firms to Montana communities meeting the company's physical, economic and/or demographic requirements; provides assistance to communities in working with recruitment prospects; works with individual communities or groups of communities and/or other organizations to design and implement proactive recruitment efforts to attract specific types of firms in industries targeted by the community; works with companies new to Montana to identify and utilize available technical assistance and resident suppliers of materials and services. If in-state demand for particular goods or services exists, the program will attempt to recruit one or more firms to fill that demand. Special services, including visa consulting and assistance, is available to investors from Canada or subsidiaries of international corporations. The program distributes prospects lists to Certified Community Lead organizations and appropriate Department of Commerce staff, unless otherwise requested and authorized by the prospective company.

The Census and Economic Information Center (CEIC): The official source of census data for Montana, the Center maintains a collection of documents and computer-retrievable files that address the economy and population of the state (historical as well as current), including special papers and annual, quarterly and monthly statistical reports from federal agencies and other Montana state agencies

Montana Health Facility Authority: Issues revenue bonds or notes to finance or refinance projects involving construction, renovation, or equipment purchases for public or private non-profit health care programs. The MHFA lends its bond proceeds to participating health care facilities at costs below those offered by commercial lending institutions, thereby substantially lowering the facilities' borrowing expenses. In some instances, however, the MHFA includes commercial lending institutions in the financing to provide credit enhancement or private placement for the bonds. The MHFA may issue its notes and bonds, which are not general obligations of the state, for a single entity or a pool of health care facilities. Eligible health facilities may include hospitals, clinics, nursing homes, centers for the developmentally disabled or a variety of other health facilities.

Montana Manufacturing Extension Center (MMEC): Improves the competitiveness of Montana manufacturers through direct, unbiased engineering and managerial assistance in partnership with public and private resources. MMEC field engineers help companies obtain the highest output from their people, equipment, and capital.

They make "house calls" and provide free initial consultation. Their assistance includes, but is not limited to: productivity and quality audits, facility layouts, materials handling, ISO 9000 and quality assurance, benchmarking, managing growth, capacity planning, feasibility assessment, equipment justification, process design and improvement, cycle time reduction, production management, cost/benefit analysis, cost reduction, product costing, make/buy analysis, inventory analysis, supplier identification and relations, payroll incentive systems, materials requirements planning (MRP), and more. Contact: MMEC/ UTAP, 315 Roberts Hall, Montana State University-Bozeman, Bozeman, MT 59717; 406-994-3812.

University Technical Assistance Program: For more than 10 years, the University Technical Assistance Program (UTAP) has provided technical assistance to Montana manufacturers through engineering graduate students who work half-time during the academic year and full-time in the summers. It continues as an integral part of MMEC with the MMEC Bozeman field engineer serving as the UTAP supervisor. Undergraduates who have completed certain engineering course work may be hired as summer interns under the supervision of other field engineers. The UTAP staff engineers complete some projects and provide valuable support to the MMEC field engineers on other projects. Contact: MMEC/ UTAP, 315 Roberts Hall, Montana State University-Bozeman, Bozeman, MT 59717; 406-994-3812.

Business Financing

Microbusiness Finance: Montana "micro" business companies with fewer than 10 full-time equivalent employees and annual gross revenues under $500,000 can receive loans of up to $35,000 from the program's network of regional revolving loan funds lending directly to businesses. The loan program is designed to fund economically sound business projects that are unable to obtain commercial financing. Companies must provide a detailed written business plan and may be required to participate in business training classes. In addition to financing, borrowers receive technical assistance and consulting to help assure their success.

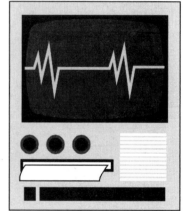

Job Investment Loans (JIL): This program is intended to provide funding for loans to Montana businesses as part of a financing package to permit business expansion, job creation and job retention. The program will provide a portion of the financing necessary to permit business expansion, job retention, and job creation. JIL monies will be used only in conjunction with equity and other debt financing in cases where other funding would not satisfy the total need and would not be available without this piece of additional financing.

Research and Development Financing: Montana Science and Technology Alliance provides $13.1 million in matching capital, from the Permanent Coal Tax Trust Fund, for research and development projects at Montana public universities.

Risk Capital Financing: The Montana Science and Technology Risk Capital Financing program may provide additional funding for current Montana companies. To receive MSTA financing, these businesses must meet the MSTA Board's investment criteria and have potential for achieving significant growth, benefiting the state's economy, and providing a substantial return on the board's investment. The MSTA structures all risk capital financing as loans. These loans may be convertible to company stock or would otherwise be structured to provide a risk-adjusted return on investment.

Growth Through Agriculture: Projects must embody innovative agricultural products or processes. Amounts: $50,000 in any one round, $150,000 to any one firm.

REA Loan and Grant Program: Provides zero-interest loans and grant to RE Act borrowers for relending to projects promoting rural economic development and job creation.

Seed Capital Program: provides funding for early-state entrepreneurial companies. The emphasis for funding is on technological companies but other companies can receive financing as well. The program may loan up to $350,000 in a single financing round, and up to a maximum of $750,000 to any one company over time.

Tax Incentives

New and Expanding Industry Tax Credit: Credit is equal to 1% of new wages paid by any corporation that is either brand new or has expanded its number of jobs by 30% or more.

Reclamation and Recycling Equipment Credit: Investment tax credit for businesses equal to 25% of the cost of property purchased to collect or process reclaimable material or to manufacture a product from reclaimed material.

Recycling Tax Credit: Income tax deduction for purchase of recycled material.

Wind Energy Generation Tax Credit: Income tax or license severance tax credit equal to 35% of the eligible costs for an investment of $5,000 or more in a commercial wind-powered energy generation system.

Small Business Investment Tax Credit: Corporation income, licenses, or coal severance tax credit for investment in a small business investment company. Credit is limited to 50% of the investment to a maximum credit of $250,000 for each taxpayer.

Research and Development Exemption: Exemption from the corporation income of license tax on the net income of a newly organized research and development firm during its first 5 years of operation.

Dependent Care Assistance Credit: A company can claim a credit for the amount paid or incurred during the taxable year for dependent care assistance actually provided to or on behalf of an employee.

Infrastructure Fees Credit: A nonrefundable tax credit is available against the corporation license tax or income tax for the portion of the fees that are charged to a specified new business for the use of the infrastructure that is built with loans.

Inventory Tax Exemption: Business inventories are exempt from property tax.

Property Tax Incentives for Selected Businesses: Reduction in property tax rates are available to: real and personal property used in the production of gasohol, machinery and equipment used in electrolytic reduction facilities (production of aluminum), market value on machinery and equipment used in a maltiny barley facility, market value on machinery and equipment used in a canola seed oil processing facility.

Property Tax Incentives for Specific Industries: Reduction in property tax rates are available to: industries that manufacture, mill, mine, produce, process, or fabricate materials; that convert materials unserviceable in their natural state into commercial products or materials, engage in the mechanical or chemical transformation of materials of substance into new products, engage in the transportation, warehousing or distribution of commercial products or materials, or if 50% or more of their annual gross income comes from out of state sales. Additional property tax reductions are available to: research and development firms, agricultural or timber product processing plants, and property used in the production of motion pictures or television commercials.

Local Option Property Tax Incentives: Property tax reduction is available to: new and expanding industries, businesses making improvements, machinery and equipment, business incubators, industrial parks, buildings or land sold or donated to a local economic development organization, and air and water pollution-control equipment.

Exports

Trade Program: Mission is to identify opportunities for worldwide and domestic trade and to provide representation, information and technical assistance. More specifically, the Trade Program provides: trade consultation, Marketing/Country reports, trade leads, trade show assistance, special promotions for Montana made products and services, tourism promotion services in the Far East.

Made in Montana program: Works to elevate the status of Montana-made products in the marketplace and to educate Montanans about the diversity of products manufactured in their state.

Nebraska

Department of Economic Development
P.O. Box 94666
301 Centennial Mall South
Lincoln, NE 68509
402-471-3111
800-426-6505 (in NE)
Fax: 402-471-3365
TDD: 402-471-3441
www.neded.org

Business Assistance

One-Stop Business Assistance Program: Provides assistance on identifying, marketing and finance information; business information and research, regulations, licenses, fees, and other state requirements for business operation.

Skilled Training Employment Program (STEP): Offers a comprehensive, on-the-job training program for new and expanding businesses.

Government Procurement Assistance: Helps create additional markets.

Match Marketing: Assists with matching Nebraska buyers and suppliers.

Technical Assistance: Increases productivity and competitiveness.

Site Location Assistance: Includes facilitating access to programs.

Business Financing

Industrial Revenue Bonds (IRB): All Nebraska counties and municipalities, as well as the Nebraska Investment Finance Authority, are authorized to issue IRBs to finance land, buildings and equipment for industrial projects. The rate of interest is normally lower than on most loans.

Nebraska Investment Finance Authority: Issues IRBs for land, building and equipment for industrial enterprises, as well as provides financing for housing.

Dollar and Energy Saving Loans: Energy saving loans are offered statewide by the Nebraska Energy Office and the state's lending institutions. The interest rate is 6% or less, but may be adjusted semi-annually. Adjustments do not affect existing loans. Check with a lender or the Nebraska Energy Office for the current rate. Contact: Nebraska Energy Office, Box 95085, Lincoln, NE 68509; 402-471-2867.

Community Improvement Financing: This is Nebraska's version of Tax Increment Financing, a method of financing public improvements associated with a private development project in a blighted and substandard area by using the projected increase in the property tax revenue which will result from the private development.

Local Option Municipal Economic Development Act: Provides the ability for communities to add a sales or property tax for economic development projects.

Nebraska Energy Fund: Provides low-interest loans for energy efficiency improvements.

Nebraska Redevelopment Act: Authorizes Community Improvement Financing for real estate and equipment in a project that adds at least 500 new jobs and $50 million of new investment.

Nebraska Agriculture Opportunities and Value-Added Partnership Act

Adams County Central Community College: Total Loan Funds: $30,000 as of April 24, 1996. Sources: Private money. Loan Terms: Low interest rates, 3 year term, collateral required, payments put on amortization schedule,

$10,000 maximum. Loan Eligibility: Serves the 25-county Central Community College area. Services: Counseling, CCC business courses, SCORE available. Contact Person: Jim Svoboda, Coordinator, P.O. Box 1054, Hastings, NE 68902-1024; 402-461-2461; 402-461-2506; Email: {svohbus@cccadm. gi.cccneb.edu}.

Mid-Nebraska Community Services: A caring, non-profit community action agency that provides resources to help people and communities in 27 counties grow within themselves for a better future. Total Loan Fund: $130,000. Contact Person: Robert E. Hobbs, Loan Coordinator, 16 West 11th Street, P.O. Box 2288, Kearney, NE 68848-2288; 308-865-5675; 308-865-5681.

Rural Business Development Fund, Small Enterprises Economic Development Project, Rural Economic and Community Development, State of Nebraska. LB144, private grants. Provides microenterprise loans, loan counseling, credit analysis, developing business plan and entrepreneurial training. Contact Person: Robert E. Hobbs, Loan Coordinator, 16 West 11th Street, P.O. Box 2288, Kearney, NE 68848-2288; 308-865-5675; 308-865-5681.

Northeast Nebraska Development District Business Loan Programs: Exists to promote and assist the growth and development of business and industrial concerns within Northeast Nebraska. Priority will be given to fixed asset financing (land, building, equipment); however, working capital can also be financed. Generally, loans will range from $10,000 to $100,000 (maximum). Contact: Northeast Nebraska Economic Development District, 111 S. 1st St., Norfolk, NE 68701; 402-379-1150; {www.nenedd.org}.

Tax Incentives

Employment and Investment Growth Act: With a $3 million investment in qualified property and addition of 30 full-time employees, a business qualifies for: direct refund of all sales and use taxes paid on purchases of qualified property; 5% tax credit on the amount of the total compensation paid to employees; 10% tax credit on total investment in qualified property, 5 and 10% tax credits applied to income tax liability or used to obtain refund of sales and use taxes paid on other purchases.

With a $10 million investment in qualified property and addition of 100 full-time employees, a business qualifies for: all of the above plus up to a 15 year personal property tax exemption on newly acquired: turbine-powered aircraft, mainframe computers and peripheral components, equipment used directly in processing agricultural products. Investment in qualified property resulting in a net gain of $20 million with no increased employment qualifies a business for direct refund of all sales and use taxes paid on purchases of qualified property.

Employment Expansions and Investment Incentive Act: Provides tax credits for any business which increase investment by at least $75,000 and increase net employment by an average of two full-time positions during a taxable year. Credits of $1,500 per net new employee and $1,000 per $75,000 net new investment may be used to reduce a portion of the taxpayer's income tax liability or to obtain a refund of sales and use taxes paid.

Enterprise Zones: Within these areas, tax credits are given for qualifying businesses which increase employment and make investments in the area.

For more information, contact Nebraska Department of Revenue, 301 Centennial Mall South, P.O. Box 94818, Lincoln, NE 58609-4818; 402-471-2971; 800-742-7474.

Exports

Office of International Trade and Investment (OITI): Works with existing businesses to expand their international marketing efforts, as well as foster international manufacturing investments in the state.

Nevada

State of Nevada Commission on Economic Development
108 E. Proctor St.
Carson City, NV 89710
775-687-4325
800-336-1600
Fax: 775-687-4450
www.expand2nevada.com

555 E. Washington Avenue
Suite 5400
Las Vegas, NV 89101
702-486-2700
Fax: 702-486-2701

Business Assistance

Commission on Economic Development: Publishes a pamphlet, *Business Assistance*. Acts as a clearinghouse for information and technical assistance. Operates several business assistance programs and performs advertising and public relations activities on behalf of Nevada business. Maintains a computerized inventory of available manufacturing and warehousing buildings, land and corporate office space, and customized site selection.

Procurement Outreach Program: Assists businesses in successfully tapping into this lucrative market by: introducing firms to federal agencies that purchase the products and services they sell; providing assistance to ensure that companies are prepared with all of the tools, knowledge and skills necessary to meet the federal government's specifications and standards, and properly complete bids; offering seminars, marketing fairs, mailing lists and direct assistance as well as the Automated Bidline which is a fax-on demand system allowing instant access to the latest bid and requests for proposal information.

Community Business Resource Center: A one-stop center for business information designed to enhance the economic self-sufficiency of low-and moderate-income individuals by developing their entrepreneurial skills. Services available include training, technical assistance and access to credit. Contact Community Business Resource Center, 116 E. 7th St., Suite 3, Carson City, NV 89701; 800-337-4590.

Business Financing

Nevada Development Capital Corporation: A private development fund designed to finance growth opportunities for small, sound Nevada businesses which do not qualify for conventional financing. The financing provided by NDCC includes but is not limited to the following: working capital loans secured by primary or subordinated assets; loans secured by fixed assets with longer terms than could be provided by conventional lending sources; loans for the acquisition of a business or interest in a business; subordinated loans in cases where available bank financing is sufficient; loans to refinance existing debt in cases where existing terms present a hardship for the business. Most loans will probably be in the $50,000 to $150,000 range. Contact: Nevada State Development Corporation, 350 S. Center St., Suite 310, Reno, NV 89501; 702-323-3625; 800-726-2494.

Nevada Self-Employment Trust: A start-up business may be eligible to borrow from $100 to $7,500 while existing companies may borrow a maximum of $25,000. Contact: Community Business Resource Center, 116 E. 7th St., Suite 3, Carson City, NV 89701; 800-337-4590.

Venture Capital: A potential source of venture capital is the State Public Employees Retirement System that disperses funds through several venture capital pools.

Industrial Revenue Bonds: A special type of loan to qualified manufacturers who are buying land, building new facilities, refurbishing existing buildings and purchasing new equipment.

Rural Business Loans: Companies in rural Nevada have additional avenues for financial assistance designed to: lend money to small businesses in need of expansion or start-up financing; assist small businesses in obtaining gap financing to complete their business expansion projects; provide financing to small businesses which meet job creation requirements. Assistance is available through the Nevada Revolving Loan Fund, Rural Economic and Community Development Services, and Rural Nevada Development Corporation.

Train Employees Now: Grants to training providers up to 75% of the total eligible costs with a cap of $1,000 per trainee.

Business Assistance Program: Helps businesses understand environmental rules and explain the permitting process as well as identify sources of financing for pollution control equipment and provide access to the latest information regarding environmental issues.

Tax Incentives

No Personal Income Tax
No Corporate Income Tax
No Franchise Tax on Income
No Unitary Tax
No Inheritance, Estate, or Gift Tax
No Admissions or Chain Store Tax

Freeport: Protects shipments in transit from taxation and cuts the cost of doing business both domestically and internationally.

Sales and Use Tax Abatement: Partial sales/use tax exemption on machinery and equipment purchases.

Sales and Use Tax Deferral: Tax deferral on machinery and equipment purchases in excess of $100,000.

Business Tax Abatement: A 50% tax exemption determined on a case by case basis.

Property Tax Abatement: 75% tax exemption on real and personal property for qualified recycling businesses.

Exports

Nevada's International Trade Program: Goal is to assist Nevada businesses to begin, or expand, exporting to international markets. Services include: Trade Missions, Export Seminars, Export Counseling, International Trade Database, Foreign Buyers Delegations, International Trade Directories.

Foreign Trade Zones: Two zones allow international importers duty-free storage and assembly of foreign products.

Export Financing: Assistance is available through private sector financial institution, the International Trade Program and the federal Export/Import Bank.

New Hampshire

State of New Hampshire
Department of Resources and Economic Development
172 Pembroke Road
P.O. Box 1856
Concord, NH 03302-1856
603-271-2341
800-204-5000 (in NH)
Fax: 603-271-6784
www.ded.state.nh.us/obid

Business Assistance

Office of Business and Industrial Development: Provides assistance and publications designed to support and promote business and industry in the state. Information in areas such as licensing and permits, financial counseling, marketing, and exporting, labor markets, and more.

Economic Development Data System: A comprehensive database of all the communities and available industrial properties within the state.

Business Visitation Program: Local volunteers visit businesses to gather information about firms' development issues, economic concerns and opinions about their community as a place to do business. Once aware of these issues, local, state and federal programs can be accessed to assist the firms. A referral network coordinates questions, issues and concerns.

Vendor Matching Program: A database that can be used to match a prospective client's product needs with the appropriate New Hampshire vendor of those products.

Procurement Technical Assistance Program: Provides the necessary tools to be competitive in the federal marketplace through procurement counseling; contract announcements; specifications and standards; and support databases.

Industrial Research Center: Assistance in basic and applied research, development and marketing through a matching grants program; hands-on training in Design of Experiment methods; and helping inventors develop patent and commercialize their ideas. Contact: New Hampshire Industrial Research Center, University of New Hampshire, 222 Kingsbury Hall, Durham, NH 03824; 603-862-0123.

Job Training Council: Provides job training for citizens while helping businesses gain capable workers. Contact: New Hampshire Job Training, 64 Old Suncook Rd., Concord, NH 03301; 603-228-9500.

Manchester Manufacturing Management Center: Serves as a crucial link between the university and the manufacturing community through sponsorship of industry-specific programs, including seminars, symposia, expos, and internships. Contact: Manchester Manufacturing Management Center, 150 Dow St., Manchester, NH 03101; 603-625-0106.

Business Financing

Regional and Local Revolving Loan Funds: Many local and regional revolving loan funds exist throughout New Hampshire. These funds have been capitalized from a variety of services, many with federal monies. The administration of these funds is generally handled by a non-profit corporation, while the local funds most often are overseen by governing bodies with the help of a loan committee. The loans may be used in conjunction with other sources to leverage additional monies or independently finance the project. Check out {www.kisbc.org/s_finsource.html}

Finance Clearinghouse: Offers companies assistance in obtaining financing. A complete listing of programs can be obtained through the clearinghouse.

Business Finance Authority: Has several loan programs designed to foster economic development and create employment with an emphasis on small business assistance.

1. Capital Access Program: Start-up businesses or business expansion are eligible for loans from $5,000 to $250,000 for business purposes.
2. Working Capital Line of Credit Guarantee: Up to $2,000,000 for business needing working capital line of credit.
3. Guarantee Asset Program: Provides assistance to capital intensive businesses.
4. Industrial Development Revenue Bond: Up to $10 million for any trade or business that is eligible for tax-exempt financing for acquisition of land, buildings and improvements, machinery and equipment.
5. Assistance to Local Development Organizations: Provides funding to municipalities and development organizations to assist in the promotion and development of New Hampshire businesses.

Contact: New Hampshire Business Finance Authority, Suite 101, 14 Dixon Ave., Concord, NH 03301; 603-271-2391; {www.state.nh.us/bfa/bfa.htm}.

Business Development Corporation: A non-profit company in the business of funding loans to small businesses that qualify. For more information, contact Business Development Corporation, 1001 Elm Street, Manchester, NH 03101; 603-623-5500; Fax: 603-623-3972; {www.nhbdc.com}.

Capital Consortium: A venture capital partnership that makes investments between $250,000 and $12,000,000 in high-potential companies. For more information, contact Business Development Corporation, 1001 Elm Street, Manchester, NH 03101; 603-623-5500; Fax: 603-623-3972; {www.nhbdc.com}.

Tax Incentives

No general sales or personal income tax
No tax on personal property or inventories
No property tax on machinery or equipment
No higher assessments or higher property tax rates for commercial or industrial real estate

Exports

International Trade Resource Center: A one-stop location when businesses, both current and potential exporters, can access the assistance and information necessary to effectively explore, develop and penetrate the foreign marketplace. Offers counseling, education and training seminars, automated trade leads, market research, marketing promotion, library and finance assistance.

New Hampshire Export Finance Program: To support export sales in providing working capital for the exporter to produce or buy a product for resale; provide political and/or commercial risk insurance in order to provide open account terms to foreign buyers; provide access to funding to qualified foreign buyers who need medium-term financing in order to purchase capital goods and services from New Hampshire Exporters. Rates and premiums arranged per sale or as needed. No dollar limit. Contact: New Hampshire Office of International Commerce, 17 New Hampshire Ave., Portsmouth, NH 03801; 603-334-6074.

Foreign Trade Zones: Provides economic incentives to companies doing business in foreign countries.

New Jersey

New Jersey Economic Development Authority
P.O. Box 990
Trenton, NJ 08625-0990
609-292-1800
www.njeda.com

Business Assistance

Division of Economic Development: Develops and administers comprehensive marketing and support programs. Helps access public and private services which address a broad array of issues, ranging from financial, technical and regulatory concerns to employee training and site location.

Office of Account Management: Offers assistance to existing companies to maintain or expand operations.

Office of the Business Advocate and Business Information: Assists businesses that are having difficulty navigating through State regulations.

Entrepreneurial Training Institute: An eight week program is offered to help new and aspiring entrepreneurs learn the basics of operating a business.

Small Business Contracts: State law requires that at least 15% of the contracts awarded by the State be given to small businesses. In the first half of 1998, these "set-aside contracts" amounted to more than $425 million.

Doing Business in New Jersey Guidebook: Provides information on starting and operating a business in the state. Topics include requirements and advice for starting a new business, information on tax and employee regulations, state and federal financial information, franchising, procurement opportunities, and exporting.

Selective Assistance Vendor Information Database: A computer database designed especially to assist business owners that wish to do business with the State of New Jersey and the private sector. SAVI-II matches buyers and vendors for public and private contracting opportunities.

Department of Labor's Division of Field Support: New Jersey provides the Business Resource Network, a coordinated interdepartmental resource to identify and market programs available to employers through various New Jersey agencies.

Department of Labor's Division of Workforce Development: The State provides matching customized training grants and technical assistance to upgrade the technical skills of incumbent workers.

Maritime Services: New Jersey offers several services to support businesses engaged in this enterprise. These include advice and assistance with permits and economic development issues, facilitation of dredging-related activities, and assistance in reducing or minimizing the creation of sediment.

Manufacturing Extension Partnership: Provides assistance to manufacturers in securing a wide variety of technical resources.

New Jersey Economic Development Authority's Trade Adjustment Assistance Center: Can provide technical assistance to manufacturers or certify manufacturers for eligibility for federal government assistance.

Real Estate Development Division: Businesses may be able to lease state-of-the-art, affordable laboratory, production, and research facilities in the Technology Centre of New Jersey. New high-technology businesses may be able to utilize inexpensive lab and office space at one of several technology business incubators throughout the state. These incubators typically offer administrative and consulting services to their tenants.

Technology Transfer Program: Businesses may be able to partner with an academic institution, facilitating the transfer of new technology from research to commercial application.

Technology Help Desk Hotline: Businesses may take advantage of a one-stop Technology Help Desk Hotline, 1-800-4321-TEC. The hotline offers answers to business and technology questions as well as financial advice, referrals to sources of commercialization assistance, help with research and development grant proposals, and advice on using a statewide and national network of business development resource organizations.

The New Jersey Economic Development Authority's Finance Finder: Helps match companies with appropriate finance programs administered by the NJEDA.

Technology Centre of New Jersey: State-of-the-art, affordable laboratory production and research facilities are available for emerging and advanced technology driven companies.

Consulting Assistance for Manufacturers Impacted By Imports: Manufacturers who can demonstrate that their employment and either sales or production have declined due to foreign competition of a like or similar product may be eligible for consulting assistance.

Business Financing

Bond Financing: Bonds are issued to provide long-term loans at attractive, below-market interest rates for real estate acquisitions, equipment, machinery, building construction, and renovations. Minimum loan size is approximately $1 million. Maximum tax-exempt bond amount for manufacturers is $10 million.

Statewide Loan Pool For Business: Loans from $50,000 up to $3 million for fixed assets and up to $500,000 for working capital are available to businesses that create or maintain jobs in a financially targeted municipality or represent a targeted industry such as manufacturing, industrial, or agricultural. Assistance usually will not exceed $35,000 per job created or maintained.

Business Employment Incentive Program (BEIP) Grant: Businesses creating at least 25 new jobs in designated urban areas, or 75 jobs elsewhere, may be eligible to receive a BEIP grant. These grants, which may last for up to 10 years, may be for up to 80% of the value of the income taxes withheld annually from the paychecks of new employees.

Loan Guarantees: Guarantees of conventional loans of up to $1 million for working capital and guarantees of conventional loans or bond issues for fixed assets of up to $1.5 million are available to credit worthy businesses that need additional security to obtain financing. Preference is given to businesses that are either job intensive, will create or maintain tax ratables, are located in an economically distressed area, or represent an important economic sector of the state and will contribute to New Jersey's growth and diversity.

Direct Loans: Loans are made for up to $500,000 for fixed assets and up to $250,000 for working capital for up to 10 years to businesses that are unable to get sufficient bank credit on their own or through the Statewide Loan Pool or with and EDA guarantee. Preference is given to job-intensive enterprises located in economically targeted areas or representing a targeted business sector.

New Jersey Seed Capital Program: Loans are made from $25,000 to $200,000 at a market rate of interest for working capital and fixed assets to technology businesses that have risked their own capital to develop new technologies and need additional funds to bring their products to market.

New Jersey Technology Funding Program: EDA participates with commercial banks to make term loans from $100,000 to $3 million for second stage technology enterprises.

Fund For Community Economic Development: Loans and loan guarantees are made to urban-based community organizations that in turn make loans to micro-enterprises and small businesses which may not qualify for traditional bank financing.

Urban Centers Small Loans: Loans ranging from $5,000 - $50,000 are available to existing retail and commercial businesses located in the commercial district of a targeted municipality.

Local Development Financing Fund: Loans ranging from $50,000 to $2 million may be made for fixed assets form commercial and industrial projects located in Urban Aid communities.

Hazardous Discharge Site Remediation Loan and Grant Program: Businesses may qualify for loans of up to $1 million for remediation activities due to a closure of operations or transfer of ownership.

Petroleum Underground Storage Tank Remediation Upgrade and Closure Program: Owners/operators may qualify for 100% of the eligible project costs.

Small Business Loans: Loans and loan guarantees administered by the New Jersey Economic Development Authority's Community Development and Small Business Lending Division.

The New Jersey Redevelopment Authority (NJRA): An independent state financing agency whose mission is to focus on investing in neighborhood-based redevelopment projects. NJRA offers low and no-interest loans, loan guarantees, equity investment and technical assistance to eligible businesses and municipalities. Contact: New Jersey Redevelopment Authority, 50 W. State St., P.O. Box 790, Trenton, NJ 08625; 609-292-3739; {www.state.nj.us/njra}.

New Jersey Economic Development Authority's Investment Banking Division: Loans may be available for the purchase of manufacturing equipment.

R&D Excellence Grant Program: Businesses may receive financial support for research and development in critical fields, such as healthcare (especially biomaterials, pharmaceuticals, and biotechnologies), software/information, and environmental and civil infrastructure technologies.

Very young technology enterprises may be eligible to receive seed-stage investments ranging from $50,000 to $1.5 million. Contact the managing partners of Early Stage Enterprises, LP, Mr. Ronald R. Hahn (e-mail rrhahn@aol.com) and Mr. James J. Millar (e-mail jimmillar@aol.com), or call ESE at 609-921-8896, Fax 609-921-8703. Such investments may also be available through the New Jersey Seed Capital Program.

Small Business Innovation Research Grants: Applicants for federal grants may receive technical consulting and bridge loans.

Edison Venture Fund: Provides funding assistance to high-technology companies in New Jersey. This private enterprise enjoys a close relationship with the State of New Jersey, having been selected through a competitive process to manage certain funds on behalf of the New Jersey Economic Development Authority. Contact: Edison Venture Fund, 1009 Lenox Dr. #4, Lawrenceville, NJ 08648; 609-896-1900; {www.edisonventure.com}.

New Jersey Redevelopment Authority and the New Jersey Economic Development Authority's Commercial Lending Division: Businesses and municipalities involved in urban redevelopment may be eligible for low- and no-interest loans, loan guarantees, equity investments, and technical assistance.

New Jersey Redevelopment Authority and the New Jersey Economic Development Authority's Community Development and Small Business Lending Division: Loans, loan guarantees, equity investments, and technical assistance may be available to finance investments in neighborhood-based redevelopment projects, small business lending, renovation, relocation, and/or real estate development in urban areas.

Business Relocation Assistance Grant: Provides grants to relocating companies that create a minimum of 25 new full-time jobs in New Jersey.

Tax Incentives

Urban Enterprise Zones: Provide significant incentives and benefits to qualified businesses located within their borders. Such benefits include sales tax to customers (3% instead of 6%), corporation tax credits for the hiring of certain employees, and subsidized unemployment insurance costs.

No net worth tax, no business personal property tax, no commercial rent or occupancy tax and no retail gross receipts tax.

Property Tax Abatements and Exemptions: Available for commercial and industrial properties in areas in need or redevelopment.

New Jobs Investment Tax Credit: Companies that make certain investments in new or expanded business facilities that are directly related to the creation of new jobs may be eligible for credits.

Manufacturing Equipment and Employment Investment Tax Credit: Certain investments made by companies for manufacturing equipment with a recovery life of four years or more are eligible for a credit.

Recognition of Subchapter S Status for Corporations: S corporations are provided a reduced corporation tax rate.

Research and Development Tax Credit for Corporation Business Tax: Businesses may be eligible for a credit for certain increased research expenditures in the state.

Exports

International Trade Services: Services include financing assistance, strategic advocacy in foreign markets, opportunities to network and receive information and advice regarding international commerce, and assistance in taking advantage of federal international trade programs and Foreign Trade Zones.

Export Financing: Up to a $1 million one-year revolving line of credit will be provided to finance confirmed foreign orders to assist businesses that want to enter the export market or expand export sales but are unable to do so because they cannot get the financing they need on their own.

Foreign Trade Zones: Within these zones, which are outside U.S. Customs territory, businesses may manufacture, assemble, package, process and exhibit merchandise with a substantial duty and cash flow savings.

Women and Minorities

New Jersey Department of Commerce and Economic Development
Division of Development for Small Businesses and Women and Minority Businesses
CN 835
Trenton, NJ 08625
609-292-3860
Fax: 609-292-9145

Services For Businesses Owned By Women And Minorities: Businesses owned by women and minorities play an important role in the New Jersey economy. New Jersey offers a number of services to help these businesses compete and overcome the special challenges they face. These services include financial assistance, advice and instructional materials, training and education, and certification necessary to receive certain contracts.

Set Aside Contracts: State law requires that 7% of the contracts awarded by the State be given to businesses owned by minorities, and 3% to businesses owned by women. In the first half of 1998, these "set-aside contracts" amounted to more than $180 million.

Women and minorities interested in establishing franchise businesses may receive investments from the Small Business Investment Company, which works in conjunction with the New Jersey Economic Development Authority's Commercial Lending Division.

Contractors Assistance Program: Small contracting businesses owned by women or minorities may receive training courses and consultations with experienced executives of large construction companies designed to make it easier to get performance bonds and successfully bid on major construction projects. This service is provided by the New Jersey Economic Development Authority's Community Development and Small Business Lending Division.

New Jersey Development Authority For Small Businesses, Minorities' And Women's Enterprises: This office offers women and minority-owned small businesses financial, marketing, procurement, technical and managerial assistance. Loans of up to $1 million can be made for real estate, fixed asset acquisition, and working capital. Guarantees to banks are also available for fixed asset acquisition and for working capital. To be eligible, a business must be certified as a small, minority-owned or women-owned enterprise. Most of the funds are targeted to enterprises located in Atlantic City or providing goods or services to customers in Atlantic City, including but not limited to the casinos. Limited monies are available for businesses located in other parts of the state.

New Mexico

Economic Development Department
Joseph M. Montoya Bldg.
1100 St. Francis Drive
Santa Fe, NM 87505-4147
505-827-0170
800-374-3061
Fax: 505-827-0407
www.edd.state.nm.us

Business Assistance

Technology Ventures Corporation: Promotes the commercialization of technology. Offers technical, business and management assistance for its clients. Contact: Technology Ventures Corporation, 1155 University Blvd. SE, Albuquerque, NM 87106; 505-246-2882.

Technology: New Mexico offers a wide range of assistance for technology-oriented companies such as research centers, partnerships with universities, and facility use.

Business Financing

ACCION: A private non-profit organization that extend microloans to small business entrepreneurs designed to help home-based and other self-employed people grow to be self sufficient. Contact: ACCION New Mexico, 219 Central NW, #620, Albuquerque, NM 87102; 505-243-8844.

Advanced Technology Program (ATP): Provides cost shared-funding to select industries for high-risk research and development projects that have the potential to launch important broad-based economic benefits to the U.S. economy.

Airport Improvement Program (AIP): Supports the development and improvement of airports in an effort to create a nationwide airport system capable of supporting the nation's civil air travel.

Albuquerque Development Capital Program: Provides loan guarantees and interest supplements for acquisition of real property, purchase of fixed assets and/or working capital purposes. Contact: City of Albuquerque, Economic Development Department, P.O. Box 1293, Albuquerque, NM 87103; 505-768-3270.

Business Participation Loans: The State Investment Council may invest a portion of the Severance Tax Permanent Fund in real property related business loans. There is a minimum of $500,000 and a maximum of $2 million.

Cibola Foundation Revolving Loan Fund: A variety of financial incentives offered to encourage economic development in Cibola County. Contact: Cibola Communities, Economic Development Foundation Inc., P.O. Box 277, Grants, NM 87020; 505-285-6604.

Community Development Loan Fund: Provides loans to businesses and organizations that have tangible benefits for low-income people. Typical loans are from $5,000 to $25,000. Contact: NM Community Development Loan Fund, P.O. Box 705, Albuquerque, NM 87103; 505-243-3196.

Community Foundation: Offers small grants, technical assistance, "capacity building" workshops, and serves as a convener around important issues for nonprofit organizations, communities and people throughout New Mexico, especially in rural areas.

FSA Farmer Programs: Guarantees loans made by agricultural lenders for family farmers and ranchers for farm ownership, improvements and operating purposes. The FSA describes a family farm as one which a family can operate and manage itself. Guarantee of up to $300,000 for farm ownership, water and soil loans; and $400,000 for operating loans. The maximum guarantee is 90%.

Industrial Development Training Program: Provides funds for classroom or on-the-job training to prepare New Mexico residents for employment. Trainee wages are reimbursed to the company at 50% during hours of training; 65% in rural New Mexico. Instructional costs involving classroom training will be reimbursed to the educational institution at 100% of all costs outlined in the training contract.

Job Training Partnership Act (JTPA): A federally funded program intended to provide job training assistance to both eligible employees and employers. Employers can receive financial reimbursement of up to 50% of the costs associated with hiring and training JTPA eligible employees.

ilagro Fund: Programs designed to promote economic development opportunities for organizations which utilize natural resources, involve small scale growers or producers, strengthen traditional skills in agriculture and production, or defend land and water rights. Funds are available to facilitate problem identification, provide training in community organizing, and to improve business skills and production techniques.

North Central New Mexico Economic Development Revolving Loan Fund: Provides loans up to $100,000 to assist small businesses in the creation and/or saving of jobs in economically disadvantaged areas. Contact: North Central New Mexico Economic Development Revolving Loan Fund, P.O. Box 5115, Santa Fe, NM 87502; 505-827-7313.

RD Housing Preservation Grants: Grants to tribes, political subdivisions and other non-profit entities to enable them to rehabilitate housing owned and occupied by very-low and low-income rural persons.

RD Rural Business Enterprise Grant Program: The purpose of the program is to support the development of small and emerging private business enterprise in rural areas under 50,000 in population, or more and adjacent urbanized areas. Priority is given to applications for projects in rural communities of 25,000 in population and under.

RD Guaranteed Business and Industry Program: The purpose of the program is to improve, develop or finance business, industry and employment, and improve the economic and environmental climate in rural communities (under 50,000 population) and non-urbanized or non-urbanizing areas. This is achieved by bolstering the existing private credit structure through the guarantee of quality loans that will provide lasting community benefits.

Severance Tax Loan Program: New Mexico can purchase up to $20 million of bonds, notes, debentures or other evidence of indebtedness, excluding commercial paper, whose proceeds are used for the establishment or expansion of business outlets or ventures located in state.

Tax Incentives

Aerospace Research and Development Deduction: The Aerospace Research and Development tax deduction was implemented to facilitate the location of a spaceport in New Mexico.

Agriculture-Related Tax Deductions/Exemptions: Feed and fertilizer, warehousing, threshing, harvesting, growing, cultivating and processing agricultural products, agricultural products.

Compensating Tax Abatement: "Compensating tax" is an excise tax imposed for the privilege of using property in New Mexico. In New Mexico it is called gross receipts tax for purchases made within the state. For purchases made outside New Mexico and imported into the state, it is called compensating tax. Abatement of the state's portion of any sales, gross receipts, compensating or similar tax on machinery and equipment, and other movable personal property for an eligible facility. In New Mexico construction or rehabilitation of non-speculative office buildings, warehouses, manufacturing facilities, and service oriented facilities not primarily engaged in the sale of goods or commodities at retail are eligible.

Enterprise Zones: The Enterprise Zone Act is designed to stimulate the creation of new jobs and to revitalize economically distressed areas. $50,000 tax credit to property owners for the rehabilitation of qualified business facilities, technical assistance, training reimbursement, and other benefits.

Filmmakers Gross Receipts Tax Incentive: Implemented to facilitate the filming of movies, television shows and commercials in New Mexico. A qualified production company may execute nontaxable transaction certificates with its suppliers for tangible personal property or services. The suppliers may then deduct their receipts from the gross receipts tax.

Historic Preservation Tax Credit Program: Offers a maximum tax credit of 20% of the substantial rehabilitation of historic buildings for commercial, industrial and rental residential purposes, and a 10% credit for substantial rehabilitation for non-residential purposes for structures built before 1936.

Indian Employment Credit: Provides for a tax credit to employers of Indians on Indian lands to encourage economic development. The maximum credit per employee is $4,000.

Low-income Housing Tax Credit Program (LIHTC): This program can be used for new construction and/or rehabilitation of rental units. The annual credit equals a fixed percentage of the project's total cost.

Modified Accelerated Cost Recovery System: Provides for a favorable deduction for property on Indian lands to encourage economic development. Capital outlays for depreciable business or income-producing property are recoverable through the depreciation deduction allowances. A business that acquires property for use in the business is entitled to deduct the cost of the property over time for the purposes of computing income tax liability.

Cultural Property Preservation Tax Credit: Property owners are eligible to receive a personal or corporate tax credit for restoring, rehabilitating or otherwise preserving cultural properties. Specifically, a tax credit is available where historic structures are certified as having received rehabilitation to preserve and enhance their historic character. Offers a maximum tax credit of 50% of the cost of restoration, rehabilitation or preservation up to $25,000.

Gross Receipts Tax Deduction: Equipment that goes into a plant financed with industrial revenue bonds is exempt for the gross receipts or compensating tax of 5%.

Interstate Telecommunications Gross Receipts Tax Exemption: This program exempts receipts from the provision of wide area telephone services (WATS) and private communications services from the interstate telecommunications gross receipts tax. Wide-area telephone service means a telephone service that entitles a subscriber to either make or receive large volumes of communications to or from persons in specified geographical areas.

Investment Tax Credit Program: Provides a general incentive for manufacturers to locate in New Mexico and to hire New Mexicans. Equipment is eligible if essential, used directly and exclusively in a manufacturing facility, and depreciated for federal income tax purposes. The creation of new, full time jobs is required to qualify for the credit. The credit allows the manufacturer to offset the amount of compensating tax paid on eligible equipment. The credit equals the amount of compensating tax actually paid, and may be applied against compensating tax, gross receipts tax or withholding tax due.

Preferential Tax Rate for Small Wineries and Breweries: Wine produced by a small winery carries a tax of 10 cents per liter on the first 80,000 liters; 20 cents on production over that level. The basic tax rate for wine is 45 cents per liter. Beer produced by a microbrewery is taxed at 25 cents per gallon. The basic tax rate for beer is 41 cents per gallon.

Property Tax Exemption: For industry financed with industrial revenue bonds, a local government may offer a real and personal property tax exemption of up to 30 years.

Targeted Jobs Tax Credit Program (TJTC): An employer may claim a tax credit equal to 40% of the first $6,000 in wages paid to the worker during the first year of employment for a maximum credit of $2,400 per employee. For economically disadvantaged summer youth, employers may claim a tax credit equal to 40% of the first $3,000 in wages for a maximum credit of $1,200 per employee.

Tax Increment Financing: At the beginning of a project, the valuation of the project properties is summed. As the project proceeds, these properties are developed or otherwise improved, increasing their valuations. The tax proceeds flowing from the increase in valuation may be diverted to finance the project. Tax increment financing in New Mexico is available only in a designated enterprise zone.

Taxpayer's Assistance Program (TAP): Enables home buyers to qualify for a larger mortgage because of reduced tax liabilities.

Property Tax Abatement: Land, buildings and equipment associated with an eligible project are exempt from ad valorem tax, generally to promote economic development.

Exports

Foreign Sales Corporations Tax Incentive Program: Regulations exempt from taxation part of the profit earned on exports, which can be 15% of the net income or 1.2% of gross receipts, whichever is greater.

Export-Import Bank (Eximbank) City/State Program: Assists exporters in accessing federal loan guarantees and credit insurance through the Export/ Import Bank. Eximbank working capital loan guarantees may be used to finance such pre-export activities as the purchase of raw materials, finished products, labor and other services needed for processing export orders. They may also be used to cover the cost of freight, port charges and certain forms of overseas business development. Loan guarantees may be used for a specific transaction or as a revolving line of credit. There are no minimum or maximum amounts of funding.

Foreign Trade Zones: Merchandise in these zones is considered to be outside U.S. Customs territory and is subject to duty only when it leave the zones for consumption in the U.S. Market. New Mexico offers three such zones.

Export Financing Assistance: Often, even the most credit-worthy small and medium-sized businesses find that commercial banks are reluctant to approve their loan request for export financing. The New Mexico Export Finance Team (NMEFT) exists to help such businesses finance their export activities.

International Trade Division: Provides assistance to manufacturing, agricultural and other production concerns in developing their worldwide export capabilities. Services include:
- Export market development counseling
- Foreign trade shows and missions
- Foreign buying and reverse trade missions
- Identifying and disseminating overseas trade leads
- Attracting foreign businesses
- Developing, maintaining and using a database of potential domestic and international customers for New Mexico goods and services.

Women and Minorities

Administration for Native Americans (ANA) Grant: Provides financial assistance through grants or contracts to further the three goals of the ANA: governance, economic development and social development. Technical assistance and training to develop, conduct and administer projects. Funding to public or private agencies to assist local residents in overcoming special obstacles to social and economic development. Maximum Program Benefits: Up to 80% of program cost, however, no set maximum or minimum grant amount.

BankAmerica Foundation - Community Economic Development Initiative: A special grant program targeted toward nonprofit organizations supporting community economic development and the growth of minority businesses. Maximum Program Benefits: Up to $500,000 in cash grants.

Eagle Staff Fund: Seeks to support Native grassroots and tribal organizations that are working to create Native-controlled reservation economies. Promotes economic development through technical assistance and financial resources.

EDA District, Indian and Area Planning Program: Grant assistance to defray administrative expenses in support of the economic development planning efforts of Economic Development Districts, Redevelopment Areas and Indian tribes.

BIA Indian Loan Guarantee Fund: Guaranteed loans that are made by private lenders to eligible applicants for up to 90% of the unpaid principal and interest due. Funds may be used to finance Indian-owned commercial, industrial or business activities organized for profit, provided eligible Indian ownership constitutes at least 51%

of the business. Loans must benefit the economy of an Indian reservation. Also, interest subsidies might be granted when the business is incurring losses. Individual guarantees are limited to $500,000; $5.5 million maximum for tribes or organizations.

Navajo Business and Industrial Development Fund: Provides loans or loan guarantees to qualified Navajo individuals or Navajo-owned businesses. The program is intended to foster the establishment of new businesses or the expansion of existing businesses within the Navajo Nation's territorial jurisdiction. Minimum loan is $10,000; maximum loan is $100,000. Loan not to exceed 90% of purchase price of assets, or 95% of value of permanent improvements on a reservation site.

Women's Economic Self-Sufficiency Team: Provides consulting, training and support programs as well as financial assistance (loans). For more information, contact WESST Corp., 414 Silver SW, Albuquerque, NM 87102; 505-848-4760; Fax: 505-241-4766.

New York

Empire State Development
One Commerce Plaza
Albany, NY 12245
518-474-7756
800-STATE-NY
www.empire.state.ny.us

633 Third Ave.
New York, NY 10017
212-803-3100

Business Assistance

Small Business Division: Offers fast, up-to-date information on the State's economic development programs and can help in making contact with appropriate agencies in such areas as financing, job training, technical assistance, etc.

Small Business Advocacy Program: Reviews regulations affecting small business, maintains liaison with small business groups, assists business owners in the regulatory process, assists in expediting innovative business programs and projects, develops and presents workshops, seminars, conferences, and other training programs.

Technical Advisory Services; Provides free, confidential technical assistance concerning compliance to federal and state air quality requirements for small businesses.

Small Business Stationary Source Technical And Environmental Compliance Assistance Program: Provides technical assistance and advocacy services to eligible businesses in achieving environmental regulatory compliance.

Business Ombudsmen Services: Counseling and problem solving assistance to resolve complaints from small businesses concerning interactions with government authorities available to businesses employing 100 or less that are not dominant in their fields.

Entrepreneurial Assistance Program: Referrals of recipients to ESD funded assistance provides classroom instruction and individual counseling, business plan development for minorities, women, dislocated workers, public assistance recipients, public housing recipients and those seeking to start a new business or who have owned a business for five years or less.

Agricultural Business Development Assistance: Technical assistance to help locate public and private funding for food processors and agricultural producers. Contact: New York State Department of Agriculture and Markets, The Winners Circle, Albany, NY 12235; 518-457-7076.

Agricultural Ombudsman Services: Helps agricultural businesses communicate with regulatory agencies.

Food & Agricultural Industry Marketing Assistance: Marketing assistance for agricultural industries including trade shows, information distribution, and export financing.

Apprentice Training Program: Provides on-the-job training for more than 250 skilled occupations. Contact: Apprentice Training Program, Room 223, Bldg. 12, State Office Campus, Albany, NY 12240; 518-457-6820.

Business Development Office: Industrial and manufacturing companies are targeted for a variety of services.

New York State Contract Reporter: Provides listings of contracts made available for bidding by New York State agencies, public benefit corporations, and its public authorities.

Procurement Assistance: Provides technical assistance to businesses seeking to compete for contracts valued at $1,000,000 or more from the state.

Workforce Training: Empire State Development offers financial support and technical resources to companies to offset the cost of employee training.

High Technology Program: The Science and Technology Foundation maintains a mission to create and administer programs that promote scientific and technical education, industrially relevant research and development, manufacturing modernization and the capitalization of high-tech companies. Contact: New York State Science and Technology Foundation, 99 Washington Ave., Suite 1731, Albany, NY 12210; 518-473-9741.

Recycling Assistance: New York State has one of the largest concentrations of recycling companies in the world. Works with companies to demonstrate that, in addition to being an important environmental activity, recycling makes good business sense. To this end, they diagnose the research and development, capital, and marketing needs of recycling companies and tailor-make a package of technical and financial assistance. Identifies new markets and assist companies retooling to reach those markets. Assists companies to implement waste prevention practices.

Technical Assistance: New York State has developed a host of business-friendly products ranging from understanding the federal Clean Air Act and its impact on small business to ownership transition plans that can help a company grow and prosper. A hotline (800-STATE NY) puts business people directly in touch with a business ombudsman. The experts staffing this hotline are ready to answer questions. In addition, they serve as advocates for business.

Ownership Transition Services: Technical assistance.

Rural Employment Program: Recruits workers for farm, landscaping and food processing industries. Contact: Rural Employment Program, Room 282, Bldg. 12, State Office Campus, Albany, NY 12240; 518-457-6798.

Technology Development Organizations; Provides assistance to technology based companies competing for state and federal research and development grant programs, business plan review and development, management, marketing and financial packaging assistance, venture capital assistance, information systems development, technology business development training, incubator facility management and technology transfer services. Contact: Industrial Technology Programs, New York State Science and Technology Foundation, 99 Washington Ave., Suite 1730, Albany, NY 12210; 518-473-9746.

Advanced Controls for Efficiency Program (ACE): Applied research, product design, demonstration and testing, and product commercialization for individuals or enterprises with an innovative, energy-related product.

Business Financing

Financial Services: Companies that plan to locate, expand or modernize their facilities in New York State are eligible for financial assistance. Generally, this assistance supports the acquisition of land and buildings or machinery and equipment. It also can help fund construction or renovation of buildings or the infrastructure and working capital required for the establishment or expansion of an eligible company.
Funds may be available through:
- direct loans to business for a portion of the cost of the project;
- interest rate subsidies to reduce the cost of borrowing from private or public sector financial institutions, in the form of a grant or linked deposit with the lending institution;
- loan guarantees for working capital assistance;
- assistance in the form of a loan and grant combination for a portion of the cost of an infrastructure project.

Economic Development Fund:
1. *Industrial Effectiveness Program*: Direct technical assistance for identifying, developing and implementing improved management and production process and grants to pay the cost of feasibility studies up to $60,000.
2. *Employee Training Assistance*: Offers skills training grant from $15,000 to $25,000.
3. *Commercial Area Development*: Loans, loan guarantees, and grants to improve commercial buildings, commercial strips, downtown areas, and business districts from $75,000 to $100,000.
4. *General Development*: Loans and loan guarantees for manufacturers, non-retail service firms, headquarters facilities of retail firms, retail firms in distressed areas, and businesses developing tourist attractions from $75,000 to $2,000,000.

5. *Infrastructure Development*: Loans and grants for businesses located in distressed areas or a business that develops a tourist attraction from $25,000 to $2,000,000 for construction or renovation of basic systems and facilities.
6. *Capital Access*: For small and medium size businesses including minority and women-owned businesses and day care centers, financing from $100,000 to $300,000.
7. *General Development Financing*: Loans and loan guarantees for manufacturing, non-retail service firms, retail headquarters, retail firms located in distressed areas and businesses which develop recreational, cultural or historical facilities for tourist attractions. Amounts are determined case-by-case.
8. *Competitiveness Improvement Services - Global Export Marketing Service*: Grants up to $5,000 for consulting services to assess organizational and product readiness for exporting. Grants up to $25,000 for an individual business or up to $50,000 for a business or industry group to create market development plans.

Industrial Waste Minimization Program: Technical assistance and grants up to $50,000 to assist, develop, and demonstrate energy-efficient methods to reduce, reuse, or recycle industrial wastes at the point of generation. Contact: NYS Energy Research and Development Authority, Corporate Plaza West, 286 Washington Ave. Extension, Albany, NY 12203; 518-862-1090, ext. 3206.

Environmental Finance Corporation: Grants for resource recovery facilities, solid waste disposal facilities, hazardous waste treatment facilities, Brownfields redevelopment, water supply and management facilities and sewage treatment works.

Recycling Investment Program: Technical assistance funding up to $75,000, capital project funding up to $300,000, research, development and demonstration project funding up to $100,000 for firms seeking to improve productivity and competitiveness by reducing solid waste and using recovered materials.

Energy Products Center: Product development demonstration and commercialization costs for technology-related businesses.

Retail and Office Development Assistance: Loans up to $5,000,000 for projects that retain or create significant numbers of private sector jobs in economically distressed areas.

Venture Capital Fund: High Tech entrepreneurs, companies with technologies ready for market, and leading-edge enterprises each have different needs for investment capital. New York State has the seed and growth capital that will enable a high tech business to grow. The Small Business Technology Investment Fund program (SBTIF) is a source of early-stage debt and equity funding for high tech companies. Initial investments range as much as $300,000 and later stage investment up to $500,000. New York State is banking on a strong high tech future.

Transportation Capital Assistance Program: Loans up to $1,000,000 for small business enterprises and NYS-certified minority and women-owned business enterprises that have transportation-related construction contracts.

Commercial District Revolving Loans Trust Fund: Loans up to $15,000 for retail, professional or commercial service for profit businesses with 50 or fewer full-time employees.

Metropolitan Economic Revitalization Fund: Loans, capital access and linked deposits up to $5,000,000 for businesses and non-profits located in economically distressed area.

Regional Revolving Loan Trust Fund: Loans and loan guarantees up to $80,000 for businesses employing fewer than 100 people.

Small Business Technology Investment Fund: For small technology based companies, financing from $25,000 to $500,000 for seed or capital.

Job Development Authority: Loans to small and medium sized businesses in manufacturing and services from $50,000 to $1,500,000.

Jobs Now Program: Capital loans and grants to private businesses creating at least 300 new full time jobs not to exceed $10,000 per job.

Linked Deposit Program: Interest rate subsidies to a variety of businesses seeking to improve competitiveness and performance up to $1,000,000.

Commercial District Revolving Loan Trust Fund: Loans up to $20,000 to businesses with 50 or fewer employees.

Empowerment Zone Program: Triple tax exempt bond financing up to $3,000,000 per zone for a variety of businesses located within a zone.

EMPOWERMENT ZONES

Enterprise Communities: Triple tax exempt bond financing up to $3,000,000 per community.

Economic Development through Greater Energy Efficiency: Grants and technical support for detailed engineering studies of manufacturing operations up to $50,000. Capital financing for demonstrations for energy efficient process technology up to $250,000. Contact: NYS Energy Research and Development Authority, Corporate Plaza West, 286 Washington Ave. Extension, Albany, NY 12203; 518-262-1090, ext. 3257.

Centers for Advanced Technology: Financial and technical assistance for commercially relevant research, technology transfer to industry, start up of new companies to commercialize research results, and incubator space. Amounts are determined case-by-case.

Tax Incentives

Investment Tax Credit: Businesses that make new investments in production property and equipment and create new jobs may qualify for tax credits of up to 10% of their eligible investment.

Research and Development Tax Credit: Investments in research and development facilities are eligible for a 9% tax credit against corporate tax.

Sales Tax Exemptions: Purchases of production machinery and equipment, research and development property, and fuels/utilities used in manufacturing and R&D.

Real Property Tax Abatement

No Personal Property Tax

Economic Development Zones: New York State has currently designated 52 economically distressed areas - certified as Economic Development Zones. They want to encourage the creation of jobs in these areas. In a zone they offer an investment tax credit of up to 19 percent. They can provide a tax break of up to 25% for new investors in these areas. They offer a host of benefits to make doing business easier, ranging from discounts on electric power to wage tax credits for new employees. They also have set aside Zone Equivalent Areas for special tax credits.

Empowerment Zone Program: Wage tax credits for businesses in severely distressed areas.

Pollution Control Facilities: Facilities are exempt from local real property taxes and ad valorem levies.

Commercial and Industrial Facilities: Property tax exemptions of up to 50% .

Corporate Franchise Tax Allocation Percentage: Business corporations are subject to tax only on the portion of their activities that are deemed to be attributable to their activities in New York State.

Credits for Bank Corporation Tax: For corporations which service mortgages acquired by the New York State Mortgage Agency, the credit is equal to the amount paid for the special recording tax on mortgages recorded after 1/1/79.

- *Credits for Insurance Corporation Tax*: Credits for additional taxes of premiums written on premiums. Credit of up to 90% or retaliatory taxes paid to the state by New York domiciled or organized insurers.
- Credit equaling the amount paid in the special additional mortgage recording tax. Credit for a portion of the cost of assessments paid to the Life Insurance Company Guaranty Corporation up to $40 million or 40% of the total tax liability.

International Banking Facility: A deduction for the adjusted net income for banking corporations that establish international banking facilities in New York to accept deposits from and make loans to foreign customers.

Retail Enterprise Credit: Investment tax credit for rehabilitation expenditures of a retail facility.

Exports

Empire State Development: International market experts help a company enter and expand in the global economy. Offers a step-by-step analysis of a company's capabilities and matches them with the demands of the international marketplace. If a company has what the global marketplace needs, they will work with that company to find the niche, the spot on the globe where they can sell. Then, they will assist them in determining how to reach those markets. They provide information about tariffs, industry specifications and government regulations. They can put a company in touch with representatives, distributors, agents and strategic allies to sell a product or service abroad.

- Assistance in identifying foreign sales agent or distributor
- Matching grants of up to $5,000 to assess product sales potential in foreign markets
- Matching grants of up to $25,000 to assist in creating export market development plans
- Low cost participation in international trade shows.

Women and Minorities

Division of Minority and Women's Business Development: Administers, coordinates, and implements a statewide program to assist the development of M/WBE's and facilitate their access to state contracting opportunities. Through the process of certification, the agency is responsible for verifying minority and women-ownership and control of firms participating in the program.

Division of Minority and Women's Business Development Lending Program: Loans up to $7,000 from the Microenterprise Loan Fund and up to $50,000 from the Minority and Women Revolving Loan Trust Fund.

North Carolina

Department of Commerce
Commerce Finance Center
301 N. Wilmington St.
P.O. Box 29571
Raleigh, NC 27626-0571
919-733-4977
Fax: 919-715-9265
www.commerce.state.nc.us/

Business Assistance

Retention and Expansion Programs: Professional assistance is provided for all aspects of business including environmental consultation, financing alternative, human resources consulting, marketing information, energy process surveys and other issues that impact business and industry.

Master License Application Program: Offers the business applicant a streamlined approach to applying for required business licenses.

Industrial Extension Service: Provides technical and industrial management assistance, conducts applied research, advocates industrial use of technology and modern managerial practices, as well as conducts continuing education programs for business, industry, entrepreneurs, engineers and local governments.

Biotechnology Center: Carries out a variety of programs and activities strengthening North Carolina's biotechnology community. NC Biotechnology Center, P.O. Box 13547, 15 TW Alexander Dr., Research Triangle Park, NC 27709; 919-541-9366; {www.ncbiotech.org}.

MCNC: A private nonprofit corporation that supports advanced education, research and technology programs to enhance North Carolina's technology infrastructure and businesses. Contact: MCNC, 3201 Cornwallis Rd., P.O. Box 12889, Research Triangle Park, NC 27709; 919-248-1800; {www.mcnc.org}.

Industrial Training Program: State funded customized job training programs for new and expanding industries that create 12 or more new jobs in a community within one year.

Small Business and Technology Development Center: Organized as an inter-institutional program of The University of North Carolina, the Small Business and Technology Development Center (SBTDC) is the primary organization through which the state of North Carolina provides counseling and technical assistance to the business community. SBTDC services are well-defined and designed to meet client needs. The primary focus is in-depth, one-on-one, confidential counseling. Assistance is provided, free of charge, to the small business owner or aspiring entrepreneur. As the only full service counseling resource statewide, the SBTDC helps with the myriad of tasks facing a business owner, including:
- assessing the feasibility of a business idea
- preparing a business plan
- finding sources of capital
- developing marketing strategies
- operations and human resource management

For more information, contact Small Business and Technology Development Center, 333 Fayetteville Street Mall, Suite 1150, Raleigh, NC 27601; 919-715-7272; 800-258-0862 (NC only); {www.sbtdc.org}.

SBTDC Special Market Development Assistance:

- *Procurement Technical Assistance Program*: The SBTDC provides comprehensive assistance in selling goods and services to the federal government. Services include help in finding out about contracting opportunities, preparing bid and proposal packages, obtaining 8(a) certification, interpreting regulations, and resolving contract administration problems. An integral part of this program is PRO-BID, a computer-based bid matching service that provides accurate and timely information on procurement opportunities.
- *International Business Development*: North Carolina businesses are increasingly looking at exporting as a vehicle to increase sales and profits. The SBTDC helps successful domestic, new-to-export businesses to identify, target and then penetrate foreign markets. SBTDC counselors provide marketing research information, assist with market planning, and then identify implementation procedures.
- *The Technology Group*: Part of the SBTDC's mission is to help emerging businesses commercialize innovative new technologies, and to facilitate the transfer of technology developed within the small business and university communities. Technology Group services include assistance in maritime technology transfer, identifying markets for scientific discoveries, guiding the development of strategies to protect intellectual property and providing referrals to specialized organizations and resources.
- *Marine Trades Program*: The SBTDC's Marine Trades Program provides business development support to marine industry firms. Specific services include assistance in marketing marine products and services, complying with environmental regulations, and maintaining safe operations. The program also provides marine specific training, education and research.

Business Financing

Industrial Revenue Bonds: Revenue Bonds have a variety of names and purposes but essentially three basic types exist. These bonds whose proper name is Small Issue Industrial Development Bonds are referred to as Industrial Revenue Bond's (IRB's). The state's principal interest in these bonds is assisting new and expanding industry while insuring that North Carolinians get good jobs at good wages. The regulations governing bond issuance are a combination of federal regulations and North Carolina statutes. The amount each state may issue annually is designated by population. There are three types of bond issuances as follows:

- Tax Exempt - Because the income derived by the bondholder is not subject to federal income tax, the maximum bond amount is $10 million in any given jurisdiction. According to federal regulations, the $10 million total includes the bond amount and capital expenditures over a six-year period going both backwards and forwards three years. The maximum any company may have is $40 million nationwide outstanding at any given period.
- Taxable - They are not exempt from federal tax (they are however exempt from North Carolina tax). The essential difference is that the Taxable bond rate is slightly higher to the borrower and not being subject to the federal volume cap, may exceed $10 million in bond amount.
- Pollution Control/Solid Waste Disposal Bond - These bonds are subject to volume cap although there is no restriction on amount, and the interest on these bonds is federally tax exempt.

Economic Development Category: Projects may involve assistance for public facilities needed to serve the target business, or loans to the private business to fund items such as machinery and equipment, property acquisition or construction. Public facility projects may provide grants of up to 75% of the proposed facility costs, with a 25% cash match to be paid by the local government applicant.

Industrial Development Fund: Purpose is to provide an incentive for jobs creation in the State's most economically distressed counties, also identified as Tier 1, 2, and 3 areas. Funds for the renovation of manufacturing buildings and the acquisition of infrastructure are made available by the Department of Commerce to eligible counties or their local units of government, which apply for the funds on behalf of their existing or new manufacturing businesses. A commitment to create jobs is executed by the benefiting firm. The amount of funds available to participating firms is determined by multiplying the number of jobs committed to be created times $4,000.00, up to a maximum of $400,000.00 or the cost of the project, whichever is less. Of course, the availability of funds also applies.

Business Energy Improvement: Program provides loans between $100,000 and $500,000 to industrial and commercial businesses located or moving to North Carolina. Loans can be financed for up to seven years at interest rates equal to 50% of the average (high and low) T-bill rate for the past year or five percent, whichever is lower. Current rate is 5%, which is the maximum. Funds are provided from a pool of $2,500,000 designated for energy related capital improvement such as cogeneration, energy saving motors, boiler improvements and low energy use lighting. A participating bank will process loans on a first-come-first-served based upon the date of receipt of a letter of credit.

Partnerships for Regional Economic Development: The counties of North Carolina have been organized into seven regional partnerships for economic development. North Carolina's regional partnerships will enable regions to compete effectively for new investment and to devise effective economic development strategies based on regional opportunities and advantages.

North Carolina SBTDC Small Business Innovation Research (SBIR): Program is a highly competitive three-phase award system which provides qualified small businesses with opportunities to propose innovative ideas that meet specific research and research and development needs of the Federal government. Phase I is a feasibility study to evaluate the proposed project's technical merit for which an awardee may receive a maximum of $100,000 for approximately six months. Phase II is the principal R&D effort which expands on the Phase I results. This two-year project may receive up to $750,000 in funding. Only Phase I awardees are eligible to compete for Phase II funds. Phase III is the commercialization of the Phase II results and moves the innovation from the laboratory to the marketplace. This requires use of private sector or other non-SBIR funding. Contact: Small Business and Technology Development Center, 333 Fayetteville Street Mall, Suite 1150, Raleigh, NC 27601; 919-715-7272; 800-258-0862 (in NC); {www.sbtdc.org}.

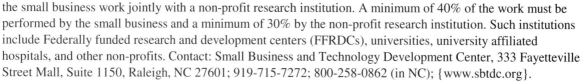

North Carolina SBTDC Small Business Technology Transfer (STTR): STTR is much like that of the Small Business Innovation Research (SBIR) program. Its unique feature is its requirement that the small business work jointly with a non-profit research institution. A minimum of 40% of the work must be performed by the small business and a minimum of 30% by the non-profit research institution. Such institutions include Federally funded research and development centers (FFRDCs), universities, university affiliated hospitals, and other non-profits. Contact: Small Business and Technology Development Center, 333 Fayetteville Street Mall, Suite 1150, Raleigh, NC 27601; 919-715-7272; 800-258-0862 (in NC); {www.sbtdc.org}.

Industrial Access/Road Access Fund: Administered by the Department of Transportation, this program provides funds for the construction of roads to provide access to new or expanded facilities.

The Rail Industrial Access Program: Provides grant funding to aid in financing the cost of constructing or rehabilitating railroad access tracks required by a new or expanded industry which will result in a significant number of new jobs or capital investment.

Tax Incentives

Double-Weighted Sales Factor in Corporate Income Tax: Structured so a business in North Carolina that makes significant sales outside the state would be taxed at a lesser level than a comparable business that is located elsewhere but makes significant sales within North Carolina.

Inventory Tax Exemption: There is no local or state property tax on inventory held by manufacturers, wholesale and retail merchants or contractors.

Computer Software Tax Exemptions: There are no local or state sales taxes on custom computer programs. Additionally, there is no property tax on computer software.

Recycling Equipment: Equipment or facilities installed for the purpose of recycling solid waste or resource recovery from solid waste receives the same treatment under the tax laws as that given to pollution abatement equipment described below.

Pollution Abatement Equipment: Property used to reduce air or water pollution receives special treatment under the tax law if the Board of Environmental Management certifies that the property complies with the requirements of the Board.

OSHA Equipment: The cost of equipment and facilities mandated by the Occupational Safety and Health Act may be amortized over 60 months for income tax purposes.

Equipment to Reduce Hazardous Waste: Equipment and facilities acquired for the purpose of reducing the volume of hazardous waste generated may be amortized over a period of 60 months for income tax purposes.

Jobs Creation Tax Credit: Provides a tax credit for creating jobs based on the number of jobs created and the location of the business.

Investment Tax Credit: Available to eligible companies that invest in machinery and equipment and based on the amount of machinery purchased.

Worker Training Tax Credit: Up to a 50% credit against eligible training expenses if the firm provides training for 5 or more employees. Maximum credit is $1,000 per employee.

Research and Development Tax Credit: A line item tax credit taken by an eligible company.

Business Property Tax Credit: Equals 4.5% of tangible personal business property capitalized under the tax code, up to a maximum single-year credit of $4,500.

Central Administrative Office Tax Credit: Available to companies who have purchased or leased real property in North Carolina to be used as a central administrative office for the company. Maximum credit is $500,000.

Ports Authority Wharfage and Handling Charges: Both importers and exporters who use the North Carolina ports can apply and qualify for a tax credit up to 50% of the total state tax liability for each tax year.

Credit for Construction of Cogenerating Power Plants: Any corporation that constructs a cogenerating power plant in North Carolina is allowed a credit equal to 10% of the costs required to purchase and install the electrical or mechanical power generation equipment of that plant.

Credit for Conversion of Industrial Boiler to Wood Fuel; Any corporation that modifies or replaces an oil or gas-fired boiler or kiln and the associated fuel and residue-handling equipment used in the manufacturing process of a manufacturing business in North Carolina with a furnace capable of burning wood is permitted a credit equal to 15% of the installation and equipment costs resulting from such a conversion.

Credit for Construction of a Peat Facility: Any corporation that constructs a facility in North Carolina that uses peat as the feedstock for the productions of a commercially manufactured energy source to replace petroleum, natural gas or other nonrenewable energy sources is allowed a credit equal to 20% of the installation and equipment costs of construction.

Sales Tax Exemptions and Discounts: Available for industrial machinery and equipment; coal, coke and fuel oil used in manufacturing; electricity or piped natural gas used in connection with manufacturing; raw materials used for production, packaging, and shipping, as well as things bought for resale; motor vehicles; aircraft, boats, railway cars, and mobile offices; purchases of ingredients or component parts of manufactured products; packaging material that becomes a part of a manufactured product. Contact: NC Department of Revenue, Box 25000, Raleigh, NC 27640; 919-733-3991; {www.dor.state.nc.us/DOR/}.

Exports

Export Ready Program: A series of workshops designed to walk a company through every facet of the export process. In cooperation with the North Carolina Community College Small Business Network, the International Trade Division has made this program available in seven regional centers across the state. The Export Outreach Program is a hard-core, intense program where commitment, preparation and action are instilled as the basis for successful exporting. North Carolina is the only state to offer such a program, which increases the quality and competitiveness of North Carolina products.

Trade Events Program: This program consists of Catalog Shows, Trade Fairs and Trade Mission in carefully selected markets worldwide. The Trade Events Calendar is updated periodically to inform North Carolina companies of these opportunities.

International Trade Division: Because North Carolina companies are prepared and committed prior to entering international markets, North Carolina is recognized in the major trading blocs of the world as one of the most aggressive international business development states in the United States. Senior Trade Specialists of the

International Trade Division represent the three major trading blocks of the world: Europe/Africa/The Middle East, The Americas, and Far East.

Women and Minorities

SBTDC Minority Business Enterprise Development: More businesses are being started by minorities than ever before. While minorities owned only 6% of North Carolina's small businesses in 1987, the number of minority-owned firms in the state jumped by 46% between 1982 and 1987 (U.S. Small Business Administration). Realizing the importance of North Carolina's minority-owned companies to future job creation and economic growth, the SBTDC is committed to providing responsive and effective support to minority business enterprises.

The SBTDC offers specialized market development assistance in the areas of government procurement, international business development, and new product and technology development. The SBTDC provides the strongest counseling resource for minority clients in the state. 25% of the 5,200 clients counseled each year are minority businesses. In addition to extensive business counseling, special focus training programs on topics such as "Equal Access to Credit" & "Minority, Women and Disadvantaged Business Enterprise Certification" are presented periodically across the state. Contact: Small Business and Technology Development Center, 333 Fayetteville Street Mall, Suite 1150, Raleigh, NC 27601; 919-715-7272; 800-258-0862 (in NC); {www.sbtdc.org}.

North Dakota

Department of Economic Development and Finance
1833 East Bismarck Expressway
Bismarck, ND 58504-6708
701-328-5300
Fax: 701-328-5320
TTY: 800-366-6888
www.growingnd.com

Business Assistance

Department of Economic Development and Finance (ED&F): This office can provide information and expertise in dealing with state, federal, and local agencies. They also have information on financing programs and other services offered by the state government.

Technology Transfer, Inc.: Serves as a liaison between ED&F, the North Dakota University System and entrepreneurs and manufacturers. The North Dakota University System provides services that help stimulate, produce and sell new ideas. Services include outreach programs designed to discover new technology; design, licensing, and patenting technical help; business development assistance; and production engineering.

North Dakota Manufacturing Technology Partnership (MTP): Approximately 400 targeted manufacturers in the state will be able to receive direct assistance from dedicated manufacturing specialists experienced in manufacturing and will be able to access other appropriate assistance through managed referrals. Manufacturers can expect benefits from improved manufacturing processes; enhanced management skills; better business practices; research and development funding and technical assistance; expanded market opportunities; defense conversion assistance; new product development resources; better trained staff; intercompany working relationships; increased revenue; and increased profit.

Community Economic Development Team: Guides communities through an intensive community inventory, a public input phase, and an ongoing process of business retention, new business start-up and recruitment. Community Services Team helps communities and counties by:
- Helping them assess the level of local interest in economic development.
- Helping them understand and assess their strengths and weaknesses.
- Identifying an organization or group of people in the community who will coordinate local development.
- Helping citizens understand the process of economic development and their role in it.
- Helping to identify community leaders and financial resources available for economic development.

Research and Information Services: A broad program to strengthen economic development efforts statewide. Its major responsibilities are:
- Responding to requests from businesses seeking to grow and wish to learn more about opportunities in North Dakota.
- Helping identify new economic development opportunities.
- Exploring ways to enhance the state's and community's climate for business growth and investment.
- Providing services that assist economic developers in conducting research, accessing and using information.
- Information Fulfillment System (IFS) which is customer driven and includes all of the systems and processes used by the Team to better manage the information needed to provide quality communications, responses and services to both external and internal clients.

Center for Innovation at University of North Dakota: Provides comprehensive, hands-on assistance for technology entrepreneurs, innovators, and manufacturers interested in starting up new ventures, commercializing new products, and licensing university technologies. Contact: Center for Innovation, UND Rural Technology Center, 4300 Dartmouth Dr., P.O. Box 8372, Grand Forks, ND 58202; 701-777-3132; {www.innovators.net}.

Rural Technology Incubator: Located in the Center for Innovation, the Rural Technology Incubator is designed to provide a seedbed to help innovators and entrepreneurs grow their businesses. Their highly diversified staff assists startups by providing them with supportive, creative places in which to work as a team. Located next to the University of North Dakota campus, the Rural Technology Incubator offers university talent, technology, training, and technical assistance to help business startups develop and test-market new products, ideas, technologies, and ventures. Contact: Center for Innovation, UND Rural Technology Center, 4300 Dartmouth Dr., P.O. Box 8372, Grand Forks, ND 58202; 701-777-3132; {www.innovators.net}.

Skills & Technology Training Center: Located in Fargo. A partnership between NDSU-Fargo, North Dakota State College of Science, and Wahpeton private sector leaders. Contact: Skills and Technology Training Center, 1305 19th Ave. North, Fargo, ND 58102; 701-231-6900; {www.sttc.nodak.edu}.

Job Services North Dakota: Has labor, employment, and other statistical information available. For more information, contact Job Services North Dakota, P.O. Box 5507, Bismarck, ND 58506; 800-732-9787; 701-328-2868; {www.state.nd.us/jsnd/lmi.htm}.

Publications:

North Dakota You Should See Us Now: Information on ND labor, infrastructure, taxes and quality of life targeted to primary sector site selectors.

North Dakota Tax Incentives for Business

Financing North Dakota's Future Brochure: Summary of ND commercial financing programs

Mini-Grants for Research & Development

Business Financing

The North Dakota Development Fund: Provides gap financing for primary sector businesses expanding or relocating in the state. Primary sector is defined as: "an individual, corporation, partnership or association which, through the employment of knowledge or labor, adds value to a product, process or service that results in the creation of new wealth." Primary sector businesses are typically considered to be manufacturing, food processing, and exported services. Types of investments include equity, debt, and other forms of innovative financing up to a limit of $300,000. One of the criteria for dollars invested is projected job creation within 24 months of funding.

Technology Transfer, Inc.: Provides leadership and funding to bring new technology developed in North Dakota to the marketplace. TTI is the only resource in North Dakota for high-risk research and development. A vital source for R&D funds, TTI invests financial resources in North Dakota companies and inventors. Individuals or companies with marketable ideas for products or manufacturing processes may use TTI funds to evaluate the product or process to find out if it has any commercial potential. They may also use TTI funds for expenses such as market research, prototyping, product testing, patenting, test marketing, and business plan development. The maximum amount allowed for each project is $100,000. TTI expects repayment through royalties if the product or process is successfully commercialized. Typically, royalties are based on gross sales, usually between 3 and 5 percent. TTI then reinvests these funds in other viable projects. If a funded project fails, TTI expects no repayment.

Agricultural Products Utilization Commission: Mission is to create new wealth and jobs through the development of new and expanded uses of North Dakota agricultural products. The commission accomplishes its mission through the administration of a grant program.

Basic and Applied Research Grants: This program centers on research efforts that focus on the uses and processing of agricultural products and by-products. Further, consideration is given to products which develop an expanded use of technology for the processing of these products.

Marketing & Utilization Grants: Funds from this category are used for the development or implementation of a sound marketing plan for the promotion of North Dakota agricultural products or by-products.

Cooperative Marketing Grants: This category encourages groups of agricultural producers to develop innovative marketing strategies.

Farm Diversification Grants: This category focuses on the diversification of a family farm to non-traditional crops, livestock or non-farm value-added processing of agricultural commodities. Traditional crops and livestock are generally defined as those for which the North Dakota Agricultural Statistics Service maintains records. The proposed project must have the potential to create additional income for the farm unit.

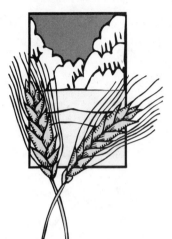

About The One Stop Capital Center: Located at the Bank of North Dakota, the One Stop Capital Center offers one-stop access to over twenty financing programs. Together, the five partners work with local financial institutions and economic developers to offer integrated financial packages. The One Stop Capital Center has loan officers available from each of the agencies who jointly work to streamline the financing process and provide timely service. Contact: Bank of North Dakota, 700 E. Main, 2nd Floor, P.O. Box 5509, Bismarck, ND 58506; 800-544-4674; {http://webhost.btigate.com/ ~onestop}.

Tax Incentives

No personal property tax including equipment, inventory, materials in process or accounts receivable.

Allows the entire amount of federal income tax liability to be deducted before calculating state corporate tax.

County Property Tax Exemptions: Any new or expanding business may be granted an exemption for up to five years. Other possible exemptions include: rehabilitation of buildings more than 25 years old; Geothermal, solar or wind energy systems.

Corporate Tax Credits: A primary sector business such as manufacturing, agricultural processing and back office operations such as telemarketing may qualify for a five-year income tax exemption. Other items that may qualify for corporate tax credits include: research expenditures within the state; seed capital investments; wages and salaries for new businesses.

Sales and Use Tax: New or expanding businesses qualify for an exemption on machinery, building materials and equipment used for manufacturing, processing or recycling. There is no sales tax on electricity, water or money when used for manufacturing purposes.

Exports

International Trade Program: Mission is to increase the number of jobs in North Dakota by helping companies expand their business into foreign markets. Staff counsels companies on export procedures, international marketing, banking and financing. They also provide referrals to translators, customs brokers, consultants and opportunities for participation in international trade show events. Offers a series of international business workshops, titled "Hands-On Training in International Business," to provide North Dakota businesses with the tools to target global markets and expand export opportunities.

Women and Minorities

Women's Business Program assists women:
- by providing counseling and technical assistance for women entrepreneurs
- by maintaining a database of women-owned businesses
- by administering the women's incentive grant program
- by certifying women-owned businesses for federal and state contracting
- by supporting the Women's Business Leadership Council
- by providing information and support through trade shows and conferences
- by serving as an information clearinghouse on economic development service providers.

For more information about Women's Business Program, contact Tara Holt, ND Women's Business Program, 418 East Broadway, Suite 25, Bismarck, ND 58501; 701-258-2251; Fax: 701-222-8071; {email: holt@btigate.com}; {www.growingnd.com/}.

Publications:

North Dakota Women's Business Development Program Packets: Materials on programs, assistance providers and guides for ND women-owned businesses.

Ohio

Ohio Department of Development
P.O. Box 1001
Columbus, OH 43216-1001
614-466-5017
800-345-OHIO
Fax: 614-463-1540
www.odod.state.oh.us

Business Assistance

Small Business Innovation Research (SBIR) Technical Assistance Services: Increases the number of research
contracts won by Ohio companies from eleven participating federal agencies. Provides small businesses with
direct, hands-on assistance in identifying research
topics; guides businesses through the proposal writing
process from design to review; and offers educational
and technical services. Also helps companies prepare
proposals for SBIR Phase I awards of up to $100,000
and Phase II awards up to $500,000.

Business Development Assistance: Assists domestic and
foreign businesses with up-to-date information on
sites, buildings, labor, markets, taxes and financing.
Development specialists act as liaison between the
companies and state/local agencies. Works to
maintain and create Ohio jobs through retention and
expansion of established businesses and attraction of
new businesses; assists local community development organizations and acts as a liaison for communities when
dealing with issues under local control.

Labor Market Information: Measurements of economic conditions. Local and national employment/labor-force data
to aid in market research, business development and planning. Attracts new employers by identifying skilled
workforce. Supplies free information on the training/education available to help workers meet business needs.

Ohio Data Users Center: Census and statistical data; demographic; economic; specific trade, industry and labor
analyses. Develops and disseminates population estimates, projections. Provides tools for better coordinated
decision-making in public/private sectors.

Ohio Procurement Technical Assistance: Free in-depth counseling, technical resources and historical contracting
data, military specifications, financial guidance and advocacy services for federal procurement opportunities.
Increases the federal dollars invested in Ohio; increase job and business market opportunities; increase
awareness of procurement programs and opportunities.

One-Stop Business Permit Center: Supplies new entrepreneurs with information about licenses and permits required
by the State of Ohio; directs callers to proper area for technical, financial and management resources; acts as
advocate for licensing and permit problems.

Buy Ohio Program: Provides marketing consultation for Ohio-made products; assists with promotions, special
events, and media coverage; develops buyer/seller relationships; disseminates program logo and materials.
Builds consumer awareness and support for quality Ohio-made products; creates more business opportunities for
Ohio companies; uses taxpayers' dollars efficiently; helps maintain jobs; develops state and local pride. No
charge for consulting or start-up packet to all Ohio travel-related businesses and organizations.

Edison Technology Centers: Provides businesses with access to state-of-the-art applied research performed in-house
or obtained through linkages with universities, federal laboratories and other institutions; education and training

programs; plant site assessments; technical problem solving; conferences, seminars and other networking opportunities.

Edison Technology Incubators: Low-cost space that reduces operating costs during start-up phase for technology-based businesses; access to business, technical, and professional services, including legal, accounting, marketing, and financial counseling.

Federal Technology Transfer Program: "Gateway" organizations to resources of the federal laboratory system including intellectual property, engineering expertise, facilities, and equipment.

Labor Market Information: Measurements of economic conditions. Local and national employment/labor-force data to aid in market research, business development and planning.

Enterprise Ohio: Matches qualified workers to job opportunities; administers job training programs, including JTP Ohio, the Work Incentive Program and the Veterans Job Training Act.

Business Financing

166 Regional Loan Program: Land and building acquisition, expansion or renovation, and equipment purchase; industrial projects preferred. Up to 40% of total eligible fixed cost ($350,000 maximum); rate negotiable for 5-15 years; equity minimum 10%, bank minimum 25%. Ohio prevailing wage rate applies.

Direct Loan (166 Loan): Land and building acquisition, expansion or renovation, and equipment purchase;

industrial projects preferred. Up to 30% of total eligible fixed cost ($1 million maximum, $350,000 minimum), two-thirds of prime fixed rate for 10-15 years; equity minimum 10%, bank minimum 25%. In distressed areas of the State, preferential rates and terms are available. However, the Director of Development may authorize a higher loan amount or modified terms that address a unique and demonstrated economic development need. Must show repayment and management capabilities; must create one job for every $15,000 received; Ohio prevailing wage rate applies.

Labor/Management Cooperation Program: Enhances relationship between labor and management through regular meetings, seminars, conferences, and work-site labor/management training programs. Creates a stable and positive work environment by nurturing cooperative labor/management relationships and by dispelling negative labor images. Matching grants support community-based area labor/management committees, regional centers for the advancement of labor-management cooperation, and an employee stock ownership assistance program.

Linked Deposit Program: Fixed assets, working capital and refinanced-debt for small businesses, creating or retaining jobs. A similar Agricultural Linked Deposit Program provides funds for Ohio farmers to help meet planning deadlines. 3% below current lending rate fixed for 2 years (possible 2-year extension); bank may then extend term at current rates. (All other sources of funds allowable.) The Agricultural Linked Deposit Program provides up to $100,000 per farm at reduced rate, approximately 4% below borrower's current rate. Must have Ohio headquarters and no divisions out of state, create one job for every $15,000 to $25,000 received, have 150 or fewer employees, be organized for profit, and have bank loan from eligible state depository.

Ohio Enterprise Bond Fund: Land and building acquisition, construction, expansion or renovation, and equipment purchase for commercial or industrial projects between $1 million and $10 million in size. Long-term, fixed rate for up to 16 years; interest rate based on Standard & Poor's A-minus rating, for up to 90% of total project amount.

Revolving Loan Funds: Projects must create or retain jobs; 51% of all jobs must be for persons from low- and moderate-income households; federal prevailing wage rates may apply; and an environmental review covering entire project must be performed. All CDBG guidelines must be met, including documentation of all project aspects. Loan ceiling determined locally or by availability. Available to user or developer, typically at 5% to 7% fixed; flexible term. Appropriate use of federal program income funds determines participation level of community. Projects must create and/or retain jobs and help develop, rehabilitate or revitalize a participating "small city" community. Financing is usually approved for fixed assets related to commercial, industrial or infrastructure.

Ohio Coal Development Program: Financial assistance for clean coal research and development projects. Advances promising technology into the commercial market. Installed technologies will result in cleaner air, better use of by-products, greater demand for Ohio coal and the jobs associated with its production and use. Strong potential also exists for the export of the technologies. For research: up to $75,000 or two-thirds of total project costs (TPC). Pilot and demonstration scale projects: up to $5 million or one-half of TPC for a pilot project, or one-third TPC for demonstration project. Funds can be issued in the form of a grant, loan, or loan guarantee.

Small Business Innovation Research Program (SBIR) Winners' Support System: Offers SBIR winners a wide range of services including: funding between federal Phase I and Phase II awards through the Bridge Grant Program; assistance in identifying potential partners or customers through the Winners' Portfolio; assistance in securing funding for commercialization through Phase III Funding conferences; and access to a network of public and private experts through a Mentor Network.

Scrap Tire Loan and Grant Program: Financing available to scrap tire recyclers who locate or expand in Ohio and who demonstrate that they will create new/reuse scrap tire products.

Defense Adjustment Program: Provides assistance to communities and technology-based companies impacted by economic losses because of company and military base drawdowns, realignments and closures.

Industrial Training Program: Up to 50% funding for orientation, training, and management program; instructional materials, instructor training.

Buckeye Fund Loan Program: Provides direct loans for businesses locating or expanding in Ohio's priority investment areas. Funds may be used for acquisition of land and buildings, new construction, renovation and expansion of existing facilities and acquisition of new or used machinery and equipment. Interest rate is no more than half of prime rate.

Port Authority Bond Reserve Fund: Provides direct financial assistance to eligible port authorities for economic development activities in the areas of manufacturing, distribution and warehousing, research and development, high technology, and commerce or service businesses paying at least the state minimum wage.

Economic Development Program: Provides funding for development and revitalization of local communities for fixed assets related to commercial, industrial or infrastructure.

Pioneer Rural Loan Program: Provides direct loans for businesses locating or expanding in Ohio's rural areas. Must demonstrate that they will create new jobs.

Tax Incentives

Community Reinvestment Areas: Local tax incentives for businesses that expand or locate in designated areas of Ohio. Up to 100% exemption of the improved real estate property tax valuation for up to 15 years. In some instances, local school board approval may be required. Business must undertake new real estate investment.

Enterprise Zones: Local and state tax incentives for businesses that expand or locate in designated areas of Ohio. Up to 75% exemption in incorporated areas and up to 60% in unincorporated areas of the improved real estate or new tangible personal property tax valuation for up to 10 years.

Ohio Manufacturing Machinery & Equipment Investment Tax Credit: A non-refundable corporate franchise or state income tax credit for a manufacturer that purchases new machinery and equipment that is located in Ohio and is used in the production or assembly of a manufactured good. The manufacturer shall receive a 7.5% tax credit on the increase of the investment that is in excess of the three-year annual average investment on machinery and equipment.

Ohio Job Creation Tax Credit: State and municipal tax incentives are available for businesses that expand or locate in Ohio. State guidelines regulate the type of business and project eligible for the incentive. A business can receive a tax credit or refund against its corporate franchise tax based on the state income withheld on new, full-time employees. The amount of the tax credit can be up to 75% for up to ten years. The tax credit can exceed 75% upon recommendation of the Director of ODOD when there is an extraordinary circumstance. Municipalities can provide a similar arrangement with their local employee income taxes.

Export Tax Credit: Credits of up to 10% from pre-tax profits that result from expanded export operations with a cap of $250,000 per year.

Technology Investment Tax Credit: Taxpayers who invest in small, research and development and technology-oriented firms may reduce their state taxes by up to 25% of the amount they invest.

Exports

International Trade Division: Assists Ohio companies to develop export markets worldwide. Ohio's trade staff in Columbus, Tokyo, Hong Kong, Toronto, Mexico City, Sao Paulo, Brussels, and Tel Aviv provide custom-tailored assistance in international marketing and export finance and lead Ohio companies on trade missions and to the world's leading trade shows. Services include:
- Export Counseling
- Trade Shows and Trade Missions
- Electronic Trade
- Export Finance
- Export Incentives
- Japan Trade Program

Women and Minorities

Minority Management and Technical Services: Provides assistance in management analysis, technical assistance, educational services and financial consulting. Supports overall growth and development of minority firms throughout the State. Counseling is provided at no charge.

Minority Contractor and Business Assistance Program: Provides management, technical, financial, and contract procurement assistance; loan, grant, bond packaging services. Networks with all levels of government, private businesses. Aids in economic growth and development of the minority community; increases awareness of local, state, and federal business assistance programs. Counseling is provided at no charge. Fees may be charged for some programs using federal funding.

Minority Contract Procurement Services: Assists primarily minority firms in procuring public and private sector contracts. Supports efforts of minority firms to obtain contract awards that will aid in sustaining and developing these firms. Counseling is provided at no charge.

Minority Business Bonding Program: Surety bonding assistance for state-certified minority businesses. Maximum bond pre-qualification of up to $1,000,000 per Minority Business. The bond premium for each bond issued will not exceed 2% of the face value of the bond.

Minority Direct Loan: Purchase or improvement of fixed assets for state-certified minority-owned businesses. Up to 40% of total project cost at 4.5% fixed for up to 10 years (maximum).

Ohio Mini-Loan Program: Fixed assets and equipment for small businesses. Start-up or existing business expansion. Projects of $100,000 or less. Up to 45% guarantee of an eligible bank loan. Interest rate of the State guarantee of the loan is currently 5.5%, and may be fixed for 10 years. Eligibility: Small business entrepreneurs with fewer than 25 employees, targeted 50% allocation to businesses owned by minorities and women.

Women's Business Resource Program: Assistance for start-up, expansion and management of businesses owned by women; assures equal access to state business assistance and lending programs; direction to purchase and procurement opportunities with government agencies. Researches legislation that may impact businesses owned by women. Increases start-ups and successes of women-owned businesses. No charge.

Oklahoma

Department of Commerce
900 North Stiles
P.O. Box 26980
Oklahoma City, OK 73126-0980
405-815-5261
800-879-6552.
Fax: 405-815-5199
www.locateok.com
www.odoc.state.ok.us/index.html

Business Assistance

Office of Business Recruitment: Provides comprehensive site location assistance to companies considering new investment in Oklahoma.

Business Development Division: Promotes growth by addressing the needs of existing and start-up businesses. Provides information and seminars directly to businesses. Offers business information and a referral network to assist companies through the maze of regulatory requirements and introduces local resource providers.

Site Location Planner: On CD-ROM and the web at {www.locateok.com}. Provides comprehensive site location data including available buildings, community information, state incentives, and statistical and other information.

Market Research:

- *National Trade Data Bank (NTDB)*-the U. S. Government's most comprehensive source of world trade data, consisting of more than 130 separate trade- and business-related programs (databases). NTDB offers one-stop-shopping for trade information from more than 20 federal sources.
- *The Economic Bulletin Board (EBB)* provides on-line trade leads, time-sensitive market information, and the latest statistical releases from a variety of federal agencies.
- *Country Commercial Guides (CCG)* present a comprehensive look at a particular country's commercial environment including economic, political, and market analysis.
- *Industry Sector Analyses (ISA)* are in-depth, structured reports on a broad range of industries regularly compiled by commercial specialists at U. S. embassies and consulates abroad.

Technology Partnerships: Testing of technologies developed by private business may be performed in partnership with research universities. Such institutions may devote resources such as laboratory usage and faculty time to a particular business's need in return for a portion of business's profits.

Business Financing

Oklahoma Finance Authorities: Provides permanent financing for real estate and equipment. Contact: Oklahoma Finance Authorities, 301 NW 63rd, Suite 225, Oklahoma City, OK 73116; 405-842-1145.

Small Business Linked Deposit Program: Provides below market interest rates for qualified small businesses and certified industrial parks through local financing sources. Contact Oklahoma State Treasurer's Office, 4545 N. Lincoln Blvd., #169, Oklahoma City, OK 73105; 405-521-3191.

Public Trust Financing: Oklahoma authorizes public trust financing for economic development purposes at the county and city level.

General Obligation Limited Tax Bonds: Revenue bonds are issued in association with a particular project.

Tax Increment Financing: Provides economic development in distressed areas for up to 25 years.

Sales Tax Financing: Oklahoma cities and counties are authorized, upon a vote of the people, to build facilities and provide other economic development benefits for businesses financed by sales tax collections.

Private Activity Bond Allocation: Generally allocations are on a first-come, first-served basis, with some size limitation.

Capital Investment Board: Facilitates investment in venture capital companies that focus on investing in quality Oklahoma companies. Contact: Oklahoma Capital Investment Board, 301 NW 63rd, Suite 520, Oklahoma City, OK 73116; 405-848-9456.

Capital Access Program: Provides a credit insurance reserve for Oklahoma banks through a fee-matching arrangement for loans enrolled in the program. Contact: Oklahoma Capital Investment Board, 301 NW 63rd, Suite 520, Oklahoma City, OK 73116; 405-848-9456.

Training for Industry: Assists qualifying businesses by paying for training for new employees.

Quality Jobs Program: Provides quarterly cash payments of up to 5% of new taxable payroll directly to a qualifying company, for up to ten years.

Small Employer Quality Jobs Program: Provides annual cash payments of 5% of taxable payroll for new employees to a qualifying company, for up to 5 years.

Enterprise Zones: The enterprise district management authorities created in some enterprise districts are empowered to establish venture capital loan programs and to solicit proposals from enterprises seeking to establish or expand facilities in the zones.

Tax Incentives

Ad Valorem Tax Exemptions: New and expanding qualifying manufacturers, research and development companies, certain computer services and data processing companies with significant out-of-state sales, aircraft repair and aircraft manufacturing may be eligible for ad valorem exemptions.

Exempt Inventory: Oklahoma's Freeport Law exempts goods, wares, and merchandise from taxation that come into Oklahoma from outside the state and leave the state within nine months.

Sales Tax Exemptions: Exemptions are available in the following areas: machinery and equipment used in manufacturing; tangible personal property used in manufacturing including fuel and electric power; tangible personal property which becomes part of the finished product; packaging materials; items sold by the

manufacturer and immediately transported out of state for exclusive use in another state; machinery, equipment, fuels and chemicals used directly or in treating hazardous industrial waste, tangible personal property used in design and warehousing and located on the manufacturing site.

Aircraft Maintenance Facilities: Sales tax exemption on aircraft and parts.

Telecommunications: Exemptions apply to various services as part of an inducement to contract for wireless telecommunications services.

Sales and Use Tax Refunds: Refunds of sales/use tax are available for purchase of data processing equipment, related peripherals and telephone or telecommunications services or equipment and for construction materials.

Income Tax Credits/Exclusions: Reduces tax liability for the taxpayer that invests in qualifying property and also hires new employees. The credit is doubled for companies that locate in state Enterprise Zones.

Technology Transfer Income Tax Exemption: The taxable income of any corporation is decreased for transfers of technology to qualified small businesses located in Oklahoma not to exceed 10% of the amount of gross proceeds received by such corporation as a result of the technology transfer.

New Products Development Income Tax Exemption: Royalties earned by an inventor on products developed and manufactured in Oklahoma are exempt from state income tax.

Agricultural Commodity Processing Facility Income Tax Exclusion: Owners of agricultural commodity processing facilities may exclude a portion from taxable income based on investment.

Income Tax Credit for Investment in Oklahoma Producer-Owned Agriculture Processing: An income tax credit of 30% of investment is available to agricultural producer investors in Oklahoma producer-owned agricultural processing ventures, cooperative, or marketing associations.

Income Tax Credit for Computer/Data Processing/ Research & Development Jobs: Credit is available for a net increase in the number of full-time employees engaged in computer services, date processing or R & D. The credit allowed is $500 per employee, up to 50 employees.

Insurance Premium Tax Credit: Insurance companies which locate or expand regional home offices in Oklahoma are eligible for special tax credits against the tax imposed in the Insurance Code ranging from 15% to 50% based on number of full-time employees.

Small Business Capital Formation Tax Credit: Authorizes an income tax credit of 20% of equity investment for investors in qualified businesses.

Rural Small Business Capital Formation Tax Credit: Authorizes an income tax credit of 30% of equity investment for investing in a small business in a rural area.

Qualified Venture Capital Company Tax Credit: Freely transferable tax credits for investors in qualified venture capital companies.

Recycling, Reuse and Source Reduction Incentive Act: Manufacturing and service industries may receive an income tax credit of up to 20% of investment cost for equipment and installation or processes used to recycle, reuse, or reduce the source of hazardous waste. Credits are limited $50,000.

Income Tax Exemption for Interest Paid on Bonds: Interest payment received as a result of bonds issued by non-profit corporations on behalf of towns, cities, or counties for housing purposes are not subject to state income tax.

Tax Incentives on Former Indian Reservation Lands:

1. Employee Credit: Businesses located on qualified areas of former Indian reservations are eligible for a tax credit based on the increase in qualifying annual wages paid to enrolled Indian tribal members or their spouses. The credit equal 20% of the increased wages.

2. Depreciation Incentive: Provides a shorter recovery period of approximately 40% for most non-residential depreciable property being used in an active trade or business.

Work Opportunity Tax Credit Program: A tax credit is available up to $2,400 for each new hire from a target group of individuals.

Welfare-to-Work Tax Credit: Available to employers who hire individuals certified and long-term assistance recipients. The credit is as much as $8,500 per new hire.

Investment/Jobs: Allows a five-year tax credit on the greater of (1%) per year of investment in qualified new depreciable property or a credit of $500 per year per new job, doubled in an Enterprise Zone.

Exports

International Trade and Investment Division: Provides diverse services including hands on assistance for companies wishing to learn more about exporting to promoting Oklahoma products at trade shows throughout the world. Also works closely with the international business community to develop top of mind awareness of Oklahoma's business climate advantages. Provide confidential, reliable site location assistance, site selection assistance, tax comparisons, and incentive projections.

International Market Insights (IMI): Commercial specialists also regularly report on specific foreign market conditions and upcoming opportunities for U.S. business.

Customized Market Analysis (CMA): Provides detailed information needed to make the most efficient and beneficial export marketing decisions. CMA will give an accurate assessment of how a product or service will sell in a given market.

Trade Opportunities Program (TOP): Up-to-the-minute sales leads from around the world are prescreened and transmitted every work day to commercial specialists in U. S. embassies and consulates abroad.

Agent/Distributor Service (ADS): Customized search needed to successfully launch an export marketing campaign. Provides pertinent information on up to six prequalified potential representatives per market.

International Company Profiles (ICP): Thorough, up-to-date background checks on potential clients.

Country Directories of International Contacts (CDIC): Provides the name and contact information of importers, agents, trade associations, government agencies, etc., on a country-by-country basis.

Trade Fair Certification: Selects events in the countries and industries with the best opportunities for U. S. exporters. Only major shows within a given industry are certified-those that have proven to be well-established, high-quality events.

Foreign Trade Zones: Businesses engaged in international trade within these zones benefit from special customs procedures.

Export Finance Program: Assistance is available through a relationship with the Export-Import Bank of the United States to facilitate export financing with working capital guarantees, credit insurance and foreign buyer financing.

Women and Minorities

Women-owned Business Certification Program: Established to facilitate contracting capabilities for women-owned businesses with public and private sector entities.

Minority Business: Provides a forum to network with banking organizations, utility companies, state agencies and other that can be valuable resources for a business. Each month several business owners are selected to give a brief presentation about their business.

Minority Business Development Centers: A vehicle for small minority-owned businesses that are seeking help in start-up information. The centers provide assistance in business plans, procurement assistance and works with the SBA in the certified lenders program and 8(a) certification.

Oklahoma Minority Supplier Development Council (OMSDC): The mission of the OMSDC is to assist corporations and public sector agencies in creating a business environment that promotes access and increased opportunities for minority-owned businesses. The Council also helps to promote, educate and develop minority-owned businesses. Contact Oklahoma Minority Supplier Development Council, 6701 N. Broadway, Suite 216, Oklahoma City, OK 73116; 405-767-9900.

Oklahoma Consortium for Minority Business Development, Inc.: Provides a forum whereby government/private agencies and organizations may coordinate functions and activities to increase overall effectiveness in advocating and supporting the minority business community.

Minority Assistance Program, Office of Central Services: Created to increase the level of Oklahoma minority business participation in state purchases. The State has designated a percentage of contract awards to properly certified minority vendors.

Native American: Almost two-thirds of Oklahoma is considered "former Indian reservation land." Businesses located in these lands before the end of the year 2003 receive accelerated depreciation rates on capital investment. Federal employment tax credits are also available to businesses in these areas that employ American Indians or spouses.

Oregon

Economic Development Department
775 Summer St., NE
Salem, OR 97310
503-986-0260
Fax: 503-581-5115
www.econ.state.or.us/javahome.htm

Business Assistance

Economic Development Department: This office can provide information and expertise in dealing with state, federal, and local agencies. They also have information on financing programs and other services offered by the state government.

Small Business Advocate: Entrepreneurs can find connections to a network of private sector advisers who can help them access capital. Inventors, entrepreneurs and mature companies can obtain information on how to access research and development federal grants, assessment of their technology concepts and innovative best practices from the technology transfer services supported by the department. All of Oregon's small and emerging businesses can benefit from the efforts of a public/private partnership to design and implement tools, incentives and policies that can make it easier to start and grow a company in Oregon. Small Business Advocate, Economic Development Department, 775 Summer St., NE, Salem, OR 97310; 503-986-0057.

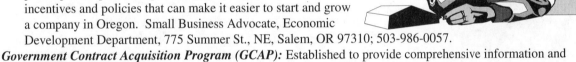

Government Contract Acquisition Program (GCAP): Established to provide comprehensive information and assistance to Oregon small businesses desiring to compete in this market.

Impact: Provides business management, marketing and financing assistance to start-up, small businesses and existing business expansion.

Oregon Business Network: Helps Portland minority start-up businesses and established businesses in a group environment.

Oregon Downtown Development Association works to revitalize and maintain the heritage and economic health of Oregon's downtowns and older business districts.

Rural Development Initiatives: A non-profit corporation that builds the capacity of rural communities to make strategic decisions about their futures and to act on those decisions to ensure high quality of life and a vital economy.

Employment Department: Comprehensive source of qualified job applicants for new businesses in Oregon communities.

Industry Workforce Training: Provides grants to community colleges for the development and implementation of training programs for multiple firms within an industry. Employers must provide matching funds or in-kind services.

Business Financing

Capital Access Program: Offered through the Oregon Economic Development Department, is designed to increase the availability of loans to Oregon small businesses from banks. The program provides loan portfolio insurance so lenders may make loans that carry higher than conventional risks. Borrowers pay a fee of between 3% and 7% of the loan amount, which is matched by the department and contributed to a loan loss reserve account in an enrolled bank. The loans must be within soundness and safety requirements of federal and state banking regulations. A Capital Access Program loan is a private transaction between the borrower and lender. The

Oregon Economic Development Department is not a party to loan negotiations or to the loan agreement. The department does not monitor the loan or require reporting from the borrower. Loan may be used for virtually any purpose, except to construct or purchase residential housing, to purchase real property that is not used for business operations of the borrower, or to refinance the principal balance of an existing loan.

Credit Enhancement Fund: Administered by the Oregon Economic Development Department, provides guarantees to enrolled banks to increase capital availability to small Oregon firms, helping them create jobs. The maximum guarantee for a loan is $500,000. The department has authority to guarantee up to $75 million of financial institution loans.

Entrepreneurial Development Loan Funds: Entrepreneurial businesses can receive loans of up to $25,000 through the Oregon Entrepreneurial Development Loan Fund.

Resource and Technology Development Fund: Equity-based capital is available for Oregon "basic-sector" businesses through the Oregon Resource and Technology Development Fund. Areas of focus include biological and biomedical services, high technology, and natural resource industries. For more information, contact Oregon Resource and Technology Development Fund, 4370 NE Halsey, Suite 233, Portland, OR 97213; 503-282-4462.

Oregon Enterprise Forum: Provides assistance to help companies that are in transition by providing mentoring services. For more information, contact Oregon Enterprise Forum, 2611 S.W. Third Ave., Suite 200, Portland, OR 97201; 503-222-2270.

Rural Development: Offers loan guarantees to banks to further business and industrial development in rural areas of the country. Loan guarantees may be made in any rural area or communities with a population of 50,000 or less. The maximum loan guarantee is $10 million. 10% equity is required. Projects must comply with certain federal requirements. Loans may be for land, facilities, equipment or working capital. Ineligible purposes include agricultural production (other federal programs are available for this purpose), hotels, motels, convention centers and tourist facilities. For more information, contact Rural Development Services, Business and Cooperative Programs, 101 SW Main, Suite 1410, Portland, OR 97204-3222; 503-414-3366.

Subordinated and Direct Loans: Subordinated loans usually fill a gap in a financing package, where commercial and private debt financing and equity have been maximized and additional funds are required to complete the financing transaction. Often these loans will "subordinate" or take a lesser security interest in the assets being financed, which will allow the senior lender first priority on project assets in the event of a default. The subordinated loan is often secured with additional assets to help collaterize its position. Direct loans and, in some limited cases, grants are available to finance businesses when the project will further the public objectives of the entity making the loan or grant.

Business Development Fund: Manufacturing, processing and regionally significant tourism projects are eligible for the Oregon Business Development Fund. The fund provides long-term, fixed rate financing for land, buildings, equipment and machinery.

Local Revolving Loan Funds: Many local and regional development groups and local governments throughout Oregon administer revolving loan funds for small business financing. In most cases, funding has been provided by the federal Department of Housing and Urban Development (HUD), the federal Economic Development Administration (EDA), the U.S. Department of Agriculture Rural Economic and Community Development Administration (RECD) or the Oregon Economic Development Department. Loan criteria may reflect some of the objectives of those funding organizations or may have special requirements of those agencies.

Oregon Port Revolving Fund Loans: Provides long-term loans to ports at below-market interest rates. Individual loans may be made to a maximum of $700,000 per project. The total outstanding loan amount any individual port can have at any one time cannot exceed $2 million. Funding may be used for port development projects (infrastructure) or to assist port-related private business development projects. The 23 legally formed Port Districts are the only entities eligible for Port Revolving Fund loans. The variety of projects eligible is very broad. These include, but are not limited to, water-oriented facilities, industrial parks, airports and eligible commercial or industrial developments. Projects must be located within port district boundaries. For more information contact Ports Division, Oregon Economic Development Department, 775 Summer Street NE, Salem, OR 97310; 503-986-0143.

Industrial Development Revenue Bonds: The Economic Development Commission may issue industrial development revenue bonds for manufacturing and processing facilities in Oregon. Industrial development bonds can finance fixed assets only, along with some limited transaction costs. If a project qualifies the bonds can be issued on a tax-exempt basis which lowers the overall cost of financing. Revenue bonds are not direct obligations of the State of Oregon. The individual or corporation on whose behalf the bonds are issued is legally obligated to repay them. An eligible company may borrow up to $10 million through the Oregon Industrial Development Revenue Bond Program. Typically, the minimum bond is for $2 million.

Small Scale Energy Loan Program: The Small Scale Energy Loan Program (SELP), administered by the Oregon Department of Energy, finances energy conservation and renewable energy projects in Oregon, through the issuance of general obligation bonds. Bond proceeds can be loaned to finance eligible equipment costs, construction, certain design and consultation fees, some reserves, construction interest and most loan closing costs. Eligible costs are those incurred after loan approval. Land and working capital are normally not financed. Costs not part of the energy project also are not eligible. All Oregonians, Oregon businesses, nonprofit organizations, municipal corporations and state agencies can apply for loans. Eligible projects are those which conserve conventional energy, such as electricity and natural gas; or projects which produce renewable energy from geothermal or solar sources or from water, wind, biomass and some waste materials. For more information, contact Oregon Department of Energy, 625 Marion Street NE, Salem, OR 97310; 503-373-1033; 800-221-8035 (in OR).

Regional Development: Cities, counties and other governmental entities also can obtain loans and grants to help pay for construction projects. The department uses grant and loan funds to support public works, safe drinking water and housing rehabilitation projects. The department also provides funding for community facilities projects to improve or build day care, senior centers, emergency shelters and family counseling facilities, among others.

Tax Incentives

Corporate Income Tax Credits: Oregon businesses may be eligible for a number of tax credits allowed under Oregon law. Some of these business-related tax credits include:
- pollution control tax credit,
- business energy tax credit,
- research tax credit,
- reclaimed plastics product tax credit,
- dependent child care tax credit, and
- donation of computers and scientific equipment in Oregon.

Enterprise Zone Program: Created as a business incentive to create new jobs by encouraging business investment in economically lagging areas of the state. Construction of new facilities in an enterprise zone entitles a business to a 100% property tax abatement for three to five years on a new plant and most of the equipment installed.

Construction in Progress Exemption: Under Oregon law, new facilities are exempt from property taxes for up to two years while they are under construction and not in use on July 1 of the taxing year. The Construction in Progress Exemption also applies to any machinery or equipment installed in the unoccupied facility on July 1. The exemption does not apply to land. For more information, contact the county assessor or Oregon Department of Revenue, Property Tax Division, Room 256, Revenue Building, Salem, OR 97310; 503-945-8290.

Strategic Investment Program: Provides property tax exemptions for significant projects that will benefit Oregon's key industries. Properties developed under this program are exempted from local property taxes for up to 15 years on assessed value in excess of $100 million. With local government approval, participating companies pay property taxes on the first $100 million in assessed value for the approved project. This base amount ($100 million) is increased by 6% per year. Participating companies also make a direct community service payment to the local government equal to 25% of the abated amount, not to exceed $2 million per year. After local government approval, the Oregon Economic Development Commission is authorized to determine that the project is eligible for the program and determine the maximum eligible cost of real and personal property for the project.

Exports

International Division of the Oregon Economic Development Department: The international arm of state government. It provides "export ready" Oregon companies assistance in export markets, assists the Governor's Office on protocol and other assignments, and works with public and private organizations to promote Oregon in the international business community. The Division is located at One World Trade Center, Suite 300, 121 SW Salmon, Portland, OR 97204; 503-229-5625; 800-448-7512.

Women and Minorities

Southern Oregon Women's Access to Credit: Offers a business development program for new and existing business owners in Jackson, Josephine and Klamath counties. Focuses on training, mentoring and financing. Contact SOWAC, 33 N. Central Avenue, Suite #209, Medford, OR 97501; 541-779-3992; Fax: 541-779-5195.

Association Of Minority Entrepreneurs: A non-profit, tax exempt organization formed to promote and develop entrepreneurship and economic development for ethnic minorities in the State of Oregon. OAME works as a partnership between ethnic minorities, entrepreneurs, education, government and established corporate business. OAME provides a core of services to start-up and/or existing minority businesses. These services include:
- Technical Assistance
- Access To Capital/Loan Fund
- Capability And Opportunity Matching (OAME's Marketing/Clearinghouse)
- Administrative Services
- Incubator With & Without Walls Development

Contact Oregon Association of Minority Entrepreneurs, 4134 N. Vancouver, Portland, OR 97217; 503-249-7744; Fax: 503-249-2027.

Native American Business Entrepreneurs Network: Created by Northwest Indian Tribes to increase the success of private businesses owned by Native Americans. ONABEN's approach consists of technical training, access to capital, (conditional on an on-going consulting relationship), access to markets and mentors. The program is organized to integrate community resources. It assists and encourages tribes to share business development resources amongst themselves and with non-Indian neighbors. The program works where no predecessor has succeeded because it approaches business ownership as an expression of Native Americans' common values; inter-generation and community awareness, mutual respect, non-destructive harvest. Contact: ONABEN, 520 SW 6th Ave., Suite 930, Portland, OR 97204; 800-854-8289; {www.onaben.org}.

Pennsylvania

Department of Community and Economic Development
433 Forum Building
Harrisburg, PA 17120
800-379-7448
www.dced.state.pa.us

Governor's Action Team
100 Pine Street, Suite 100
Harrisburg, PA 17101
717-787-8199
Fax: 717-772-5419
www.teampa.com

Business Assistance

Entrepreneurial Assistance Office: Established to ensure small business owners receive the support and assistance they require. The Entrepreneurial Assistance Office works to build an environment which encourages the creation, expansion and retention of small, women and minority owned businesses.

Small Business Resource Center: The single point of contact and hub of information for small businesses, answering state related and general business questions about licenses and permits. The Center has select state forms and applications available as well as other sources of information and technical assistance.

Environmental Business Advocate: Assists small businesses in complying with requirements of the Federal Clean Air Act and appropriate state regulations. Housed in the PA Department of Environmental Protection, (DEP), the EBA represents the interests of small businesses in matters affecting them with DCED and the U.S. Environmental Protection Agency.

Industrial Resource Centers: Assists companies in solving problems through the deployment of technologies.

Job Centers: Provide employers with a wide array of employment and training services.

Small Business Incubators: Sites where young businesses can start and grow. Offers businesses the opportunity to rent small units of space at a lower than market rate. Provides tenants with business development services that help to reduce costs and increase profits.

Business Financing

PA Industrial Development Authority: Low-interest financing through Industrial Development Corporations for land and building acquisitions, construction and renovation resulting in the creation or retention of jobs. Amounts: Loans up to $1 million (within Enterprise Zones, $1.5 million) no more than 30 to 40% of the total eligible project costs, advanced technology projects and those in an Act 47 or within an Enterprise Zone qualify for lower interest rates.

Machinery and Equipment Loan Fund: Low-interest loan financing to acquire and install new or used machinery and equipment or to upgrade existing machinery and equipment. Amounts: Loans up to $500,000 or 50% of the total eligible project costs, whichever is less.

Small Business First: Funding for small businesses including: low-interest loan financing to small businesses for land and building acquisition and construction; machinery and equipment purchases and working capital; financing to comply with environmental regulations; for businesses involved in municipal or commercial recycling; and for those impacted by defense conversion. Amounts: $200,000 or 50% of the total eligible project costs, whichever is less. Maximum loan amount is $100,000 for working capital.

PA Infrastructure Investment Authority (PennVEST): Low-interest loans for design, engineering and construction of publicly and privately owned drinking water distribution and treatment facilities, storm water conveyance and wastewater treatment systems. Amounts: Loans up to $11 million per project for one municipality, up to $20 million for more than one municipality, up to $350,000 for design and engineering, up to 100% of the total project costs.

PA Capital Access Program: Through participating banks, loan guarantees are provided to support a wide variety of business purposes. Amounts: Loan guarantees up to $500,000.

PA Economic Development Financing Authority: An issuer of tax-exempt and taxable bonds, both in pooled transactions and stand-alone transactions. Bond funds are loaned to businesses and can be used to finance land, building, equipment, working capital and refinances. Amounts: Loans no less them $400,000 and no more than $10 million for manufacturers, no upper limits for other projects, up to 100% of project costs.

Customized Job Training: Provides grants to businesses in need of training assistance for new hires, retraining efforts and upgrading employees in an effort to retain and create jobs in Pennsylvania. Amounts: Grants up to 100% of the eligible costs for new job creations, grants up to 70% of eligible costs for job retention, grants up to 25% of the eligible costs for upgrade training. Contact: Office of Workforce and Technology Development, 464 Forum Bldg., Harrisburg, PA 17120; 717-787-4117.

Job Training Partnership Act: Up to 50% of wage rate for employees while in training.

Opportunity Grant Program: Provides grant funds to create or preserve jobs within the Commonwealth. Funds may be used for job training, infrastructure improvements, land and building improvements, machinery and equipment, working capital and environmental assessment and redemption. Amounts: No minimum or maximum grant amount.

Infrastructure Development Program: Grant and low-interest loan financing for public and private infrastructure improvements. Amounts: Loans and grants up to $1.25 million, no more than 20% of the annual appropriation for a single municipality.

Industrial Sites Reuse Program: Grant and low-interest loan financing is provided to perform environmental site assessment and remediation work at former industrial sites. Amounts: Grants and loans up to $200,000 for environmental assessment, grants and loans up to $1 million for remediation.

Rail Freight Assistance: Grants to build or repair rail lines and spurs. Amounts: Grants up to $250,000 for maintenance, up to $100,000 for construction.

Enterprise Zone Program: Grants available for loans to businesses: Planning Grant up to $50,000; Basic Grant up to $50,000; Competitive Grant: up to $250,000.

Industrial Resource Center Network: Provides financial and technical assistance to manufacturers to improve their manufacturing operations.

Seed Venture Program: Provides product development and working capital to early-stage venture companies.

Small Business First Export Loan Program: Provides short-term loans to meet the pre and post-export financing needs of small businesses. Amounts: Pre-Export loans: Up to $350,000 or 50% of total eligible project costs, whichever is less. Post-Export loans: Loans not to exceed 80% of the face amount of the contract.

Underground Storage Upgrade Loan: Loans to assist owners of regulated storage tanks in upgrading their underground storage tank systems to meet federal Environmental Protection Agency upgrade requirements. Amounts: $500,000 or 75% of the total eligible project costs, whichever is less.

Challenge Grant Program: Provides grants ranging from $5,000 to $100,000 for research and development, technology transfer, joint research and development.

Tax Incentives

Job Creation Tax Credits: A $1,000-per-job tax credit to approved businesses that agree to create jobs in the Commonwealth within three years.

Keystone Opportunity Zones: Zones in which businesses and residents will be exempt from virtually all state and local taxes.

Manufacturing, processing and research and development activities are exempt from the Capital Stock and Franchise Tax.

Pollution control devices are exempt from the Capital Stock and Franchise Tax.

Machinery and equipment used in manufacturing are exempt from the Sales and Use Tax.

Computer services are exempt from the Sales and Use Tax.

Machinery and equipment, business inventories and personal property are exempt from Pennsylvania's real property tax.

Improvements to property can be exempted from the real property tax for up to ten years.

Capital gains are taxed at a rate of 2.8%.

Films: A sales tax exemption is available for most purchases made by producers of full-length feature films.

Local Economic Revitalization Tax Assistance Act: Local municipalities, school districts and counties can offer up to 100% abatements on property taxes for up to 10 years.

Neighborhood Assistance Tax Credit: Up to 70% of the amount invested in programs that help families or communities in impoverished areas.

Employment Incentive Payments Program: Provides credits to employers that hire welfare recipients.

Enterprise Zone Credit Program: Allows corporations a tax credit of up to 20% on investments to rehabilitate or improve buildings or land in an Enterprise Zone.

Exports

Headquartered in Harrisburg, the Office of International Business Development maintains offices around the world. The Office, together with the Team Pennsylvania Export Network Regions, supports Pennsylvania firms wishing to do business in the overseas market. The Office coordinates a range of trade development activities including:

- industry sector trade initiatives
- provision of market intelligence
- export financing programs
- in-country support for firms in association with the Commonwealth's overseas offices

Contact Office of International Business Development, 308 Forum Building, Harrisburg, PA 17120; 888-PA EXPORT.

Women and Minorities

PA Minority Business Development Authority: Low-interest loan financing to businesses which are owned and operated by minorities. Amounts: Manufacturing, industrial, high-tech, international trade or franchise companies with loans up to $500,000 (within Enterprise Zones, $750,000) or 75% of total eligible project costs, whichever is less, retail or commercial firms loans of up to $250,000 ($350,000 in Enterprise Zones).

Minority Business Development Agency: Provides minority entrepreneurs with management and technical assistance services to start, expand, or mange a business.

National Minority Supplies Development Council: A non-profit corporation chartered in 1972 to expand business opportunities for minority owned companies, to encourage mutually beneficial economic links between minority suppliers and the public and private sectors, and to help build a stronger, more equitable society by supporting and promoting minority business development.

Independence Capital Network Fund: Provides grants to small employers to enable them to make special accommodations for workers with disabilities.

50 Best Women in Business: Awards program recognizes and applauds the significant contributions Pennsylvania's women business owners and leaders make to their communities, to their families and to their work.

Minority Business Advocate: Encourages the development of minority-owned businesses as part of the overall economic development strategy of the Commonwealth. Serves as an advocate for minority owned business owners in resolving issues with state agencies and interacting with other government agencies.

Women's Business Advocate: Works to assist women businesses in the development of their business, specifically assisting in resolving issues with state agencies, exploring marketing options and identifying financing strategies.

Bureau of Contract Administration and Business Development (Formerly the Minority and Women Business Enterprise Office): Benefits small, minority and women businesses. Provides the necessary resources and direction for business owners to compete for and participate in the state contracting process. Furthermore, it is the statewide agency for certification as a Minority Business Enterprise and Women Business Enterprise.

Rhode Island

Economic Development Corporation
One West Exchange St.
Providence, RI 02903
401-222-2601
Fax: 401-222-2102
www.riedc.com

Business Assistance

Economic Development Corporation: This office can provide information and expertise in dealing with state, federal, and local agencies. They also have information on financing programs and other services offered by the state government.

Economic Development Set Aside: The Set-Aside for Economic Development is designed to provide matching job training funds to companies that are either relocating to Rhode Island or expanding present operations in the state. The funds are used for the training of new employees through either customized training programs or on the job training.

Customized Upgrade Training to Improve Productivity: This program allows an employer to upgrade the skills of existing employees, thus improving the productivity of the business. The program awards matching grants of up to $25,000 per company through a competitive Request for Proposal process. In some cases, the company will be a fast growing firm, while others may be marginal with the training program becoming part of an overall business strategy to improve competitiveness. Businesses are urged to work through trade associations and local colleges and universities to increase the effectiveness of the training programs.

Customized Training (new hires): This type of program involves occupational skills with training provided either by the employer or by an outside trainer. The training location can be the employer's worksite or at an educational facility (or some combination). The employer makes the final decision on program design, curriculum content, and trainee selection.

First Stop Business Center: Helps businesses deal with federal, state, and local requirements and provides information and referral assistance. Contact First Stop Business Center, 100 North Main St., Providence, RI 02903; 401-277-2185; Fax: 401-277-3890; {www.state.ri.us/bus/frststp.htm}.

Business Financing

Industrial Revenue Bonds: Industrial Revenue Bonds may be used to finance qualified commercial and industrial projects. The bonds offer a competitive interest rate and state sales tax exemption on building materials that may be significant for projects involving new construction. Financing is available through the Rhode Island Industrial Facilities Corporation and covers the entire project cost. The project and the credit of the user provides the security for the bonds which may be issued on the financial strength of the user when the user is appropriately rated. The bonds may also be issued with an enhancement letter of credit from a financial institution.

Tax-Exempt "Small Issue Bonds": Under the small-issue bond provisions of the Omnibus Budget Reconciliation Act of 1993, interest on certain bonds with face amounts of less than $10 million is excluded from income if at least 95% of the bonds' proceeds is used to finance manufacturing facilities. Industrial Revenue Bonds are tax-exempt obligations of the issuer, the interest on which is exempt from federal and state income tax. The interest rate on such obligations is normally below that available for conventional mortgages.

Bond and Mortgage Insurance Program: The Program reduces the capital necessary for new manufacturing facilities, renovation of manufacturing facilities, the purchase of new machinery and equipment in financing projects up to $5,000,000.

The Small Business Loan Fund: The SBLF provides eligible Small Business Fixed Asset Loans from $25,000 to a maximum of $250,000 and Working Capital Loans to a maximum of $30,000.

Ocean State Business Development Authority: Through the SBA 504 and 7A program the Authority can provide up to 90% financing on loan requests to $2,000,000 with a participating bank. Loan proceeds may be used to purchase land, renovate, or construct buildings and acquire new and used machinery and equipment.

Samuel Slater Innovation Partnership Program: Designed to provide public-sector supporting funds on a matching, cost reimbursement basis to private-sector initiated activities designed to improve the competitiveness of Rhode Island-based firms. It is designed to foster and support efforts by companies to increase their competitiveness through the development and/or better use of technology that directly and indirectly lead to an improved Rhode Island economy. By the nature of this program, the EPC is looking for creative, yet feasible, approaches to improving their industrial competitiveness through collaboration with institution of higher education and/or other firms or through the development of new technology-based businesses. A total of $1,375,000 in matching funds is available in the Innovation Partnership Program and will be awarded on a competitive, merit basis in three distinct grant programs:

- Industry-Higher Education Partnership Grants Available Funds: $750,000
- Multi-firm Collaboration Grants Available Funds: $500,000
- Technology Entrepreneur Seed Grants Available Funds: $125,000

Tax Incentives

No Income Tax for Insurance Carriers.

Passive Investment Tax Exemption: A corporation's investment income may be exempt from the Rhode Island income tax if it confines its activity to the maintenance and management of its passive intangible assets, maintains an office in Rhode Island, and employs at least five persons in Rhode Island.

Telecommunication Sales Tax Exemption: Regulated investment companies with at least 500 full-time equivalent employees are exempt from the sales and use tax imposed on toll-free terminating telecommunication service.

Insurance and Mutual Holding Companies: Rhode Island allows a mutual insurance company to create a mutual holding company, owned by the policy holders exactly as they now own the mutual company. This holding company, however, would then own the actual insurance company as a stockholder, while the insurance company itself could issue stock to raise capital. The process could be controlled by the mutual holding company, which means that policyholders would be protected from any dilution of control over the majority stockholder of the company. Policyholders ownership of the insurance subsidiary would be shared with other stockholders only to the extent that they choose to issue stock to raise capital for expansion.

Captive Insurance Companies: Rhode Island allows captive insurance companies to capitalize with a letter of credit or cash as in other states.

Insurance Company Retaliatory Tax Exemption: Foreign insurance companies are exempt from gross premiums retaliatory taxes in Rhode Island when their home jurisdiction does not impose a like tax.

Income Allocation Modification for Manufacturers of Medical Instruments and Supplies (SIC Code 384) and Drugs (SIC Code 283): A Rhode Island manufacturer of Medical Instruments and Supplies or Drugs registered and certified by the United States Food and Drug Administration with a place of business outside the state may modify the numerator in the allocation formula for the current tax year.

4% Credit for Equipment and Facilities Used in Manufacturing: Manufacturers may take a 4% tax credit for new tangible personal and other tangible property that is located in Rhode Island and is principally used by the taxpayer in the production of goods by manufacturing, processing, or assembling.

Research and Development Expense Credit: A special Rhode Island credit is allowed against the business corporation taxes and Rhode Island personal income tax for qualified research expenses. The credit is computed at 22.5% of the expense as defined in Section 41 of the

Internal Revenue Code for companies increasing research and development expenditures, making Rhode Island the highest in the nation. The credit drops to 16.9% for R&D expenditures above the first $25,000 of credit. Unused credit may be carried forward for up to seven years.

Rhode Island Job Training Tax Credit: A special Rhode Island credit allows companies to receive a credit of $5,000 per employee against the business corporation taxes in any three year period against the cost of offering training and/or retraining to employees. This tax credit is critically important to existing Rhode Island employers, which formerly were not provided any tax incentives for the retraining of existing employees. With this tax credit, Rhode Island businesses will be able to reduce costs, be more efficient, and add to their competitiveness.

Rhode Island Employer's Apprenticeship Tax Credit: The annual credit allowed is 50% of the actual wages paid to the qualifying apprentice or $4,800, whichever is less. The credit applies to the following trades in the metal and plastic industries: machinist, toolmaker, modelmaker, gage maker, patternmaker, plastic process technician, tool & machine setter, diesinker, moldmaker, tool & die maker, machine tool repair.

Educational Assistance and Development Credit: A credit is 8% of the contribution in excess of $10,000 made to a Rhode Island institution of higher education and the contribution is to be for the establishment or maintenance of

programs of scientific research or education. "Contributions" include the cost or other basis (for federal income tax purposes) in excess of $10,000 of tangible personal property excluding sale discounts and sale-gift arrangements concerning the purchase of equipment. Amounts of unused credit may be carried over for 5 years and documentation of the credit requires a written statement from the institution.

Adult Education Tax Credit: The Rhode Island Adult Education Tax Credit allows for both a worksite and nonworksite tax credit for vocational training or basic education of 50% of the costs incurred up to a maximum of $300 per employee and $5,000 per employer per calendar year.

Child and Adult Daycare Tax Credit: Credits are available against the business corporation tax, the bank excise tax, the insurance companies gross premiums tax and the personal income tax. These credits are computed at 30% of the amount of Rhode Island licensed daycare purchased and 30% of the cost to establish and/or operate a Rhode Island licensed daycare facility whether established and/or operated by the taxpayer alone or in conjunction with others. The maximum annual credit for purchased daycare is $30,000 per year and the amounts of unused credit may not be carried forward. For daycare facilities and rents/lease foregone, the maximum total credit is $30,000 per year and amounts of unused may be carried forward for 5 years.

Tax Incentives for Employers to hire unemployed Rhode Island Residents: The incentive of 40% of an eligible employee's first year wages up to a maximum of $2,400 may be used to reduce the gross Rhode Island income of businesses and individuals that employ and retain previously unemployed Rhode Island residents.

SBA Credit for Loan Grantee Fee: A small business may take a tax credit equal to any guaranty fee they pay to the United States Small Business Administration pursuant to obtaining SBA financing.

Rhode Island Enterprise Zone Program Tax Benefits: Rhode Island offers an Enterprise Zone Program developed to revitalize distressed urban areas in Rhode Island. The program provides an aggressive and comprehensive incentive package to businesses willing to relocate or expand into the designated Enterprise Zones.

Resident Business Owner Tax Modification: Business owners who operate a qualified business and who live in the same Enterprise Zone are eligible for a three year modification of $50,000 from their federal adjusted gross income when computing their state income tax liability and a $25,000 modification for years four and five.

Interest Income Tax Credit: Corporations or taxpayers that make new loans to qualified Enterprise Zone businesses are eligible to receive a 10% tax credit on interest earned from the loan. The maximum credit per taxpayer is $10,000 per year.

Donation Tax Credit: A taxpayer is eligible for a credit of 20% for any cash donation against the state tax imposed for donations to public supported improvement projects in the zone.

Tax Credit Available to Certified Mill Building Owner(s): A specialized investment tax credit equal to 10% of the cost of the substantial rehab. The rehab must occur within two years following certification.

Tax Credits Available to Lenders: A credit equal to 10% of the interest earned on loans to eligible businesses. Maximum of $10,000 per taxable year. A credit equal to 100% of the interest on loans made solely and exclusively for the purpose of substantial rehab of a Certified Building. Maximum of $20,000 per taxable year.

Alternative Transportation: 50% of the capital, labor, and equipment costs incurred by businesses for construction of or improvements to any filling station that provides alternative fuel or recharging of electric vehicles and 50% of the incremental costs incurred by a taxpayer for the purchase of alternative fueled motor vehicles or for the cost of converting vehicles into alternative fueled vehicles. The amount of either of the two credits may be transferred by one taxpayer to another if the transferee is a parent, subsidiary, affiliate, or is subject to common ownership, management, and control with the transferor. A taxpayer who has not transferred a credit and whose credit exceeds its tax liability may carry forward any unused portion of the credit to one or more of the succeeding five years.

Disabled Access Credit for Small Business: The expenses must be made to enable the small business to comply with federal or state laws protecting the rights of persons with disabilities. The credit is equal to 10% of the total amount expended during the tax year in Rhode Island, up to a maximum of $1,000, for removing architectural, communication, physical, or transportation barriers; providing qualified interpreters or other effective methods of delivering aurally delivered materials to persons with hearing impairments; providing readers, tapes, or other effective means of making visually delivered materials available to persons with visual impairments; providing job coaches or other effective means of supporting workers with severe impairments in competitive employment; providing specialized transportation services to employees or customers with mobility impairments; buying or modifying equipment for persons with disabilities; and providing similar services, modifications, material or equipment for persons with disabilities.

Sales and Use Tax Exemptions: Manufacturers' machinery and equipment is exempt; Manufacturers' machinery, equipment, replacement parts and computer software used in the manufacturing process are exempt.

Professional Services: Services such as those provided by physicians, attorneys, accountants, engineers, and others are exempt. However, the tax applies to any tangible personal property that may be sold at retail by such professionals (i.e.--opera glasses, field glasses, etc.).

Occupational Services: Services such as provided by barbers, beauty parlors, bootblacks, cleaning and pressing shops, laundries, and similar service establishments are exempt. However, if delivery to the purchaser or his agent is consummated within, the tax applies to any tangible personal property that may be sold at retail by such establishments.

Sales in interstate commerce: A shipment by common carrier, United States mail, or delivery facilities not operated by the seller to a purchaser outside Rhode Island is not subject to the tax. If the purchaser takes delivery within the state, the tax applies.

Intangibles: Sales or transfers of intangible personal property such as stocks, bonds, accounts receivable, money, or insurance policies are exempt.

Pollution Control Equipment: Sales of air and water pollution control equipment for incorporation into or used and consumed directly in the operation of a facility or installation approved by the Rhode Island Director of Environmental Management are exempt.

Scientific Equipment: Sales of scientific equipment, computers, software and related items to a qualifying firm to be used predominantly by that firm for research and development purposes. The qualifying firm must furnish the vendor with a Rhode Island Research and Development Exemption Certificate.

Boat Sales: The sale of boats has been exempted from the state sales tax. Boats are also exempt from local property taxes.

Local Property Taxes: Intangible property is not taxed.

Inventory & Equipment Tax Exemption For Manufacturer: Manufacturers' machinery and equipment used in the production process and inventories of manufacturers in Rhode Island are exempt from property taxes.

Real Estate Property Tax Exemption/Stabilization: Any city or town in Rhode Island may exempt or stabilize the tax on real and personal property used for manufacturing, or commercial purposes, for a period not exceeding ten years. The incentive may not be used to encourage a firm to move from one municipality to another in Rhode Island.

Property Tax Exemption/Stabilization For Wholesaler's Inventory: Any city or town in Rhode Island may exempt or stabilize the tax on a wholesaler's inventory for a period of up to twenty five years. The incentive may not be used to encourage a firm to move from one municipality to another in Rhode Island.

Property Tax Exemption/Stabilization Office Equipment: Any city or town in Rhode Island may exempt or stabilize the tax on computers, telephone equipment and other office personal property for a period of up to twenty five years. The incentive may not be used to encourage a firm to move from one municipality to another in Rhode Island.

Energy Related Property Tax Exemptions: For local tax purposes, solar, wind, or cogeneration equipment shall not be assessed at more than the value of the conventional heating, cooling, or energy production capacity that would otherwise be necessary to install in the building.

Air and Water Pollution Control Equipment: Air and water pollution control equipment used to treat waste water and air contaminants produced as the result of industrial processing is exempt from local property taxes for ten years and may continue to remain exempt with municipal approval.

Hazardous Waste Equipment: Tangible personal property used for the recycling, recovery or reuse of "hazardous

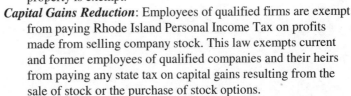

waste" generated by the same taxpayer on the same or adjacent property is exempt.

Capital Gains Reduction: Employees of qualified firms are exempt from paying Rhode Island Personal Income Tax on profits made from selling company stock. This law exempts current and former employees of qualified companies and their heirs from paying any state tax on capital gains resulting from the sale of stock or the purchase of stock options.

Estate and Gift Tax: An estate is required to file Rhode Island Estate Tax Form 100 with a $25 filing fee. There is no Estate Tax unless the gross value of the estate exceeds $600,000 and there is no surviving spouse. Then, the Estate Tax due is an amount equal to the Federal Credit apportioned to Rhode Island. Rhode Island has no ***Gift Tax***.

Exports

International Trade Partnership: As the official arm of state government, RIEDC is the principal liaison with foreign governments and hosts in-coming trade delegations from other countries. As the entity charged with developing the state's economic agenda, RIEDC is the partner responsible for providing business services directly to companies. These services include: development and execution of trade shows and trade missions; customized export management training and general trade assistance to Rhode Island companies.

South Carolina

Department of Commerce
P.O. Box 927
Columbia, SC 29202
803-737-0400
877-751-1262
Fax: 803-737-0418
www.callsouthcarolina.com

Business Assistance

Department of Commerce: This office can provide information and expertise in dealing with state, federal, and local agencies. They also have information on financing programs and other services offered by the state government.

Enterprise Development, Inc.: Develops strategic initiatives and business resources for new capital investments. Initiatives are in the development of finances, technology and human resources.

South Carolina Research Authority: A public, self-funded, non-profit organization that works to attract and support technology-based companies in South Carolina by: encouraging collaboration between industry, government, and educational institutions; providing unique site locations in specialized research parks; offering technology management specialization. Contact: South Carolina Research Authority, P.O. Box 12025, Columbia, SC 29211; 803-799-4070; {www.scra.org}.

Business Financing

Industrial Revenue Bonds

Jobs-Economic Development Authority (JEDA): Loan and investment programs for creation and retention of jobs.

Carolina Capital Investment Corporation: A bank consortium administered by JEDA to provide funding to small, growth oriented firms.

Taxable and Tax-Exempt Industrial Development Bonds: Bond for individual company funding range from $1 million to $10 million.

Taxable Bond Financing Program: Assists commercial business and real estate development firms with affordable long-term debt financing. Proceeds may be used to fund the acquisition, construction or renovation of buildings and land, the purchase of new or used equipment, and for working capital purposes as well as the refinancing of existing debt.

Venture Capital Funding: Loans to businesses for innovative products or processes.

Center for Applied Technology: Provides assistance in the formation and development of technology based companies, and offers access to capital, business development, as well as access to federal laboratory technologies. Contact Center for Applied Technology, Office of Technology Transfer, Clemson University, P.O. Box 345701, Clemson, SC 29634; 864-656-5708.

Tax Incentives

Jobs Tax Credit: Provides income tax credits for companies locating in or expanding current business in any county in South Carolina ranging from $1,500 to $4,500.

Child Care Credit: Payments made to licensed and/or registered child care facilities for the benefit of an employee are eligible for a credit against state corporate income tax not to exceed a maximum of $3,000 per employee.

Corporate Headquarters Credit: Firms establishing headquarters or expanding existing headquarters in South Carolina are eligible for credits to state corporate income taxes or corporate license fees.

Net Operating Loss: Net operating losses incurred may be carried forward for up to 15 years.

Credit for Former Military Employees: Offers a credit to state corporate income taxes of 10% of the first $10,000 of income per employee to firms hiring laid off defense workers.

Sales and Use Tax Exemptions: The following items are exempt for manufacturers from sales and use tax: production machinery and equipment; repair parts; materials which will become an integral part of the finished product; industrial electricity and fuels used in the manufacturing process; packaging materials.

Property Tax Exemptions: The following items are exempt from property tax: manufacturing inventory; intangible property; facilities or equipment of industrial plants designed for elimination, mitigation, prevention, treatment, abatement, or control of water, air, or noise pollution.

Other Corporate Income Tax Incentives:
- No state property tax
- No unitary taxes on worldwide profits
- No wholesale sales taxes
- No value-added taxes
- No intangible taxes
- No local income tax
- No inventory tax
- No sales tax on manufacturing machinery, industrial power or materials for finished products

Enterprise Program: Offers tax advantages for new jobs to businesses located anywhere in the state.

Exports

Trade Development Program: Mission is twofold: to increase awareness among South Carolina companies of world market profitability and the valuable export resources available; and to promote South Carolina companies and products to prospective overseas importers, resulting in an increased international market share and direct sales for South Carolina companies.
- Hands-on trade services include such matters as answering export-related inquiries and extending referrals to other export assistance providers. In addition, they regularly co-host trade-related conferences and seminars.
- Promotional activities include assistance to and the recruitment of companies for participation in trade shows and trade missions overseas and the hosting of visiting international trade missions sourcing South Carolina products. These activities are accomplished through staff-organized meetings with South Carolina manufacturers.
- Technological capabilities allow the trade staff to provide the most efficient service through both targeted events scheduling, and the ability to disseminate the most current international sales leads and trade-related reports to South Carolina firms with the push of a button.
- Exporters Database & Directory allows the matching of South Carolina firms with overseas requests for products, and serves as a resource for storing useful promotional information on in-state exporters. South Carolina firms may request their addition to this database, which doubles as the trade programs' mailing list, by completing an Export Questionnaire available from their office.

Export Trade and Finance Program: Assistance through financial counseling, facilitating services and lending/guarantee program.

Foreign Trade Zones: Operating with an FTZ offers several cost benefits: possible reduction or elimination of customs duty, deferral of duty payment, efficiency gains of bypassing customs through direct delivery.

South Dakota

Governor's Office of Economic Development
711 East Wells Ave.
Pierre, SD 57501-3369
605-773-5032
800-872-6190
Fax: 605-773-3256
www.state.sd.us/goed

Business Assistance

Governor's Office of Economic Development: This office can provide information and expertise in dealing with state, federal, and local agencies. They also have information on financing programs and other services offered by the state government

Workforce Development Program: Trains new employees, retrains current employees, and upgrades current employee skills.

Business Financing

Economic Development Finance Authority: Allows enterprises to pool tax-exempt or taxable development bonds for the purpose of constructing any site, structure, facility, service or utility for the storage, distribution or manufacturing of industrial or agricultural or nonagricultural products or the purchase of machinery and equipment used in an industrial process. Generally, the Authority will not consider loan requests for enterprises for amounts less than $300,000 and will not pool projects unless the pool volume is $1 million or more.

Revolving Economic Development and Initiative (REDI) Fund: Objective is to create "primary jobs" in South Dakota. Primary jobs are defined as "jobs that provide goods and services which shall be primarily exported from the state, gain market shares from imports to the state or meet an unmet need in the area resulting in the creation of new wealth in South Dakota. Primary jobs are derived from businesses that bring new income into an area, have a stimulative effect on other businesses or assist a community in diversification and stabilization of its economy." All for-profit businesses or business cooperatives are encouraged to apply, whether they are business start-ups, expansions, or relocations from outside South Dakota. The REDI Fund may provide up to 45% of the total project cost and requires the applicant to secure the matching funds before applying to the Board of Economic Development for the REDI Fund, including a 10% minimum equity contribution.

Tax Incentives

South Dakota is one of only two states with no corporate income tax, no personal income tax, no personal property tax and no business inventory tax.

Exports

International Trade Directory: Identifies South Dakota traders (i.e. exporters and importers) of manufactured products, agribusiness products, services and technologies. The directory also offers a list of various private companies and public agencies that are available to serve the special needs of South Dakota exporters and importers. Exporters Directory is available in hard copy upon request. Contact: Mr. Joop Bollen, South Dakota International Business Institute - NSU, 1200 S. Jay Street, Aberdeen, SD 57401-7198; 605-626-3149; Fax: 605-626-3004; {Email: bollenj@wolf.northern.edu}; {http://sdibi.northern.edu/sdibi.html}.

Foreign Direct Investment: For information on Foreign Direct Investment opportunities in South Dakota, contact one of the out-of-state development specialists at the Governor's Office of Economic Development.

Tennessee

Department of Economic and Community Development
Rachel Jackson Building, 8th Floor
320 Sixth Avenue North
Nashville, TN 37243-0405
615-741-1888
Fax: 615-741-7306
www.state.tn.us

Business Assistance

Self Help: There are two self help resource centers sponsored by Nations Bank and 1st Tennessee. The centers offer information on starting a business; preparing business plans; pro forma financial statements, small business management.

- 1st Tennessee has sponsored a center at the Memphis Public Library, Main Branch, 1850 Peabody, Memphis, TN 38104; 901-725-8877. It is open library hours. Nations Bank operates their own Business Resource Center at their West End Office in Nashville and Beale Street Office in Memphis. Each center has a large business library, plus PC-based access to national magazines and newspapers. They offer videos, cassettes and slide presentations, as well as self-help guides. Entrepreneurs do not have to be bank clients to use the centers and can even schedule early evening appointments with bank staff. Contact TN Small Business Center, 3401 West End Avenue, Suite 110, Nashville, TN 37203-1069; 615-749-4088; 800- 342-8217 Ext. 4088; or Business Resource Center, 555 Beale Street, Memphis, TN 38103; 901-526-9300.
- The Tennessee Economic Development Center provides conference rooms equipped with video conferencing and multimedia capability. The demonstration room offers computers with internet access that is available for people wishing to conduct research related to business and economic development.

Manufacturing Services: Utilizes field representatives, each with extensive industrial experience and expertise, to work with Tennessee's existing industries as they strive to succeed in today's competitive marketplace. Through its Manufacturing Means Jobs Initiative the division seeks to provide businesses an environment in which to prosper and expand, creating new jobs in the process and adding strength to the state's economic growth.

Agricultural Extension Service: Assistance in areas such as research based agricultural practices, agribusiness management, small and home based businesses in a rural setting. The extension service can draw on the resources of the university for many areas of technical expertise in rural based businesses.

Consulting Services: There are several no fee consulting services available in Tennessee. Funded by federal, state, local and private sources; these services can aid business owners in a variety of ways. However, these services are in great demand. In order to maximize the effectiveness of the programs, new business owners should examine their situations to determine the most appropriate form of assistance.

For these services, contact Tennessee Economic Development Center, Bellsouth Building, 300 Commerce Street, Nashville, TN 37201-33011; 615-214-3003.

Industrial Extension:

1) University of Tennessee Center for Industrial Services
CIS is a state wide industrial extension program dedicated to helping managers of Tennessee business and manufacturing firms find solutions to technical and managerial problems they face. CIS provides information and counseling services and strives to link resources of higher education with industrial needs. Contact UT Center for Industrial Services, Suite 606, 226 Capitol Boulevard, Nashville, TN 37219-1804; 615-532-8657; {www.cis.utk.edu}.

2) Tennessee Technological University Center for Manufacturing Research and Technology Utilization
   The Manufacturing Center was created to help improve the manufacturing productivity of state industry and to enhance instructional quality in manufacturing-related areas. The Center seeks to assist industry not only in research and development, but also in integrating manufacturing processes with a systems approach. At any given time in the Manufacturing Center, over 30 separate, but complimentary projects may be in progress. Contact Tennessee Tech Manufacturing Center, College of Business Administration, TTU Box 5077, Cookeville, TN 38505; 615-372-6634; Fax: 423-372-6249.

Small Business Incubation Centers: Incubation centers offer a low cost way for entrepreneurs to start their businesses in an office/light manufacturing environment. Offering low cost rental rates per square foot, incubators also offer shared resources such as conference rooms, utility hook ups, office copiers, some telephone support. The most valuable commodity they offer is a shared environment in which business owners can discuss common problems and reach solutions.

Small Business Information Guide: A resource manual that assists start-up and existing small businesses with issues like state and federal business taxes, business regulations and government assisted funding programs.

Industrial Training Service: Helps recruit, screen and train new employees, provide job-specific training and overall workforce development. They partner with over 40 community colleges, and technical institutes and technology centers across the state.

Business Financing

ACCE$$: The Nashville Area Chamber of Commerce, U.S. Small Business Administration and area banks started a financing program for small businesses. ACCE$$ serves the small business loan market, booking loans of $5000 and up. The program enables entrepreneurs the opportunity to present their business plans orally to a panel of bank loan officers. Panelists can qualify good credit risks immediately, improving the presenter's chances of obtaining an SBA guarantee. Regardless of the decision, small business owners receive valuable outside appraisal of their business plans. Contact: Nashville Area Chamber of Commerce, 161 Fourth Ave. N., Nashville, TN 37219; 615-259-4775; {www.nashvillechamber.com}.

Small And Minority Owned Telecommunications Business Assistance Program (Loan Guarantee): Designed to enhance and stimulate the growth, development and procurement opportunities for small, minority, and women owned businesses in the telecommunications industry in Tennessee.

Revolving Loan Funds: Available through nine community development corporations in Tennessee. The revolving loan fund combines funds secured from the Economic Development Administration and Farmer's Home Administration with regional funding sources to provide new or expanding businesses with financing at below market rates.

Tennessee Valley Authority Special Opportunity Counties Program: Designed to provide capital to finance projects which support the recruitment of new industry, the expansion of existing industry, the growth of small business, and the creation of new companies in the Tennessee Valley.

a) The Economic Development Loan Fund (EDLF): $20 million per year revolving loan program targeted on low interest loans to established companies relocating or expanding their operations in the Tennessee Valley. Loans are made for buildings, plant equipment, infrastructure, or property based on the capital investment leveraged, the number of jobs created, power load generated and geographic diversity. TVA Economic Development staff market the program, manage the loan review process, and manage the loan portfolio. Primary Focus: Sustained Growth.

b) Special Opportunities County Fund: $15 million revolving loan program targeted on low interest loans for companies expanding or relocating in the Tennessee Valley's most economically distressed counties. Loans are made for buildings, plant equipment, infrastructure, or property based on the capital investment leveraged and the number of jobs created. TVA Economic Development staff market the program, manage the loan review process, and manage the loan portfolio. Primary Focus: Sustained Growth.

c) Minority Business Development Loan Fund: Revolving loan fund targeted to socially and economically disadvantaged businesses in the Valley.

d) Commerce Capital LP. A Small Business Investment Company chartered by the Department of Commerce. Administration Commerce Capital's $5 million equity fund leverages up to $90 million federal dollars for rapidly growing small business operating capital needs in the Tennessee Valley. These investments are made in both debt and equity financing for companies in health care, manufacturing, environmental services, communications and information systems. Investments range from $500,000 to $3,000,000. TVA Economic Development staff market the SBIC program to valley businesses and submit the projects for review by the Commerce Capital General Partner. A TVA representative sits on the Commerce Capital board to review investment decisions and monitor return on investment. Primary Focus: Initial growth.

Contact: Tennessee Valley Authority, P.O. Box 292409, Nashville, TN 37229; 615-232-6000.

Tennessee Child Care Facilities Program: Assists child care providers by enabling them to upgrade facilities, create or expand the number of child care slots. The Program was established to accomplish two main goals: assist child care providers in attaining higher standards of safety and environment; increase the number of child care slots especially in rural and economically distressed areas. The program also assists companies and organizations wishing to establish day care centers for employees or groups of employees. The Program has three components:

*   Guarantees to lenders up to $250,000 for new construction
*   Direct loans to providers up to $10,000 for upgrade of facilities
*   Direct loans to providers up to $25,000 for new or addition of slots

As of spring, 1998, the guarantee portfolio totaled $2.3 million, close to its cap for prudent risk. Direct loans are subject to funding on an annual basis from different sources. Maturities as well as interest rates vary based on uses of the loans.

Rural Electric Administration (REA), Rural Economic Development Revolving Loan Program For Rural Electric And Telephone Cooperatives: Designed to promote rural economic development and job creation by providing zero interest loans to REA borrowers. The program will fund up to $100,000 per project. The maximum term of the loan is ten years at zero interest rate with a two-year deferred payment. For more information, contact your local electric utility company.

Small Business Energy Loan Program: Designed to assist in the identification, installation, and incorporation of approved energy efficiency measures onto, or into, the existing Tennessee located facilities processes, and for operations of approved applicants. The Energy Division currently maintains a loan portfolio of $4,560,000 to 115 borrowers. Approved loan requests average $39,000.

Rural Business & Cooperative Development Service Loan Guarantees: The U.S. Department of Agriculture, through the RBCDS (formerly Farmers Home Administration), guarantees term loans to non-farm businesses in rural areas; that is, localities with populations below 50,000 not adjacent to a city where densities exceed 100 persons per square mile. The Tennessee RBCDS currently maintains a loan portfolio in excess of $40,000,000 (in addition to their relending program with the Development Districts listed above) with 40 industrial borrowers. Approved loan requests average just over $1,000,000.

Small Business Investment Companies: Private investment and loan companies established to serve the small business market. They are funded with a combination of private and federal investment. SBICs assist only businesses below $6,000,000 in net worth and less than $2,000,000 in annual net income. They may prioritize investments in type (equity or loan); dollar amount, location or industry.

Occupational Safety And Health Grant: The goal of this program is to fund the education and training of employees in safe employment practices and conduct in the employer's own business for the employer's own employees; and promote the development of employer - sponsored health and safety programs in the employer's own business for the employer's own employees. Grants average in the $5000 range with some greater amounts. Contact Tennessee Department of Labor, Occupational Safety and Health Grant Program, Gateway Plaza, 2nd Floor, 710 James Robertson Parkway, Nashville, TN 37243; 800-332-2667.

Pollution Prevention Loan Program: Loans for the purchase of equipment and/or construction to complete pollution prevention activities at small and medium sized businesses.

Tennessee Technology Development Corporation: Provides seed capital fund for promising technology companies. Contact Tennessee Technology Development Corporation, 1020 Commerce Park Dr., Oak Ridge, TN 37830; 865-220-8832; {www.tennesseetechnology.org}.

Tax Incentives

Personal Income: Earned income is not taxed in Tennessee; however, certain dividend and interest income received by a Tennessee resident is taxable.

Energy Fuel and Water: Reduced sales tax on manufacturers' use of energy fuel and water at manufacturing site; tax-exempt if they have direct contact with product during manufacturing process.

Pollution Control Equipment: Exempt from sales tax.

Raw Materials: Exempt from sales tax.

Industrial Machinery: Exempt from sales tax.

Work-In-Progress: Exempt from property tax.

Finished Product Inventory: Exempt from property tax.

Investment Tax Credit: Manufacturers are allowed a tax credit of 1% of the cost of industrial machinery.

Franchise Tax Jobs Credit: Allows a $2,000 or $3,000 tax credit against franchise tax liability for each new full-time employee of qualified business that increases employment by 25 or more and meets required capital investment.

Exports

Export Assistance: Five core agencies provide assistance to Tennessee firms interested in or already exporting products abroad. Tennessee Department of Economic and Community Development, International Development Group provides strategic counsel support and coordination for the expansion of Tennessee's non-agricultural business and export interests in selected international markets. Contact International Development Group, 8th Floor Rachel Jackson Building, 320 Sixth Avenue, N., 7th Floor, Nashville, TN 37243; 615-741-5870; Fax: 615-741-7306.

International Trade Centers: Export efforts focus on novice and new to exporting firms. Maintaining offices in Memphis and Knoxville, the ITC can offer one on one counseling at any SBDC office across the state. ITC counselors:

- Assists in evaluating a company's export potential.
- Assists in market research.
- Assists with market entry strategies.
- Advises on market opportunities.
- Advises on export practices.
- Advises on export procedures.
- In addition to counseling, ITC sponsors continuing education seminars and workshops across the state. Those firms interested in exporting for the first time should contact the Small Business Development Center nearest them for ITC assistance. Contact SBDC - International Trade Center, University of Memphis, Memphis, TN 38152; 901-678-4174; Fax: 901-678-4072; or SBDC - International Trade Center, 301 East Church Street, Knoxville, TN 37915; 423-637-4283; Fax: 423-523-2071.

Tennessee Department of Agriculture, Division of Marketing: Offers similar services as the Tennessee Export Office, however specifically catering to the Tennessee farmers and agri-business people in the state. Their services include:

- hosting foreign buyer visits from abroad
- participating in trade shows and sales missions to key agricultural market destinations
- identifying foreign import requirements and assistance in obtaining appropriate documentation
- conducting seminars highlighting agricultural exports
- disseminate trade leads and other trade information

Contact Tennessee Department of Agriculture, Division of Marketing, Ellington Agricultural Center, P.O. Box 40627, Nashville, TN 37204; 615-837-5160.
Foreign Trade Zones: Tennessee has five foreign trade zones with eight sub-zones.

Women and Minorities

Office of Minority Business Enterprise: Facilitates the resources needed in assisting minority businesses in growth and business development by identifying sources of capital; linking successful businesses with minority businesses which need help in areas like training, quality control, supplier development or financial management; providing education and training, specialized technical assistance and identification of procurement opportunities in the public and private sectors; and publishing the Minority and Women Business Directory profiling minority businesses and their capabilities for public and private organizations which use their services or products. Contact Office of Minority Business Enterprise, 312 8th Ave. North, 11th Floor, Nashville, TN 37248; 615-741-2545.

Purchasing Councils: Encourages mutually beneficial economic links between ethnic minority suppliers and major purchasers in the public and private sectors. Contact Tennessee Minority Purchasing Council, Metro Center, Plaza 1 Building, 220 Athens Way, Suite 105, Nashville, TN 37225; 615-259-4699; or Mid-South Minority Purchasing Council, 4111 West Park Loop, Memphis, TN 38124; 901-678-2388.

Minority Business Development Center: Provides management, marketing, and technical assistance to increase business opportunities for minority entrepreneurs. Each center provides accounting, administration, business planning, construction, and marketing information to minority firms. The MBDC also identifies minority firms for contract and subcontract opportunities with government agencies and the private sector.

Tennessee Minority Business Automotive Initiative: Provides assistance in enhancing minority manufacturing opportunities, as well as subcontracting awards to minority businesses.

Texas

Department of Economic Development
P.O. Box 12728
Austin, TX 78711
512-936-0260
800-888-0511
www.tded.state.tx.us

Business Assistance

Department of Economic Development: Provides business counseling for both new and established firms. Helps firms locate capital, state procurement opportunities, state certification programs for minority and women-owned businesses, and resources management and technical assistance. An Office of Business Permit Assistance serves as a clearinghouse for permit-related information throughout the state and refers applicants to appropriate agencies for permit and regulatory needs. Publications are available containing information and resources for start-up and existing businesses. It also has a program for corporate expansion and recruitment.

Office of Small Business Assistance: Charged with helping the state's small businesses become more globally competitive. The Office provides information and assistance to establish, operate and expand small and historically underutilized businesses (HUBS). In addition, the Office is charged with being the focal point for comments, suggestions and information regarding HUBS and small businesses to develop and suggest proposals for changes in state and federal policies in response to this information.

Texas Manufacturing Assistance Center: Works for all Texans by enabling small manufacturers to better compete in the international marketplace. It's a manufacturing brain trust with a single mission: To improve and expand manufacturing in Texas through free technical assistance to small business manufacturers. Contact: Texas Manufacturing Assistance Center, P.O. Box 12728, Austin, TX 78711; 800-488-TMAC.

General Service Commission: To facilitate the ordering needs of the State of Texas, the General Services Commission has established procedures for procuring goods and services. Contact: General Services Commission, P.O. Box 13047, Austin, TX 78711; 512-463-3416.

Economic Development Clearinghouse: A one-stop center for information about economic development programs and technical assistance offered by state and federal agencies, local governments and other organizations. The clearinghouse's website is {www.edinfo.state. tx.us}.

Texas Marketplace: Offers businesses access to the internet including free web page, daily posting of all major procurement opportunities with the State of Texas, electronic bulletin board for posting information about commodities for sale or to buy, and other resources and government procurement opportunities. Contact: Texas Marketplace, Texas Department of Economic Development, Internet Services Group, P.O. Box 12728, Austin, TX 78711; 512-936-0236; {www.marketplace.state.tx.us}.

Business & Industry Data Center (BIDC): Provides one-stop access to data, information, and analyses on the Texas economy. Contact Business and Industry Data Center, P.O. Box 12728, Austin, TX 78711; 512-936-0550; {www.bidc.state.tx.us}.

Office of Defense Affairs: Develops pro-active statewide strategy to prevent future defense closures and realignments and assist defense-dependent communities to prepare for future base realignments or closures.

Business Financing

Linked Deposit Program: Established to encourage lending to historically underutilized businesses, child-care providers, non-profit corporations, and/or small businesses located in distressed communities by providing lenders and borrowers a lower cost of capital. Minimum loan amount is $10,000; maximum loan amount is $250,000, fixed borrower loan rate.

Capital Fund Infrastructure Program: This economic development program is designed to provide financial resources to non-entitlement communities. Funds can be utilized for public infrastructure to assist a business, which commits to create and/or retain permanent jobs, primarily for low and moderate-income persons. This program encourages new business development and expansions located in non-entitlement communities. The minimum & maximum award is $50,000 & $750,000 inclusive of administration. The award may not exceed 50% of the total project cost.

Capital Fund Real Estate Development Program: This economic development program is designed to provide financial resources to non-entitlement communities. Funds can be utilized for real estate development to assist a business that commits to create and/or retain permanent jobs, primarily for low and moderate-income persons. The minimum and maximum award is $50,000 and $750,000 inclusive of administration. The award may not exceed 50% of the total project cost.

Capital Fund Main Street Improvements Program: The Texas Capital Fund Main Street Improvements Program is designed to foster and stimulate the development of small businesses by providing financial assistance to non-entitlement cities (designated by the Texas Historical Commission as a Main Street City) for public improvements. This program encourages the elimination of slum or blighted areas. Minimum awards are $75,000. Maximum awards are $150,000. Matching funds must be provided.

Small Business Industrial Revenue Bond Program: Designed to provide tax-exempt financing to finance land and depreciable property for eligible industrial or manufacturing projects. The Development Corporation Act allows cities, counties, conservation and reclamation districts to form non-profit industrial development corporations or authorities on their behalf. Program objective is to issue taxable and tax-exempt bonds for eligible projects in cities, counties, conservation and reclamation districts. The industrial development corporation acts as a conduit through which all monies are channeled. Generally, all debt services on the bonds are paid by the business under the terms of a lease, sale, or loan agreement. As such, it does not constitute a debt or obligation of the governmental unit, the industrial development corporation, or the State of Texas.

Capital Access Fund: Established to increase the availability of financing for businesses and nonprofit organizations that face barriers in accessing capital . Through the use of the Capital Access Fund, businesses that might otherwise fall outside the guidelines of conventional lending may still have the opportunity to receive financing. The essential element of the program is a reserve account established at the lending institution to act as a credit enhancement, inducing the financial institution to make a loan. Use of proceeds may include working capital or the purchase, construction, or lease of capital assets, including buildings and equipment used by the business. There is no minimum or maximum loan amount, only a maximum amount that the state will provide to the financial institution's reserve fund.

Smart Jobs Fund: Provides grants to businesses to train their employees. Although a company is limited to $1.5 million per fiscal year, subject to certain limitations, the Fund recommends that applicants limit their applications to a maximum of $2,500 per trainee for small businesses and $1,200 per trainee for large businesses.

Leverage Fund: An economic development bank offering an added source of financing to communities that have passed the economic development sales tax. This program allows the community to make loans to local businesses for expansion or to recruit new industries.

Tax Incentives

Enterprise Zone Program: Designed to induce capital investment and create new permanent jobs into areas of economic distress. Qualified businesses located in an enterprise zone may qualify for a variety of local and state incentives including a refund of state sales and use taxes, franchise tax reductions, and state administered program priority.

Texas does not have statewide business tax incentives. These are handled at the city and/or county level in the city/county in which a business enterprise is based.

Exports

Office of International Business (OIB) helps Texas companies expand their business worldwide. By providing a forum for international business exchange through international trade missions, trade shows, seminars and inbound buyers missions, OIB gives Texas companies the opportunity to promote their products and services to international buyers and partners. OIB also helps to connect companies with counseling and training available through the International Small Business Development Centers and works with entities such as the U.S. Department of Commerce, the Japan External Trade Organization, the Texas consular corps and its counterparts in the Mexican border states to ensure that Texas business interests are represented abroad. The State of Texas office in Mexico City is an invaluable resource for facilitating business between Texas and Mexico. Programs include:

- Trade Missions and Trade Shows
- Export Counseling
- Partnerships
- Trade Lead Distribution
- Texas International Center
- Research Publications

Utah

Business and Economic Development Division
324 South State St., Suite 500
Salt Lake City, UT 84111
801-538-8800
Fax: 801-538-8889
www.dced.state.ut.us

Business Assistance

Business and Economic Development Division: Provides information on regulations, sources of assistance, and other important information for starting a business.

Custom Fit Training: Provides training for new or expanding companies. A Custom Fit representative will discuss with the company the training needs anticipated and then develop a specific customized training plan to meet those needs. The required training can take place at a variety of locations including the business or a local institution. Often training is provided in both locations. The program can provide instructors from the State's learning institutions, private sector, consultants or instructors within the business. The program is designed to be flexible to meet the specific needs of the company. Contact: Utah State Office of Education, Applied Technology Division, 250 East 500 South, Salt Lake City, UT 84111; 801-538-7867; {www.usoe.k12.ut.us/ate/CF/custom.htm}.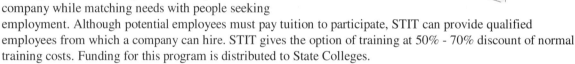

Short Term Intensive Training (STIT): Programs are customized and designed to meet full-time job openings. Programs are usually less than one year in length and will be designed to meet the specific training needs of a company while matching needs with people seeking employment. Although potential employees must pay tuition to participate, STIT can provide qualified employees from which a company can hire. STIT gives the option of training at 50% - 70% discount of normal training costs. Funding for this program is distributed to State Colleges.

Job Service: A computerized job matching system that quickly screens applicants to ensure that they meet the qualifications set by a company. Over 16,000 active applicants are presently registered with the Salt Lake Office. Job Service personnel can save countless hours by taking all of company applications and then referring only the most qualified applicants.

Centers of Excellence Program: Supports selected research programs at Utah's universities. Programs are selected based on leading edge research activities that have projected commercial value. The primary objective is to encourage the commercialization of leading edge technologies through licensing patented technologies and by creating new companies. The Centers of Excellence Program impacts Utah's economic development by the creation of jobs, the flow of licensing royalties, the expansion of the tax base, and the leveraged use of matching fund dollars to strengthen research and development at Utah's institutions of higher learning.

Utah Partners in Education: Facilitates business/ education/ government partnerships statewide. Purpose is to find ways in which those three entities can work together to meet common needs and thereby strengthen the economy of Utah. Contact: Utah Partners in Education, 324 South State St., Suite 500, Salt Lake City, UT 84111; 801-538-8628; {www.utahpartnership.utah.org}.

Utah Directory of Business and Industry: A listing of more than 9,800 individual employers sorted by Standard Industrial Classification (SIC), which is a standard method for classifying what businesses or other organizations do.

Environmental Permitting: One-stop shopping for the environmental permitting process through the Department of Environmental Quality.

Business Financing

Utah Ventures: a privately financed venture fund focusing on investments in the life sciences and information technology in Utah, other Intermountain states and California. Utah Ventures seeks to identify the best opportunities, secure subsequent coinvestments from other venture funds and corporate investors, and works with the entrepreneur to help build the business. Contact Utah Ventures, 423 Wakara Way Suite 206, Salt Lake City, UT 84108; 801-225-5395.

Revolving Loan Funds: In an effort to create jobs and improve the business climate of a community, some cities, counties, and Associations of Governments (geographical regions) will lend money to small businesses located in their areas. The amount available to a business goes from a few thousand dollars to over $100,000. Typically, the money is used for plant and equipment, working capital, inventory or accounts receivable financing. Rates are usually less than or equal to conventional lender financing, and the term for repayment may be either short (6 months) or extended (many years). This type of financing is often used in conjunction with other lender financing since most revolving loan programs will accept a second or third position on financed assets.

Microenterprise Loan Fund (UMLF) is a tax-exempt, nonprofit corporation. It provides a modestly secured form of financing up to $10,000, with terms up to five years, to owners of startup and existing firms who do not have access to traditional funding sources, especially those who are socially or economically disadvantaged. The interest rate is prime plus 3% fixed, and the business must be located in Salt Lake County. Contact: Utah Microenterprise Loan Fund, 3595 S. Main St., Salt Lake City, UT 84115; 801-269-8408; {www.umif.com}

The Utah Technology Finance Corporation is an independent corporation of the state that makes debt investments in Utah companies. UTFC leverages state and federal funds as a catalyst in capital formation for the creations, growth, and success of Utah Businesses. UTFC offers various types of debt financing through such programs as Early Technology Business Capital, Utah Rural Loan Program, MicroLoan Program, Utah Revolving Loan Fund, Bank Participation Loan Program, and Defense Conversion Loan Program. Contact Utah Technology Finance Corporation (UTFC), 177 East 100 South, Salt Lake City, UT 84111; 801-364-4346; Fax: 801-364-4361; {www.utfc.org}.

Industrial Assistance Fund: Can be used for relocation costs. This incentive loan can be repaid as Utah jobs created meet the IAF requirements resulting in higher quality jobs, and as Utah purchases merit enough earned credits to convert the loan to a grant. Three basic programs exist: 1) rural Utah program with funding up to $100,000 for relocation expenses; 2) Corporate Funding which is dependent on the amount of Utah purchases and wages: 3) Targeted Industries which is primarily aimed at information technology, biomedical and aerospace.

Industrial Development Bonds (IDB's): A financing tool used by private sector developers for manufacturing facilities. The federal tax code places a limit of $10.0 million per project on IDB financing.

Tax Incentives

No inventory or worldwide unitary taxes.

New Equipment: An exemption of sales and use taxes are available for the purchase or lease of new equipment or machinery for manufacturing facilities.

Economic Development Area/Tax Increment Financing: Tax increment financing (TIF) is utilized in areas that have been targeted for economic development. Redevelopment areas are determined by local municipalities. Portions of the new property tax generated by new development projects are returned to project developers in the form of infrastructure development, land cost write down or other appropriate means. Details of TIF are site specific. Development of a proposal is relatively simple, yet the benefits can be great.

Enterprise Zones: The act passed by the Utah State Legislature provides tax credits for manufacturing companies locating in rural areas that qualify for assistance. A $750 tax credit is given for all new job created plus a credit of $1,250 for jobs paying at least 125% of the average wage for the industry. In addition, investment tax credits are available for all investment in new plant and equipment as follows: 10% for first $100,000; 5% of next

$250,000. Tax credits can be carried forward for 3 years. Enterprise Zones benefits are only available in certain non-metro counties.

Special programs such as Affirmative Action, Targeted Job Tax Credits and veterans programs are also available.

Exports

International Business Development Office: Programs offered include:
- Trade Representatives
- Country Information
- Market Research Reports
- Trade Lead Resource Center
- Foreign Business Directories
- Trade Shows and Exhibits

Women and Minorities

Offices of Ethnic Affairs: Recognizing that state government should be responsive to all citizens, and wishing to promote cooperation and understanding between government agencies and its ethnic citizens, these offices were created:
- Office Of Asian Affairs
- Office Of Black Affairs
- Office Of Hispanic Affairs
- Office Of Polynesian Affairs
- Division of Indian Affairs

Minority and Women Owned Business Source Directory: Offered by the Utah PTAC (Procurement Technical Assistance Center). The directory includes approximately 850 companies, and is the most complete such listing available. However, listings are voluntary, having been obtained through surveys, and this is not to be construed as a comprehensive catalog. There are some 4,400 minority-owned employers in the state, and 46,000 that are women-owned.

Vermont

Department of Economic Development
National Life Building, Drawer 20
Montpelier, VT 05620-0501
802-828-3221
800-341-2211
Fax: 802-828-3258
www.thinkvermont.com

Business Assistance

Department of Economic Development: A one-stop shop ready to help with businesses to support the economic growth of the state through job creation and retention. Areas in which the Department can assist Vermont businesses are entrepreneurs; international trade; financing; government contracts, marketing; permits; site location; and training.

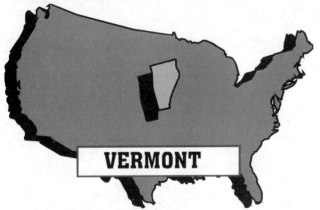

Regional Development Corporations: Twelve RDCs serve every geographic region of the state serving as satellites of the Department of Economic Development, and provide many of the same services. Their primary function is to coordinate job and business development activities within their geographic region.

Manufacturing Extension Center: Provides one-on-one support and services through Field Engineers to small and mid-sized manufacturers. Their goal is to assist Vermont manufacturers increase productivity, modernize processes, and improve their competitiveness. Ongoing training opportunities designed specifically for manufacturers are also offered. Contact: Vermont Manufacturing Extension Center, VT Technical College, P.O. Box 500, Randolph Center, VT 05061; 802-728-1432; {www.vmec.org}.

Business Assistance Network: An accessible series of resources designed to provide timely and pertinent information to businesses interested in participating in new markets for their products or services, increasing competitiveness, or building "teaming arrangements" with other businesses. The information may be accessed through the Internet at {www.state.vt.us}.

Micro Business Development Program: Promotes self-employment and business expansion opportunities for low income Vermonters. Offers free, one-to-one technical assistance and business development workshops for income eligible persons. Contact Bruce Whitney, c/o SEVCA, 91 Buck Dr., Westminster, VT 05158; 802-722-4575, ext. 142.

Northeast Employment and Training Organization: Manages the Entrepreneurial Training Program which provides statewide small business management courses to enterprises of all sizes, including individuals interested in self-employment and micro businesses. Contact: Northeast Employment Training Organization, P.O. Box 186, 145 Railroad St., St. Johnsbury, VT 05819; 802-748-8935; {http://vt-neto.org}.

Government Marketing Assistance Center: Exists to design, implement, and maintain resources that promote economic expansion by providing assistance to Vermont businesses' which allow them to pursue and compete in the public procurement process and introduce them to new markets for their goods and/or services. The GMAC can provide a business with a customized search to receive Federal bid opportunities, including bids available through Electronic Data Interchange (EDI). A business must be registered to receive Federal Bids opportunities.

Vermont Business Registry: An on-line registry of businesses throughout Vermont involved in manufacturing, manufacturing support, product distribution, services, research and development, and construction.

Vermont Bid Opportunities: An electronic resource which provides businesses with a current listing of bid opportunities available through Vermont based federal, state and local governments and by the private sector purchasing organizations.

Business Calendar of Events: Lists business assistance seminars, training workshops, trade shows, etc., which are sponsored by various organizations.

The Vermonter's Guide to Doing Business: Provides information relating to public and private institutions that can assist local businesses on any aspect of successful business operation.

Department of Employment and Training: Offers a full range of workforce-related services and information through a network of 12 One-Stop Career Resource Centers. {www.det.state.vt.us}.

Market Vermont Program: A cooperative effort among the Departments of Economic Development; Agriculture, food and Markets; Tourism and Marketing; Forest, Parks and Recreation; Fish and Wildlife; Historic Preservation; Vermont Life Magazine; Vermont Economic Progress Council; and Vermont Council on the Arts to identify and promote goods made, and services offered, in Vermont.

Agricultural Marketing: Provides resource for the promotion of various agricultural projects and works with commodity groups to improve market opportunities. Marketing representatives help with promotion, marketing, packaging, support publications, etc. Contact: Department of Agriculture, Development Division, 116 State St., Drawer 20, Montpelier, VT 05620; 802-828-2416.

Business Financing

Rural Economic Activity Loans: REAL loans are available to assist rural entrepreneurs who cannot obtain adequate financing from other sources on reasonable terms to establish or expand their business. These businesses must demonstrate the potential to significantly improve or retain employment opportunities. Loans up to $25,000 may be made to fund the cost of an eligible project, but cannot exceed 75% of total project costs. For loans greater than $25,000, funds may be provided for up to 40% of fixed asset project costs and/or 50% of working capital loan projects.

Small Business Development Corporation: A non-profit corporation offering loans between $2,500 and $50,000 to assist growing Vermont small businesses who cannot access conventional sources of credit. Funds may be used to finance the acquisition of fixed assets or for working capital with restrictions.

Job Start Program: Helps develop self-employment opportunities for low and moderate income Vermonters through loans used to start, strengthen or expand small businesses. Funds may be used to purchase equipment, inventory or for working capital.

Financial Access Program: Designed to enhance opportunities for small businesses to access commercial credit utilizing a pooled reserve concept. Loans must be in an amount up to and including $200,000 made to businesses with sales less than $5 million.

Mortgage Insurance Program: Designed to aid businesses by insuring loans made by commercial banks. Proceeds may be used to insure loans made for the acquisition of land, buildings, machinery and equipment or working capital, for use in an eligible facility. Maximum is $2 million per project.

Local Development Corporation Loans: Loans to nonprofit local development corporations are available through VEDA-s Subchapter 3 program. "Spec" buildings and incubators can provided low cost, flexible leased space for businesses which prefer not to own their own facility. Loan proceeds may be used for the purchase of land for industrial parks, industrial park planning and development, and the construction or improvement of speculative buildings or small business incubator facilities.

Industrial Revenue Bonds: Designed to aid businesses through VEDA's issuance of tax-exempt, low interest bonds to provide funds for the acquisition of land, buildings, and/or machinery and equipment for use in a manufacturing facility.

Direct Loan Program: Designed to finance the establishment or expansion of eligible facilities through the acquisition, construction and installation of fixed assets. Provides attractive variable rate loans to business for the purchase of land, the purchase or construction (including renovation) of buildings, and the purchase and installation of machinery and equipment for use in an eligible facility.

For above loans, contact Vermont Economic Development Authority, 58 E. State St., Montpelier, VT 05602; 802-828-5627; {www.veda.state.vt.us}.

Vermont Sustainable Jobs Fund: The goal of the fund is to develop and support projects throughout the State leading to the creation or retention of quality jobs, and the protection and enhancement of Vermont's human and natural resources. Grants and technical assistance will be available for collaborative activity including the development of flexible manufacturing networks, business clusters, and networks. A specific area of focus will be adding value to agricultural products that use the natural resource of grass. Contact: Vermont Sustainable Jobs Fund, Inc., 58 E. State St., Montpelier, VT 05602; 802-828-5320; {www.vsif.org}.

Agricultural Facility and Debt Stabilization Loans: Provides loans and refinancing for family farms or agricultural facility operators.

Regional/Local Revolving Loan Funds: Existing through the state, the administration of these funds is generally a non-profit development corporation.

Business and Industrial Loan Guarantees: Designed to serve the credit needs of large rural businesses. Emphasis is placed on loan guarantees between $500,000 and $3 million, but may be issued up to $10 million.

Business and Industry Direct Loans: A limited amount of funding is available for direct business loans in designated areas of economic distress. The program is targeting loans in the $100,000 to $250,000 range.

Intermediary Relending Program: Designed to finance small and emerging business and community development projects in rural areas. Loans are made to qualified intermediaries who in turn relend to small businesses and community development organizations. Business or organizations borrowing from the intermediary must be located in a rural area. The maximum loan to an intermediary is $2 million and the maximum loan that the intermediary can relend for a project is $150,000.

Rural Business Enterprise Grant: Provides grants to public bodies and non-profit corporations for the benefit of small and emerging businesses. Grant funds may be used to establish revolving loan funds, construct facilities, provide planning, or technical assistance.

Burlington Micro Loan Program: Available for asset financing, inventory financing, and working capital to businesses located in the City of Burlington. Typical loans range from $500 to $5,000. Contact Community and Economic Development Office, Room 32, City Hall, Burlington, VT 05401; 802-865-7187.

Green Mountain Capital, L.P.: Established as a Small Business Investment Company to provide working capital loans to rapidly growing small businesses in Vermont. Companies that qualify will probably have achieved a level of sales in excess of $1 million dollars annually. GMC does not finance start-ups. Contact Green Mountain Capital, RD 1, Box 1503, Waterbury, VT 05676; 802-244-8981.

North Atlantic Venture Fund, L.P.: A private enterprise that seeks to invest from $100,000 to $750,000 in high-quality opportunities that have outgrown seed capital resources and are either not ready for or have exceeded the limits of commercial bank lending resources. Contact Vermont Venture Capital Fund, 76 St. Paul St., Burlington, VT 05401; 802-658-7820.

Tax Incentives

Payroll Tax Credit: A firm may receive a credit against income tax liability equal to a percentage of its increased payroll costs.

Research and Development Tax Credit: A firm may receive a credit against income tax liability in the amount of 10% of qualified research and development expenditures.

Workforce Development Tax Credit: A firm may receive a credit against income tax liability in the amount of 10% of its qualified training, education and workforce development expenditures. A 20% credit may be taken for qualified training, education and workforce development expenditures for the benefit of welfare to work participants.

Small Business Investment Tax Credit: A firm may receive a credit against income tax liability in the amount equal to 5% to 10% of its investments within the state in excess of $150,000 in plants, facilities, and machinery and equipment.

Sales and Use Tax Exemptions:
1. Sales of electricity, oil, gas and other fuels used on site directly in the production of projects or services.
2. Sales of building materials within any three consecutive years in excess of $1 million in purchase value used in the construction, renovation or expansion of facilities that are used exclusively for the manufacture of tangible personal property for sales. The threshold for sales of building materials can be reduced to $250,000 for businesses that receive approval from VEDC or are located in a designated downtown development district.
3. Machinery and equipment, including system-based software used directly in the production of products or services.

Construction In Progress Property Tax Exemption: A tax exemption for a period not to exceed two years is available for real property, excluding land, consisting of unoccupied new facilities, or unoccupied facilities under renovation or expansion that are less than 75% complete.

Brownfields Property Tax Exemption: Exempt from the statewide education property tax are real property consisting of the value of remediation expenditures incurred by a business for the construction of new, expanded or renovated facilities on contaminated property.

Rehabilitation Investment Tax Credit: A federal income tax credit is available for 20% of the costs of rehabilitating income-producing historic buildings.

Sprinkler System Rebate: A building owner who installs a complete automatic fire sprinkler system in an older or historic building that has been certified for one of the state building rehabilitation tax credits is eligible for a rebate for the cost of a sprinkler system, not to exceed $2,000.

Money Management Industry Tax Credit: An income tax credit of up to 75% for the money management industry that can be taken every year and is easy to understand and therefore claim.

Employee Training Tax Credit: An employer can claim up to $400 in tax credits per year for training qualified employees if the employer does business in a designated downtown district with the intent of providing permanent employment.

Credit For Income From Commercial Film Production: A credit shall be available against the tax imposed for that taxable year upon the taxable income received from a dramatic performance in a commercial film production during that taxable year. The credit shall be in the amount by which the Vermont tax on such income, without regard to this credit, exceeds the highest personal income tax rate in the taxpayer's state of residence, multiplied by the Vermont commercial film production income.

Exports

Vermont World Trade Office: Assists businesses wishing to export their products and services, to expand by developing sales in new markets, and by encouraging suitable foreign companies to establish operations within the state. Contact World Trade Office, 60 Main St., Suite 102, Burlington, VT 05401; 802-865-0698; {www.vermontworldtrade.org}.

VEDA Export Financing: In addition to the Export Working Capital Guarantee Program, VEDA offers a number of other loan and insurance programs for Vermont's exporting community. This includes small business credit insurance, and environmental exports program, and export credit insurance short-term multi-buyer policy, and a medium-term single-buyer policy.

Export Tax Credit: A firm which makes sales outside of Vermont may take as a credit against their income tax liability, the difference between the income tax calculated under the existing state apportionment formula and the proposed formula which double weights the sales factor and disregards throwback provision. The incentive is favorable to exporters, encouraging Vermont businesses that export to declare a greater amount of taxable income.

Women and Minorities

Women's Small Business Program: Offers a continuum of services to women seeking to identify, start, stabilize and expand a small business. Services include: Getting Serious, a workshop to determine a business idea and whether business meets personal goals; Start-Up, a 15 week intensive course to develop a business plan and business management skills; Working Solution, topic specific workshops for micro-business owner; and a graduate association to foster ongoing networking and access to information. They also offer comprehensive skills training and the opportunity to connect with other women entrepreneurs. Grants and scholarships for training are available to income eligible women. Contact: Women's Small Business Program, Trinity College, 208 Colchester Ave., Burlington, VT 05401; 802-846-7338; 877-770-VWBC.

Virginia

Economic Development Partnership
P.O. Box 798
Richmond, VA 23206
804-371-8100
Fax: 804-371-8112
www.yesvirginia.org

Business Assistance

Economic Development Partnership: Helps new and expanding businesses by answering questions about licensing, taxes, regulations, assistance programs, etc. The office can also locate sources of information in other state agencies, and it can identify sources of help for business planning, management, exporting, and financing.

Virginia Department of Business Assistance: A good starting point for new businesses to learn about financial programs, workshops, business planning and more. Contact Virginia Department of Business Assistance, P.O. Box 466, Richmond, VA 23218; 804-371-8200; Fax: 804-371-2142; {www.dba.state.va.us}.

Existing Industry Division (EID): Discovers needs and identifies resources that allow existing businesses and industries to take advantage of opportunities and avoid problems. EID professionals generally call on organizations within geographic territories and discuss business conditions. Information collected is processed and analyzed for further action.

Workforce Services Division (WFS): Works with new and existing businesses and industries to recruit and train qualified workers at all skill levels for newly created jobs. The programs addressing these efforts support State and local Economic Development marketing efforts.

Workforce Services: Mission is to train and retrain Virginians for specific employment opportunities. Offers consulting, video production for training purposes, and funding.

Center for Innovative Technology: Exists to stimulate economic growth by serving technology businesses. Services include: access to 11 technology development centers; assistance with pursuing joint product development with a Virginia university and provide co-funding for projects; entrepreneurship programs designed to help early stage companies bring new products to market; assistance solving manufacturing production problems. Contact Center for Innovative Technology, 2214 Rock Hill Rd, Suite 600, Herndon, VA 20170; 800-383-2482; {www.cit.org}

Virginia's Business Development Network: Designed to provide management and technical assistance to small and medium-sized companies. Provides one-on-one counseling and group training on a variety of subjects and assists entrepreneurs with pre-business planning.

Business Financing

Virginia Small Business Financing Authority: Offers financing programs to provide businesses with access to capital needed for growth and expansion. Programs include:
1. *Industrial Development Bonds (IDBs) and the Umbrella IDB Program*: VSBFA issues tax-exempt and taxable revenue bonds (IDBs) statewide to provide creditworthy businesses with access to long term, fixed asset financing at favorable interest rates and terms. Tax-exempt IDBs may be used to finance new or expanding manufacturing facilities and exempt projects, such as solid waste disposal facilities. In addition, VSBFA offers

an Umbrella IDB Program that provides a cost-effective means for businesses to sell their bonds in the public bond market, particularly for smaller projects with limited access to this market.

2. *Virginia Economic Development Revolving Loan Fund*: This fund provides loans of up to $700,000 to bridge the gap between private debt financing and private equity for projects that will result in job creation or retention. Funding is available for fixed asset financing to new and expanding manufacturing companies and other industries that derive 50% or more of their sales outside of Virginia.

3. *Virginia Defense Conversion Revolving Loan Fund*: This fund provides loans of up to $700,000 to assist defense dependent companies seeking to expand into commercial markets and diversify their operations. Funding is available for fixed assets and working capital.

4. *Loan Guarantee Program*: This program is designed to reduce the risk to banks in making loans thereby increasing the availability of short-term capital for small businesses. Under the program, VSBFA will guarantee up to $250,000 or 50%, whichever is less, of a bank loan. Typical borrowings include revolving lines of credit to finance accounts receivable and inventory, and short-term loans for working capital and fixed asset purchases, such as office or research equipment.

5. *Virginia Capital Access Program (VCAP):* VCAP provides a form of loan portfolio insurance for participating banks through special loan loss reserve accounts which are funded by loan enrollment premiums paid by the bank/borrower and matched by the VSBFA. This allows the banks to exceed their normal risk thresholds for commercial loans of all types and, thereby, accommodate a broader array of loan requests from Virginia businesses.

6. *Export Financing*: Offers bank loans for export working capital, and continues to work in partnership with the Export-Import Bank of the United States.

7. *Child Day Care Financing Program*: VSBFA provides small direct loans to child day care providers for quality enhancement projects or to meet or maintain child care standards. Eligible loan uses include infant care equipment or equipment needed to care for children with special needs, playground improvements, vans, and upgrades or minor renovations to kitchens, bathrooms, and plumbing and electrical systems.

Contact: Virginia Small Business Financing Authority, P.O. Box 446, Richmond, VA 23218; 804-371-8254; {www.vsbfa.state.va.us}.

Financial Services Division (FSD): Identifies potential financial resources to meet the capital needs of Virginia business clients, and administers loan and guarantee programs designed to foster growth and private financing in Virginia business.

Governor's Opportunity Fund: Supports economic development projects that create new jobs and investment in accordance with criteria established by state legislation. Funds can be used for such things as site acquisition and development; transportation access; training; construction or build-out of publicly owned buildings; or grants or loans to Industrial Development Authorities.

Solar Photovoltaic Manufacturing Grants: Designed to encourage the product development and manufacture of a high technology, renewable energy source in Virginia. Any manufacturer who sells solar photovoltaic panels, manufactured in Virginia, is entitled to receive an annual grant of up to seventy-five cents per watt of the rated capacity of panel sold. Contact: Virginia Department of Mines, Minerals, and Energy, 202 N. Ninth St., Ninth Street Office Bldg., 8th Floor, Richmond, VA 23219; 804-692-3200.

Virginia Coalfield Economic Development Authority: Designed to enhance the economic base of specific areas. The Authority provides low interest loans or grants to qualified new or expanding industries through its financing program to be used for real estate purchases, construction or expansion of buildings, and the purchase of machinery and equipment. Contact: Virginia Coalfield Economic Development Authority/ The Virginia Southwest Promise, P.O. Box 1060, Lebanon, VA 24266; 540-889-0381.

Virginia Capital L.P.: A private venture capital firm. Investments that are attractive include ownership transactions and profitable, growing companies whose needs exceed senior bank debt capacity. Typical investments range between $500,000 and $1,500,000. Contact: Virginia Capital L.P., 9 South 12th St., Suite 400, Richmond, VA 23219; 804-648-4802.

Enterprise Zone Job Grants: Businesses creating new-full-time positions are eligible to receive grants of up to $500 per position ($1,000 if a zone resident fills a position). The maximum grant to any one firm is $100,000 a year for the three consecutive years in the grant period.

Tax Incentives

Major Business Facility Job Tax Credit: Qualified companies locating or expanding in Virginia receive a $1,000 corporate income tax credit for each new full-time job created over a threshold number of jobs

Recycling Equipment Tax Credit: An income tax credit is available to manufacturers for the purchase of certified machinery and equipment for processing recyclable materials. The credit is equal to 10% of the original total capitalized cost of the equipment.

Job Tax Credits

Day Care Facility Investment Tax Credit: Corporations may claim a tax credit equal to 25% of all expenditures incurred in the construction, renovation, planning or acquisition of facilities for the purpose of providing day care for children of company employees. The maximum credit is $25,000.

Neighborhood Assistance Tax Credit: An income tax credit is provided for companies that make donations to neighborhood organizations conducting approved community assistance programs for impoverished people. The credit equals 45% of the total donation.

Clean Fuel Vehicle Job Creation Tax Credit: Businesses manufacturing or converting vehicles to operate on clean fuel and manufacturers of components for use in clean fuel vehicles are eligible to receive an income tax credit for each new full-time job created over and above the previous year's employment level. The credit is equal to $700 in the year the job is created, and in each of two succeeding years if the job is continued, for a maximum of $2,100 per job.

Clean Fuel Vehicle Tax Credit: An income tax credit is available to companies which purchase clean fuel vehicles or invest in related refueling facilities. The credit is equal to 10% of the IRS allowed deduction or credit for these purchases.

Worker Retraining Tax Credit: Employers are eligible to receive an income tax credit equal to 30% of all expenditures made by the employer for eligible worker retraining.

Property Tax Incentives: No property tax at the state level; real estate and tangible personal property are taxed at the local level. Virginia differs from most states in that its counties and cities are separate taxing entities. A company pays either county or city taxes, depending on its location. No tax on intangible property; manufacturers' inventory, manufacturers' furniture, fixtures, or corporate aircraft. Exemptions include: certified pollution control facilities and equipment; certified recycling equipment, rehabilitated commercial/industrial real estate; manufacturers' generating equipment; certified solar energy devices.

Sales and Use Tax Exemptions: Manufacturers' purchases used directly in production; items purchased for re-sale by distributors; certified pollution control equipment and facilities; custom computer software; purchases used in research and development; most film, video and audio production related purchases.

Enterprise Zones: Designed to stimulate business development in distressed urban and rural areas. Incentives include:

1. General Tax Credit: A 10 year tax credit is available against state income tax liability (80% first year and 60% in years two through ten) that results from business activity within an enterprise zone.
2. Refundable Real Property Improvement Tax Credit: A tax credit equal to 30% of qualified zone real property improvements is available to businesses that rehabilitate property or undertake new construction in an enterprise zone. The maximum credit within a five-year period is $125,000.
3. Investment Tax Credit For Large Qualified Zone Projects: Projects with an investment of at least $100 million and creating at least 200 jobs are eligible for a negotiated credit of up to 5% of total investment in real property, machinery and equipment.

Exports

Export Financing Assistance Program: VSBFA provides guarantees of up to the lesser of $750,000 or 90% of a bank loan for export working capital, and also works with the Export-Import Bank of the United States (Eximbank) and the U.S. Small Business Administration (SBA) to provide Virginia exporters with easier access to federal loan guarantees. In addition, VSBFA administers an Eximbank Export Credit Insurance Umbrella Policy to assist Virginia exporters in obtaining insurance on their foreign receivables.

International Market Planning: Designed to assist companies developing new export markets and increase sales. Offers international marketing research; current market analyses; specific strategies to access selected markets.

Women and Minorities

VWBE Certification Program: Helps Virginia's women-owned and operated companies certify themselves as WBE's to better compete in government and corporate procurement markets. In addition to being listed in the directory, certified companies will be registered in the WBE website, as well as in the Virginia Procurement Pipeline website. Certified WBE's also have the privilege of using the WBE seal on marketing materials and letterhead. They also receive information on other resources available to women-owned businesses regarding government contracting, management issues, and women's ownership. Contact: Women's Enterprise Program, P.O. Box 446, Richmond, VA 23218; 804-371-8200; {www.dba.state.va.us/SBDWBE.htm}.

Washington

Department of Community, Trade and Economic Development
906 Columbia St. SW
P.O. Box 48300
Olympia, WA 98504-8300
800-237-1233
www.cted.wa.gov

Business Assistance

Business Assistance Center:
1. ***The Business Assistance Center Hotline***: A statewide, toll-free information and referral service, provides information regarding state business licensing, registration, technical assistance, other state agencies or one-to-one business counseling. To contact a person from the Business Assistance Hotline, call 800-237-1233; 360-586-4840; TDD 360-586-4852.
2. ***Education & Training***: Efforts are focused on providing practical application of economic development techniques along with providing a forum for practitioners for the interchange of economic development ideas. Contact Business Assistance Center, 2001 6th Ave., Suite 2600, Seattle, WA 98121; 800-237-1233; 360-664-9501.

One-Stop Licensing Center: A convenient, one-stop system that takes care of basic registration requirements and offers information about any additional licensing.

Business Retention & Expansion Program: Works with at-risk manufacturing and processing firms to reduce the number of business closures, layoffs and failures that result in significant job loss. State and local staff provide technical and problem solving assistance for these companies.

Job Skills Program: Provides grants for customized training projects. It requires at least 50% matching support from industry which may be in the form of donated or loaned equipment, instructional time contributed by company personnel, use of company facilities or training materials.

Loan Portfolio Management: Staff evaluate and process loan applications.

Business Investment Program: Support the creation of family wage jobs by providing technical assistance and consulting services to businesses considering expansion in the state.

Downtown Revitalization Service: Encourages partnerships between business and government that revitalize a community's economy, appearance and traditional business image.

Education and Training: Works in partnership with local Economic Development Councils to provide businesses and communities with practical application of economic development techniques.

Business Financing

Child Care Advantages: Provides businesses with financial and technical assistance to develop on-site or near-site child care facilities. Qualified businesses are eligible to receive direct loans, loan guarantees, or grants through the Facilities Fund to start or expand their child care facilities.

Coastal Revolving Loan Fund: This fund lends to public agencies and businesses in Jefferson, Clallam, Grays Harbor, Pacific and Wahkiakum counties. Borrowers must demonstrate job creation and private investment to qualify for loans up to $150,000. The program also provides technical assistance loans up to $50,000 for public agencies and $30,000 for businesses for feasibility studies and planning.

Industrial Revenue Bonds: Up to $10 million may be issued to finance a project. Taxable nonrecourse economic development bonds are also available through the Washington Economic Development Finance Authority.

Forest Projects Revolving Loan Fund: Provides financial assistance to small-and medium-sized forest projects companies. Loans up to $750,000 are available for secondary wood product companies and their suppliers.

Community Development Finance: Program is available to help business and industry secure long-term expansion loans. By combining private financial resources with federal and state lending assistance and local leadership, this program focuses on business expansion through community development activities.

Loan programs are available for real estate, new construction, renovation, major leasehold improvements, machinery, equipment, and working capital. Government financing for a start-up business is possible, but more difficult and requires a larger down payment by the business.

Rural Washington Loan Fund: Gap financing for businesses that will create new jobs or retain existing jobs in non-entitlement areas of the state.

Cascadia Revolving Fund: private nonprofit community development loan fund which is lent to small businesses that cannot access traditional sources of credit. Maximum loan is $150,000. Contact Cascadia Revolving Fund, 119 1st Ave. South, Seattle, WA 98104; 206-447-9226; {www.cascadiafund.org}.

Tax Incentives

Sales/Use Tax Exemption On Machinery And Equipment: Manufacturers and processors for hire are not required to pay the sales or use tax on machinery and equipment used directly in manufacturing operations. In addition, charges made for labor and services for installing the machinery and equipment are not subject to the sales tax.

Distressed Area Sales/ Use Tax Deferral/Exemptions: Grants a waiver of sales/use tax for manufacturing, research and development, or computer-related businesses (excluding light and power businesses) locating in specific geographical areas. In certain other locations, the sales/use taxes on qualified construction and equipment costs are waived when all qualifications are met for a specified period of time.

Distressed Area Business And Occupation Tax Credit: A program for increasing employment provides a $1,000 credit against the B&O tax for each new employment position created and filled by certain businesses located in distressed areas. A distressed county is one with unemployment rates at 20% or above.

High Technology Sales/Use Tax Deferral/Exemption: Businesses in the following research and development technology categories may be eligible for a sales/use tax deferral/exemption, if they start new research and development or pilot scale manufacturing operations, or expand or diversify a current operation by expanding, renovating or equipping an existing facility anywhere in Washington.

High Technology Business And Occupation Tax Credit: An annual credit of up to $2 million is allowed for businesses that perform research and development in Washington in specified high technology categories and meet the minimum expense requirements. The credit cannot exceed the amount of the business and occupation tax due for that calendar year. The rate for the credit is: Nonprofit corporation or association: 515% (.00515) of the expenses. For profit businesses: 2.5% (.025) of the expenses.

Investment Tax Credits for Rehabilitation of Historic Structures: Office of Archaeology and Historic Preservation helps businesses apply for a 20% investment tax credit for the certified rehabilitation of historic structures.

Exports

International Trade Division: Works to expand future and existing export markets by distributing trade statistics, a bi-monthly newsletter, industry directories, organizing trade missions, participating in trade shows and managing state office in Europe, Japan, Taiwan, Tokyo, and Vladivostock.

Export Finance Assistance Center: Provides information and guidance on the repayment risk of financing aspects of export transactions. Contact: Export Finance Assistance Center of Washington, 2001 Sixth Ave., Suite 650, Seattle, WA 98121; 206-464-7152.

Women and Minorities

Linked Deposit Loan Program: Allows minority or women-owned businesses with 50 or fewer employees to apply at participating banks for reduced rate loans.

Minority and Women-Owned Business Loan: Loans can be available to assist certified minority and woman-owned businesses that are located in non-metropolitan areas.

Office of Minority and Women's Business Enterprises: Mission is to enhance the economic vitality of Washington State by creating an environment which mitigates the effects of race and gender discrimination in public contracting and promotes the economic development and growth of minority and women businesses. Certifies Women's business ventures and publishes a directory. Contact Office of Minority and Women's Business Enterprise, P.O. Box 41160, Olympia, WA 98504; 360-753-9693.

Minority & Women Business Development: Access resources and technical assistance to start or expand a business. MWBD provides entrepreneurial training, contract opportunities, bonding assistance, export assistance, and access to capital for start-ups or expanding businesses in the minority and women's business community. Contact Minority and Women's Business Development, Department of Community, Trade and Economic Development, 2001 Sixth Ave., Suite 2600, Seattle, WA 98121; 206-956-3164.

West Virginia

West Virginia Development Office
1900 Kanawha Blvd., East
Charleston, WV 25305-0311
304-558-2234
800-982-3386
Fax: 304-558-0449
www.wvdo.org

Business Assistance

West Virginia Development Office: This office can provide information and expertise in dealing with state, federal, and local agencies. They also have information on financing programs and other services offered by the state government.

Business Counseling: Confidential free service is available to those exploring the option of starting or purchasing a new business and to current owners of small businesses.

Seminars and workshops: Small group training is provided in areas such as starting a business in West Virginia, the basics of business planning, accounting and record keeping, business management techniques, tax law, personnel management techniques, quality customer service, etc. Most seminars and workshops may be attended for a nominal fee.

Other services: Staff members are well networked to the business and banking community and can make referrals to state, federal, and private agencies. The staff can provide problem solving assistance, business plan assistance; financial planning assistance; loan packaging assistance; minority/woman/veterans business outreach; a minority-owned and women-owned business directory; and an employee training program called the Small Business Work Force Program. Most of these services are free of charge. In addition, the SBDC is creating a customer learning center which will allow the entrepreneur to use SBDC owned computers to generate a business plan, devise and print corporate plans, learn about the internet, and the use of Electronic Data Interchange (EDI) for the purpose of electronic commerce.

Site Selection: Industrial specialists assist out-of-state companies, existing state businesses and site location consultants with the identification of suitable locations for their proposed operations utilizing a computerized inventory.

Small Business Work Force Program: Designed to serve businesses with fewer than 20 employees that are established, viable small businesses with demonstrable growth potential. Training programs will be developed based upon a comprehensive needs analysis and the business plan.

Regional Contracting Assistance Center: A private non-profit corporation founded to create information and assistance programs to help West Virginia businesses understand, adapt to, and excel in the evolving business environment. Services include:

1. *Bid Network* which links local businesses, based on their product and/or service capabilities, to opportunities represented by internal, national, regional, and local purchasing requirements.

2. *West Virginia Information Connection*: This business resource is a modem accessible series of five interactive databases on a 24-hour basis. Using the system, businesses can utilize a searchable electronic yellow pages of West Virginia businesses to locate sources of supply or in-state marketing leads. It also offers a bid board that displays contracts available through local government and private sector purchasing organizations; a directory of West Virginia industrial plants, sites, and office buildings; a demographic file providing information on West Virginia cities and counties; and a directory or resources available through

government agencies and non-profit organizations. To access the WVIC: Modem Dial: 304-344-0685 (2400 bad) 304-344-0687 (1200 baud).

3. *Information Exchange System*: A business-to-business information distribution network designed to allow West Virginians to send and receive electronic mail, distribute and collect marketing leads, and directly access the Information Connection. Through this program, West Virginians may also borrow computer modems that will allow them to electronically connect to information resources such as on-line services.

4. *Quality From The Outset*: A direct in-plant technical assistance program aimed at helping businesses improve their quality, productivity, and competitiveness. The consulting service is offered at no charge.

5. *Other Services*: Bid assistance; assistance with government contracts; market location assistance; access to a computer-assisted library of federal, military, and industry adopted standards and specifications as well as technical assistance to understand and comply with specifications and standards.

Robert C. Byrd Institute: A teaching factory to help small and medium-sized manufacturing companies increase their competitiveness through the adoption of world-class manufacturing technologies and modern management techniques. Contact Robert C. Byrd Institute, 1050 4th Avenue, Huntington, WV 25755; 304-696-6273.

Business Financing

Direct Loans: The WVEDA can provide up to 45% in financing fixed assets by providing low interest, direct loans to expanding state businesses and firms locating in West Virginia. Loan term is generally 15 years for real estate intensive projects and 5 to 10 years for equipment projects.

Indirect Loans: The WVEDA provides a loan insurance program and a capital access program through participating commercial banks to assist firms that cannot obtain conventional bank financing. The program insures up to 80% of a bank loan for a maximum loan term of four years.

Industrial Revenue Bonds: This provides for customized financing through the federal tax exempt industrial revenue bonds. $35 million of the state's bond allocation is reserved for small manufacturing projects.

Leveraged Technology Loan Insurance Program: This program expands the loan insurance coverage to 90% for those businesses involved in the development, commercialization, or use of technology- based products and processes.

West Virginia Capital Company Act: WVEDA administers a program that provides for debt and equity venture capital investment to small business.

For the above loans, contact: West Virginia Economic Development Authority, 1018 Kanawha Blvd., East, Suite 501, Charleston, WV 25301; 304-558-3650.

Small Business Development Loans: This program provides capital to entrepreneurs for new or expanded small business with loans from $500 to $10,000. Please contact the West Virginia Small Business Development Center.

Jobs Investment Trust: A $10 million public venture capital fund that uses debt and equity investments to promote and expand the state's economy.

Governor's Guaranteed Work Force Program: Provides training funds to assist new employees in learning their jobs, as well as to improve and expand the skills of existing employees for companies moving to or expanding in West Virginia.

Tax Incentives

Super Tax Credit Program: Provides substantial tax credits for companies that create jobs in industries such as manufacturing, information processing, distribution, and destination tourism projects. A business that creates 50 jobs or more can offset up to 80% of its basic business tax liability over ten years with this credit. This innovative program is based on a formula calculated by using a job creation and a qualified investment factor. In addition, small businesses in industries previously mentioned may qualify for the credit by creating at least 10 jobs over three years.

Corporate Headquarters Relocation Credit: Available to corporations in particular industries that relocate their headquarters to West Virginia. If at least 15 jobs are created, the allowable credit is 10% of qualified investment. If the corporate headquarters relocation results in 50 or more new jobs, then the allowable credit is 50% of qualified investment. Qualified investment includes the reasonable and necessary expenses incurred by the corporation to move its headquarters to this state.

West Virginia Capital Company Credit: Established to encourage the formation of venture capital in West Virginia. Investors in qualified capital companies are entitled to a state tax credit equal to 50% of their investment. Capital companies must have a capital base of at least $1 million but not greater than $4 million.

Warehouse Freeport Amendment: Allows goods in transit to an out-of-state destination to be exempt from local ad valorem property tax when "warehoused" in West Virginia. This exemption is specifically applicable to finished goods inventories.

Research and Development Project Credits: Manufacturers, producers of natural resources, generators of electric power and persons providing manufacturing services may qualify for the credit for research activities conducted within the state. The credit generally equals 10% of the qualified investment in depreciable personal property, wages and other expenses incurred for conducting a qualified research or development project.

Wood Processing Tax Credit: This credit is available for new wood processing operations. The tax credit is $250 per year per full time employee for 10 years to new or expanding companies involved in the manufacture of value-added wood products. The finished product must be consumer ready.

Sales Tax Exemption: For materials and equipment used directly in manufacturing process.

Industrial Expansion or Revitalization Tax Credit: Available for manufacturers as a credit against the business franchise tax.

Major Project Appraisal: Available for expansions at facilities that have original investment of more than $ 100 million. This requires the property tax for capital improvements of more than $ 50 million be appraised at salvage value.

Exports

Office of International Development: Offers export counseling and trade promotion opportunities to West Virginia companies. Maintains overseas offices.

Business and Industry Development Division: The Industrial Development Division of the West Virginia Development Office, in cooperation with the Department of Commerce and SBA, cosponsors workshops in international marketing.

West Virginia Export Council: A non-profit export promotion organization committed to expanding West Virginia exports. The Council assists public sector organizations in planning, promoting, and implementing activities that assist international export efforts.

Center for International Programs: For information on this program, contact Dr. Will Edwards, Director, Marshall University, Huntington, WV 25755; 304-696-6265; Fax 304-696-6353.

Women and Minorities

Center for Economic Options: A non-profit statewide, community-based organization which promotes opportunities that develop the economic capacity of West Virginia's rural citizens and communities. Working with members of society who traditionally have been excluded from economic decision-making, the Center advocates equity in the workplace, coordinates alternative approaches for economic development, and works to impact the direction of public policy. The Center coordinates three strategies to accomplish these goals:

1. *Community Resources*: Coordinates a pool of facilitators and training specialists who provide technical assistance to individuals, organizations, and community groups in many areas including strategic planning, business plan development, board development, and community assessments. The program also provides workshops and resource materials on community-based development.

2. *Enterprise Development*: Promotes rural job creation through self-employment and links small-scale, sector-specific entrepreneurs in statewide production and marketing networks. The Center facilitates the development of these flexible networks and connects the business owners with information, resources, training opportunities, and markets.

3. *Public Policy*: Researches and recommends policy in several areas including worker equity, enterprise development, sustainable development, work force training, and economic equity. Through the program,

consultants on establishing equity in the workplace and meeting state and federal sex equity regulations are provided.

Contact: Center for Economic Options, 601 Delaware Ave., Charleston, WV 25302; 304-345-1298.

West Virginia Women's Commission: Offers women opportunities to learn to be advocates for themselves and to work with others to address systemic change. Projects include leadership and legislative conference like the Women's Town Meeting and Women's Day at the Legislature among others. Contact West Virginia Women's Commission, Building 6, Room 637, 1900 Kanawha Boulevard, East, Charleston, WV 25305; 304-558-0070; Fax: 304-558-3240.

Minority-owned and Women-owned Business Directory: Each year the West Virginia Small Business Development Center publishes a "Minority-owned and Women-owned Business Directory" This directory is distributed to public and private purchasing agents, Chambers of Commerce, Economic Development Authorities, legislators and many privately owned businesses including contractors and all of the listees. There is no cost for the directory nor is there a charge for being included. The only requirement is that the business be located in West Virginia, be a for profit company and be 51% owned by a minority or woman.

Wisconsin

Department of Commerce (COMMERCE)
201 W. Washington Avenue
Madison, WI 53707
608-266-1018
Business Helpline: 800-HELP-BUSiness
Fax Request Hotline: 608-264-6154
Export Helpline: 800-XPORT-WIsconsin
www.commerce.state.wi.us

Business Assistance

Department of Commerce: The Wisconsin Department of Commerce is the state's primary agency for delivery of integrated services to businesses. Services include business financing, technical and managerial services to a wide range of businesses.

Business Development Resources: The Area Development Manager Program assists business expansions, promotes business retention, and helps local development organizations in their respective territories. Area development managers use their knowledge of federal, state, and regional resources to provide a variety of information to expanding or relocating firms. They also mobilize resources to help struggling businesses.

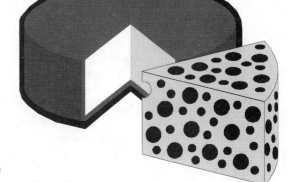

Brownfields Initiative Technical Assistance Program: Provides information and assistance related to brownfields redevelopment. The program can assist in the identification and resolution of regulatory issues, and electronically link prospective buyers with information on available brownfield sites.

Business Development Assistance Center: Provides assistance to small businesses. The office furnishes information on government regulations, and refers businesses to appropriate resources. Call 800-HELP BUSiness.

Dairy 2020 Initiative: A state, business, and education partnership that works to enhance the competitive edge of the Wisconsin dairy industry. Contact: Dairy 2020 Program, P.O. Box 7970, Madison, WI 53707; 608-266-7370.

Assistance with Environmental Regulations and Permits is available to manufacturers. COMMERCE can also expedite regulatory and permit clearance and resolve delays and communications problems. Businesses storing or handling flammable or combustible liquids can receive compliance assistance.

Wisconsin Health Consultation Program: Provides free assistance to employers who request help to establish and maintain a safe and healthful workplace. Health Consultants will conduct an appraisal of physical work practices and environmental hazards, will perform an ergonomics analysis, review various aspects of the employers present occupational safety and health program, and will present occupational health related training.

Industrial Recycling Assistance Program: Conducts site visits and detailed assessments to help manufacturers find the best available solutions for waste management and waste reduction problems.

Manufacturing Assessment Center: Helps small and medium manufacturers improve quality and productivity through professional assessment of operations, systems, and layouts. The center maintains a list of related seminars available throughout the country, and can arrange plant tours of leading-edge manufacturers in the state.

Plan Review Program provides plan review and consultation for structures, plumbing, elevators, HVAC, lighting, erosion control, and private onsite wastewater treatment systems. The services help designers, installers, and owners protect public safety and promote economic efficiency.

Recycling Technical Assistance Program: Helps companies switch to recycled feedstock or reduce waste generation.

Small Business Clean Air Assistance Program: Designed to help small businesses comply with standards established by the federal Clean Air Act.

Small Business Ombudsman: Provides information on government regulations and financing alternatives to small businesses, particularly entrepreneurs. Through its advocacy function, the office promotes special consideration for small businesses in Wisconsin administrative rules.

WiSCon Safety Consultation Program: Assesses current safety programs and suggests improvements; evaluates physical work practices; identifies available assistance; and provides training and education for managers and employees. The consultants do not issue citations, propose penalties, or report possible safety violations to the Occupational Safety and Health Administration.

Wisconsin TechSearch is the fee-based information outreach program of the Kurt F. Wendt Library. TechSearch offers document delivery and reference services to businesses and industry. On-line literature, patent and trademark searches are available. TechSearch provides access to the information resources of the Wendt Library, which contains outstanding collections in science and engineering, and is a US Patent and Trademark Depository Library and more than 40 libraries and information centers on the UW-Madison campus. For more information and a fee schedule, call 608-262-5913/5917 or E-mail {wtskfw@ doit.wisc.edu}.

UW-Madison Engineering Cooperative Education and Internship Program: Provides student engineering interns that can help companies undertake a variety of technical and engineering initiatives. Interns are paid commensurate with their educational level and previous experience. Advantages to the employer include developing a stronger, experienced workforce; identifying outstanding students for potential employment at graduation; evaluating an individual's performance prior to making a full-time commitment; and sharing new technology, research, and procedures.

Solid and Hazardous Waste Education Center: Provides technical assistance to businesses and communities on emissions reduction, pollution prevention, recycling, and solid waste management. The Center also offers grants that companies can use for hazardous waste reduction audits. UW- Green Bay Campus, 2420 Nicolet Dr., ES317, Green Bay, WI 54311; 920-465-2327.

Business Financing

Customized Labor Training Fund: Provides training grants to businesses that are implementing new technology or production processes. The program can provide up to 50% of the cost of customized training that is not available from the Wisconsin Technical College System.

Dairy 2020 Initiative: Awards grants and loans for business and feasibility planning to dairy producers and processors considering a modernization or expansion project.

Employee Ownership Assistance Loan Program: Can help a group of employees purchase a business by providing individual awards up to $25,000 for feasibility studies or professional assistance. The business under consideration must have expressed its intent to downsize or close.

Division of Vocational Rehabilitation Job Creation Program: Designed to increase employment opportunities for DVR clients by providing equipment grants, technical assistance grants, and customized assistance to companies that will hire persons with disabilities as part of a business expansion.

Major Economic Development Program: Offers low-interest loans for business development projects that create a significant economic impact.

Rural Economic Development Program: Makes individual awards up to $30,000 for feasibility studies and other professional assistance to rural businesses with fewer than 25 employees. Businesses and farms that have completed their feasibility evaluations are eligible for individual micro loans up to $25,000 for working capital and the purchase of equipment.

Technology Development Fund: Helps businesses finance Phase I product development research. Firms completing Phase I projects can receive Phase II product-commercialization funding.

Tax Incremental Financing: Helps cities in Wisconsin attract industrial and commercial growth in underdeveloped and blighted areas. A city or village can designate a specific area within its boundaries as a TIF district and develop a plan to improve its property values. Taxes generated by the increased property values pay for land acquisition or needed public works.

Brownfields Initiative: Provides grants to persons, businesses, local development organizations, and municipalities for environmental remediation activities for brownfield sites where the owner is unknown, cannot be located or cannot meet the cleanup costs.

BDI Micro Loan Program: Helps entrepreneurs with permanent disabilities and rehabilitation agencies finance business start-ups or expansions.

BDI Self-Employment Program: Helps severely disabled DVR clients start micro-businesses.

Industrial Revenue Bonds (IRBs): A means of financing the construction and equipping of manufacturing plants and a limited number of non-manufacturing facilities. The municipality is not responsible for debt service on IRBs, nor is it liable in the case of default. IRBs are also exempt from federal income tax.

Petroleum Environmental Clean-up Fund: Reimburses property owners for eligible clean-up costs related to discharges for petroleum tank systems.

Recycling Demonstration Grant Program: Helps businesses and local governing units fund waste reduction, reuse, and recycling pilot projects.

Recycling Early Planning Grant Program: Awards funds to new and expanding business plans, marketing assistance, and feasibility studies on the start-up or expansion of a recycling business.

Recycling Loan Program: Awards loans for the purchase of equipment to businesses and nonprofit organizations that make products from recycled waste, or make equipment necessary to manufacture these products.

Recycling Technology Assistance Program: Provides low cost loans to fund research and development of products or processes using recovered or recyclable materials. Eligible activities include product development and testing, process development and assessment, specialized research, and technical assistance.

Wisconsin Fund: Provides grants to help small commercial businesses rehabilitate or replace their privately owned sewage systems.

Wisconsin Housing and Economic Development Authority (WHEDA): Offers a program that buys down commercial interest rates, enabling Wisconsin lenders to offer short-term, below-market-rate loans to small, minority- or women-owned businesses. A loan guarantee program is available for firms ramping-up to meet contract demands; for firms in economically-distressed areas; and for tourism and agribusiness projects. The authority also operates a beginning farmer bond program.

Recycling Loan Program

Community-Based Economic Development Program: Awards grants to community-based organizations for development and business assistance projects and to municipalities for economic development planning. The program helps community-based organizations plan, build, and create business and technology-based incubators, and can also capitalize an incubator tenant revolving-loan program.

Early Planning Grant: Helps entrepreneurs and small businesses obtain professional services necessary to evaluate the feasibility of a proposed start-up or expansion.

Economic Diversification Loan Program: Low-interest loan to finance a portion of the costs to establish and expand operations.

Wisconsin Small Business Innovative Research (SBIR) Support Program: Coordinates resources to help businesses pursue federal SBIR grants and contracts. The federal SBIR program provides Phase I awards of up to $100,000 for feasibility studies and Phase II awards of up to $750,000 for project development.

Tax Incentives

Development Zone Program: A tax benefit initiative designed to encourage private investment and to improve both the quality and quantity of employment opportunities. The program has $21 million in tax benefits available to assist businesses that meet certain requirements and are located or willing to locate in one of Wisconsin's 20 development zones.

Enterprise Development Zone Program: This program promotes a business start-up or expansion on a particular site in any area of the state that suffers from high unemployment, declining incomes and property values, and other indicators of economic distress. The program pays on performance. Tax credits can be taken only on income generated by business activity in the zone. The maximum amount of tax credits per zone is $3 million. Up to 50 sites can be designated around the state for projects that are not likely to occur or continue unless a zone is created. Types of Credits: A business in an enterprise development zone is eligible to earn the following tax credits:

1. The jobs credit: Equal to 40% of the first $6,000 in qualified wages for the first and second years of employment of a member of a "target group."

2. The sales tax credit: Equal to the amount of sales tax paid on building materials and equipment.
3. The location credit: Equal to 2.5% of the cost of acquiring, constructing, rehabilitating, remodeling or repairing real property.
4. The investment credit: Equal to 2.5% of the cost of depreciable tangible personal property.
5. The research credit: Equal to 5% of increased expenditures on research.
6. The child care credit: Equal to expenses incurred by an employer for child care provided to children of target group members. Up to $1,200 per year per child for two years.
7. The environmental remediation credit: Equal to 7.5% of cost of the remediation of contaminated land.

Exports

COMMERCE maintains International Offices in Frankfurt, Mexico City, Seoul, Toronto and Sao Paolo. They also contract with consultants in Hong Kong/China, Japan, Singapore and Southeast Asia, Chile, Peru, and Ecuador to provide export services to state firms. Participating in a variety of promotional activities, such as trade shows and Wisconsin product exhibits, the offices forward trade leads and set up business meetings between state firms and potential clients. Overseas firms interested in sites or investment in Wisconsin can contact the offices for assistance.

Wisconsin Trade Project Program: Can help small export-ready firms participate in international trade shows. The business covers its own travel and lodging expenses. COMMERCE can then provide up to $5,000 in reimbursements to a business for costs associated with attending a trade show, such as booth rental or product brochure translation.

Trade Shows and Trade Missions: Showcase Wisconsin firms and products to prospective international clients. The Department sponsors a Wisconsin-products booth at approximately 12 international trade fairs per year, and also arranges trade and reverse investment missions abroad, many of them led by the Governor.

Women and Minorities

Bureau of Minority Business Development
Department of Commerce
123 W. Washington Ave.
P.O. Box 7970
Madison, WI 53707
608-267-9550
www.commerce.state.wi.us

Certifies companies to be eligible to participate in state's minority business bid preference. Company must be at least 51% owned, controlled, and managed by minority (being a woman is not considered a minority).

Certification to participate in the state's minority business purchasing and contracting program is available to minority vendors. Interested firms may apply through the department. They are then listed in the *Annual Directory of Minority-Owned Firms*.

Marketing Assistance of various kinds is offered to minority-owned firms. Certified minority vendors are listed in the department's database for access by the purchasing community. Minority-owned firms can receive help developing marketing plans. Each year, the department sponsors the Marketplace Trade Fair to encourage business contacts between minority vendors and state and corporate buyers.

American Indian Liaison: Provides advice, training, technical assistance, and economic development information to the Wisconsin tribes, tribal communities, and American Indian entrepreneurs, and serves as state economic development liaison.

Minority Business Development Fund Revolving Loan Fund (RLF) Program: Designed to help capitalize RLFs administered by American Indian tribal governing bodies or local development corporations that target their loans to minority-owned businesses. The corporation must be at least 51-percent controlled and actively managed by minority-group members, and demonstrate the expertise and commitment to promote minority business development in a specific geographic area.

Minority Business Development Fund: Offers low-interest loans for start-up, expansion or acquisition projects. To qualify for the fund, a business must be 51-percent controlled, owned, and actively managed by minority-group members, and the project must retain or increase employment.

Minority Business Early Planning Grant Program: Provides seed capital to minority entrepreneurs for feasibility studies, business plans, and marketing plans.

Wisconsin Women's Business Initiative Corporation (WWBIC): Offers micro loans to businesses owned by women, minorities, and low-income individuals. WWBIC also offers training and technical assistance.

Wyoming

Wyoming Business Council
214 W. 15th St.
Cheyenne, WY 82002
307-777-2800
Fax: 307-777-2838
www.wyomingbusiness.org

Business Assistance

Wyoming Business Council: This office can provide information and expertise in dealing with state, federal, and local agencies. They also have information on financing programs and other services offered by the state government.

Science, Technology and Energy Authority: Helps to improve the development of research capability, stimulate basic and applied technological research and facilitate commercialization of new products and processes.

Mid-America Manufacturing Technology Centers: A non-profit organization that assists small and medium-sized manufacturers in becoming more competitive, improve quality, boost sales and locate production resources.

Business Financing

The state offers a wide spectrum of public sector financial and technical assistance programs.

Wyoming Industrial Development Corporation: Matches resources in both private and public sectors that best fit the needs of business.

Workforce Training: Financial support is available for on-the-job training, classroom training, or a combination of both.

Tax Incentives

No personal income tax.
No corporate income tax.
No tax on intangible assets such as bank accounts, stocks, or bonds.
No tax on retirement income earned and received from another state.
No inventory tax.
No tax on goods-in-transit or made from out-of-state.

SMALL BUSINESS DEVELOPMENT CENTERS
The Best Place To Start

Small Business Development Centers (SBDCs) could be the best deal the government has to offer to entrepreneurs and inventors, and a lot of people don't even know about them! Where else in the world can you have access to a $150 an hour consultant for free? There are over 700 of these offices all over the country and they offer free (or very low cost) consulting services on most aspects of business including:

- how to write a business plan

- how to get financing

- how to protect your invention

- how to sell your idea

- how to license your product

- how to comply with the laws

- how to write a contract

- how to sell overseas

- how to get government contracts

- how to help you buy the right equipment

You don't even have to know how to spell ENTREPRENEUR to contact these offices. They cater to both the dreamer, who doesn't even know where to start, as well as to the experienced small business that is trying to grow to the next stage of development. In other words, the complete novice or the experienced professional can find help through these centers. Why spend money on a consultant, a lawyer, an accountant, or one of those invention companies when you can get it all for free at your local SBDC?

Recently, I spoke with some entrepreneurs who used a California SBDC and each of them had nothing but praise for the services. A young man who dropped out of college to start an executive cleaning business said he received over $8,000 worth of free legal advice from the center and said it was instrumental in getting his business off the ground. A woman who worked in a bank started her gourmet cookie business by using the SBDC to help her get the money and technical assistance needed to get her venture up and running. And a man who was a gymnast raved about how the SBDC helped him get his personal trainer business off the ground. All kinds of businesses being started, and all kinds of compliments for the SBDC's role in assisting these entrepreneurs, in whatever they are attempting. It sounds like a solid recommendation to me.

Can something that is free be so good? Of course it can. Because most of the people who work there are not volunteers, they are paid for by tax dollars. So it's really not free to us as a country, but it is free to you as an entrepreneur. And if you don't believe me that the SBDCs are so good, would you take the word of Professor James J. Chrisman from the University of Calgary in Calgary, Alberta, Canada? He was commissioned to do an independent study of SBDCs and found that 82% of the people who used their services found them beneficial. And the businesses who used SBDCs had average growth rates of up to 400% greater than all the other businesses in their area. Not bad. Compare this to the Fortune 500 companies who use the most expensive consulting firms in the country and only experience growth rates of 5% or less. So, who says you get what you pay for?

Small Business Development Centers

Alabama

Lead Center:
Office of State Director
Alabama Small Business Development Consortium
University of Alabama at Birmingham
2800 Milan Court
Birmingham, AL 35211
205-943-6750
www.asbdc.org

Auburn University
Small Business Development Center
108 College of Business
Auburn University, AL 36849-5243
334-844-4220
Fax: 334-844-4268
Email: Mrutherford@business.auburn.edu

University of Alabama at Birmingham
Small Business Development Center
901 South 15th Street
Birmingham, AL 35924-2060
205-934-6760
Fax: 205-934-0538
Email: sbdc@uab.edu

University of North Alabama
Small Business Development Center
P.O. Box 5248
Keller Hall
Florence, AL 35632-0001
256-765-4629
Fax: 256-760-4813
Email: clong@unanov.una.edu

North East Alabama Regional
Small Business Development Center
P.O. Box 168
225 Church Street, NW
Huntsville, AL 35804-0168
256-535-2061
Fax: 256-535-2050
Email: dtaylor@hsvchamber.org

Jacksonville State University
Small Business Development Center
700 Pelham Road
114 Merrill Hall
Jacksonville, AL 36265
256-782-5271
Fax: 256-782-5179
Email: sbdc@jsucc.jsu.edu

Livinsgston University
Small Business Development Center

Station 35
Livingston, AL 35470
205-652-3665
Fax: 205-652-3516
Email: adeaver@uwa.edu

University of South Alabama
Small Business Development Center
College of Business and Management Studies
BMSB, Room 1
Mobile, AL 36688
334-460-6004
Fax: 334-460-6246
Email: ttucker@usamail.usouthal.edu

Alabama State University
Small Business Development Center
915 South Jackson Street
Montgomery, AL 36195
334-229-4138
Fax: 334-269-1102
Email: lpatrick@asunet.alasu.edu

Troy State University
Small Business Development Center
102 Bibb Graves
Troy, AL 36082-0001
334-670-3771
Fax: 334-670-3636
Email: jkervin@trojan.troyst.edu

Alabama International Trade Center
University of Alabama
Bidgood Hall, Room 201
Tuscaloosa, AL 35487-0396
205-348-7621
Fax: 205-348-6974
Email: aitc@aitc.cba.ua.edu

University of Alabama
Small Business Development Center
Bidgood Hall, Room 201
Tuscaloosa, AL 35487-0396
205-348-7621
Fax: 205-348-6974
Email: phaninen@cba.ua.edu

Alaska

Lead Center:
Jan Fredericks
University of Alaska
Small Business Development Center

430 West 7th Avenue, Suite 110
Anchorage, AK 99501
902-274-7232
800-478-7232 (Outside Anchorage)
Fax: 907-274-9524
www.aksbdc.org
Email: anja@uaa.alaska.edu

University of Alaska-Anchorage
Small Business Development Center
Rural Outreach Program
430 West 7th Avenue, Suite 110
Anchorage, AK 99501
907-274-7232
800-478-7232 (Outside Anchorage)
Fax: 907-274-9524
Email: answb1@uaa.alaska.edu

University of Alaska-Fairbanks
Small Business Development Center
613 Cushman Street, Suite 209
Fairbanks, AK 99701
907-456-7232
800-478-1701 (Outside Fairbanks)
Fax: 907-456-7233
Email: fnsts@aurora.uaf.edu

Southeast Alaska
Small Business Development Center
3100 Channel Drive, 3rd Floor
Juneau, AK 99801
907-463-3789
Fax: 907-463-3478
Email: anjas3@uaa.alaska.edu

Kenai Peninsula
Small Business Development Center
P.O. Box 3029
11896 Kenai Spur Highway
Kenai, AK 99611-3029
907-283-3335
Fax: 907-283-3913
Email: mgregory@kpedd.org

Ketchikan Area
Small Business Development Center
306 Main Street, Suite 325
Ketchikan, AK 99901
907-225-1388
Fax: 907-225-1385
Email: anrl1@uaa.alaska.edu

Matanuska-Susitna Borough
Small Business Development Center
P.O. Box 3029
201 North Lucielle Street, Suite 2A

Wasilla, AK 99654
907-373-7232
Fax: 907-373-7234
Email: antjs@uaa.alaska.edu

Arizona
Lead Center:
Arizona Small Business Development Center
2411 West 14th Street
Tempe, AZ 85281
480-731-8720
Fax: 480-731-8729
www.dist.maricopa.edu/sbdc

Central Arizona College
Small Business Development Center
1015 East Florence Boulevard, Suite B
Casa Grande, AZ 85222
520-426-4341
Fax: 520-876-5966

Coconino Community College
Small Business Development Center
3000 North 4th Street, Suite 17
Flagstaff, AZ 86004
520-526-5072
Fax: 520-526-8693

Northland Pioneer College
Small Business Development Center
P.O. Box 610
Holbrook, AZ 86025
951 West Deuce of Clubs
Show Low, AZ 85901
520-532-6170
Fax: 520-532-6171
www.npsbdc.com
Email: mengle99@yahoo.com

Mojave Community College
Small Business Development Center
1971 Jagerson Avenue
Kingman, AZ 86401
520-757-0895
Fax: 520-757-0836

Maricopa Community Colleges
Small Business Development Center
702 East Osborn Road, Suite 150
Phoenix, AZ 85014
602-230-7308
Fax: 602-230-7989

Yavapai College
Small Business Development Center
117 East Gurley Street, Suite 206

Prescott, AZ 86301
520-717-7621
Fax: 520-717-7621
www.yavapai.cc.az.us/sbdc.nsf

Cochise College
Small Business Development Center
901 North Colombo, Room 308
Sierra Vista, AZ 85635
520-515-5478
Fax: 520-515-5437
800-966-7943 ext. 478
www.cochise.cc.az.us
Email: sbdc@cochise.cc.az.us

Eastern Arizona College
Small Business Development Center
622 College Avenue
Thatcher, AZ 85552-0769
520-428-8590
Fax: 520-428-8591
www.eac.cc.az.us/community.htm

Pima Community College
Small Business Development Center
4905 A East Broadway, Suite 101
Tucson, AZ 85709-1260
520-206-4906
Fax:520-206-4585
http://pimacc.pima.edu/~econdev/
economic_develop/business/index.htm
Email: sbdtc@pimacc.pima.edu

Arizona Western College
Small Business Development Center
281 West 24th Street
Yuma, AZ 85364
520-341-1650
Fax: 520-726-3626

Arkansas

Lead Center:
Arkansas Small Business Development Center
University of Arkansas at Little Rock
Little Rock Technology Center Building
100 South Main, Suite 401
Little Rock, AR 72201
501-324-9043
800-862-2040 (AR only)
Fax: 501-324-9049
http://asbdc.ualr.edu
Email: jmnye@ualr.edu

Henderson State University
Small Business Development Center

P.O. Box 7624
Arkadelphia, AR 71999
870-230-5224
www.hsr.edu/dept/sbdc.index.html
Email: jacksol@hsu.edu

University of Arkansas at Fayetteville
Small Business Development Center
Sam M. Walton College of Business, Room 117
Fayetteville, AR 72701
501-575-5148
Fax: 501-575-4013
http://waltoncollege.uark.edu/sbdc
Email: lsexton@walton.uark.edu

W. Arkansas Regional Office
Small Business Development Center
5111 Rogers Avenue, Suite 510
Fort Smith, AR 72903
501-484-5032
http://asbdc.ualr.edu/fortsmith
Email: rvvanzant@ualr.edu

NW Arkansas Regional Office
Small Business Development Center
P.O. Box 190
Harrison, AR 72601
870-741-8009
Fax: 870-741-1905
http://asbdc.ualr.edu/harrison
Email: rdpenquite@ualr.edu

SW & Western Regional Offices
Small Business Development Center
835 Central Avenue
Box 402-D
Hot Springs, AR 71901
501-624-5448
http://asbdc.ualr.edu/hotsprings
Email: rxevans2@ualr.edu

Southern Arkansas University
Small Business Development Center
P.O. Box 9379
Magnolia, AR 71754-9379
870-235-5033
http://asbdc.ualr.edu/magnolia
Email: dgwilliams@ualr.edu

Osceola Field Office
Small Business Development Center
2868 West Semmes
Osceola, AR 72730
870-563-5763
http://asbdc.ualr.edu/osceola
Email: rlbrothers@ualr.edu

Pine Bluff Field Office
121 West 6th, Suite 3C
Pine Bluff, AR 71601
870-850-8900
http://asbdc.ualr.edu/pinebluff
Email: rlbarker@ualr.edu

Arkansas State University
Small Business Development Center
P.O. Box 2650
State University, AR 72467
870-972-3517
Fax: 870-972-3678
www.astate.edu/docs/acad/coba/sbdc
Email: hlawrence@cherokee.astate.edu

Phillips Community College
Small Business Development Center
P.O. Box 289
2807 Highway 165 South
Suite A109
Stuttgart, AR 72160
870-673-8708
http://asbdc.ualr.edu/stuttgart
Email: lelefler@ualr.edu

California
Lead Center:
California Small Business Development Center
California Trade and Commerce Agency
801 K Street, Suite 1700
Sacramento, CA 95814
916-324-5068
Help Line: 800-303-6600
Fax: 916-322-5084
www.commerce.ca.gov/business/small/
starting/sb_sbdc.html

Outreach Center
Calaveras County Economic Development Company
571 Stanislaus Avenue, Suite E
P.O. Box 1082
Angeles Camp, CA 95222
209-736-4994
Fax: 209-736-4944
Email: ccedc@volcano.net

Central Coast Small Business Development Center
c/o Cabrillo College
6500 Soquel Drive
Aptos, CA 95003
831-479-6136
Fax: 831-479-6166
www.businessonline.org
Email:BusinessOnline@Cabrillo

Sierra College
Small Business Development Center
560 Wall Street, Suite J
Auburn, CA 95603
530-885-5488
Fax: 530-823-2831
www.sbdcsierra.org
Email: sbdcinfor@sierra.org

Weill Institute
Small Business Development Center
1706 Chesterfield Avenue, Suite 200
Bakersfield, CA 93301
805-322-5881
Fax: 805-322-5663
www.kccd.cc.ca.us/sbdc.html
Email: weill@lightspeed.net

Butte College
Small Business Development Center
260 Cohasset Road, Suite A
Chico, CA 95926
530-895-9017
Fax: 530-895-9099
www.bcsbdc.org
Email: konuwaso@butte.cc.ca.us

Southwestern College
Small Business Development Center
International Trade Center
900 Otay Lakes Road
Building 1600
Chula Vista, CA 91910
619-482-6391
Fax: 619-482-6402
www.sbditc.com
Email: support@sbditc.org

Outreach Center
Commerce Small Business Development Center
500 Citadel Drive, Suite 213
Commerce, CA 90040
323-887-9627
Fax: 323-887-9670

Contra Costa Small Business Development Center
2425 Bisso Lane, Suite 200
Concord, CA 94520
925-646-5377
Fax: 925-646-5299
Email: Bhamile@hotmail.com

Satellite Operation
North Coast Small Business Development Center
207 Price Mall, Suite 500

Crescent City, CA 95531
707-464-2168
Fax: 707-465-6008
Email: fransbdc@northcoast.com

Satellite Operation
Imperial Valley Small Business Development Center
1240 State Street
El Centro, CA 92243
760-312-9800
Fax: 760-312-9838
Email: ivsbdc@quix.net

Export Small Business Development Center
222 North Sepulveda, Suite 1690
El Segundo, CA 90245
310-606-0166
Fax: 310-606-0155
www.exportsbdc.org
Email: info@exportsbdc.org

North Coast Small Business Development Center
520 E Street
Eureka, CA 95501
707-445-9720
Fax: 707-445-9652
www.northcoastsbdc.org
Email: fransbdc@northcoast.com

Outreach Center
West Company Coast Office
306 Redwood Avenue
Fort Bragg, CA 95437
707-964-7571

Satellite Operation
Fremont Small Business Development Center
3100 Mowry Avenue, Suite 404
Fremont, CA 94538
510-505-9725
Fax: 510-505-9727

Central California Small Business Development Center
3419 West Shaw Avenue, Suite 102
Fresno, CA 93711
559-275-1223
800-974-0064
Fax: 559-275-1499
www.ccsbdc.org
Email: Dennisw@ccsbdc.org

Gavilan College
Small Business Development Center
7436 Monterey Street
Gilroy, CA 95020
408-847-0373

Fax: 408-847-0393
www.gavilansbdc.org
Email: l.nolan@gilroy.com

Satellite Operation
Glendale Small Business Development Center
330 North Brand Boulevard, Suite 190
Glendale, CA 91203
818-552-3254
Fax: 818-552-3322
Email: sbdcgln@attglobal.net

Tech Coast Small Business Development Center
Orange County Business Council
2 Park Plaza, Suite 100
Irvine, CA 92614
949-476-2242
Fax: 949-476-0763
www.venturepoint.org
Email: jdelong@venturepoint.org

Outreach Center
Amador Small Business Development Center
P.O. Box 1077
1500 S Highway 49
Jackson, CA 95642
209-223-0351
Fax: 209-223-2261

Satellite Operation
Lake County Small Business Development Center
55 First Street, 3rd Floor, MS-J
Lakeport, CA 95453
707-263-0330
Fax: 707-263-8516
Email: lakesbdc@jps.net

Satellite Operation
South Central Small Business Development Center
Los Angeles One Stop Capital Shop
10221 Compton Avenue, Suite 103
Los Angeles, CA 90002
213-473-5111
Fax: 213-473-5115

Outreach Center
Alpine Chamber of Commerce and Visitor Authority
P.O. Box 265
3 Webster Street
Markeleeville, CA 96120
530-694-2475
Fax: 530-694-2748

Yuba College Small Business Development Center
330 9th Street
P.O. Box 262

Marysville, CA 95901
530-749-0153
Fax: 530-749-0155
Email: phpd@aol.com

Satellite Operation
Valley Sierra
Small Business Development Center
2000 M Street
Merced, CA 95340
209-385-7686
800-323-2623
Fax: 209-383-4959
Email: msoaza@inreach.com

Valley Sierra Small Business Development Center
1012 11th Street, Suite 400
Modesto, CA 95354
209-521-6177
Fax: 209-521-9373
http://smallbizcenter.org
Email: bearden@scedo.org

Napa Valley College
Small Business Development Center
1556 First Street, Suite 103
Napa, CA 94559
707-253-3210
Fax: 707-253-3068
www.napasbdc.org
Email: nvcsbdc@pacbell.net

East Bay Small Business Development Center
519 17th Street, Suite 210
Oakland, CA 94612
510-893-4114
Fax: 510-8935532
Email: fhameed@ebsbdc.org

North San Diego County Small Business Development
Center
1823 Mission Avenue
Oceanside, CA 92054
760-795-8740
Fax: 760-795-8728
www.sandiegosmallbiz.com
Email: centerinfor@sandiegosmallbiz.com

Satellite Operation
Northeast Valley Small Business Development Center
12502 Van Nuys Boulevard
Suite 119
Pacoima, CA 91331
818-834-9860
Fax: 818-897-8007
Email: nevsbdc@vedc.org

Satellite Operation
Coachella Valley Small Business Development Center
Palm Springs Satellite Center
5005 Palm Canyon Drive, Suite 222
Palm Springs, CA 92264
760-864-1311
Fax: 760-864-1319

Eastern Los Angeles County
Small Business Development Center
300 West Second Street, suite 203
Pomona, CA 91766-1634
909-629-2247
800-450-72323
Fax: 909-629-8310
http://vclass.mtsac.edu/sbdc

Cascade Small Business Development Center
737 Auditorium Drive, Suite A
Redding, CA 96001
530-225-2760
Fax: 530-225-2769
www.scedd.org
Email: bnash@scedd.org

Inland Empire Small Business Development Center
1157 Spruce Street
Riverside, CA 92507
909-781-2345
Fax: 909-781-2353
www.ecsbdc.org

Greater Sacramento Small Business Development Center
1410 Ethan Way
Sacramento, CA 958125
916-563-3210
Fax: 916-563-3266
www.sbdc.net
Email: csteimle@sbdc.net
Satellite Operation
Inland Empire Business Incubator
155 South Memorial Drive, Suite B
San Bernardino, CA 92408-909-382-0065
Fax: 909-382-8543

San Francisco Small Business Development Center
455 Market Street, 6th Floor
San Francisco, CA 94105
415-908-7501
Fax: 415-974-6035
Email: sbdcsf@pacbell.net

Silicon Valley
Small Business Development Center
84 West Santa Clara
San Jose, CA 95113-1815

408-494-0240
888-726-2712
Fax: 408-494-0245
www.siliconvalley-sbdc.org
Email: sbdc@siliconvalley-sbdc.org

South Central Coast Small Business Development Center
3566 South Higuerea Street
Suite 100
San Luis Obispo, CA 93401
805-549-0401
877-549-8349
Fax: 805-543-5198
Email: sccsbdc@fix.net

Orange County Small Business Development Center
901 East Santa Ana Boulevard
Suite 101
Santa Ana, CA 92701
714-564-5202
Fax: 714-647-1168
www.ocsbdc.org
Email: O'Brien_Joh@rsccd.org

Satellite Operation
Westside Small Business Development Center
3233 Donald Douglas
Loop South, Suite C
Santa Monica, CA 90405
310-398-8883
Fax: 310-398-3024

Redwood Empire Small Business Development Center
607 Healdsburg Avenue
Santa Rosa, CA 95401
707-524-1770-888-346-7232
Fax: 707-524-1772
www.santarosa.edu/sbdc
Email: sbdc@santarosa.edu

San Joaquin Delta College
Small Business Development Center
445 North San Joaquin Street
Stockton, CA 95204
209-943-5089
Fax: 209-943-8325
http://sbdc.deltacollege.org
Email: gmurphy@sjdccd.cc.ca.us

Solano County Small Business Development Center
424 Executive Court North, Suite C
Suisun, CA 94585
707-864-3382
Fax: 707-864-8025
www.solanosbdc.com
Email: epratt@solano.cc.ca.us

Southwest Los Angeles County Small Business
Development Center
2377 Crenshaw Boulevard
Torrance, CA 90501
310-787-6466
Fax: 310-782-8607
www.swlasbdc.org
Email: dennismorrison@hotmail.com

Outreach Center
West Company Small Business Development Center
367 North State Street, Suite 201
Ukiah, CA 95482
707-468-3553
Fax: 707-468-3555
Email: westco@pacific.net

Vallejo Chamber Small Business Development Center
c/o Vallejo Chamber of Commerce
Two Florida Street
Vallejo, CA 94590
707-644-5551
Fax: 707-644-5590

North Los Angeles County SBDC
4717 Van Nuys Boulevard, Suite 201
Van Nuys, CA 91403-2100
818-907-9922
Fax: 818-907-9890
www.vedc.org/sbdc.htm
Email: vnsbdc@vedc.org

Satellite Operation
Export Small Business Development Center Satellite
Center
5700 Ralston Street, Suite 310
Ventura, CA 93003
805-644-6191
Fax: 805-658-2252
Email: esbdc@primenet.com

Satellite Operation
Gold Coast Small Business Development Center
5700 Ralston Street, Suite 310
Ventura, CA 93003
805-658-2688
Fax: 805-658-2252
Email: gcsbdc@vedc.org

Satellite Operation
Victorville Satellite Center
15490 Civic Drive, Suite 102
Victorville, CA 92392
760-951-1592
Fax: 760-951-8929
Email: hd_sbdc@eee.org

Satellite Operation
Central California Small Business Development Center
720 West Mineral King Avenue
Visalia, CA 93291
P.O. Box 787
Visalia, CA 93279-0787
Email: wendi@ccsbdc.org
559-625-3051
Fax: 559-625-3053

Colorado

Lead Center:
Mary Madison
Colorado Small Business Development Center
Office of Economic Development
1625 Broadway, Suite 1710
Denver, CO 80202
303-892-3763
Fax: 303-892-3848
www.state.co.us/gov_dir/oed/sbdc.html
Email: mary.madison@state.co.us

Alamosa Small Business Development Center
Adams State College
208 Edgemont Street
Alamosa, CO 8102
719-587-7372
Fax: 719-587-7603
Email: mchoffman@adams.edu

Aurora Small Business Development Center
Community College of Aurora
9905 East Colfax
Aurora, CO 80010-2119
303-341-4849
Fax: 303-361-2953
www.ci.aurora.co.us/develop/sbdc.htm
Email: asbdc@henge.com

Boulder Small Business Development Center
Boulder Chamber of Commerce
2440 Pearl Street
P.O. Box 73
Boulder, CO 80302
303-442-1475
Fax: 303-938-8837
Email: marilynn@chamber.coulder.co.us

Canon City Small Business Development Center
3080 East Main
Canon City, CO 81212
719-275-5335
Fax: 719-269-7334
Email: allancmconnell@pcc.cccbes.edu

Douglas County Small Business Development Center
Castle Rock Chamber of Commerce
P.O. Box 282
420 Jerry Street
Castle Rock, CO 80104
303-814-0936
Fax: 303-688-2688

Colorado Springs Small Business Development Center
University of Colorado at Colorado Springs
CITTI Building
1420 Austin Bluffs Parkway
Colorado Springs, CO 80933
719-592-1904
Fax: 719-533-0545
www.uccs.edu/~sbdc
Email: iclark@brain.uccs.ed

Craig Small Business Development Center
Colorado Northwestern Community College
50 College Drive
Craig, CO 81625
970-824-7078
Fax: 970-824-5004
Email: SBDC@mail.cmn.net

Delta Small Business Development Center
Delta Montrose Vocational Center
1765 U.S. Highway 50
Delta, CO 81416
970-874-8772
Fax: 970-874-8796
www.dci-press.com/schools/votech/dmavte.sbdc.html
Email: MBA1st@aol.com

Denver Small Business Development Center
Community College of Denver/Greater Denver Chamber
of Commerce
1445 Market Street
Denver, CO 80202
303-620-8076
Fax: 303-534-3200
www.denverchamber.org/business_center/sbdc.htm
Email: tame.lee@den-chamber.org

Durango Small Business Development Center
Fort Lewis College
1000 Rim Drive
Durango, CO 81301-3999
970-247-7009
Fax: 970-247-7250
http://soba.fortlewis.edu/sbdc
Email: sbdc@fortlewis.edu

Fort Collins Small Business Development Center
125 South Howes Street, Suite 150

Key Tower Building
Fort Collins, CO 80521
970-498-9295
Fax: 970-498-8924
Email: sbdc@webaccess.net

Fort Morgan Small Business Development Center
Morgan Community College
300 Main Street
Fort Morgan, CO 80701
970-542-3263
Fax: 970-867-3352
Email: sbdc@twol.com

Glenwood Springs Small Business Development Center
Colorado Mountain College
P.O. Box 10001
831 Grand Avenue
Glenwood Springs, CO 81602-0001
800-621-1647
970-928-0120
Fax: 970-947-8324
www.coloradomtn.edu/sbdc/home.html
Email: janetren@coloradomtn.edu

Lakewood Small Business Development Center
1726 Cole Boulevard, Building 22, Suite 310
Golden, CO 80401
303-277-1840
Fax: 303-277-1899
www.state.co.us/gov_dir/oed/sbdc/RR.html
Email: sbdcrrcc@rmi.net

Grand Junction Small Business Development Center
Mesa State College
Western Co. Business Development
2591 B 3/4 Road
Grand Junction, CO 81503
970-243-5242
Fax: 970-241-0771
Email: jmorey@gj.net

Greeley Small Business Development Center
Aims Community College/Greeley and Weld Chamber of
Commerce
902 7th Avenue
Greeely, CO 80631
970-352-3661
Fax: 970-352-3572
Email: r.anderson@aims.edu

Lamar Small Business Development Center
South Eastern C. Enterprise Development
804 South Main
Lamar, CO 81052
719-336-8141

Fax: 719-336-3835
Email: seced@ria.net

Pueblo Small Business Development Center
Pueblo Community College
900 West Orman Avenue
Pueblo, CO 81004
719-549-3224
Fax: 719-549-3139
Email: mary.mcmahon@pcc.ccoes.edu

Trinidad Small Business Development Center
Trinidad State Junior College
136 West Main Street
Trinidad, CO 81082
719-846-5644
Fax: 719-846-4550
www.tsfc.cccoes.edu/sbdc/sbdc.htm

Westminster Small Business Development Center
Front Range Community College
3645 West 112th Avenue
Westminster, CO 80030
303-460-1032
Fax: 303-469-7143
Email: fr_bao@cccs.cccoes.edu

Connecticut

Lead Center:
Connecticut Small Business Development Center
University of Connecticut
School of Business Administration
2 Bourn Place, U-94
Storrs, CT 06269-5094
860-486-4135
Fax: 806-486-1576
www.sbdc.uconn.edu
Email: CSBDC.information@sba.uconn.edu

Small Business Development Center
c/o Business Regional Business Council
10 Middle Street, 14th Floor
Bridgeport, CT 06604-4229
203-330-4813
Fax: 203-366-0105
Email: BridgeportCSBDC@sba.uconn.edu

The Greater Danbury Chamber of Commerce
Small Business Development Center
72 W Street
Danbury, CT 06810
203-743-5565
Fax: 203-794-1439
Email: DanburyCSBDC@sba.uconn.edu

Quinebaug Valley Community & Technical College
Small Business Development Center
742 Upper Maple Street
Danielson, CT 06239-1440
860-774-1133
Fax: 860-774-6737
Email: DanielsonCSBDC@sba.uconn.edu

Asnuntuck Community College Continuing Education
Small Business Development Center
170 Elm Street
Enfield, CT 06082
860-253-3125
Fax: 860-253-3067
Email: EnfieldCSBDC@sba.uconn.edu

University of Connecticut
Small Business Development Center
Administration Building, Room 300
1084 Shennecossett Road
Groton, CT 06340-6097
860-405-9002
Fax: 860-405-9041
Email: GrotonCSBDC@sba.uconn.edu

Middlesex County Chamber of Commerce
Small Business Development Center
393 Main Street
Middletown, CT 06457
860-344-2158
Fax: 860-346-1043
Email: MiddletownCSBDC@sba.uconn.edu

New Haven Small Business Development Center
Greater New Haven Chamber of Commerce
900 Chapel Street, 10th Floor
New Haven, CT 06510
203-782-4390
Fax: 203-782-4329
Email: NewHavenCSBDC@sba.uconn.edu

Stamford Small Business Development Center
c/o Southwestern Area Commerce and Industry
Association
One Landmark Square
Stamford, CT 06901
203-359-3220
Fax: 203-967-8294
Email: StamfordCSBDC@sba.uconn.edu

Naugatuck Valley Community Technical College
Small Business Development Center
750 Chase Parkway
Ekstrom Hall, 3rd Floor, Room 308
Waterbury, CT 06708-3011
203-575-8256
Fax: 203-575-8241
WaterburyCSBDC@sba.uconn.edu

Greater Hartford Area Small Business Development
Center
1800 Asylum Avenue
West Hartford, CT 06117-2659
860-570-9109
Fax: 860-570-9170
Email: WestHartford CSBDC@sba.uconn.edu

Eastern Connecticut State University
Small Business Development Center
83 Windham Street
Willmantic, CT 06226-2295
860-465-5349
Fax: 960-465-5143
Email: WillmanticCSBDC@sba.uconn.edu

Delaware
Lead Center:
Delaware Small Business Development Center
University of Delaware
1318 North Market Street
Wilmington, DE 19801
302-571-1555
Fax: 302-571-5222
www.delawaresbdc.org
Email: wilmington@delawaresbdc.org

Delaware State University
146 South Governor's Avenue
Dover, DE 19904
302-678-1555
Fax: 302-739-2333
dover@delawaresbdc.org

Delaware Technical Community College
Small Business Development Center
103 West Pine Street
Georgetown, DE 19947
302-856-1555
Fax: 302-854-6979
Email: georgetown@delawaresbdc.org

Delaware Technology Park
Small Business Development Center
One Innovation Way
Newark, DE 19711
302-831-1555
Fax: 302-831-1423
Email: newark@delawaresbdc.org

District of Columbia
Lead Center:
Howard University
Small Business Development Center

2600 6th Street, NW, Room 128
Washington, DC 20059
202-806-1550
Fax: 202-806-1777
http://howardsbdc.net

Center for Urban Progress/Office of Latino Affairs
2000 14th Street, NW
Washington, DC 20002
202-671-2828
Fax: 202-671-4557

UDC David Clarke School of Law
Small Business Development Center
4200 Connecticut Avenue, NW
Building 38
Washington, DC 20008
202-274-7235
Fax: 202-274-3583

Florida

Lead Center:
Florida Small Business Development Center
University of West Florida
Downtown Center
19 West Garden Street, Suite 302
Pensacola, FL 32501-5750
850-595-5480
Fax: 850-595-5487
www.sbdc.uwf.edu
Email: lstrain@uwf.edu

Central Florida Development Council
Small Business Development Center
600 North Broadway, Suite 300
Bartow, FL 33830
941-534-4370
Fax: 941-533-1247
Email: mstan@cfdc.org

Florida Atlantic University
Small Business Development Center
777 Glades Road, Building T-9
P.O. Box 3091
Boca Raton, FL 33431
561-362-5620
Fax: 561-362-5623
www.fau.edu/divdept/sbdc
Email: sbdc@fau.edu

Florida Gulf Coast University
Seminole Community College
Small Business Development Center
1445 Dolgner Place
Sanford, FL 32771

407-321-3495
Fax: 407-321-4184
http://sbdc.seminole.cc.fl.us
Email: hardyw@mail.seminole.cc.fl.us

24311 Walden Center Drive, Suite 100
Bonita Springs, FL 34134
941-948-1820
Fax: 941-948-1814
Email: dregelsk@fgcu.edu

Small Business Development Center
46 SW 1st Avenue
Dania, FL 33304
954-987-0100
Fax: 954-987-0106

Daytona Beach Community College
Small Business Development Center
Center for Business & Industry
1200 West International Speedway Boulevard
P.O. Box 2811
Daytona Beach, FL 32120-2811
904-947-5463
Fax: 904-254-4465
www.thebci.com/sbdc

Florida Atlantic University
Small Business Development Center
Commercial Campus
1515 West Commercial Boulevard, Room 11
Fort Lauderdale, FL 33309
954-771-6520
Fax: 954-351-4120
Email: jhudson@fau.campus.mci.net

Indian River Community College
Small Business Development Center
3209 Virginia Avenue, Room 114
Fort Pierce, FL 34981-5599
561-462-4756
Fax: 561-462-4830
Email: mthompso@ircc.fl.us

Okaloosa-Walton Community College
University of West Florida
Small Business Development Center
1170 Martin Luther King Boulevard
Fort Walton Beach, FL 32547
850-863-6543
Fax: 850-863-6564
Email: jbiere@uwf.edu

Small Business Development Center
1031 NW 6th Street, Suite B-2
Gainesville, FL 32601

352-377-5621
Fax: 352-372-4132
Email: sbdcgnv@atlantic.net

University of North Florida
Small Business Development Center
College of Business
12000 Alumni Drive
Jacksonville, FL 32224-2678
904-620-2428
Fax: 904-620-2567
Email: nmartine@unf.edu

Gulf Coast Community College
Small Business Development Center
2500 Minnesota Avenue
Lynn Haven, FL 32444
904-271-1108
Fax: 904-271-1109
www.northfloridabiz.com
Email: gcccsbdc@knolog.net

Small Business Development Center
8500 SW 8th Street, Suite 224
Miami, FL 33144
786-388-9040
Fax: 786-388-9060
Email: fuillar@msn.com

Florida International University
Small Business Development Center
University Park, CEAS 2620
Miami, FL 33199
305-348-2272
Fax: 305-348-2965
www.fiu.edu/~sbdc
Email: sbdc@fiu.edu

Florida International University
North Miami Campus
Small Business Development Center
Academic Building 1, Room 350
Miami, FL 33150
305-919-5790
Fax: 305-919-5792
Email: jarrettr@servax.fiu.edu

Brevard Community College
Small Business Development Center
3865 North Wickham Road
Room 10-122
Melbourne, FL 32935
321-632-111 ext. 33201, 32760
888-747-2802
www.brevard.cc.fl.us/melbourne/sbdc/melb_sbdc.html
Email: Peadev@brevard.cc.fl.us

Small Business Development Center
110 East Silver Springs Boulevard
Ocala, FL 34470
352-622-8763
Fax: 352-351-1031
Email: sbdcoca@atlantic.net

University of Central Florida
Small Business Development Center
12565 Research Parkway, Suite 300
Orlando, FL 32826-2909
407-823-5554
Fax: 407-384-2868
www.bus.ucf.edu/sbdc
Email: sbdcucf@pegasus.cc.ucf.edu

Seminole Community College
Small Business Development Center
1445 Dolgner Place
Sanford, FL 32771
407-321-3495
Fax: 407-321-4184
http://sbdc.seminole.cc.fl.us
Email: hardyw@mail.seminole.cc.fl.us

Florida A&M University
Small Business Development Center
1157 East Tennessee Street
Tallahassee, FL 32308
850-599-3407
Fax: 850-561-2049
www.famu.edu/acad/centers
Email: goreilly@freenet.fsu.edu

University of South Florida
Small Business Development Center
1101 Channelside Drive, Suite 210
Tampa, FL 33602
813-905-5800
Fax: 813-905-5801
www.coba.usf.edu/centers/sbdc

Georgia
Lead Center:
Hank Logan
Georgia Small Business Development Center
University of Georgia
Chicopee Complex
1180 East Broad Street
Athens, GA 30602-5412
706-542-6762
Fax: 706-542-6776
www.sbdc.uga.edu
Email: hlogan@sbdc.uga.edu

Small Business Development Center
University of Georgia Business Outreach Center
230 South Jackson Street, Suite 333
Albany, GA 31701-2885-912-430-4303
Fax: 912-430-3933
www.graycommuniites.com/sites/sbdc
Email: sbdcalb@sbdc.uga.edu

Small Business Development Center
University of Georgia
Chicopee Complex
1180 East Broad Street
Athens, GA 30602-5412
706-542-7436
Fax: 706-542-6803
www.sbdc.uga.edu
Email: nancys@sbdc.uga.edu

Small Business Development Center
University of Georgia Business Outreach Center
University Plaza, Box 874
Atlanta, GA 30303-3083
404-651-3550
Fax: 404-651-1035
www.gsu.edu/!wwwsbp
Email: sbdbjm@langate.gsu.edu

Small Business Development Center
University of Georgia Business Outreach Center
1054 Claussen Road, Suite 301
Augusta, GA 30907-3215
706-737-1790
Fax: 706-731-7937
Email: jmoore@sbdc.uga.edu

Small Business Development Center
University of Georgia Business Outreach Center
1107 Fountain Lake Drive
Brunswick, GA 31525-3039
912-264-7343
Fax: 912-262-3095
Email: dlewis@sbdc.uga.edu

State University of West Georgia
Small Business Development Center
Room 130 Cobb Hall
Carrollton, GA 30118
770-838-3082
Fax: 770-838-3083
www.westga.edu/~busn/sbdc.html
Email: bdeegan@westga.edu

Small Business Development Center
University of Georgia Business Outreach Center
1030 First Avenue
Columbus, GA 31901-2402

706-649-7433
Fax: 706-649-1928
Email: lorie@sbdc.uga.edu

Small Business Development Center
University of Georgia Business Outreach Center
Technical Building, Room 112
213 North College Drive
Dalton, GA 30260
706-272-2707
Fax: 706-272-2701
Email: rhennier@sbdc.uga.edu

DeKalb Chamber of Commerce
Small Business Development Center
750 Commerce Drive
Decatur, GA 30030-2622
404-373-6930
Fax: 404-687-9684

Small Business Development Center
University of Georgia Business Outreach Center
3675 Crestwood Parkway, Suite 280
Duluth, GA 30096
770-806-2124
Fax: 770-806-2129
Email: sbdcgw@sbdc.uga.edu

Small Business Development Center
University of Georgia Business Outreach Center
500 Jesse Jewel Parkway, Suite 304
Gainesville, GA 30501-3773
770-531-5681
Fax: 770-531-5684
Email: resimmon@sbdc.uga.edu

Small Business Development Center
University of Georgia Business Outreach Center
601 Broad Street
LaGrange, GA 30240-2999
706-880-8353
Fax: 706-845-0391

Small Business Development Center
University of Georgia Business Outreach Center
401 Cherry Street, Suite 701
Macon, GA 31201-6592
912-751-6592
Fax: 912-751-6607

Kennesaw State University
Small Business Development Center
Busbee Drive
KSU Center, Suite 405
Kennesaw, GA 30144-5591
770-423-6450

Fax: 770-423-6564
http://coles.kennesaw.edu/pages/sbdc
Email: carobert@ksumail.kennesaw.edu

Clayton College and State University
Small Business Development Center
P.O. Box 285
Morrow, GA 30260
770-961-3440
Fax: 770-961-3428
Email: JeanneHaas@mail.clayton.edu

Floyd College Small Business Development Center
P.O. Box 1864
Rome, GA 30720
706-295-6326
Fax: 706-295-6732
Email: Peter_matthews@mail.fc.peachnet.edu

Small Business Development Center
University of Georgia Business Outreach Center
111 East Liberty Street, Suite 200
Savannah, GA 31401
912-651-3200
Fax: 912-651-3209
Email: lvos@sbdc.uga.edu

Small Business Development Center
University of Georgia Business Outreach Center
College of Business Administration
P.O. Box 8156
Statesboro, GA30460-8156
912-681-5194
Fax: 912-681-0648
Email: jmdavisWsgvms2.cc.gasou.edu

Valdosta State University
Small Business Development Center
107 Thaxton Hall
Valdosta, GA 31698
912-245-3738
Fax: 912-245-3741
www.valdosta.edu/sbdc
Email: sbarnett@valdosta.edu

Hawaii

Lead Center:
Hawaii Small Business Development Center
University of Hawaii at Hilo
200 West Kawili Street
Hilo, HI 96720-4091
808-974-7515
Fax: 808-974-7683
www.hawaii-sbdc.org
Email: darrylm@interpac.net

Small Business Development Center
Maui Research and Technology Center
590 Liposa Parkway
Kihei, HI 96726-6900
808-875-2402
Fax: 808-875-2452
www.hawaii-sbdc.org/maui.htm
Email: dfisher@maui.com

Small Business Development Center
Kauai Community College
3-1901 Kaumualii Highway
Lihue, HI 96766-9591
808-246-1748
Fax: 808-246-1748
www.hawaii-sbdc.org/kauai.htm
Email: randyg@aloha.net

Hawaii Island Fax: 808-875-2452
www.hawaii-sbdc.org/maui.htm
Email: dfisher@maui.com

100 Pauahi Street, Suite 109
Hilo, HI 96720
808-969-1814
Fax: 808-969-7669
www.hawaii-sbdc.org/hawaii.htm
Email: winters@interpac.net

Small Business Development Center
Business and Information Counseling Center
1111 Bishop Street, Suite 204
Honolulu, HI 96813
808-522-8131
Fax: 808-522-8135
www.hawaii-sbdc.org/oahu.htm
Email: lunoda@aloha.net

Idaho

Lead Center:
Idaho State Business Development Center
Boise State University
College of Business
1910 University Drive
Boise, ID 83725
208-426-1640
800-225-3815
Fax: 208-426-3877
www.boisestate.edu/isbdc
Email; jhogge@boise.state.edu

Boise State University
Small Business Development Center
1910 University Drive
Boise, ID 83725
208-426-3875

800-225-3815
Fax: 208-426-3877
Email: bshepard@bsa.idbsu.edu

Idaho State University
Small Business Development Center
2300 North Yellowstone
Idaho Falls, ID 83401
208-523-1087
800-658-3829
Fax: 208-523-1049
Email: cappmary@fs.isu.edu

Lewis-Clark State College
Small Business Development Center
500 8th Avenue
Lewiston, ID 83501
208-799-2465
800-933-5272
Fax: 208-799-2878
www.lcsc.edu
Email: hleboeuf@lcsc.edu

Boise Satellite Office
Small Business Development Center
P.O. box 1901
McCall, ID 83638
208-634-2883

Caldwell County Center
Small Business Development Center
2407 Caldwell Boulevard
Nampa, ID 83651
208-467-5707
Email: bdicus@bsu.idbsu.edu

Idaho State University
Small Business Development Center
1651 Alvin Ricken Drive
Pocatello, ID 83201
208-234-7541
800-232-4921
Fax: 208-233-0268
Email: coxpaul@isu.edu

North Idaho College
Small Business Development Center
525 West Clearwater Loop
Post Falls, ID 83854
208-769-3444
Fax: 208-769-3223
www.nic.edu/wft/ISBDC.htm
Email: jalynn@nic.edu

College of Southern Idaho
Small Business Development Center

Evergreen Building, Room C78
315 Falls Avenue
P.O. Box 1238
Twin Falls, ID 83303-1238
208-733-9554 ext. 2450
800-680-0274 ext. 2450
Fax: 208-733-9316
www.csi.edu/support/isbdc/SBDC.html
Email: bmatsuoka@csi.edu?subject-ISBDC

Illinois
Lead Center:
Mark Petrelli
Illinois Small Business Development Center
Department of Commerce
620 East Adams Street, 3rd Floor
Springfield, IL 62701
www.commerce.state.il.us/doingbusiness/
First_Stop/SBCDServices.htm

Waubonsee Community College
Small Business Development Center
5 East Galena Boulevard
Aurora, IL 60506-4178
630-801-7900 ext. 4139
Fax: 630-892-4668
www.cc.il.us/sbdc
Email: rstevens@mail.wcc.cc.il.us

Southern Illinois University-Carbondale
Dunn Richard Small Business Development Center
150 East Pleasant Hill Road
Carbondale, IL 62901-6702
618-536-2424
Fax: 618-453-5040
Email: sbdc@siu.edu

Kaskaskia College
Small Business Development Center
27210 College Road
Centralia, IL 62801-7878
618-532-2049
Fax: 618-532-4983

Asian American Alliance
222 West Cermak, Suite 302
Chicago, IL 60616-1986
312-326-2200
Fax: 312-326-0399
Email: aasbdc@igcom.net

Back of the Yards Neighborhood Council
Small Business Development Center
1751 West 47th Street
Chicago, IL 60609-3889

773-523-4419
Fax: 773-254-3525
Email: bync1751@aol.com

Chicago State University
Greater Southside Small Business Development Center
9501 South King Drive, BHS 601
Chicago, IL 60628-1598
773-995-3938
Fax: 773-995-2269
www.csu.edu/CollegeofBusiness
Email: I_conda@csu.edu

Greater North Pulaski Development Corporation
Small Business Development Center
4054 West North Avenue
Chicago, IL 60639
773-384-2262
Fax: 773-384-3850
www.gnpdc.org/sbdc.htm
Email: sbdc@gnpdc.org

Hull House Association
500 East 67th Street
Chicago, IL 60657
773-493-1306
Fax: 773-561-3507
www.hullhouse.org
Email: lalexander@hullhouse.org

North Business and Industrial Council
5353 West Armstrong Avenue
Chicago, IL 60646-6509
773-594-0891/9292
Email: sbdc@norbic.org

Women's Business Development Center
Small Business Development Center
8 South Michigan, Suite 400
Chicago, IL 60603
312-853-3477
Fax: 312-853-0145
www.wbdc.org
Email: wbdc@wbdc.org

Industrial Council of NW Chicago
Small Business Development Center
2023 West Carroll Avenue
Chicago, IL 60612
312-421-3941
Fax: 312-421-1871
www.industrygroup.com/icnc/index.html
Email: icnc@industrygroup.com

Latin American Chamber of Commerce
Small Business Development Center

3512 West Fullerton Avenue
Chicago, IL 60647
773-252-5211
Fax: 773-252-7065
www.laccl.com/sbdc.html
Email: sbdclacc@ix.netcom.com

Eighteenth Street Development Corporation
Small Business Development Center
1839 South Carpenter
Chicago, IL 60608-3347
312-733-2287
Fax: 312-733-8242

Chicago Loop Small Business Development Center
DCCA/James R. Thompson Center
100 West Randolph, Suite 3-400
Chicago, IL 60601-3219
312-814-6111
Fax: 312-814-5247

McHenry County College
Small Business Development Center
8900 U.S. Highway 14
Crystal Lake, IL 60012-2761
815-455-6098
Fax: 815-455-9319
www.mchenry.cc.il.us/depts/cced/cced_sbdc.asp
Email: SBDC@pobox.mchenry.cc.il.us

Danville Area Community College
Small Business Development Center
28 West North Street
Danville, IL 61832-5729
217-442-7232
Fax: 217-442-6228
Email: dsbdc@soltec.net

Cooperative Extension Service
Small Business Development Center
2525 East Federal Drive
Building #11, Suite 1105Decatur, IL 62526-2184
217-875-8284
Fax: 217-875-8288
Email: wilkingsonw@idea.ag.uiuc.edu

Sauk Valley College
Small Business Development Center
173 Illinois Route #2
Dixon, IL 61021-3188
815-288-5511 ext. 320
Fax: 815-288-5958
Email: nelsonJ@hpux1.succ.cc.il.us

Black Hawk College
Small Business Development Center

301 42nd Avenue
East Moline, IL 61244-4038
309-755-2200 ext. 211
Fax: 309-755-9847
Email: scalfd@outrol.bhc.edu

East St. Louis Small Business Development Center
Federal Building
650 Missouri Avenue
East St. Louis, IL 62201-2955
618-482-3833
Fax: 618-482-4359
Email: robertahart@ahartgroup.com

Southern Illinois University-Edwardsville
Small Business Development Center
Campus Box 1107
Edwardsville, IL 62026-0001
618-692-2929
Fax: 618-692-2647
Email: ahauff@siue.edu

Elgin Community College
Small Business Development Center
1700 Spartan Drive, BCC-115
Elgin, IL 60123
847-214-7488
Fax: 847-622-3068
www.elgin.cc.il.us/corpcom/smallbuss.html
Email: elginsbdc@mail.elgin.cc.il.us

Evanston Business and Technology Center
Small Business Development Center
1840 Oak Avenue
Evanston, IL 60201-3670
847-866-1817
Fax: 847-866-1808
Email: rch@iss.com

College of DuPage
Small Business Development Center
425 22nd Street
Glen Ellyn, IL 60137-6599
630-942-2771
Fax: 630-942-3789
www.cod.edu/BPI/BPI_SBDC.htm
Email: gaydav@cdnet.cod.edu

College of Lake County
Small Business Development Center
19351 West Washington Street, Room B201
Grayslake, IL 60030-1198
847-543-2033
Fax: 847-223-9371
www.clc.cc.il.us/dept/cee/sbd/index.htm
Email: ecd384@clc.cc.il.us

Southeastern Illinois College
303 South Commercial
Harrisburg, IL 62946-2125
618-252-5001
Fax: 618-252-0210
Email: sbdc@intrnet.net

Rend Lake College
Small Business Development Center
Route #1
Ina, IL 62846-9801
618-437-5321 ext. 335
Fax: 618-437-5677

Joliet Junior College
Small Business Development Center
Renaissance Center
214 North Ottawa Street
Joliet, IL 60432
815-281-1400
Fax: 815-722-1895
www.jjciet.org/SBDC.htm
Email: sbdc@jjc.cc.il.us

Kankakee Community College
Small Business Development Center
Box 888 River Road
Kankakee, IL 60901-7878
815-933-0376
Fax: 815-933-0217
www.kcc.cc.il.us
Email: kberry@kcc.cc.il.us

Western Illinois University
Small Business Development Center
214 Seal Hall
Macomb, IL 61455
309-298-2211
TDD: 309-292-4444
Fax: 309-298-2520
www.wiusbdc.org

Maple City Business and Technology
Small Business Development Center
620 South Main Street
Monmouth, IL 61462-2688
309-734-4664
Fax: 309-734-8579

Illinois Valley Community College
Small Business Development Center
815 North Orlando Smith Avenue, Building 11
Oglesby, IL 61348-9692
815-223-1740
Fax: 815-224-3033
Email: bpalmer@rs6000.ivcc.edu

Illinois Eastern Community College SBDC
401 East Main Street
Olney, IL 62450-2119
618-395-3011
Fax: 618-395-1922
Email: sbdc@omegabbs.com

Moraine Valley College
Small Business Development Center
10900 South 88th Avenue
Palos Hills, IL 60465-0937
708-974-5735
Fax: 708-974-0078
Email: lavaiano@moraine.cc.il.us

Bradley University
Small Business Development Center
141 North Jobst Hall 1st Floor
Peroria, IL 61625-0001
309-677-2992
Fax: 309-677-3386
Email: sbdc@bradley.bradley.edu

Triton College
2000 Fifth Avenue
River Grove, IL 60171-1995
708-456-0300 ext.3696
www.triton.cc.il.us/edi/small.html
Email: gbarnes@triton.cc.il.us

Rock Valley College
Small Business Development Center
1220 Rock Street
Rockford, IL 61101-1737
815-968-4087
Fax: 815-968-4157
Email: rvcsbdc@inwave.com

Lincoln Land Community College
Small Business Development Center
100 North 11th Street
Springfield, IL 62703-1002
217-789-1017
Fax: 217-789-0938
Email: fschreck@cabin.llcc.cc.il.us

Shawnee College
Small Business Development Center
8364 Shawnee College Road
Ullin, IL 62992-2206
618-634-9618
Fax: 618-634-2347
Email: sccsbdc@shawnee.cc.il.us

Governors State University
Small Business Development Center

College of Business, Room 3370
University Park, IL 60466
708-534-4929
Fax: 708-534-1646
www.govst.edu/users/gcbpa/comserv/sbdc.htm
Email: h_gereg@govst.edu

Indiana

Lead Center:
Indiana Small Business Development Center
Small Business Development Center Corporation
One North Capitol, Suite 1275
Indianapolis, IN 46204
317-264-2820
888-ISBD-244
Fax: 317-264-2806
www.isbdcorp.org
Email: dbishop@isbdccorp.org

Bloomington Area Small Business Development Center
Greater Bloomington Chamber of Commerce
216 Allen Street
Bloomington, IN 47403
812-339-8937
Fax: 812-335-7352
www.sbdcbiz.com

Columbus Regional Small Business Development Center
Columbus Enterprise Development Center
4920 North Warren Drive
Columbus, IN 47203
812-372-6480
Fax: 812-372-0228

Southwestern Small Business Development Center
Evansville Chamber of Commerce
100 NW Second Street, Suite 100
Evansville, IN 47708
812-425-7232
Fax: 812-421-5884
www.mevcc.org

Northeastern Small Business Development Center
1830 Wayne Trace
Fort Wayne, IN 46803
219-426-0040
Fax: 219-424-0024
www.fwuea.org/Small_Business_Development/small_business_development.html
Email: jomare@fwi.com

Indianapolis Regional Small Business Development
Center
Indiana University
342 North Senate Avenue

Indianapolis, IN 46204
317-261-3030
Fax: 317-261-3053
www.indysbdc.com

Kokomo-Howard County Chamber of Commerce
Small Business Development Center
106 North Washington Street
Kokomo, IN 46901
765-457-5301
Fax: 765-452-4564
www.kokomochamber.com
Email: infor@kokomochamber.com

Greater Lafayette Area Small Business Development
Center
122 North third
Lafayette, IN 47901
765-742-2394
Fax: 765-742-6276

Madison Area Chamber of Commerce
Small Business Development Center
975 Industrial Drive
Madison, IN 47250
812-265-3127
800-595-3127
Fax: 812-265-5544
www.madisonchamber.org/sbdc.html
Email: info@madisonchamber.org

East Central Indiana Small Business Development Center
Muncie-Delaware County Chamber of Commerce
401 South High Street
Muncie, IN 47308
765-284-8144
Fax: 765-851-9151
www.muncie.com/small-business.asp

Northwest Indiana Forum, Inc.
Small Business Development Center
6100 Southport Road
Portage, IN 46368
219-762-1696
Fax: 219-763-2653
www.nwisbdc.org

Richmond/Wayne County Small Business Development
Center
Richmond Area Chamber of Commerce
33 South 7th Street
Richmond, IN 47374-5462
765-962-2887
www.sbdc1.org

South Bend Area
Small Business Development Center

300 North Michigan Street
South Bend, IN 46601
219-282-4350
Fax: 219-282-4344
Email: jfye@michianatoday.com

Indiana State University
Small Business Development Center
School of Business
Ninth & Sycamore Streets
Terre Haute, IN 47809-5402
812-237-7676
800-227-7232
Fax: 812-237-7675
www.indstate.edu/schbus/sbdc
Email: SBDC@indstate.edu

Brazil-Clay County Chamber of Commerce
Small Business Development Center
Twelve North Walnut Street
Brazil, IN 47834
812-448-8457

Clinton Chamber of Commerce
Small Business Development Center
292 North Ninth Street
Clinton, IN 47482
765-832-3844

Connersville Small Business Development Center
504 Central Avenue
Connersville, IN 47331
765-825-8328
Fax: 765-825-4613

Madison County
Small Business Development Center
Elwood Chamber of Commerce
108 South Anderson Street
Elwood, IN 46036
765-552-0180

Northlake Small Business Development Center
576 Carolina Street
Gary, IN 46402
219-885-9663
Fax: 219-885-9675

Greencastle Small Business Development Center
Greencastle Chamber of Commerce
Two South Jackson Street
Greencastle, IN 46135
765-653-4517

Blackford County Economic Development Corporation
Small Business Development Center
111 North High Street

Hartford, IN 47348
765-348-4944

LaPorte Small Business Development Center
414 Lindolnway
LaPorte, IN 46350
219-326-7232
Fax: 219-324-7439

Grant county Small Business Development Center
Ivy Tech State College
1015 East 3rd Street
Marion, IN 46952
765-284-8144

Merrillville Small Business Development Center
1919 West 81st Avenue
Merrillville, IN 46410
219-762-1696 (Portage Office contact)
Fax: 219-763-2653

Michigan City Small Business Development Center
200 East Michigan Boulevard
Michigan City, IN 46360
219-874-6221

Southern Indiana Small Business Development Center
4100 Charlestown Road
New Albany, IN 47150
812-945-0054
Fax: 812-948-4664

Henry County Small Business Development Center
NC/HC Economic Development Corporation
100 South Main Street
New Castle, IN 47362
765-521-7402

Pike County Chamber of Commerce
714 Main Street
Petersburg, IN 47567
812-354-8155

Jay County Development Corporation
Small Business Development Center
122 East Main Street
Portland, IN 47371
219-726-9311

Saint Mary-of-the-Woods College
Center for Women in Small Business
St. Mary-of-the-Woods, IN 47885
812-535-5151

Sullivan County Chamber of Commerce
Small Business Development Center

112 West Washington Street
Sullivan, IN 47882
812-268-4830

Tell City Chamber of Commerce
Small Business Development Center
645 Main Street
Tell City, IN 47586
812-547-4011
Fax: 812-547-8378

Valparaiso Small Business Development Center
150 Lincolnway
Valparasio, IN 46383
219-462-1105

Vincennes University
Small Business Development Center
P.O. Box 887
Vincennes, IN 47591
812-885-5749

Washington, Davies County Small Business Development
Center
One Train Depot Street
Washington, IN 47501
812-254-5262
Fax: 812-254-2550

Randolf County Small Business Development Center
Randolph county and Community Economic Development
Foundation
111 South Main Street
Winchester, IN 47394
765-584-3266

Iowa
Lead Center:
Iowa Small Business Development Center
Iowa State University
College of Business Administration
Chamblynn Building
137 Lynn Avenue
Ames, IA 50014-7126
515-292-6351
800-373-7232
Fax: 515-292-0020
www.iabusnet.org/sbdc/index.html
Email: SBDCWebmaster@iastate.edu

Iowa State University
Small Business Development Center
2501 North Loop Drive
Building 1, Suite 615
Ames, IA 50010-8283

515-296-7828
Fax: 515-296-6714

Des Moines Area Community College
Small Business Development Center
Circle West Incubator
P.O. Box 204
Lot 3, Industrial Park
Audubon, IA 50025
712-563-2301
Fax: 712-563-2301
Email: circlew@netins.net

Iowa Western Community College
Small Business Development Center
2700 College Road, Box 4C
Council Bluffs, IA 51502
712-325-3260
Fax: 712-325-3408
www.iwcc.cc.ia.us/ContEducation/CBI/sbdc.htm
Email: ronsbdc@aol.com

Southwestern Community College
Small Business Development Center
1501 West Townline
Creston, IA 50801
515-782-4161
Fax: 515-782-1334
www.swcc.cc.ia.us/AdultEd/sbdc
Email: taylor@swcc.cc.ia.us

Eastern Iowa Community College District
Small Business Development Center
314 West Second Street
Davenport, IA 52801
319-336-3440
800-462-3255
Fax: 319-322-5236
www.eiccd.cc.ia.us/shared/bic/biznind.html
Email: gryan@eiccd.cc.ia.us

Drake University
Small Business Development Center
Drake Business Center
2507 University Avenue
Des Moines, IA 50311-4505
515-271-2655
Fax: 515-271-1899

Northeast Iowa Community College
Small Business Development Center
770 Town Clock Plaza
Dubuque, IA 52001
319-588-3350
Fax: 319-557-1591

Iowa Central Community College
Small Business Development Center
900 Central Avenue, Suite 4
Fort Dodge, IA 50501
515-576-5090
Fax: 515-576-0826
www.iccc.cc.ia.us/btech

University of Iowa-Oakdale Campus
Small Business Development Center
108 Pappajohn Business Administration Building
Suite S-160
Iowa City, IA 52242-1000
319-335-3742
Fax: 319-335-2445
Email: paul_heath@uiowa.edu

Kirkwood Community College
Small Business Development Center
2901 Tenth Avenue
Marion, IA 52302
319-377-8256
Fax: 319-398-1053

North Iowa Area Community College
Small Business Development Center
500 College Drive
Mason City, IA 50401
515-422-4342
Fax: 515-422-4129
http://venus.niacc.cc.ia.us/progserv/smbusdev.html
Email: peterric@niacc.cc.ia.us

Indian Hills Community College
Small Business Development Center
623 Indian Hills Drive, Building 12
Ottumwa, IA 52501
515-683-5127
Fax: 515-683-5263
Email: bziegler@incc.cc.ia.us

Western Iowa Tech Community college
Small Business Development Center
4647 Stone Avenue, Building B
P.O. Box 5199
Sioux City, IA 51102-5119
712-274-6418
Fax: 712-274-6429

Iowa Lakes Community College
Small Business Development Center
1900 North Grand Avenue, Suite 8
Spencer, IA 51301
712-262-4213
Fax: 712-262-4047
Email: kmccarty@ilcc.cc.ia.us

University of Northern Iowa
Small Business Development Center
200 East 4th Street
Waterloo, IA 50703
319-236-8123
Fax: 319-236-8240
www.sbdc.uni.edu
Email: maureen.collins-williams@uni.edu

Southeastern Community College
Small Business Development Center
P.O. Box 180
1015 South Gear Avenue
West Burlington, IA 52655-0180
319-752-2731 ext. 8103
Fax: 319-752-3407
www.sccc.cc.ia.us/workforce/smallbus.html
Email: cgrimm@secc.cc.ia.us

Kansas

Lead Center:
Kansas Small Business Development Center
Fort Hays State University
214 SW 6th Street, Suite 205
Topeka, KS 66603-3719
785-296-6514
Fax: 785-291-3261
www.fhsu.edu/dsbdc
Email: ksbdc@cjnetworks.com

Neosho County Community College
Small Business Development Center
1000 South Allen
Chanute, KS 66720
316-431-2820
Fax: 316-431-0082

Coffeyville Community College
Small Business Development Center
11th and Willow Street
Coffeyville, KS 67337-5064
316-251-7700 ext. 2117
Fax: 316-252-7098
Email: charless@raven.ccc.cc.ks.us

Colby Community College
Small Business Development Center
1255 South Range
Colby, KS 67701
785-462-3984 ext. 239
Email: bob@Katie.colby.cc.ks.us

Dodge City Community College
Small Business Development Center
2501 North 14th Avenue

Dodge City, KS 67801
316-227-9247
Fax: 316-227-9200

Emporia State University
Small Business Development Center
1320 Cof E Drive
Emporia, KS 66801
316-342-5308
Fax: 316-341-5418
www.emporia.edu/sbdc/index.html
Email: brumbaul@esumail.emporia.edu

Fort Scott Community College
Small Business Development Center
2108 South Horton
Fort Scott, KS 66701
316-223-2700
Fax: 316-223-6530

Garden City Community College
Small Business Development Center
801 Campus Drive
Garden City, KS 67846
316-276-9632
Fax: 316-275-3249
www.westernkansas.net/sbdc
Email: sbdc@gcnet.com

Barton County Community College
Small Business Development Center
245 NE 30th Road
Great Bend, KS 67530
316-792-9214
Email: simmonse@barton.cc.ks.us

Fort Hays State University
Small Business Development Center
109 West 10th Street
Hays, KS 67601
785-628-6786
Fax: 785-628-0533
Email: sbdc@fhsu.edu

Hutchinson Community College
Small Business Development Center
815 North Walnut, #225
Hutchinson, KS 67501
316-665-4950
Fax: 316-665-8354

Independence Community College
Small Business Development Center
11th and Main, Arco Building
Independence, KS 37301
316-332-1420
Fax: 316-331-5344

Allen County Community College
Small Business Development Center
1801 North Cottonwood
Iola, KS 66749
316-365-5116 ext. 218
Fax: 316-365-3284

Kansas City Kansas Community College
7250 State Avenue
Kansas City, KS 66112
913-596-9659
Fax: 913-596-9663

University of Kansas
Small Business Development Center
734 Vermont, Suite 104
Lawrence, KS 66044
785-843-8844
Fax: 785-843-8878
www.bschool.ukans.edu/kusbdc/kusbdc.htm
Email: kusbdc@idir.net

Seward County Community College
Small Business Development Center
1801 North Kansas
P.O. Box 1137
Liberal, KS 67905-1137
316-629-2650
Fax: 316-629-2689

Kansas State University
Small Business Development Center
2323 Anderson Avenue, Suite 100
Manhattan, KS 66502-2947
785-532-5529
Fax: 785-532-5827
www.cba.ksu.edu/cba/depart/sbdc/default.htm
Email: sbdc@ksu.edu

Johnson County Community College
Small Business Development Center
12345 College Boulevard
Carlsen Center, Room 223
Overland Park, KS 66210-1299
913-469-3878
Fax: 913-469-2547
www.centerforbusiness.org/program.asp?sb
Email: sbdc@jcc.net

Labette Community College
Small Business Development Center
200 South 14th
Parsons, KS 67357
316-421-6700
Fax: 316-421-0921

Pittsburg State University
Small Business Development Center
Shirk Hall
1501 South Joplin
Pittsburg, KS 66762
316-235-4920
Fax: 316-235-4919
www.pittstate.edu/bti/sbdc.html
Email: drichard@pittstate.edu

Pratt Community College
Small Business Development Center
Highway 61
Pratt, KS 67124
316-672-5641 ext. 200
Fax: 316-672-5288

Salina Area Chamber of Commerce
Small Business Development Center
120 West Ash
Salina, KS 67401
785-827-9301
Fax: 785-827-9758
www.salinakansas.org/SBDC/Sbdc.htm
Email: gaines@informatics.net

Washburn University
Small Business Development Center
101 Henderson Learning Center
Topeka, KS 66621
785-231-1010 ext. 1305
Fax: 785-231-1063
www.washburn.edu/sbdc
Email: zzsbdc@washburn.edu

Kentucky

Lead Center:
Kentucky Small Business Development Center
University of Kentucky
225 Gatton College of Business and Economics
Lexington, KY 40506-0034
859-257-7668
Fax: 859-323-1907
www.ksbdc.org
Email: IrnaugO@uky.edu

Ahsland Small Business Development Center
Moorehead State University
1401 Winchester Avenue, Suite 305
Ashland, KY 41101
606-329-8011
Fax: 606-324-4570
www.ksbdc.org
Email: k.jenkin@moorehead-st.edu

Bowling Green Small Business Development Center
Western Kentucky University
2355 Nashville road
Bowling Green, KY 42101
270-745-1905
Fax: 270-745-1931
www.ksbdc.org
Email: rick.horn@wku.edu

Elizabethtown Small Business Development Center
1105 Julianna Court, #6
Elizabethtown, KY 42701
270-765-6737
Fax: 270-769-5095
www.ksbdc.org
Email: pksbdc@kvnet.org

North Kentucky Small Business Development Center
Northern Kentucky University
BEP Center, Room 463
Highland Heights, KY 41009-0506
859-572-6524
Fax: 859-572-6177
www.kjsbdc.org
Email: landrys@nku.edu

Hopkinsville Small Business Development Center
Murray State University
300 Hammond Drive
Hopkinsville, KY 42240
270-886-8666
Fax: 270-886-3211
www.ksbdc.org
Email: mocartner@hotmail.com

Lexington Areas Small Business Development Center
4th Floor Central Library Building
140 East Main Street
Lexington, KY 40507-1376
859-257-7666
Fax: 859-257-1751
www.ksbdc.org
Email: dmcknt1@pop.uky.edu

Greater Louisville Small Business Development Center
600 West Main, Suite 400
Lousiveille, KY 40202
502-574-4770
Fax: 502-574-4771
www.ksbdc.org
Email: mashcraft@louky.org

Southeast Kentucky Small Business Development Center
Southeast Community College-Bell County Campus
1300 Chichester Avenue
Middlesboro, KY 40965-2265
606-242-2145 ext. 2021

888-225-7232
Fax: 606-242-4514
www.ksbdc.org
Email: John.Moore@kctcs.net

Moorehead Small Business Development Center
Moorehead State University
CB 309, UPO 2479
Moorehead, KY 40351
606-783-2895
Fax: 606-783-5020
www.ksbdc.org
Email: k. berry@moorehead-st.edu

West Kentucky Small Business Development Center
Murray State University
Business Building South, Room 253
Murray, KY 42071
270-762-2856
Fax: 270-762-3049
www.ksbdc.org
Email: rosemary.miller@murraystate.edu

Owensboro Small Business Development Center
Murray State University
3860 U.S. Highway 60 West
Owensboro, KY 42301
270-926-8085
Fax: 270-684-0714
www.ksbdc.org
Email: mickeyjohnson@gradd.com

West Kentucky Small Business Development Center
MSU-Harry L. Crisp Sr. Regional Higher Ed Campus
300 Irvin Cobb
Paduch, KY 42001
270-442-3897
Fax: 270-762-5473
www.ksbdc.org
Email: loretta.daniel@murraystate.edu

Pikeville Small Business Development Center
Moorehead State University
3455 North Mayo Trail #4
Pikeville, KY 41501
606-432-5848
Fax: 606-432-8924
www.ksbdc.org
Email: m.morley@moorehead-st.edu

South Central Small Business Development Center
Eastern Kentucky University
The Center for Rural Development
2292 South Highway 27, Suite 260
Somerset, KY 42501
606-677-6120

859-622-1384 (Richmond)
877-EKU-SBDC
Fax: 859-622-1414
www.ksbdc.org
Email: kdmoat1@pop.uky.edu

Louisiana

Lead Center:
Louisiana Small Business Development Center
University of Louisiana at Monroe
Admin. 2-57
Monroe, LA 71209-6435
318-342-5506
Fax: 318-342-5510
http://lsbdc.net1.nlu.edu
Email: brrathburn@ulm.edu

Small Business Development Center
Dunbar Plaza, Suite 114C
3600 Jackson Street Extension
Alexandria, LA 71303
318-484-2123
Fax: 318-484-2126
www.nsula.edu/nsusbdc

Capital Small Business Development Center
1933 Wooddale Boulevard, Suite E
Baton Rouge, LA 70806
225-922-0998
Fax: 225-922-0024

Louis State University
Small Business Development Center
South Stadium Drive
Baton Rouge, LA 70803-6100
225-388-4872
Fax: 225-388-3975
www.bus.lsu.edu/btc/sbdc.htm
Email: lsu-sbdc@lsu.edu

Southeastern Louisiana University
Small Business Development Center
College of Business
SLU 10522
Hammond, LA 70402
504-549-3831
Fax: 504-549-2127
www.selu.edu/Academics/Business/SBDC
Email: tfontenot@selu.edu

University of Louisiana at Lafayette
Acadiana Small Business Development Center
P.O. Box 43732
Lafayette, LA 70504

337-262-5344
Fax: 337-262-5296
www.louisiana.edu/Research/SBDC
Email: sbdc@louisiana.edu

McNeese State University
Small Business Development Center
Lake Charles, LA 70609
318-475-5529
Fax: 318-475-5528
www.mcneese.edu/colleges/business/depts/sbdc
Email: msusbdc@mail.mcneese.edu

University of Louisiana at Monroe
College of Business Administration
Admin 2-123
Monroe, LA 71209
318-342-1224
Fax: 318-342-1209
http://lsbdc.net1.nlu.edu/ulm/ulm.htm
Email: esc@ulm.edu

Northwestern State University
Small Business Development Center
Russell Hall, Room 114A
Natchitoches, LA 71497
318-357-5611
Fax: 318-357-6810
www.nsula.edu/nsusbdc
Email: sbdc@alpna.nsula.edu

University of New Orleans
Small Business Development Center
LA International Trade
2926 World Trade Center
New Orleans, LA 70130
504-568-8222
Fax: 504-568-8228
www.uno.edu/~litc
Email: litc@uno.edu

Loyola University
Small Business Development Center
Box 134
New Orleans, LA 70118
504-865-3474
Fax: 504-865-3496
Email: sbdc@nadal.loyno.edu

Southern University
Small Business Development Center
College of Business Administration
New Orleans, LA 70126
504-286-5308
Fax: 504-284-5512

University of New Orleans
Small Business Development Center
UNO Technology Enterprise Center
1600 Canal Street, Suite 620
New Orleans, LA 70112
504-539-9292
Fax: 504-539-9295
www.gnofn.org/~unosbdc
Email: unosbdc@gnofn.org

Louisiana Tech University
Small Business Development Center
College of Administration and Business
Box 10318, Tech Station
Ruston, LA 71272
318-257-3537
Fax: 318-257-4253
Email: jeffers@cab.latech.edu

Louisiana State University Shreveport
Small Business Development Center
College of business Administration
Shreveport, LA 71115
318-797-5144
Fax: 318-797-5208

Nicholls State University
Small Business Development Center
P.O. Box 2015
Thibodaux, LA 70310
504-448-4242
Fax: 504-448-4922
Email: BA-WH@nich-nsunet.nich.edu

Maine

Lead Center:
Maine Small Business Development Center
University of Southern Maine
96 Falmouth Street
P.O. Box 9300
Portland, ME 04104-9300
207-780-4420
TTY: 207-780-5646
Fax: 207-780-4810
www.mainesbdc.org
Email: msbdc@usm.maine.edu

Androscoggin Valley Council of Governments (AVCOG)
Small Business Development Center
125 Manley Road
Auburn, ME 04210
207-783-9186
Fax: 207-783-5211
www.avcog.org/sbdc.htm
Email: mdubois@avcog.org

Coastal Enterprises, Inc
Small Business Development Center
Weston Building
7 North Chestnut Street
Augusta, ME 04330
207-621-0245
Fax: 207-622-9739
www.ceimaine.org/business.htm
Email: wbs@ceimaine.org

Eastern Maine Development Corporation
Small Business Development Center
One Cumberland Place, Suite 300
P.O. Box 2579
Bangor, ME 04401
207-942-6389
800-339-6389
Fax: 207-942-3548
www.emdc.org
Email: mleonard@emdc.org

Satellite Operation
Brunswick Small Business Development Center
11 Cumberland Street
Brunswick, ME 04011-1903
207-373-0851
Email: jburbank@nqi.net

Satellite Operation
Brunswick Small Business Development Center
Curtis Memorial Library
26 Pleasant Street
Brunswick, ME 04011
207-882-4340 (Wiscasset Office)
Fax: 207-882-4456
Email: tar@ceimaine.org

Satellite Operation
MidCoast Council for Business Development
9 Lincoln Street
Brunswick, ME 04011
207-729-0144
Fax: 207-725-0989
http://mcb.nqi.net
Email: mcdbmcog@blazenetme.net

Satellite Operation
Calais Small Business Development Center
Washington County Technical College
RR1, Box 22C, River Road
Calais, ME 04619
207-454-1033
Email: jtoth@emdc.org

Northern Maine Regional Planning Commission
Small Business Development Center

302 Main Street
Caribou, ME 04736
207-498-8736
800-427-8736
Fax: 207-493-3108
www.mndc.org/sbdc/sbdchome.html
Email: rthompson@nmdc.org

Satellite Operation
Dover-Foxcroft Small Business Development Center
Piscataquies County Economic Development Council
55 High Street
Dover-Foxcroft, ME 04426
800-339-6389
207-942-6389
Email: mdubois@emdc.org

Satellite Operation
East Millinocket Small Business Development Center
KATEC Center
1 Industrial Drive
East Millinocket, ME 04430
800-339-6389 (ME)
207-942-6389
Email: balexander@emdc.org

Satellite Operation
Wilton Small Business Development Center
Career Center
Route 2 & 4
East Wilton, ME 04234
207-783-9186 (Auburn Office)
207-645-5824 (Wilton Office)
Fax: 207-783-5211

Fairfield Small Business Development Center
Kennebec Valley Council of Governments
17 Main Street
Fairfield, ME 04937
207-453-4258 ext. 16
Fax: 207-453-4264
Email: jrm@ceimaine.org

Satellite Operation
Fort Kent Small Business Development Center
Aroostook County Register of Deeds
Corner of Elm & Hall Streets
Fort Kent, ME 04743
207-498-8736
800-427-8736 (ME)
Fax: 207-493-3108

Satellite Operation
Houlton Small Business Development Center
39 Bangor Street
Houlton, ME 04730

207-498-8736
800-427-8736 (ME)
Fax: 207-493-3108

Satellite Operation
Kittery Small Business Development Center
Gateway of Maine Chamber of Commerce
306 US Route 1
Kittery, ME 03904
207-439-7545

Satellite Operation
Lewiston Small Business Development Center
Business Information Center
Bates Mill Complex 35
Canal Street
Lewiston, ME 04240
207-783-9186 (Auburn Office)
Fax: 207-783-5211

Satellite Operation
Machias Small Business Development Center
Sunrise County Economic Council
1 Struck Pole Road
Machias, ME 04654
800-339-6389 (ME)
207-942-6389

Small Business Development Center
University of Southern Maine
96 Falmouth Street
Portland, ME 04104-9300
207-780-4949
Fax: 207-780-4810
Email: entwstle@maine.maine.edu

Satellite Operation
Portland Small Business Development Center
Portland Resource Hub
441 Congress Street
Portland, ME 04101
207-780-4949 (USM Office)
Fax: 207-780-4810
Email: entwstle@maine.maine.edu

Satellite Operation
Rockland Small Business Development Center
Key Bank of Maine
331 Main Street
Rockland, ME 04841
204-882-4340 (Wiscasset Office)
207-882-4456
Email: tar@ceimaine.org

Satellite Operation
Rockland Small Business Development Center

Rockland Chamber of Commerce
Harbor Park
Rockland, ME 04841
800-339-6389 (ME)
207-942-6389
Email: mdubois@emdc.org

Satellite Operation
Biddeford-Saco Small Business Development Center
Biddeford-Saco Chamber of Commerce and Industry
110 Main Street
Saco, ME 04072
207-282-1567
Fax: 207-282-3149
Email: aiello@usm.maine.edu

Southern Maine Regional Planning Commission
Small Business Development Center
21 Bradeen Street, Suite 403
Springvale, ME 04083
207-324-0316
Fax: 207-324-2958
Email: jvitko@server.eddmaine.org

Coastal Enterprises, Inc.
Small Business Development Center
36 Water Street, Box 268
Wiscasset, ME 04578
207-882-4340
Fax: 207-882-4456
www.ceimaine.org/business.htm
Email: cfm@ceimaine.org

Satellite Operation
York Small Business Development Center
York Chamber of Commerce
449 Route 1
York, ME 03909
207-363-4422

Maryland
Lead Center:
University of Maryland
Small Business Development Center
Administrative Offices
7100 Baltimore Avenue, Suite 401
College Park, MD 20740
301-403-8300
Fax: 301-403-8303
www.bsos.umd.edu/sbdc

Central Small Business Development Center
3 West Baltimore Street #170
Baltimore, MD 21201
888-898-2073

Satellite Operation
St. Mary's Business Resource Center
22930 Three notch road
California, MD 20619
301-737-1500
800-762-7232 (appointments)
Fax: 301-737-1500
www.sbdchelp.com

Western Region Small Business Development Center
3 Commerce Drive
Cumberland, MD 21502
301-724-6716
800-457-7232
Fax: 301-777-7504

Satellite Operation
Cecil Community College
Small Business Development Center
107 Railroad Avenue
Elkton, MD 21921
www.sbdchelp.com

Charles County Community College
Southern Region Small Business Development Center
P.O. Box 910, Mitchell Road
LaPlate, MD 20646-0910
301-934-7583
800-762-7232
Fax: 301-934-7681
www.sbdchelp.com

Satellite Operation
Calvert County Department of Economic Development
Small Business Development Center
Courthouse Annex, Suite 101
176 Main Street
Prince Frederick, MD 20678
410-535-4583 ext. 484
800-762-7232 (appointments)
Fax: 410-535-4585

Eastern Shore Small Business Development Sub-Center
Salisbury State University
Franklin P. Purdue School of Business
Salisbury, MD 21801
410-548-3991
800-999-7232
Fax: 410-548-5389
www.ssu.edu/Community/SBDC.html

Towson University
Small Business Development Center
8000 York Road
Towson, MD 21252-0001
410-832-5001

877-421-0830
Fax: 410-830-5009
www.towson.edu/sbdc
Email: sstockton@towson.edu

Satellite Operation
Small Business Development Center
Chesapeake College
P.O. Box 8
Wye Mills, MD 21679

Massachusetts

Lead Center:
Massachusetts Small Business Development Center
University of Massachusetts Amherst
205205 Isenberg School of Management
Amherst, MA 01003-4935
413-545-6301
Fax: 413-545-1273
http://msbdc.som.umass.edu
Email: gep@msbdc.umass.edu

Procurement Technical Assistance Center
Small Business Development Center
University of Massachusetts Amherst
205 Isenberg School of Management
Amherst, MA 01003
413-545-6303
Fax: 413-545-1273
http://msbdc.som.umass.edu/ptac.htm
Email: mrobinson@msbdc.umass.edu

Satellite Operation
Massachusetts Export Center
Boston Fish Pier
Building 2W, Suite 305
Boston, MA 02210
617-478-4133
Fax: 617-478-4135
www.magnet.state.ma.us/export
Email: pmurphy@massport.com

Satellite Operation
Minority Business Assistance Center
Small Business Development Center
100 Morrissey Boulevard
Boston, MA 02125-3393
617-287-7750
Fax: 617-287-7767
www.mgmt.umb.edu/centers/mbac/index.html
Email: MBAC@umb.edu

Boston College
Metropolitan Regional Small Business Development
Center

142 Beacon Street
Chestnut Hill, MA 02167
617-552-4091
Fax: 617-552-2730

Boston College
Capital Formation Service/East
Small Business Development Center
142 Beacon Street
Chestnut Hill, MA 02467
617-552-4091
Fax: 617-552-2730
www.bc.edu/bc_org/avp/csom/executive/sbdc
Email: sbdcmail@bc.edu

University of Massachusetts at Dartmouth
Southeastern Massachusetts Regional Small Business
Development Center
200 Pocasset Street
P.O. Box 2785
Fall River, MA 02772
508-673-9783
Fax: 508-674-1929
http://web.meganet.net/sbdc
Email: sbdc@meganet.net

Satellite Operation
Chamber of Commerce of the Berkshires
Small Business Development Center
75 N Street, Suite 360
Pittsfiled, MA 01201
413-499-0933
Fax: 413-447-9641
Email: smongue@msbdc.umass.edu

Salem State College
Northeast Region Small Business Development Center
Enterprise Center
352 Lafayette Street
Salem, MA 01970
978-542-6343
Fax: 978-542-6345
www.msbdcn-ne.org

University of Massachusetts
Western Regional Small Business Development Center
101 State Street, Suite 424
Springfield, MA 01103
413-737-6712
Fax: 413-737-2312
www.umass.edu/linkumass/springfield/
massachusetts_54.html

Clark University
Central Regional Small Business Development Center
5 Maywood Place

Worcester, MA 01610
508-793-7615
Fax: 508-793-8890
www.clark.edu/~sbdc
Email: lmarsh@clarku.edu

Michigan
Lead Center:
Wayne State University
Michigan Small Business Development Center
2727 Second Avenue
Detroit, MI 48201
313-964-1798
Fax: 313-964-3648
www.michigansbdc.org
Email: stateoffice@msbdc.wayne.edu

Satellite Operation
Lenaweee County Chamber of Commerce
Small Business Development Center
202 North Main Street, Suite A
Adrian, MI 49221
517-266-1488
Fax: 517-263-6065
Email: spin@orchard.washtenaw.cc.mi.us

Satellite Operation
Ottawa County Economic Development Office, Inc.
Small Business Development Center
6676 Lake Michigan Drive
P.O. Box 539
Allendale, MI 49401-0539
616-892-4120
Fax: 616-895-6670
Email: drizzo@altelco.net

Alpena Community College
666 Johnson Street
Alpena, MI 49707
517-356-9021 ext. 383
Fax: 517-354-0698
Email: bourdelc@alpena.cc.mi.us

Specialty Center
Michigan Manufacturing Technology Center
2901 Hubbard Road
P.O. Box 1485
Ann Arbor, MI 48106-1485
734-769-4110
Fax: 734-769-4064
Email: wrl@iti.org

Satellite Operation
Huron County Economic Development Center
Small Business Development Center

Huron County Building, Room 303
250 East Huron
Bad Axe, MI 48413
517-269-6431
Fax: 517-269-7221
Email: cjo@avci.net

Satellite Operation
Lake Michigan College
Small Business Development Center
Corporate and Community Development Department
2755 East Napier
Benton Harbor, MI 49022
616-927-8179
Fax: 616-927-8103
Email: richter@raptor.lmc.cc.mi.us

Satellite Operation
Mecosta County Development Corporation
246 North State Street, Suite B
Big Rapids, MI 49307
616-592-3403
Fax: 616-796-1625

Satellite Operation
Livingston County Small Business Development Center
131 South Hyne
Brighton, MI 48116
810-227-3556
Fax: 810-227-3080
Email: livibusi@bizserve.com

Satellite Operation
Tuscola County Economic Development
Small Business Development Center
194 North State Street, Suite 200
Caro, MI 48723
517-673-2849
Fax: 517-673-2517

Satellite Operation
University of Detroit-Mercy College of Business Administration
Small Business Development Center
4001 West McNichols
P.O. Box 19900
Detroit, MI 48219-0900
313-933-1115
Fax: 313-933-1052
Email: kesavar@udmercy

Wayne State University
Small Business Development Center
2727 Second Avenue, Suite 121
Detroit, MI 48201
313-577-4850

Fax: 313-577-8933
Email: bob@wayne.edu

1st Step, Inc.
Small Business Development Center
2415 14th Avenue, S
Escanaba, MI 49829
906-786-9234
Fax: 906-786-4442

Community Capital Development Corporation
Small Business Development Center
711 North Saginaw Street
Suite 102
Flint, MI 48503
810-239-5847
Fax: 810-239-5575

Satellite Operation
Association of Commerce and Industry
Small Business Development Center
1 South Harbor Avenue
P.O. Box 509
Grand Haven, MI 49417
616-846-3153
Fax: 616-842-0379
Email: acisbdc@hotmail.com

Grand Valley State University
301 West Fulton
Room 718S Eberhard Center
Grand Rapids, MI 49504
616-771-6693
Fax: 616-458-3872
Email: lopuckic@gvsu.edu

Satellite Operation
Oceana Economic Development Corporation
Small Business Development Center
P.O. Box 168, 100 State Street
Hart, MI 49420-0168
616-873-7141
Fax: 616-873-5914
Email: edc@oceana.com

Satellite Operation
Gogebic County Economic Development Corporation
Gogebic County Community College
E4946 Jackson Road
Ironwood, MI 49938
906-932-4231 ext. 257
Fax: 906-932-2129
Email: JerryM@Admin1.Gogebic.cc.MI.US

Satellite Operation
Jackson Business Development Center

414 North Jackson Street
Jackson, MI 49201
517-787-0442
Fax: 517-787-3960
Email: jbdc@jacksonmi.com

Kalamazoo College
Small Business Development Center
Stryker Center
1327 Academy Street
Kalamazoo, MI 49006
616-337-7350
Fax: 616-337-7415
Email: sbdc@kzoo.edu

Lansing Community College
Small Business Development Center
P.O. Box 40010
333 North Washington Square
Lansing, MI 48901
517-483-1921
Fax: 517-483-9803
Email: ds1921@lois.lansing.cc.mi.us

Satellite Operation
Lapeer Development Corporation
Small Business Development Center
449 McCormick Drive
Lapeer, MI 48446
810-667-0080
Fax: 810-667-3541

Satellite Operation
Midland Chamber of Commerce
Small Business Development Center
300 Rodd Street
Midland, MI 48640
517-839-9522 ext. 207
Fax: 517-835-3701
Email: biz@macc.org

Satellite Operation
Monroe County IDC
111 Conant Avenue
Monroe, MI 48161
313-243-5947
Fax: 313-242-0009
Email: mcidc@tdi.net

Macomb County Business Assistance Center
Small Business Development Center
1 South Main Street, 7th Floor
Mt. Clemens, MI 48043
810-469-5118
Fax: 810-469-6787
Email: bacmac@bizserve.com

Central Michigan University
Small Business Development Center
256 Applied Business Studies Complex
Mt. Pleasant, MI 48859
517-774-3270
Fax: 517-774-7992
Email: 34tjen@cmuvm.csv.cmich.edu

Satellite Operation
Muskegon Economic Growth Alliance
Small Business Development Center
230 Terrace Plaza
P.O. Box 1087
Muskegon, MI 49443-1087
616-724-3180
Fax: 616-728-7251

Satellite Operation
Ontonagon County Economic Development Corporation-
Courthouse
725 Greenland Road
Ontonagon, MI 49953
906-884-4188
Fax: 906-884-2916
ONTCOED@UP.net

Satellite Operation
Pontiac Economic Development Corporation
8 North Saginaw Avenue
Pontiac, MI 48342
248-857-5603
Fax: 248-857-5713

Satellite Operation
Economic Development Alliance of St. Clair Shores
Small Business Development Center
800 Military Street, Suite 320
Port Huron, MI 48060
810-982-9511
Fax: 810-982-9531
Email: IDC@Stclair.cc.mi.us

Satellite Operation
Kirtland Community College
10775 North St. Helen Road
Roscommon, MI 48653
517-275-5121 ext. 297
Fax: 517-275-8745
Email: loiacanj@kirtland.cc.mi.us

Satellite Operation
Saginaw County Minority Business Development Center
901 South Washington
Saginaw, MI 48601
517-752-6693
Fax: 517-752-8195

Satellite Operation
Saginaw Future, Inc.
Small Business Development Center
301 East Genessee, Third Floor
Saginaw, MI 48607
517-754-8222
Fax: 517-754-1715
Email: sblack@compuserve.delta.edu

Satellite Operation
Marquette Area Chamber of Commerce
Eastern U.P. Planning and Development Corporation
P.O. Box 520
Sault Ste. Marie, MI 49783
906-635-1580
Fax: 906-632-4255
Email: EURPDC@NorthernWay.net

Satellite Operation
West Shore Community College
Business and Industrial Development Institute
3000 North Stiles Road
P.O. Box 277
Scottville, MI 49545-0277
616-845-6211
Fax: 616-845-0207
Email: mabertstrom@westshore.cc.mi.us

Satellite Operation
Parkwood Professionals
26211 Central Park Boulevard, Suite 415
Southfield, MI 48076
248-945-3867
Fax: 248-352-7615

Satellite Operation
Downriver Community Conference
15100 Northline Road
Southgate, MI 48195
313-281-0700 ext. 190
Fax: 313-281-3418
Email: pboase@bizserve.com

Satellite Operation
Sterling Heights Chamber of Commerce
12900 Hall Road, Suite 110
Sterling Heights, MI 48313
810-731-5400
Fax: 810-731-3521
Email: ladams@suscc.com

Satellite Operation
Northwestern Michigan College
Center for Business and Industry
1701 East Front Street

Traverse City, MI 49686
616-922-1720
Fax: 616-922-1722
Email: cbailey@nmc.edu

Travers Bay Economic Development Corporation
Traverse City Small Business Development Center
202 East Grandview Parkway
Traverse City, MI 49684
231-947-5075
Fax: 231-946-2565

Satellite Operation
Northwest Michigan Council of Governments
2200 Dendrinos Drive
P.O. Box 506
Traverse City, MI 49685-0506
616-929-5000
Fax: 616-929-5017
Email: dbeldin@nwm.cog.mi.us

Saginaw Valley State University
Small Business Development Center
7400 Bay Road
University Center, MI 48710
517-790-7748
Fax: 517-790-1955

Satellite Operation
Warren/Centerline/Sterling Heights Chamber of
Commerce
30500 Van Dyke Avenue, Suite 118
Warren, MI 48093
810-751-3939
Fax: 810-751-3995
Email: jmasi@wcschamber.com

Washtenaw Satellite Operation
Small Business Development Center
301 West Michigan Avenue, Suite 101
Ypsilanti, MI 48197
734-547-9170
Fax: 734-547-9178
Email: rking@orchard.washtenaw,cc.mi.us

Minnesota
Lead Center:
Minnesota Small Business Development Center
Department of Trade and Economic
500 Metro Square
121 7th Place East
St. Paul, MN 55101-2146
612-297-5770
Fax: 612-296-1290
www.dted.state.mn.us
Email: marykruger@dted.state.mn.us

Northwest Technical College
Small Business Development Sub-Center
905 Grant Avenue, SE
Bemidji, MN 56601
218-755-4286
Fax: 218-755-4289

Normandale Community College
Small Business Development Sub-Center
9700 France Avenue South
Bloomington, MN 55431
612-832-6221
Fax: 612-832-6352
www.normandale.mnscu.edu/main/
continuingeducation/bpdc/bdo/smalldev.html

Central Lakes College
Small Business Development Sub-Center
501 West College Drive
Brainerd, MN 56401
218-825-2028
Fax: 218-855-8141

University of Minnesota at Duluth
Small Business Development Center
150 School of Business and Economics
10 university Drive
Duluth, MN 55812
218-726-6192
Fax: 218-726-6338
Email: ljensen@d.umn.edu

Vermillion Community College
Small Business Development Sub-Center
1900 East Camp Street
Room NS-110
Ely, MN 55731
218-726-6192

Itasca Development Corporation
Small Business Development Sub-Center
19 NE Third Street
Grand Rapids, MN 55744
218-327-2241
Fax: 218-327-2242
www.itasacadv.org
Email: idsbdc@uslink.net

Hibbing Community College
Small Business Development Sub-Center
1515 East 25th Street
Hibbing, MN 55746
218-262-6703
Fax: 218-262-6717
Email: j.antilla@hi.cc.mn.us

Small Business Development Center
Rainy River Community College
1501 Highway 71
International Falls, MN 56649
218-285-2255
Fax: 218-285-2239

Region Nine Development Commission
Small Business Development Center
P.O. Box 3367
410 Jackson Street
Mankato, MN 56002-3367
507-389-8863
Fax: 507-387-7105
www.rndc.org/programs/sbdc

Southwest State University
Small Business Development Center
ST #105
Marshall, MN 56258
507-537-7386
Fax: 507-537-6094
www.southwest.msus.edu
Email: struve@ssu.southwest.msus.edu

Minnesota Project Innovation
Small Business Development Center
100 Mill Place
111 Third Avenue South
Minneapolis, MN 55401
612-347-6751
Fax: 612-338-3483
www.mpi.org
Email: pdillon@mpi.org

University of St. Thomas
Small Business Development Center
Graduate School of Business
1000 LaSalle Avenue
Suite 25 #225
Minneapolis, MN 55403
651-962-4500
800-328-6819 ext. 2-4500
Fax: 651-962-4410
www.gsb.stthomas.edu/sbdc
Email: gwschneider@stthomas.edu

Moorhead State University
Small Business Development Center
615 11th Street
MSU Box 303
Moorhead, MN 56563
218-236-2289
Fax: 218-239-2280
ww.mnstate.edu/SBDC.htm
Email: sliwoski@mhd1.moorehead.msus.edu

Small Business Development Sub-Center
Owatonna Incubator, Inc.
P.O. Box 505
Owatonna, MN 55060
507-451-0517

Pine Technical College
Small Business Development Sub-Center
1000 4th Street
Pine City, MN 320-629-7340
Fax: 320-629-7603
Email: sparlinj@ptc.tec.mn.us

Rochester Community and Technical College
Small Business Development Center
Riverland Hall
851 30th Avenue, SE
Rochester, NN 55904
507-285-7425
Fax: 507-285-7110

Dakota County Technical Institute
Small Business Development Sub-Center
1300 145th Street, East
Rosemount, MN 55068
651-423-8262
Fax: 651-423-8761

Small Business Development Sub-Center
SE Minnesota Development Corporation
111 W. Jessie Street
Rushford, MN 55971
507-864-7557
Fax: 507-864-2091

St. Cloud State University
Small Business Development Center
Business Resource Center
720 4th Avenue, South
St. Cloud, MN 56301-3761
320-255-4842
Fax: 612-255-4957

North Shore Business Enterprise Center
Small Business Development Sub-Center
5 Fairgrounds Road
P.O. Box 248
Two Harbors, MN 55616
218-834-3494
Fax: 218-834-5074
www.nsbec.com
Email: ajackso2@d.umn.edu

Minnesota Technology Inc.
Small Business Development Sub-Center
Olcott Plaza

820 North 9th Street
Virginia, MN 55792
218-741-4241
Fax: 218-741-4251

Mississippi

Lead Center:
Mississippi Small Business Development Center
University of Mississippi
P.O. Box 1848
B19 Jeanette Phillips Drive
University, MS 38677
662-951-5001
800-725-7232 (MS)
Fax: 662-951-5650
www.olemiss.edu/depts/mssbdc
Email: msbdc@olemiss.edu

Northeast Mississippi Community College
Small Business Development Center
Holliday Hall, 2nd Floor
Cunningham Boulevard
Booneville, MS 38829
662-720-7448
Fax: 662-720-7464
Email: kholt@necc.cc.ms.us

Delta State University
Small Business Development Center
P.O. Box 3235 DSU
1417 College Street
Cleveland, MS 38733
662-846-4236
Fax: 662-846-4235
www.deltast.edu/sbdc/online/index.html
Email: sbdc@deltast.edu

East Central Community College
Small Business Development Center
P.O. Box 129
275 Broad Street
Decatur, MS 39327
601-635-2111 ext. 297
Fax: 601-635-4031
Email: rwestbrook@eccc.cc.ms.us

Jones Jr. College
Small Business Development Center
900 Court Street
Ellisville, MS 39437
601-477-4235
Fax: 601-477-4166
Email: greg.butler@jcjc.cc.ms.us

Mississippi Gulf Coast Community College
Small Business Development Center

P.O. Box 100
2300 Highway 90
Gautier, MS 39553
228-497-7723
Fax: 228-497-7788
Email: janice.mabry@mgccc.cc.ms.us

Delta Community College
Small Business Development Center
P.O. Box 5607
1656 East Union
Greenville, MS 38704-5607
662-378-8183
Fax: 662-378-5349
Email: mdccsbdc@tecinfo.com

Pearl River Community College
Small Business Development Center
5448 U.S. Highway 49 South
Hattiesburg, MS 39401
601-544-5533
Fax: 601-544-5549
Email: smyers@prcc.cc.ms.us

Mississippi Valley State University Affiliate
Small Business Development Center
1400 Highway 82 West
P.O. Box 992
Itta Bena, MS 38941
662-254-3712
Fax: 662-254-3600
Email: wsimms@fielding.mvsu.edu

Jackson State University
Small Business Development Center
Suite 2A-1, Jackson Enterprise Center
931 Highway 80 West, Unit 43
Jackson, MS 39204
601-979-2795
Fax: 601-979-2796
Email: bbreazea@ccaix.jsums.edu

University of Southern Mississippi
Small Business Development Center
136 Beach Park Place
Long Beach, MS 39560
228-865-4578
Fax: 228-865-4581
www.gp.usm.edu/sbdc/index.html
Email: Lucy.Betcher@usm.edu

Alcorn State University
Small Business Development Center
P.O. Box 90
Lorman, MS 39096
601-877-3901

601-877-6450
Fax: 601-877-3900

Meridian Community College
Small Business Development Center
910 Highway 19 North
Meridian, MS 39307
601-482-7445
800-MCC-THE1
Fax: 601-482-5803
www.mcc.cc.ms.us/webcenter/sbdchome.htm

Co-Lin Community College
Small Business Development Center
11 Co-Lin Circle
Natchez, MS 39120
601-445-5254
Fax: 601-446-1221
Email: RobertRuss@colin.cc.ms.us

Hinds Community College
Small Business Development Center
International Trade Center
PMB 11263, 1500 Raymond Lake Road, 3rd Floor
P.O. Box 1170
Raymond, MS 39154-1100
601-857-3536
Fax: 601-857-3474
Email: mhwall@hinds.cc.ms.us

Holmes Community College
Small Business Development Center
413 West Ridgeland Avenue
Ridgeland, MS 39157
601-605-3355
Fax: 601-605-3396
Email: jdeddens@holmes.cc.ms.us

Northwest MS Community College
Small Business Development Center
Desoto Center Room 208
5197 W.E. Ross Parkway
Southaven, MS 38671
662-342-7648
662-280-1421
Fax: 662-280-6174
Email: smbusdev@nwcc.cc.ms.us

Mississippi State University
Small Business Development Center
#1 Research Boulevard
P.O. Drawer 5288
Starkville, MS 39763
662-325-8684
Fax: 662-325-4016
Email: sfisher@cobilan.msstate.edu

Southwest MS Community College
Small Business Development Center
College Drive
Summit, MS 39666
601-276-3890
Fax: 601-276-3883
www.smcc.cc.ms.us/support/ccenter/webdoc6.htm
Email: waller@smcc.cc.ms.us

Itawamba Community College
Small Business Development Center
2176 South Eason Boulevard
Tupelo, MS 38804-5999
601-620-5230
Fax: 601-620-5232
Email: rbhollingsworth@icc.cc.ms.us

University of Mississippi
Small Business Development Center
P.O. Box 1848
B19 Jeanette Phillips Drive
University, MS 38677-1848
662-234-2120
662-951-1291
Fax: 662-951-5650
www.olemiss.edu/depts/umsbdc
Email: sbdc@olemiss.edu

Missouri
Lead Center:
Missouri Small Business Development Center
University of Missouri-System
1205 University Avenue, Suite 300
Columbia, MO 65211
573-882-0344
Fax: 573-884-4297
www.mo-sbdc.org
Email: sbdcmso@missouri.edu

Southeast Missouri State University
Small Business Development Center
Rovert A Dempster Hall
One University Plaza MS-5925
Cape Girardeau, MO 63701
573-986-6084
Fax: 573-986-6083
www.semo.edu/sesbdc/homepage.html
Email: c402sbiWsemovm.semo.edu

Satellite Operation
Small Business Development Center
Chillicothe City Hall
715 Washington Street
Chillicothe, MO 64601-2229
660-646-6920

Fax: 660-646-6811
Email: jcdau@greenhills.net

University of Missouri at Columbia
Small Business Development Center
Suite 1800, 1205 University Avenue
Columbia, MO 65211
573-882-7096
Fax: 573-882-9931
http://business.missouri.edu/Research/Training/
sbdc/homepage.html
Email: sbdc-c@ext.missouri.edu

Jefferson College
Small Business Development Center
1000 Viking Drive
Hillsboro, MO 63050-2441
636-942-3000 ext. 493

Missouri Southern State College
Small Business Development Center
3950 Newman Road
Joplin, MO 64801-1595
417-625-9313
Email: sbdcj@missouriedu

Truman State University
Small Business Development Center
100 East Normal
Kirksville, MO 63501-4419
660-785-4307
Email: sbdck@missouri.edu

Rockhurst University
Small Business Development Center
1100 Rockhurst Road
Kansas City, MO 64110-2561
816-501-4572
www.rockhurst.edu/3.0/services_and_resources/
sbdc/index.html
Email: sbdckc@missouri.edu

Thomas Hill Enterprise Center
Small Business Development Center
1709 Prospect Drive, Suite B
Macon, MO 63552
660-385-6550
www.e-center.org
Email: JV@e-center.org

Northwest Missouri State University
Small Business Development Center
423 North Market Street
Maryville, MO 64468
660-562-1701
Fax: 660-582-3071

www.nwmissouri.edu/~sbdc/index.htm
Email: sbdcm@missouri.edu

Small Business Development Center
Mineral Area College
5270 Flat River Road
P.O. Box 1000
Park Hills, MO 63601-1000
573-518-2169
Email: sbdcph@missouri.edu

University of Missouri-Rolla
Small Business Research and Information Center
104 Nagogami Terrace
Rolla, MO 65409-1340
573-341-4559
Fax: 573-341-6495
www.umr.edu/~tscsbdc
Email: sbdc@umr.edu

Southwest Missouri State University
Small Business Development Center
Center for Business Research
901 South National
Springfiled, MO 65804-0089
417-836-5685
Email: SBDC@mail.smsu.edu

St. Charles Small Business Development Center
5988 Mid Rivers Mall Drive
St. Charles, MO 63304-7119
636-928-7714
Fax: 636-441-6881
http://mo-sbdc.org/stlouis/index.html
Email: sbdc@stcc-edc.com

Satellite Operation
St. Joseph Chamber of Commerce
St. Joseph Satellite Center
3003 Frederick Avenue
St. Joseph, MO 64506
816-232-4460
Fax: 816-364-4873
http://mo-sbdc.org/stlouis/index.html
Email: sbdc@saintjoseph.com

Satellite Operation
Grace Hill Satellite Center
2614 14th Street
St. Louis, MO 63106
314-588-8856
Fax: 314-539-9666
Email: wilsonkr@missouri.edu

SBA One-Stop Capital Shop
Small Business Development Center

706 North Jefferson
St. Louis, MO 63103
314-436-2202 ext. 329
Fax: 314-436-2627
http://mo-sbdc.org/stlouis/index.html
Email: Wilsonkr@missouri.edu

St. Louis Enterprise Center
315 Lemay Ferry Road, Suite 131
St. Louis, MO 63125
314-631-5327
Fax: 314-631-7996
http://mo-sbdc.org/St.louis/index.html
Email: TuckerGD@missouri.edu

Central Missouri State University
Small Business Development Center
Center for Technology and Small Business Development
Grinstead #14
Warrensburg, MO 64093-5037
660-543-4402
Fax: 660-543-8159
http://153.91.1.141
Email: ctr4tech@cmsu1.cmsu.edu

Southwestern Missouri State University-West Plains
Small Business Development Center
128 Garfield
West Plains, MO 65775-2715
417-255-7966
Email: Lwright@wp.smsu.edu

Montana

Lead Center:
Montana Small Business Development Center
Department of Commerce
1429 Ninth Avenue
Helena, MT 59601
406-444-4780
http://commerce.state.mt.us/EconDev/SBDC/SBDC.htm
Email: rkloer@state.mt.us

Billings Small Business Development Center
Big Sky Economic Development Authority
222 North 32nd Street
Bilings, MT 59101
406-256-6875
Fax: 406-256-6877
Email: langman@bigskyeda.org

Bozeman Small Business Development Center
Gallatin Development corporation
222 East Main, Suite 102
Bozeman, MT 59715
406-587-3113

Fax: 406-587-9565
www.bozeman.org/sbdc.html
Email: botmline@bozeman.org

Butte Small Business Development Center
Headquarters RC&D
305 West Mercury, Suite 211
Butte, MT 59701
406-782-7333
Fax: 406-782-2990
Email: connietd@in-tch.com

Colstrip Small Business Development Center
Southeastern Montana Development Corporation
P.O. Box 1935
6200 main Street
Colstrip, MT 59323
406-748-2990
Fax: 406-748-2990
www.se-mdc.org/service.html

Great Falls Small Business Development Center
High Plains Development Authority
710 1st Avenue North
P.O. Box 2568
Great Falls, MT 59403-2568
406-453-8834
Fax: 406-454-2995
www.hpda.org/smallbusiness.htm
Email: suzie@hpda.org

Havre Small Business Development Center
Bear Paw Development Corporation
P.O. Box 170
48 2nd Avenue
Havre, MT 59501
406-265-4945
Fax: 406-265-5602
www.bearpaw.org/
small_business_development_center.htm
Email: tjette@bearpaw.org

Helena Small Business Development Center
Gateway Economic Development Corporation
1015 Poplar
Helena, MT 59601
406-447-1512
Fax: 406-447-1514
Email: hlnsbdc@mt.net

Kalispell Area Chamber of Commerce
Small Business Development Center
15 Depot Park
Kalispell, MT 59901
406-758-2802
Fax: 406-758-2805

www.kalispellsmallbusiness.com
Email: kalsbdc@centrurytel.net

Missoula Community Development Corporation
Small Business Development Center
103 East Main
Missoula, MT 59802
406-728-9234
fax: 406-542-6671
www.mtcdc.org/sbdc.html
Email: medc@mtcdc.org

Wolf Point Small Business Development Center
Missouri Valley Development Corporation
233 Cascade Street
Wolf Point, MT 59201
406-653-2590
Fax: 406-653-1840
Email: laursbdc@midrivers.com

Nebraska

Lead Center:
Nebraska Business Development Center
University of Nebraska at Omaha
College of Business Administration, Room 415
Omaha, NE 68182
402-554-2521
http://nbdc.unomaha.edu
Email: robert_bernier@unomaha.edu

Chadron State College
Nebraska Business Development Center
Administration Building 354
1000 Main Street
Chadron, NE 69337
308-432-6282
www.csc.edu/r/Regional/NBDC.htm
Email: chanson@cscl.csc.edu

University of Nebraska at Kearney
Nebraska Business Development Center
Men's Hall
9th Avenue and 26th Street, Room 207
Kearney, NE 68849-3035
308-865-8344
www.unk.edu/departments/NBDC
Email: Jensens@unk.edu

Nebraska Business Development Center
1135 M Street, Suite 200
Lincoln, NE 68508
402-472-3358
Fax: 402-472-3363
NBDCLincolnNE@aol.com

Northeast Community College
801 East Benjamin Avenue, Room 113WA
Norfolk, NE 68702-0469
402-644-0580
Email: Renee_Held@unomaha.edu

Mid-Plains Community College
Nebraska Business Development Center
1101 Halligan Drive
Vocational Technical Campus
North Platte, NE 69101
308-534-5115
Email: mdkurth@ziggy.mpcc.cc.me.us

Entrepreneur Shop at Kinko's
2727 South 140th Street
Omaha, NE 68144
402-595-1158
desarae_fichepain@unomail.unomaha.edu

Nebraska Business Development Center
Omaha Business and Technology Center
2505 North 24th Street, Suite 101
Omaha, NE 68110
402-595-3511

University of Nebraska at Omaha
Nebraska Business Development Center
1313 Farnam, Suite 132
Omaha, NE 68182-0164
402-595-2381
Fax: 402-595-2385
http://nbdc.unomaha.edu
Email: thomas_mccabe@unomaha.edu

Peru State College
Nebraska Business Development Center
T.J. Majors Hall, Room 248
Peru, NE 68421
402-872-2274
http://bobcat.peru.edu/~nbdc
Email: breazile@pscosf.peru.edu

Nebraska Business Development Center
US Bank Building
1620 Broadway, Room 201
Scottsbluff, NE 69361
308-635-7513
Email: ibatters@unomaha.edu

Wayne State College
Nebraska Business Development Center
Gardner Hall
1111 Main Street
Wayne, NE 68787
402-375-7575

Fax: 402-375-7574
www.wsc.edu/academic/business/nbdc.htm
Email: nbdc@wscgate.wsc.edu

Nevada
Lead Center:
Nevada Small Business Development Center
University of Nevada Reno
College of Business Administration
Business Building, Room 411
Reno, NV 89577-0100
775-784-1717
Fax: 775-784-4337
www.nsbdc.org
Email: nsbdc@unr.nevada.edu

Great Basin College
Small Business Development Center
1500 College Parkway
Elko, NV 89801
775-753-2245
Fax: 775-753-2242
www.nsbdc.org/offices/elko
Email: judye@gbcnv.edu

University of Nevada at Las Vegas
Small Business Development Center
College of Business and Economics
3720 Howard Hughes Parkway
Las Vegas, NV 89109
702-734-7575
Fax: 702-734-7633
www.nsbdc.org/offices/lasvegas
Email: nsbdc@nevada.edu

Carson City Chamber of Commerce
Small Business Development Center
1900 South Carson Street, #100
Carson City, NV 89702
775-882-1565
Fax: 775-882-4179
www.nbdc.org/offices/carson-city
Email: ccchamber@semp.net

Ely Small Business Development Center
rural Nevada Development Corporation
740 Park Avenue
Ely, NV 89301
775-289-8519
Email: rbart@idsely

Fallon Small Business Development Center
Churchill County Economic Development Authority
448 West Williams Street
Fallon, NV 89406

775-423-8587
Fax: 775-423-0381
www.nsbdc.org/offices/fallon
Email: jshields@sci-nevada.com

Carson Valley Small Business Development Center
Carson Valley Chamber of Commerce
1512 Highway395, Suite 1
Gardnerville, NV 89410
775-782-8144
Email: khalbard@scs.unr.edu

Henderson Small Business Development Center
Community College of Southern Nevada
700 College Drive
Building B, Suite 130-1
Henderson, NV 89015
702-651-3520
Fax: 702-651-3194
www.nsbdc.org/offices/henderson
Email: bernief@nevada.edu

Small Business Development Center
19 West Brooks Avenue, Suite B
North Las Vegas, NV 89030
702-399-6300
Fax: 702-399-6301
www.nsbdc.org/offices/n_lasvegas
Email: stevenj@nevada.edu

Hi-Desert Economic Development Authority
Small Business Development Center
P.O. Box 820
Winnemucca, NV 89446
775-623-5777
Fax: 775-623-5999
www.nsbdc.org/offices/winnemucca
Email: sbdc@desertlink.com

New Hampshire
Lead Center:
New Hampshire Small Business Development Center
University of New Hampshire
The Whittemore School of Business
108 McConnell Hall
Durham, NH 03824
603-862-2200
Fax: 603-862-4876
www.nhsbdc.org
Email: mec@christa.unh.edu

Keene State College
Small Business Development Center
Mail Stop 2101
Keene, NH 03435-2101

603-358-2602
Fax: 603-358-2612
www.nhsbdc.org/keene.htm
Email: gc@christa.unh.edu

Small Business Development Center
120 Main Street
Littleton, NH 03561
603-444-1053
Fax: 603-444-5463
www.nhsbdc.org/littleto.hmt
Email: eward@moose.neia.net

Small Business Development Center
1000 Elm Street, 12th Floor
Manchester, NH 03101
603-634-2000
Fax: 603-647-4410
www.nhsbdc.org/manchest.htm
Email: sbdcinfo@nhsbdc.org

Plymouth State College
Small Business Development Center
Outreach Center
MSC 24A
Plymouth, NH 03264-1595
603-535-2523
Fax: 603-535-2850
www.nhsbdc.org/plymouth.htm
Emaill: gchabot@mail.plymouth.edu

Small Business Development Center
151 Main Street
Nashua, NH 03060
603-886-1233 ext. 225
Fax: 603-598-1164
www.nhsbdc.org/nashua.htm
Email: sbdcinfo@nhsbdc.org

International Trade Resource Center
17 New Hampshire Avenue
Peace International Tradeport
Portsmouth, MH 03801-2838
603-334-6074
Fax: 603-334-6110
www.nhsbdc.org/itrc.htm
Email: sbdcinfo@nhsbdc.org

New Hampshire Small Business Development Center
c/o Rochester Chamber of Commerce
18 South Main Street, Suite 3A
Rochester, NH 03867
603-330-1929
Fax: 603-330-1948
www.nhsbdc.org/rocheste.htm

New Jersey
Lead Center:
New Jersey Small Business Development Center
Rutgers Graduate School of management
49 Bleeker Street
Newark, NJ 07102
973-353-1927
Fax: 973-353-1110
www.nj.com/njsbdc_new/index.ssf?/main.html
Email: sbdcinfo@yourbizpartner.com

Small Business Development Center
Greater Atlantic City Chamber of Commerce
11 South Iowa
Atlantic City, NJ 08401
609-572-0950

Rutgers University Campus at Camden
Small Business Development Center
School of Business
227 Penn Street
13th Floor, Room 334
Camden, NJ 08101
856-225-6221
http://camden-sbc.rutgers.edu/sbdc

Brookdale Community College
Small Business Development Center
765 Newman Springs Road
Lincroft, NJ 07738
732-224-2738/2751
www.brookdale.cc.nj.us/staff/sbdc

Rutgers University Campus at Newark
Small Business Development Center
Rutgers Graduate School of Management
49 Bleeker Street
Newark, NJ 07102
973-353-5950
www.nj.com/njsbdc

Bergen Community College
Small Business Development Center
400 Paramus Road
3rd Floor, Room A328
Paramus, NJ 07652
201-447-7841
www.bergen.cc.nj.us/sbdc
Email: vdelia@bergen.cc.nj.us

Paterson Small Business Development Center
133 Ellison Street
Paterson, NJ 07505
973-754-8695
Fax: 973-754-9153

Mercer County Community College
Small Business Development Center
1200 Old Trenton Toad
Trenton, NJ 08690
609-586-4800 ext. 3469
www.mcc.edu/business/sbdc
Email: sbdc@mcc.edu

Kean University
Small Business Development Center
East Campus, Room 242
1000 Morris Avenue
Union, NJ 07083
908-527-2946
www.kean.edu/~cont-ed/small_business_dev_center.htm

Warren County Community College
Skylands Small Business Development Center
475 Route 57 West
Washington, NJ 07882
908-689-9620
www.warren.cc.nj.us/ssbdc

New Mexico

Lead Center:
New Mexico Small Business Development Center
Santa Fe Community College
6401 Richards Avenue
Santa Fe, NM 87502-4187
505-428-1362
800-281-7232
Fax: 505-438-1237
www.mnsbdc.org

New Mexico State University at Alamogordo
Small Business Development Center
2230 Lawrence Boulevard
Alamogrodo, NM 88310
505-434-5272
Fax: 505-434-1432
Fax: 505-439-3643

Albuquerque Technical Vocational Institute
Small Business Development Center
801 University SE, Suite 300
Albuquerque, NM 87106
505-272-7980
Fax: 505-272-7969
http://fpweb.tvi.cc.mn.us/wtc/tvisbdc.htm
Email: sbdc@tvi.cc.nm.us

South Valley Small Business Development Center
700 4th Street, SW
Albuquerque, NM 87102
505-248-0132
Fax: 505-248-0127

New Mexico State University at Carlsbad
Small Business Development Center
1500 University Drive, Room 254
Carlsbad, NM 88220
505-234-9435
Fax: 505-885-1515

Clovis Community College
Small Business Development Center
417 Schepps Boulevard
Clovis, NM 88101
505-769-4136
Fax: 505-769-4190
www.clovis.cc.nm.us/communityservices/SBDC.htm
Email: sbdc@clovis.cc.nm.us

Northern New Mexico Community College
Small Business Development Center
921 Paseo de Onate
Espanola, NM 87532
505-747-2236
Fax: 505-747-2234
http://nnm.cc.nm.us/www/pionews/sbdc3-2-2k.htm
Email: icarrillo@nnm.cc.nm.us

San Juan College
Small Business Development Center
4601 College Boulevard
Farmington, NM 87402
505-599-0528
Fax: 505-599-0385
www.sjc.cc.nm.us/QCB/qcb.html

University of New Mexico at Gallup
Small Business Development Center
103 West Highway 66
Gallup, NM 87301
505-722-2220
Fax: 505-863-6006

New Mexico State University at Grants
Small Business Development Center
709 East Roosevelt Avenue
Grants, NM 87020
505-287-8221
Fax: 505-287-2125
www.grants.nmsu.edu/gr_general/sbdc.html
Email: sbdcgrant@7cities.net

New Mexico Junior College
Small Business Development Center
5317 Lovington Highway
Hobbs, NM 88240
505-392-5603 ext. 651
Fax: 505-392-2594

Dona Ana Branch Community College
Small Business Development Center
Box 30001, Department 3DA
34005 Espina, Room 99
Las Cruces, NM 88003-8001
505-527-7601
Fax: 505-527-7515
http://dabcc-www.nmsu/edu/comm/sbdc
Email: tsullivan@nmsu.edu

Luna Vocational Technical Institute
Small Business Development Center
P.O. Box 1510
Las Vegas, NM 87701
505-454-2595
800-588-7232
Fax: 505-454-2588
Email: lvtisbdc@nmhu.campus.mci.net

University of New Mexico at Los Alamos
Small Business Development Center
P.O. Box 715
190 Central Park Square
Los Alamos, NM 87544
505-622-0001
Fax: 505-662-0099

University of New Mexico at Valencia
Small Business Development Center
280 La Entrada
Los Lunas, NM 87031
505-925-8980
Fax: 505-925-8981
www.unm.edu/~vcsbdc

Eastern New Mexico University at Roswell
Small Business Development Center
P.O. Box 6000
Roswell, NM 88201-6000
505-624-7133
Fax: 505-624-7132

Santa Fe Community College
Small Business Development Center
6401 Richards Road
Santa Fe, NM 87505
505-428-1343
Fax: 505-428-1469
www.santa-fe.cc.nm.us/community.html#sbdc

Western New Mexico University
Southwest Small Business Development Center
P.O. Box 2672
Silver City, NM 88062
505-538-6320

Fax: 505-538-6341
Email: sbdc@silver.wnmu.edu

Mesa Technical College
Small Business Development Center
911 South 10th
Tucumcari, NM 88401
505-461-4413 ext. 133 or 140
Fax: 505-461-1901/4318

New York
Lead Center:
New York Small Business Development Center
State University of New York
42 State Street
Albany, NY 12246
518-443-5398
800-732-7232
Fax: 518-465-4992
www.nyssbdc.org
Email: conroyds@nyssbdc.org

State University of New York at Albany (SUNY)
Small Business Development Center
1 Pinnacle Place, Suite 218
Albany, NY 12203-3439
518-453-9567
Fax: 518-453-9572
Email: crsbdc@global2000.net

Binghamton University
Small Business Development Center
P.O. Box 6000
Binghamton, NY 13902-6000
607-777-4024
Fax: 607-777-4029
http://sbdc.binghamton.edu
Email: sbdc@binghamton.edu

State University College at Brockport
Small Business Development Center
350 New Campus Drive
Brockport, NY 14420
716-395-2334
Fax: 716-395-2467
http://cc.brockport.edu/~smallbus/index.html
Email: sbdc@brockport.edu

Lehman College
Bronx Small Business Development Center
250 Bedford Park Boulevard, West
Old Gym Building, Room 007
Bronx, NY 10468
718-960-8806
Email: bxsbdc@binc.org

Boricua College
9 Graham Avenue
Brooklyn, NY 11206
718-963-4112 ext. 563
Fax: 718-963-3473
Email: SBDC@mindspring.com

State University College at Buffalo
Small Business Development Center
Bacon hall 117
1300 Elmwood Avenue
Buffalo, NY 14222
716-878-4030
Fax: 716-878-4067
Email: smallbiz@buffalostate.edu

SUNY Canton College of Technology
Canton Small Business Development Center
Faculty Office Building, Room 430
Cornell Drive
Canton, NY 13617
315-386-7312
Fax: 315-379-3814
www.canton.edu/scripts/t3cgi.exe/can/
can_start.taf?_function=lead&page_name=
community&type= community

Corning Community College
Small Business Development Center
24 Denison Parkway West
Corning, NY 17830
607-962-9461
Fax: 607-936-6642
www.corning-
cc.edu/workforcedevelopment/training/backup/ index.html
Email: gestwicki@corning-cc.edu

Mercy College Outreach Center
Small Business Development Center
555 Broadway
Dobbs Ferry, NY 10522-1189
914-674-7845
Fax: 914-693-4996
www.sbdc.rockland.ny.us
Email: sbdc@sbdc.rockland.ny.us

State University College of Technology at Farmingdale
Small Business Development Center
Campus Commons
Melville, NY 11735
516-420-2765
Fax: 516-293-5343
www.farmingdale.edu/CampusPages/CampusAffiliates/
SmallBusinessCenter/smallbusinesscenter.html
Email: southard@farmingdale.edu

SUNY Geneseo
Small Business Development Outreach Center
South Hall 111
1 College Circle
Geneseo, NY 14454-1485
716-245-5429
Fax: 716-245-5430
www.geneseo.edu/~founddev/corporaterel/bic/sbdc.shtml
Email: SBDC@uno.cc.geneseo.edu

EOC Hempstead Outreach Center
Small Business Development Center
269 Fulton Avenue
Hempstead, NY 11550
516-564-8672
Fax: 516-564-1895
www.farmingdale.edu/CampusPages/CampusAffiliates/
SmallBusinessCenter/smallbusinesscenter.html
Email: schwarjf@farmingdale.edu

York College, The City University of New York
Small Business Development Center
94-50 159th Street
Science Building, Room 107
Jamaica, NY 11451
718-262-2880
Fax: 718-262-2881
Email: cook@ycvax.york.cuny.edu

Jamestown Community College
Small Business Development Center
Community Services Center
525 Falconer Street
Jamestown, NY 14701
716-665-5754
800-522-7232
Fax: 716-665-6733
www.sunyjcc.edu/sbdc/sbdc.html
Email: dobiesia@jccw22.cc.sunyjcc.edu

Mid-Huron Small Business Development Center
Business Resource Center
1 Development Court
Kingston, NY 12401
914-339-0025
Fax: 914-339-1631
http://208.234.27.47/conted/sbdc.html
Email: hardingf@sunyulster.edu

Midtown Outreach Center
Small Business Development Center
Baruch College
360 Park Avenue, Box F-1101
New York, NY 10010
212-802-6620

Fax: 212-802-6613
Email: sonica_puri@baruch.cuny.edu

Pace University
Small Business Development Center
1 Pace Plaza, Room W 483
New York, NY 10038
212-346-1900
Fax: 212-346-1613
www.pace.edu/sbdc
Email: sbdc@pace.edu

International Trade Center
Niagara Falls Small Business Development Center
Carborundum Center
345 Third Street
Niagara, Falls, NY 14303-117
716-285-4793
Fax: 716-285-4797
www.sunyniagara.cc.ny.us/pathways/internat.html
Email: nialTRC@macronet.com

Plattsburgh State University of New York
Small Business Development Center
Ward Hall 118
101 Broad Street
Plattsburgh, NY 12901
518-564-2042
Fax: 518-564-2043
www2.plattsburgh.edu/center/tac/sbdc
Email: SBDC@plattsburgh.edu

Manufacturing and Defense Development Center
Small Business Development Center
East Campus
One University Place, Suite A207
Rensselaer, NY 12144
518-525-2644
Fax: 518-525-2649
www.defensedollars.com
Email: MDDC@nyssbdc.org

Riverhead Outreach Center
Small Business Development Center
Suffolk County Community College
Orient Building, Room 132
Riverhead, NY 11901
516-369-1409
Fax: 516-369-3255
www.research.sunysb.edu/research/sbdc

Small Business Development Outreach Center-SUNY
Brockport
25 Franklin Street, Suite 1238
Rochester, NY 14607
716-232-7310

Fax: 716-232-7274
http://cc.brockport.edu/~smallbus/index.html

Niagara County Community College at Sanborn
Small Business Development Center
3111 Saunders Settlement Road
Sanborn, NY 14132
716-614-6480
Fax: 716-731-3595
www.niagarasbdc.org
Email: sbdc@alpha.sunyniagara.cc.ny.us

Southampton Outreach Small Business Development
Center
Long Island University
Abney Peak, Montauk Highway
Southhampton, NY 11968
631-287-0059
Fax: 631-287-8287
www.research.sunysb.edu/research/sbdc
judity.McEvoyWsunysb.edu

The College of Staten Island
Small Business Development Center
2800 Victory Boulevard
South Administration Building 1A-111
Staten Island, NY 10314
718-982-2560
Fax: 718-982-2323
www.library.csi.cuny.edu/sbdc
Email: schwartzm@postbox.csi.cuny.edu

SUNY at Stony Brook
Small Business Development Center
College of Engineering and Applied Science
Harriman Hall, room 109
Stony Brook, NY 11794-3775
516-632-9070
Fax: 516-632-7176
www.research.sunysb.edu/research/sbdc

Rockland Community College
Small Business Development Center
145 College Road
Suffern, NY 10901-3611
914-356-0370
Fax: 914-356-0381
www.sbdc.rockland.ny.us
Email: sbdc@sbdc.rockland.ny.us

Onondaga Community College at Syracuse
Small Business Development Center
Ralph and Fay Whitney Applied Technology Center
Suite W210, 4941 Onondaga Road
Syracuse, NY 13215-2099
315-498-6070

Fax: 315-492-3704
www.sunyocc.edu/business/sbdc.html
Email: millerr@aurora.sunyocc.edu

Brookhaven National Laboratory
Small Business Development Outreach Center
Building 464, Bell Avenue
Upton, NY 11973
631-344-2393
Fax: 631-344-3543
Email: Judity.McEvoy@sunysb.edu

SUNY Institute of Technology at Utica/Rome
Small Business Development Center
Route 12
P.O. Box 3050
Utica, NY 13504-3050
315-792-7547
Fax: 315-792-7554
www.sbdc.sunyit.edu
Email: sbdc@sunyit.edu

Jefferson Community College
Small Business Development Center
Coffeen Street
Watertown, NY 13601
315-782-9262
Fax: 315-782-0901
Email: sbdc@ccmgate.sunyjefferson.edu

The Small Business Resource Center
Small Business Development Center
222 Bloomingdale Road
White Plains, NY 10605-1500
914-948-4349/4450
Fax: 914-948-4985
www.sbdc.rockland.ny.us
Email: sbdc@sbdc.rockland.ny.us

North Carolina

Lead Center:
North Carolina Small Business and Technology
Development Center
University of North Carolina
333 Fayette Street Mall, Suite 1150
Raleigh, NC 27601-1742
919-715-7272
800-258-0862
Fax: 919-715-7777
www.sbtdc.rog
Email: info@sbtdc.org

Asheville Office
Western Region Small Business and Technology
Development Center

P.O. Box 2510
Wachovia Bank building
Asheville, NC 28802-9958
828-251-6025
Fax: 828-232-5126

Small Business and Technology Development Center
Marine Trades
P.O. Box 406
Beaufort, NC 28516
252-728-2144
Fax: 252-728-6988
www.uncwil.edu/dpsee/sbtdc
Email: bradleymp@uncwil.edu

Appalachian State University
Small Business and Technology Development Center
Appalachian-Foothills Region
Walker College of Business
P.O. Box 32114
Boone, NC 28608
828-262-2492
Fax: 828-262-2027

Small Business and Technology Development Center
Central Carolina Region
608 Airport Road, Suite B
CD#1280 UNC-CH
Chapel Hill, NC 27514
919-962-0389
800-815-8906
Fax: 919-962-3291

Small Business and Technology Development Center
Southern Piedmont Region
The Ben Craig Center
8701 Mallard Creek Road
Charlotte, NC 28262
704-548-1090
Fax: 704-548-9050

Western Region Small Business and Technology
Development Center
Western Carolina University, Bird Building
Cullowhee, NC 28723
828-227-7494
Fax: 828-227-7422
www.wcu.edu/mrc/sbtdc.html
Email: steinber@WPOFF.wcu.edu

Elizabeth City State University
Small Business and Technology Development Center
Northeastern Region
Box 874
Elizabeth City, NC 27909
252-335-3247
800-258-0862

Fax: 252-335-3648
www.ecsu.edu/ECSU/Alumni/SBTDC.html

Fayetteville State University
Small Business and Technology Development Center
Continuing Education Center
P.O. Box 1334
Fayetteville, NC 28302
910-486-1727
Fax: 910-486-1949

NC A&T University/
CH Moore Agricultural Research Center
Small Business and Technology Development Center
Box D-22
Greensboro, NC 27411
336-334-7005
Fax: 336-334-7073

East Carolina University
Small Business and Technology Development Center
300 1st Street, Willis Building
Greenville, NC 27858-4353
252-328-6157
Fax: 252-328-6992
www.ecu.edu/rds/sbtdc/sbtdc.html
Email: RDS@mail.ecu.edu

Appalachian-Foothills Small Business and Technology
Development Center
514 Highway 321 NW, Suite A
Hickory, NC 28601
828-345-1110
Fax: 828-326-9117

University of North Carolina at Pembroke
P.O. Box 1510
Pembroke, NC 28272-1510
910-521-6611
Fax: 910-521-6550

MCI Small Business Resource Center
800 1/2 South Salisbury Street
Raleigh, NC 27601
919-715-0520
Fax: 919-715-0518

NC Wesleyan College
Small Business and Technology Development Center
3400 North Wesleyan Boulevard
Rocky Mount, NC 27804-9906
252-985-5130
Fax: 252-977-3701

University of North Carolina at Wilmington
Small Business and Technology Development Center
Southeastern Region

601 South College Road
Wilmington, NC 28403
910-962-3744
Fax: 910-962-3014
www.uncwil.edu/dpsee/sbtdc
Email: langerl@uncwil

Winston-Salem University
Small Business and Technology Development Center
Northern Piedmont Region
P.O. Box 19483
Winston-Salem, NC 27100
306-750-2030
Fax: 306-750-2031
www.wssu.edu/academics/bus-econ/sbtdc.asp
Email: tjohnson@sbtdc.org

North Dakota

Lead Center:
North Dakota Small Business Development Center
University of North Dakota
118 Gamble Hall
Grand Forks, ND 58202
701-777-3700
800-445-7232
Fax: 701-777-3225
http://bpa.und.nodak.edu/sbdc
Email: ndsbc@sage.und.nodak.edu

Small Business Development Center
Bismarck Regional Center
700 East Main Avenue, 2nd Floor
Bismarck, ND 58502
701-328-5865
701-328-5865
877-596-6622
Fax: 701-250-4304
Email: carl_kvanig@und.nodak.edu

Small Business Development Center
Fargo Regional Center
657 2nd Avenue N, Room 219
Fargo, ND 58102
701-237-0986
800-698-5726
Fax: 701-237-9734
Email: linda_licbert_hall@und.nodak.edu

Procurement Assistance
P.O. Box 1309
Fargo, ND 58107-1309
701-237-9678
800-698-5726
Fax: 701-237-9706
Email: jackie_neubauer@und.nodak.edu

Small Business Development Center
Grand Forks Regional Center
202 North 3rd, Suite 200
Grand Forks, ND 58203
701-772-8502
Fax: 701-772-9238
Email: george_younerman@und.nodak.edu

Small Business Development Center
Minot Regional Center
900 North Broadway, Suite 301
Minot, ND 58703
701-852-8861
Fax: 701-839-3889
Email: mitchell_monson@und.nodak.edu

Willston Outreach Center
Small Business Development Center
Box 1326, Creighton Building
Williston, ND 58802-1326
701-774-4235
Fax: 701-774-4201
Email: gary_sukat@und.nodak.edu

Ohio

Lead Center:
Ohio Small Business Development Center
Department of Development
77 South High Street, 28th Floor
Columbus, OH 43226-0101
614-466-2480
Fax: 614-466-0829
www.ohiosbdc.org

University of Akron
Western Reserve Business Center for Women
Polsky M-185 West
Akron, OH 44325-6002
330-972-5592
Fax: 330-972-5573
www.commtech.uakron.edu/current/programs/WRBCW
Email: kdf@uakron.edu

Akron Regional Development Board
Small Business Development Center
One Cascade Plaza, 8th Floor
Akron, OH 44308-1192
330-376-3170
800-621-8001
Fax: 330-379-3164
www.ardb.org
Email: smith@ardb.org

Ohio University
Small Business Development Center
20 East Circle Drive, Suite 155

Athens, OH 45701
740-593-1797
Fax: 740-593-1795
Email: aa428@seorf.ohio.edu

Wood County Small Business Development Center
Bowling Green State University
BGSU Training Center
40 College Park
Bowling Green, OH 43403
419-372-9536
877-650-8165
Fax: 419-372-8667
www.bgsu.edu/offices/sbdc
Email: fligor@bgnet.bgsu.edu

Kent State University Geagua Campus
14111 Claridon-Troy Road
Burton, OH 44021
440-834-4187
Fax: 440-834-8846
www.geauga.kent.edu/sbdc.html
Email: emcconnell@geauga.kent.edu

Kent Stark Small Business Development Center
Office of Corporate and Community Services
6000 Frank Avenue, NW
Canton, OH 44720
330-499-9600
Fax: 330-494-6121
www.stark.kent.edu/occs/main_pages/sbdc.htm
Email: ccollings@stark.kent.edu

Wright State University Lake Campus
Small Business Development Center
7600 State Route 703
Celina, OH 45822
419-586-0355
800-237-1477 ext. 8355
Fax: 419-586-0358
www.wright.edu/lake/webpages/sbdc.html
Email: tomas.knapke@wright.edu

Clemont County Chamber of Commerce
Small Business Development Center
4440 Glen Este-Withamsbille Road
Cincinnati, OH 45245
513-753-7141
Fax: 513-753-7146

Cincinnati Small Business Development Center
7162 Reading Road, Suite 725
Cincinnati, OH 45237-3844
513-556-2072
Fax: 513-556-2074
www.uc.edu/cece/smlbus.html

Hamilton County Development Company
Small Business Development Center
1776 Mentor Avenue
Cincinnati, OH 45213-3597
513-631-8292
Fax: 513-351-0610
www.hcdc.com/assistance.html
Email: m.meyers@hcdc.com

Greater Cleveland Growth Association
Small Business Development Center
200 Tower City
50 Public Square
Cleveland, Oh 44113-2291
216-621-3300 ext. 2389
Fax: 216-621-4617
www.clevelandgrowth.com
Email: juhlik@clevegrowth.com

Columbus Small Business Development Center
Columbus Chamber of Commerce
37 North High Street
Columbus, OH 43215-3065
614-225-6949
Fax: 614-469-8250
www.columbus-chamber.org/sbdc.html
Email: mercedes_moore@columbus.org

Dayton Area Chamber of Commerce
Dayton Small Business Development Center
Chamber Plaza- 5th and Main Street
Dayton, OH 45402-2400
937-226-1444
Fax: 937-226-8254
www.daytonchamber.org
Email: harryb@dacc.org

Dayton Satellite
Center for Small Business Assistance
College of Business Administration
120 B Rike Hall
Dayton, OH 45435
937-775-3503
Fax: 937-775-3545
Email: michael.bodey@wright.edu

Maumee Valley Planning Organization
Northwest Small Business Development Center
197-2-B1 Park Island Avenue
Defiance, OH 43512
419-782-6270
Fax: 419-782-6273

Kent State University, Tuscarawas Campus
Tuscarawas Small Business Development Center
330 University Drive, NE

East Liverpool, OH 43920
330-339-9070
Fax: 330-339-2637

North Central Small Business Development Center
Fremont Office
Terra Community College
2830 Napoleon Road
Freemont, OH 43420-9967
419-334-8400 ext. 210
800-826-2431 ext. 255
Fax: 419-334-9414
Email: kern@terra.cc.oh.us

Greater Hamilton Chamber of Commerce
Small Business Development Center
201 Dayton Street
Hamilton, OH 45011
513-844-1500
Fax: 513-844-1999
www.hamilton-ohio.com/SBDC/entrance.htm

Southern State Community College
Small Business Development Center
100 Hobart Drive
Hillsboro, OH 45133
937-393-3431 ext.2619
800-628-7722
Fax: 937-393-9370
www.osbdc.net/sbdc
Email: rdaniels@osbdc.net

Growth Partnership for Ashtabula County
 Small Business Development Center
36 West Walnut Street
Jefferson, OH 44047
216-576-9134
Fax: 216-576-5003
Email: ashtabulasbdc@suite224.net

Kent State University
NEOH Manufacturing Small Business Development
Center
Van Deusen Hall
School of Technology
P.O. Box 5190
Kent, OH 44242-0001
330-672-2892
Fax: 330-672-2894
http://webcourses.tech.kent.edu/sot/partnerships.htm

Kent-Portage Small Business Development Center
Kent State University Partnership
College of Business Administration, Room 306
Kent, OH 44242
330-672-2772 ext. 254

Fax: 330-672-9338
http://business.kent.edu/SBDC/index.htm
Email: lyost@bsa3.kent.edu

Ohio Business Development Organization
Southern Area Manufacturing Small Business
Development Center
3155 Research Park, Suite 206
Kettering, OH 45420
937-258-7255
Fax: 937-252-9314
www.obdosbdc.org

Lima Technical College
Small Business Development Center
545 West Market Street, Suite 305
Lima, OH 45801-4717
419-229-5320
Fax: 419-229-5424
Email: bicdenhy@worcnet.gen.oh.us

Lorain County Chamber of Commerce
Small Business Development Center
6100 South Broadway, Suite 201
Lorain, OH 44053
440-233-6500
Fax: 440-246-4050
www.lorcham.org/econ_dev
Email: djones@lorcham.org

Mid-Ohio Small Business Development Center
Mansfield-Richland Business Incubator
P.O. Box 1208
201 East Fifth Street, Suite 200
Mansfield, OH 44902
419-521-2655
800-366-7232
Fax: 419-522-6811

Marietta College
Small Business Development Center
213 4th Street, 2nd Floor
Marietta, OH 45750
740-376-4832
800-789-7232
Fax: 740-376-4901
Email: lankforp@marietta.edu

Marion Small Business Development Center
Marion Area Chamber of Commerce
206 South Prospect Street
Marion, OH 43302
740-387-0188
Fax: 740-387-7722
www.mariononline.com/chamber
Email: heartofohio@acc-net.com

Mid-Miami Valley
Small Business Development Center
36 City Centre Plaza
Middletown, OH 45042
513-422-4551
Fax: 513-422-6831
Email: david75bsu@aol.com

Lake Erie College
Lake County Economic Development Center
391 West Washington Street
Painesville, OH 44077
440-357-2293
Fax: 440-357-2296
Email: lcedc@lcedc.org

Tuscarawas Chamber of Commerce
Small Business Development Center
300 University Drive, NE
Philadelphia, OH 44663-9447
330-339-3391 ext. 279
Fax: 330-339-2637
Email: pcomanitz@tusc.kent.edu

Upper Valley Joint Vocational School
Small Business Development Center
8811 Career Drive
North County Road 25A
Piqua, OH 45356
937-778-8419
800-589-6963
Fax: 937-778-9237
www.nationjob.com/showcomp.cgi/upvj.html
Email: uv_jackson@woco.ohio.gov

Kent State University, Salem Campus
Columbiana County/ Salem SBDC
2491 State Route #45, South
Salem, OH 44460
330-385-3805ext. 103
800-385-5150
Fax: 330-385-6348
Email: ddavis@kenteliv.kent.edu

Lawrence County Chamber of Commerce
Small Business Development Center
P.O. Box 488
216 Collins Avenue
Southpoint, OH 45680
740-377-4550
800-408-1334
Fax: 740-377-2091
Email: sesbdc@zoomnet.net

Springfield Small Business Development Center
300 East Auburn Avenue

Springfield, OH 45505
937-322-7821
Fax: 937-322-7824

Jefferson County Chamber of Commerce
Small Business Development Center
630 Market Street
P.O. Box 278
Steubenville, OH 43952
740-282-6226
Fax: 740-282-6285
Email: chamber@clover.net

Enterprise Development Corporation
Small Business Development Center
9030 Hocking Hills Drive
The Plains, OH 45780
740-797-9646
Fax: 740-797-9659
Email: djdl@compuserve.com

Toledo Chamber of Commerce
Small Business Development Center
Enterprise Suite 200
300 Madison Avenue
Toledo, OH 43604-1575
419-243-8191
Fax: 419-241-8302
www.toledochamber.com
Email: wendy.gramza@toledochamber.com

Youngstown/Warren Satellite
Small Business Development Center
180 East Market Street, Suite 225
Warren, OH 44482
330-393-2565
Fax: 330-392-6040
Email: ccsbdc@cc.ysu.edu

Youngstown Business Incubator
Small Business Development Center
241 Federal Plaza West
Youngstown, OH 44503
330-746-3350
Fax: 330-746-3324
www.ybi.org
Email: jcossler@ybi.org

Zanesville Area Chamber of Commerce
Small Business Development Center
205 North Fifth Street
Zanesville, OH 43701
740-452-4868
740-455-8282
Fax: 740-454-2963

Oklahoma

Lead Center:
Oklahoma Small Business Development Center
Southeastern Oklahoma State University
517 University
Durant, OK 74701
580-924-0277
800-522-6154
Fax: 580-745-7471
www.osbdc.org/osbdc.html
Email: gpennington@sosu.edu

East Central State University
Small Business Development Center
1036 East 10th St.
Ada, OK 74820
580-436-3190
Fax: 580-436-3190
www.ecok.edu/dept/usbdcecu
Email: mcdaniel@mailclerk.ecok.edu

Northwestern State University
Small Business Development Center
709 Oklahoma Boulevard
Alva, OK 73717
580-327-8608
Fax: 580-327-8408
www.nwosu.edu/osbdc/index.html
Email: BWGregory@nwosu.edu

Southeastern State University
Small Business Development Center
517 University
Durant, OK 74701
580-745-7577
Fax: 580-745-7471
Email: hmanning@sosu.edu

Northwestern State University
Enid Satellite Center
2929 East Randolph
Enid, OK 73701
580-213-3197
Fax: 580-213-3196
Email: nwosu.edu

Northwestern State University
Goodwell Satellite
Small Business Development Center
301 Sewell Hall
Goodwell, OK 73939
580-349-2611 ext. 317
Fax: 580-349-2302
Email: osbdc@opsu.edu

Lawton Satellite Center
Small Business Development Center
711 SW "D" , Suite 203
Lawton, OK 73501
580-248-4946
Fax: 580-357-4964
Email: sbdcswsu@sonetcom.com

Northeastern State University
Miami Satellite
P.O. Box 3985
Miami, OK 74354-0985
918-540-0575
Fax: 918-540-0575
Email: clcoy@neoam.cc.ok.us

Rose State College
Procurement Specialty Center
6420 SE 15th Street
Midwest City, OK 73110
405-733-7348
Fax: 405-733-7495
www.rose.cc.ok.us/sbdc
Email: mcure@ms.rose.cc.ok.us

University of Central Oklahoma
Small Business Development Center
115 Park Avenue
Oklahoma City, OK 73102
405-232-1968
Fax: 405-232-1967
www.osbdc.org
Email: surbch@osbdc.org

Langton University
Minority Assistance Center
4205 North Lincoln Boulevard
Oklahoma City, OK 73105
405-962-1628
Fax: 405-962-1639
Email: mbfisher@lunet.edu

Eastern Central University
Poteau Satellite Center
Small Business Development Center
1507 South McKenns
Poteau, OK 74953
918-647-4019
Fax: 918-647-4019
www.casc.cc.ok.us/~brec/osbd.html
Email: dqualls@casc.cc.ok.us

Northeastern State University
Small Business Development Center
309 North Muskogee
Tahlequah, OK 74464

918-458-0802
Fax: 918-458-2105
Email: meigs@nsuok.edu

Northeastern State University
Tulsa Satellite
Small Business Development Center
Metropolitan Tulsa Chamber of Commerce
616 South Boston, Suite 100
Tulsa, OK 74119
918-5813-2600
Fax: 918-599-6173

Southwestern State University
Small Business Development Center
100 Campus Drive
Weatherford, OK 73096
580-774-7095
Fax: 580-774-7096
www.swosu.edu/academics/bdc
Email: ClarkR@swosu.edu

Oregon

Lead Center:
Oregon Small Business Development Center
44 West Broadway, Suite 501
Eugene, OR 97401-3021
541-726-2250
Fax: 541-345-6006
www.bizcenter.org
E-ma9il: sandy_cutler@bizcenter.org

Linn-Benton Community College
Small Business Development Center
6500 Pacific Boulevard SW
Albany, OR 97321
541-917-4923
Fax: 541-917-4445
www.lbcc.cc.or.us/bdc

Central Oregon Community College
Small Business Development Center
The Welcome Center
63085 North Highway 97
Bend, OR 97701
541-383-7290
Fax: 541-317-3445
www.co.cc.edu.classes/cp/bizdevcenter.htm

Southwestern Oregon Community College
Small Business Development Center
New Mark Center
2110 Newmark
Coos Bay, OR 97420
541-888-7100

Fax: 541-888-7113
http://mail.coos.or.us/~bdc
Email: bdc@mail.coos.or.us

lane Community College
Small Business Development Center
1445, Suite 1
Eugene, OR 97401-4087
541-726-2255
Fax: 541-686-0096
www.lanecc.edu/cc_gen/bdc/busde.htm
Email: scheideckerj@lanecc.edu

Rogue Community College
Small Business Development Center
214 SW 4th Street
Grants Pass, OR 97526
503-491-7658
Fax: 503-666-1140
www.roguecc.or.us/sbdc
Email: dlove@rogue.cc.or.us

Mount Hood Community College
Small Business Development Center
323 NE Roberts Street
Gresham, OR 97030
503-491-7658
Fax: 503-666-1140
www.bizcenter.org/gresham
Email: donking@teleport.com

Oregon Institute of Technology
Small Business Development Center
3201 Campus Drive, South Hall 314
Klamath Falls, OR 97601-8801
541-885-1760
Fax: 541-885-1761
www.oit.edu/other/sbdc
Email: sbdc@oit.edu

LaGrande Small Business Development Center
Eastern Oregon University
1410 L Avenue
LaGrande, OR 97850
541-962-3391
Fax: 541-962-3369
www.bizcenter.org/LaGrande
Email: LaGrande@bizcenter.org

Small Business Development Center
Oregon Coast Community College
North County Center
4157 NW Highway 101, Suite 123
Lincoln City, OR 97367
541-765-2515
Fax: 541-996-4958

www.occc.cc.or.us/isbdc.html
Email: gfaust@occc.cc.or.us

Small Business Development Center
322 West 6th Street
Medford, OR 97501
541-772-3478
Fax: 503-776-2224
www.sou.edu/business/SBDC.htm

Clackamas Community College
Small Business Development Center
7736 SE Harmony Road, Room 170 & 172
Milwaukie, OR 97222
503-656-4447
Fax: 503-650-7358
www.cccsbdc.org

Treasure Valley Community College
Small Business Development Center
650 College Road
Ontario, OR 97914
541-889-6493 ext. 356
Fax: 541-881-2743
www.tvcc.or.us/del/page40.htm
Email: ontario@bizcenter.org

Blue Mountain Community College
Small Business Development Center
37 SE Dorion
Pendelton, OR 97801
541-276-6233
Fax: 541-276-6819
www.bizcenter.org/Pendelton
Email: Pendelton@bizcenter.org

Portland Community College
Small Business Development Center
2701 NW Vaughn Street, Suite 730
Portland, OR 97210
503-978-5080
Fax: 503-222-2570
www.bizcenter.org/Portland
Email: tlowles@pcc.edu

Small Business International Trade Program
121 SW Salmon Street, Suite 300
Portland, OR 97204
503-274-7482
Fax: 503-228-6350
Email: portland@bizcenter.org

Umpqua Community College
Small Business Development Center
744 SE Rose Street
Rosenburg, OR 97470

541-672-2535
Fax: 541-672-3679
www.umpqua.cc.or.us/dsbdc.htm

Chemeketa Community College
Small Business Development Center
365 Ferry Street, SE
Salem, OR 97301
503-399-5088
Fax: 503-581-6017
www.chemeketa.edu/programs/tedcenters/sbdc.html
Email: jimmiew@chemeketa.edu

Clatsop Community College
Small Business Development Center
1761 North Holladay
Seaside, OR 97138
503-338-3347
800-206-7352
Fax: 503-738-7843
www.clatsop.cc.or.us/services/srvframe.html
Email: panic@clatsop.cc.or.us

Columbia Gorge Community College
Small Business Development Center
400 East Scenic Drive, Suite 257
The Dalles, OR 97058
541-298-3118
Fax: 541-298-3119
www.cgcc.cc.or.us/SBDC/SBDC.htm
Email: sbdc@cgcc.or.us

Tillamook Bay Community College Service District
Small Business Development Center
401 B Main Street
Tillamook, OR 97141
503-842-2551
Fax: 503-842-2555
www.tbcc.cc.or.us/~Oofl/sbdc.htm
Email: jcasey@tbcc.cc.or.us

Pennsylvania
Lead Center:
Pennsylvania Small Business Development Center
University of Pennsylvania
The Wharton School, 409 Vance Hall
3733 Spruce Street
Philadelphia, PA 19104
215-898-1219
Fax: 215-573-2135
www.pasbdc.org
Email: pasbdc@wharton.upenn.edu

Lehigh University
Small Business Development Center

Rauch Business Center
621 Taylor Street
Bethlehemn, PA 18015-3117
610-758-3980
Fax: 610-758-5205
www.leigh.edu/~insbdc
Email: insbdc@lehigh.edu

Clarion University of Pennsylvania
Small Business Development Center
102 Dana Still Business Administration Building
Clarion, PA 16214-1232
814-393-2060
Fax: 814-393-2636
www.clarion.edu/sbdc/index.html
Email: yearney@clarion.edu

Gannon University
Small Business Development Center
120 9th Street
Erie, PA 16501
814-871-7232
Fax: 814-871-7383
www.gannon.edu/resource/other/sbdc
Email: gusbdc@mail.gannon.edu

Kutztown University
Small Business Development Center
Dixon University Center SSHE
2986 North 2nd Street
Harrisburg, PA 17110
717-720-4230
800-457-7743 ext. 4230
Fax: 717-720-4262
www.kutztown.edu/~sbdc
Email: mckowen@kutztown.edu

Indiana University of PA
Small Business Development Center
108 Eberly College of Business
Indiana, PA 15705
724-357-7915
Fax: 724-357-5985
http://shade.grove.iup/edu/gradua/iracs/sbdc.htmlx

St. Vincent College
Small Business Development Center
Center for Global Competitiveness
300 Fraser Purchase Road
First Floor, Benedict Hall
Latrobe, PA 15650
724-537-4572
866-SBDC-CGC (Toll free)
Fax: 724-537-0919
http://sbdc.stvincent.edu
Email: sbdc@stvincent.edu

Bucknell University
Small Business Development Center
125 Dana Engineering building
Lewisburg, PA 17837
570-577-1249
Fax: 570-577-1768
www.departments.bucknell.edu/sbdc
Email: sbdc@bucknell.edu

Lock Haven University of Pennsylvania
Small Business Development Center
105 Annex Building
Lock Haven, PA 17745
570-893-2589
www.lhup.edu/sbdc

St. Francis College
Small Business Development Center
117 Evergreen Drive
Loretto, PA 15940
814-472-3200
Fax: 814-472-3202
www.sfcpa.edu/sbdc
Email: brc@sfepa.edu

Temple University
Small Business Development Center
1510 Cecil B. Moore Avenue
Philadelphia, PA 191221
215-204-7282
Fax: 215-204-4554
www.sbm.temple.edu/~sbdc
Email: sbdc@sbm.temple.edu

University of Pennsylvania
Small Business Development Center
The Wharton School, 409 Vance Hall
3733 Spruce Street
Philadelphia, PA 19104-6374
215-898-4861
Fax: 215-898-1063

Chrysler Corporation Small Business Development Center
Duquesne University
108 Rockwell Hall
600 Forbes Avenue
Pittsburgh, PA 15282-0103
412-396-6233
Fax: 412-396-5884
http://srvl.sbdc.duq.edu.html

University of Pittsburgh
Small Business Development Center
Katz Graduate School of Business
Pittsburgh, PA 15213
412-648-1542

Fax: 412-648-1636
www.sbdc.pitt.edu
Email: sbdc@katz.pitt.edu

University of Scranton
Small Business Development Center
St. Thomas Hall, Room 588
Scranton, PA 18510-4639
717-941-7588
800-829-7232
Fax: 717-941-4053

Pennsylvania State University
Small Business Development Center
117 Technology Center
University Park, PA 16802-7000
814-863-4293
www.researchpsu.edu/sbdc
Email: sbdc@psu.edu

Wilkes College
Small Business Development Center
Hollenback Hall
192 South Franklin Street
Wilkes-Barre, PA 18766
570-408-4340
800-945-5378 ext. 4340
Fax: 570-824-2245

Outreach Center
Small Business Development Center
McDade Trust & Transit Centre
100 West 3rd Street
Willliamsport, PA 17701
570-320-4230 ext. 5555
www.lhup.edu/sbdc

Rhode Island
Lead Center:
Rhode Island Small Business Development Center
Bryant College
1150 Douglas Pike
Smithfield, RI 02917-1284
401-232-6111
Fax: 401-232-6933
www.risbdc.org
Email: Admin@risbdc.org

Northern Rhode Island Chamber of Commerce
Small Business Development Center
6 Blackstone Valley Place, Suite 105
Lincoln, RI 02865-1105
401-334-1000 ext. 113
Fax: 401-334-1009
www.nichamber.org

East Bay Office
Small Business Development Center
Newport County Chamber of Commerce
45 Valley Road
Middletown, RI 02842-6377
401-849-6900
Fax: 401-841-0570
www.newportchamber.com
Email: scarr@bryant.edu

South County Rhode Island SBDC
QP/D Industrial Park
35 Belver avenue, Room 212
North Kinstown, RI 02852-7556
401-294-1227
Fax: 401-294-6897
Email: dfournar@bryant.edu

Rhode Island Small Business Development Center
Enterprise Community Office
550 Broad Street
Providence, RI 02907-1445
401-272-1083
Fax: 401-272-1186
www.risbdc.org/bic.htm
Email: sgoudiab@bryant.edu

Bryant College
Small Business Development Center
30 Exchange Terrace, 4th Floor
Providence, RI 02903-1793
401-831-1330
Fax: 401-454-2819
www.bryant.edu/BUSINESS.HTM

Bell Atlantic Telecommunications Center
Small Business Development Center
Bryant College Koffler Technology Center
1150 Douglas Pike
Smithfield, RI 02917-1284
401-232-0220
Fax: 401-232-0242
www.risbdc.org
Email: belltel@bryant.edu

Export Assistance Center
Bryant Colllege EAC
1150 Douglas Pike
Smithfield, RI 02917-1284
401-232-6407
Fax: 401-232-6416
www.rieac.org
Email: postoffice@rieac.org

East Bay Chamber of Commerce
654 Metacom Avenue, Suite 2

Warren, RI 02885-0250
401-245-0750
Fax: 401-245-0110
www.eastbaychamberri.org

Central Rhode Island Chamber of Commerce
3288 Post Road
Warwick, RI 02886-7151
401-732-1101
Fax: 401-732-1107
www.centralrichamber.com
Email: infor@centralrichamber.com

South Carolina

Lead Center:
Small Business Development Center
South Carolina Small Business Development Center
University of South Carolina
College of Business Administration
Columbia, SC 29208
803-777-4907
Fax: 803-777-4403
http://sbdcweb.badm.sc.edu
Email: sbdc@darla.badm.sc.edu

University of South Carolina-Aiken
Small Business Development Center
171 University Parkway, Box 9
School of Business
Aiken, SC 29801
803-641-3646
Fax: 803-641-3647
www.usca.sc.edu/sbdc/sbdc001.htm
Email: sbdc@aiken.sc.edu

University of South Carolina at Beaufort
Small Business Development Center
801 Carteret Street
Beaufort, SC 29902
843-521-4142
Email: Goodman@gwm.sc.edu

Clemson University
Small Business Development Center
425 Sirrine Hall
Clemson, SC 29634-1392
864-656-3227
Fax: 864-656-4869
http://business.clemson.edu/sbdc
Email: jillb@clemson.edu

University of South Carolina
Small Business Development Center
Darla Moore School of Business
Columbia, SC 29208

803-775-5118
Fax: 803-777-4403

Columbia Manufacturing Field Office
1136 Washington Street, Suite 300
Columbia, SC 29201
803-252-6976 ext. 237

Coastal Carolina University
Small Business Development Center
School of Business Administration
P.O. Box 261954
Wall Building, Suite 111
Conway, SC 29528-6054
843-349-2170
Fax: 803-349-2445
http://cba.winthrop.edu/sbdc
Email: sbdcweb.badm.sc.edu

Florence/Darlington Technical College
Small Business Development Center
P.O. Box 100548
Florence, SC 29501-0548
843-661-8256
Fax: 843-661-8041
http://cba.winthrop.edu/sbdc

Greenville Area Small Business Development Center
216 South Pleasantburg Drive
Greenville, SC 29607
864-250-8894
Fax: 864-250-8897

Manufacturing Field Office
1324 Miller Road
Greenville, SC 29607
864-288-5687

Spartanburg Area Small Business Development Center
University Center
216 South Pleasantburg Drive, Room 140
Greenville, SC 29607
864-316-0170
www.business.clemson.edu/sbdc

Upper Savannah Area Small Business Development
Center
600 Monument Street, Suite 106
Greenwood, SC 29648
864-943-8028
Fax: 864-942-8592
http://business.clemson.edu/sbdc

University of South Carolina at Hilton Head
Small Business Development Center
1 College Center Drive
Hilton Head Island, SC 29928

843-785-3995
Fax: 843-785-3995
Email: Jenkins@gwn.sc.edu

Kingstree Area Small Business Development Center
Williamsburg Enterprise Community
128 Mill Street
P.O. Box 428
Kingstree, SC 29556
843-354-9070

Charelston Area Small Business Development Center
5400 Core Drive, Suite 104
North Charelston, SC 29406
843-740-6160
Fax: 843-740-1607
Email: Lenr@Infoave.net

South Carolina State College
Small Business Development Center
School of Business
Algernon S. Belcher Hall
300 College Street
Campus Box 7176
Orangeburg, SC 29117
803-536-8445
Fax: 803-536-8066

Winthrop University
Small Business Development Center
118 Thurmond Building
Rock Hill, SC 29733
803-323-2283
Fax: 803-323-4281
http://cba.winthrop.edu/sbdc
Email: sbdctech@winthrop.edu

Spartanburg Office
Small Business Development Center
P.O. Box 5626
Spartanburg, SC 29304-5626
864-585-1731
http://business.clemson.edu/sbdc
Email: Dtinsel@clemson.edu

Sumter Area Small Business Development Center
University of South Carolina at Sumter
200 Miller Road
Sumter, SC 29150-2498
803-938-3833
Email: Leron@uscsumter.uscsu.sc.edu

South Dakota
Lead Center:
South Dakota Small Business Development Center
University of South Dakota

414 East Clark
Vermillion, SD 57069
605-677-5287
Fax: 605-677-5427
www.usd.edu/brbinfo/sbdc/index.htm
Email: wdruin@usd.edu

Aberdeen Small Business Development Center
416 Production Street
Aberdeen, SD 57401
605-626-2565
Fax: 605-626-2667
Email: kweaver@midco.net

Pierre Small Business Development Center
221 South Central
Pierre, SD 57501
605-945-1661
Fax: 605-224-8320

Small Business Development Center
444 North Mount Rushmore Road, Room 204
Rapid City, SD 57701
605-394-5311
Fax: 605-394-6140
Email: cmartin@tie.net

Small Business Development Center
1000 North West Avenue, #400B
Sioux Falls, SD 57104
605-367-5757
Fax: 605-367-5755
Email: mslade@usd.edu

Watertown Small Business Development Center
124 First Avenue, NW P.O. Box 1207
Watertown, SD 57201
605-882-5115
Fax: 605-882-5049
Email: sbdc@dailypost.com

Yankton Small Business Development Center
1808 Summit Avenue
P.O. Box 687
Yankton, SD 57078
605-665-0751
Fax: 605-665-0303
Email: troysbdc@dtgnet.com

Tennessee
Lead Center:
State University and Community College
Tennessee Small Business Development Center
1415 Murfreesboro Road, Suite 350
Nashville, TN 37217

615-366-3900
Fax: 615-366-4464
www.tsbdc.org
Email: alaabs@tbr.state.tn.us

Chattanooga State Technical Community College
Small Business Development Center
100 Cherokee Boulevard, Suite 202
Chattanooga, TN 37405
423-752-1774
www.sbdc.chattanooga.org
Email: dmarsh@sbdc.chattanooga.org

Southeast Tennessee Development District
Small Business Development Center
P.O. Box 4757
Chattanooga, TN 37405-0757
423-266-5781
Fax: 423-267-7705

Cleveland State Community College
Small Business Development Center
TA Valley Programs Division
P.O. Box 3570
Cleveland, TN 37320-3570
423-478-6247
Fax: 423-478-6251
www.clscc.cc.tn.us/SBDC/index.htm
Email: dgeren@clscc.cc.tn.us

Small Business Development Center
Maury County Chamber of Commerce
Memorial Building
Room 205, 106 West Sixth Street
P.O. Box 8069
Columbia, TN 38402
615-898-2745
Fax: 615-893-7089

Tennessee Technological University
Small Business Development Center
College of Business Administration
P.O. Box 5023
Cookeville, TN 37203-3401
931-372-3648
Fax: 931-372-6249

Dyersburg Community College
Small Business Development Center
1510 Lake Road
Dyersburg, TN 38024
901-286-3201
Fax: 901-286-3271

Four Lakes Regional Industrial Development Authority
Small Business Development Center

P.O. Box 63
Hartsville, TN 37074-0063
615-374-9521
Fax: 615-374-4608

Jackson State Community College
Small Business Development Center
2046 North Parkway Street
Jackson, TN 38301-3797
901-424-5389
800-355-5722 ext. 627
Fax: 901-425-2641
www.jscc.cc.tn.us/conted/sbdc.htm
Email: croth@jscc.cc.tn.us

East Tennessee State University
Small Business Development Center
College of Business
 P.O. Box 70698
Johnson City, TN 37614-5630
Fax: 423-461-7080
http://business.etsu.edu/Tsbdc
Email: justiceB@etsu.edu

Kingsport Small Business Development Center
1501 University Boulevard
Kingsport, TN 37660
432-392-8017
http://business.etsu.edu/Tsbdc
Email: Lytle@etsu.edu

International Trade Center
601 West Summit Hill Drive
Knoxville, TN 37915
423-632-2990
Fax: 423-521-6367
www.tsbdc.org/itm.htm

Pellissippi State Technical Community College
Small Business Development Center
601 West Summit Hill Drive
Knoxville, TN 37902-2011
423-632-2980
Fax: 423-971-4439
www.pst.cc.cc.tn.us/bcs/TNsbdc.html

Memphis State University
Small Business Development Center
320 South Dudley Street
Memphis, TN 38101-3206
901-527-1041
Fax: 901-527-1047
www.tsbdc.memphis.edu

University of Memphis
Small Business Development Center

Technology and Energy Services
South Campus, Building One
Memphis, TN 38152
901-678-4057
Fax: 901-678-4072
www.tsbdc.org/tes/tes.htm
Email: Pjennings@cc.emephis.edu

Middle Tennessee State University
Small Business Development Center
Chamber of Commerce Building
501 Memorial Boulevard
Murfreesboro, TN 37129
615-898-2745
Fax: 615-893-7089

Tennessee State University
Small Business Development Center
330 10th Avenue, North
Nashville, TN 37203-3401
615-963-7179
Fax: 615-963-7160
www.cob.tnstate.edu/research/sbdc/sbdc.htm
Email: wlatham@tnstate.edu

Texas

Lead Centers:
North Texas Small Business Development Center
Dallas County Community College
1402 Corinth Street
Dallas, TX 75215
214-860-5833
Fax: 214-860-5813
www.bizcenter.org
Email: daw1404@dccd.edu

Texas Gulf Coast Small Business Development Center
University of Houston
2302 Fannin
Houston, TX 77002
713-752-8444
Fax: 713-756-1500
http;//smbizsolutions.uh.edu
Email: gshelton@uh.edu

Northwest Texas Small Business Development Center
2579 South Loop 289, Suite 210
Lubbock, TX 79423
806-745-3973
800-992-7232
Fax: 806-745-6207
http://nwtsbdc.org
Email: SBDCweb@nwtsbdc.org

South Texas Border Small Business Development Center
University of Texas at San Antonio Downtown
1222 North Main, Suite 450
San Antonio, TX 78212
210-458-2450
Fax: 210-458-2464
http://sbdc.utsa.edu/regional/index.htm
Email: jmcnamee@utsa.edu

SUL Ross State University
Big Bend Region Minority and Small Business
Development Center
Room 319, Briscoe Administration Building
P.O. Box C-47
Alpine, TX 79832
915-837-8694
Fax: 915-837-8104
www.sulross.edu/~sbdc
Email: lgarcia@sulross.edu

Trinity Valley Small Business Development Center
500 South Prairieville
Athens, TX 75751
903-675-7403
Fax: 903-675-5199
www.bizcoach.org
Email: sbdctvcc@flash.net

Austin Community College
Small Business Development Center
5930 Middle Fiskville Road
Austin, TX 78752
512-223-7754
Fax: 512-223-7734
wws2.austin.cc.tx.us/wcell/sbdc.html
Email: cfegley@austin.cc.tx.us

Lee College
Small Business Development Center
P.O. Box 818
Baytown, TX 77522-0818
281-425-6309
www.lee.edu/workforce

John Gray Institute/Lamar University
Small Business Development Center
855 Florida Avenue, Suite 101
Beaumont, TX 77705
409-880-2367
800-722-3443
Fax: 409-880-2201
http://hal.lamar.edu/~sbdc
Email: sbdc@hal.lamar.edu

Blinn College
Small Business Development Center

902 College Avenue
Brenham, TX 77833
409-830-4137
Fax: 409-830-4135
www.blinncol.edu/sbdc
Email: pnelson@acmail.blinncol.edu

Brazos Valley Small Business Development Center
4001 East 29th Street, Suite 175
Bryan, TX 77802
409-260-5222
Fax: 409-260-5208
www.bvsbdc.org

Del Mar College, East Campus
Small Business Development Center
101 Baldwin Boulevard
Corpus Christi, TX 78404-3897
512-698-1021
888-698-6111
Fax: 512-882-4256
www.delmar.edu/sbdc
Email: lfarr@delmar.edu

Navarro Small Business Development Center
120 North 12th Street
Corsicanna, TX 75110
903-874-0658
Fax: 903-874-4187
www.bizcoach.org
Email: lalla@nav.cc.tx.us

Dallas Small Business Development Center
1402 Corinth
Dallas, TX 75215
214-860-5850
Fax: 214-860-5881
www.billpriestinstitute.org
Email: sms9415@dcccd.edu

International Small Business Development Center
2050 Stemmons Freeway
World Trade Center, Suite 156A
P.O. Box 20451
Dallas, TX 75342
214-747-1300
800-337-7232
Fax: 214-748-5774
http://rampages.onramp.net~sbdc
Email: sbdc@onramp.net

Grayson Small Business Development Center
6101 Grayson Drive
Denison, TX 75020
903-463-8787
Fax: 903-463-5437

www.bizcoach.org
Email: stidhamk@grayson.edu

Best Southwest Small Business Development Center
214 Main, Suite 102A
Ducanville, TX 75116
972-709-5878
972-709-5990
Fax: 972-709-56089
www.bizcoach.org
Email: nsmall@dcccd.edu

Sul Ross State University
Rio Grande College Small Business Development Center
Route 2, Box 1200
Eagle Pass, TX 78852
830-758-5025
Fax: 830-758-5001

University of Texas/Pan American
Small Business Development Center
1201 West University Drive
Edinburg, TX 78539-2999
956-381-3361
Fax: 956-381-2322
http://coservelpanam.edu/sbdc
Email: sbdc@panam.edu

El Paso Community College
Small Business Development Center
4191 North Mesa, Suite 137
El Paso, TX 79902-1423
915-831-4744
www.epcc.edu/Community Sbdc
Email: roques@epcc.edu

Small Business Development Center for Excellence
7300 Jack Newell Boulevard
Fort Worth, TX 76118
817-272-5930
Fax: 817-272-5952
http://arri.uta.edu/sime/sbdcinde.htm
Email: jweddle@arri.uta.edu

Tarrant Small Business Development Center
100 East 15th Street, Suite 400 #24
Fort Worth, TX 76102
817-871-6028
Fax: 817-871-0031
www.fwbac.com
Email: tcjc.sbdc@swbac.com

North Central Texas Small Business Development Center
1525 West California
Gainesville, TX 76240
817-668-4220

Fax: 817-668-6049
www.bizcoach.org
Email: ckeeler@nctc.cc.tx.us

Galveston College
Small Business Development Center
4015 Avenue Q
Galveston, TX 77550
409-762-7380
888-743-7380
Fax: 409-762-7898

North Harris Community College District
Small Business Development Center
250 North Sam Houston Parkway East, Suite 200
Houston, TX 77060-2000
281-260-3174
Fax: 281-260-3162
www.cbed.org/sbdc/index.htm

Sam Houston State University
Small Business Development Center
College of business Administration
2424 Sam Houston Avenue
Huntsville, TX 77340
936-294-3737
Fax: 936-294-3738
www.shsu.edu/~sbd
Email: sbd_rab@shsu.edu

Brazosport College
Small Business Development Center
500 College Drive, Room K-201
Lake Jackson, TX 77566
970-230-3380
Fax: 970-230-3482
www.brazosport.cc.tx.us/~sbdc

Satellite Operation
College of the Mainland/LaMarque
1130 Delmar
LaMarque, TX 77568
409-762-7380
Fax: 409-762-7898
www.gc.edu/sbda

Satellite Operation
League City Bank & Trust
303 East Main Street
League City, TX 77573
409-762-7380
Fax: 709-762-7898
www.gc.edu/sbda

Laredo Development Foundation
Small Business Development Center

616 Leal Street
Laredo, TX 78041
956-722-0563
800-820-0564
Fax: 956-722-6247
www.laredo-ldf.com/ldfsbdc.htm
Email: ldf@icsi.net

Kilgore College
Small Business Development Center
110 Triple Creek Drive, Suite 70
Longview, TX 75601
903-757-5857
Fax: 903-753-7920
www.bizcoach.org
Bbunt@aol.com

Texas Tech University
Small Business Development Center
2579 South Loop 289, Suite 210
Lubbock, TX 79423
806-745-3973
800-992-7232
Fax: 806-745-6207
www.nwtsbdc.org/Texas_Tech/Texas_Tech.htm
Email: SBDCWeb@nwtsbdc.org

Angelina Community College
Small Business Development Center
3500 South First Street
P.O. Box 1768
Lufkin, TX 75902
936-639-1887
Fax: 936-639-3863
www.angelina.cc.tx.us/
SBDC/CS%20SBDC%20.INDEX.htm
Email: bmcclain@agelina.cc.tx.us

Northeast/Texarkana Small Business Development Center
P.O. Box 1307
Mt. Pleasant, TX 75455
903-572-1911
Fax: 903-572-0598
www.bizcoach.org

Paris Small Business Development Center
2400 Clarksville Street
Paris, TX 75460
903-784-1802
Fax: 903-784-1801
www.bizcoach.org
Email: paasbdc@stargate.lstarnet.com

San Jacinto College District
Small Business Development Center
8060 Spencer Highway B105E

Pasadena, TX 77501
281-542-2024
Fax: 281-478-2790
www.sjcd.cc.tx.us/sbdc

Collin County Small Business Development Center
Courtyard Center for Professional and Economic
Development
4800 Preston Park Boulevard, Suite A126/Box 15
Plano, TX 75093
972-985-3770
Fax: 972-985-3775
www.bizcoach.org

Lamar State College
Small Business Development Center
1401 Proctor Street
Port Arthur, TX 77640
409-983-5973
Fax: 409-983-1546
www.portarthur.com/sbdc/main.htm
Email: ltait@ih2000.net

Angelo State University
Small Business Development Center
P.O. Box 10910, ASU Station
San Angelo, TX 76909
915-942-2098
Fax: 915-942-2096
www.angelo.edu/services/sbdc
Email: SBDC@angelo.edu

UTSA Downtown
International Small Business Development Center
1222 North Main, Suite 450
San Antonio, TX 78212
210-458-2470
Fax: 210-458-2464
Email: friojas@utsa.edu

Tyler Small Business Development Center
1530 South SW Loop 323, Suite 100
Tyler, TX 75701
903-510-2975
Fax: 903-510-2978
www.bizcoach.org
Email: dpro@tjc.tyler.cc.tx.us

University of Houston-Victoria
Small Business Development Center
700 Main Center, Suite 102
Victoria, TX 77901
512-575-8944
Fax: 512-575-8852
www.vic.uh.edu/sbdc
Email: parksc@viptx.net

McLennan Small Business Development Center
401 Franklin
Waco, TX 76701
817-714-0077
Fax: 817-714-1668
http://mcweb.mcc.cc.tx.us/sbdc

Wharton County Junior College
Small Business Development Center
Administration Building, Room 102
911 Boling Highway
Wharton, TX 77488
979-244-8463

Utah

Lead Center:
Salt Lake Community College
Small Business Development Center
1623 South State Street
Salt Lake City, UT 84115
801-957-3489
Email: FinnerMi@slccc.edu

College of Eastern Utah
Small Business Development Center
639 West 100 South
Blanding, UT 84511
435-678-2201 ext. 173
Fax: 435-678-2220
Email: Bill_olderog@sanjuan.ceu.edu

Southern Utah University
Small Business Development Center
351 West Center
Cedar City, UT 84720
435-586-5400
Fax: 435-586-5493
Email: snow@suu.edu

Snow College
Small Business Development Center
345 West 100 North
Ephraim, UT 84627
435-283-7372
Fax: 435-283-6913
Email: Johnson@snow.edu

Utah State University
Small Business Development Center
East Campus Building, Room 24
Logan, UT 84322-8330
435-797-2277
Fax: 435-797-3317
Email: fprante@ext.usu.edu

Moab Higher Education Center
125 West 200 South
Moab, UT 84532
435-259-3622
www.ext.usu.edu/comm/index.htm
Email: BrianD@ext.usu.edu

Weber State University
Small Business Development Center
School of Business and Economics
3806 University Circle
Ogden, UT 84408-3806
801-626-7051
Fax: 801-626-7423
http://weber.edu/sbdc
Email: kfry@weber.edu

College of Eastern Utah
Utah Valley State College
800 West 1200 South
Orem, UT 84058
801-222-8230
Fax: 801-225-1229
Email: cozzench@uvsc.edu

Small Business Development Center
P.O. Box 1106
Price, UT 84501
435-637-5444
Fax: 435-637-7336
Email: Drigby@seuaognet.seuaog.dist.ut.us

Salt Lake Community College
8811 South 700 East
Sandy, UT 84070
801-255-5878
Fax: 801-255-6393

Salt Lake Community College
1623 South State Street
Salt Lake city, UT 84070
801-957-3480
Fax: 801-957-3489

Dixie College
Small Business Development Center
225 South 700 East
St. George, UT 84770
435-652-7751
Fax: 435-652-7870
www.dixie.edu/dba/sbdc.htm
Email: bauer@dixie.edu

Utah State University Extension
Small Business Development Center
1680 West Highway 40

Vernal, UT 84078
435-789-6100
Fax: 435-789-3916
Email: markh@ext.usu.edu

Vermont
Lead Center:
Vermont Small Business Development Center
Vermont Tech. College
P.O. Box 422
Randolph, VT 05060-0422
802-728-9101
Fax: 802-728-3026

Northwestern Vermont Small Business Development
Center
P.O. Box 786 NW VT SBDC
Burlington, VT 05402-0786
802-658-9228
Fax: 802-860-1899

Southwestern Vermont Small Business Development
Center
256 N. Main St.
Rutland, VT 05701
802-773-9147
Fax: 802-773-2772

Southeastern Vermont Small Business Development
Center
P.O. Box 58
Springfield, VT 05156-0058
802-885-2071
Fax: 802-885-3027

Central Vermont Small Business Development Center
Green Mountain SBDC
P.O. Box 246
White River Jct., VT 05001-0246
802-295-3710
Fax: 802-295-3779

Brattleboro Dev. Credit Corp.
Small Business Development Center
P.O. Box 1177
Brattleboro, VT 05301-1177
802-257-7731
Fax: 802-258-3886

Addison Co. Econ. Dev. Corp
Small Business Development Center
2 Court St.
Middlebury, VT 05753
802-388-7953
Fax: 802-388-8066

Central VT Econ. Dev. Center
Small Business Development Center
P.O. Box 1439
Montpelier, VT 05601-1439
802-223-4654
Fax: 802-223-4655

Lamoille Econ. Dev. Center
Small Business Development Center
P.O. Box 455
Morrisville, VT 05661-0455
802-888-4923
Fax: 802-888-5640

Bennington Co. Industrial Corp.
Small Business Development Center
P.O. Box 357
No. Bennington, VT 05257
802-442-8975
Fax: 802-442-1101

Lake Champlain Islands
Chamber of Commerce SBDC
P.O. Box 213
No. Bero, VT 05474-0213
802-372-5683
Fax: 802-372-6104

Franklin County Industrial Dev. Corp.
Small Business Development Center
P.O. Box 1099
St. Albans, VT 05478-1099
802-524-2194
Fax: 802-527-5258

Northeastern VT Dev. Assn.
Small Business Development Center
P.O. Box 630
St. Johnsbury, VT 05819
802-748-1014
Fax: 802-748-1223

Virginia
Lead Center:
Department of Business Assistance
Virginia Small Business Development Center
707 East Main Street, Suite 300
Richmond, VA 23219
804-371-8253
Fax: 804-225-3384
www.dba.state.va.us/SBDMain.html
Email: rwilburn@dba.state.va.us

VA Highland Community College
Small Business Development Center

P.O. Box 828
Abingdon, VA 24212
540-676-5615

Alexandria Small Business Development Center
1055 North Fairfax Street, Suite 204
Alexandria, VA 22314
703-299-9146

South Fairfax Small Business Development Center
6911 Richmond Highway, Suite 290
Alexandria, VA 22306
703-768-1440
www.sbdc.org/rgnloffc.htm
Email: cbp@gmu.edu

George Mason University/Arlington Campus
Small Business Development Center
4001 North Fairfax Drive, Suite 450
Arlington, VA 22201
703-993-8129
Fax: 703-993-8130
www.gmu.edu/departments/ii/gmar/sbdc.html

Mountain Empire Community College
Small Business Development Center
PO Drawer 700, Route 23S
Big Stone Gap, VA 24219
540-523-6529
Fax: 540-523-8139
www.me.cc.va.us/sbdc.html
Email: tblankenbecler@me.cc.va.us

Central Virginia Small Business Development Center
1001 East Market Street, Suite 101
Charlottesville, VA 22902
804-295-8198
Fax: 804-295-7066
http://monticello.avenue.org/Market/SBDC
Email: sbdc@cstone.net

Northern Virginia Small Business Development Center
4031 University Drive, Suite 200
Fairfax, VA 22030
703-277-7700
Fax: 703-277-7722
www.sbdc.org

Longwood Small Business Development Center
515 Main Street
Farmville, VA 23909
804-395-2086
Fax: 804-395-2359
www.lwc.edu/sbdc
Email: kcopelan@longwood.lwc.edu

Rappahannock Region Small Business Development
Center
The James Monroe Center
121 University Boulevard
Fredericksburg, VA 22406
540-286-8060
Fax: 540-286-8005
http://departments.mwc.edu/sbdc/www/Default.htm
Email: rrsbdc@mwc.edu

Small Business Development Center
525 Butler Farm Road, Suite 102
Hampton, VA 23666
725-825-2957
757-622-6414

James Madison University
Small Business Development Center
College of Business
Zane Showker Hall, Room 527
Harrisonburg, VA 22807
540-568-3227
Fax: 703-568-3299
www.jmu.edu/sbdcenter

Lynchburg Regional Small Business Development Center
147 mill Ridge Road
Lynchburg, VA 24502
804-582-6170
800-876-7232
Fax: 804-582-6106

Martinsville Small Business Development Center
115 Broad Street
Martinsville, VA 24114
540-632-4462
Fax: 540-632-5059
Email: jtberry@neocomm.net

Hampton Roads Chamber of Commerce
Small Business Development Center
P.O. Box 327
420 Bank Street
Norfolk, VA 23501-0327
757-825-2957
Fax: 757-622-5563
www.hrccva.com/busdevr.htm
Email: infor@hrccva.com

Crater Small Business Development Center
1964 Wakefield Street
Petersburg, VA 23805
804-862-6129
Fax: 804-862-6109
www.craterpdc.state.va.us/longwood.htm
Email: dhowerton.lwc@va.visi.net

Radford University
Business Assistance Center
P.O. Box 6953
Radford, VA 24142
540-831-6056
www.radford.edu/~bac
Email: bac@runet.edu

Southwest Virginia Community College
Small Business Development Center
P.O. Box SVCC
Richlands, VA 24641
540-964-7345
Fax: 540-964-7575
www.sw.cc.va.us/sbdc/svccsbdc.htm
Email: Jim_boyd@sw.cc.va.us

Greater Richmond Small Business Development Center
116 East Franklin Street, Suite 100
Richmond, VA 23219
804-783-9314
www.grsbdc.com

Regional Chamber Small Business Development Center
212 South Jefferson Street
Roanoke, VA 24011
540-983-0717
Fax: 540-983-0723 ext. 239
www.roanokechamber.org/sbdc.htm
Email: sbdc@roanokechamber.org

South Boston Small Business Development Center
515 Broad Street
South Boston, VA 24592
804-575-0044
Fax: 804-575-1762
Email: decker@halifax.com

Loudoun County Small Business Development Center
207 East Holly Avenue, Suite 214
Sterling VA 20164
703-430-7222
Fax: 703-430-7258
www.loudounsbdc.org
Email: sbdc@loudounsbdc.org

Lord Fairfax Small Business Development Center
6480 College Street
Warrenton, VA 20187
540-351-1595
Fax: 540-351-1597
www.lfsbdc.org
Email: dburch@lfsbdc.org

Warsaw Small Business Development Center
P.O. Box 490

479 Main Street
Warsaw, VA 22572
804-33-0286
800-524-8915
http://homepages.sylvaninfo.net/sbdc
Email: sbdcwarsaw@sylvaninfo.net

Lord Fairfax Small Business Development Center
156 Dowell J Circle
Winchester, VA 22602
540-722-7580
Fax: 540-722-7582
www.flsbdc.org
Email: bsirbaugh@lfsbdc.org

Wytheville Community College
Small Business Development Center
1000 East Main Street
Wytheville, VA 24382
540-223-4715
800-468-1195 ext. 4715 or 4798
Fax: 540-223-4715
www.wc.cc.va.us/sbdc

Washington

Lead Center:
Washington Small Business Development Center
Washington State University
601 West First Street
Spokane, WA 99201-3899
509-358-7765
Fax: 509-358-7764
www.sbdc.wsu.edu
Email: clrk@wsu.edu

Bellevue Community College
Small Business Development Center
12400 SE 38th Street
Bellevue, WA 98007-6484
425-643-2888
Fax: 425-649-3094
Email: bhuenefe@bcc.ctc.edu

Western Washington University
Small Business Development Center
College of Business and Economics
119 North Commercial Street, Suite 195
Bellingham, WA 98225
360-733-4014
Fax: 360-733-5092
www.cbe.www.edu/SBDC
Email: Tom.Dorr@www.edu

Olympic College Small Business Development Center
Affiliated Counseling Center

654 4th Street
Bremerton, WA 98337
360-478-4839
Fax: 360-478-6978
www.oc.ctc.edu/instruction/e_continuinged.shtml#ce
Email: ssegler@oc.ctc.edu

Edmonds Community College
Small Business Development Center
20000 68th Avenue West
72813 4th Street SW
Everett, WA 98204
425-640-1435
Fax: 425-640-1371
www.cce.edcc.edu/cce/ccecatalog/cbet.html
Email: rbattles@edcc.ctc.edu

Big Bend Community College
Small Business Development Center
7662 Chanute Street, Building 1500
Moses Lake, WA 98837-3299
509-762-5351 ext. 289
Fax: 509-762-6289
http://bbcc.ctc.edu/business.htm
Email: business@bbcc.ctc.edu

Skagit Valley College
Small Business Development Center
2405 East College Way
Mt. Vernon, WA 98273
360-416-7872/7873
Fax: 360-336-6116
www.svc.ctc.edu/pub_html/dept/sbrc
Email: aamot@skagit.ctc.edu

Okanogan County Council for Economic Development
Small Business Development Center
Wenatchee Valley College
Box 741
203 South 2nd
Okanogan, WA 98840
509-826-5107
Fax: 509-826-1812
Email: cd_occed@northcascades.net

South Puget Sound Community College
Small Business Development Center
721 Columbia Street, SW
Olympia, WA 98501
360-753-5616
Fax: 360-586-5493
Email: DouglasHammel@olywa.net

Port Angeles Small Business Development Center
102 East Front Street
P.O. Box 1085

Port Angeles, WA 98362
360-457-7299
Fax: 360-457-9618
Email: kpurdy@clallam.org

Seattle Small Business Development Center
Parkplace Building
1200 6th Avenue, Suite 1700
Seattle, WA 98101
206-553-7328
Fax: 206-553-7044
Email: mfranz@connectexpress.com

South Seattle Community College
Small Business Development Center
6000 16th Avenue, SW
Seattle, WA 98106
206-768-6855
Fax: 206-768-6699
Email: Chansen@sccd.ctc.edu

Washington State University at Seattle
Small Business Development Center
180 Nickerson, Suite 207
Seattle, WA 98109
206-464-5450
Fax: 206-464-6357
www.spokane.org/bic/sbdc.htm
Email: wwong@wolfenet.com

North Seattle Community College
Small Business Development Center
International Trade Institute
2001 6th Avenue, Suite 650
Seattle, WA 98121
206-553-0052
Fax: 206-553-7253
Email: atamura@sttl.uswest.net

Community College of Spokane
Small Business Development Center
SIRTI Building
665 North Riverpoint Boulevard
Spokane, WA 99202
509-358-7890
Fax: 509-358-7896
Email: mdillon@wsu.edu

Washington State University at Tacoma
Small Business Development Center
950 Pacific Avenue, Suite 300
Box 1933
Tacoma, WA 98401-1933
253-272-7232
Fax: 253-597-7305

www.sbdc.wsu.edu
Email: sbdctaco@telishpere.com

Washington State University
Small Business Development Center
200 SE Park Plaza Drive, Suite 1005
Vancouver, WA 98684
360-260-6372
Fax: 360-694-6369
www.sbdc.wsu.edu
Email: harte@vancouver.wsu.edu

Yakima Valley Community College
Small Business Development Center
P.O. Box 1647
113 South 14th Avenue
Yakima, WA 98902
509-574-4935
Fax: 509-574-4943
www.yvcc.cc.wa.us/programsofstudy/pace/
business/bdc/sbdc.html
Email: Arice@yvcc.cc.wa.us

Columbia Basin College
Tri-Cities Small Business Development Center
901 North Colorado
Kennewick, WA 9936
509-735-6222
Fax: 509-735-6609
Email: BlakesCafe@3-cities.com

Port of Walla Walla
Small Business Development Center
500 Tausick Way
Walla Walla, WA 99362
509-527-4681
Fax: 509-525-3101
www.portwallawalla.com/Pages/smallbiz.htm
Email: rm@portwallawalla.com

West Virginia
Lead Center:
West Virginia Small Business Development Center
West Virginia Development Office
1900 Kanawha Boulevard East
Building 6 Room 652
Charleston, WV 25305
304-558-2960
888-WVA-SBDC
Fax: 304-558-0127
www.wvsbdc.org

Charelston Small Business Development Sub Center
State Capitol Complex
Building 6, Room 652

Charleston, WV 25305
304-558-2960
Fax: 304-558-0127
www.wvsbdc.org

Elkins Satellite Small Business Development Center
10 Eleventh Street, Suite One
Elkins, WV 26241
304-637-7205
Fax: 304-637-4902
Email: jrjm@westvirginia.com

Fairmont State College
Small Business Development Center
3000 Technology Drive, Suite 20
Fairmont, WV 26554
304-367-2712
Fax: 304-367-2717
www.fscwv.edu/sbdc
Email: jkirby@mail.fscwv.edu

Marshall University
Small Business Development Center
2000 Seventh Avenue
Huntington, WV 25703-1527
304-696-6246
Fax: 304-696-4835
http://web.marshall.edu/ibd/sbdc.htmlx
Email: emcclain@murc.marshall.edu

Eastern WV Community and Technical College
Small Business Development Center
204 Washington Street
Moorefield, WV 26836
304-538-8147

West Virginia University
Small Business Development Center
P.O. Box 6025
Morgantown, WV 26506
304-293-5839
Fax: 304-293-8905
Email: stratton@be.wvu.edu

Southern WV Community and Technical College
Small Business Development Center
P.O. Box 2900
Mt. Gay, WV 25637
304-792-7160 ext. 235
Fax: 304-792-7046
www.southen.wvnet.edu
Email: joannek@southern.wvnet.edu

WVU Institute of Technology
Small Business Development Center
912 East Main Street

Oak Hill, WV 25901
304-255-4022
Fax: 304-252-9584
Email: sbdc@netphase.net

West Virginia University at Parkersburg
Small Business Development Center
Route 5, Box 167-A
Parkersburg, WV 26101
304-424-8277
Fax: 304-424-8266
www.wvup.wvnet.edu/www/BIDS/Sbdc.htm
Email: ghill@alpha.wvup.wvnet.edu

Shepherd College
Small Business Development Center
Shepherdstown, WV 25443
304-876-5261
800-344-5231 ext. 5261
Fax: 304-876-5467
www.shepherd.edu/sbdc.web
Email: clunber@shepherd.edu

Glenville State College
Small Business Development Center
249 Skidmore Lane
Sutton, WV 26601-9272
304-765-7300
Fax: 304-765-7724
Email: cook@glenville.wvnet.edu

West Virginia Northern Community College
Small Business Development Center
College Square
Wheeling, WV 26003
304-233-5900 ext. 4355
Fax: 304-232-3819
http://techctr1.northern.wvnet.edu/northern/
CBDS_sbdc.htm
Email: daberegg@northern.wvnet.edu

McDowell Satellite
Small Business Development Center
P.O. Box 158
State Highway 103
Wilcoe, WV 24895
304-448-2118 ext. 28
Fax: 304-448-3287
Email: hpatterson@citilink.net

Wisconsin
Lead Center:
Wisconsin Small Business Development Center
University of Wisconsin
432 North Lake Street, Room 423

Madison, WI 53706
608-263-7794
Fax: 608-262-3878
http://cf.uwex.edu/sbdc

University of Wisconsin at Eau Claire
Small Business Development Center
P.O. Box 4004
1105 Garfield
Eau Claire, WI 54702-4004
715-836-5811
Fax: 715-836-5263
www.uwec.edu/Academics/CDB/programs/
traindev/frametraindev.home.htm
Email: ask_sbdc@wuec.edu

University of Wisconsin at Green Bay
Small Business Development Center
2420 Nicolet Drive
Green Bay, WI 54311
902-465-2089
Fax: 902-465-2660
www.uwab.edu/outreach/sbdc

Kenosha County Small Business Development Center
c/o Job Center/Human Services Building
8600 Sheidan
Kenosha, WI 53141
262-697-4525
Fax: 262-697-4563
Email: dschacht@co.kenosha.wi.us

University of Wisconsin at LaCrosse
Small Business Development Center
School of Business
120 North Hall
La Crosse, WI 54601
608-785-8782
Fax: 608-785-6919
http://perth.uwlax.edu/bdc
Email: gallaghejani@uwlax.edu

University of Wisconsin at Madison
Small Business Development Center
School of Business
975 University Avenue
Madison, WI 53706
608-263-7680
Fax: 608-263-0818

University of Wisconsin at Milwaukee
Small Business Development Center
161 West Wisconsin Avenue, Suite 600
Milwaukee, WI 53203
414-227-3142

www.uwm.edu/University/Outreach/catalog/
DBM_SBDC/index.shtml

University of Wisconsin at Oshkosh
Small Business Development Center
347 Park Plaza
Oshkosh, WI 54901
920-424-1456
800-232-8939
Fax: 920-424-2005
www.ccp.uwosh.edu/services/
services_smallbusiness.html

University of Wisconsin at Platteville
Southwest Wisconsin Small Business Development Center
133 Warner Hall
Plateville, WI 53818
608-342-1038
Fax: 608-342-1454

Racine County Small Business Development Center
4701 Washington Avenue, Suite 215
Racine, WI 53404
262-638-1713
Fax: 262-638-0250
Email: larsonj@uwp.edu

University of Wisconsin at River Falls
Small Business Development Center
410 South Third Street
River Falls, WI 54022
715-425-0620
Fax: 715-425-0624
Email: Kathy.bartelt@uwrf.edu

University of Wisconsin at Stevens Point
Small Business Development Center
2100 Main Street
103 Main Building
Stevens Point, WI 54481
715-346-3838
800-898-9472
Fax: 715-346-4045
www.uwsp.edu/extension/NonCredit/SBDC/index.htm
Email: vloberme@uwsp.edu

University of Wisconsin at Superior
Small Business Development Center
Belknap & Catlin
P.O. Box 2000
Superior, WI 54880-2898
715-394-8351
Fax: 715-394-8592
http://staff.uwsuper.edu/bdc
Email: mpekklal@staff.uwsuper.edu

University of Wisconsin at Whitewater
Small Business Development Center
2000 Carlson Hall
Whitewater, WI 53190
262-472-3217
800-621-7235
Fax: 262-472-5692
www.sbdc.uww.edu

Wyoming
Lead Center:
University of Wyoming
Small Business Development Center
P.O. Box 3922
Laramie, WY 82071-3922
307-766-3505
800-348-5194
Fax: 307-766-3406
http://marshal.uwyo.edu/sbdc
Email: ddw@uwyo.edu

Wyoming Small Business Development Center
300 South Wolcott, Suite 300
Casper, WY 82601
307-234-6683
800-348-5207
Fax: 307-577-7014
Email: sbdc@trib.com

Laramie County Community College
Small Business Development Center
1400 East College Drive
Cheyenne, WY 82007-3298
307-632-6141
800-348-5208
Fax: 307-632-6061
www.lcc.whecn.edu/areainfo/bus_ind/WSBDC.html
Email: sewsbdc@wyoming.com

Small Business Development Center
First Interstate Bank Building
222 South Gilette Avenue, Suite 402
Gilette, WY 82716
307-682-5232
Fax: 307-686-5792
Email: sbdc@vcn.com

Northwest Community College
Small Business Development Center
143 South Bent Street
Powell, WY 82435
307-754-2139
800-383-0371
Fax: 307-754-0368
Email: nwwsbdc@wave.park.wy.us

Freemont County Satellite Small Business Development
Center
Riverton Branch Public Library
1330 West Park Avenue
Riverton, WY 82501-1790
307-857-1174
Fax: 307-857-1175
Email: wsbdc@tcine.net

Wyoming Small Business Development Center
P.O. Box 1168
1400 Dewar Drive, Suite 205
Rock Springs, WY 82902-1168
307-352-6894
800-348-5205
Fax: 307-352-6876
Email: bellis@uwyo.edu

VENTURE CAPITAL
Finding A Rich Angel

With federal and state money getting harder to come by, and banks experiencing serious problems of their own that restrict their willingness to loan money, anyone interested in starting his own business or expanding an existing one may do well to look into venture capital. Venture capitalists are willing to invest in a new or growing business venture for a percentage of the equity. Below is a listing of some of the associations, government agencies, and businesses that have information available on venture capital.

In addition, there are Venture Capital Clubs throughout the country where entrepreneurs have a chance to present their ideas to potential investors and learn about the process of finding funds for ventures that might be long on innovative ideas for a business, but short on proven track records.

Associations

The National Venture Capital Association (NVCA)
1655 N. Fort Meyer Dr., Suite 850
Arlington, VA 22209
703-524-2549
Fax: 703-524-3940
www.nvca.org

The association works to improve the government's knowledge and understanding of the venture capital process. Staff members can answer questions about federal legislation and regulations, and provide statistical information on venture capital. NVCA members include venture capital organizations, financiers, and individuals interested in investing in new companies. The association publishes a membership directory that includes a listing of their members with addresses, phone numbers, tax numbers and contacts. There are currently about 289 members. The directory is available for $99.

The Western Association of Venture Capitalists
3000 San Hill Rd.
Bldg. 1, Suite 190
Menlo Park, CA 94025
650-854-1322

Publishes a directory of its 130 members. The cost is $100.

National Association of Investment Companies
733 15th St. NW, Suite 700
Washington, DC 20005
202-289-4336
Fax: 202-289-4329

It is composed of specialized Small Business Investment Companies (SSBICs). The SSBIC Directory lists about 120 companies across the country including names, addresses, and telephone numbers. It also describes each company's investment preferences and policies. The 23-page publication costs $25.98. It also publishes *Perspective*, a monthly newsletter geared toward specialized small business investment companies. This newsletter includes articles about legislation and regulations affecting SSBICs. (Note: This association was formerly called the American Association of Minority Enterprise Small Business Investment Companies (AAMESBIC)).

Technology Capital Network at MIT
201 Vassar St.
Cambridge, MA 02139

617-253-7163
Fax: 617-258-7395
www.tcnmit.org

This nonprofit corporation tries to match entrepreneurs in need of capital with venture capital sources. Investors and entrepreneurs register with the network for up to 12 months for $300.

Venture Capital Clubs

There are more than 150 Venture Capital Clubs worldwide where inventors can present their ideas to potential investors. At a typical monthly meeting, several entrepreneurs may give short presentations of their ideas. It is a great way for entrepreneurs and potential investors to talk informally.

The International Venture Capital Institute (IVCI)
P.O. Box 1333
Stamford, CT 06904
203-323-3143

The IVCI publishes an annual directory of domestic and international venture groups (venture capital clubs). The cost of the *1995 IVCI Directory of Domestic and International Venture Groups*, which includes contact information for all of the clubs, is $19.95.

Below is a partial listing of clubs in the United States.

Venture Capital Clubs

Alabama
Birmingham Venture Club
Chamber of Commerce
P.O. Box 10127
Birmingham, AL 35202
205-323-5461
Fax: 205-250-7669
www.birminghamchamber.com

Mobile Venture Club
c/o Mobile Area Chamber of Commerce
451 Government St.
Mobile, AL 36652
334-433-6951
Fax: 334-431-8646
www.mobcham.org
Attn: Walter Underwood

Arkansas
Venture Capital Investors
400 W. Capital, Suite 1845
Little Rock, AR 72201
501-372-5900
Fax: 501-372-8181

California
Tech Coast Venture Network
195 S. C St., Suite 250
Tustin, CA 92780
714-505-6493

Fax: 714-669-9341
www.tcvn.org
Attn: Alonzo

Orange Coast Venture Group
P.O. Box 2011
Laguna Hills, CA 92654
949-859-3646
Fax: 949-859-1707
www.ocvg.org
Attn: Gregory Beck

Community Entrepreneurs Organization
P.O. Box 9838
San Rafael, CA 94912
415-435-4461
Attn: Dr. Rick Crandall

San Diego Venture Group
750 B St., Suite 2400
San Diego, CA 92101
619-272-1985
Fax: 619-272-1986
www.sdvgroup.org

Colorado
Rockies Venture Club, Inc.
190 E. 9th Ave., Suite 440
Denver, CO 80203
303-831-4174

Fax: 303-832-4920
www.rockiesventureclub.org
Attn: Josh

Connecticut
Connecticut Venture Group
1891 Post Rd., Suite F
Fairfield, CT 06430
203-256-5955
Fax: 203-256-9949
www.ct-venture.org

District of Columbia
Baltimore-Washington Venture Group
Michael Dingman Center for Entrepreneurship
College Park, MD 20742-7215
301-405-2144
Fax: 301-314-9152
www.rhsmith.umd.edu/dingman

Florida
Gold Coast Venture Capital Club
22783 S. State Rd. 7, #56
Boca Raton, FL 33428
561-488-4505
Fax: 561-451-4746
www.beaconmgmt.com/gcvcc

Hawaii
Hawaii Venture Group
University of Hawaii, OTTED
2800 Woodlawn Dr., Suite 280
Honolulu, HI 96822
808-533-1400
Fax: 808-524-2775
www.hawaiiventuregroup.com

Idaho
Rocky Mountain Venture Group
2300 N. Yellowstone, Suite E
Idaho Falls, ID 83402
208-526-9557
Fax: 208-526-0953
Attn: Dennis Cheney

Treasure Valley Venture Capital Forum
Idaho Small Business Development Center
Boise State University College of Business
1910 University Dr.
Boise, ID 83725
208-426-1640
Fax: 208-426-3877
www.boisestate.edu/isbdc

Iowa
Iowa City Development
ICAD Group
P.O. Box 2567
Iowa City, IA 52244
319-354-3939
Fax: 319-338-9958
Attn: Marty Kelley

Illinois
Madison Dearborn Partners
70 W. Madison, 8th Floor
Chicago, IL 60602
312-895-1000
Fax: 312-895-1001

Kentucky
Kentucky Investment Capital Network
67 Wilkinson Blvd.
Frankfort, KY 40601
502-564-4300, ext. 4315
Fax: 502-564-9758
www.state.kentucky.us
Attn: Norris Christian

Mountain Ventures Inc.
P.O. Box 1738
London, KY 40743
606-864-5175
Fax: 606-864-5194
www.ezec.gov

Louisiana
Chamber Small Business Hotline
1-800-949-7890

Maryland
Mid Atlantic Venture Association (MAVA)
2345 York Rd.
Timonium, MD 21093
410-560-5855
Fax: 410-560-1910
www.mava.org
Attn: Maryanne Gray

Massachusetts
Venture Capital Fund of New England
160 Federal St., 23rd Floor
Boston, MA 02110
617-439-4646
Fax: 617-439-4652

Michigan
Southeastern Venture Capital
The Meyering Corporation

206 30 Harper Ave., Suite 103
Harper Woods, MI 48225
313-886-2331
Attn: Carl Meyering

Ann Arbor Chamber of Commerce
425 S. Main St.
Ann Arbor, MI 48104
734-665-4433
www.annarborchamber.org
Attn: Barb Sprague

Minnesota
The Entrepreneurs Network
4555 Erin Dr., Suite 200
Eagan, MN 55122
651-683-9141
Fax: 651-683-0584
www.ens.net

St. Paul Venture Capital
10400 Viking Drive, Suite 550
Bloomington, MN 55444
612-995-7474
Fax: 612-995-7475
www.st.paulvc.com

Missouri
Kansas City Venture Group
10551 Barkley, Suite 400
Overland Park, KS 66212
913-341-8992
Fax: 913-341-8981

Missouri Innovation Center
5650 A S. Sinclair Rd.
Columbia, MO 65203
573-446-3100
Fax: 573-446-3106

Montana
Montana Private Capital Network
7783 Valley View Rd.
Poulson, MT 59860
406-883-5677
Fax: 406-883-5677
Attn: Jon Marchi, President

Nebraska
Grand Island Industrial Foundation
309 W. 2nd St.
P.O. Box 1486
Grand Island, NE 68802-1486
308-382-9210
Fax: 308-382-1154

www.gichamber.com
Attn: Andrew G. Baird, II CED

New Jersey
Venture Association of New Jersey, Inc.
177 Madison Ave., CN 1982
Morristown, NJ 07960
973-631-5680
Fax: 973-984-9634
www.zanj.com
Attn: Amy or Jay Trien

New York
Long Island Venture Group
CW Post Campus
Long Island University
College of Management
Deans Office, Worth Hall
Room 309, North Blvd.
Brookville, NY 11548
516-299-3017
Fax: 516-299-2786
www.liv.edu
Attn: Carol Caracappa

New York Venture Group
605 Madison Ave., Suite 300
New York, NY 10022-1901
212-832-7300
Fax: 212-832-7338
www.nybusiness.com
Attn: Burt Alimansky

Westchester Venture Capital Network
c/o Chamber of Commerce
235 Mamaroneck Ave.
White Plains, NY 10605
914-948-2110
Fax: 914-948-0122
www.westchesterny.org

Rochester Venture Capital Group
100 Corporate Woods, Suite 300
Rochester, NY 14623

Ohio
Greater Columbus Chamber of Commerce
Columbus Investment Interest Group
37 N. High St.
Columbus, OH 43215
614-225-6087
Fax: 614-469-8250
www.columbus.org
Attn: Diane Essex

Ohio Venture Association, Inc.
1120 Chester Ave.
Cleveland, OH 44114
216-566-8884
Fax: 216-696-2582
Attn: Joan McCarthy

Oklahoma
Oklahoma Venture Forum
211 Robinson, Suite 210
P.O. Box 26788
Oklahoma City, OK 73126-0788
405-636-9736
405-270-1050
Fax: 405-416-1035
Attn: Steve Thomas

Oregon
Oregon Entrepreneur Forum
2611 Southwest Third Ave., Suite 200
Portland, OR 97201
503-222-2270
Fax: 503-241-0827
www.oes.org

Portland Venture Group
P.O. Box 2341
Lake Oswego, OR 97035
503-697-5907
Fax: 503-697-5907
Attn: Glen Smith

Pennsylvania
Enterprise Venture Capital Corporation of
Pennsylvania
111 Market St.
Johnstown, PA 15901
814-535-7597
Fax: 814-535-8677

South Dakota
Dakota Ventures Inc.
P.O. Box 8194
Rapid City, SD 57709
605-348-8441
Fax: 605-348-8452
Attn. Don Frankenfeld

Texas
Capital Southwest Venture Corporation
12900 Preston Rd., Suite 700
Dallas, TX 75230
972-233-8242
Fax: 972-233-7362
www.capitalsouthwest.com

Utah
Utah Ventures
423 Wakara Way, Suite 306
Salt Lake City, UT 84108
801-583-5922
Fax: 801-583-4105

Vermont
Vermont Venture Network
P.O. Box 5839
Burlington, VT 05402
802-658-7830
Fax: 802-658-0978

Virginia
Richmond Venture Capital Club
c/o 4900 Augusta Ave., Suite 103
Richmond, VA 23230
804-359-1139
www.ventureclub.com
Attn: Smoky Sizemore

Washington
Northwest Venture Group
P.O. Box 21693
Seattle, WA 98111-3693
425-746-1973

West Virginia
Enterprise Venture Capital Company
P.O. Box 460
Summerville, WV 26651
304-872-3000
Fax: 304-872-3040
Attn: William Bright

Wisconsin
Wisconsin Venture Network
P.O. Box 510103
Milwaukee, WI 53203
414-224-7070
www.maxnetwork.com/wvn
Attn: Paul Sweeny

International Clubs
Puerto Rico Venture Capital Club
P.O. Box 2284
Hato Rey, PR, 00919
1-809-787-9040
Attn: Danol Morales

Johannesburg Venture Capital Club
162 Anderson St.
P.O. Box 261425

EXCOM 2023 RSA
Johannesburg, South Africa, 2001
Attn: Graham Rosenthal

Cape Town Venture Capital Association
c/o Arthur Anderson and Company
12th Floor, Shell House
Capetown, South Africa, 8001
Attn: Colin Hultzer

Canada Clubs
Edmonton Chamber of Commerce

600 10123 99th St.
Edmonton, Alberta Canada, T5J 3G9
780-426-4620
Attn: Ace Cetinski

Venture Capital/
Entrepreneurship Club of Montreal, Inc.
1670 Sherbrooke St.
East Montreal (Quebec) Canada, H2L 1M5
514-526-9490
Attn: Claude Belanger

Other groups with information on venture capital include:

The CPA Firm Coopers and Lybrand
1177 Avenue of the Americas
New York, NY 10020
212-596-8000
Fax: 212-596-8910
www.pwc.com

The firm publishes several publications on venture capital including *Venture Capital: The Price of Growth*, 1998, and *Venture Capital Advisory and Survey*, 1996 update. There is no charge for these publications.

Venture Economics, Inc.
22 Thompson Place
Boston, MA 02210
617-345-2504
Attn: Kelly McGow

Publications are available from:
Securities Data Publishing
40 W. 57th St., 11th Floor
New York, NY 10019
212-765-5311
Fax: 212-956-0112
Attn: Esther Miller

Venture Capital Journal, a monthly periodical that cites new issues and trends in venture capital investments. Subscription rate is $1095.

Pratt's Guide to Venture Capital Sources, an annual directory that lists 800 venture capital firms in the U.S. and Canada. It also includes articles recommending ways to raise venture capital. The cost is $385 plus shipping and taxes.

Additional Reading Material

A Venture Capital Primer for Small Business, a U.S. Small Business Administration publication that identifies what venture capital resources are available and explains how to develop a proposal for obtaining these funds ($2). SBA Publications, P.O. Box 30, Denver, CO 80201-0030. Item number FM5.

The Ernst & Young Guide to Financing for Growth. This is part of their entrepreneur series and includes bibliographical references and index. ($14.95) John Wiley & Son, 1 Wiley Dr., Somerset, NJ 08875; 800-225-5945. 1994.

Uncle Sam's Venture Capital

What Do Federal Express, Apple Computer, Staples and A Porno Shop on 42nd Street All Have In Common? They All Used Government Venture Money To Get Started

A few years ago I read that the government provided money to a porno shop in New York City through a program call Small Business Investment Companies (SBIC). Since 1960 these organizations have provided venture capital to over 75,000 businesses, so it's easy to see that one of those businesses might be a porno shop. Porno is a legitimate businesses in many areas of the country.

SBICs are licensed by the U.S. Small Business Administration but are privately owned and operate on a for profit basis. Their license allows companies to pool their money with borrowed money from the government in order to provide financing to small businesses in the form of equity securities or long-term debt. These government subsidized investment companies have helped Compaq, Apple, Federal Express and Staples make it to the big time. They have also helped smaller companies achieve success. They've financed Spencer and Vickie Jacobs' hot tub business in Columbus, Ohio, as well as taxi drivers in New York City who needed money to pay for the medallions which allows them to operate their own cabs.

Uncle Sam's Venture Capital Boom

In 1994, new government regulations were imposed that make it easier to become an SBIC. The budget for this program was also greatly expanded. As a result of this change, there will now be over $6 billion worth of financing available to entrepreneurs over the next several years. Now, that's not small change, even to a hotshot entrepreneur. With these new regulations and budget in place, the government expects that there will soon be 200 additional SBICs waiting to serve American entrepreneurs.

Who Gets The Money?

Basically you have to be a small business to apply for this money, and the government's definition includes companies that have less than $18 million in net worth and less than $6 million in profits. Wow, that's some small business! They seem particularly interested in businesses that offer a new product or service that has a strong growth potential. There is special consideration given to minorities and Vietnam Veterans applying for this money.

You do have to be armed with a business plan which should include the following:
1. Identify Your Company
2. Identify Your Product Or Service
3. Describe Your Product Facilities And Property
4. Detail Your Marketing Plan
5. Describe Your Competition
6. Describe Your Management Team
7. Provide A Financial Statement

Where to Apply

You can apply to more than one SBIC at the same time. Each acts as an independent company and they can provide money to both local or out-of-state businesses. At the end of this section is a listing of SBA licensed Small Business Investment Companies. However, this list is growing every day so it would be wise to contact the following office to obtain a current list: Associate Administrator for Investment, U.S. Small Business Administration, Washington, DC 20416; 202-205-6510; {www.sba.gov/inv}.

States Have Venture Money, Too

It's not enough to only look at federal venture capital programs, because some state governments also have venture capital programs. More and more states continue to start new programs every month. Some states, like Maryland, see the value in the new rule changes for becoming an SBIC, and are beginning to apply to become a licensed participant of the Small Business Administration's program. Here is what is available from state governments at the time this book went to press. Be sure to check with your state to see what's new:

1) Arkansas - Seed Capital Investment Program
2) Connecticut - Risk Capital
   - Product Design Financing
   - Seed Venture Fund
3) Illinois - Technology Investment Program
   - Illinois Venture Capital Fund
4) Iowa - Venture Capital Resources Fund
5) Kansas - Venture Capital and Seed Capital
   - Seed Capital Fund
   - Ad Astra Fund
   - Ad Astra Fund II
6) Louisiana - Venture Capital Incentive Program
7) Massachusetts - Venture Capital Program
8) Michigan - Enterprise Development Fund
   - Onset Seed Fund
   - Diamond Venture Associates
   - Semery Seed Capital Fund
   - Michigan Venture Capital Fund
9) Montana - Venture, Equity & Risk Capital
10) New Mexico - Venture Capital Investment Program
11) New York - Corporation for Innovation Development
12) North Carolina - North Carolina First Flight Inc.
13) North Carolina - Seed and Incubator Capital
14) Pennsylvania - Seed Venture Capital
15) South Carolina - Venture Capital Funding Program
16) Tennessee - Venture Capital

Contact your state office of economic development in your state capital for further information on venture capital available in your state.

Alabama

Alabama Capital Corporation
David C. DeLaney, President
16 Midtown Park East
Mobile, AL 36606
334-476-0700
Fax: 334-476-0026

FJC Growth Capital Corporation
William B. Noojin, Manager
200 Westside Court Square, Suite 340
Huntsville, AL 35801
256-922-2918
Fax: 256-922-2909

First SBIC of Alabama
David C. DeLaney, President
16 Midtown Park East
Mobile, AL 36606
334-476-0700
Fax: 334-476-0026

Hickory Venture Capital Corporation
J. Thomas Noojin, President
301 Washington St.
Suite 301
Huntsville, AL 35801
256-539-1931
Fax: 256-539-5130
www.hvcc.com

Javelin Capital Fund, L.P.
Lyle Hohnke and Joan Neuschaler, Partners
2850 Cahaba Rd.
Suite 240
Birmingham, AL 35223
205-870-4811
Fax: 205-870-4822

Arizona

Sundance Venture Partners, L.P.
Brian Burns, General Manager
5030 E. Sunrise Dr., Suite 200
Phoenix, AZ 85044
602-785-0725
Fax: 602-785-0753

Sundance Venture Partners, L.P.
(Main Office: Cupertino, CA)
Gregory S. Anderson, Vice President
5030 E. Sunrise Dr., Suite 200
Phoenix, AZ 85004
480-785-0725
Fax: 480-257-8111

Arkansas

Small Business Inv. Capital, Inc.
Jerry W. Davis, President
12103 Interstate 30
P.O. Box 3627
Little Rock, AR 72203
501-455-6599
Fax: 501-455-6556

California

Allied Business Investors, Inc. (SSBIC)
Jack Hong, President
301 W. Valley Blvd., Suite 208
San Gabriel, CA 91776
626-289-0186
Fax: 626-289-2369

Ally Finance Corp.
Eric Steinmann, CEO
14011 Park Ave., Suite 310
Victorville, CA 92392
760-241-7025
Fax: 760-241-8232

Asian American Capital Corporation
Jennie Chien, Manager
1251 W. Tennyson Rd., Suite #4
Hayward, CA 94544
510-887-6888
Fax: 510-887-6897

Aspen Ventures West II, L.P.
Alexander Cilento and David Crocket, Managers
1000 Fremont Ave., Suite V
Los Altos, CA 94024
650-917-5670
Fax: 650-917-5677
www.aspenventures.com

Astar Capital Corp.
George Hsu, President
9537 E. Gidley St.
Temple City, CA 91780
626-350-1211
Fax: 626-443-5874

AVI Capital, L.P.
P. Wolken, B. Weinman and B. Grossi, Managers
One First St., Suite 12
Los Altos, CA 94022
650-949-9862
Fax: 650-949-8510
www.avicapital.com

BT Capital Partners, Inc.
(Main Office: New York, NY)
300 S. Grand Ave.
Los Angeles, CA 90071
www.bankerstrust.com/btcapital

BankAmerica Ventures, Inc.
Carla Perumean, Senior VP
950 Tower Lane, Suite 700
Foster City, CA 94404
650-378-6000
Fax: 650-378-6040

Bay Partners SBIC, L.P.
John Freidenrich and Neal Dempsey, Managers
10600 N. De Anza Blvd., Suite 100
Cupertino, CA 95014
408-725-2444
Fax: 408-446-4502
www.baypartners.com

Bentley Capital
John Hung, President
592 Vallejo St., Suite #2
San Francisco, CA 94133
415-362-2868
Fax: 415-398-8209

Best Finance Corporation
Yong Ho Park, General Manager
3540 W. Wilshire Blvd., Suite 804
Los Angeles, CA 90010
213-385-7030
Fax: 213-385-7130

Calsafe Capital Corp.
Ming-Min Su, President,
Director and Manager
245 E. Main St., Suite 107
Alhambra, CA 91801
626-289-3400
Fax: 626-300-8025

Canaan Venture Partners
Main Office: Rowayton, CT-
Eric Young, Manager
2884 Sand Hill Rd.
Menlo Park, CA 94025
650-854-8092
Fax: 650-854-8127
www.canaan.com

Capstone Ventures SBIC, L.P.
Barbara Santry and Gene Fischer, Managers

3000 Sand Hill Rd.
Building 1, Suite 290
Menlo Park, CA 94025
650-854-2523
Fax: 650-854-9010
www.capstonevc.qpg.com

Charterway Investment Corporation
Edmund C. Lau, Chairman
9660 Flair Dr., Suite 328
El Monte, CA 91731
626-279-1189
Fax: 626-279-9062

Critical Capital Growth Fund, L.P.
Steven Sands and Allen Gold, Managers
17 E. Sir Francis Drake Blvd.
Suite 230
Larkspur, CA 94939
415-464-5720
Fax: 415-464-5701

Draper Associates (a California LP)
Timothy C. Draper, President
400 Seaport Court, Suite 250
Redwood City, CA 94063
650-599-9000
Fax: 650-599-9726
www.drapervc.com

Draper-Richards L.P.
William Draper III, President
50 California St., Suite 2925
San Francisco, CA 94111
415-616-4050
Fax: 415-616-4060
www.draperintl.com

Far East Capital Corp.
Tom Wang, Manager
977 N. Broadway, Suite 401
Los Angeles, CA 90012
213-687-1361
Fax: 213-626-7497

First American Capital Funding, Inc.
Chuoc Vota, President
10840 Warner Ave., Suite 202
Fountain Valley, CA 92708
714-965-7190
Fax: 714-965-7193

Fourteen Hill Capitol
Bradley Rotter and Alan Perper, Managers

1700 Montgomery St., Suite 250
San Francisco, CA 94111
415-394-9469
Fax: 415-394-9471
www.fourteenhill.com

Fulcrum Venture Capital Corporation
Brian Argrett, President
3683 Corporate Pointe, Suite 380
Culver City, CA 90230
310-645-1271
Fax: 310-645-1272

Hall Capital Management
Ronald J. Hall, Managing Director
26161 La Paz Rd., Suite E
Mission Viejo, CA 92691
949-707-5096
Fax: 949-707-5121

Imperial Ventures, Inc.
Christian Hobbs, VP
9920 S. La Cienega Blvd., Suite 1030
(P.O. Box 92991, L.A. 90301)
Inglewood, CA 90301
310-417-5960
Fax: 310-417-5781

Kline Hawkes California SBIC, LP
Frank R. Kline, Manager
11726 San Vicente Blvd., Suite 300
Los Angeles, CA 90049
310-442-4700
Fax: 310-442-4707
www.klinehawkes.com

LaiLai Capital Corp.
Danny Ku, Pres. & General Mgr.
223 E. Garvey Ave., Suite 228
Monterey Park, CA 91754
626-288-0704
Fax: 626-288-4101
www.lailai.com

Magna Pacific Investments
David Wong, President
330 N. Brand Blvd., Suite 670
Glendale, CA 91203
818-547-0809
Fax: 818-547-9303

Marwit Capital Corp.
Matthew Witte, President
180 Newport Center Dr., Suite 200

Newport Beach, CA 92660
949-640-6234
Fax: 949-720-8077
www.marwit.com

New Vista Capital Fund
Roger Barry, Manager
540 Cooper St., Suite 200
Palo Alto, CA 94301
650-329-9333
Fax: 650-328-9434
www.nvcap.com

Novus Ventures, L.P.
Daniel Tompkins, Manager
20111 Stevens Creek Blvd., Suite 130
Cupertino, CA 95014
408-252-3900
Fax: 408-252-1713

Opportunity Capital Corporation
J. Peter Thompson, President
2201 Walnut Ave., Suite 210
Fremont, CA 94538
510-795-7000
Fax: 510-494-5439

Opportunity Capital Partners II, L.P.
J. Peter Thompson, Gen. Partner
2201 Walnut Ave., Suite 210
Fremont, CA 94538
510-795-7000
Fax: 510-494-5439

Pacific Mezzanine Fund, L.P.
Nathan W. Bell, General Partner
2200 Powell St., Suite 1250
Emeryville, CA 94608
510-595-9800
Fax: 510-595-9801

Pinecreek Capital Partners, L.P.
Randall F. Zurbach, President
24 Corporate Plaza, Suite 160
Newport Beach, CA 92660
949-720-4620
Fax: 949-720-4629

Positive Enterprises, Inc.
Kwok Szeto, President
1489 Webster St., Suite 228
San Francisco, CA 94115
415-885-6600
Fax: 415-928-6363

San Joaquin Business Investment Group Inc.
Eugene Waller, President
1900 Mariposa Mall, Suite 100
Fresno, CA 93721
559-233-3580
Fax: 559-233-3709

Sorrento Growth Partners
Robert Jaffe, Manager
4370 La Jolla Village Dr., Suite 1040
San Diego, CA 92122
619-452-3100
Fax: 619-452-7607
www.sorrentoventures.com

Tangent Growth Fund
Alexander Schilling, Manager
180 Geary St., Suite 500
San Francisco, CA 94108
415-392-9228
Fax: 415-392-1928

TeleSoft Partners IA L.P.
Arjun Gupta, Manager
1450 Fashion Island Blvd., Suite 610
San Mateo, CA 94404
650-358-2500
Fax: 650-358-2501

UnionBanCal Venture Corporation
Robert S. Clarke, President
445 S. Figueroa St., 9th Floor
P.O. Box 3100
Los Angeles, CA 90071
213-236-4092
Fax: 213-629-5328

VK Capital Company
Franklin Van Kasper, Gen Partner
600 California St., Suite 1700
San Francisco, CA 94108
415-391-5600
Fax: 415-397-2744
www.vkco.com

Viridian Capital, L.P.
Christine Cordaro, Contact
220 Montgomery St., Suite 946
San Francisco, CA 94104
415-391-8950
Fax: 415-391-8937

Walden-SBIC, L.P.
Arthur S. Berliner, Manager

750 Battery St., 7th Floor
San Francisco, CA 94111
415-391-7225
Fax: 415-391-7262
www.waldenvc.com

Wells Fargo SBIC, Inc.
Richard Green and Steven Burge, Managers
One Montgomery St.
West Tower, Suite 2530
San Francisco, CA 94104
800-411-4932
Fax: 415-765-1569
www.wallsfargo.com

Western General Capital Corporation
Alan Thian, President
13701 Riverside Dr., Suite 610
Sherman Oaks, CA 91423
818-907-8272
Fax: 818-905-9220

Woodside Fund III SBIC, L.P.
Vincent Occhipinti and Frank Mendicino
850 Woodside Dr.
Woodside, CA 94062
650-368-5545
Fax: 650-368-2416
www.woodsidefund.com

Colorado

CapEx, L.P.
Jeffrey Ross, Manager
1670 Broadway, Suite 3350
Denver, CO 80202
303-869-4700
Fax: 303-869-4602

Hanifen Imhoff Mezzanine Fund, L.P.
Edward C. Brown, Manager
1125 17th St.
Suite 1820
Denver, CO 80202
303-291-5209
Fax: 303-291-5327
www.rockycapital.com

Rocky Mountain Mezzanine Fund II
Edward Brown and Paul Lyons, Managers
1125 17th St., Suite 1500
Denver, CO 80202
303-291-5209
Fax: 303-291-5327
www.rockycapital.com

Connecticut
AB SBIC, Inc.
Adam J. Bozzuto, President
275 School House Rd.
Cheshire, CT 06410
203-272-0203
Fax: 203-250-2954

Canaan SBIC, L.P.
Gregory Kopchinsky, Manager
105 Rowayton Ave.
Rowayton, CT 06853
203-855-0400
Fax: 203-854-9117
www.canaan.com

Capital Resource Co. of Connecticut
Morris Morgenstein, General Partner
Two Bridgewater Rd.
Framington, CT 06032
860-677-1113
Fax: 860-677-5414

Imprimis SB, L.P.
Charles Davidson, Joseph Jacobs, Managers
411 W. Putnam Ave.
Greenwich, CT 06830
203-862-7074
Fax: 203-862-7374

First New England Capital, LP
Richard C. Klaffky, President
100 Pearl St.
Hartford, CT 06103
860-293-3333
Fax: 860-293-3338
www.firstnewenglandcapital.com

Marcon Capital Corp.
Robert Mahoney and Todd Enright, Managers
1470 Barnum Ave., Suite 301
Bridgeport, CT 06610
203-337-4444
Fax: 203-337-4449
www.marconcapital.com

RFE Capital Partners, L.P.
Robert M. Williams, Managing Partner
36 Grove St.
New Canaan, CT 06840
203-966-2800
Fax: 203-966-3109

SBIC of Connecticut Inc. (The)
Kenneth F. Zarrilli, President
965 White Plains Rd.
Trumbull, CT 06611
203-261-0011
Fax: 203-452-9699

Delaware
Blue Rock Capital, L.P.
Virginia Bonker and Paul Collison, Managers
5803 Kennett Pike, Suite A
Wilmington, DE 19807-1135
302-426-0981
Fax: 302-426-0982

District of Columbia
Allied Investment Corporation
Kelly Anderson, Controller
1919 Pennsylvania Ave., NW
Washington, DC 20006-3434
202-973-6328
Fax: 202-659-2053
www.alliedcapital.com

Broadcast Capital, Inc. SSBIC
John E. Oxendine, President
1700 K St., NW, Suite 405
Washington, DC 20006
202-496-9250
Fax: 202-496-9259

Capitol Health Partners, L.P.
Debora Guthrie, Manager
2620 P St., NW
Washington, DC 20007
202-342-6300
Fax: 202-342-6399

Multimedia Broadcast Investment Corp. SSBIC
Walter L. Threadgill, President
3101 South St., NW
Washington, DC 20007
202-293-1166
Fax: 202-293-1181

Women's Growth Capital Fund, LLLP
Patty Abramson and Rob Stein, Managers
1029 31st St., NW
Washington, DC 20007-1203
202-342-1431
Fax: 202-342-1203
www.womensgrowthcapital.com

Florida

Capital International
Marvel Iglesias, Contact
One SE Third Ave.
Suite 2255
Miami, FL 33131
305-373-6500
Fax: 305-373-6700
www.net-invest.com

Market Capital Corp.
Eugene C. Langford
1715 W. Cleveland St.
Tampa, FL 33606
813-251-6055
Fax: 813-251-1900
www.langfordhill.com

PMC Investment Corporation
(Main Office: Dallas, TX)
AmeriFirst Bank Building
2nd Floor S
18301 Biscayne Blvd.
N. Miami Beach, FL 33160
305-933-5858
Fax: 305-931-3054

Western Financial Capital Corp.
(Main Office: Dallas, TX)
AmeriFirst Bank Bldg., 2nd Floor S
18301 Biscayne Blvd.
N. Miami Beach, FL 33160
305-933-5858
Fax: 305-932-3730
www.pmcapital.com

Georgia

Cordova Enhanced Fund, L.P.
Paul DiBella and Ralph Wright, Managers
2500 North Winds Parkway, Suite 475
Alpharetta, GA 30004
678-942-0300
Fax: 678-942-0301
www.cordovaventures.com

EGL/NatWest Ventures USA, L.P.
Salvatore Massaro, Manager
6600 Peachtree-Dunwoody Rd.
300 Embassy Row, Suite 630
Atlanta, GA 30328
404-949-8300
Fax: 404-949-8311
www.eglholdings.com

First Growth Capital, Inc.
Vijay K. Patel, President
P.O. Box 815
I-75 and GA 42
Best Western Plaza
Forsyth, GA 31029
912-994-4620
Fax: 912-994-1280

Waschovia Capital Associates, Inc.
Matthew J. Sullivan, Managing Director
191 Peachtree St., NE, 26th Floor
Atlanta, GA 30303
404-332-1437
Fax: 404-332-1455
www.waschovia.com

Hawaii

Pacific Century SBIC, Inc.
Robert Paris, President
130 Merchant St., 12th Floor
(P.O. Box 2900,
Honolulu, 96846-6000)
Honolulu, HI 96813
808-537-8613
Fax: 808-521-7602
www.boh.com

Pacific Venture Capital, Ltd.
Dexter J. Taniguchi, President
222 S. Vineyard St., PH.1
Honolulu, HI 96813
808-521-6502
Fax: 808-521-6541
E-mail: hedco@gle.com

Illinois

ABN AMRO Capital
Paul Widuch, Chairman
135 S. Lasalle St.
Chicago, IL 60674
312-904-6445
Fax: 312-904-6376
www.abnamro.com

BMO Nesbitt Burns Equity Investments
William Morro, President
111 W. Monroe St., 20th Floor
Chicago, IL 60603
312-461-2021
Fax: 312-765-8000

Continental Illinois Venture Corp.
Christopher J. Perry, President

209 S. LaSalle St.
(Mail: 231 S. LaSalle St.)
Chicago, IL 60697
312-828-8021
Fax: 312-987-0763
www.civc.com

First Chicago Equity Corp.
David J. Vitale, President
Three First National Plaza, Suite 1330
Chicago, IL 60670
312-895-1000
Fax: 312-895-1001

Heller Equity Capital Corporation
Charles Brisman, Steven Miriani
500 W. Monroe St.
Chicago, IL 60661
312-441-7000
Fax: 312-441-7208
www.hellersin.com

Midwest Mezzanine Fund
David Gezon and Allan Kayler, Managers
208 S. Lasalle St., 10th Floor
Chicago, IL 60604
312-855-7140
Fax: 312-553-6647
www.abnequity.com

Peterson Finance and Investment Company
James S. Rhee, President
3300 W. Peterson Ave., Suite A
Chicago, IL 60659
773-539-0502
Fax: 773-583-6714

Polestar Capital, Inc.
Wallace Lennox, President
180 N. Michigan Ave., Suite 1905
Chicago, IL 60601
312-984-9875
Fax: 312-984-9877
www.polestarvc.com

Prairie Capital Mezzanine Fund, L.P.
Bryan Daniels and Stephen King, Partners
300 S. Wacker Dr., Suite 1050
Chicago, IL 60606
312-360-1133
Fax: 312-360-1193

Shorebank Capital Corp.
David Shryock, CEO

7936 S. Cottage Grove Ave.
Chicago, IL 60619
773-371-7030
Fax: 773-371-7035
www.sbk.com

Walnut Capital Corp.
Burton W. Kanter, Chairman of the Board
Two N. LaSalle St., Suite 2200
Chicago, IL 60602
312-269-1700
Fax: 312-269-1747

Indiana

1st Source Capital Corporation
Eugene L. Cavanaugh, Jr., VP
100 N. Michigan St.
(Mailing address: P.O. Box 1602
South Bend 46634)
South Bend, IN 46601
219-235-2180
Fax: 219-235-2227

Cambridge Ventures, LP
Ms. Jean Wojtowicz, President
8440 Woodfield Crossing, #315
Indianapolis, IN 46240
317-469-9704
Fax: 317-469-3926

White River Venture
Sam Surphin and Mark Delong, Managers
3603 E. Raymond St.
Indianapolis, IN 46203
317-780-7789
Fax: 317-791-2935

Iowa

Berthel SBIC, LLC
Jim Thorp and Henry Madden, Managers
100 2nd St., SE
Cedar Rapids, IA 52407
319-365-2506
Fax: 319-365-9141
www.berthel.com

MorAmerica Capital Corporation
David R. Schroder, President
101 2nd St., SE, Suite 800
Cedar Rapids, IA 52401
319-363-8249
Fax: 319-363-9683

North Dakota SBIC, L.P.
David R. Schroder, Manager
101 Second St. SE, Suite 800
Cedar Rapids, IA 52401
701-298-0003
Fax: 701-293-7819

Kansas
Kansas Venture Capital, Inc.
Carol Laddish, Manager
6700 Antioch Plaza, Suite 460
Overland Park, KS 66204
913-262-7117
Fax: 913-262-3509

Enterprise Fund
Randall Humphreys, Manager
7400 W. 110th St., Suite 560
Overland Park, KS 66210
913-327-8500
Fax: 913-327-8505

Kentucky
Equal Opportunity Finance, Inc.
David A. Sattich, President
420 S. Hurstbourne Pkwy., Suite 201
Louisville, KY 40222
502-423-1943
Fax: 502-423-1945

Mountain Ventures, Inc.
L. Ray Moncrief, Executive VP
P.O. Box 1738
362 Old Whitely Rd.
London, KY 40743
606-864-5175
Fax: 606-864-5194

Louisiana
Banc One Equity Investors, Inc.
Thomas J. Adamek, President
451 Florida St.
P.O. Box 1511
Baton Rouge, LA 70821
225-332-4421
Fax: 225-332-7377

Hibernia Capital Corp.
Thomas Hoyt, President
313 Carondelet St.
New Orleans, LA 70130
504-533-5988
Fax: 504-533-3873
www.hibernia.com

Maine
North Atlantic Venture Fund
David M. Coit, Manager
Seventy Center St.
Portland, ME 04101
207-772-1001
Fax: 207-772-3257
www.northatlanticcapital.com

Maryland
Anthem Capital
William Gust, Manager
16 S. Calvert St., Suite 800
Baltimore, MD 21202
410-625-1510
Fax: 410-625-1735
www.anthemcapital.com

MMG Ventures
Stanley W. Tucker, Manager
826 E. Baltimore St.
Baltimore, MD 21202
410-333-2548
Fax: 410-333-2552
www.mmggroup.com

Security Financial and Investment Corp.
7720 Wisconsin Ave., Suite 207
Bethesda, MD 20814
301-951-4288
Fax: 301-951-9282

Syncom Capital Corp.
Terry L. Jones, President
8401 Colesville Rd., #300
Silver Spring, MD 20910
301-608-3207
Fax: 301-608-3307

Massachusetts
Argonauts MESBIC Corporation
Kevin Chen, General Manager
929 Worcester Rd.
Framingham, MA 01701
508-875-6939
Fax: 508-872-3741

BancBoston Ventures, Inc.
Frederick M. Fritz, President
100 Federal St.
P.O. Box 2016
Stop 01-32-01
Boston, MA 02106
617-434-2442

Fax: 617-434-1153
www.bancboscap.com

Cadeuceus Capital Health Ventures
Bill Golden, Manager
101 Arch St., Suite 1950
Boston, MA 02110
617-330-9345
Fax: 617-330-9349

Chestnut Street Partners, Inc.
David D. Croll, President
75 State St., Suite 2500
Boston, MA 02109
617-345-7220
Fax: 617-345-7201
www.mcventurepartners.com

Citizens Ventures, Inc.
Robert Garrow and Gregory Mulligan, Managers
28 State St., 15th Floor
Boston, MA 02109
617-725-5635
Fax: 617-725-5630

Commonwealth Enterprise Fund Inc
Charles G. Broming, Fund Manager
10 Post Office Square, Suite 1090
Boston, MA 02109
617-482-1881
Fax: 617-482-7129

GMN Investors II, L.P.
James M. Goodman, Manager
20 William St.
Wellesley, MA 02481
781-237-7001
Fax: 781-237-7233
www.gemini-investors.com

Geneva Middle Market Investors
James Goodman, Manager
20 William St.
Wellesley, MA 02481
781-237-7001
Fax: 781-237-7233
www.gemini-investors.com

Marathon Investment Partners
10 Post Office Square, Suite 1225
Boston, MA 02109
617-423-2494
Fax: 617-423-2719
www.marathoninvestment.com

New England Partners Capital, L.P.
Robert Hanks, Prin. and Todd Fitzpatrick
One Boston Place, Suite 2100
Boston, MA 02108
617-624-8400
Fax: 617-624-8416

Northeast SBI Corp.
Joseph Mindick, Treasurer
212 Tosca Dr.
Stoughton, MA 02072
781-297-9235
Fax: 781-297-9236

Norwest Equity Partners IV
Main Office: Minneapolis, MN
40 William St., Suite 305
Wellesley, MA 02181
617-237-5870
Fax: 617-237-6270
www.norwestvc.com

Pioneer Ventures Limited Partnership
Leigh Michl, General Partner
60 State St., 19th Floor
Boston, MA 02109
617-742-7825
Fax: 617-742-7315
www.pioneerfunds.com

Seacost Capital Partners
Walt Leonard, Manager
55 Ferncroft, Rd.
Danvers, MA 01923
978-750-1310
Fax: 978-750-1301

UST Capital Corp.
Arthur F. Snyder, President
40 Court St.
Boston, MA 02108
617-726-7000
Fax: 617-695-4185
www.ustrustboston.com

Zero Stage Capital V, L.P.
Paul Kelley, Manager
Kendall Square
101 Main St., 17th Floor
Cambridge, MA 02142
617-876-5355
Fax: 617-876-1248
www.zerostage.com

Michigan

Capital Fund, Inc.
Barry Wilson, President
6412 Centurion Dr., Suite 150
Lansing, MI 48917
517-323-7772
Fax: 517-323-1999

Dearborn Capital Corp.
Michael J. Kahres, President
c/o Ford Motor Credit Corp.
P.O. Box 1729
Dearborn, MI 48121
313-337-8577
Fax: 313-248-1252

Investcare Partners
Malcolm Moss, Manager
31500 Northwest Highway
Suite 120
Farmington Hill, MI 48334
248-851-9200
Fax: 248-851-9208

Merchants Capital Partners, L.P.
Pat Beach, Dick Goff, Ross Martin, Managers
24 Frank Lloyd Wright Dr.
Lobby L, 4th Floor
Ann Arbor, MI 48106
734-994-5505
Fax: 734-994-1376
www.captec.com

Motor Enterprises, Inc.
Mark Fischer, VP and Treasurer
NAO Headquarters Bldg., 1-8
30400 Mound Rd., Box 9015
Warren, MI 48090
810-986-8420
Fax: 810-986-6703

Pacific Capital
Lois F. Marler, VP
2401 Plymouth Rd., Suite B
Ann Arbor, MI 48105
734-747-9401
Fax: 734-747-9704
www.whitepines.com

White Pines Capital Corp.
Mr. Ian Bund, President
2401 Plymouth Rd.
Ann Arbor, MI 48105
734-747-9401

Fax: 734-747-9704
www.whitepines.com

Minnesota

Agio Capital Partners
Kenneth F. Gudolf, Pres. and CEO
First Bank Place
601 Second Ave. S., Suite 4600
Minneapolis, MN 55402
612-339-8408
Fax: 612-349-4232
www.agio-capital.com

Baynew Capital Partners
Cary Musech, Manager
61 E. Lake St., Suite 230
Waycata, MN 55391
612-475-4935
Fax: 612-476-7820
www.bayviewcap.com

Milestone Growth Fund, Inc.
Esperanza Guerrero, President
401 Second Ave. S., Suite 1032
Minneapolis, MN 55401
612-338-0090
Fax: 612-338-1172

Mezzain Capital Partners
Gerald Slater and Lar Sovenson
150 S. 5th St., Suite 1720
Minneapolis, MN 55402
612-343-5540
Fax: 612-333-6118

Medallion Capital, Inc.
Tom Hunt, President
7831 Glenroy Rd., Suite 480
Minneapolis, MN 55439-3132
612-831-2025
Fax: 612-831-2945
www.medallionfinancial.com

Norwest Venture Partners
Robert F. Zicarelli, Manager
2800 Piper Jaffray Tower
222 S. Ninth St.
Minneapolis, MN 55402
612-667-1650
Fax: 612-667-1660
www.norwestvc.com

Piper Jaffray Healthcare Capital
Lloyd Benson, Manager

222 S. Ninth St.
Minneapolis, MN 55402
612-342-6335
Fax: 612-342-8514
www.pjc.com

Piper Jaffray Technology Capital
Gary Blauer and Buzz Benson, Managers
222 South 9th St.
Minneapolis, MN 55402
612-342-6368
Fax: 612-342-8514
www.pjc.com

Norwest Venture Partners
Daniel J. Haggerty, Manager
2800 Piper Jaffray Tower
Minneapolis, MN 55402
612-667-1650
Fax: 612-667-1660
www.norwestvc.com

Wells Fargo SBIC, Inc.
John Whaley
2800 Piper Jaffray Tower
222 S Ninth St.
c/o Norwest Venture Capital
Minneapolis, MN 55402
612-667-1667
Fax: 612-667-1660
www.norwestvc.com

Mississippi

CapSource Fund, L.P.
Bobby Weatherly and James Herndon, Managers
800 Woodlands Parkway, Suite 102
Ridgeland, MS 39157
601-899-8980
Fax: 601-952-1334

Sun-Delta Capital Access Center, Inc.
Howard Boutte, Jr., VP
819 Main St.
Greenville, MS 38701
601-335-5291
Fax: 601-335-5295

Missouri

Bankers Capital Corp.
Raymond E. Glasnapp, President
3100 Gillham Rd.
Kansas City, MO 64109
816-531-1600
Fax: 816-531-1334

BOME Investors, Inc.
Gregory R. Johnson and John McCarthy, Managers
8000 Maryland Ave., Suite 1190
St. Louis, MO 63105
314-721-5707
Fax: 314-721-5135
www.gatewayventures.com

CFB Venture Fund I, Inc.
James F. O'Donnell, Chairman
11 S. Meramec, Suite 1430
St. Louis, MO 63105
314-746-7427
Fax: 314-746-8739

CFB Venture Fund II, Inc.
James F. O'Donnell, President
11 S. Meramec, Suite 1430
St. Louis, MO 63105
314-746-7427
Fax: 314-746-8739

Civic Ventures Investment Fund, L.P.
Bryon E. Winton, Manager
One Metropolitan Square
211 North Broadway, Suite 2380
St. Louis, MO 63102
314-436-8222
Fax: 314-436-2070

Enterprise Fund, L.P.
Joseph D. Garea, Managing Director
150 North Meramec
Clayton, MO 63105
314-725-5500
Fax: 314-725-1732

Gateway Partners
John S. McCarthy
8000 Maryland Ave.
Suite 1190
St. Louis, MO 63105
314-721-5707
Fax: 314-721-5135
www.gatewayventures.com

KCEP I, L.P.
William Reisler, Manager
233 W. 47th St.
Kansas City, MO 64112
816-960-1771
Fax: 816-960-1777
www.kcep.com

MorAmerica Capital Corporation
(Main Office: Cedar Rapids, IA)
911 Main St., Suite 2424
Commerce Tower Bldg.
Kansas City, MO 64105
816-842-0114
Fax: 816-471-7339

United Missouri Capital Corporation
Noel Shull, Manager
1010 Grand Blvd.
P.O. Box 419226
Kansas City, MO 64141
816-860-7914
Fax: 816-860-7143
www.umb.com

Nevada
Atalanta Investment Company, Inc.
L. Mark Newman, Chairman of the Board
601 Fairview Blvd.
Call Box 10,001
Incline Village, NV 89450
775-833-1836
Fax: 775-833-1890

New Jersey
DFW Capital Partners
Donald Demuth, Manager
Glenpointe Center East, 5th Floor
300 Frank W. Burr Blvd.
Teaneck, NJ 07666
201-836-2233
Fax: 201-836-5666

CIT Group/Venture Capital, Inc.
Colby W. Collier, Manager
650 CIT Dr.
Livingston, NJ 07039
973-740-5429
Fax: 973-740-5555
www.citgroup.com

Capital Circulation Corporation
Judy Kao, Manager
2035 Lemoine Ave., Second Floor
Fort Lee, NJ 07024
201-947-8637
Fax: 201-585-1965

Early Stage Enterprises
Ronald Hahn and James Miller, Managers
995 Rte 518
Skillman, NJ 08558

609-921-8896
Fax: 609-921-8703

First Fidelity
Stephen Lane, President
190 River Rd.
Summit, NJ 07901
908-598-3363
Fax: 908-598-3375

Midmark Capital
Dennis Newman, Manager
466 Southern Blvd.
Chatham, NJ 07928
973-822-2999
Fax: 973-822-8911
www.midmarkcapital.com

Rutgers Minority Investment Co.
Oscar Figueroa, President
180 University Ave., 3rd Floor
Newark, NJ 07102
973-353-5627

Tappan Zee Capital Corporation
Jeffrey Birnberg, President
201 Lower Notch Rd.
P.O. Box 416
Little Falls, NJ 07424
973-256-8280
Fax: 973-256-2841

Transpac Capital Corporation
Tsuey Tang Wang, President
1037 Route 46 East
Clifton, NJ 07013
973-470-8855
Fax: 973-470-8827

Penny Lane Partners
Stephen Shaffer, Resident Manager
One Palmer Square, Suite 309
Princeton, NJ 08542
609-497-4646
Fax: 609-497-0611

New Mexico
TD Origen Capital Fund
J. Michael Schafer, Manager
150 Washington Ave., Suite 201
Santa Fe, NM 87501
505-982-7007
Fax: 505-982-7005

New York

399 Venture Partners
William Comfort, Chairman
399 Park Ave.
14th Floor, Zone 4
New York, NY 10043
212-559-1127
Fax: 212-888-2940

BOCNY, LLC
Shelley G. Whittington, Manager
10 E. 53rd St., 32nd Floor
New York, NY 10022
225-332-7721
Fax: 225-332-7377

American Asian Capital Corporation
Howard H. Lin, President
130 Water St., Suite 6-L
New York, NY 10005
212-422-6880
Fax: 212-422-6880

Argentum Capital Partners, LP
Daniel Raynor, Chairman
405 Lexington Ave., 54th Floor
New York, NY 10174
212-949-6262
Fax: 212-949-8294

Bank Austria Creditanstalt SBIC, Inc.
Dennis O'Dowd, President
245 Park Ave., 32nd Floor
New York, NY 10167
203-861-1410
Fax: 203-861-1477
www.bacai.com/

BT Capital Partners, Inc.
Doug Brent, Managing Director
130 Liberty St., 25th Floor
New York, NY 10006
212-250-7577
Fax: 212-250-7651
www.bankerstrust.com/btcapital

Barclays Capital Investors Corp.
Lorne Stapleton, President
222 Broadway, 11th Floor
New York, NY 10038
212-412-5832
Fax: 212-412-7600
www.barcat.com

CB Investors, Inc.
George E. Kells, Managing Director
380 Madison Ave., 12th Floor
New York, NY 10017
212-622-3100
Fax: 212-622-3799
www.chasecapitalpartners.com

CIBC Wood Gundy Ventures, Inc.
Robi Blumenstein, Managing Director
425 Lexington Ave., 9th Floor
New York, NY 10017
212-856-3713
Fax: 212-697-1554
www.cibcwm.com

CMNY Capital II, L.P.
Robert G. Davidoff, G.P.
135 E. 57th St., 26th Floor
New York, NY 10022
212-909-8432
Fax: 212-980-2630

Cephas Capital Partners
Clint Campbell, Jeff Holmes, Managers
16 W. Main St.
Rochester, NY 14614
716-231-1528
Fax: 716-231-1530

Capital Investors & Management Corp.
Rose Chao, Manager
210 Canal St., Suite 611
New York, NY 10013
212-964-2480
Fax: 212-349-9160

Chase Manhattan Capital Corp.
George E. Kells, Managing Director
380 Madison Ave., 12th Floor
New York, NY 10017
212-552-6275
Fax: 212-622-3799
www.chase.com

Chase Venture Capital Assoc.
Jeffrey C. Walker, Managing General Partner
380 Madison Ave., 12th Floor
New York, NY 10017
212-270-3220
Fax: 212-622-3101
www.chase.com

Credit Suisse First Boston SB Fund
David DeNunzio, John Hennessy, Managers
11 Madison Ave., 26th Floor
New York, NY 10010
212-325-2000
Fax: 212-325-2699
www.csfb.com

Citicorp Venture Capital, Ltd
William Comfort
Chairman of the Board
399 Park Ave.
14th Floor, Zone 4
New York, NY 10043
212-559-1127
Fax: 212-793-6164

Dresdner Kleinwort Benson Private Equity
Christopher Wright, President
75 Wall St., 24th Floor
New York, NY 10005
212-429-2100
Fax: 212-429-2929
www.dresdner-bank.com

Edwards Capital Corporation
Michael Kowalsky, President
437 Madison Ave.
New York, NY 10022
212-328-2110
Fax: 212-328-2125
www.medallionfinancial.com

Eos Partners SBIC II, L.P.
Steven Friedman and Brian Young, Managers
320 Park Ave., 22nd Floor
New York, NY 10022
212-832-5800
Fax: 212-832-5805
www.eospartners.com

East Coast Venture Capital, Inc.
Zindel Zelmanovitch, President
570 Seventh Ave., Suite 1802
New York, NY 10018
212-869-7778
Fax: 212-819-9764

East River Ventures
Alexander Paluch and Walter Carozza
150 E. 58th St., 16th Floor
New York, NY 10155
212-644-6211
Fax: 212-980-6603

Elk Associates Funding Corp.
Gary C. Granoff, President
747 Third Ave.
New York, NY 10017
212-421-2111
Fax: 212-759-3338

Empire State Capital Corporation
Dr. Joseph Wu, President
170 Broadway, Suite 1200
New York, NY 10038
212-513-1799
Fax: 212-513-1892

Esquire Capital Corp.
Wen-Chan Chin, President
69 Veterans Memorial Highway
Commack, NY 11725
516-462-6944
Fax: 516-864-8152

Exim Capital Corp.
Victor K. Chun, President
241 5th Ave., 3rd Floor
New York, NY 10016
212-683-3375
Fax: 212-689-4118

Fair Capital Corp.
Rose Chao, Manager
210 Canal St., Suite 611
New York, NY 10013
212-964-2480
Fax: 212-349-9160

EOS Partners, SBIC
Steven Friedman, Partner
520 Madison Ave., 42nd Floor
New York, NY 10022
212-832-5814
Fax: 212-832-5815
www.eospartners.com

Exeter Capital Lenders
Keith Fox, Manager
10 E. 53rd St.
New York, NY 10022
212-872-1170
Fax: 212-872-1198
www.exeterfunds.com

First County Capital, Inc.
Orest Glut, Financial Manager
135-14 Northern Blvd., 2nd Floor

Flushing, NY 11354
718-461-1778
Fax: 718-461-1835

Flushing Capital Corporation
Frank J. Mitchell, President
39-06 Union St., Room 202
Flushing, NY 11354
718-886-5866
Fax: 718-939-7761

Freshstart Venture Capital Corporation
Zindel Zelmanovich, President
24-29 Jackson Ave.
Long Island City, NY 11101
718-361-9595
Fax: 718-361-8295
www.defertax.com

Fundex Capital Corp.
Larry Linksman, President
780 Third Ave., 48th Floor
New York, NY 10017
212-527-7135
Fax: 212-527-7134

Genesee Funding, Inc.
Stuart Marsh, President & CEO
70 Linden Oaks, 3rd Floor
Rochester, NY 14625
716-383-5550
Fax: 716-383-5305

Hanam Capital Corp.
Robert Schairer, President
38 W. 32nd St., Suite 1512
New York, NY 10001
212-564-5225
Fax: 212-564-5307

Hudson Venture Partners, L.P.
Lawrence Howard and Marilyn Adler
660 Madison Ave., 14th Floor
New York, NY 10022
212-644-9797
Fax: 212-583-1849

ING Furman Selz Invest
Brian Friedman, Manager
230 Park Ave.
New York, NY 10169
212-309-8348
Fax: 212-692-9147

IBJ Whitehall Capital Corp.
Pete Hardy, President
One State St., 8th Floor
New York, NY 10004
212-858-2000
Fax: 212-952-1629

Ibero American Investors Corp.
Emilio Serrano, President
104 Scio St.
Rochester, NY 14604
716-262-3440
Fax: 716-262-3441
www.iberoinvestors.com

InterEquity Capital Corporation
Irwin Schlass, President
220 Fifth Ave., 12th Floor
New York, NY 10001
212-779-2022
Fax: 212-779-2103
www.interequity-capital.com

International Paper Cap. Formation, Inc.
(Main Office: Memphis, TN)
John Jepsen, President
Two Manhattanville Rd.
Purchase, NY 10577
914-397-1578
Fax: 914-397-1909
www.internationalpaper.com

J.P. Morgan Investment Corp.
Brian F. Watson, Managing Director
60 Wall St.
New York, NY 10260
212-483-2323
Fax: 212-648-5032
www.jpmorgan.com

KOCO Capital Company
Paul Echausse, President
111 Radio Circle
Mount Kisco, NY 10549
914-242-2324
Fax: 914-244-3985

M & T Capital Corp.
Tom Scanlon, President
One Fountain Plaza, 9th Floor
Buffalo, NY 14203
716-848-3800
Fax: 716-848-3150
www.mandtbank.com

LEG Partners Debenture
Lawrence Golub, Manager
230 Park Ave., 19th Floor
New York, NY 10169
212-207-1423
Fax: 212-207-1579

Medallion Funding Corporation
Alvin Murstein, President
437 Madison Ave.
New York, NY 10022
212-328-2110
Fax: 212-328-2125
www.medallionfinancial.com

Mercury Capital, L.P.
David Elenowitz, Manager
153 E. 53rd St.
New York, NY 10022
212-838-0888
Fax: 212-759-3897

NBT Capital Corporation
Daryl Forsythe and Joe Minor, Managers
19 Eaton Ave.
Norwich, NY 13815
607-337-6810
Fax: 607-336-8730
www.nbtbank.com

NYBDC Capital Corp.
Robert W. Lazar, President
41 State St.
P.O. Box 738
Albany, NY 12207
518-463-2268
Fax: 518-463-0240
www.nybdc.com

NatWest USA Capital Corporation
Elliot Jones, President
660 Madison Ave., 14th Floor
New York, NY 10021
212-401-1330
Fax: 212-401-1390
www.natwest.com

Norwood Venture Corp.
Mark R. Littell, President
1430 Broadway, Suite 1607
New York, NY 10018
212-869-5075
Fax: 212-869-5331
www.norven.com

Needham Capital
John Michaelson, Manager
445 Park Ave.
New York, NY 10022
212-705-0297
Fax: 212-751-1450
www.needhamco.com

Paribas Principal Incorporated
Steven Alexander, President
787 Seventh Ave., 32nd Floor
New York, NY 10019-8018
212-841-2000
Fax: 212-841-3558
www.parbas.com

Pierre Funding Corp.
Elias Debbas, President
805 Third Ave., 6th Floor
New York, NY 10022
212-888-1515
Fax: 212-688-4252

Prospect Street NYC Discovery Fund, L.P.
Richard E. Omohundro, CEO
250 Park Ave., 17th Floor
New York, NY 10177
212-448-0702
Fax: 212-448-0702
www.prospectstreet.com

Pyramid Ventures, Inc.
Brian Talbot, VP
130 Liberty St., 31st Floor
New York, NY 10006
212-250-9571
Fax: 212-250-7651
www.bankerstrust/btcapitalpartners

RBC Equity Investments
Stephen Stewart, Manager
One Liberty Plaza
New York, NY 10002
212-428-3035
Fax: 212-858-7468

Regent Capital Partners
J. Oliver Maggard, Managing Partner
505 Park Ave.
Suite 1700
New York, NY 10022
212-735-9900
Fax: 212-735-9908

Situation Ventures Corp.
Sam Hollander, President
56-20 59th St.
Maspeth, NY 11378
718-894-2000
Fax: 718-326-4642

Sixty Wall Street
Brian Watson, Managing Director
60 Wall St.
New York, NY 10260
212-344-7538
Fax: 212-648-5032

Societe Generale Capital Corp.
Steven Baronoff, President
1221 Ave. of the Americas, 8th Floor
New York, NY 10020
212-278-5400
Fax: 212-278-5387
www.socgen.com

Sterling/Carl Marks Capital, Inc.
Harvey L. Granat, President
175 Great Neck Rd., Suite 408
Great Neck, NY 11021
516-482-7374
Fax: 516-487-0781

TLC Funding Corp.
Philip G. Kass, President
660 White Plains Rd.
Tarrytown, NY 10591
914-939-0518
Fax: 914-332-5660

Transportation Capital Corp.
Michael Fanger, President
437 Madison Ave.
New York, NY 10022
212-328-2110
Fax: 212-328-2125
www.medallionfinancial.com

Triad Capital Corp. of New York
Oscar Figueroa, Manager
305 Seventh Ave., 20th Floor
New York, NY 10001
212-243-7360
Fax: 212-243-7647
www.bcf-triad.org

Trusty Capital Inc.
Yungduk Hahn, President

350 Fifth Ave.
Suite 2026
New York, NY 10118
212-736-7653
Fax: 212-629-3019

United Capital Investment Corp.
Paul Lee, President
60 E. 42nd St., Suite 1515
New York, NY 10165
212-682-7210
Fax: 212-573-6352

UBS Capital, II LLC
Justin S. Maccarone, President
299 Park Ave.
New York, NY 10171
212-821-6490
Fax: 212-821-6333

Venture Opportunities Corp.
A. Fred March, President
150 E. 58th St., 16th Floor
New York, NY 10155
212-832-3737
Fax: 212-980-6603

Wasserstein Adelson Ventures, L.P.
Townsend Ziebold, Jr., Manager
31 West 52nd St., 27th Floor
New York, NY 10019
212-969-2690
Fax: 212-969-7879
www.wassersteinparilla.com

Winfield Capital Corp.
Stanley M. Pechman, President
237 Mamaroneck Ave.
White Plains, NY 10605
914-949-2600
Fax: 914-949-7195

Walden Capital Partners
John Costantino, Allen Greenberg, Managers
150 E. 58th St., 34th Floor
New York, NY 10155
212-355-0090
Fax: 212-755-8894
www.waldencapital.com

North Carolina
BB&T Capital Partners, LLC
David Townsend and Martin Gilmore, Managers
200 West Second St., 4th Floor

Winston-Salem, NC 27101
336-733-2420
Fax: 336-733-2419
www.bbtcapital.com

First Union Capital Partners Inc
Tracey M. Chaffin, CFO
One First Union Center, 5th Floor
301 S. College St.
Charlotte, NC 28288
704-374-4768
Fax: 704-374-6711
www.firstunion.com

Blue Ridge Investors
Edward McCarthy, Executive VP
300 N. Greene St., Suite 2100
Greensboro, NC 27401
336-370-0576
Fax: 336-274-4984

Centura SBIC, Inc.
Robert R. Anders, Jr., President
200 Providence Rd., 3rd Floor
P.O. Box 6261
Charlotte, NC 28207
704-331-1451
Fax: 704-331-1761
www.centura.com

NationsBanc SBIC Corporation
George Carter, President
Elyn Dortch, VP
101 S. Tryon St., 18th Floor
NC-1-002-18-02
Charlotte, NC 28255
704-386-7549
Fax: 704-386-1930

NationsBanc Capital Corporation
Walter W. Walker, Jr., President
100 North Tryon St., 25th Floor
NCI-007-25-02
Charlotte, NC 28255
704-386-8063
Fax: 704-388-9049
www.bankofamerica.com

Oberlin Capital
Robert Shepley, Manager
702 Oberlin Rd., Suite 150
Raleigh, NC 27605
919-743-2544
Fax: 919-743-2501

North Dakota
North Dakota SBIC, L.P.
Main Office: Cedar Rapids, IA
406 Main Ave.
Suite 404
Fargo, ND 58103
701-298-0003
Fax: 701-293-7819

Ohio
Enterprise Ohio
Steven Budd, President
8 N. Main St.
Dayton, OH 45402
937-226-0457
Fax: 937-222-7035

Banc One Capital Partners Corp.
William Leahy, Managing Director
150 E. Gay St., 24th Floor
Columbus, OH 43215
614-217-1100
Fax: 614-217-1217

Financial Opportunities, Inc.
Gregg R. Budoi, Manager
300 Executive Parkway West
Hudson, OH 44236
330-342-6664
Fax: 330-342-6675

Key Equity Capital Corp.
David Given, President
127 Public Square, 28th Floor
Cleveland, OH 44114
216-689-5776
Fax: 216-689-3204

Clarion Capital Corp.
Morris H. Wheeler, President
Ohio Savings Plaza, Suite 510
1801 E. 9th St.
Cleveland, OH 44114
216-687-8941
Fax: 216-694-3545

National City Capital Corp
William H. Schecter, President & GM
1965 E. Sixth St.
Suite 1010
Cleveland, OH 44114
216-575-2491
Fax: 216-575-9965

River Cities Capital
R. Glen Mayfield, Manager
221 E. Fourth St.
Suite 2250
Cincinnati, OH 45202
513-621-9700
Fax: 513-579-8939
www.rccf.com

Key Mezzanine Capital
Stephen Stewart, Manager
10th Floor, Banc One Bldg.
600 Superior Ave.
Cleveland, OH 44114
216-858-6090
Fax: 216-263-3577

Oklahoma
BancFirst Investment Corporation
T. Kent Faison, Manager
101 North Broadway
Mail: P.O. Box 26788
Oklahoma City, OK 73126
405-270-1000
Fax: 405-270-1089
www.bancfirst.com

First United Venture Capital Corporation
John Massey and Greg Massey, Managers
1400 West Main St.
Durant, OK 74701
580-924-2256
Fax: 580-924-2228

Oregon
Northern Pacific Capital Corp.
Joseph P. Tennant, President
937 S.W. 14th St., Suite 200
P.O. Box 1658
Portland, OR 97207
503-241-1255

Shaw Venture Partners
Ralph R. Shaw, Manager
400 SW Sixth Ave., Suite 1100
Portland, OR 97204
503-228-4884
Fax: 503-227-2471
www.shawventures.com

Pennsylvania
CIP Capital, Inc.
Winston Churchill, Jr., Manager
435 Devon Park Dr., Bldg. 300

Wayne, PA 19087
610-964-7860
Fax: 610-964-8136

CEO Venture Fund
James Colker, Manager
2000 Technology Dr., Suite 160
Pittsburgh, PA 15219
412-687-0200, ext. 236
Fax: 412-687-8139
www.ceoventurefund.com

GS Capital, L.P.
Kenneth S. Choate, Managing Director
433 Devon Park Dr., Suite 612
Wayne, PA 19087
610-293-9151
Fax: 610-293-1979

Greater Phila. Venture Capital Corp., Inc.
Fred S. Choate, Mgr.
351 E Conestoga Rd.
Wayne, PA 19087
610-688-6829
Fax: 610-254-8958

Mellon Ventures
Lawrence Mock, Ronald Coombs, Managers
One Mellon Bank Center, Room 3200
Pittsburgh, PA 15258
412-236-3594
Fax: 412-236-3593
www.mellon.com

Meridian Venture Partners
Raymond R. Rafferty, Gen Part
The Fidelity Court Building
259 Radnor-Chester Rd., Suite 140
Radnor, PA 19087
610-254-2999
Fax: 610-254-2996

Argosy Investment Partners
Kunte Albrecht, Manager
950 W. Valley Rd., Suite 2902
Wayne, PA 19087
610-971-0558
Fax: 610-964-9524
www.argosycapital.com

Liberty Ventures
Thomas R. Morse, Manager
The Bellevue
200 Broad St.

Philadelphia, PA 19102
215-732-4445
Fax: 215-732-4644

Puerto Rico
North American Inv. Corporation
Marcelino Pastrana Torres, President
Mercantil Plaza Bldg., Suite 813
P.O. Box 1831
Hato Rey, PR 00919
787-754-6178
Fax: 787-754-6181

Rhode Island
Domestic Capital Corp.
Nathaniel B. Baker, President
815 Reservoir Ave.
Cranston, RI 02910
401-946-3310
Fax: 401-943-6708
www.domesticbank.com

Fleet Equity Partners
Robert Van Degna, Habib Gorgi, Managers
50 Kennedy Plaza, 12th Floor
Providence, RI 02903
401-278-6770
Fax: 401-278-6387
www.fleetequity.com

Fleet Venture Resources, Inc.
Robert M. Van Degna, President
50 Kennedy Plaza, 12th Floor
Mail Stop: RI MO F12C
Providence, RI 02903
401-278-6770
Fax: 401-278-6387
www.fleetequity.com

South Carolina
Charleston Capital Corporation
Henry Yaschik, President
111 Church St.
P.O. Box 328
Charleston, SC 29402
843-723-6464
Fax: 843-723-1228

CF Investment Co.
William S. Hummers, III, Manager
102 S. Main St.
Greenville, SC 29601
864-255-4919
Fax: 864-239-6423

TransAmerica Mezzanine
John J. Sterling, President
7 N. Laurens St., Suite 603
P.O. Box 10447
Greenville, SC 29601
864-232-6198
Fax: 864-241-4444

South Dakota
Bluestem Capital Partners II, L.P.
Steve Kirby and Paul Schock, Managers
122 South Phillips Ave., Suite 300
Sioux Falls, SD 57104
605-331-0091
Fax: 605-334-1218

Tennessee
Capital Across America
Whitney Johns and Chris Brown, Managers
414 Union St., Suite 2025
Nashville, TN 37219
615-254-1414
Fax: 615-254-1856

Commerce Capital, L.P.
Andrew Higgins, Pres and Rudy Ruark, V.P.
611 Commerce St., Suite 2602
Nashville, TN 37203
615-726-0202
Fax: 615-242-1407

Equitas, L.P.
D. Shannon LeRoy, President of CGP
2000 Glen Echo Rd., Suite 100
Mail: P.O. Box 158838
Nashville, TN 37215
615-383-8673
Fax: 615-383-8693
E-mail: sleroy@equitaslp.com

International Paper Cap. Formation, Inc.
Bob J. Higgins, VP and Controller
International Place II
6400 Poplar Ave.
Memphis, TN 38197
901-763-6282
Fax: 901-763-6076
www.internationalpaper.com

Pacific Capital, L.P.
Clay R. Caroland, III, President
3100 West End Ave., Suite 1070
Nashville, TN 37203
615-292-3166

Fax: 615-292-8803
www.whitepine.com

Sirrom Investments, Inc.
George M. Miller, II, President
500 Church St., Suite 200
Nashville, TN 37219
615-256-0701
Fax: 615-726-1208
www.finova.org

Southern Venture Fund
Don Johnston, President
310 25th Ave., N., Suite 103
Nashville, TN 37203
615-329-9448
Fax: 615-329-9237
www.masseyburch.com

Valley Capital Corp.
Lamar J. Partridge, President
Suite 212, Krystal Building
100 W. Martin Luther King Blvd.
Chattanooga, TN 37402
423-265-1557
Fax: 423-265-1588

West Tennessee Venture Capital Corporation
Frank Banks, President
5 N. Third St.
Memphis, TN 38103
901-522-9237
Fax: 901-527-6091

Texas
AMT Capital, Ltd.
Tom H. Delimitros, CGP
8204 Elmbrook Dr., Suite 101
Dallas, TX 75247
214-905-9760
Fax: 214-905-9761
www.amtcapital.com

Alliance Business Investment Co.
(Main Office: Tulsa, OK)
1221 McKinney St., Suite 3100
Houston, TX 77010
713-659-3131
Fax: 713-659-8070

Legacy Private Capital Management
Suzanne B. Kriscunas, Managing Director
3811 Turtle Creek Blvd., Suite 1600
Dallas, TX 75219

214-219-0363
Fax: 214-219-0769
www.legacyfund.com

Capital Southwest Venture Corp.
William R. Thomas, President
12900 Preston Rd., Suite 700
Dallas, TX 75230
972-233-8242
Fax: 972-233-7362
www.capitalsouthwest.com

Catalyst Fund, Ltd., (The)
Richard L. Herrman, Manager
Three Riverway, Suite 770
Houston, TX 77056
713-623-8133
Fax: 713-623-0473
www.the-catalyst-group.com

Chen's Financial Group, Inc.
Samuel S. C. Chen, President
10101 Southwest Freeway, Suite 370
Houston, TX 77074
713-772-8868
Fax: 713-772-2168

First Capital Group of Texas
Messrs. Blanchard, Greenwood & Lacy
750 E. Mulberry, Suite 305
San Antonio, TX 78212
210-736-4233
Fax: 210-736-5449
www.firstcapitalgroup.com

HCT Capital Corp.
Vichy Woodward Young, Jr., Pres.
4916 Camp Bowie Blvd., Suite 200
Ft. Worth, TX 76107
817-763-8706
Fax: 817-377-8049

Houston Partners, SBIP
Glenda Overbeck, President, CGP
401 Louisiana, 8th Floor
Houston, TX 77002
713-222-8600
Fax: 713-222-8932
www.houstonpartners.com

Jardine Capital Corporation
Lawrence Wong, President
7322 Southwest Parkway, Suite 787
Houston, TX 77074

713-271-7077
Fax: 713-271-7577

MESBIC Ventures, Inc.
Donald R. Lawhorne, President
12655 N. Central Plaza, Suite 710
Dallas, TX 75243
972-991-1598
Fax: 972-991-1647

Mapleleaf Capital Ltd.
Patrick A. Rivelli, Manager
Three Forest Plaza, Suite 935
12221 Merit Dr.
Dallas, TX 75251
972-239-5650
Fax: 972-701-0024

NationsBanc Capital Corporation
(Main Office: Charlotte, NC)
901 Main St., 66th Floor
Dallas, TX 75202
214-508-0932
Fax: 214-508-0985

North Texas MESBIC, Inc.
Allan Lee, President
9500 Forest Lane, Suite 430
Dallas, TX 75243
214-221-3565
Fax: 214-221-3566

PMC Investment Corporation
Andrew S. Rosemore, President
18111 Preston Rd., Suite 600
Dallas, TX 75252
972-349-3200
Fax: 972-349-3265
www.pmccapital.com

Retail and Restaurant Growth Capital, L.P.
Raymond Hemmig, Joseph Harberg, Managers
10000 N. Central Expressway, Suite 1060
Dallas, TX 75231
214-750-0065
Fax: 214-750-0060
www.rrgcsbic.com

SBIC Partners
Gregory Forsot and Jeffrey Brown, Managers
201 Main St., Suite 2302
Fort Worth, TX 76102
949-729-3222
Fax: 949-729-3226

SBIC Partners II, L.P.
Nicholas Binkley and Gregory Forrest, Managers
201 Main St., Suite 2302
Fort Worth, TX 76102
817-339-7020
Fax: 817-338-2047

Southwest/Catalyst Capital, Ltd.
Ronald Nixon and Rick Herrman, Managers
Three Riverway, Suite 770
Houston, TX 77056
713-623-8133
Fax: 713-623-0473
www.the-catalyst-group.com

Stratford Capital
Michael Brown, John Fannin, Darin Winn
200 Crescent Court, Suite 1650
Dallas, TX 75201
214-740-7377
Fax: 214-740-7340

United Oriental Capital Corp.
Jai Min Tai, President
908 Town and Country Blvd.
Suite 310
Houston, TX 77024
713-461-3909
Fax: 713-465-7559

Victoria Capital Corp.
Steve Selinske, Acting President
16416 San Pedro
San Antonio, TX 78232
210-856-4468
Fax: 210-856-8848

Western Financial Capital Corp.
Andrew S. Rosemore, President
17290 Preston Rd., Suite 600
Dallas, TX 75252
972-349-3200
Fax: 972-349-3265
www.pmccapital.com

Utah
First Security Business Investment Corporation
Louis D. Alder, Manager
15 East 100 South
Suite 100
Salt Lake City, UT 84111
801-246-5737
Fax: 801-246-5740
www.firstsecurity.com

Utah Ventures II L.P.
Alan Dishlip and James Dreyfous, Managers
423 Wakara Way
Suite 206
Salt Lake City, UT 84108
801-583-5922
Fax: 801-583-4105

Wasatch Venture Corporation
Todd J. Stevens, Secretary
1 South Main St., Suite 1400
Salt Lake City, UT 84133
801-524-8939
Fax: 801-524-8941
www.wasatchvc.com

Vermont
Green Mountain Capital, L.P.
Michael Sweatman, General Mgr.
RR1 Box 1503
Waterbury, VT 05676
802-244-8981
Fax: 802-244-8990
E-mail: ims@gmtcap.com

Virginia
Continental SBIC
Arthur Walters, President
4141 N. Henderson Rd., Suite 8
Arlington, VA 22203
703-527-5200
Fax: 703-527-3700

East West United Investment Company
Dung Bui, President
1568 Spring Hill Rd.
Suite 100
McLean, VA 22102
703-442-0150
Fax: 703-442-0156
www.ewmortgage.com

Virginia Capital SBIC
Frederick Russell, Tom Deardorff, Managers
9 S. 12th St., Suite 400
Richmond, VA 23219

Waterside Capital Corp.
Alan Lindower, President
300 E. Main St., Suite 1380
Norfolk, VA 23510
757-626-1111
Fax: 757-626-0114
www.watersidecapital.com

Walnut Capital Corp.
(Main Office: Chicago, IL)
8000 Tower Crescent Dr., Suite 1070
Vienna, VA 22182
703-448-3771
Fax: 703-448-7751

Washington
Northwest Venture Partners II, L.P.
Thomas Simpson and Jean Balek-Miner, Managers
221 North Wall St., Suite 628
Spokane, WA 99201
509-747-0728
Fax: 509-747-0758
www.nwva.com

Pacific Northwest Partners SBIC, L.P.
Theodore M. Wight, Manager
305 - 108th Ave. NE, 2nd Floor
Bellevue, WA 98004
425-455-9967
Fax: 425-455-9404
www.pnwp.com

West Virginia
Shenandoah Venture Capital L.P.
Thomas E. Loehr, President
208 Capital St., Suite 300
Charleston, WV 25301
304-344-1796
Fax: 304-344-1798

WestVen Limited Partnership
Thomas E. Loehr, President
208 Capitol St., Suite 300
Charleston, WV 25301
304-344-1794
Fax: 304-344-1798

Whitney Capital Corporation
Thomas Loehr, Manager
707 Virginia St., East, Suite 1700
Charleston, WV 25301
304-345-2480
Fax: 304-345-7258

Wisconsin
Capital Investments, Inc.
Steve Ripple, Executive VP
1009 W. Glen Oaks Lane, Suite 103
Mequon, WI 53092
414-241-0303
Fax: 414-241-8451
www.capitalinvestmentsinc.com

Future Value Ventures, Inc.
William P. Beckett, President
2821 N. 4th St., Suite 526
Milwaukee, WI 53212
414-264-2252
Fax: 414-264-2253

M & I Ventures L.L.C.
John T. Byrnes, President
770 North Water St.
Milwaukee, WI 53202

414-765-7910
Fax: 414-765-7850
www.masonwells.com

MorAmerica Capital Corporation
(Main Office: Cedar Rapids, IA)
600 East Mason St.
Suite 304
Milwaukee, WI 53202
414-276-3839
Fax: 414-276-1885

GOVERNMENT CONTRACTS
How to Sell Your Goods and Services To The World's Largest Buyer

If you produce a product or service, you've probably always wondered how you could offer what you produce to the biggest client in the world — the Federal government. Have you thought of the government as being a "closed shop" and too difficult to penetrate? Well, I'm happy to say that you're entirely wrong on that score. The Federal government spends over $180 billion each year on products ranging from toilet paper to paper clips and writes millions of dollars in contracts for services like advertising, consulting, and printing. Most Americans believe that a majority of those federal purchasing contracts have been eliminated over the last few years, but that's simply not true — they've just been replaced with new contracts that are looking for the same kinds of goods and services. Last year the government took action (either initiating or modifying) on over 350,000 different contracts. They buy these goods and services from someone, so why shouldn't that someone be you? To be successful doing business with the government, you need to learn to speak "governmenteze" to get your company into the purchasing loop, and I can show you how to accomplish that in just a few easy steps.

Step 1

Each department within the Federal government has a procurement office that buys whatever the department requires. Most of these offices have put together their own *Doing Business With the Department of* _____ publication, which usually explains procurement policies, procedures, and programs. This booklet also contains a list of procurement offices, contact people, subcontracting opportunities, and a solicitation mailing list. Within each department there is also an Office of Small and Disadvantaged Business Utilization, whose sole purpose is to push the interests of the small business, and to make sure these companies get their fair share of government contracts. Another good resource is your local Small Business Administration Office which should have a listing of U.S. Government Procurement Offices in your state.

Step 2

Once you have familiarized yourself with the process, you need to find out who is buying what from whom and for how much. There are three ways to get this important information.

A. Daily Procurement News
Each weekday, the *Commerce Business Daily* (CBD) gives a complete listing of products and services (that cost over $25,000) wanted by the U.S. government — products and services that your business may be selling. Each listing includes the following: the product or service, along with a short description; name and address of the agency; deadline for proposals or bids; phone number to request specifications; and the solicitation number of the product or service needed. Many business concerns, including small businesses, incorporate CBD review into their government marketing activities. To obtain a subscription for $275 a year, contact: Superintendent of Documents, U.S. Government Printing Office, Washington, DC 20402; 202-512-1800; {www.gpo.gov}.

B. Federal Data Systems Division (FDSD)

This Center distributes consolidated information about federal purchases, including research and development. FDSD can tell you how much the Federal government spent last quarter on products and services, which agencies made those purchases, and what contractors did business with the government. FDSD summarizes this information through two types of reports: The FDSD standard report and the FDSD special report. The standard report is a free, quarterly compilation containing statistical procurement information in "snapshot" form for over 60 federal agencies, as well as several charts, graphs, and tables which compare procurement activities by state, major product and service codes, method of procurement, and contractors. The report also includes quarterly and year-to-year breakdowns of amounts and percentages spent on small, women owned, and minority businesses. Special reports are prepared upon request for a fee, based on computer and labor costs. They are tailored to the specific categories, which can be cross-tabulated in numerous ways. A special report can help you analyze government procurement and data trends, identify competitors, and locate federal markets for individual products or services. Your Congressman may have access to the Federal Procurement Database from his/her office in Washington, which you may be able to use for free. For more information, contact: Federal Data Systems Division, General Services Administration, 7th and D St., SW, Room 5652, Washington, DC 20407; 202-401-1529.

C. Other Contracts

For contracts under $25,000, you must be placed on a department's list for solicitation bids on those contracts. The mailing list forms are available through the Procurement Office, the Office of Small and Disadvantaged Business Utilization, or your local Small Business Association office. Last year 18.7 billion dollars was spent on these "small" purchases, so these contracts should not be overlooked. Smaller contracts, completed over the course of a fiscal year, can mean lots of revenue for your business bottom line.

Step 3: Subcontracting Opportunities

All of the federal procurement offices or Offices of Small and Disadvantaged Business Utilization (SDBU) can provide you with information regarding subcontracting. Many of the departments' prime contracts require that the prime contractor maximize small business subcontracting opportunities. Many prime contractors produce special publications which can be helpful to those interested in subcontracting. The SDBU Office can provide you with more information on the subcontracting

Offices of Small and Disadvantaged Business Utilization

process, along with a directory of prime contractors. Another good source for subcontract assistance is your local Small Business Administration (SBA) office, 1-800-827-5722. SBA develops subcontracting opportunities for small business by maintaining close contact with large business prime contractors and by referring qualified small firms to them. The SBA has developed agreements and close working relationships with hundreds of prime contractors who cooperate by offering small firms the opportunity to compete for their subcontracts. In addition, to complete SBA's compliance responsibilities, commercial market representatives monitor prime contractors in order to assess their compliance with laws governing subcontracting opportunities for small businesses.

Step 4: Small Business Administration's 8(a) Program

Are you a socially or economically disadvantaged person who has a business? This group includes, but is not limited to, Black Americans, Hispanic Americans, Native Americans, Asian Pacific Americans, and Subcontinent Asian Americans. Socially and economically disadvantaged individuals represent a significant percentage of U.S. citizens, yet account for a disproportionately small percentage of total U.S. business revenues. The 8(a) program assists firms in participating in the business sector and to become independently competitive in the marketplace. SBA may provide participating firms with procurement, marketing, financial, management, or other technical assistance. A Business Opportunity Specialist will be assigned to each firm that participates, and is responsible for providing the firm with access to assistance that can help the firm fulfill its business goals. SBA undertakes an extensive effort to provide government contracting opportunities to participating businesses. The SBA has the Procurement Automated Source System (PASS) which places your company's capabilities online so that they may be available to government agencies and major corporations when they request potential bidders for contracts and subcontracts. To apply for the 8(a) program, you must attend an interview session with an official in the SBA field office in your area. For more information, contact your local Small Business Administration Office, or call 1-800-827-5722 or {www.sba.gov} for the SBA office nearest you.

Step 5: Bond

A Surety bond is often a prerequisite for government and private sector contracts. This is particularly true when the contract involves construction. In order for the company to qualify for an SBA Guarantee Bond, they must make the bonding company aware of their capabilities based on past contract performance and meeting of financial obligations. SBA can assist firms in obtaining surety bonding for contracts that do not exceed $1,250,000. SBA is authorized, when appropriate circumstances occur, to guarantee as much as 90 percent of losses suffered by a surety resulting from a breach of terms of a bond.

Step 6: Publications

The Government Printing Office has several publications for sale which explain the world of government contracts. For ordering information, contact: Superintendent of Documents, Government Printing Office, Washington, DC 20402; 202-512-1800; {www.gpo.gov}.

* *U.S. Government Purchasing and Sales Directory* ($25): The Directory is an alphabetical listing of the products and services bought by the military departments, and a separate listing of the civilian agencies. The Directory also includes an explanation of the ways in which the SBA can help a business obtain government prime contracts and subcontracts, data on government sales of surplus property, and comprehensive descriptions of the scope of the government market for research and development.

* *Selling to the Military* ($14.00)

* *Women Business Owners; Selling to the Federal Government* ($3.75)

* *Subcontracting Opportunities with DOD Major Prime Contractors* ($23.00)

Step 7: What is GSA?

General Services Administration (GSA) is the Government's business agent. On an annual budget of less than half a billion dollars, it directs and coordinates nearly $8 billion a year worth of purchases, sales, and services. Its source of supply is private enterprise, and its clients include all branches of the Federal government. GSA plans and manages leasing, purchase, or construction of office buildings, laboratories, and warehouses; buys and delivers nearly $4 billion worth of goods and services; negotiates the prices and terms for an additional $2.3 billion worth of direct business between federal groups and private industry; sets and interprets the rules for federal travel and negotiates reduced fares and lodging rates for federal travelers; and manages a 92,000 vehicle fleet with a cumulative yearly mileage of over 1 billion. For a copy of *Doing Business With GSA, GSA's Annual Report*, or other information regarding GSA, contact: Office of Publication, General Services Administration, 18th and F Streets, NW, Washington, DC 20405; 202-501-1235. For information on GSA's architect and engineer services, such as who is eligible for GSA professional services contracts, how to find out about potential GSA projects, what types of contracts are available, and where and how to apply, contact: Office of Design and Construction, GSA, 18th and F Streets, NW, Washington, DC 20405; 202-501-1888. Information on specifications and standards of the Federal government is contained in a booklet, *Guide to Specifications and Standards*, which is available free from Specifications Sections, General Services Administration, 470 E L'Enfant Plaza, SW, Suite 8100, Washington, DC 20407; 202-619-8925.

Step 8: Bid and Contract Protests

The General Accounting Office (GAO) resolves disputes between agencies and bidders of government contracts, including grantee award actions. The free publication, *Bid Protests at GAO; A Descriptive Guide*, contains information on GAO's procedures for determining legal questions arising from the awarding of government contracts. Contact Information Handling and Support Facilities, General Accounting Office, Gaithersburg, MD 20877; 202-512-6000. For Contract Appeals, the GSA Board of Contract Appeals works to resolve disputes arising out of contracts with GSA, the Departments of Treasury, Education, Commerce, and other independent government agencies. The Board also hears and decides bid protests arising out of government-wide automated data processing (ADP) procurements. A contractor may elect to use either the GSA Board or the General Accounting Office for resolution of an ADP bid protest. Contractors may elect to have their appeals processed under the Board's accelerated procedures if the claim is $50,000 or less, or under the small claims procedure if the claim is $10,000 or less. Contractors may also request that a hearing be held at a location convenient to them. With the exception of small claims decisions, contractors can appeal adverse Board decisions to the U.S. Court of Appeals for the Federal Circuit. For more information, contact: Board of Contract Appeals, General Services Administration, 18th and F Streets, NW, Washington, DC 20405; 202-501-0720. There are other Contract Appeals Boards for other departments. One of the last paragraphs in your government contract should specify which Board you are to go to if a problem with your particular contract should arise.

Free Local Help:
The Best Place To Start To Sell To The Government

Within each state there are offices that can help you get started in the federal procurement process. As stated previously, your local Small Business Administration (SBA) office is a good resource. In addition to their other services, the SBA can provide you with a list of Federal Procurement Offices based in your state, so you can visit them in person to gather valuable information. Another place to turn is your local Small Business Development Center (look under Economic Development in your phone book). These offices are funded jointly by federal and state governments, and are usually associated with the state university system in your area. They are aware of the federal procurement process, and can help you draw up a sensible business plan that will be successful.

Some states have established programs to assist businesses in the federal procurement process for all departments in the government. These programs are designed to help businesses learn about the bidding process, the resources available, and provide information on how the procurement system operates. They can match the product or service you are selling with the appropriate agency, and then help you market your product. Several programs have online bid matching services, whereby if a solicitation appears in the *Commerce Business Daily* that matches what your company markets, then the program will automatically contact you to start the bid process. The program office can then request the appropriate documents, and assist you in achieving your goal. These Procurement Assistance Offices (PAOs) are partially funded by the Department of Defense to assist businesses with Defense Procurement. For a current listing of PAOs contact:

Defense Logistics Agency
Office of Small and Disadvantaged Utilization
Bldg. 4, Cameron Station, Room 4B110
Alexandria, VA 22304-6100   703-767-1661
{www.dla.mil}, then go to the small business site

Let Your Congressman Help You

Are you trying to market a new product to a department of the Federal government? Need to know where to try to sell your wares? Is there some problem with your bid? Your Congressman can be of assistance. Because they want business in their state to boom, most Congressmen will make an effort to assist companies in obtaining federal contracts. Frequently they will write a letter to accompany your bid, or if you are trying to market a new product, they will write a letter to the procurement office requesting that they review your product. Your Congressman can also be your personal troubleshooter. If there is some problem with your bid, your Congressman can assist you in determining and resolving the problem, and can provide you with information on the status of your bid. Look in the blue pages of your phone book for your Senators' or Representatives' phone numbers, or call them in Washington at 202-224-3121.

Small Business Set-Asides

The Small Business Administration (SBA) encourages government purchasing agencies to set aside suitable government purchases for exclusive small business competition. A purchase which is restricted to small business bidders is identified by a set aside clause in the invitation for bids or request for proposals. There is no overall listing of procurements which are, or have been, set aside for small business. A small business learns which purchases are reserved for small business by getting listed on bidders' lists. It also can help keep itself informed of set aside opportunities by referring to the *Commerce Business Daily*. Your local SBA office can provide you with more information on set asides, and so can the Procurement Assistance Offices listed at the end of this section. To locate your nearest SBA office, call 1-800-827-5722 or {www.sba.gov}.

Veterans Assistance

Each Small Business Administration District Office has a Veterans Affairs Officer which can assist veteran-owned businesses in obtaining government contracts. Although there is no such thing as veterans set aside contracts, the Veterans Administration does make an effort to fill its contracts using veteran-owned businesses whenever possible. Contact your local SBA office for more information.

Woman-Owned Business Assistance

> **Procurement Assistance Offices**

There are over 3.7 million women-owned businesses in the United States, and the number is growing each year. Current government policy requires federal contracting officers to increase their purchases from women-owned businesses. Although the women-owned firms will receive more opportunities to bid, they still must be the lowest responsive and responsible bidder to win the contract. To assist these businesses, each SBA district office has a Women's Business Representative, who can provide you with information regarding government programs. Most of the offices hold a *Selling to the Federal Government* seminar, which is designed to educate the business owner on the ins and outs of government procurement. There is also a helpful publication, *Women Business Owners: Selling to the Federal Government*, which provides information on procurement opportunities available. Contact your local SBA office or your Procurement Assistance Office (listed below) for more information.

Minority and Labor Surplus Area Assistance

Are you a socially or economically disadvantaged person who has a business? This group includes, but is not limited to, Black Americans, Hispanic Americans, Native Americans, Asian Pacific Americans, and Subcontinent Asian Americans. Socially and economically disadvantaged individuals represent a significant percentage of U.S. citizens yet account for a disproportionately small percentage of total U.S. business revenues. The 8(a) program assists firms to participate in the business sector and to become independently competitive in the marketplace. SBA may provide participating firms with procurement, marketing, financial, management, or other technical assistance. A Business Opportunity Specialist will be assigned to each firm that participates, and is responsible for providing that company with access to assistance that can help it fulfill its business goals.

Some areas of the country have been determined to be labor surplus areas, which means there is a high rate of unemployment. Your local SBA office can tell you if you live in such an area, as some contracts are set asides for labor surplus areas. For more information, contact your local Small Business Administration office (call 1-800-827-5722 for the SBA office nearest you; or online at {www.sba.gov}), or call the Procurement Assistance Office in your state (listed below).

Federal Procurement Assistance Offices

Alabama
Charles A. Hopson
University of Alabama at Birmingham
1717 11th Ave., S, Suite 419
Birmingham, AL 35294-4410
205-934-7260
Fax: 205-934-7645

Alaska
Mike Taylor
University of Alaska Anchorage
Small Business Development Center
430 W. 7th Ave., Suite 100
Anchorage, AK 99501-3550
907-274-7232
Fax: 907-274-9524

Arizona
Linda Alexius Hagerty
The National Center for AIED
National Center Headquarters
953 E. Juanita Ave.
Mesa, AZ 85204
602-545-1298
Fax: 602-545-4208

Paul R. Roddy
Aptan, Inc.
1435 N. Hayden Rd.
Scottsdale, AZ 85257-3773
602-945-5452
Fax: 602-945-4153
E-mail: aptan@pnmenet.com
www.aptan.com

Arkansas
Toni Tosch
Board of Trustees
University of Arkansas
Cooperative Extension Service
103 Page
Malvern, AR 72104
501-337-5355
Fax: 501-337-5045
E-mail: info@apacua.org
www.apacua.org

California
Lane Stafford
Riverside Community College District
3985 University Ave.
Riverside, CA 92501-3256

909-684-8469
Fax: 909-684-8369
E-mail: stafford@rccd.cc.ca.us
www.rccd.resources4u.com/pac/

Jane E. McGinnis
Action Business Center
California Central Valley PTAC
3180 Collins Dr., Suite A
Merced, CA 95348
209-385-7686
Fax: 209-383-4959
E-mail: cpc@cell2000.net
www.cell2000.net/cpc

J. Gunnar Schalin
Southwestern Community College
Contracting Opportunities Center
3443 Camino Del Rio South, Suite 116
San Diego, CA 92108-3913
619-285-7020
Fax: 619-285-7030
E-mail: sdcoc@pacbell.net
http://home.pacbell.net/sdcoc

Colorado
No PTA awarded

Connecticut
Arlene M. Vogel
Southeastern Connecticut Enterprise Region (seCTer)
190 Governor Winthrop Blvd., Suite 300
New London, CT 06320
860-701-6056
1-888-6-SECTER
Fax: 860-437-4662
E-mail: avogel@secter.org
www.secter.org/cptap/main.htm

Delaware
No PTA awarded

District of Columbia
No PTA awarded

Florida
Laura Subel
University of West Florida
Florida PTA Program
19 W. Garden St.
Suite 300
Pensacola, FL 32501

850-595-6066
Fax: 850-595-6070

Georgia
Zack Osborne
Georgia Technical Research Corp.
GA Institute of Technology
400 Tenth St.
CRB Room 246
Atlanta, GA 30332-0420
912-953-1460
Fax: 912-953-3169

Hawaii
No PTA awarded

Idaho
Larry Demirelli
Idaho Department of Commerce
State of Idaho
700 West State St.
Boise, ID 83720-0093
208-334-2470
Fax: 208-334-2631

Illinois
D. Lorenzo Padron
Latin American Chamber of Commerce
The Chicago Pac
2539 N. Kedzie Ave.
Chicago, IL 60647
773-252-5211
Fax: 773-252-7065
www.lacc1.com

Lois Van Meter
State of Illinois
Dept. of Commerce and Community Affairs
620 E. Adams St., Third Floor
Springfield, IL 62701
217-557-1823
Fax: 217-785-6328
E-mail: ivanmete@commerce. state.il.us
www.commerce.state.il.us

Indiana
Kathy DeGuilio-Fox
Partners in Contracting Corporation
PTA Center
6100 Southport Rd.
Portage, IN 46368
219-762-8644
Fax: 219-763-1513

A. David Schaaf
Indiana Small Business Development Corporation
Government Marketing Assistance Group
One N. Capitol Ave., Suite 1275
Indianapolis, IN 46204-2026
317-264-5600
Fax: 317-264-2806
www.isbdcorp.org

Iowa
Bruce Coney
State of Iowa
Iowa Department of Economic Development
200 E. Grand Ave.
Des Moines, IA 50309
515-242-4888
Fax: 515-242-4893
E-mail: bruce.coney@ided. state.ia.us
www.state.ia.us/sbro/ptac.htm

Kansas
Terri Bennett
Missouri Southern State College
3950 E. Newman Rd.
Joplin, MO 64801-1595
417-625-3049
Fax: 417-625-9782
E-mail: bennett-t@mail.mssc.edu

Kentucky
James A. Kurz
Kentucky Cabinet For Economic Development
Department of Community Development
500 Mero St.
22nd Floor Cap Plaza Tower
Frankfort, KY 40601
800-838-3266
Fax: 502-564-5932
E-mail: jkurz@mail.state.ky.us
www.state.ky.us/edc/kpp.htm

Louisiana
Sherrie Mullins
Louisiana Productivity Center
University of Southwest Louisiana
P.O. Box 44172
241 E. Lewis St.
Lafayette, LA 70504-4172
318-482-6767
Fax: 318-262-5472
E-mail: sbm3321@usl.edu

Kelly Ford
Northwest Louisiana Government Procurement
Center

Shreveport COC
400 Edwards St.
P.O. Box 20074
Shreveport, LA 71120-0074
318-677-2529
Fax: 318-677-2534
E-mail: kmford@iamenca.net

Maine
Michael Robinson
Eastern Maine Development Corp.
Market Development Center
One Cumberland Pl., Suite 300
P.O. Box 2579
Bangor, ME 04402-2579
207-942-6389
Fax: 207-942-3548
E-mail: mrobinson@emdc.org
www.mdcme.org

Maryland
Michael J. Wagoner, Inc.
Tri County Council For Western Maryland
111 S. George St.
Cumberland, MD 21502
301-777-2158
Fax: 301-777-2495

Massachusetts
No PTA awarded

Michigan
Sheila A. Auten
Genesee County Metropolitan Planning Commission
PTA Center
1101 Beach St., Room 223
Flint, MI 48502-1470
810-257-3010
Fax: 810-257-3185

Amy Reid
Schoolcraft College
18600 Haggerty Rd.
Livonia, MI 48152-2696
734-462-4400, ext. 5309
Fax: 734-462-4439
E-mail: 2382@softshare.com
www.schoolcraft.cc.mi.us

Michael Black
Kalamazoo Chamber of Commerce
SW & NE Michigan Technical Assistance Center
346 W. Michigan Ave.
Kalamazoo, MI 49007-3737
616-381-2977, ext. 3242

Fax: 616-343-1151
E-mail: swmitac@iserv.net

Paula Boase
Downriver Community Conference
Economic Development
15100 Northline
Southgate, MI 48195
734-281-0700, ext. 129
Fax: 734-281-3418

Janet E. Masi
Warren, Center Line
Sterling Heights Chamber of Commerce
30500 Van Dyke Ave., Suite 118
Warren, MI 48093
810-751-3939
Fax: 810-751-3995
E-mail: jmasi@wcschamber.com
www.michigantac.org

Pamela Vanderlaan
West Central Michigan Employment and Training
Consortium
PTA Center
110 Elm St.
Big Rapids, MI 49307
616-796-4891
Fax: 616-796-8316

James F. Haslinger
Northwestern Michigan Council of Governments
PTA Center
P.O. Box 506
2194 Dendrinos Dr.
Traverse City, MI 49685-0506
616-929-5036
Fax: 616-929-5012

Minnesota
George Johnson
Minnesota Project Innovation, Inc.
Procurement Technical Assistance Center
100 Mill Place
Suite 100, 111 Third Ave. South
Minneapolis, MN 55401-2551
612-347-6745
Fax: 612-349-2603
E-mail: gjohnson@mpi.org
www.mpi.org

Mississippi
Richard L. Speights
Mississippi Contract Procurement Center, Inc.
1636 Poppsferry Rd., Suite 229

Biloxi, MS 39532
228-396-1288
Fax: 228-396-2520
E-mail: mprogoff@aol.com
www.mscpc.com

Missouri
Morris Hudson
The Curators of University of Missouri
Outreach & University Extension
310 Jesse Hall
Columbia, MO 65211
573-882-3597
Fax: 573-884-4297

Guy M. Thomas
Missouri Southern State College
3950 E. Newman Rd.
Joplin, MO 64801-1595
417-625-3001
Fax: 417-625-9782

Montana
James Ouldhouse
Big Sky Economic Development Authority
2722 Third Ave., North
Suite 300 West
Billings, MT 59101-1931
406-256-6871
Fax: 406-256-6877
E-mail: jewell@bigskyeda.org
E-mail: ouldhouse@bigskyeda.org

Nebraska
Jerry Dalton
Board of Regents of the University of Nebraska
Nebraska Business Development Center
1313 Farnam St., Suite 132
Omaha, NE 68182-0210
402-595-3511
Fax: 402-595-3832

Nevada
Roger Tokarz
State of Nevada
Commission on Economic Development
5151 S. Carson St.
Carson City, NV 89701
702-687-1813
Fax: 702-687-4450

New Hampshire
Joseph Flynn
State of New Hampshire

Office of Business and Industrial Development
P.O. Box 1856
172 Pembroke Rd.
Concord, NH 03302-1856
603-271-2591
Fax: 603-271-6784
E-mail: j-flynn@drred.state.nh.us
www.ded.state.nh.us/obid/ptac

New Jersey
John Fedkenheuer
County Economic Development Corp.
PTA Program
1085 Morris Ave., Suite 531
Lib Hall Center
Union, NJ 07083
908-527-1166
Fax: 908-527-1207

Dolcey Chaplin
Foundation At New Jersey Institute of Technology
(NJIT)
PTA Center
University Heights
Newark, NJ 07102
973-596-3105
Fax: 973-596-5806
E-mail: chaplin@admin.njit.edu
www.nyit.edu/DPTAC

New Mexico
Charles Marquez
State of New Mexico General Services Department
Procurement Assistance Program
1100 St. Francis Dr., Room 2006
Santa Fe, NM 87503
505-827-0425
Fax: 505-827-0499
E-mail: cmarquez@state.nm.us

New York
Keith Cook
South Bronx Overall Economic Development
Corporation
370 E. 149th St.
Bronx, NY 10455
718-292-3113
Fax: 718-292-3115

Thomas M. Livak
Cattaraugus County
Department of Economic Development
Plan and Tour
303 Court St.

Little Valley, NY 14755
716-938-9111
Fax: 716-938-9431

Solomon Soskin
Long Island Development Corporation
PTA Program
255 Executive Dr.
Plainview, NY 11803
516-349-7800
Fax: 516-349-7881
E-mail: gov_contracts@lidc.org
www.lidc.org

Gordon Richards
New York City Dept. of Business Services
Procurement Outreach Program
110 William St., 2nd Floor
New York, NY 10038
212-513-6472
Fax: 212-618-8899

Roberta J. Rodriquez
Rockland Economic Development Corporation
Procurement
One Blue Hill Plaza, Suite 1110
Pearl River, NY 10965-1575
914-735-7040
Fax: 914-735-5736

North Carolina
Robert Truex
University of North Carolina at Chapel Hill
Small Business and Tech Development Center
Room 300, Bynum Hall
Chapel Hill, NC 27599-4100
919-715-7272
Fax: 919-715-7777
E-mail: rtruex@sbtdc.org

North Dakota
No PTA awarded

Ohio
Caretha Brown-Griffin
Community Improvement Corporation of Lake
County Ohio
NE Ohio Government Contract Assistance Center
Lake Erie
391-W. Washington College
Painesville, OH 44077
440-357-2294
Fax: 440-357-2296
E-mail: neogcac@lcedc.org

Connie S. Freeman
Lawrence Economic Development Corporation
Procure Outreach Center
216 Collins Ave.
P.O. Box 488
South Point, OH 45680-0488
740-377-4550
Fax: 740-377-2091
E-mail: procure@zoomnet.net
www.zoomnet.net/~procure/

Oklahoma
C.L. Vache
Oklahoma Department of Vocational and Technical
Education
Oklahoma Bid Assistance Network
1500 W. Seventh Ave.
Stillwater, OK 74074-4364
405-743-5571
Fax: 405-743-6821

Roy Robert Gann, Jr.
Tribal Government Institute
421 E. Comanche, Suite B
Norman, OK 73071
405-329-5542
Fax: 405-329-5543

Oregon
Jan Hurt
The Organization for Economic Initiatives
Government Contract Acquisition Program
99 W. 10th Ave., Suite 330
Eugene, OR 97401
541-344-3537
Fax: 541-687-4899

Pennsylvania
Joseph E. Hopkins
Mon-Valley Renaissance
CA University of Pennsylvania
250 University Ave.
California, PA 15419
724-938-5881
Fax: 724-938-4575
E-mail: wojak@cup.edu

Richard A. Mihalic
NW Pennsylvania Regional Planning and
Development Commission
614 Eleventh St.
Franklin, PA 16323
814-677-4800

Fax: 814-677-7663
E-mail: nwpaptac@nwpian.org

Chuck Burtyk
PIC of Westmoreland/Fayette, Inc.
Procurement Assistance Center
531 S. Main St.
Greensburg, PA 15601
724-836-2600
Fax: 724-836-8058
E-mail: cburtyk@sgi.net

Robert J. Murphy
Johnstown Area Regional Industries
Defense PAC
111 Market St.
Johnstown, PA 15901
814-539-4951
Fax: 814-535-8677

A. Lawrence Barletta
Seda Council of Governments
RR 1, Box 372
Lewisburg, PA 17837
570-524-4491
Fax: 570-524-9190
E-mail: sedapta@seda.cog.org
www.seda.cog.org

Thomas E. Wren
University of Pennsylvania-Wharton
SE-PA PTAP
3733 Spruce St.
Vance Hall, 4th Floor
Philadelphia, PA 19104-6374
215-898-1282
Fax: 215-573-2135

David Kern
Economic Development Council of Northeast
Pennsylvania
Local Development District
1151 Oak St.
Pittston, PA 18640
570-655-5581
Fax: 570-654-5137

Kerry A. Meehan
Northern Tier Regional Planning and Development
Commission
Economic/Community Development
507 Main St.
Towanda, PA 18848-1697
570-265-9103
Fax: 570-265-7585

E-mail: meehan@northerntier.org
www.northerntier.org

Millicent Brown
West Chester University
Procurement Assistance Center
211 Carter Dr., Suite E
West Chester, PA 19383
610-436-3337
Fax: 610-436-2593
pac.btcwcu.org

Puerto Rico
Wilson Baez
Commonwealth of Puerto Rico
Economic Development Administration
355 Roosevelt Ave.
Hato Rey, PR 00918
787-753-6861
Fax: 787-751-6239

Rhode Island
Michael H. Cunningham
Rhode Island Development Corporation
Business Expansion Division
One W. Exchange St.
Providence, RI 02903
401-277-2601
Fax: 401-277-2102
E-mail: mcunning@riedc.com

South Carolina
John M. Lenti
University of South Carolina
Frank L. Roddey SBDC of South Carolina
College of Business Administration
Columbia, SC 29208
803-777-4907
Fax: 803-777-4403

South Dakota
No PTA awarded

Tennessee
Becky Peterson
Center for Industrial Services
University of Tennessee
226 Capitol Blvd., Suite 606
Nashville, TN 37219-1804
615-532-4906
Fax: 615-532-4937

Texas
Doug Nelson
Panhandle Regional Planning Commission

Economic Development Unit
P.O. Box 9257
Amarillo, TX 79105-9257
806-372-3381
Fax: 806-373-3268

Rogerio Flores
University of Texas at Arlington
Automation and Robotics Research Institute
Office of President
Box 19125
Arlington, TX 76019
817-272-5978
Fax: 817-272-5952

Rosalie Manzano
University of Texas at Brownsville ITSC
Center for Business and Economic Development
1600 E. Elizabeth St.
Brownsville, TX 78520
956-548-8713
Fax: 956-548-8717

Carey Joan White
University of Houston, TIPS
1100 Louisiana, Suite 500
Houston, TX 77204
713-752-8466
Fax: 713-756-1515

Otilo Castellano
Texas Technical University
College of Business Administration
203 Holder
Lubbock, TX 79409-1035
806-745-1637
Fax: 806-745-6207

Thomas E. Breuer, Jr.
Angelina College
Procurement Assistance Center
P.O. Box 1768
Lufkin, TX 75902-1768
409-639-3678
Fax: 409-639-3863
E-mail: acpac@lcc.net
www.oecrc.org/acpac/

Terri L. Williams
San Antonio Procurement Outreach Program
Economic Development Department
P.O. Box 839966
San Antonio, TX 78283
210-207-3910
Fax: 210-207-3909

Frank Delgado
El Paso Community College
Resource Development
P.O. Box 20500
El Paso, TX 79998
915-831-4405
Fax: 915-831-4420

Utah
Johnny C. Bryan
Utah Department of Community and Economic Development
Utah Procurement Technical Assistance Center (UPTAC)
324 South State St., Suite 504
Salt Lake City, UT 84111
801-538-8791
Fax: 801-538-8825

Vermont
Greg Lawson
State of Vermont
Department of Economic Development
109 State St.
Montpelier, VT 05609
802-828-5237
Fax: 802-828-3258

Virginia
James Regan
George Mason University
Entrepreneurship Center
4400 University Dr.
Fairfax, VA 22030
703-277-7750
Fax: 703-352-8195
E-mail: ptap@gmu.edu
www.gmu.edu/gmu/PTAP

Dennis K. Morris
Crater Planning District Commission
The Procurement Assistance Center
1964 Wakefield St.
P.O. Box 1808
Petersburg, VA 23805
804-861-1667
Fax: 804-732-8972
E-mail: ptac111@aol.com

Glenda D. Calver
Southwestern Virginia Community College
Economic Development Division
P.O. Box SVCC
Richlands, VA 24641

540-964-7334
Fax: 540-964-7575
www.sw.cc.va.us/pac.html

Washington
Brent C. Helm
Economic Development Council of
Snohomish County
728 134th St., SW
Bldg. A, Suite 219
Everett, WA 98204
425-743-4567
Fax: 425-745-5563
E-mail: ptac@snoedc.org
www.snoedc.org/patc/html

West Virginia
R. Conley Salyer
Regional Contracting Assistance Center, Inc.
1116 Smith St., Suite 202
Charleston, WV 25301
304-344-2546
Fax: 304-344-2574
www.rcacwv.com

Belinda Sheridan
Mid-Ohio Valley Regional Council

PTA Center
P.O. Box 5528
Parkersburg, WV 26105
304-428-6889
Fax: 304-428-6891
E-mail: ptac@access.mountain.net

Wisconsin
Denise Kornetzke
Madison Area Technical College
Small Business PAC
211 North Carroll St.
Madison, WI 53703
608-258-2350
Fax: 608-258-2329
http://bpac.madison.tec.wi.us

Joseph W. Hurst
Wisconsin Procurement Institute, Inc.
756 N. Milwaukee St.
Milwaukee, WI 53202
414-443-9744
Fax: 414-443-1122
E-mail: wispro@execpc.com

Wyoming
No PTA awarded in this state

How To Become a Consultant With The Government

If you are between jobs or just thinking about quitting the one you have and want something to tide you over until you get your next one, you should seriously think about freelancing for the Federal government.

The Interior Department hires ecologists and geologists. The Justice Department hires business consultants. The Department of Energy hires conservation consultants. Here's a sample listing of the kinds of projects freelance consultants do for the Federal government:

Types of Government Freelancing

Landscaping
Carpentry Work
Painting and Paper Hanging
Security Guards
Computer Services
Data Processing
Detective Services
Electrical Work
Plumbing
Accounting Services
Chaplain Services (Priest)
Management Consulting
Engineering Services
Information Retrieval
   Services
Real Estate Agents
Secretarial Services
Court Reporting
Legal Services
Business Consulting
Photography
Insurance Agents
Computer Programming
Research
Drafting
Interior Decorating
Library Services
Word Processing

Translation Services
Courier and Messenger Services
Cleaning Services
Food Service
Auditing Services
Advertising Services
Nursing Services
Housekeeping Services
Administrative Support
   Services
Education and Training
Medical Services
Social Services
Special Study and Analysis
Wildlife Management
Salvage Services
Travel Agent
Personnel Testing Services
Photography
Animal Care
Mathematics and Computer
   Science
Environmental Research
Historians
Recreation Research
Economic Studies
More, More, More...

Practically every major government agency hires freelance consultants to work on both small and large projects which might be exactly what you need until you land a full time job down the road.

The feds hire all kinds of professionals to perform consulting work, from accountants and business specialists, to computer experts, social scientists, and security and surveillance consultants. The offices listed below, called Offices of Small and Disadvantaged Business Utilization, specialize in helping individuals and small businesses get involved in contracting with their agency.

Subcontracting

Not only do the feds themselves hire consultants, so do the large prime contractors who sell their products and services to the government. By law, any large company that receives contracts worth $500,000 or more from the Federal government must make an effort to subcontract some of that work to small businesses. So, for example, if a company gets a large computer consulting contract with the Defense Department, they have to make an effort to hire some freelance computer consultants to work on that contract. And that could be you.

How to Find Subcontracting Work

All of the federal procurement offices or Offices of Small and Disadvantaged Business Utilization (SADBU) (see list below) can provide you with information regarding subcontracting. Many of the departments' prime contracts require that the prime contractor maximize small business subcontracting opportunities. The SADBU offices can show you the way to get this work.

Each of the large federal agencies listed below, except the Department of Education, maintain directories of large contractors who are looking to do work with the feds in your area of expertise. And since the companies listed in these directories, for the most part, have just landed big government contracts, they might very well be looking to take on more full-time employees to help fulfill those contracts. A great lead on new job openings that probably won't be listed in the Sunday newspaper!

Offices of Small and Disadvantaged Business Utilization

Note: Offices designated as Offices of Small and Disadvantaged Business Utilization (OSDBUs) provide procurement assistance to small, minority, 8(a) and women-owned businesses. Their primary function is to ensure that small and disadvantaged businesses receive their fair share of U.S. Government contracts. "OSDBUs" are the contacts for their respective agencies and are excellent sources of information.

Agency for International Development
Ronald Reagan Building
1300 Pennsylvania Ave., NW
Washington, DC 20523-1414
202-712-1500
Fax: 202-216-3056
www.info.usaid.gov

Corporation for National and Community Service
1100 Vermont Ave., NW
Room 2101
Washington, DC 20525
202-606-5020
Fax: 202-606-5126

Department of Agriculture
14th and Independence Ave., SW
Room 1323, South Bldg.
Washington, DC 20250-9400

202-720-7117
Fax: 202-720-3001
www.usda.gov/da/smallbus.html

Department of Commerce
14th and Constitution Ave, NW
Room 6411
Washington, DC 20230
202-482-1472
Fax: 202-482-0501
www.osec.doc.gov/osdbu

Department of Education
600 Independence Ave., SW
Room 3120-ROB-3
Washington, DC 20202-0521
202-708-9820
Fax: 202-401-6477
www.ed.gov/offices/ODS

Department of Energy
1000 Independence Ave., SW
Room 5B110
Washington, DC 20585
202-586-8383
Fax: 202-586-3075
www.hr.doe.gov/ed/osdbu.htm

Department of Health and Human Services
200 Independence Ave., SW
Room 517D
Washington, DC 20201
202-690-7300
Fax: 202-690-8772

Department of Housing and Urban Development
451 7th St., SW, Room 3130
Washington, DC 20410
202-708-1428
Fax: 202-708-7642
www.hud.gov/osdbu/osdbu.html

Department of the Interior
18th & C St., NW, Room 2727
Washington, DC 20240
202-208-3493
Fax: 202-208-5048
www.doi.gov/osdbu/osdbu.html

Department of Justice
1331 Pennsylvania Ave., NW
Room 1010
National Place Bldg.
Washington, DC 20530
202-616-0521
Fax: 202-616-1717
www.usdoj.gov/jmd/pss/home.osd.htm

Department of Labor
200 Constitution Ave., NW
Room C-2318
Washington, DC 20210
202-219-9148
Fax: 202-219-0167
www.dol.gov/dol/ospl

Department of State
Room 633 (SA 6)
Washington, DC 20522-0602
703-875-6824
Fax: 703-875-6825
http://statebuy.inter.net/osdbul.htm

Department of Transportation
400 7th St., SW, Room 9414
Washington, DC 20590
202-366-1930
Fax: 202-366-7228
http://osdbuweb.dot.gov

Department of the Treasury
1500 Pennsylvania Ave., NW
Room 6100 - Annex
Washington, DC 20220
202-622-0530
Fax: 202-622-2273
www.ustreas.gov/sba

Department of Veterans Affairs
810 Vermont Ave., NW
Washington, DC 20420
202-565-8124
Fax: 202-565-8156
www.va.gov/osdbu

Environmental Protection Agency
401 M St., SW
Mail Code A-123O-C
Washington, DC 20460
202-260-4100
Fax: 202-401-1080

Export-Import Bank of the U.S.
811 Vermont Ave., NW, Room 1017
Washington, DC 20571
202-565-3338
Fax: 202-565-3528

Federal Emergency Management Agency
500 C St., SW, Room 726
Washington, DC 20472
202-646-3743
Fax: 202-646-3846
www.fema.gov/ofm

Federal Trade Commission
6th and Pennsylvania Ave., NW
Room H-700
Washington, DC 20580
202-326-2258
Fax: 202-326-3529
www.ftc.gov

General Services Administration
18th and F Sts., NW, Room 6029
Washington, DC 20405
202-501-1021

Fax: 202-208-5938
www.gsa.gov/oed

National Aeronautics and Space Administration
Headquarters, Code K
Room 9K70, 300 E St., SW
Washington, DC 20546
202-358-2088
Fax: 202-358-3261
www.hq.nasa.gov/office/codek

National Science Foundation
4201 Wilson Blvd.
Arlington, VA 22230
703-306-1390
Fax: 703-306-0337
www.eng.nsf.gov/sbir/index.html

Nuclear Regulatory Commission
Mailstop T2 F-18
Washington, DC 20555
301-415-7380
301-415-5953

Executive Office of the President
725 17th St., NW, Room 5001
Washington, DC 20503
202-395-7669
Fax: 202-395-1155

Office of Personnel Management
1900 E St., NW, Room 5542
Washington, DC 20415
202-606-2180
Fax: 202-606-1464

Small Business Administration
Director
Office of Procurement and Grants Management
409 Third St., SW, 8th Floor
Washington, DC 20416
202-205-7701
Fax: 202-693-7004

Smithsonian Institution
Small and Disadvantaged Business Utilization
Program
995 L'Enfant Plaza, SW
Washington, DC 20506
202-287-3343
Fax: 202-287-3492

Tennessee Valley Authority
1101 Market St., EB2B
Chattanooga, TN 37402-2801
423-751-7203
Fax: 423-751-7613
www.usps.gov

U.S. Postal Service
475 L'Enfant Plaza, SW
Room 3821
Washington, DC 20260-5616
202-268-6578
Fax: 202-268-6573
www.usps.gov

United States Information Agency
400 6th St., SW
Room 1725
Donahue Building
Washington, DC 20547
202-205-9662
Fax: 202-401-2410

Office of Federal Procurement Policy
725 17th St., NW
Room 9013
Washington, DC 20503
202-395-3302
Fax: 202-395-5705
www.arnet.gov

Civic Transportation Board
12th & Constitution Ave., NW
Room 3148
Washington, DC 20423
202-565-1674
202-565-1596

Railroad Retirement Board
844 N. Rush St.
Chicago, IL 60611
312-751-4565
Fax: 312-751-4923
www.rrb.gov

Minority Business Development Agency
Department of Commerce
14th & Constitution Ave., NW
Room 5093
Washington, DC 20230
202-482-1712
Fax: 202-482-5117

State Procurement Assistance

Have you ever wondered where the government buys all of the products that it works with each day? You might be surprised to learn that they buy from small businesses just like yours
that produce products such as:

♦ work clothing
♦ office supplies
♦ cleaning equipment
♦ miscellaneous vehicles
♦ medical supplies and equipment

Imagine what your bottom line could look like each year if you won just ONE lucrative government contract that would provide your business with a secure income! It might even buy you the freedom to pursue other clients that you wouldn't have the time or money to go after otherwise. If your business performs well and completes a government contract satisfactorily, chances are you'll have a shot at more and maybe even bigger contracts.

The offices listed below are starting places for finding out who in the state government will purchase your products or services.

State Procurement Offices

Alabama
Finance Department
Purchasing Division
100 N. Union, Suite 192
Montgomery, AL 36104
334-242-7250
Fax: 334-242-4419
www.purchasing.state.al.us

Alaska
State of Alaska
Department of Administration
Division of General Services
P.O. Box 110210
Juneau, AK 99811-0210
907-465-2250
Fax: 907-465-2189
www.state.ak.us/local/akpages/
ADMIN/dgs/home.htm

Arizona
State Procurement Office
15 S. 15th Ave.
Suite 103
Phoenix, AZ 85007
602-542-5511
Fax: 602-542-5508
http://sporas.ad.state.az.us

Arkansas
Office of State Purchasing
P.O. Box 2940
Little Rock, AR 72203
501-324-9316
Fax: 501-324-9311

California
Office of Procurement
Department of General Services
1823 14th St.
Sacramento, CA 95814
916-445-6942
Fax: 916-323-4609
www.td.dgs.ca.gov/

Colorado
Division of Purchasing
225 E. 16th Ave., Suite 900
Denver, CO 80203
303 866-6100
Fax: 303-894-7444
www.gssa.state.co.us

Connecticut
State of Connecticut
Department of Administrative Services
Bureau of Purchases
165 Capitol Ave.

Hartford, CT 06106
860-713-5095
Fax: 860-713-7484
www.das.state.ct.us/busopp.htm

Delaware
Purchasing Division
Purchasing Bldg.
P.O. Box 299
Delaware City, DE 19706
302-834-4550
Fax: 302-836-7642
www.state.de.us/purchase

District of Columbia
Office of Contracts and Procurement
441 4th St. NW, Suite 800
Washington, DC 20001
202-727-0252
Fax: 202-724-5673
www.ci.washington.dc.us

Florida
General Service Department
Division of Purchasing
4050 Esplanade Way
Tallahassee, FL 32399-0950
850-488-5498
http://purchasing.state.us/

Georgia
Administrative Services Department
200 Piedmont Ave., Room 1308 SE
Atlanta, GA 30334
404-656-3240
Fax: 404-651-6963
www.doas.state.ga.us

Hawaii
Purchasing Branch
Purchasing and Supply Division
Dept. of Accounting and General Services
Room 416, 1151 Punch Bowl St.
Honolulu, HI 96813
808-586-0575
Fax: 808-586-0570
www.state.hi.us/icsd/dags/spo.html

Idaho
Division of Purchasing
Administration Department
5569 Kendall St.
State House Mall
Boise, ID 83720

208-327-7465
Fax: 208-327-7320
www2.state.id.us/adm/purchasing

Illinois
Department of Central Management Services
Procurement Services
801 Stratton Bldg.
Springfield, IL 62706
217-782-2301
Fax: 217-782-5187
www.state.il.us/cms

Indiana
Department of Administration
Procurement Division
402 W. Washington St., Room W-468
Indianapolis, IN 46204
317-232-3032
Fax: 317-232-7213
www.state.in.us/idoa/proc

Iowa
State of Iowa
Department of General Services
Purchasing Division
Hoover State Office Building
Des Moines, IA 50319
515-281-3089
Fax: 515-242-5974
www.state.ia.us/government/dgs/
csap/purhome/business.htm

Kansas
Division of Purchasing
Room 102 North
Landon State Office Bldg.
900 SW Jackson St.
Topeka, KS 66612
785-296-2376
Fax: 785-296-7240
http://da.state.ks.us/purch

Kentucky
Purchases, Department of Finance
Room 367, Capital Annex
Frankfort, KY 40601
502-564-4510
Fax: 502-564-7209
http://purch.state.ky.us

Louisiana
State Purchasing Office
Division of Administration

P.O. Box 94095
Baton Rouge, LA 70804-9095
225-342-8010
Fax: 225-342-8688
www.doa.state.la.us/osp/osp.htm

Maine
Bureau of Purchases
State House Station #9
Augusta, ME 04333
207-287-3521
Fax: 207-287-6578
http://janus.state.me.us/purchase

Maryland
Purchasing Bureau
301 W. Preston St.
Mezzanine, Room M8
Baltimore, MD 21201
410-767-4600
Fax: 410-333-5482
www.dgs.state.md.us

Massachusetts
Purchasing Agent Division
One Ashburton Place
Room 1017
Boston, MA 02108
617-727-7500
Fax: 617-727-4527
www.comm-pass.com

Michigan
Office of Purchasing
Mason Bldg.
P.O. Box 30026
Lansing, MI 48909
or 530 W. Ellegan, 48933
517-373-0330
Fax: 517-335-0046
www.state.mi.us/dmd/oop

Minnesota
State of Minnesota
Department of Administration
Suite 112, Administration Bldg.
50 Sherburne Ave.
St. Paul, MN 55155
651-296-6152
Fax: 651-297-3996
www.mmd.admin.state.mn.us

Mississippi
Office of Purchasing and Travel
1504 Sillers Bldg.

550 High St., Suite 1504
Jackson, MS 39201
601-359-3409
Fax: 601-359-3910
www.dfa.state.ms.us

Missouri
State of Missouri
Division of Purchasing
P.O. Box 809
Jefferson City, MO 65102
573-751-2387
Fax: 573-751-2387
www.oa.state.mo.us/purch/bids.htm

Montana
Department of Administration
Procurement Division
165 Mitchell Bldg.
Helena, MT 59620-0135
406-444-2575
Fax: 406-444-2529
www.state.mt.us/doa/ppd

Nebraska
State Purchasing Division
301 Centennial Mall S.
P.O. Box 94847
Lincoln, NE 68509
402-471-2401
Fax: 402-471-2089
www.nol.org/home/DASMAT

Nevada
Nevada State Purchasing Division
209 E. Musser St., Room 304
Blasdel Bldg.
Carson City, NV 89710
702-684-0170
Fax: 702-684-0188
www.state.nv.us/purchasing/

New Hampshire
State Purchasing Department
25 Capitol St.
State House Annex, Room 102
Concord, NH 03301
603-271-2201
Fax: 603-271-2700
www.state.nh.us/das/purchasing/index.html

New Jersey
Division of Purchase and Property
P.O. Box 039

Trenton, NJ 08625
609-292-4886
Fax: 609-984-2575
www.state.nj.us/treasury/purchase

New Mexico
State Purchasing Division
1100 St. Frances Dr.
Room 2016
Joseph Montoya Bldg.
Santa Fe, NM 87503
505-827-0472
Fax: 505-827-2484
www.state.nm.us/spd

New York
Division of Purchasing
Corning Tower
Empire State Plaza, 38th Floor
Albany, NY 12242
518-474-3695
Fax: 518-486-6099
www.ogs.state.ny.us

North Carolina
Department of Administration
Division of Purchase and Contract
116 W. Jones St.
Raleigh, NC 27603-8002
919-733-3581
Fax: 919-733-4782
www.state.nc.us/pandc/

North Dakota
Central Services Division of State Purchasing
Purchasing
600 E Blvd., I Wing
Bismarck, ND 58505-0420
701-328-2683
Fax: 701-328-1615
www.state.nd.us/centserv

Ohio
State Purchasing
4200 Surface Rd.
Columbus, OH 43228-1395
614-466-4635
Fax: 614-466-2059
www.gsa.ohio.gov/gsa/ods/pur/pur.html

Oklahoma
Office of Public Affairs
Central Purchasing Division
Suite 116, Rogers Bldg.

2401 N. Lincoln
Oklahoma City, OK 73105
405-521-2110
Fax: 405-521-4475
www.dcs.state.ok.us

Oregon
General Services
Purchasing and Print Services Division
1225 Ferry St.
Salem, OR 97310
503-378-4643
Fax: 503-373-1626
tpps.das.state.or.us/purchasing

Pennsylvania
Procurement Department Secretary
N. Office Bldg., Room 414
Commonwealth and North St.
Harrisburg, PA 17125
717-787-5733
Fax: 717-783-6241
www.dgs.state.pa.us

Rhode Island
Department of Administration
Purchases Office
One Capital Hill
Providence, RI 02908-5855
401-222-2317
Fax: 401-222-6387
www.purchasing.state.ri.us

South Carolina
Materials Management Office
General Service Budget and Control Board
1201 Main St., Suite 600
Columbia, SC 29201
803-737-0600
Fax: 803-737-0639
www.state.sc.us/mmo/mmo/

South Dakota
Division of Purchasing
523 E. Capitol Ave.
Pierre, SD 57501
605-773-3405
Fax: 605-773-4840
www.state.sd.us/boa

Tennessee
Department of General Services
Division of Purchasing
Third Floor, Tennessee Towers

312 8th Ave. North
Nashville, TN 37243-0557
615-741-1035
Fax: 615-741-0684
www.state.tn.us/generalser/purchasing

Texas
State Purchasing and General Services Commission
P.O. Box 13047
Austin, TX 78711
512-463-3445
Fax: 512-463-7073
www.gsc.state.tx.us

Utah
Purchasing Division
Department of Administrative Services
State Office Bldg., Room 3150
Salt Lake City, UT 84114
801-538-3026
Fax: 801-538-3882
www.purchasing.state.ut.us

Vermont
Purchasing and Contract Administration Division
128 State St., Drawer 33
Montpelier, VT 05633-7501
802-828-2211
Fax: 802-828-2222
www.bgf.state.vt.us/pca

Virginia
Department of General Services
Purchasing Division
P.O. Box 1199
Richmond, VA 23209
804-786-3842
Fax: 804-371-8936
www.dgs.state.va.us/dps

Washington
Office of State Procurement
Suite 201, General Admin Bldg.
210 11th Ave. SW
Olympia, WA 98504-1017
360-902-7400
Fax: 360-586-2426
www.ga.wa.gov/proc.htm

West Virginia
Department of Administration
Purchasing Section
Building 15
2019 Washington St. East
Charleston, WV 25305-0110
304-558-2306
Fax: 304-558-6026
www.state.wv.us/admin/purchase

Wisconsin
Division of State Agency Services
Bureau of Procurement
101 E. Wilson, 6th Floor
P.O. Box 7867
Madison, WI 53707-7867
608-266-2605
Fax: 608-267-0600
http://vendornet.state.wi.us

Wyoming
Department of Administration
Procurement Services
2001 Capitol Ave.
Cheyenne, WY 82002
307-777-7253
Fax: 307-777-5852
www.state.wy.us

GRANTS FOR LIVING EXPENSES

Sometimes you just need a little help getting through to the end of the month. Whether you need help with your heating or phone bill, or help with transportation and medical issues, resources are available. The trick is knowing who to call. What we have done is pulled together information on programs and services across the country. Some are available to anyone, whereas others are only for a specific target group or residents of a particular town. This may give you ideas of who in your area may offer grants or other forms of assistance to those in need. Many of these groups and organizations are small and have limited funds, so they asked not to be included in a major publication for fear of being inundated with requests for funds. But they do exist and they do provide help, so call around and ASK. You will be surprised by what you hear. There are also organizations to help with issues such as:

* Free child care
* Money to fix your car
* Money for adoptions
* Private school tuition for your kids
* Child support help
* Money for heating, phone or food bills
* Free hospitalization and medications
* Discounts for seniors
* Dental and vision care assistance
* Free mammograms and immunizations

We have touched the tip of the iceberg. Read on and see what else is out there waiting for you to call.

STATES OFFER MONEY FOR: CARS, BUS FARE, AUTO REPAIRS, INSURANCE AND DRIVERS ED

The following are examples of what just some of the states are offering in transportation assistance for those who have serious transportation needs. Transportation is a growing concern in the workforce and programs are being added and changed every day. Be sure to contact your state transportation agency for the latest benefits your state has to offer.

* Alaska: $85 a month towards transportation
* Arizona: $5 a day towards transportation
* Arkansas: $200 for car repairs
* Colorado: Free cars and 3 months of insurance
* Delaware: 30 free transit ride tickets with a new job
* Florida: Money for gas, repairs and insurance
* Illinois: $60 a month for gas or $88 a month to take the bus
* Kansas: $30 a month for gas and money for car repairs
* Kentucky: $60 a month for gas and $300 to get a drivers license, pay for auto registration, taxes or repairs, and $900 to move to another city to get a job

- Louisiana: $100 a year for auto repairs
- Massachusetts: $150 a month towards transportation
- Michigan: Money for auto repairs and insurance
- Mississippi Provides Door to Door Service
- Nebraska: Money for insurance, auto repairs; $2,000 to buy you a car; 3 months of auto insurance, $500 for taxes, licensing, etc.
- New Hampshire: $130 a month for transportation; $240 a year for auto repairs; and money to take drivers education
- New Jersey: $500 for car repairs
- New York: $500 for car repairs
- Oklahoma: Money for auto repairs and insurance
- Pennsylvania: $200 for auto repairs
- South Dakota: Money for auto repairs
- Vermont: $200 for auto repairs
- Washington: $546 a month for transportation
- Wisconsin: $1600 interest free to buy a car or repay with community service

FREE TAXI SERVICE
To Work, School, or Day Care

One county in Oregon has a program that picks up you and your child, taking your child to day care and you to work. It doesn't charge you anything, and doesn't even ask your income. North Carolina has programs where counties are given vans to transport people back and forth to work, with lower fees charged to those in welfare-to-work programs. Mississippi has a program that will pick you up at your house, almost anywhere in the state and take you back and forth to work if you are working to get off welfare.

Some communities, like Fairfax County in Virginia, maintain a database that helps locate the necessary transportation for work and day care needs. And Kentucky operates an 800 hotline that tries to solve any work-related transportation need, and soon they will have a separate hotline for each county. Do these people want you to get to work, or what?

To start looking for programs like this in your area, contact your local congressman's office or your local social service agency. They won't know about all the programs but can probably give you some starting places. You should also find out about local vanpool and rideshare programs. Your local chamber of commerce or library should have this kind of information for you.

Get $65 a Month Free From Your Boss
For Commuting To Work

Your employer can give you $65 a month to help pay for bus, train, ferry, or vanpool commuting expense and neither you nor the employer has to pay taxes on this money. Contact your local transit authority for more details on the program called *Tax Free Qualified Transportation Fringe Benefits*, or contact: Commuter Check Services Corporation, 401 S. Van Brunt Street, Suite 403, Englewood, NJ 07631; 201-833-9700; Fax: 201-833-8704; {www.commutercheck.com}.

Money For Auto Repairs, Car Insurance, Driver's Ed, Or Just A Tank Of Gas

Whatever it takes to keep you on the road! There are federal programs as well as state programs to help people with limited incomes keep their vehicles on the road so that they can get back and forth to work, focusing on those trying to get off welfare.

Some states will even give you money for driver's education or to pay for a driver's license. The issue, like the programs for free cars, is to **help people make it to work**. Illinois and Kentucky offer $60 a month for gas money. New York and New Jersey give people up to $500 for car repairs. Pennsylvania and Vermont only give $200 for car repairs. But Washington State provides people up to $546 a month for their transportation.

Limousines anyone? These programs are organized like a patchwork quilt in most areas involving federal, state, county and non-profit organizations.

To start looking for programs like this in your area, contact your local congressman's office or your local Social Services. They won't know about all the programs but can probably give you some starting places.

Here is just a *SAMPLING* of the Wheels to Work programs that we found:

Wheels to Work
Forsyth County Department of
Social Services
P.O. Box 999
Winston-Salem, NC 27102
910-727-2175

Cooperative Ministry
Art Collier
P.O. Box 1705

Columbia, SC 29202
803-799-3853

New Leaf Services
3696 Greentree Farms Dr.
Decatur, GA 30034
404-289-9293

Cars for Work
Good Will and Crisis Assistance
Ministry

2122 Freedom Dr.
Charlotte, NC 28266
704-332-0291

Wheels to Work
Resource Conservation &
Development Council
240 Oak St., Suite 101
Lawrenceville, GA 30245
770-339-6071

One Month of Free Bus Passes

Detroit's **Suburban Mobility Authority for Regional Transportation (SMART)** has a program called "Get a Job/Get a Ride" that gives a month's worth of free rides to anyone in the Detroit area who gets a job.

The only requirement is that you started a new job within the last 30 days. You can be making $100,000 a year and they'll still give you the free passes. New Jersey will give a free one-month pass to those on low income that get a job or are going to training.

Check with your local Chamber of Commerce, Transit Authority, or your state Department of Transportation.

Free Legal Help To Fight
A Car Dealer Or Repair Shop

When you can't get satisfaction from the manager or owner, then it is time to bring in the big guns:

✦ Your state attorney general's office is set up to handle automobile complaints. Sometimes all you have to do is send a letter to the attorney general with a copy to the business owner.

✦ Automotive Consumer Action Program (AUTOCAP) is a complaint handling system sponsored by the automobile industry for new or used car purchases from NEW car dealers only. To find a source in your area, contact: National Automobile Dealers Association, 8400 Westpark Drive, McLean, VA 22102; 703-821-7000; {www.nada.org/}

✦ Better Business Bureau (BBB) Auto Line is a FREE, out-of-court arbitration program, paid for by the business community to handle automobile complaints between consumers and most auto manufacturers. Contact your local Better Business Bureau or BBB Auto Line, Dispute Resolution Division, Council of Better Business Bureaus, Inc., 4200 Wilson Blvd, Suite 800, Arlington, VA 22202; 703-276-0100; {www.bbb.org/complaints/BBBautoLine.asp}.

Free and Low Cost Seminars on How To Buy a Car

You can't just go on color alone! You need to become savvy as to what options to look for and how to negotiate with the dealer. Do you really need rust proofing? What is the difference between the invoice and the sticker price? How can I find out what the dealer paid for the car?

Don't be intimidated by salesmanship. The dealer wants your money, so they don't want you to leave without signing on the bottom line. Many different organizations and groups offer classes on how to buy a car. Contact your county cooperative extension service, your local adult education department, or women's organizations in your area to see what they may have to offer.

GET YOUR CAR REPAIRED
FOR FREE

June Rapp of Massachusetts took her family van into a dealer to have it fixed and they wanted to charge her over $1000 to make the repairs. She called the U.S. Department of Transportation and found out that her problem was part of a manufacturer recall. Recalls have to be fixed for free and the repair shop didn't know that. To find out about recalls for any car, contact:

❏ **Auto Safety Hotline**, US Dept. of Transportation, NEF-11.2HL, 400 Seventh St., SW, Washington, DC 20590; 888-327-4236; {www.nhtsa.dot.gov/cars/problems/recall/recmmy1.cfm}

❏ The **Consumer Report** people have a searchable database for car recall information. Contact Consumers Union, 101 Truman Ave., Yonkers, NY 10703; 914-378-2000; {consumerreports.org}.

FREE AND LOW COST SEMINARS ON HOW TO FIX UP A CAR

What do you do if you are driving on a freeway and you get a flat tire? How often should you change the oil and can you do it yourself? How do you jump a car? It is better to plan ahead for emergencies, but where do you go for help?

Many different organizations and groups offer classes on how to fix up a car. Begin by contacting your local car insurance company, automobile road service company, or department of motor vehicles. I have even seen classes being offered by automobile dealerships. Once you are there, maybe they can sell you a new car as well.

Other places to check include your county Cooperative Extension Service, your local adult education department, or women's organizations in your area. You can save yourself worry, stress, and money if you are prepared and knowledgeable regarding your car.

GRANDMA NEEDS A RIDE TO THE DOCTOR

Many seniors have to give up driving their cars, perhaps because of the cost or illness. But then how do they get to the doctor or the bank or the store? Many rely upon their friends and children to solve their transportation needs, but there are times when you need to come up with another alternative.

The Eldercare Locator provides access to an extensive network of organizations serving older people at state and local community levels. This service can connect you to information sources for a variety of services including transportation.

For more information, contact Eldercare Locator, National Association of Area Agencies on Aging, 1112 16th St., NW, Washington, DC 20024; 800-677-1116 between 9 a.m. and 8 p.m. EST; {www.aoa.gov}.

I DON'T HAVE A CAR & MY CHILD IS SICK AT SCHOOL

Suppose your child is sick at school and needs you in the middle of the day, but you don't have a way to get there because you go to work most days by some other way than using your car. Don't panic. You can probably get a free ride, taxi, or free rental car from the local *"Guaranteed Ride Home Program"*.

You can also use the service for most family emergencies if your normal ride falls through, or if you have to work late unexpectedly. Call your local carpool or vanpool service to see if they have a similar program. Most of these programs require that you pre-register, but it is always best to plan ahead for emergencies anyway.

If you do a computer search using the terms (including the quotes) "guaranteed ride home program," you will find a listing of many of the programs offered. You can also contact your state Department of Transportation for starting places.

DISCOUNTS on
Buses, Trains and Subways

If you are a senior citizen, you can usually ride most forms of transportation for about half-price. Amtrak and Greyhound offer discounts of 10-15% for the senior set. Children even get to take advantage of discount programs, with the youngest group often getting a free ride.

Don't forget to ask about a variety of reduced fare programs, including student and military discounts. Often job training programs will compensate you for your travel, so before you begin training, inquire about support services such as transportation and child care.

Free & Discounted
Child Safety Seats

It's easy to spend $100 on a child's car seat, so look for the deals. There are hospitals that give out free child safety seats as you leave with your new baby, with no questions asked and no income requirements. Local police and fire departments inspect child safety seats to see that they are in proper order and properly installed, and sometimes provide free seats to those whose current equipment is not considered safe. Local organizations, like the Easter Seals Society were part of a federal program that gives out millions of dollars worth of free seats because of a settlement the U.S. Department of Transportation made with General Motors. Other groups will lend you a seat for as little as $5. The state of Minnesota alone has over 225 such programs.

To find a program near you, contact your local police or fire department. Or contact your state information operator listed in the Appendix and ask them for your state office for Highway Safety or Traffic Safety. These national organizations may also be able to give you a local source:

- *National SAFEKIDS Campaign*, 1301 Pennsylvania Ave., NW, Suite 1000, Washington, DC 20004; 202-626-0600; fax 202-393-2072; {www.safekids.org}

- *National Highway Traffic Safety Administration*, U.S. Department of Transportation, 400 Seventh St., SW, Washington, DC 20590; 800-424-9393; {www.nhtsa.dot.gov}

Cheap Air Fare To See a Sick Relative

Not free, but at least you don't have to pay full price. When a family member is very ill or has died, families have to make last minute airline reservations. Obviously you lose out on the 21-day advance purchase rates, but almost all airlines offer *bereavement* or *compassion* fares for domestic travel.

Generally the fares are available to close family members, and the discount on the full-fare rate varies from airline to airline. Many require that you provide the name of the deceased and the name, address and phone number of the funeral home handling arrangements. In the case of a medical emergency, the name and address of the affected family member and the name, address and phone number of the attending physician or hospital are required. Contact the airline of your choice to learn more about the "Bereavement/Compassion Fares." Full fare rate varies from airline to airline, but you could save up to 50%.

Free Cars and Air Fare To Go On Vacation

Not quite as easy as it sounds, but there are programs out there to help people move their cars. Most of the cars need to be driven across the country and in exchange, many car moving companies offer free gas and airline travel home.

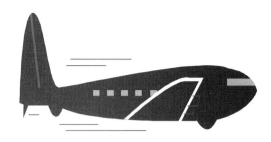

This is not to say that you can take your family on a minivan vacation across the country. Certain rules and restrictions apply. But I have known many a college kid that has gotten to drive across the U.S. for free.

Obviously, you do not get to pick your make and model, and you need to be flexible as to the departure time and destination, but this is one way to see America. Contact local moving companies to see what they have to offer. There is even a website for those interested in having their cars moved at {www.movecars.com}, and they may be able to provide you with information.

Air courier services operate the same way, but you are required to have a valid passport. Most air freight services don't do enough business to send a plane overseas each day. As a courier, you carry a package checked as baggage to an overseas destination. There have been no incidences of contraband problems, and customs is familiar with this service. You deliver the package to a company representative in the customs section of the airport, then you are on your own. In exchange, you get to fly to exotic ports for FREE or cheap. Children are not allowed to accompany couriers. Contact companies listed in the air courier section of your phone book, do a web search using the terms "air courier service," or contact the Air Courier Association at 800-282-1202; or online at {www.aircourier.org}.

Discounts on Car Rentals

You never should pay full-price for car rentals and there are deals aplenty if you keep your eyes opened. AAA and AARP membership will save you a few bucks, as will many other membership programs. Car rental agencies also often offer discounts to senior citizens (check what age they consider "senior"). Many times, if you book your flight and car rental at the same time, you can get a discount rate, plus get miles added to your frequent flyer program. All you have to do is ask!

The free brochure, *Renting a Car*, outlines some points to consider and questions to ask when you reserve a rental car. You can learn how to choose a rental car company and understand the terms they use for insurance and charges. For your copy, contact Public Reference, Room 130, Federal Trade Commission, Washington, DC 20580; 202-326-2222, 877-FTC-HELP; or online at {www.ftc.gov}.

$65/Mo Bus Money or $170/Mo Parking Money From Your Boss

Your employer can give you $65 a month to pay for going to work in a bus, van or metro, or give you $170 a month for parking. You get the money tax free, and the employer gets to take a tax deduction. Everybody wins! It's called the *Qualified Transportation Fringe Benefit* or *Transit Benefit Program*. Get a copy of IRS Publication 535, *Business Expenses* and show your boss the section entitled "Qualified Transportation Fringe". The publication is available from your local IRS office or from 800-TAX-FORM or from their web site at {www.irs.ustreas.gov}.

Tax Deductions For Your Car

You can deduct:

- 31 1/2 cents per mile if you use your car for business (IRS Publication 463, Travel Entertainment, Gift, and Car Expenses)
- 12 cents per mile if you use your car during charity work (IRS Instructions for Schedule A, Itemized Deductions)
- 10 cents per mile if you use your car for medical care (IRS Instructions for Schedule A, Itemized Deductions)
- 10 cents per mile if you use your car to move to a new job (IRS Publication 521, Moving Expenses)

These publications are free from your local IRS office, by calling 1-800-829-3676 or download from {www.irs.ustreas.gov}

Your Child Has A Doctor's Appointment and Your Car Won't Work

The Federal Transit Administration provides over $50 million a year to over 1,000 local organizations to provide free non-emergency transportation for people who are old or have a disability. But the groups who get this federal money can also provide free transportation services to moms who are in a jam.

The regulations state that the vehicles can also be used to "serve the transportation needs of the general public on an incidental basis". You may have to do some educating to get a local group to give you a ride. Tell them to see Circular FTA C9070, 1D, for Section 5310 Program, Chapter V, Program Management, paragraph 3b. It's available from the U.S. Federal Transit Administration or on the web at {www.fta.dot.gov/library/ policy/circ9070/ chapter5.html}.

To find groups in your area who receive these FTA Section 5310 grants for Elderly and Persons With Disabilities, contact your state department of transportation or the U.S. Federal Transit Administration, Office of Program Management, Office of Resource Management and State Programs, 400 7th St., SW, Washington, DC 20590; 202-366-4020; {www.fta.dot.gov}.

MAKE $39,000 AND GET FREE CHILD CARE

In Connecticut your income can be $39,168 and you can get $640 a month for child care. Make $25,332 in Indiana and get $1,260 a month for infant care. Earn $38,244 in Alaska and receive $583 a month for child care.

The Child Care and Development Block Grant gives money to states to help families meet their child care needs. Parents may choose from a variety of child care providers, including center-based, family child care and in-home care, care provided by relatives, and even sectarian child care providers. You can even get money to start a day care center! Income qualifications vary from state to state, and each state operates their programs slightly differently.

To find out how to take advantage of this program in your state and to learn the eligibility requirements, contact National Child Care Information Center, 243 Church St., NW, Vienna, VA 22180; 800-616-2242; {http://nccic.org}.

Free Child Care
When Training Or Looking For A Job

Welfare reform, called *Temporary Assistance for Needy Families (TANF),* does more to help people not wind up on welfare. The new program includes free training, education, child care, and transportation assistance necessary to help you obtain employment.

Child care is an important part of the program. Eligibility requirements vary from state to state, so contact your TANF office nearest you to learn what options are available to you. For more information, contact Office of Family Assistance, Administration for Children and Families, 370 L'Enfant Promenade, SW, Washington, DC 20447; 202-401-9215; {www.acf.dhhs.gov/programs/opa/facts/tanf.htm}.

$9 a Week Child Care at Local Nonprofits

Local non-profits around the country get grants from the United Way or other institutions and offer free and sliding scale day care services. The United Way spends about a third of its funds, about $1 billion a year, on programs for children and families.

For example, the Community Partnerships for Children Program in Brockton, MA provides child care for a family of 2 with weekly income of $210 for only $9.00 a week, and families of 4 with income of $1,000 a week can get care for $114 a week per child. There are about 500 local United Way Information and Referral Services around the country that can point you to local groups that can help you solve your child care problems.

Look in the phone book for your local United Way agency, or contact United Way of America, 701 N. Fairfax Street, Alexandria, VA 22314-2045; 703-836-7100; 800-411-UWAY (8929); {www.unitedway.org}.

Free Child Care For AmeriCorp
and VISTA Workers

Over $10,000,000 a year is paid out to cover child care services for people working with AmeriCorps or VISTA. These programs allow you to tackle community problems on everything from disaster relief to tutoring. National Service jobs also provide a stipend, housing, and even college money; child care is a bonus.

Contact Corporation of National Service, 1201 New York Ave., NW, Washington, DC 20525; 202-606-5000; {www.nationalservice.org}.

YOUR CHILD MAY BE ELIGIBLE FOR A HEAD START

Head Start is one of those government programs that has proven to actually work. It's preschool that has a great student teacher ratio and all teachers are certified in early childhood development. It prepares the children with school readiness, and research shows that these children enter kindergarten with the skills necessary to succeed. Some Head Start programs are even home-based. There are income requirements for acceptance into the program, but the program does allow 10% of the students to have higher incomes. And 10% of the program needs to be offered to kids who have a disability.

To learn more about Head Start programs near you, contact your local board of education, the state Department of Social Services, or Administration for Children and Families, U.S. Department of Health and Human Services, Head Start Bureau, 330 C Street, SW, Washington, DC 20447; 202-205-8572; {www.acf.dhhs.gov/programs/hsb}.

WORK FOR COMPANIES THAT OFFER FREE/DISCOUNT CHILD CARE

You may be surprised at the number of daycare centers offering services right inside company office buildings. In fact the federal government may be in the lead as they have over 1,000 child care centers that are sponsored by various governmental agencies. Talk to other moms and dads on the playground, call human resources departments, and even check with your local chamber of commerce. All may be able to direct you to companies providing this benefit.

A directory of sites is available for $25 from the Work and Family Connection, 5197 Beachside Dr., Minnetonka, MN 55343; 800-487-7898; {www.workfamily.com}. Another resource is your local Child Care Resource and Referral Agency, who should be aware of programs in their area. To locate your local referral agency, contact Child Care Aware, 1319 F Street, NW, Suite 500, Washington, DC 20004; 800-424-2246, {www.childcareaware.org}.

Besides child care centers, some employers offer a dependent care assistance plan that allows you to pay for child care out of pre-tax dollars. You get more care for your buck. Other employers offer direct subsidies to offset child care costs. Talk to your company human resources office to learn more.

Free Child Care For Teens With Disabilities

48 states provide a subsidy to parents who qualify for childcare for children ages 14 to 19 who are physically and/or mentally incapable of self-care. Each state sets their eligibility requirement and the amount of funds they have available for this type of care. To learn what your state has to offer, contact your state Child Care and Development Block Grant lead agency.

GET MONEY FOR YOUR OWN CHILD CARE CENTER

Child Care Works is a new partnership between the District of Columbia, eight area banks and three community organizations that make training, grants and loans available to licensed neighborhood day care providers to provide slots for 1,000 children. Maryland and Ohio provide special low-interest loans through their Department of Economic Development to fund child care centers. Even the Child Care and Development Block Grant provides money to develop child care centers and before and after school programs. For more information, contact your state Department of Economic Development or your Child Care and Development Block Grant lead agency.

Get $4,800 From The IRS To Pay For Child Care

Remember that the Internal Revenue Service (IRS) offers some benefits for child care costs. IRS Publication 503, *Child and Dependent Care Expenses*, outlines the rules covering this benefit and describes how to figure the benefit if your employer covers some of the cost. You may claim up to $2,400 for the care of one child (or $4,800 for two or more).

For more information, contact the IRS Information Line at 800-829-1040; or {www.irs.gov}. In addition, 25 states and the District of Columbia offer some type of child care income tax benefit either in the form of credits or deductions. Contact your state Tax Revenue office to see what your state offers.

GRANTS AND LOANS FOR ADOPTIONS

The National Adoption Foundation (NAF) is a national non-profit organization dedicated to providing financial support, information, and services for adoptive and prospective adoptive families. They recently announced the expansion of its programs to include home equity loans, as well as unsecured loans and grants for adoption expenses. A grant program to cover adoption expenses is also available on a limited basis for prospective adoptive parents.

Other sources of money for adoption include:

- Ask your employer for employee adoption assistance benefits. Approximately 65 percent of Fortune 500 companies now offer some kind of adoption benefit.

- Take advantage of the new adoption expense tax credit in advance by modifying your income tax withholding to reflect your tax savings when you file your return. This frees up cash for adoption expenses due now.

Contact: National Adoption Foundation, 1415 Flag Ave., So. , Minneapolis, MN 55426; 800-448-7061; 203-791-3811; Fax: 612-544-6698; {Email: SFreivalds@aol.com}.

Free Credit Repair

It always seemed strange to me that if you're in debt enough to need help with credit repair, why in the world would you spend more money on a credit repair services? You can do it for free, yourself!

Spending money needlessly is what got you there in the first place. And more importantly, federal and state regulators have been warning consumers against using credit counseling companies. Companies, lawyers and others will charge you $300 to $1000 for something you can do for free.

Here are some of the free reports you can get from the Federal Trade Commission:

- ❏ *Credit Repair: Self-Help May Be The Best*
- ❏ *Knee Deep in Debt*
- ❏ *How To Dispute Credit Reporting Errors*
- ❏ *How To Deal With Credit Problems*
- ❏ *How to Dispute Credit Report Errors*

For your copies, contact Public Reference, Room 130, Federal Trade Commission, Washington, DC 20580; 202-326-2222; 877-FTC-HELP; {www.ftc.gov}.

If you don't want to do it ALL yourself, you can ask for **FREE HELP**. The following non-profit and government organizations provide free, or low-fee credit counseling services. You can contact them to find the office nearest you. Some of these offices are financed by the bank and credit card industry, who are biased toward having you pay all your bills without using the bankruptcy option. So be sure that they explain your bankruptcy options.

- ❏ *National Foundation for Consumer Credit*, 8611 Second Avenue, Suite 100, Silver Spring, MD 20910; 800-388-2227; Spanish: 800-68AYUNDA; {www.credit.org}.
- ❏ Free internet credit counseling services from the non-profit organization, *Credit Counseling Center of America,* P.O. Box 830489, Richardson, TX 75083-0489; 800-493-2222; {www.cccamerica.org}.
- ❏ *County Cooperative Extension Service*: to find your local office, see the blue pages of your phone book.

GET FREE COPIES OF YOUR CREDIT REPORT

You can get a free copy of your credit report if:

- ★ you have been denied credit, insurance, or employment within the last 60 days
- ★ you're unemployed and plan to look for a job within 60 days
- ★ you're on welfare, or
- ★ your report is inaccurate because of fraud.

Otherwise they can charge you up to $8 for a copy of your report. For copies of your report, contact the credit reporting agencies listed in the yellow pages of your telephone book, or contact the three major national credit bureaus:

Equifax
   PO Box 740241, Atlanta, GA 30374; 800-685-1111
Experian (formerly TRW)
   PO Box 949, Allen, TX 75013; 800-682-7654
Trans Union
   760 West Sproul Road, Springfield, PA 19064; 800-916-8800

If you have trouble getting satisfaction from a credit reporting agency contact: Consumer Response Center, Federal Trade Commission, CRC-240, Washington, DC 20580; 877-FTC-HELP; {www.ftc.gov}.

Free Help Fighting a High ELECTRIC BILL Or Stopping A TURN-OFF

The state utility commissions can help you fight high gas or electric bills. Some will even come out and make sure that your meter is not over charging you. They don't have money to pay for your bills, but they can negotiate payment arrangements with the company for you or suggest non-profit organizations that may have emergency funds to help. For example Maryland suggests the Fuel Fund for Central Maryland or the Maryland Energy Assistance program. The office can also force the utility not to cut off your service because of medical emergencies or cold weather. Contact your state utility commission listed in the blue pages of your phone book for further assistance.

Check For A $100 Heating Bill Tax Credit

The state of Michigan offers a home heating bill tax credit (that means you pay less in taxes) for people who are low income, receiving public assistance or unemployment. Call your state department of taxation to learn about tax credits available to you. Michigan Department of Treasury, Lansing, MI 48956; 800-487-7000; {www.treas.state.mi.us/formspub/forms/indtax/}.

Free Voice Mail

If you are unemployed and the phone company cut off your phone, how does a potential employer get in touch with you? Free voice mail. You can get set up with your own personalized greeting, as well as get a security code and instructions on how you can retrieve your messages 24 hours a day. The program is available in over 27 cities and is growing.

See if you're eligible for your area by contacting Community Technology Institute, P.O. Box 61385, Seattle, WA 98121; 206-441-7872; Fax: 206-441-4784; {www.cvm.org/home.html}.

GET AN $84 REDUCTION ON YOUR TELEPHONE BILL

Link-Up and *Lifeline* are two government programs that offers up to $84 a year in discounts on your monthly bill and a 50% reduction for your hook-up service, or $30 which ever is less. These programs have income requirements that vary from state to state.

Ask your phone company about them or contact your state Utility Commissioner listed in the blue pages of your phone book or Federal Communications Commission, 445 12th St., SW, Washington, DC 20554; 888-CALL-FCC, 202-418-0190; {www.fcc.gov}.

Dress For Success For Free

Looking for work and can't afford the right wardrobe? There are about 50 non-profit organizations around the country that provide women with two separate outfits for free. One can be used to go to an interview and the other can be used once you get the job. The following organization acts as a clearinghouse for similar opportunities around the country. Bottomless Closet, 445 North Wells, Chicago, IL 60610; 312-527-9664; Fax: 312-527-4305; {www.bottomlesscloset.org}.

$800 FOOD MONEY

You don't get the cash, but you do get it in the form of Food Stamps. The Food Stamp Program was designed to help low-income families buy the food they need to stay healthy and productive. The amount of Food Stamps you get each month is determined by the number of people in your family and by the household income. The average benefit is about $71 dollars a month, but a 4-person household could get up to $408 a month. There are obviously income requirements you must meet.

To apply for the Program, look in the blue pages of your telephone book under "Food Stamps," "Social Services," or "Public Assistance." You can also find more information by contacting U.S. Department of Agriculture, Food and Nutrition Service, 3101 Park Ctr. Dr., Park Office Center Bldg., Alexandria, VA 22302; 703-305-2276; {www.fns.usda.gov/fsp}.

Extra Money to Live On

Struggling to pay bills because you or your child are disabled? Supplemental Security Income (SSI) provides funds to individuals who are 65 or older, or blind, or have a disability and who don't own much or have a lot of income.

SSI isn't just for adults. Monthly checks can go to disabled and blind children. There are income requirements you must meet and you or your child's disability will be screened. But it could mean an extra $400 a month and that could help a great deal!

For more information, contact Social Security Administration, Office of Public Inquiries, 6401 Security Blvd., Room 4-C-5 Annex, Baltimore, MD 21235; 800-772-1213; {www.ssa.gov}.

$500 For Seniors and Disabled

The state of Pennsylvania offers up to $500 for seniors and people with disabilities who pay property taxes or rent. If you live in Pennsylvania, contact Department of Aging, 555 Walnut St., 5th Floor, Harrisburg, PA 17101; 717-783-1549. If you live elsewhere, contact your state Office on Aging listed in the blue pages of your phone book, or your state Department of Revenue.

Money When You're Out Of Work

In Massachusetts, you can receive up to $402 a week for 30 weeks, and in special circumstances they will extend the benefits another 18 weeks. Mass lay-offs, base closings, trade agreements, and high unemployment in your state, all affect your ability to find and keep a job. If you are out of work, take advantage of unemployment insurance. This is the government's first line of defense against the ripple effects of unemployment.

All states are required to provide benefits up to 26 weeks and some extend them further. If your state has very high unemployment, you may be eligible for 13 additional weeks of compensation. If you lost your job because of an increase in imports, you may qualify to have your benefits extended up to an extra 52 weeks if you are in a job-retraining program.

Your weekly benefit amount depends upon your past wages within certain minimum and maximum limits that vary from state to state. Many states also will add additional funds depending upon the number of dependents. If you are denied benefits, learn about the appeal process, as your chances of winning are good. For more information, contact your state Unemployment Insurance office listed in the blue pages of your phone book.

Free Help In Writing A Will

Estate planning is not something that people often relish doing, but it is extremely important. It is difficult enough when a loved one dies, but then to have to search through papers trying to find information about insurance, or investments is often too much. When children are involved, estate planning is essential. Who will take care of the children and how can you secure their financial future?

Your local Cooperative Extension Service often offers classes or publications on estate planning. The time to plan ahead is now. Look in the blue pages of your phone book for the nearest Cooperative Extension office, as they are in almost every county across the country.

$700 Discount On Your Utility Bills

The legislature in Massachusetts passed a law giving discounts up to $700 on heating bills for families making up to $30,000, along with up to 40% discount on electric bills, $108 off telephone bills, and $100 off oil bills. It's in the Massachusetts Budget for FY 99 (Line Item 4403-2110). Also:

✡ **Mason County** in the state of Washington offers a utility bill discount of $12.00 a month for seniors making less than $18,000, and disabled people at 125% of poverty. Contact Public Utility District #3, 307 W. Cota St., Shelton, WA 98584; 800-424-5555; {www.olywa.net}.

✡ **Phoenix, Arizona** offers discounts on utility bills, discounts on phone bills and even help paying utility deposits and heating repairs for low-income residents through the Arizona Public Service Energy Support Program, P.O. Box 6123-086Z, Phoenix, AZ 85008; 800-582-5706.

✡ **Ameritech in Illinois** gives a 100% discount on connection charges and $5.25 off the monthly bill to low-income residents. To sign up, call Ameritech at 800-244-4444.

✡ **Ohio** offers reduced or free phone hook up service and possibly $8.00 a month off your phone bill for low-income residents. Contact Public Utilities Commission, 180 E. Broad St., Columbus, OH 43215; 800-686-7826; {www.puc.state.oh.us}.

✡ **Pennsylvania Bell Atlantic** offers free telephone hook up and $9.00 monthly discount to low-income residents through Lifeline and Universal Telephone Assistance Programs. To sign up, call 800-272-1006.

Contact your state's utilities office in the blue pages of your phone book to find out about special discounts on your gas, electric, cable or telephone in your state.

Free Tax Help for Seniors

It is nice to get special treatment every now and then, and tax time is no exception. The Tax Counseling for the Elderly program was designed to provide free taxpayer assistance to those ages 60 and above. The staff usually consists of retired individuals associated with nonprofit organizations that receive grants from the IRS to perform this service. Often they provide counseling in retirement homes, neighborhood sites or private houses of the homebound.

For information on the Tax Counseling for the Elderly program near you, contact your local IRS office, call the hotline at 800-829-1040; {www.irs.gov}.

Volunteers Get a 50% Discount On Food

It's called the Self-Help and Resource Exchange (SHARE), and it distributes food at 50% discounts to 5,415 community-based organizations, which in turn give it to individuals. The only catch is that you have to volunteer your time in the community for at least 2 hours a month. You can coach little league or help fix up a playground. To find a SHARE affiliate near you, contact SHARE, 6950 Friars Road, San Diego, CA 92108; 888-742-7372; Fax: 618-686-5185; {www.worldshare.org}.

Government Supported Agencies Offer Free Money And Help When You Don't Know Where To Turn

If you need emergency money to pay a bill, or for housing, training, health care, or just additional support, these organizations can be of service and they are likely to have an office near you. Although these are private organizations, they do receive a portion of their funds from your favorite Uncle Sam.

1) Community Action Agencies
Nearly 1,000 agencies around the country received funds from the U.S. Government's Community Services Block Grants to offer education, counseling, employment, training, food packages, vouchers, weatherization and utility assistance, life skills, affordable housing, transportation, furnishings, recreation, emergency services, information and referral services. To locate an agency serving your area, contact: National Association Of Community Action Agencies. 1100 17th St., NW, Suite 500, Washington, DC 20036; 202-265-7546; Fax: 202-265-8850; {www.nacaa.org}.

2) Catholic Charities
Over 14,000 local organizations offer a variety of services for many different communities including: child care, elderly services, emergency financial services, emergency shelter, food pantries, housing assistance, job training, out-of-home care, parenting education, youth services, rental assistance, utility assistance, and health care. For an office near you, contact Catholic Charities USA, 1731 King Street #200, Alexandria, VA 22314; 703-549-1390; Fax: 703-549-1656; {www.catholiccharitiesusa.org}.

3) *Salvation Army*

Families in need can receive a wide range of services including: utility assistance, transitional housing, emergency food, furnishings, Section 8 tenant counseling, counseling, rent or mortgage assistance, and even clothing. Most services are for households who are below 150% of the poverty level (about $24,000 for family of 4). For an office near you, contact Salvation Army National Headquarters, 615 Slaters Lane, P.O. Box 269, Alexandria, VA 22313; 703-684-5500; Fax: 703-684-3478; {www.salvationarmy.org}.

FREE DIRECTORY/OPERATOR ASSISTANCE IF YOU HAVE A DISABILITY

Directory assistance can cost up to 95 cents per request and an additional 50 cents for the connection. To assist persons with visual, hearing, or other disabilities, local telephone companies offer directory and operator assistance exemptions. Simply request and complete a form from the local telephone company and have your physician complete the appropriate section. When you return the form to the phone company, you'll be eligible for the exemptions. Contact the business office of your local telephone company.

GET EXTRA CASH FINDING LOST MONEY AND SURPLUS PROPERTY

Make $2,000 in 45 minutes. That's what the author, Mary Ann Martello, did when she searched state databases looking for old forgotten utility deposits and bank accounts set up by grandparents. Every state has an office that collects money in that state that has been abandoned, forgotten, or left unclaimed, including:

- ✖ Savings and checking accounts
- ✖ Uncashed payroll or cashiers checks
- ✖ Money orders and travelers checks
- ✖ Certificates of deposit
- ✖ Customer deposits or overpayment
- ✖ Paid up life insurance policies
- ✖ Health and accident insurance payments
- ✖ Uncashed death benefit checks
- ✖ Gift certificates and Christmas club accounts
- ✖ Stock and dividends
- ✖ Utility deposits
- ✖ Oil and gas royalty payments

The money could be a savings account that grandma set up for you when you were born. Or it could be a Christmas fund Great Aunt Rose contributed to before she passed away. Your father may have even had a safe deposit box he never told you existed.

According to reports, state agencies across the U.S. may be holding over $8 billion dollars in abandoned money. Although the rules vary from state to state, generally after two or more years without activity on an account (no deposits or withdrawals), the bank will try to contact you. If their efforts fail, the property is considered abandoned and transferred to the state of your last known address.

To locate funds, contact the unclaimed property office in the state (usually part of the state treasurer's department) where you or your benefactors have lived or conducted business. Most state agencies have websites, and many have searchable databases. You can contact the National Association of Unclaimed Property Administrators, P.O. Box 7156, Bismarck, ND 58507; {www.unclaimed.org}. Not only does the website give you a listing of state offices, it also links you to those that have existing websites..

Checking Into Your Retirement Check

Did you work some place twenty years ago that is no longer in business? What about an old pension fund that was in financial trouble? Don't give up. The Pension Benefit Guaranty Corporation (PBGC) monitors and sometimes takes over private sector-defined benefit plans. These are traditional pensions that promise a specified monthly benefit at retirement.

The PBGC operates a Pension Search Directory to find people who are owed pensions from the plans PBGC now controls. You can search by name, company worked for, or by state where the company is/was headquartered. In the last eighteen months, the directory found 1,400 people owed more that $4 million with the average benefit being $4,100. There is still $13 million just waiting to be claimed.

For more information, contact Pension Benefit Guaranty Corporation, Pension Search Program, 1200 K St., NW, Washington, DC 20005; 800-326-LOST; {www.pbgc.gov}.

The IRS Has "GOOD NEWS" For 100,000 Taxpayers

Seems impossible, doesn't it? Close to 100,000 taxpayers are due a refund, yet their checks have been returned to the tune of over $62.6 million. The average check is $627. What do you do if you think you or someone you love is missing a check? Contact the IRS toll-free hotline at 800-829-1040 and talk to a customer service representative. They can plug your name in the computer and see if your name pops up on their screen.

165,000 Unclaimed Social Security Checks

Social Security checks go out to 92% of those over the age of 65, so once in awhile a check may go astray. If you think you are missing some checks, or if you find un-negotiated checks, contact your local Social Security Administration office. They can reissue the checks to the person or to the estate.

Social Security assures me that this occurs rarely, as they send out 612 million payments with only 165,000 checks that were not endorsed. Contact Social Security Hotline at 800-772-1213.

The same deal holds true with the Veterans Affairs Administration. If you feel you are missing checks or find checks that have not been endorsed, contact your local Veterans Affairs office so that checks can be reissued to you or to the estate of a loved one. Contact Veterans Affairs at 800-827-1000.

Free Private Eye and Mediation For Missing Children

Besides location and investigative services, as well as mediation services for families estranged by parental abduction, you can also get free kidnapping prevention programs and referral and support services.

Contact Find-A-Child of America, Inc., P.O. Box 277, New Paltz, NY 12561; 800-I-AM-LOST; 914-255-1848; 800-A-WAY-OUT (for mediation and support); {www.childfindofamerica.org}.

AN EXTRA $6,000 A YEAR IF YOU CAN'T WORK

Is your check too small to live on? If so, don't be discouraged. If you don't qualify for Social Security, or if your benefits are very low, you may qualify for Supplemental Security Income (SSI).

This program was established to help poor seniors over 65, as well as the blind and disabled, meet basic living needs. To qualify, you must meet a maximum monthly income test. Some of the income and services you receive are excluded when they calculate your monthly income in relation to your personal expenses.

Those who meet SSI's eligibility usually automatically qualify for Medicaid coverage and food stamp benefits. Studies have found that only between 40 and 60 percent of those who qualify for SSI actually receive benefits under the program. To find out if you qualify, contact your local Social Security office or call the Social Security Hotline at 800-772-1213.

Law Gives Kids With ADD Free Special Classes

The nonprofit organization, *Children and Adults with Attention Deficit Disorder (CHADD),* identifies a number of federal laws that require the government to provide children with this disorder special educational services. It is only recently that these children became eligible for such services, so many eligible children may not be receiving what they deserve.

To learn more about these free educational services, or to find out more and how to treat a child with ADD, or what's good and bad about available treatments, contact: CHADD, 8181 Professional Place, Suite 201, Landover, MD 20785; 800-233-4050; Fax: 301-306-7090; {www.chadd.org}.

Vet Services Hotline

The Department of Veterans Affairs hotline can provide you with information on such programs as life insurance, comprehensive dental and medical care, nursing homes, home loan programs, burial services, and more. Contact Department of Veterans Affairs, 810 Vermont Ave., NW, Washington, DC 20420; 800-827-1000; {www.va.gov}.

Get Money While You're Waiting For Government Money

General Public Assistance or just Public Assistance (it is known by many different names) is a welfare program offered in 42 states. This is a program of last resort for people either waiting to qualify for other government

programs such as disability benefits, or who do not qualify for any programs, yet need money to live. The program eligibility and benefit levels vary within and across state lines. In some states, this benefit is only available in certain areas. There are strict income and asset levels that you must meet to qualify.

In Kansas, General Assistance pays families $278 per month while they are waiting for other government money. In California, the benefit is $225. Contact your local welfare office, your state Department of Social Service, or your state Temporary Assistance to Needy Families office to see what your state offers and the eligibility requirements.

10% Off Your Airline Tickets

Every airline offers discounts to seniors amounting to usually 10%. What happens, though, is that some of the airlines' special offers may be exempt from the discount. It is best to see what the lowest available rate is and then inquire about the discount.

All the major airlines also offer coupon books for seniors that are four round-trip tickets good for wherever the airline flies. The price of the coupon books is around $540. In many instances, the airline only requires that one person meet the age requirement for a discount, so your companion can receive the lower rate as well.

50% Off Camping

Almost all states offer discounts to seniors at state parks. Entrance fees are usually waived for seniors, or states like Illinois offer 50% off camping fees. Eighteen states have no residency requirements to receive the discount, so if you are planning a cross country camping trip, contact the state Parks Department to find out about eligibility criteria.

For those wanting to camp in the National Forest, the Golden Age Passport is available to those 62 and over. For $10 you receive free lifetime admission to the parks, plus 50% off on camping and many other services. The Passport is available at all National Forests.

10-50% OFF HOTEL ROOMS

Almost all major hotel chains offer discounts from 10-30% off the cost of rooms. Some require that you belong to AARP or AAA, so it is best to call ahead and ask.

Three hotel chains, Ramada, Hilton, and Red Roof Inns offer special deals to seniors who frequent their hotels. Ramada's Best Years Club charges $15 for a lifetime membership fee. The fee entitles you to 25% off regular two double bed room rates, plus you receive points redeemable for travel and prizes (800-672-6232; available at most

Ramadas). Hilton Senior HHonors program charges $50 ($40 annual renewal fee), and seniors receive up to 50% off rooms and 20% off hotel restaurants (800-492-3232). Red Roof has a lifetime Redicard for seniors that costs $10. The card gets you 10% off rooms, plus 3 $5 off coupons for lodging (800-843-7663).

10-15% OFF
WHEN YOU TRAVEL

All car rental chains offer senior discounts, but again AARP or AAA membership may be required. The amount of discount varies from location to location, but usually is 10%. You should call ahead to see if a discount is available. Some chains also require reservations 24 hours in advance.

For those that prefer to leave the driving to others, two other discount programs include AMTRAK and Greyhound. Amtrak offers 15% off any fare available to those 62 and older (800-USA-RAIL). Greyhound has an 8% discount for people 55 and over (800-231-2222).

50% Discount On Telephone Service

Under the Federal Communication Commission's Link-Up America and Lifeline programs, low-income households seeking telephone service are given a 50% discount on local connection charges, and may be able to pay installment payments on the remaining charge. These programs are available in most states.

To sign up for this service, contact the customer service representative at your local telephone company.

10% OFF AT RESTAURANTS

The Early Bird specials can happen all day once you hit a certain age. Many restaurant chains offer special deals for seniors. Most restaurant chains are independently owned and operated, but they usually follow the recommendations from the headquarters.

Places like Denny's, Bob Evan's, and International House of Pancakes frequently offer seniors a reduced price menu. Other chains, such as Applebee's, Kentucky Fried Chicken, and Wendy's, often give seniors a 10% discount on their meals. It never hurts to ask if a discount is offered.

5-10% Off When You Shop

Banana Republic offers seniors age 62 and older 10% off every day, while Ross, Stone & Thomas, and Glik's offer 10% off to seniors on specific days during the week. Other stores like Wal-mart and May Co. frequently offer advertised senior specials. Sears and Montgomery Ward have discount cards or clubs you can join for a fee that entitles you to discounts and other services. Ask at the main offices of stores where you shop to see what may be available to you. Even grocery stores are getting into the act!

Free (Or Cheap) Hunting and Fishing Licenses

Practically every state has a special license rate for seniors. States such as Alabama, Alaska, Delaware, Georgia, Kansas, and others do not require that people age 65 and over to carry a fishing and hunting license. Other states offer seniors, on average, half off the cost of licenses.

Inquire where you usually purchase these licenses to learn what age you need to be to receive the discount and the specific details.

Save Money When You Bank

First Citizens Bank has **Senior Quest Accounts** where customers 60 and over receive unlimited check writing, no per check charge, interest bearing checking, no monthly service charge, free safe deposit box, no ATM fees, free cashier's checks, travelers' checks, and money orders. They even offer special rates on 6 and 12 month CD's, no annual fee credit card, free direct deposit and discount brokerage fees, with some of these services requiring a minimum balance. Not a bad deal. Other banks offer similar services, with most offering free checks, no minimum balance, and unlimited check writing.

Grants Aid Needy Professional Musicians and Singers

Assistance is available to financial needy New York residents once prominent in opera and classical music through the Bagby Foundation for the Musical Arts, Inc. The Foundation also provides monetary support for coaching assistance to students desiring to make their professional opera debut. Contact The Bagby Foundation for the Musical Arts, Inc., 501 5th Ave., Suite 1401, New York, NY 10017; 212-986-6094.

10%-100% Off On Your Glasses

Pearle Vision Centers offer 50% off either the lenses or frames when you purchase a complete set of glasses to people 50-59, 60% off to those 60-69, 70% to those 70-79, and so on until seniors reach 100 and they give them 100% off either the lenses or frames when they purchase a complete set of glasses. Lens Crafters and Eye Glass Factory also offer a 10% discount to seniors, and Sears Optical Centers give 15% off to AARP members. Now it makes seeing clearly less costly.

$5,000
Extra Spending Money

If your check is too small to live on, don't be discouraged. If you don't qualify for Social Security, or if your benefits are very low, you may qualify for supplemental Security Income (SSI).

This program was established to help poor seniors over 65 and the blind and disabled meet basic living expenses. To qualify you must meet a maximum monthly income test. Some of the income and services you receive are excluded when they calculate your monthly income in relation to your personal expenses. Studies have found that only between 40 and 60 percent of seniors who meet the income

General Welfare Grants Support Utah Residents

The Marion D. and Maxine C. Hanks Foundation, Inc. offers general welfare grants and support for medical expenses to needy Utah residents. Contact The Marion D. and Maxine C. Hanks Foundation, Inc., 8 E. Broadway, Suite 405, Judge Building, Salt Lake City, UT 84111; 801-364-7705.

requirements for SSI actually receive benefits. To find out more about the program, contact your local Social Security office or contact the Social Security Hotline at 800-772-1213.

Christian Scientists Assisted by Two Agencies

The New Horizons Foundation provides financial assistance to residents of Los Angeles County, CA, who are over 65 years of age and active Christian Scientists. Contact: New Horizons Foundation, c/o Gifford & Dearing, 700 S. Flower St., Suite 1222, Los Angeles, CA 90017-4160; 213-626-4481.

Grants and camperships are available through the Sunnyside Foundation, Inc. to underprivileged Christian Science children under the age of 20 who regularly attend Sunday School and are Texas residents. Contact Sunnyside Foundation, Inc., 8222 Douglas Ave., Suite 501, Dallas, TX 75225-5936; 214-692-5686.

Pittsburgh-Area Jewish Families In Need Receive Aid

Financial assistance is offered to needy Jewish families residing in the Pittsburgh area through the Jewish Family Assistance Fund for living, personal, food and medical expenses. Contact Jewish Family Assistance Fund, 5743 Bartlett St., Pittsburgh, PA 15217-1515; 412-521-3237.

Indiana Presbyterians Offered Financial Assistance

The Frank L. and Laura L. Smock Foundation offers Presbyterian Indiana residents who are ailing, physically disabled, blind, needy or elderly medical and nursing care assistance. Contact Frank L. and Laura L. Smock Foundation, c/o Norwest Bank Indiana, N.A., P.O. Box 960, Fort Wayne, IN 46801-6632; 219-461-6451.

Three Funds Assist Senior Citizens

1. The de Kay Foundation offers financial subsidies for living expenses to needy NY, NJ and CT residents with no assets. Applications must be submitted by social service agencies. Contact The de Kay Foundation, 1211 Avenue of the Americas, New York, NY 10036; Attn: Jean P. Wilhelm; 212-789-5255.

2. Monetary assistance is available for living expenses such as food and medicine through the Sarah A.W. Devens Trust to economically disadvantaged women over age 65 residing in MA. Contact Sarah A.W. Devens Trust, c/o Rice, Heard & Bigelow, Inc., 50 Congress St., Suite 1025, Boston, MA 02109; 617-557-7415.

3. Supplemental monthly income is available to elderly indigent residents of the Southeastern U.S. through the Alfred I. Dumont Foundation. Contact Alfred I. duPont Foundation, 1650 Prudential Dr., Suite 302, Jacksonville, FL 32207; 904-858-3123.

EMERGENCY Aid AVAİLABLE TO MUSİC TEACHERS

Emergency aid for medical needs is available to U.S. music teachers through the Presser Foundation. Assistance is primarily given to retired teachers. Contact Presser Foundation, 385 Lancaster Ave., #205, Haverford, PA 19041; 610-652-9030.

Oregon Masons Assisted

The Portland Area Acacia Fund provides relief assistance is to distressed Masons and their widows and orphans living in Oregon. Contact Portland Valley Acacia Fund, 709 SW 15th Ave., Portland, OR 97205; 503-228-9405

Health Care Grants

3 Million Seniors & Disabled
Don't Apply for Their Free $1,000 For Health Care

Each year over 3 million eligible seniors and people with disabilities fail to apply for a little-known program that will give them up to an extra $1,051 in their Social Security check. That's how much the government deducts from their Social Security to pay for their Medicare premiums. It amounts to $87.60 a month for couples and $43.80 for individuals. There are three basic programs:

1) *Pays for Medicare premiums, deductibles and co-payments under the Qualified Medicare Beneficiaries (QMBs) plan.*
2) *Pays for Medicare Part B premiums under the Specified Low-Income Medicare Beneficiaries (SLMBs) plan.*
3) *Pays for Medicare Part B premiums under the Qualified Individuals Plan for people with incomes up to $14,892.*

Studies show that only 5,000 of the 500,000 eligible apply for this program. With so few eligible people applying, it's understandable that many people don't know about this program.

Here's where to go. Contact your local Social Security Office. If they don't know, contact your state Office of Social Services. You can also contact the Medicare Hotline and request the publication, *Guide to Health Insurance for People With Medicare*. Contact Medicare Hotline at 800-638-6833; {www.medicare.gov}.

Discounts On Dental And Vision Care

If you live near a university that has a dental or optometry school, then you may be in luck. Many of these schools offer reduced fee services for dental care or vision screening. You will receive treatment from students, but they will be supervised by some of the best people in the field.

These schools also often conduct research studies, so you if you

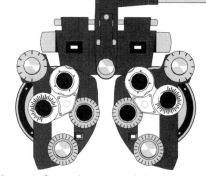

qualify, you may be able to receive treatment for free. My eleven-year-old daughter gets glasses, contacts, plus free contact solution for three years, because she is part of a study on nearsightedness in children. Not a bad deal! To locate schools near you, you can contact American Association of Dental Schools, 1625 Massachusetts Ave., NW, Suite 60, Washington, DC 20036; 202-667-9433; [www.aads.jhu.edu]. You can also contact American Optometric Association, 243 N. Lindbergh Blvd., St. Louis, MO 63141; 314-991-4100; [www.aoanet.org].

Grants Assist with Eye Treatment, Eye Surgery and Low Vision Equipment

The Pearle Vision Foundation offers grants to U.S. residents for low vision equipment. Funding is also available to non-profit organizations for vision-care assistance. Contact Pearle Vision Foundation, 2534 Royal Lane, Dallas, TX 75229; 972-277-6191.

Free Plastic Surgery For Children

Austin Smiles provides free reconstructive plastic surgery, mainly to repair cleft lip and palate, to the children around Austin, Texas. They do about 75 surgeries a year. Austin Plastic Surgery Foundation, P.O. Box 26694, Austin, TX 78755-0694; 512-451-9300; Fax: 512-451-9312; {www. main.org/smiles/}. To see if similar services are available anywhere near you contact Cleft Palate Foundation, 104 S. Estes Dr., Suite 204, Chapel Hill, NC 27514; 800-24-CLEFT; 919-933-9044; {www.cleft.com/ cpf.htm}.

Grants Up To $2,500 and Loans To Finance Adoptions

The National Adoption Foundation helps arrange loans and provides limited grants for parents to cover expenses before and after adoption. They also provide information on sources of other financial help like the 325 Fortune 500 companies who offer an average cash reimbursement of $4,000 for their employees who adopt, or the new adoption expense tax credit that is available from the IRS. Contact: National Adoption Foundation, 100 Mill Plain Rd, Danbury, CT 06811; 203-791-3811.

The following organizations also provide free publications, referral services and advice on adoption and searching for birth relatives:

★ **National Adoption Information Clearinghouse**, 330 C Street, NW, Washington, DC 20447; 888-251-0075; 703-352-3488; {www.calib.com/naic}.
★ **National Adoption Center**, 1500 Walnut St, Suite 701, Philadelphia, PA, 19102; Answer Line: 215-735-9988; {www.adopt.org}.
★ **National Council For Adoption**, 1930 17th Street, NW, Washington, DC 20009; 202-328-8072; fax: 202-332-0935; {www.ncfa-usa.org}.

Camp Wheezeaway Is Free For Kids With Asthma

Every year, about 80 kids with asthma, between 8 and 12 years of age, can go to summer camp for free in Jackson Cap, Alabama. For information on how to apply, contact American Lung Association of Alabama, 900 South 18th St., Birmingham, AL 35205; 205-933-8821.

For more information on other camps for children with asthma, or other questions concerning asthma, contact The American Lung Association, 1740 Broadway, New York, NY 10019; 212-315-8700; 800-LUNG-USA; {www.lungusa.org}.

Free Speech Therapy For Toddlers

It doesn't matter how much money you earn. You can have your child tested to see if any speech problems are developing and even get free speech therapy. It's part of the U.S. Individuals with Disabilities Education Act (IDEA) to make sure that children in need receive special education beginning on their third birthday, and in some states, like Virginia, it starts at age 2.

The program is run through your local school district, so check with them first, or your state Department of Education. You can also contact Division of Educational Services, Office of Special Education Programs, U.S. Department of Education, 330 C St., SW, Washington, DC 20202; 202-205-9172; {www.ed.gov/offices/OSERS/OSEP/osep.html}.

Free Flu Shots

Who should get flu shots? The U.S. Center for Disease Control recommends it for

- adults over 65
- residents of nursing home
- persons over 6 months of age with chronic cardiovascular or pulmonary disorders, including asthma
- persons over 6 months of age with chronic metabolic diseases including diabetes, renal dysfunction, hemoglobinipathies, immunosupressive or immunodeficiency disorders
- women in their 2nd or 3rd trimester of pregnancy during flu season
- persons 6 months to 18 years receiving aspirin therapy
- groups, including household members and care givers who can infect high risk persons

Almost anyone can get free or low cost ($10-$15) flu shots from their county health office or other community sources. Some doctors, like Dr. Donald McGee in New Hampshire {www.drmcgee.com}, offer free shots in their office. Medicare Part B also pays for flu shots.

Contact your county office of public health listed in your telephone book or your state Department of Health. If you have trouble finding a local low cost source, or would like more information on the flu vaccine contact the National Immunization Information Hotline at 800-232-2522 (English); 800-232-0233 (Spanish); {www.cdc.gov/nip}.

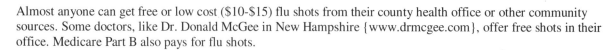

Free Help • At Your Home, • Every Day • For The First 3 Weeks After Childbirth

The Healthy Families America Project operates 300 programs in 40 states. It helps new mothers cope with the pressures of being a new parent by offering volunteer home visitors who come to your home for the first three weeks after birth. They are trained to show you how to deal with the physical, emotional and financial strains of a new baby. First time mothers and older mothers are among those considered for the program.

To see if there is a program in your area and if you qualify, contact National Committee to Prevent Child Abuse, 200 S. Michigan Ave., 17th Floor, Chicago, IL 60604; 312-663-3520; Fax: 312-939-8962; {www.childabuse.org}.

Kids Get Free Expert Care At 22 Hospitals

Children suffering from orthopedic injuries, diseases of the bones, joint and muscles, or burns can get free treatment from one of the 22 Shriners Hospitals. The requirements for admission are that the child is under the age of 18, and there is a reasonable possibility the condition can be helped. For more information, contact Shriners Hospitals, P.O. Box 31356, Tampa, FL 33631; 800-237-5055 (in Canada 800-361-7256); {www.shrinershq.org}.

$1,300 Worth Of Dental Care For Seniors and Disabled

The National Foundation of Dentistry for the Handicapped started the Donated Dental Services program to help disabled and elderly persons who are low-income by matching them with volunteer dentists. Homeless and mentally ill people are also helped.

Volunteer dentists agree to treat one or two people each year with dental problems, and dental laboratories that make dentures, crowns, and bridges also donate services. The program now serves over 500 people each year with each patient receiving an average of $1,300 worth of services. In some areas of the country, Dental House Call projects have been started where dentists will come to homes or centers to provide dental care.

To learn where services are located in your area, contact National Foundation of Dentistry for the Handicapped, 1800 15th St., Unit 100, Denver, CO 80202; 303-534-5360, Fax: 303-534-5290.

Sightless Get Free Seeing Eye Dogs, Training, Travel and Air Fare

Pilot Dogs gives its trained animals to the blind at absolutely no charge. They also include four weeks of training in using the dog and will pay for room and board, all equipment, and round trip transportation. Other groups provide similar services:

* *Pilot Dogs, Inc.*, 625 West Town Street, Columbus, OH 43215; 614-221-6367; fax: 614-221-1577; {www.pilotdogs.org/index.shtml}.
* *Guide Dog Foundation for the Blind, Inc*, 371 East Jericho Tpke., Smithtown, NJ 11787; 800-548-4337; 516-265-2121; {www.guidedog.org}.

Alcohol and Drug Abuse
Counseling & Treatment

Georgia provides outpatient counseling services, short-term residential programs, and even school student assistance programs. Florida provides substance abuse treatment programs through a partnership with 102 public and private not-for-profit community providers. Delaware contracts with private organizations around the state to provide screening, outpatient counseling, and detoxification, as well as short term and long term treatment. Contact your state Department of Health to see what your state has to offer.

There are also nonprofit organizations who, by themselves, offer free treatment to people, like the Center for Drug-Free Living in Orlando, Florida (5029 N. Lane, Suite 8, Orlando, FL 32808; 407-245-0012; {www.cfdfl.com}). If your state can't help you get the information or treatment you need, one or both of the following hotlines should be able to help:

■ *National Drug and Treatment Routing Service*, Center for Substance Abuse Treatment, National Institute on Alcohol Abuse and Alcoholism (NIAAA), 600 Executive Blvd, Willco Bldg., Bethesda, MD 20892; 800-662-HELP; {www.niaaa.nih.gov}.

■ *The National Clearinghouse for Alcohol and Drug Information*, 11426 Rockville Pike, Suite 200, Rockville, MD 20852; 800-729-6686 24 hours a day; 301-468-2600 TDD; {www.health.org}.

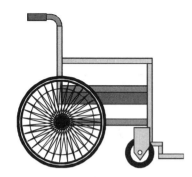

Free Wheelchairs

Easter Seals, the American Cancer Society and other helpful organizations provide free wheelchairs and other medical related equipment, like walkers, commodes, bathtub rails, bathtub chairs, crutches, transfer benches, electric wheelchairs and scooters, on a short- or long-term basis. Some programs require deposits that are completely refundable.

Check with your local office of Easter Seals and the American Cancer Society. You can also contact your state Department of Health.

- *American Cancer Society, Inc.*, 1599 Clifton Road, NE, Atlanta, GA 30329; 800-ACS-2345; {www.cancer.org}.

- *Easter Seals*, 230 West Monroe Street, Suite 1800, Chicago, IL 60606; 800-221-6825; 312-726-6200; fax: 312-726-1494; {www.seals.com}.

MAKE $40,000 & GET FREE PRESCRIPTION DRUGS – EVERYTHING BUT VIAGRA

Valium, Prozac, Dilantin are just a few of the medications you can get FREE directly from the drug companies themselves. That's right: drug companies don't want everybody to know this, but they will give certain people who can't afford their medications their drugs free of charge.

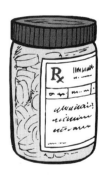

So what's the catch? It sounds too easy. The drug companies require that you participate in their "indigent patient programs." Your doctor needs to write them a note stating that you cannot afford the drugs that you need. Your doctor is the one that needs to call the drug manufacturer. Once the forms are filled out, you will be able to pick up your drugs directly from your doctor's office.

Call the Pharmaceutical Research and Manufacturers of America hotline to receive a listing of the drug companies and their programs. Contact Pharmaceutical Research and Manufacturers of America, 1100 15th St., NW, Washington, DC 20005; 800-PMA-INFO; {www.phrma.org}.

Make $38,657 And Get Free Health Care For Your Kids

Over 4.7 million children are eligible for this program and are not enrolled. Almost every state now has a Children's Health Insurance Program (CHIPS) which extends medical coverage to many children who may not be covered.

A family of four living in Connecticut can make up to $38,657 and get free health care for their children up to 18 years of age. For a family of two, it's $25,487. And a family of four making $49,350 will pay only $30 a month for insurance. Contact Department of Social Services, State of Connecticut, 25 Sigourney St., Hartford, CT 06105; 877-

CT-HUSKY (toll-free); {www.huskyhealth.com/qualify.htm}. A family of four living in Virginia and making up to $30,000 can get free coverage. Contact Department of Medical Assistance Services, 600 E. Broad St., Suite 1300, Richmond, VA 23219; 877-VA-CMSIP (toll free); {http://dit1.state.va.us/~dmas/cmsip.htm}.

Maryland's program covers pregnant women of any age and children up to 19 if the family of four have an income below $32,900. Their program includes dental and vision care. Contact Health Choice, Maryland Department of Health and Mental Hygiene, W. Preston St., Room L, Baltimore, MD 21201; 800-456-8900; {www.dhmh.state.md.us/healthchoice/html/maqanda3.htm}.

Contact your state Department of Health to see what version of the CHIPS program is offered in your area. It is usually part of the state's Medicaid program. A new government hotline can also help you locate free health care for kids. Call toll-free 877-KIDS-NOW (877-543-7669).

Free Care
Even If You Don't Qualify

You or your child may still be able to get free health care from local government programs even if you don't qualify. Many local health offices have the authority to stretch the rules if they see fit. Others have set up special arrangements with the local medical society for people who don't qualify for their programs. These offices can direct you to local nonprofit organizations or groups that can give you the care you need at the price you can afford.

Contact your county office of public health listed in your telephone book or your state Department of Health. If you cannot get satisfaction from these offices, contact your local office of your state or federal elected official.

Free Mammograms /
Free Tests For Breast and Cervical Cancer

An estimated 2 million American women will be diagnosed with breast or cervical cancer in the 1990s, and half a million will lose their lives from these diseases. Screening could prevent up to 30% of these deaths for women over 40.

The government's Center for Disease Control will spend about $145 million a year to maintain a state-by-state program to establish greater access to screening and follow-up services. Each state runs their program a little differently. Most states have the following requirements:

➜ women starting 40 or 50 years old,
➜ are underinsured or have no insurance
➜ have income below a certain level (usually $32,000 or $40,000 for family of 4)

Some states can adjust eligibility requirements for special cases. States vary in the array of services covered but they normally include:

➜ breast and cervical cancer screening
➜ mammograms

<table>
<tr><td>

Cancer Patients Receive Help with Expenses

Limited financial assistance is available through Cancer Care, Inc. to cancer patients and their families who are residents of NY, NJ and CT for home care, child care and transportation expenses. Contact Cancer Care, Inc., 275 7th Ave., 22nd Floor, New York, NY 10001; 212-221-3300.

</td></tr>
</table>

→ treatment if diagnosed with cancer
→ breast reconstruction or prosthesis

States that don't have direct funds for treatment often make arrangements with other facilities to provide treatment for free. If your screening has been done elsewhere, you can still receive free treatment under this program. Men diagnosed with breast cancer can also receive free treatment.

Contact your county office of public health listed in your telephone book or your state Department of Health. You can also contact the main office of this program at Division of Cancer Prevention and Control, National Center for Chronic Disease Prevention and Health Promotion, Center for Disease Control and Prevention, 4770 Buford Highway, NE, MS K-64, Atlanta, GA 30341, 770-488-4751; {www.cdc.gov/nccdphp/dcpc/nbccedp/ index.htm}.

More Free Mammograms

Not all insurance companies pay for mammograms, and not every woman is eligible for the government's program described earlier. The following organizations can help you identify free and low cost mammograms in your area.

1) *The American Cancer Society*: contact your local office the national office at 800-ACS-2345.
2) *YMCA's Encore Plus Program*: contact your local office or the national office at 800-95-EPLUS
3) *National Cancer Institute*: 800-4-CANCER
4) *State Office of Breast and Cervical Cancer*: contact your state Department of Health
5) *October is National Breast Cancer Awareness Month*: many mammogram facilities offer their services at special fees during this period. Call and see what kind of deal you can get.
6) *Medicare coverage of mammograms*: call 800-638-6833

For a free copy of *How To Get A Low Cost Mammogram*, contact National Alliance of Breast Cancer Organizations, (NABCO) 9 East 37th Street, 10th Floor, New York, NY 10016; 800-719-9154; {www.nabco.org}.

Free Hospital Care

Don't have money for your gall bladder surgery? What about that hospital visit you had two months ago? You might not have to pay a cent. Call the Hill-Burton Hotline.

Under this program, certain hospitals and other health care facilities provide free or low-cost medical care to patients who cannot afford to pay. You may qualify even if your income is up to double the Poverty Income Guidelines. That's $32,900 for a family of four! You can apply before or after you receive care, and even after the bill has been sent to a collection agency.

Call the Hotline to find out if you meet the eligibility requirements and to request a list of local hospitals who are participating. For more information, contact Hill-Burton Hotline, Health Resources and Services Administration, 5600 Fishers Lane, Room 11-19, Rockville, MD 20857; 800-638-0742; 800-492-0359 (in MD); {www.hrsa.dhhs.gov/osp/dfcr/about/aboutdiv.htm}.

Free Food At School For Your Kids

A 1998 Tufts University study states: "Children who participate in the U.S. Department of Agriculture's School Breakfast Program were shown to have significantly higher standardized achievement test scores than eligible non-participants. Children getting school breakfasts also had significantly reduced absence and tardiness rates."

Your child can get a free breakfast at one of the 70,000 participating schools at one income level ($21,385 for family of 4) and at a reduced fee at another level ($30,433 for family of 4). Families who pay full price still get a bargain. Over 6.9 million kids participate and 5.9 million get it for free or at a reduced rate. Lunch is also available under the U.S. Department of Agriculture's National School Lunch program at 95,000 schools serving 26 million children. The same general requirements apply to both programs.

Ask your school if they participate, or contact your local School Food Service Authority in your school system. If all this fails, contact your state Department of Education. Check out the Food and Nutrition Services web page at {www.fns.usda.gov/fncs/}.

Rich Kids Pay 2 Cents For Half-Pint of Milk

Milk at this price is available to students, no matter what the family income, at over 8,000 schools, 1,400 summer camps, and 500 non-residential child care institutions. The program is called the U.S. Department of Agriculture's **Special Milk Program** and is available to institutions that do not use the School Breakfast Program or the National School Lunch program.

Ask your school if they participate, or contact your local School Food Service Authority in your school system. If all this fails, contact your state Department of Education. If you cannot get satisfaction from these offices, contact your local office of your state or federal elected official.

Free Immunizations For Your Kids

Only 78% of children receive their full recommended vaccinations that protect them against polio, diphtheria, mumps, whooping cough, German measles, tetanus, spinal meningitis, chicken pox, and hepatitis B. An increasing number of children are exposed to diseases in day-care settings and elsewhere.

Almost any child, no matter what their income, can receive free or very low cost immunizations in their local area. Contact your county office of health listed in your telephone book, or your state Department of Health. If you have trouble, call the National Immunization Information Hotline at 800-232-2522 (English); 800-232-0233 (Spanish); {www.cdc.gov/nip}.

Low Cost Immunizations for Travelers

In order to prevent contracting diseases like Yellow Fever, Cholera or Japanese Encephalitis when traveling in other countries, the government's Center for Disease Control recommends that certain vaccines would eliminate your risk of infection. Some local Public Health offices offer these vaccines at a fraction of what you would pay at a doctor's office.

To find your local county office of health, look in your telephone book or contact your state Department of Health. For more information about disease and vaccines for travel, contact: Center for Disease Control and Prevention, National Center for Infectious Diseases, Division of Quarantine, 1600 Clifton Road, MS E-03, Atlanta, GA 30333; 404-638-8100; Fax: 404-639-2500; {www.cdc.gov/travel/index.htm}.

Fund Helps Foster Independence of Physically Disabled

Individuals with physical disabilities residing in Oregon may be eligible to receive financial assistance through the Blanche Fisher Foundation. The fund assists with the expense of hearing aids, eyeglasses, wheelchairs, ramps, tuition and skills training. Contact Blanche Fisher Foundation, 7912 SW 35th Ave., Suite 7, Portland, OR 97219-2427; 503-819-8205; {Email: bff@bff.org}.

National Immunization Information Hotline

This hotline tells you where you can go locally to get Free Immunization shots for your kids or flu shots for yourself. Immunizations for children can run as much as $335 per child. This program is run by the U.S. Government's Center for Disease Control, which can answer almost any question you have about shots over the telephone or send you free publications. In most areas of the country, immunizations are available FREE for children. Adult services may be free or very low cost. Call 800-232-2522 (English); 800-232-0233 (Spanish); {www.cdc.gov/nip}.

How To Fight Your Doctor, Hospital, Or Insurance Company — Call The Marines

Well, not the actual Marines from the Department of Defense, dressed in fatigues and armed with high tech weapons. But you can call other government offices and advocacy groups that will do your fighting for you or give you the needed weapons to do your own fighting. Before you call a lawyer, call these free offices first:

- *State Insurance Commissioner*: will help you learn your legal rights regarding insurance.
- *State Medical Boards*: will review your complaint (including billing issues) and help resolve disputes.
- *State HMO boards*: will review your complaint (including billing issues) and help resolve disputes.
- *The Center for Patient Advocacy*, 1350 Beverly Road, Suite 108, McLean, VA 22101; 800-846-7444; {www.patientadvocacy.org}: provides free advice and publications on how to fight the system, also does advocacy work for patients rights on Capitol Hill)
- *Center for Medicare Advocacy, Inc*, P.O. Box 350, Willimantic, CT 06226; 860-456-7790; {www.medicareadvocacy.org}. Attorneys, paralegals, and technical assistants provide legal help for elderly and disabled who are unfairly denied Medicare coverage in the states of Connecticut and New York. They will send materials to people in other states to learn how to fight for themselves.
- *American Self Help Clearinghouse*, Northwest Covenant Medical Center, 25 Pocono Road, Denville, NJ 07834; 973-625-9565; Fax: 973-635-8848; TTD 973-625-9053; {www.cmhc.com/selfhelp}: makes referrals to self-help organizations world wide and helps people interested in starting their own self help group.

National Self-Help Clearinghouse, c/o CUNY, Graduate School and University Center, 25 West 43rd St., Room 620, New York, NY 10036; 212-354-8525; Fax: 212-642-1956; {www.selfhelpweb.org}: makes referrals to self-help groups nationwide.

Free Hepatitis B Shots To Children

Oswego County Health Department offers free shots for children 18 and younger. The same with Buena-Vista County in Iowa, but people 19 and over are charged $31.75 for the shot. However, you won't be turned away if you cannot pay.

Hepatitis can cause serious liver disease, cancer and even death. About 1 in 20 people in U.S. have been infected, and over 4,000 a year die. To find out about services in your area, contact the county office of health listed in your telephone book or your state Department of Health.

Medical, Dental and Educational Expense Assistance to Children of Emergency Medical Technicians

Medical and dental assistance is available to children under the age of 18 through the Eagles Memorial Foundation, Inc. Assistance is provided for doctor, dentist and hospital bills, eyeglasses, drugs, and medical and dental devices. Educational Assistance not to exceed $6000/yr. or $30,000/4 yrs. is available through the Eagles Memorial Foundation, Inc. to individuals over the age of 18.

Contact Eagles Memorial Foundation, Inc., 4710 14th St. W., Bradenton, FL 34207; 941-758-5456.

30% of All Families Eligible For Free Health Services — Others Pay Sliding Scale

Many services provided by county governments are free and persons who don't qualify for free services are charged on a sliding scale based on income. A typical fee chart is the one below from Denton, Texas. The data is based on 1996 Federal Poverty Rates from the Bureau of the Census. Denton also states that *NO ONE WILL BE REFUSED SERVICES FOR INABILITY TO PAY*, which is typical for most counties. **REMEMBER**, if you don't qualify for free services, everyone qualifies for services on a sliding scale.

Estimated Income Limits For Free Service			
Service	Single Person	Family of 2	Family of 4
Food Vouchers and Nutritional Info (185% of poverty)	$14,893	$20,073	$30,433
Prenatal Care During Pregnancy (200% of poverty)	$16,100	$21,700	$32,900
Child Medical Care (200% of poverty)	$16,100	$21,700	$32,900
Adult Health Care (150% of poverty)	$12,075	$16,275	$24,675
Dental Care (150% of poverty)	$12,075	$16,275	$24,675

Service	Single Person	Family of 2	Family of 4
HIV Counseling & Testing	No limits, $10.00 donation requested		
Sexually Transmitted Disease Clinic	No limits, $10.00 donation requested		
Tuberculosis	No limits, $4.00 for testing		
Overseas Vaccinations	No limits, $5.00 to $50.00		
Immunizations	No limits, up to $30 per family, no one refused		
Substance Abuse Screening & Referral	No limits, Free		

Estimate of Families Living At Poverty Levels		
% Of Poverty Level	**Number of Families**	**% of Total Families**
100%	12,594,000	12.3%
150%	21,055,000	20.0%
185%	28,174,000	27.4%
200%	30,078,000	29.3%
(Poverty Data from Census Report P60-198 1996 ----One Person = $7,995, Two Persons = $ 10,233, Four Persons = $16,063, Household Income Data from Census Current Population Reports, P60-200) (Poverty Data 7/1/98 USDA {www.usda.gov/fcs/cnp/ieg98-99.htm} 1=$8,050, 2=$10,850, 3=13,650, 4=16,450, 5=19,250, 6=22,050, 7=24,850, 8=27,650		

Grants and Fundraising Help For Transplant Patients

Organizations like The National Foundation for Transplants and National Transplant Assistance Fund assist patients, their families, and friends in raising significant amounts of money for the patient's transplant care when there is no public or private insurance that will cover all the costs. They also provide grants to help pay for medications required after a transplant, or money for transplant-related emergencies, and one-time assistance grants of $1,000.

Other transplant related non-profits, like the Liver Foundation's Liver Transplant Fund, provide services and help for patients and families to raise money for an organ transplant.

❑ *National Foundation for Transplants*, 1102 Brookfield, Suite 200, Memphis, TN 38119; 800-489-3836, 901-684-1697, Fax: 910-684-1128; {www.transplants.org}.

❑ *National Transplant Assistance Fund*, 6 Bryn Mawr Avenue, P.O. Box 258, Bryn Mawr, PA 19010; 800-642-8399; Fax: 610-527-5210; {www.transplantfund. org}.

❑ *American Liver Foundation*, 75 Maiden Lane, Suite 603, New York, NY 10038; 800-GO LIVER; {www.liverfoundation.org}.

Working People With Disabilities Can Get Cheap Health Insurance

A change to the Balanced Budget Act of 1997 passed by Congress allows states to offer Medicaid to individuals who are working and who have a disability. Prior to this, states could only offer Medicaid to people with disabilities who were NOT working. The income limits goes up to $40,000 and the state can charge premiums on an income-related sliding scale.

Contact your state Department of Health to identify your Medicaid office. You can contact the local office of your congressman or senator for more information on the law. You can also check out the website of the Bazelon Center at {www.bazelon.org}.

Free Transportation To Medical Appointments For Your Mom

Mom has to get to a doctor's visit in the middle of the day and you can't take her. Or you have a disability that may cause you to miss an appointment if someone else doesn't drive. You may be able to get free transportation and escort services provided by either your local health office or local office on aging. Some communities even provide very low cost door-to-door services for seniors to go anywhere.

If you can't find your local area agency on aging or public health office in your telephone book, contact your state Department of Aging or Health. If that fails, contact the Eldercare Locator Hotline at 1-800-677-1116. They are available to help anyone identify services for seniors.

Free Health Insurance Counseling

Free one-on-one counseling is available to seniors and, in most areas, people with disabilities, to answer questions like:

- ◆ How much insurance is too much?
- ◆ If something sounds like fraud, where can I go for help?
- ◆ What's the best Medigap insurance plan?
- ◆ Do I qualify for government health benefits?
- ◆ Should I buy long-term care insurance?

The program is called **Health Insurance Counseling and Advocacy Program (HICAP)** and is sponsored by the U.S. Health Care Financing Administration. In most states, it is usually run by the state Department on Aging or the State Insurance Commissioner's office. If that fails, contact the Eldercare Locator hotline at 1-800-677-1116. They can give you the local number.

Free Take Out Taxi For Seniors

People 60 and over who are homebound because of illness, incapacity, or disability, or who are otherwise isolated can receive hot meals delivered to their home. The program is funded in every state by the Older Americans Act. Contact your local area agency on aging or your state Department on Aging. If that fails, contact the Eldercare Locator hotline at 1-800-677-1116. They are available to help anyone identify services for seniors.

Low Cost Home Health Care

Montgomery County in Maryland provides home health care free or on a sliding scale, depending on income, through the local public health office. You don't have to be a senior to qualify.

A survey by the Center for Disease Control reports that about half of all local public health agencies provide similar services. To see what is available in your area, contact your county office of health listed in your telephone book or your state Department of Health. If you cannot get satisfaction from these offices, contact your local office of your state or federal elected official.

For similar services for seniors, contact your local area agency on aging or your state Department on Aging. If that fails, contact the Eldercare Locator hotline at 1-800-677-1116. They are available to help anyone identify services for seniors.

$$$$$ Money To Buy A Van, A Talking Computer Or Rubber Door Knob Grips

People with disabilities now have a place to turn to learn everything they need to know about how the latest in technology can improve their lives. It can be a specially equipped van, a talking computer, a special kitchen or eating aid, or adaptive toys for children. Or it may be a student with learning disabilities who needs special help getting through school.

A project funded by the U.S. Department of Education, called Technical Assistance Project has established an office in each state that can provide:

▲ *Information Services*: will help you identify the special products that are available to help you cope with your disability.

▲ *Equipment Loan Program*: allows people to borrow new technology devices for a number of weeks before they purchase them.

▲ *Recycling Program*: matches up people with needs for products with people who want to sell or donate products.

▲ *Funding Information*: collects information on the various sources of funding for this equipment from public and private sources.

▲ *Loans*: many states are offering special loans to help people purchase the necessary equipment; Ohio offers low interest loans up to $10,000, California has loans up to $20,000, North Carolina up to $15,000.

Contact your state information operator listed in the Appendix and ask for your state Office of Social Services or Vocational Rehabilitation. They should be aware of your state Assistance Technology Office. If you have trouble locating your state office,

---

Easter Seals in Arizona Offers Free Computers to People With Disabilities

Washington State chapter has a free loan program, and the chapters in Missouri offer computer classes. Contact you local Easter Seals Society to see what they may offer in the way of computers and computer skills for people with disabilities. If you can't find your local office, contact: Easter Seals, 230 West Monroe Street, Suite 1800, Chicago, IL 60606; 800-221-6825; 312-726-6200; Fax: 312-726-1494; {www.seals.com}.

---

you can contact the office that coordinates all state activities: Rehabilitation Engineering and Assertive Technology Society of North America, (RESNA), 1700 North Moore Street, #1540, Arlington, VA 22209; 703-524-6686; Fax: 703-524-6630; TTY: 703-524-6639; {www.resna.org}.

Free & Low Cost Dental Care for Kids, Seniors, and Certain Incomes

Many of the local health offices provide dental services to children and to income-eligible adults on a sliding fee scale. Contact your county office of health listed in your telephone book or your state Department of Health.

Many states have special free or discount services just for seniors. Contact your local Area Agency on Aging or your state Department on Aging. If that fails, contact the Eldercare Locator Hotline at 1-800-677-1116.

Service Organizations

Need help with child care, elderly services, substance abuse treatment? What about youth programs or disaster assistance? Many large service organizations have local offices that provide all this and more. Services vary depending upon the needs of the community, but before you fight your battles alone, contact these main offices to find out about local programs:

✦ *Catholic Charities USA*, 1731 King St., #200, Alexandria, VA 23314; 703-549-1390; {www.catholiccharitiesusa.org}.

✦ *Salvation Army*, 615 Slaters Lane, P.O. Box 2696, Alexandria, VA 22313; 703-684-5500; 800-SAL-ARMY; {www.salvationarmyusa.org}.

✦ *United Way of America*, 701 N. Fairfax St., Alexandria, VA 22314; 800-411-UWAY; {www.unitedway.org}.

Free Care By the Best Doctors In The World

Bob Dole knew where to go when he had his cancer surgery — The National Institutes of Health (NIH). Each year, close to 75,000 patients receive free medical care by some of the best doctors in the world. Medical research professionals receive millions of dollars each year to study the latest causes, cures, and treatments to various diseases or illnesses. If your health condition is being studied somewhere, you may qualify for what is called a "clinical trial" and get the treatment for free.

There are several ways to find out about ongoing clinical trials across the nation. Your first call should be to the National Institutes of Health Clinical Center. NIH is the federal government's focal point for health research. The Clinical Center is a 325-bed hospital that has facilities and services to support research at NIH. Your doctor can call the Patient Referral Line to find out if your diagnosis is being studied and to be put in contact with the primary investigator who can then tell if you meet the requirements for the study.

You can also search their website for your diagnosis and qualifying information. In addition, each Institute at NIH also funds research that is conducted by universities, research institutions, and others. To learn about those studies, contact the Institute that handles your diagnosis. Or conduct a CRISP (Computer Retrieval of Information on Scientific Projects) search, which is a database of research projects and programs supported by the U.S. Department of Health and Human Services.

◆ **Clinical Center**, National Institutes of Health, Patient Recruitment, Building 61, 10 Cloister Court, Bethesda, MD 20892; 301-496-4891; 800-411-1222; {www.cc.nih.gov}.

◆ **National Institutes of Health**, Office of Communications, Building 1, Room 344, 1 Center Dr., MSC0188, Bethesda, MD 20892; 301-496-4000; {www.nih.gov}.

◆ **CRISP**, Office of Reports and Analysis, Office of Extramural Research, 6700 Rockledge Dr., Room 3210, Bethesda, MD 20892-7772; 301-435-0656; {www-commons.cit.nih.gov/crisp/}.

Free Eye Care

If you or someone you love needs eye care, but cannot afford it, the following organizations can help:

♥ For those 65 and older: *National Eye Care Project*, American Academy of Ophthalmology (AAO), P.O Box 429098, San Francisco, CA 94142; 415-561-8500; 800-222-3937; {www.eyenet.org}.

♥ For low-income families and children, applications are accepted on a first come-first serve basis in January with treatment following later in the year: *VISION USA*, American Optometric Association, 243 North Linbergh Blvd., St. Louis, MO 63141; 314-991-4100; 800-766-4466; {www.aoanet.org}.

♥ *Lions Clubs International*, 300 22nd St., Oak Brook, IL 60523; 630-571-5466; {www.lionsclubs.org}.

♥ *Glaucoma 2001*, American Academy of Ophthalmology (AAO), P.O Box 429098, San Francisco, CA 94142; 415-561-8500; 800-391-EYES; {www.eyenet.org}.

ARE YOU ELIGIBLE?

Health insurance can be quite confusing. What exactly do you qualify for?

Medicare is a health insurance program, generally for people age 65 or older who are receiving *Social Security* retirement benefits. You can also receive Medicare if you are under 65 and receive Social Security or Railroad Board disability benefits for 24 months, or if you are a kidney dialysis or kidney transplant patient.

Medicaid is a federal program administered by each state, so eligibility and benefits vary from state to state. The program is administered by a state welfare agency, and it provides health insurance to people with low income and limited assets.

To determine your eligibility, contact your state Office of Social Services. For Medicare eligibility, contact Medicare Hotline, Health Care Financing Administration, 6325 Security Blvd., Baltimore, MD 21207; 800-638-6833; {www.medicare.gov}.

Money For New Hearing Aids

You can get information on different types of hearing loss, lists of hearing professionals, and information on locating financial assistance for assistive hearing devices by calling The Better Hearing Institute, P.O. Box 1840, Washington, DC 20013; 800-EAR-WELL; {www.betterhearing.org}.

Discounts On Bicycle Helmets

The Department of Health in Mesa County Colorado offers discounts on bicycle helmets for children in the county. Check with your local office of health to see if there are any programs like this in your area. If not, you can start one with a free *Toolkit for Organizers of Bicycle Helmet Programs* from Bicycle Helmet Safety Institute, 4611 Seventh Street South, Arlington, VA 22204; 703-486-0100; Fax 703-486-0576; {www.helmets.org}. This organization will also send you a free copy of *A Consumer's Guide to Bicycle Helmets*.

EYE CARE HELPLINE

The *National Eye Care Project Helpline* puts callers in touch with local ophthalmologists who have volunteered to provide medical eye care at no out-of-pocket expense. Individuals must be 65 or older and not have had access to an ophthalmologist within the past three years. The emphasis of this program is to help disadvantaged people.

For more information, contact National Eye Care Project Helpline, American Academy of Ophthalmology, P.O. Box 429098, San Francisco, CA 94142-9098; 800-222-3937 (8 a.m.- 4 p.m. PST); {www.eyenet.org}.

Free Help For Cancer Families

Local chapters of the American Cancer Society sponsor a wide range of services for cancer patients and their families, including self-help groups, transportation programs, and lodging assistance for those who must travel far for treatment. To find your local chapter or for more information on cancer detection, prevention and treatment, contact American Cancer Society, 1599 Clifton Rd., NE, Atlanta, GA 30329; 800-ACS-2345; {www.cancer.org}.

Financial Assistance for Ill and Indigent Registered Nurses

Nurses House, Inc. offers short-term financial assistance to ill and indigent U.S. Registered Nurses to help meet basic living expenses. Costs of medical and educational expenses are not funded. Contact Nurses House, Inc., 2113 Western Ave., Suite 2, Guilderland, NY 12084; 518-456-7858.

Grants Assist with Eye Treatment, Eye Surgery and Low Vision Equipment

The Pearle Vision Foundation offers grants to U.S. residents for low vision equipment. Funding is also available to non-profit organizations for vision-care assistance. Contact Pearle Vision Foundation, 2534 Royal Lane, Dallas, TX 75229; 972-277-6191.

Foundation Assists Individuals with Spinal Cord Injuries

The William Heiser Foundation for the Cure of Spinal Cord Injuries, Inc. provides general welfare assistance to individuals with spinal cord injuries residing in the Wantagh, New York area. Contact: William Heiser Foundation for the Cure of Spinal Cord Injuries, 3280 Sunrise Highway, Suite 65, Wantagh, NY 11793; 516-826-11793; {www.go.to/theheiserfoundation}.

Free Legal Help For Living Expenses

Legal Help For Millionaires

No matter what your income, you can get the most powerful organization in the world, *your government*, to fight for you to:

1) Establish paternity;
2) Set up a court order for child support;
3) Track down a missing parent and collect your child support; and even
4) Get the courts to adjust child support orders when circumstances change.

Actually I lied. There are a few states that may charge you up to $25.00. So the maximum you will pay is $25.00. So, why hire an attorney, who may or may not know the law, and will charge you up to $200 an hour, when you can call someone who wrote the law, whose duty is to enforce it for you, and who is free?

Contact your state Child Support Enforcement Office, or contact Office of Child Support Enforcement, U.S. Department of Health and Human Services, 370 L'Enfant Promenade, SW, Washington, DC 20447; 202-401-9383; {www.acf.dhhs.gov/programs/ cse/}.

More Free Legal Services

You don't have to go to your neighbor's brother's cousin's kid who is an attorney, unless you want to pay for his legal advice. Uncle Sam has set up law offices all across the country to help those who cannot afford standard legal fees. It is the Legal Services Corporation's job to give legal help to low-income individuals in civil matters. These offices are staffed by over 6,400 attorneys and paralegals. Each program follows certain guidelines as to what cases it accepts and specific financial eligibility that possible clients must meet.

To learn about the program nearest you, look in the blue pages of your phone book, or contact Legal Services Corporation, 750 First St., NE, 11th Fl., Washington, DC 20002; 202-326-8800.

Get Rid of Neighborhood Troublemakers Without the Police, For FREE

Some states allow local community groups to get tenants or property owners thrown out of the neighborhood — under civil laws, not criminal laws — if they are involved with drugs or are a nuisance to the community. It's easier to enforce a civil law than a criminal law. Which is probably why O.J. Simpson lost his civil trial, but won his criminal trial.

The Community Law Center in Maryland provides free legal assistance to communities in Maryland to enforce these laws. Their services are free to non-profit community groups who seek to rid their neighborhood of troublemakers.

To find out if your community has similar services, contact your state Attorney General's office. The Community Law Center can be reached at 2500 Maryland Avenue, Baltimore, MD 21218; 410-366-0922; Fax: 410-366-7763; {clawc@aol.com}.

10,000 Lawyers That Work For Free

If your income is less than $32,000 (for a family of 4), it's worth checking out the pro bono legal services that are available in your state. And even if your income is more, it's worth checking because some of these services have flexible requirements depending upon your situation and the problem involved. Every year tens of thousands of lawyers volunteer their services to people who need help with almost any kind of problem.

For a listing of pro bono organizations in your state, contact your state bar association listed in your state capitol. The state information operator listed in the Appendix can provide you with a number, or you can contact: American Bar Association 750 N. Lake Shore Dr., Chicago, IL 60611; 312-988-5000; {www.abanet.org/legalservices/probono}.

Free Legal Help With Family, Consumer, Housing, Income, Work, Children and Senior Citizen Issues

Legal Services Corporation is a collection of over 269 government supported local offices that provide free legal services in their area. Over 5000 attorneys and paralegals are available to individuals and families that are under certain income limits. The maximum income can be up to $30,000 for a family of four, or even more depending on certain financial obligations.

To find an office near you, contact your state information operator listed in the Appendix and ask for the Legal Services Office or contact: Legal Services Corporation, 750 First Street NE, 10th Floor, Washington, DC 20002; 202-336-8800; {www.lsc.gov}.

Help For Families Fighting For Veterans Benefits

Through low cost publications, training courses and other services, for 25 years the **National Veterans Legal Services Program** has been helping veterans get their due. Current publications include: *VA Claims*, *Agent Orange*, and *Veterans Family Benefits*. Contact: National Veterans Legal Services Program, P.O. Box 753, Waldorf, MD 20604-0753; 301- 638-1327; 800-688-5VET; Fax 301-843-0159; {www.nvlsp.org}.

Free Lawyers Will Fight For Your Rights

We've all heard of the *American Civil Liberties Union (ACLU)*. They have over 300 offices around the country and handle close to 6,000 cases a year. The ACLU has more than 60 staff attorneys who collaborate with at least 2,000 volunteer attorneys in handling cases. They have appeared before the Supreme Court more than any other organization except the U.S. Department of Justice. If you feel that your civil liberties have been violated, they may take your case. The kinds of issues they are most currently active in include: woman's rights, reproductive freedom, workplace rights, AIDS, arts censorship, capital punishment, children's rights, education reform, lesbian and gay rights, immigrants' rights, national security, privacy and technology, prisoners' rights, and voting rights.

Contact the local ACLU office listed in your telephone directory or the main office website can provide you with a local contact: ACLU - American Civil Liberties Union, 125 Broad Street, 18th Floor, New York, NY 10004-2400; {www.aclu.org/action/chapters.html}.

FREE LEGAL HELP WITH SEXUAL HARASSMENT AT WORK OR SCHOOL

Free Legal Assistance For Domestic Violence Problems

Seven days a week, 24 hours a day, you can call the hotline and not only get access to sources that will solve your immediate problem, but also get information and sources in your area that can explain your legal options and get you through the legal process. Contact: National Domestic Violence Hotline, P.O. Box 161810, Austin, TX 78716; 800-799-SAFE; TTY: 800-787-3224; {ndvh@ndvh.org}; {www.ndvh.org}.

Free assistance to women and girls who are facing sex, or race discrimination, sexual harassment at work or at school, pregnancy, discrimination, or problems with family medical leave and other employment issues related specifically to women. The staff offers information and answers questions, and occasionally can draft "demand" letters, demanding that an employer or other person or organization stop doing something. In some circumstances, they can help you pursue internal grievance or administrative procedures, and in some precedent-setting cases, they will provide legal representation.

Contact: Equal Rights Advocates, 1663 Mission Street, Suite 550, San Francisco, CA 94103; 415-621-0672; Fax: 415-621-6744; Advice and Counseling Line: 800-839-4ERA; {www.equalrights.org}.

Your Family's Rights Under the New Fair Housing Law: Protecting Families with Children from Discrimination

This book is written by one of the country's leading advocates for children's rights. It shows how to tell if families with children have been discriminated against in housing and what to do about it! A great guide for parents, as well as advocates who work with families. 1990 (ISBN: 0-938008-74-9. $4.75, plus $2.00 postage). Contact: Children's Defense Fund, CDF Publications, 25 E Street NW, Washington, DC 20001; 202-628-8787; Fax: 202-628-8333; {www.childrensdefense.org}.

Help For You Or Your Child With A Learning Or Physical Disability

The disability laws not only cover people with disabilities that everyone can see. It's also for children who aren't getting the education they need from the local school, or for the cancer patient who feels discriminated against at work.

A free hotline will help you learn about your rights, help you enforce them, and will even handle some high impact legal cases. Contact: Disability Rights Education and Defense Fund, Inc., 2212 Sixth Street, Berkeley, CA 94710; 510-644-2555 V/TTY; Fax: 510-841-8645; {edf@dredf.org}; {www.dredf.org}.

FREE LEGAL HELP FOR
BREAST CANCER PATIENTS

If you are a breast cancer patient living in California, you maybe eligible to receive free legal assistance on issues such as:

★ Debt collection problems with hospital and doctor bills.
★ Barriers to access to diagnosis and treatment.
★ Negotiations with insurance carriers for coverage and payment options.
★ Housing discrimination.
★ Employment discrimination.
★ Temporary guardianships or modification of custody arrangements.

If you don't live in California, ask them if they are aware of similar services in your area. Contact: Breast Cancer Legal Project, California Women's Law Center, 3460 Wilshire Blvd., Suite 1102, Los Angeles, CA 90010; 213-637-9900; Fax: 213-637-9909; {cwcl@cwcl.org}; {www.cwlc.org/BCLC. intro.html}.

FREE WOMEN'S LAW CENTERS

Rich or poor, women in **Maryland** can get free telephone help in filling out the forms to represent themselves in family court matters that are simple and uncontested. The hotline number is *800-845-8550* and it operates Tuesdays and Thursdays 9:30 am to 4:30 pm. Or women can call the hotline for information on family law issues, such as, how to obtain a separation, child custody, child support, and how to escape domestic violence. Contact: The Women's Law Center of Maryland, Inc., 305 West Chesapeake Ave., Towson, MD 21205; 410-321-8761; {info-flc@ wlcmd.org}; {www.wlcmd.org}.

Women in the state of **Washington** can call a free legal *Information and Referral line* that is staffed with attorneys and paralegals to respond to questions about family law or employment. They also can receive legal rights publications including *Sexual Harassment in Employment and Education*; *Family Law in Washington State: Your Rights and Responsibilities*; and *Grandparents Raising Grandchildren; A Legal Guide for Washington State*. You can also attend free legal workshops, or receive help in filling out legal forms, and free legal consultations in domestic violence cases. Contact: Northwest Women's Law Center, 119 South Main St., Suite 410, Seattle WA 98104-2515; 206 682 9552; Fax: 206 682 9556; Legal Information and Referral: 206-621-7691; {NWWLC@nwwlc.org}; {www.nwwlc.org}.

Free Help With Welfare Rights

Over 157 local organizations around the country fight for the rights of low-income people on welfare. These organizations can be a good place to turn to insure that you are getting the proper benefits, and for knowing your rights in dealing with the bureaucracy.

You can contact your local social services agency to locate an office near you or the website for the Welfare Law Center that contains a directory of all the organizations. Contact: Welfare Law Center, 275 Seventh Ave., Suite 1205, New York, NY 10001; 212-633-6967; {dirk@ welfarelaw.org}; {www.lincproject.org/lid/lid.html}.

Free Legal Help To Fight For Your Home Schooling Rights

The Home School Legal Defense Association (HSLDA) provides legal help for members on home schooling issues. Families receive legal consultation by letter and phone, and representation for negotiations with local officials, and court proceedings.

HSLDA also takes the offensive, filing actions to protect members against government intrusion and to establish legal precedent. On occasion, HSLDA will handle precedent-setting cases for non-members, as well. Contact: HSLDA, P.O. Box 3000, Purcellville, VA 20134; 540-338-5600; Fax: 540-338-2733; {www.hslda.org}.

Free Legal Rights For Women's Issues

The National Organization for Women Legal Defense and Education Fund (NOW LDEF) has a hotline that provides free information and referrals on women's issues including reproductive rights, violence against women, economic justice, and gender equity in education. They also provide low-cost legal guides, some of which are available free on the Internet, on the following topics:

- ➡ *A Guide to Court Watching in Domestic Violence and Sexual Assault Cases*
- ➡ *Divorce and Separation*
- ➡ *Domestic Violence and Child Custody*
- ➡ *Employment Sexual Harassment & Discrimination* (Spanish)
- ➡ *Incest and Child Sexual Abuse*
- ➡ *Pregnancy & Parental Leave*
- ➡ *Sexual Harassment in Housing*
- ➡ *Sexual Harassment in the Schools*
- ➡ *Sexual Harassment in the Schools: A Blueprint for Action* (Spanish)
- ➡ *Stalking*
- ➡ *Violence Against Women*
- ➡ *How to Find a Lawyer* (free)

Contact: NOW LDEF, 395 Hudson Street, New York, NY 10014; 212-925-6635 (9:30 a.m. to 11:00 p.m. EST); Fax: 212-226-1066; email your question to {astrubel@ nowldef.org}; {www.nowldef.org}.

Free Legal Help To Fight Your Union At Work

If you feel your rights have been violated by compulsory unionism, or you simply have a question about your Right to Work, legal experts are available for free to help answer your questions. Contact: The National Right to Work Legal Defense Foundation, 8001 Braddock Rd., Springfield, VA 22160; 800-336-3600; {www.nrtw.org}.

Free Consulting Services In Sex Discrimination Law Suits

If, as a woman, you feel discriminated against in higher education, the Legal Advocacy Fund (LAF) of the American Association of University Women (AAUW) may be able to help by providing financial support for sex discrimination lawsuits. LAF organizes a network of volunteer attorneys and social scientists who consult with women on legal strategy, informational resources, and the strength of current or potential lawsuits.

To find out if you're eligible, please contact: AAUW Legal Advocacy Fund, Dept. LAF.INT., American Association of University of Women, 1111 16th St., NW, Washington, DC 20036; 800-326-AAUW; Fax: 202-872-1425; TDD: 202-785-7777; {E-mail: info@aauw.org}; {www.aauw.org}.

Legal Assistance for Overseas Teachers

Free legal aid is available for teachers employed in U.S. Department of Defense schools overseas and are members of the *Federal Education Association (FEA)*. The FEA legal staff conducts arbitration and other legal actions to insure the rights and benefits of teachers. Contact: Federal Education Association, 1201 16th St. NW, Washington, DC 20036; 202-822-7850; Fax: 202-822-7867 (legal/ president); {FEA_Legal/Pres@odedodea.edu} (legal office, president); {www.feaonline.org}.

Free Legal Help For Pregnant Teens Discriminated In Honors Society

Feminists for Life of America, along with the ACLU, got the a federal court to rule that two high school seniors, whose school denied them National Honor Society membership because they became pregnant and chose to give birth, must be admitted into the society. For free legal information on these kinds of issues, contact Feminists for Life of America, 733 15th St. NW, Suite 1100, Washington, DC 20005; 202-737-FFLA; {www.serve.com/fem4life/index.htm}.

Free Legal Help On Civil Liberties and Rights

The Rutherford Institute defends people who have been denied civil and human rights without charging them for such services. The issues they cover include civil liberties, religious freedom, parental rights, and sexual harassment. You may remember them from their involvement in the Paula Jones case.

If you need legal help, contact The Rutherford Institute, Legal Department, P.O. Box 7482, Charlottesville, VA 22906; 804-978-3888; {www.rutherford.org}.

FREE HELP COLLECTING CHILD SUPPORT

An association of concerned parents helps others learn about their rights and the remedies available for collecting what is due to them. Some services are free, others are for those who join for only $20. They can show you that you don't need to use a professional collection agency, and they will even contact officials on your behalf.

Contact: Association for Children for Enforcement and Support (ACES), 260 Upton Ave., Toledo, OH 43006; 800-537-7072; Fax: 419-472-5943; {www.childsupport-aces.org}.

Free Legal Help for Lesbians, Gay Men and People With HIV/AIDS

Lambda carries out carries out legal work on issues such as discrimination in employment, housing, public accommodations, and the military; HIV/AIDS-related discrimination and public policy issues; parenting and relationship issues; equal marriage rights; equal employment and domestic partnership benefits; "sodomy" law challenges; immigration issues; anti-gay initiatives; and free speech and equal protection rights. If you are seeking assistance with a legal matter, contact one of the offices listed below. They can guide you to a solution or help you directly:

National Headquarters Lambda
120 Wall Street, Suite 1500
New York, NY 10005-3904
212-809-8585
Fax: 212-809-0055

Western Regional Office
6030 Wilshire Boulevard
Los Angeles, CA 90036-3617
323-937-2728
Fax: 323-937-0601

Midwest Regional Office
11 East Adams, Suite 1008
Chicago, IL 60603-6303
312-663-4413
Fax: 312-663-4307

Southern Regional Office
1447 Peachtree Street, NE, Suite 1004
Atlanta, GA 30309-3027
404-897-1880
Fax: 404-897-1884

Lambda's website is {www.lambdalegal.org}.

Paralegals Offer Legal Work at 75 % Discount

The only things a paralegal can't do that a lawyer can, is give legal advice and represent you in court. That means they can file uncontested divorce papers, family court petitions, wills and probate, power of attorney, bankruptcy, incorporation. etc.

There are states where paralegals can represent clients in cases like those involving evictions or government agencies. And if you are seeking a legal opinion from an attorney, you may want to get a paralegal to research the law for you, so that you can make your own decisions.

Remember 50% of all lawyers lose their cases in court. So why pay $200 an hour for a lawyer, when you can get a lot of the same services done for less than $50 and hour. Paralegals are in the yellow pages and you can contact your state or local paralegal association by contacting the national association that can give you a local contact. For more information, contact National Federation of Paralegal Associations, P.O. Box 33108, Kansas City, MO 64114; 816-941-4000; Fax: 816-941-2752; {www.paralegals. org}.

FREE LEGAL LATINO HELP

The Mexican American Legal Defense and Educational Fund (MALDEF) is a national nonprofit organization whose mission is to protect and promote the civil rights of the more than 29 million Latinos living in the United States in the areas of education, employment, political access, and more. They take cases to court and provide other legal help for the Latino community. Contact: MALDEF, 634 South Spring St., 11th Floor, Los Angeles, CA 90014; 213-629-2512; Fax: 213-629-0266; {www.maldef.org}.

Fight Your Bank, Credit Card Company, Etc.

Finding the right bank, savings and loan, or credit union means figuring out your own needs first. How much money can you keep on deposit and how many checks will you write? Examine your future loans and savings needs, as well as look at the convenience of the financial institution, its service charges, fees, and deposit and loan interest rates. You can contact one of the following offices to learn more. These offices will also help you if you think the bank is messing with your money.

National Banks (banks that have the word "National" in their names or the intitals "N.A." after their names)
> Comptroller of the Currency
> U. S. Department of the Treasury
> Customer Assistance Group
> 1301 McKinner St.
> Suite 3710
> Houston, TX 77010
> 800-613-6743
> {www.occ.treas.gov}

FDIS-Insured Banks
> Office of Consumer Affairs
> Federal Deposit Insurance Corporation
> 550 17th St., NW
> Room F-130
> Washington, DC 20429
> 202-898-3542

> 800-934-3342
> {www.fdic.gov}

Savings and Loans
> Office of Thrift Supervision
> U.S. Department of Treasury
> 1700 G St., NW
> Washington, DC 20552
> 202-906-6237
> 800-842-6929
> {www.ots.treas.gov}

State Banks
> Contact your State Government Banking Commissioner located in your state capital (look in the blue pages of your phone book or contact your state capitol operator).

Housing Discrimination

Buying your first home is a very exciting time. But for many, house shopping is more than an eye opening experience. Some people are not shown houses in particular neighborhoods or are denied a home because of their sex, race, or living arrangement. If you feel you have been treated unfairly, contact office of Fair Housing and Equal Opportunity, U.S. Department of Housing and Urban Development, 451 7th St., SW, Room 5100, Washington, DC 20410; 202-708-4252; 800-669-9777; {www.hud.gov}.

Discrimination Because You're A Woman, Pregnant, Person of Color, etc.

There's no need to take harassment or bullying on the job. Here is your chance to fight back. If you believe you have been discriminated against by an employer, labor union, or employment agency when applying for a job or while on the job because of race, color, sex, religion, national origin, age, or disability, you may file a charge with the Equal Employment Opportunity Commission (EEOC). For more information, contact Equal Employment Opportunity Commission, 1801 L St., NW, Washington, DC 20507; 800-669-4000; {www.eeoc.gov}.

Lawyers, Accountants, Pharmacists, Doctors, Real Estate Agents, and Other Professionals

Lawyer over-charging you? Do you feel you have been mistreated by your doctor?

These issues and more are handled by the agency or board that licenses that particular profession. Whether it is your accountant, real estate agent, doctor, dentist, or other professional, you can contact the licensing board directly to file a grievance. These boards will then help you to resolve the problem. To locate the correct board usually located in your state capital, contact your state operator.

Retailers, Mail Order Companies, Auto Dealers, Contractors, Etc.

You go to a store to get the best price on the gift for Uncle George, only to learn that the store is out of stock despite the product being advertised in the paper. Did the salesman try to get you to buy a higher priced item? You could be the victim of the old bait and switch scam. Is the paint peeling off of the new toy doll you bought your daughter? Problems dealing with your car dealership or car repair shop? (This is the number one complaint heard.) What about the contractor that has yet to finish the job?

There are ways to deal with all these problems and get them resolved to your satisfaction. You just need to pull in the big guns. The States' Attorney General's Offices have Consumer Protection Offices, and many also have separate offices that handle only car complaints. They will take your complaint and try to help you get the satisfaction you deserve. For other problems contact:

♦ *Defective Products* — contact Consumer Product Safety Commission, 5401 Westbard Ave., Washington, DC 20207; 800-638-2772; {www.cpsc.gov}.
♦ *Contractor or Licensed Professional Problems* — contact the state Licensing Board for the profession located in your state capitol. You can contact the state operator for assistance in finding the office.
♦ *Mail Order Problems* — contact the U.S. Postal Service, Public Affairs Branch, 475 L'Enfant Plaza, SW, Room 3140, Washington, DC 202060; 202-268-5400; {www.usps.gov}.
♦ *Fraud Issues* — contact Federal Trade Commission, Public Reference, CRC-2480, Washington, DC 20580; 202-382-4357, 877-FTC-HELP; {www.ftc.gov}.

Where to Get Help to Stop Sexual Harassment

Call **"9 to 5"** if you experience any of the following at work:

➡ Suggestive comments about your appearance
➡ Unwanted touching or other physical contact
➡ Unwanted sexual jokes or comments
➡ Sexual advances

Sexual harassment is not only offensive, it's against the law. It is illegal even if the harasser is not your boss, even if he is not threatening that you will lose your job if you don't go along. 9to5's **toll free job problem hotline** and trained job counselors give information and support to thousands of working women.

If you decide to pursue a legal remedy, contact your state discrimination agency or the federal Equal Employment Opportunity Commission (look in your phone book for the field office closest to you). The federal agency covers workplaces of 15 or more. State law covers workplaces with fewer employees.

Contact: 9to5, National Association of Working Women, 1430 West Peachtree St., Suite 610, Atlanta, GA 30309; 800-522-0925; {www.9to5.org}.

HOW AN ABUSER CAN DISCOVER YOUR INTERNET ACTIVITIES
(And what you can do about it)

The *American Bar Association's (ABA) Commission on Domestic Violence* has issued a warning concerning possible threats to you if an abuser has access to your e-mail account and thus may be able to read your incoming and outgoing mail. If you believe your account is secure, make sure you choose a password he or she will not be able to guess. If an abuser sends you threatening or harassing e-mail messages, they may be printed and saved as evidence of this abuse. Additionally, the messages may constitute a federal offense.

For more information on this issue, contact your local United States Attorney's Office. For more information about what you can do, and the efforts of the ABA's Commission on Domestic Violence, please contact American Bar Association Commission on Domestic Violence, 740 15th Street, NW, 9th Floor, Washington, DC 20005-1022; 202-662-1737/1744; Fax: 202-662-1594, {E-mail: abacdv@abanet.org}; {www.abanet.org}.

Free Legal Help If Your Child Is Suspended or Expelled From School

"Zero Tolerance" and other school system disciplinary practices can place your child's education in jeopardy if you are not aware of your rights. Your first meeting with the principal on such matters can actually serve as a trial for your child's future.

The School House Legal Services of Baltimore, Maryland provides free attorneys and paralegals to represent Maryland families in these matters. Maryland has an income limit for representation that is about $30,000 for a family of four, but information about the process is free.

If you don't live in Maryland, contact your local Legal Services Office or your State Department of Education for more information and help. School House Legal Services can be reached at Maryland Disability Law Center, 1800 N. Charles St., Suite 202, Baltimore, MD 21201; 410-727-6352.

Emergency Shelter, Housing & Counseling For Violence Victims

If violence is ripping your life apart, you have nowhere to go, and you do not know how to reclaim your life, the YWCA, the nation's leading provider of shelter and services to women and their families can help you! In the United States, more than 650,000 people come to the YWCA each year for services and support overcome violence. For more information about the services offered in your state, contact your local YWCA.

The YWCA takes a holistic approach to helping women escape, recover from and prevent violence in their lives and the lives of their families. Many local YWCAs offer programs and services including emergency shelter for women and children, transitional housing, support to victims of rape and sexual assault, individual and group counseling, peer support, self-defense training, programs for batterers and legal advocacy.

Contact: YWCA of the U.S.A., Empire State Building, Suite 301, 350 Fifth Ave., New York, NY 10118; 212-273-7800; Fax: 212- 465-2281; {www.ywca.org}. National Domestic Violence Hotline 800-799-SAFE; hearing impaired 800-787-3224.

Lawyer's Referral Service

The *American Bar Association's* lawyer referral service is designed to assist you in finding the appropriate service-provider to help you solve your legal problem. There are two steps to this process: first, helping you determine whether you need to see a lawyer, and second, referring you to a lawyer who handles your type of case or to an appropriate community or governmental agency if that will be of more help to you. Lawyer referral can also provide you with information on procedures in the courts and legal system in your community.

When you contact lawyer referral, be prepared to briefly describe your situation so that the consultant can determine what kind of help you need. Lawyer Referral does not offer legal advice or free legal services. If you are referred to an attorney, you are entitled to a half-hour initial consultation at no charge, or for a nominal fee that goes to fund the lawyer referral service's operation. If additional legal services are required, you may choose to hire the lawyer. It is important to discuss legal fees and costs with the lawyer. We strongly recommend that you and the lawyer sign a written fee agreement, so that there is no question about what services the lawyer will perform, and what those services will cost you.

Contact your state Bar Association listed in your state capitol or The American Bar Association, 750 N. Lake Shore Dr., Chicago, IL 60611; 312-988-5000; {E-mail: info@abanet.org}; {www.abanet.org}.

When All Else Fails

People forget that they can turn to their representative or senators for help resolving a complaint. You vote these people into office, and most of them want to stay there. They know that if they can help you, then you and your family will vote for them in each and every election.

Their offices have case managers whose job is to cut the red-tape and push your case through quickly. Look in your phone book for their local office or you can call U.S. House of Representatives, Washington, DC 20515; 202-224-3121; {www.house.gov}; or U.S. Senate, Washington, DC 20510; 202-224-3121; {www.senate.gov}.

GRANTS FOR THE
ARTS AND HUMANITIES

The Arts and Humanities

One of the greatest sources of funds from the government comes
from the National Endowment for the Arts and National
Endowment for the Humanities. In the year 2000, over
$177,400,000 was awarded throughout the country, about 30% of
which is funding that is administered through state arts and
humanities councils. That's a heck of a lot of money! But if you
know how to access it, some of that chunk might be able to help
you. Federal and state funding for the arts and humanities is one
of the only ways that both of these vital areas can be kept alive,
and in doing so help to keep the American cultural scene bustling
with activity.

Maybe you or your group would like to sponsor a talk at your
local library, or bring a dance group to a school -Arts and
Humanities funding is the place to go for financial assistance.
Funding also helps get traveling exhibits off the ground and helps train teachers in both the arts and humanities.
There are even fellowships available in both areas to assist artists and scholars alike. Take David Shevlino, for
example. Like most professional artists, he knew where to look for grants. "It's pretty common knowledge among
people in the arts." This painter from Wilmington, Delaware is able to pursue his art career in part due to funding he
has received in the form of fellowships. David followed the simple application process, which he says is pretty
straightforward and when he had any questions, found the councils to which he was applying more than willing to
give him a hand. Many, many artists are able to benefit from this type of individual fellowship. Look at the
following examples from around the country!

Heidi Hart	PA	$10,000	Dance
Kimi Takesue	PA	$10,000	Media Arts
Ivy H. Goodman	MD	$1000	Fiction
Katja Oxman	MD	$6000	Visual Arts
Chuck Holdeman	DE	$10,000	Music
Doug Sharples	SD	$3000	Documentary Film
Kathy Kissik	RI	$5000	Photography
J. Carlos Ferguson	VA	$4500	Painting
Jon Pineda	VA	$5000	Poetry
Dale Lynn Aadland	SD	$3000	Printmaking

Of course there are all types of programs to meet many levels of needs in the Arts and Humanities world. And
there's help to get that funding! As a matter of fact, a lot of the funding agencies have proposal writing workshops,
and most of them prefer that you consult with their staff prior to submitting your application. They will actually help
you through the process so that your project may be more likely to receive funding! So get out there and get yourself
or your community some monies to help enhance your cultural lives!

The information that follows in this chapter outlines the programs available through the National Endowment for the
Arts and the National Endowment for the Humanities, as well as each state's arts and humanities organizations. But
remember, those are not the only sources. We also list private arts organizations that provide grants funding, but all
of these are only the tip of the iceberg. Many cities and counties have their own arts councils, willing to assist those

local artists in the creation or performance of their work. Search for those by contacting your city or county government, as well as your state arts or humanities organization.

Now don't forget to read the first part of this book, "Types of Assistance and Grants Sources," as well as "More Help In Finding a Grant." These sections provide some great starting places for your money hunt. Many arts or humanities organizations can benefit from checking out the federal government's Non-Profit Gateway at {www.nonprofit.gov}. This site provides wonderful links to departments and agencies that have programs of interest to you. You can also usually find out what types of programs have been funded before to give you an idea of how your project matches with the program.

The Foundation Center is an online "gateway to philanthropy on the World Wide Web." Along with a large database of philanthropic organizations, including links to funding groups and corporate and private foundations, there are links and information on how to write a proposal, how to establish a nonprofit organization, tax info and how to receive grants for individuals. There is also an extensive library, and several books that deal specifically with the arts and humanities. For further information, contact the Foundation Center, 79 Fifth Avenue, New York, NY 10003; 800-424-9836; 202-331-1400; {http://fdncenter.org}.

Other resources to check out include:

- ArtJob which is a comprehensive site listing of not only employment opportunities in the art field, but internships, fellowships, conferences, and more. Contact artjobonline, 1543 Champ St., Suite 220, Denver, CO 80202; 888-JOBS-232; 303-629-1166; Fax: 303-629-9717; {www.artjob.org}.
- Art Deadline List provides a listing of opportunities for artists to enter competitions and contests, as well as apply for grants, scholarships, fellowships, and more. Check it out at {www.xensei.com/adl}.
- Arts Wire is an online magazine for the arts community, and includes articles, up-coming conferences, nonprofit resources, links to other sites, and much more. They also provide links to organizational member sites that include many local arts organizations. Check it out at {www.artswire.org}.
- World Wide Arts Resources provides information and resources for the arts community, including links to arts organizations, funding opportunities, arts news, portfolios, and more. Check them out at {www.wwar.com}.

The Arts

National Endowment for the Arts

National Endowment for the Arts
1100 Pennsylvania Avenue NW
Washington, DC 20506
202-682-5400
www.arts.gov

Although government administrations come and go, and controversy over public funding of provocative art rages and wanes, the National Endowment for the Arts continues to be the ultimate source of public money for the arts. For the year 2000, the NEA will give away $79.6 million in grants. As required by Congress, 40 percent, ($33.3 million) of that money goes to regional, state and local organizations that, in turn, distribute grants to local artists and organizations. (See page 478 for a listing of these important funding sources.)

You've probably seen the NEA's prestigious logo in the credits for a public television broadcast or in the printed program when the touring company from a big city opera came to town. But as an artist or presenter, you shouldn't feel that your project is not big enough to merit the NEA's attention. In fact, it's quite rare for the NEA to give a grant of $100,000 or more. Grants of $25,000 or less are far more common.

Consider these recent grants, all of which will give you a sense of what wide-ranging, yet modest, proposals are supported by the NEA.

Dayton, Ohio's Cityfolk serves a community that is 40 percent African American and 30 percent Appalachian. Cityfolk, which is the only full-time, professional presenter of traditional and ethic performing arts in the state, offers a concert season and a large summer folk festival. Cityfolk received $20,000 from the NEA in 1999 to allow it to provide additional educational programming-school and community residencies, folk arts demonstrations and "meet the artist" discussion sessions, special artist workshops, and other materials.

Cornerstones Community Partnerships in Santa Fe, New Mexico, received a $50,000 grant to support the preservation of historic adobe structures through technical assistance workshops for community-based restoration projects. Cornerstones helps rural communities throughout New Mexico preserve historic adobe buildings that are central to the Hispanic and Native American cultures of the Southwest. The grant will help Cornerstones sponsor and coordinate volunteer workdays in approximately 40 communities, provide training to volunteers, help local residents acquire the proper building supplies, lend necessary tools, and recruit additional volunteer labor.

The **Indiana State Symphony Society, Inc./Indianapolis Symphony Orchestra** received a $20,000 grant to support the Neighborhood Harmony Project, an outreach project with community centers in Indianapolis where the orchestra will provide music performances and educational programs for children in low-income families.

NEA grant applications are geared toward organizations. What that means for you is that, with a few exceptions, if you are an individual artist hoping to finish the novel you started or to paint a mural for your library, you need to work with a sponsoring organization. For instance, you could work on your novel at a writers' workshop or with the library board to design the mural. In both cases, it would be the writers' workshop and the library that would apply for the grant.

The NEA offers five different types of grants to organizations:

Creativity: Creation and Presentation of Artistic Work. These grants are intended to support the creation and refinement of artistic work, within or across art forms or disciplines. They also support public presentation, exhibition, performance, or publication of high quality works of all cultures and periods. (Literature must focus on contemporary writers.)

Organizational Capacity: Developing Strong and Valued Arts Organizations. These grants support projects that develop future arts leaders and enhance the skills of those already working in the field, as well as other projects that help arts organizations become more effective and adaptable.

Access: Access to the Arts for All. These grants support activities including exhibitions, performances, distribution of artistic work, and innovative uses of new technology that enhance public access to the arts, and touring and outreach projects that involve diverse communities and reach new audiences.

Education: Lifelong Education in the Arts. These grants support activities that promote the arts as an integral part of education for Americans of all ages and professional development opportunities for artists, arts professionals, teachers and others working in the arts with students at the elementary or secondary school level.

Heritage/Preservation: Preservation of Our Cultural Heritage. These grants are intended for festivals, exhibits, and other presentations that reflect and increase the public's appreciation for our diverse cultural traditions, for apprenticeships and other forms of instruction that pass artistic repertoire, techniques and traditions on to future generations, and for the documentation, recording or conservation of highly significant works or collections of art, artifacts or designed elements, or of cultural traditions.

If and when you decide you want to pursue one of these grants, you'll need to contact the NEA office (listed below) that oversees grants for your art form. Before you call, check out the NEA's web sites for these disciplines as well; you'll find lots of helpful information to make your call more productive.

Arts Education
AIE/Music/Opera/Presenting/Multidisciplinary
National Endowment for the Arts
1100 Pennsylvania Ave, NW, Suite 703
Washington, DC 20506
202-682-5438 (voice)
202-682-5002 (fax)
202-682-5496 (TDD/TTY)
www.arts.gov/artforms/Artsed/Artsed3.html

Arts Management
Partnership, Planning & Stabilization
National Endowment for the Arts
1100 Pennsylvania Avenue, NW, Suite 726
Washington, DC 20506
202-682-5429 (voice)
202-682-5602 (fax)
202-682-5496 (TDD/TTY)
www.arts.gov/artforms/Manage/Manage2.html

Dance
Dance/Design/Media Arts/Museums/Visual Arts
National Endowment for the Arts
1100 Pennsylvania Ave, NW, Suite 726
Washington, DC 20506
202-682-5452 (voice)
202-682-5721 (fax)
202-682-5496 (TDD/TTY)
www.arts.gov/artforms/Dance/Dance3.html

Design
Dance/Design/Media Arts/Museums/Visual Arts
National Endowment for the Arts
1100 Pennsylvania Ave, NW, Suite 726
Washington, DC 20506
202-682-5429 (voice)
202-682-5602 (fax)
202-682-5496 (TDD/TTY)
www.arts.endow.gov/artforms/Design/Design3.html

Film, Television, and Radio
Dance/Design/Media Arts/Museums/Visual Arts
National Endowment for the Arts
1100 Pennsylvania Ave, NW, Suite 726

Washington, DC 20506
202-682-5452 (voice)
202-682-5721 (fax)
202-682-5496 (TDD/TTY)
www.arts.gov/artforms/Media/Media3.html

Folk & Traditional Arts
Folk & Traditional Arts/Literature/Theater/Musical
Theater/Planning & Stabilization
National Endowment for the Arts
1100 Pennsylvania Ave, NW, Suite 720
Washington, DC 20506
202-682-5428 (voice)
202-682-5669 (fax)
202-682-5496 (TDD/TTY)
www.arts.gov/artforms/Folk/Folk1.html

Literature
Folk & Traditional Arts/Literature/Theater/Musical
Theater/Planning & Stabilization
National Endowment for the Arts
1100 Pennsylvania Ave, NW, Suite 720
Washington, DC 20506
202-682-5428 (voice)
202-682-5512 (fax)
202-682-5496 (TDD/TTY)
www.arts.gov/artforms/Lit/Lit3.html

Multidisciplinary
Multidisciplinary Projects
AIE/Music/Opera/Presenting/Multidisciplinary
National Endowment for the Arts
1100 Pennsylvania Ave, NW, Suite 726
Washington, DC 20506
202-682-5429 (voice)
202-682-5602 (fax)
202-682-5496 (TDD/TTY)
www.arts.gov/artforms/Multi/Multi1.html

Museums and Visual Arts
Museums and Visual Arts
Dance/Design/Media Arts/Museums/Visual Arts
National Endowment for the Arts
1100 Pennsylvania Ave, NW, Suite 726

Washington, DC 20506
202-682-5452 (voice)
202-682-5721 (fax)
202-682-5496 (TDD/TTY)
www.arts.gov/artforms/Museums/Museum1.html

Music
AIE/Music/Opera/Presenting/Multidisciplinary
National Endowment for the Arts
1100 Pennsylvania Ave, NW, Suite 703
Washington, DC 20506
202-682-5438 (voice)
202-682-5002 (fax)
202-682-5496 (TDD/TTY)
www.arts.gov/artforms/Music/Music1.html

Opera
Division of Education & Access
National Endowment for the Arts
1100 Pennsylvania Ave, NW, Suite 726
Washington, DC 20506
202-682-5438 (voice)
202-682-5002 (fax)

202-682-5496 (TDD/TTY)
www.arts.gov/artforms/Opera/Opera3.html

Presenting
AIE/Music/Opera/Presenting/Multidisciplinary
National Endowment for the Arts
1100 Pennsylvania Ave, NW, Suite 703
Washington, DC 20506
202-682-5438 (voice)
202-682-5002 (fax)
202-682-5496 (TDD/TTY)
www.arts.gov/artforms/Presenting/Presenting1.html

Theater
Folk & Traditional Arts/Literature/Theater/Musical
Theater/Planning & Stabilization
National Endowment for the Arts
1100 Pennsylvania Ave, NW, Suite 720
Washington, DC 20506
202-682-5428 (voice)
202-682-5512 (fax)
202-682-5496 (TDD/TTY)
www.arts.gov/artforms/Theater/Theater1.html

Securing Grants from Local, State and Regional Arts Organizations

Unfortunately, your money worries won't go away with a grant from the NEA. In fact, organizations are required to match NEA grants dollar-for-dollar with funds from other sources. So even if you're thinking globally, you'll have to begin by looking for financial support locally. Start with your local, state, or regional arts council. (Look in the phone book for your local arts organization. Sometimes these groups have names that aren't obvious, such as YourTown ArtLink, so call your local government office or the state arts council if you need help finding them. Information on state and regional arts councils is listed below.) You should also check out the NEA's web page, "Cultural Funding: Federal Opportunities" {www.arts.gov/federal.html}, which is a resource that points you to an array of funding opportunities supported by federal dollars at the national, regional, state and local levels.

Regional, State and Local Arts Agencies

Regional Arts Organizations

Arts Midwest

(Serves Illinois, Indiana, Iowa, Michigan, Minnesota, North Dakota, Ohio, South Dakota, Wisconsin)
Hennepin Center for the Arts
528 Hennepin Avenue, Suite 310
Minneapolis, MN 55403
612-341-0755
TT/Voice: 612-341-0901
www.artsmidwest.org
Arts Midwest gave $350,000 in grants through The Heartland Fund in 1999. The Heartland Fund provides up to $5,000 per performing group to organizations in the 15 states covered by Arts Midwest and the Mid-America Arts Alliance to pay for 15 to 30 percent of artists' fees for performances and educational activities by theater, dance, and music ensembles. Presenting organizations can apply for funds to pay for up to five different performing groups or a total dollar amount of $13,000.

Consortium for Pacific Arts & Cultures

2141C Atherton Road
Honolulu, HI 96822
808-946-7381

Mid-America Arts Alliance

(Serves Arkansas, Kansas, Missouri, Nebraska, Oklahoma, Texas)
912 Baltimore Avenue, Suite 700
Kansas City, MO 64105
816-421-1388
www.maaa.org
The Heartland Fund provides up to $5,000 per performing group to organizations in the 15 states covered by Arts Midwest and the Mid-America Arts Alliance to pay for 15 to 30 percent of artists' fees for performances and educational activities by theater, dance, and music ensembles. Presenting organizations can apply for funds to pay for up to five different performing groups or a total dollar amount of $13,000.

Community Catalyst Grants award up to $1,000 to organizations for projects that broaden and deepen community participation in the arts.

Meet the Composer Grants offer up to $1,000 for performance of a composer's work accompanied by an educational activity involving the composer and members of the community.

Mid-Atlantic Arts Foundation

(Serves Delaware, District of Columbia, Maryland, New Jersey, New York, Pennsylvania, West Virginia, Virginia, and the US Virgin Islands)
22 Light Street, #330
Baltimore, MD 21202
410-539-6656
TT: 410-539-4241
www.midatlanticarts.org
Mid-Atlantic Arts Foundation gave $2,400,000 to area artists and
arts organizations in Fiscal Year 1999.

Granting programs:
ArtsEmerge awards grants of up to $5,000 to artists, companies, and presenter organizations in the Mid-Atlantic states to assist in planning, creating, and presenting new work.

ArtsCONNECT provides funds to nonprofit presenting partnerships or networks based in the Mid-Atlantic states to help pay performing artists' and companies' fees for touring, residencies, and multiple engagements.

Artist as Catalyst supports residency projects designed by artists and organizations in partnership.

Peer Assistance and Mentoring Program supports peer assistance and mentoring opportunities for people engaged in the practice, presentation or conservation of folk and traditional arts in the mid-Atlantic region. The program provides a subsidy of $250 per day for up to five days for the mentor and applicant to work together according to their agreed upon consultation

Pennsylvania Performing Arts on Tour awards grants of up to $30,000 per year to nonprofit presenting organizations that engage artists or companies included on the Pennsylvania Performing Arts on Tour roster. Grants are used to pay up to 60 percent of the contracted artists fees and travel expenses.

New England Foundation for the Arts

(Serves Connecticut, Maine, Massachusetts, New Hampshire, Rhode Island, Vermont)
330 Congress Street, 6th Floor
Boston, MA 02210-1216
617-951-0010
www.nefa.org
The New England Foundation for the Arts offers three categories of grants.

Creation and Presentation grants are awarded to organizations for the development and presentation of artistic work by providing support to artists and their organizational partners.

The Presenter Travel Fund assists arts programmers in New England to investigate new or unfamiliar work by encouraging applicants to attend festivals and showcases, where they may experience as many performances and genres as possible. Grants to nonprofit, New England-based organizations will cover up to 50 percent of total expenses, generally up to $500.

The New England States Touring Program, a cooperative program with the state arts agencies of New England, provides artist fee support to presenters for performances and related community activities by over 650 artists on the New England States Touring Roster. Presenting organizations may request up to 50 percent of the artist's contractual fee, although grants are more typically in the 20 to 40 percent range. Minimum grants are $100 for engagements of individual artists and $200 for companies or ensembles.

Meet the Composer grants are awarded to organizations that allow interaction between composers and audiences in conjunction with the performance of the composer's work. Presenting organizations may request up to 50 percent of the composer's contractual fee, although grants are more typically in the 20 to 40 percent range.

The Massachusetts Touring Program, funded by the Massachusetts Cultural Council, provides support and services similar to New England States Touring, specifically within Massachusetts for Massachusetts-based artists.

The National Dance Project (NDP) provides grants for the production and touring of contemporary dance work by regionally and nationally known artists in the United States. NDP production grants support the development of new dance work. Production grants are awarded to an average of 20 dance projects annually. Grants generally range from $18,000 to $35,000. Each season, NDP touring grants support the presentation and distribution of that work and of a limited number of other projects nominated by dance presenters across the country. Presenters booking NDP-supported works are eligible to receive a fee subsidy grant. Grants generally range from 15 to 25 percent of the contracted artist's fee. Each year, the National Dance Project awards a limited number of "tour-only" grants to projects nominated by the field. These grants are competitive, and are awarded to an average of 5 projects each year. Grants generally range from $8,000 to $25,000.

Culture in Community grants strengthen the role the arts play in community development by advancing partnerships between arts and non-arts entities.

Fund for the Arts is a restricted fund of NEFA that provides support to artists and nonprofit organizations in Greater Boston for art projects of lasting public benefit.

Visible Republic is a public art program supporting the creation of new work by visual artists through grants for projects that are linked to a public site in the Greater Boston area. A total of $12,000 is available for planning grants and will be equally divided among grant recipients. A minimum of $1,000 per recipient will be awarded.

Building Communities through Culture (BCC) identifies, links, and strengthens arts-based community development projects throughout New England. These grants are characterized by arts/non-arts partnerships. BCC provides support to communities selected for participation, including fellowships for community leaders, gatherings, and project planning and implementation assistance.

Connections grants focus on professional development, technology, and research that will expand and enrich the arts infrastructure.

New England Foundation for the Arts is one of 20 sites nationwide participating in a national initiative to train the nonprofit arts community to use the World Wide Web to strengthen the ties between themselves and the communities they serve through the New England Open Studio. Now in its third year, New England Open Studio: Arts Online will work with cultural organizations to develop and introduce best business and communication practices for using technology with a focus on the Internet.

Southern Arts Federation

(Serves Alabama, Florida, Georgia, Kentucky, Louisiana, Mississippi, North Carolina, South Carolina, and Tennessee)
1401 Peachtree Street, Suite 460
Atlanta, GA 30309
404-874-7244
TT: 404-876-6240
www.southarts.org
In Fiscal Year 1999, the Southern Arts Foundation gave $239,629 in fee support for community arts presenters.

Granting programs:
The National Endowment for the Arts/Southern Arts Federation Regional Touring Program provides funding to bring artists and performers to communities, especially those that are underserved, throughout the South through block booking. Presenting organizations may receive up to 50 percent of the artist's fee to bring an out-of-state artist to their community. The maximum award for a Presenter Fee Support project is $5,000 and the maximum award for a Dance Support Project is $7,500.

Meet the Composer/South grants offer up to $750 (not to exceed 50 percent of the artist's fee) for performance of a composer's work accompanied by an educational activity involving the composer and members of the community.

Western States Arts Federation

(Serves Alaska, Arizona, California, Colorado, Idaho, Montana, Nevada, New Mexico, Oregon, Utah, Washington, and Wyoming)
1543 Champa St., Suite 220
Denver, CO 80202
303-629-1166
www.westaf.org

Granting programs:
TourWest provides funding to bring artists and performers to communities, especially those that are underserved, throughout the West through block booking. Presenting organizations may receive up to $2,500 or 50 percent of the artist's fee (whichever is less) to bring an artist or performing ensemble to their community.

State and Jurisdictional Arts Agencies

Alabama
Alabama State Council on the Arts
One Dexter Avenue
Montgomery, AL 36130
334-242-4076
TT/Relay: 1-800-548-2546
www.arts.state.al.us

The Alabama State Council on the Arts budgeted $4,350,000 in grants for fiscal year 2000-2001. The Alabama State Council on the Arts awards grants to organizations and individuals in the following program areas: Arts in Education (presentations in schools, artist residencies, scholarships), Community Arts (support for local groups, festivals, community design guidelines), Folklife (presentations and documentation, festivals, field studies, apprenticeships with master artists), Literary Arts (readings, technical assistance, fellowships), Performing Arts (performances, operating support, collaborations, program development, fellowships), and Visual Arts(exhibits, projects, operational support, program development, internships, fellowships). Grants seldom exceed $10,000; or $1,000 for technical assistance.

Organizations may apply for presenting grants to help offset the costs of artists' fees, project assistance grants for specific activities and services, operating support, technical assistance for small-scale projects, collaborative ventures, programming development, and up to $250 per week to support a temporary internship.

Individuals may apply for artist and arts administration fellowships of $5,000 or $10,000, up to $1,000 in technical assistance, artist-in-education residencies of $600 per three-day workweek, and folk arts apprenticeships of up to $5,000.

Alaska

Alaska State Council on the Arts
411 West 4th Avenue, Suite 1E
Anchorage, AK 99501-2343
907-269-6610
www.aksca.org
The Alaska State Council on the Arts provides funding and support throughout the state on a variety of levels, from project grants to technical and operational support. Some funding is provided to individual communities through local arts agencies, while other monies may go to directing support a specific project or an educational program.

There are nine distinct categories through which an organization may receive funding, depending on its need. Grants include the following types: Local Arts Agency, Operational, Project, Workshop, Career Opportunity, Master Artist and Apprentice Work in Traditional and Native Arts, Community Arts Development, funding to support Artists in the Schools, Arts Incentive.

Funds are awarded only to Alaskan nonprofit organizations and in certain categories, individuals.

American Samoa

American Samoa Council on Arts, Culture & Humanities
P.O. Box 1540
Pago Pago, American Samoa 96799
011-684-633-4347
Fax: 011-684-633-2059
www.nasaa-arts.org/new/nasaa/gateway/AS.html
The American Samoa Council on the Arts, Culture and Humanities funds its programs heavily based upon the goal of maintaining and passing on traditional arts and Samoan culture. Programs offered by the agency include: Arts in Education; Cultural Maintenance; Folk Art; Children's Summer Cultural Program; Museum, Adult Cultural.

Arizona

Arizona Commission on the Arts
417 West Roosevelt
Phoenix, AZ 85003
602-255-5882
http://az.arts.asu.edu/artscomm

The Arizona Commission on the Arts has many granting programs through several sources. In collaboration with the National Endowment for the Arts, the state of Arizona has its own statewide endowment program, Arizona ArtShare, which granted over $67,000 to the arts in 1999. Grants were made in three areas: Arts Education, Outreach and Education, and Stabilization, to help mid-sized arts organizations stay on their feet.

There are also a variety of other grants available to arts organizations, including those to help with planning and development, to help pay for consultant services and to support online development.

Arkansas

Arkansas Arts Council
1500 Tower Building
323 Center Street
Little Rock, AR 72201
501-324-9766
www.arkansasarts.com/index.html
The Arkansas Arts Council oversees and funds the arts in eight categories: Arts in Education; Arts on tour; Assistance Fund; Expansion Arts; General Operating Support; Individual Artists Fellowships; Project Support; Public Art. While most of the categories are limited to applications from nonprofit organizations, the grants in the Individual Fellowships category are extensive in their scope of media. The recipients range from filmmakers to writers to visual artists to musicians and more.

California

California Arts Council
1300 I Street, #930
Sacramento, CA 95814
916-322-6555
TT: 916-322-6569
www.cac.ca.gov
The California Arts Council is an organization serving the arts to an obviously large state.
Granting programs include those in the following categories: Artist in Residence; Artists Fellowships; California Challenge Program; Multi-Cultural Arts Development; Local Arts Education Partnership; Organizational Support; Performing Arts Touring; State-Local Partnership; Traditional Folk Arts.

As with any federally funded awards, there is a requirement that they be matched. In California that is the California Challenge program. The goal of this particular program is to assist organizations in obtaining funding and increased support from private foundations and other public sources. Applicants must be nonprofit, two years in existence, and have a minimum annual income of $100,000. The idea is that each organization, depending on its annual budget, will find matching funds of either 2:1 or 3:1 to the monies awarded by the Arts Council, the goal being to increase outside funding.

Colorado

Colorado Council on the Arts
750 Pennsylvania Street
Denver, CO 80203-3699
303-894-2617
TT: 303-894-2664
www.coloarts.state.co.us
The Colorado Council on the Arts has grants available to both nonprofit arts organizations as well as individuals.

According to the Council, recommended grantees unfortunately far exceed the abilities to fund. Grants range from $2000- $32,000, with two thirds of all of those funded being less than $10,000.

Requested proposals fall into the following categories for 2001: Increased Public Engagement; Community Building through the Arts; Folk or Traditional Arts; Collaborations between schools (K-12), Artist and Arts Organizations; Helping Youth-at-Risk; Professional Development Services for Artists and Arts organizations.

In addition to those programs listed above, there are also awards made to individual artists through a fellowship program. The categories change annually and for 2001 will be: Literature (fiction and non-fiction only); Visual Arts (three-dimensional work only); Performing Arts (dance, choreography, music composition and performance art); Folk Arts. The award amount is $4000 and you must be a Colorado resident for at least one year in order to apply.

Connecticut
Connecticut Commission on the Arts
Gold Building 755 Main Street
Hartford, CT 06103
860-566-4770
www.ctarts.org
The Connecticut Commission on the Arts has several grants and matching programs available to organizations and some individual funds available for artists. Qualified organizations may apply within the following categories: Arts Management Technical Assistance; Arts Partnerships for Stronger Communities; Arts Presentation; Arts Endowment Fund; Organization Challenge Grant. Each granting program has different requirements and application deadlines, all information which is available online.

For individual artists, categories alternate according to odd/even year designations. Visual artists may apply in odd-numbered years while choreographers, poets, playwrights, fiction writers, composers and film or video artists may apply in even-numbered years. Generally, there are between twenty and thirty-five awards made annually in amounts of either $2500 or $5000. Artists applying must be residents of Connecticut for a minimum of one year, and may not have been a recipient of a fellowship within the last four years, or a full-time enrolled student.

Delaware
Delaware Division of the Arts
State Office Building
820 North French Street
Wilmington, DE 19801
302-577-3540
TT/Relay: 1-800-232-5460
www.artsdel.org
The Delaware Division of the Arts has extensive funding available in a large variety of categories. For nonprofit arts organizations, the granting program categories are as follows: General Operating Support; Technical Assistance; Arts Stabilization; Project Support; Opportunity Grants. There are also Arts in Education programs available.

For the individual professional artist fellowships are available for Emerging Professional ($2000), Established Professional ($5000), and Masters Fellowship ($10,000). There are different and specific criteria for each of the above.

District of Columbia
District of Columbia Commission on the Arts & Humanities
410 8th Street, NW
Washington, DC 20004
202-724-5613

TT: 202-727-3148

www.capaccess.org/ane/dccah

The DC Commission on the Arts and Humanities offers grants in the following categories: Grants-in-Aid; Artist Fellowships; Arts Education; City Arts. Thirty-seven individuals received Artists Fellowships last year in performing arts, visual arts, media and literature. There are also some other smaller programs to encourage the arts among the general public like a writer's competition for young people ages 8-18. Cash prizes are awarded for excellence.

Florida

Florida Division of Cultural Affairs
Florida Department of State
The Capitol
Tallahassee, FL 32399-0250
850-487-2980
TT: 850-488-5779
www.dos.state.fl.us/dca/

With over $28,000,000 going to the arts, and more than fifteen granting programs, the Florida Division of Cultural Affairs has a lot to offer. Granting programs include: Arts in Education; Challenge Grants; Cultural Facilities; Cultural Institutions; Discipline based Arts; Individual Fellowships; International Cultural Exchange; Local Arts Agency/State Service Organization; Quarterly Assistance; Science Museum; You and Children's museum; State Touring Program; Underserved Arts Community Assistance Program.

Individual fellowships are granted annually to artists in dance, folk arts, interdisciplinary, literature, media arts, music, theatre, and visual arts and crafts. Last year 476 applications were received and only 40 of those were funded. Awards are in the amount of $5000. Applicants may only receive an award every 5 years, must be a Florida resident, and may not be a student pursuing a degree.

Georgia

Georgia Council for the Arts
260 14th Street, NE
Atlanta, GA 30318-5730
404-685-2787
www.ganet.org/georgia-arts

The Georgia Council for the Arts offers grants in the following categories:
Organizational :General Operating Support; Organizational: Project Support; Challenge Grants; Georgia Folklife Program; Traditional Arts Apprenticeship; Technical Assistance; Touring Program; Artist-in-Residence; Grassroots Arts program. More than $4,000,000 is available in the categories listed. Amounts of funding varies depending upon the program. Deadlines also vary. Call the Council directly for more information.

Guam

Guam Council on the Arts & Humanities
Office of the Governor
P.O. Box 2950
Agana, GU 96910
011-671-647-2242

Hawaii

Hawaii State Foundation on Culture & the Arts
44 Merchant Street
Honolulu, HI 96813

808-586-0300
TTD: 808-586-0740
www.state.hi.us/sfca
The goal of the granting programs of the State Foundation on Culture and the Arts is to promote and preserve the local arts, culture and humanities through the state of Hawaii. All application deadlines are in the fall, having begun during the summer of years ending in even numbers. Workshops (free) are available to help with the application process. For more information, contact the above address.

Idaho

Idaho Commission on the Arts
P.O. Box 83720
Boise, ID 83720-0008
208-334-2119
www2.state.id.us/arts
The Idaho Commission on the Arts has the initial three categories of funds available as those designated for Individuals, Arts in Education and Organizations. For the Individual category, monies are available in a QuickFund$ program, for support and professional development Fellowships that recognize excellence in various arts ($3500), and an award for The Writer-in-Residence, the highest literary honor in the state ($8000 over 3 years).

Arts in Education programs include: Artists in Schools; Artists in Communities; Folk Arts in Schools; Arts as Basic. The grants for these programs are usually between $1500-$3500. Also available is a program called School Connections: Audiences of Tomorrow. This program is to encourage the performing arts to participate in educational programs. Grants may be as high as $25,000. Applications forms for Individuals and Organizations are available online.

Illinois

Illinois Arts Council
State of Illinois Center
100 West Randolph, Suite 10-500
Chicago, IL 60601
312-814-6750
TT: 312-814-4831
www.state.il.us/agency/iac
The Illinois Arts Council offers grants in the following categories: Program Grants, which include a variety of media, and Arts in Education; Programs to Serve the Community, such as Arts-in-Education Residencies, ArtsResource, Ethnic and Folk Arts Master/Apprenticeships, and Short Term Artists Residencies (S.T.A.R.); Programs for the Artist, specifically fellowships ($7000).

Applications are due at varying times of the year and are available, along with program information and guidelines at the Council's web site.

Indiana

Indiana Arts Commission
402 West Washington Street, Room 072
Indianapolis, IN 46204-2741
317-232-1268
TT: 317-233-3001
www.state.in.us/iac/index.html
The Indiana Arts Commission has five basic categories through which funding may be found: Major Arts

Institutions, Arts Service Organizations, Technical Assistance Program, Individual Artists' Projects, and Capacity Building. Deadlines vary depending on which program you are applying for.

The Commission also has an extensive web site with lots of information about the arts in Indiana including many links.

Iowa

Iowa Arts Council
600 East Locust
State Capitol Complex
Des Moines, IA 50319
515-281-4451
www.culturalaffairs.org/iac
The Iowa Arts Council, a division of the Iowa Department of Cultural Affairs offers funding and scholarships in these categories: Artists in Schools/Communities Residency Grants; Artists Project Grants, Arts in Education Project Grants, Mini Grants; Project Grants for Organizations; Operational Support Grants; Technical Assistance.

Deadlines vary and all applications, guidelines and further information are available at the Council's web site, and are downloadable. You may also apply electronically.

Kansas

Kansas Arts Commission
Jayhawk Tower
700 Jackson, Suite 1004
Topeka, KS 66603
785-296-3335
TT/Relay: 1-800-766-3777
http://arts.state.ks.us
The Kansas Arts Commission has six programs available to organizations and communities: Operational Support; Arts in Education Projects ($2000-$9000); Arts Project Support ($2000-$7500); Technical Assistance (up to $2000); Grassroots Program (up to $2000); Kansas Touring Program. All of the above programs require matching dollar donations of at least a $ for $ match in order to be funded.

For individual artists, the categories vary depending on the year. They are rotated biennially. Ten Fellows are chosen, each receiving $5000. For fiscal year 2001 the categories are Music Composition, Choreography, Film/Video, Interdisciplinary/ Performance Art, and Playwriting. For fiscal year 2002, categories are Fiction, Poetry, Two-Dimensional Visual Art, Three-Dimensional Visual Art, and Crafts. There are also Mini Fellowships offered for $500. Artists may not apply for both Mini Fellowships and Artists Fellowships. Complete guidelines and application information are available online.

Kentucky

Kentucky Arts Council
31 Fountain Place
Frankfort, KY 40601
502-564-3757
www.kyarts.org
There are more than twenty granting programs administered by the Kentucky Arts Council! They include: Artists in Residence; Arts Development; Arts in Education Artist Roster; Challenge; Community Residence Program; Community Arts Development; Folk & Traditional Arts Apprenticeship; Folk Arts Project & Tour of KY Folk Music; Governor's Awards in the Arts; individual Artist Fellowship and Cultural Exchange; Individual Artist Professional Development; Individual Artist Project; Kentucky arts on Tour; KY Peer Advisory Network; Kentucky

Poet Laureate; Organizational Technical Assistance; Project Grant; Salary Assistance; School/Community/Arts Partnership.

The Arts Council's web site is extremely user-friendly with loads of information and great links to other arts sites.

Louisiana

Louisiana Division of the Arts
Louisiana Department of Culture, Recreation, & Tourism
1051 North 3rd Street
P.O. Box 44247
Baton Rouge, LA 70804
504-342-8180
www.crt.state.la.us/arts/index.htm
The Louisiana Division of the Arts offers funding in the following categories: General Operating Support; Local Arts Agencies; Arts-in-Education; Folklife Apprenticeships; Project Assistance; Artists Fellowships; Artists Mini Grants; Director's Grant-in-Aid Program.

Application requirements and deadlines vary, and all information is available online. Included online are sections giving examples of projects, and help with preparation of writing a proposal.

Maine

Maine Arts Commission
55 Capitol Street
State House Station 25
Augusta, ME 04333
207-287-2724
TT: 207-287-5613
www.mainearts.com/
The Maine Arts Commission Offers Individual Fellowships in the following categories: Dance; Design Arts; Media Arts; Music; Theatre Arts; Traditional Arts; Visual Arts; Literature; Multi-Disciplinary. There are also Apprenticeships available.

An Arts-in Education program is considered one of the Commission's priorities. Other organizational and community programs include: Cultural Assessment and Planning (up to $10,000); Local Culture Initiatives (up to $4000); Organizational Development (up to $2000); Leadership Initiatives (up to $25,000).

All application forms and information are available online, but the Commission does not accept electronic applications at this time. In addition to the information for the state of Maine, this web site also has a substantial listing of other opportunities available to individual artists throughout the country.

Maryland

Maryland State Arts Council
175 West Ostend, Suite E
Baltimore, MD 21230
410-767-6555
410-333-4519 (TDD)
www.msac.org
With over $9,000,000 given in grants last year, the Maryland State Arts Council's programs are considerable. Categories include General Operating Grants for Organizations, Arts Projects for Organizations, Arts in Communities Programs, Community Arts Development and County Councils, Arts in Education and Individual Artists Awards. Grants for Individuals range from $1000-$6000.

Massachusetts

Massachusetts Cultural Council
120 Boylston Street, 2nd Floor
Boston, MA 02116-4600
617-727-3668
TT: 617-338-9153
www.massculturalcouncil.org
The Massachusetts Cultural Center has many programs that offer funding. Over $16,000,000 will be awarded this year! Programs include: Mini Grants; Artists Grants; Cultural Economic Development; Education Partnership Initiative; Endowment Grant Program; Event & Residency; Local Cultural Council Grants; Local Cultural Council Matching Incentive; Massachusetts Cultural Facilities Project; Massachusetts Touring Program; Organizational Support; PASS Program (admissions subsidized for schools and youth programs); Professional Development; Science in the Community Initiative; YouthReach Initiative.

In addition to those programs listed above, there is also one called the Massachusetts Elder Arts initiative. This unusual program is designed to enrich the lives of senior citizens through the use of the arts. Funding is provided to organizations to help bring arts of all kinds to the elderly population.

$361,000 was granted to Individual Artists in 1999. Grants in various media are awarded annually with grantees receiving either a sum of $12,500 or a finalist award of $1000.

Michigan

Michigan Council for Arts and Cultural Affairs
525 West Ottawa Street
P.O. Box 30705
Lansing, MI 48909-8205
517-241-4011
www.commerce.state.mi.us/arts
The Michigan Council for Arts and Cultural Affairs offers the following matching grant programs: Arts and Learning; Artists in Schools; Anchor Organization Program; Arts Organization Development Program; Arts and cultural Projects for Cities, Townships and Villages; Discretionary Grants; Local, Regional or Statewide Arts Agencies Services program; Mini-Grant Regional Re-granting; Arts Projects; Partnership Program. The deadline for application for all of the above is May 1st of any given year. Free workshops are available throughout the state to assist with the application process.

Last year the state of Michigan awarded more than $21,000,000 in grants to the arts.

Minnesota

Minnesota State Arts Board
Park Square Court
400 Sibley Street, Suite 200
St. Paul, MN 55101-1949
651-215-1600
800-8MN-ARTS
TT/Relay: 651-297-5353
www.arts.state.mn.us
Grants to organizations in Minnesota fall into the following categories: Arts in Education Organizational Support; Arts Across Minnesota: (Festivals); Arts Across Minnesota: (Host Communities); Folk Art Sponsorship; Institutional Support; Institutional presenter Support; Series Presenter Support.

For Individuals there are Fellowships, Career Opportunity Grants, Cultural Collaborations, Folk Art Apprenticeships ($4000) and Video Documentation Grants.

Artist's fellowships are available for Visual Arts, Film and Video, Photography, Dance, Music, Theatre Arts, Prose and Poetry. All awards are $8000.

Mississippi

Mississippi Arts Commission
239 North Lamar Street, Second Floor
Jackson, MS 39201
601-359-6030
www.arts.state.ms.us
While there is no direct information about specific granting programs at the Mississippi Arts Commission web site at this time, there is a wonderful section on grant writing with terrific tips and suggestions for anyone writing a proposal in any state. Please contact the office listed above for more specific information pertaining to grants and programs in Mississippi.

Missouri

Missouri State Council on the Arts
Wainwright Office Complex
111 North Seventh Street, Suite 105
St. Louis, MO 63101
314-340-6845
www.missouriartscouncil.org
The Missouri Arts Council has programs available with applications accepted in the following categories: Arts Education; Arts Services; Community Arts; Discipline Program Assistance; Established Institutions; Festivals; Folk Arts; Mini Grants; Minority Arts; Missouri Cultural Trust Fund; Missouri Touring; Technical Assistance.

Applications and guides are available to download at the Council's web site.

Montana

Montana Arts Council
316 North Park Avenue
Room 252
Helena, MT 59620
406-444-6430
TT/Relay: 1-800-833-8503
www.art.state.mt.us
The Montana Arts Council offers both Individual and Organizational grants. Applications for organizational grants are accepted in April for projects beginning the following July. For Individual Artists, there is an annual May 1st deadline with any submissions being completed within the last four years. Artists must be 21 or over to apply.

Nebraska

Nebraska Arts Council
The Joslyn Castle Carriage House
3838 Davenport Street
Omaha, NE 68131-2329
402-595-2122
TT/Voice: 402-595-2122
www.nebraskaartscouncil.org

The Nebraska Arts Council supports a variety of programs with grants to organizations as well as Individual Artists. Through Organizational programs, funding may be secured within the following categories: Basic Support; Arts in Education; Arts projects; Nebraska Touring and Exhibits Sponsors; Special Opportunity Support. There are within those broad categories more specific programs through which organizations may apply.

Individual Artists may apply for Artists Fellowships.

All applications and guidelines are available online and may be downloaded from the Council's web site.

Nevada
Nevada Arts Council
Capitol Complex
602 North Curry Street
Carson City, NV 89710
702-687-6680
http://dmla.clan.lib.nv.us/docs/ARTS
The Nevada Arts Council offers both Organizational and Individual grants. Organizational categories consist of Arts in Education Programs, Community Arts Development, Folk Arts, and a Grants Program of six sub-categories. Those are: Challenge; Design Arts; Development; Jackpot; Organizational Support; Projects.

Individual Artist's Fellowships are awarded annually to up to six individual artists. Awards are in the amount of $5000. Applications and other information are available for download online.

New Hampshire
New Hampshire State Council on the Arts
40 North Main Street
Concord, NH 03301
603-271-2789
TT/Relay: 1-800-735-2964
www.state.nh.us/nharts
The New Hampshire Council on the Arts offers many granting programs within five major categories: Artists' Services ($100-$5000); Arts Advancement ($100-$12,000); Arts in Education ($500-$5000); Community Arts ($100-$3500); Traditional Arts ($100-$4000). The award amounts listed above represent the range for all grants given within each category.

New Jersey
New Jersey State Council on the Arts
225 West State Street
P.O. BOX 306
Trenton, NJ 08625-0306
609-292-6130
TT: 609-633-1186
www.njartscouncil.org
The New Jersey Arts Council has a wide array of programs with available funding. They include: General Operating Support; General Programming Support; Special Project Grants; Arts Education Special Initiative; Projects Serving Artists; Community Arts Collaboration; Local Arts; Local Arts Staffing Initiative; Artists' Fellowships; Folk Art Apprenticeships; Artist-in-Education Program; Artist-in-Education Sponsor Program.

An independent panel of experts reviews proposals, with submission deadlines varying from program to program. All application materials and guidelines are available online.

New Mexico

New Mexico Arts
P.O. Box 1450
Santa Fe, NM 87504-1450
505-827-6490
www.artsnet.org/nma
New Mexico Arts offers granting programs including those in the following categories: Community Arts Development; Local Arts Councils; Partnership/Arts Enterprise Projects; Traditional Folk Arts Projects; Arts Projects; Arts Education Projects; Technical Assistance; Folk Art Apprenticeships; Tumblewords.

In addition to the program listings, the New Mexico Arts web site now has eGrants, which allows you to download all applications, instructions and guidelines as well as apply electronically for funding.

New York

New York State Council on the Arts
915 Broadway
New York, NY 10010
212-387-7000
TT: 212-387-7049
www.nysca.org
The New York State Council on the Arts has divided their granting program categories into two separate entities, Organizational, and Independent Projects. The Organizational categories are General Operating Support and general Program Support. The Discipline Specific categories are as follows: Arts in Education; Capital Projects; Dance; Electronic Media and Film; Folk Arts; Individual Artists; Literature; Museum; Music; Presenting; Special Arts Services; State and Local Partnership-Decentralization; Theatre; Visual Arts.

All eligibility requirements, information, guidelines and forms are available online.

North Carolina

North Carolina Arts Council
Department of Cultural Resources
Raleigh, NC 27601-2807
919-733-2821
www.ncarts.org/
The North Carolina Arts Council has, to put it bluntly, a ton of categories! For Organizational grants alone, there are seventeen, including the following: Arts in Education Development; Arts in Education Partnership; Folklife Documentary Program; Folklife Projects; General Support; Grassroots Arts; Local Arts Council Salary Assistance; Local Government Challenge Grants; Management/Technical Assistance; Multicultural Organization Development; New Realities Program; New Works; Peer Advisory Network; Professional Development; Project Support for Literary, Performing and Visual Arts; Series Support; Special Initiatives. Whew!

In addition to those for Organizations, there is a nice array of grants for Individuals. Along with standard Artist Fellowships ($8000), there are also programs geared to folk artists ($5000) and programs for regional artists.

North Dakota

North Dakota Council on the Arts
418 East Broadway Ave., Suite 70
Bismarck, ND 58501-4086
701-328-3954

www.state.nd.us/arts
Grants offered by the North Dakota Council on the Arts fall into the following categories: Access; Arts in Education; Institutional Support; Professional Development; Special Projects; Traditional Arts Apprenticeship.

Northern Mariana Islands

Northern Mariana Islands Commonwealth Council for Arts & Culture
P.O. Box 553, CHRB
CNMI Convention Center
Commonwealth of the Northern Mariana Islands
Saipan, MP 96950
9-011-670-322-9982
www.nasaa-arts.org/new/nasaa/gateway/NorthernM.html

Ohio

Ohio Arts Council
727 East Main Street
Columbus, OH 43205
614-466-2613
TT: 614-466-4541
www.oac.state.oh.us/
Individual programs available through the Ohio Arts Council are awarded in eleven different disciplines: Choreography; Music Composition; Visual Arts; Crafts; Design Arts; photography; Media Arts; Criticism, Playwriting; Creative Writing; Interdisciplinary/Performance Art. Awards are $5000 and $10,000. Also available are Assistance awards (up to $1000).

The Arts in Education Program also has a wide variety of programs available to schools. In addition to in school programs, and Artist Residencies programs, there is also a Writing Workshop for teachers, in order to assist them in teaching poetry, non-fiction and fiction.

Oklahoma

Oklahoma Arts Council
P.O. Box 52001-2001
Oklahoma City, OK 73152-2001
405-521-2931
www.state.ok.us/~arts
The Oklahoma Arts Council has three basic categories that have funding available, Artist-in-Residence, Touring Program, and Arts-in Education. Within those categories are the following programs: Annual Project Support; Artist-in-Residence; Artists and Educators Collaborative; Arts in Alternative Education; Community Connections; DesignWorks; Festivals; Local Government Challenge Grant; master/Apprentice; Minigrant; Oklahoma Touring Program; Presenting Program; School and Museum Partnership; Technical Assistance; Youth Arts.

All forms and guidelines are available online, along with a little lesson in Latin!

Oregon

Oregon Arts Commission
775 Summer Street, NE
Salem, OR 97310
503-986-0082
TT: 503-378-3772
http://art.econ.state.or.us

The Oregon Arts Commission offers grants for Arts Industry Development, Individuals, Communities (local and regional), Arts in Education grants, and Arts Reaching Youth Initiative Grants, for high-risk youth. There is also a cultural planning group and an Oregon Folklife program that works in conjunction with the Oregon Historical Society.

For Individual Artists, there are up to ten fellowships awarded annually for $3000 each. In even-numbered years disciplines are Literature, and Performing Arts. Odd-numbered years feature awards in the Visual Arts, and Design Arts.

Deadlines vary for all of the programs. Guidelines and applications are available online.

Pennsylvania
Commonwealth of Pennsylvania Council on the Arts
Finance Building, Room 216A
Harrisburg, PA 17120
717-787-6883
TT/Relay: 800-654-5984
www.artsnet.org/pca
The Pennsylvania Council on the Arts' grants and awards are divided into the following categories: Those for Arts organizations and programs; Entry Track, for organizations just getting started; Projects; Individual Artists; Accessibility to the Arts in PA for Individuals with Disabilities; Arts in Education; Local Government; PA Partners in the Arts; Preserving Cultural Diversity; Professional Development & Consulting.

Individual Artists Fellowships are granted for amounts ranging from $5000-$10,000. Deadlines vary according to which discipline your work falls into. The PCA also offers programs supporting apprenticeships.

Puerto Rico
Institute of Puerto Rican Culture
Apartado Postal 4184
San Juan, PR 00902-4184
809-723-2115

Rhode Island
Rhode Island State Council on the Arts
83 Park Street, 6th Floor
Providence, RI 02903-1037
401-222-3880
www.risca.state.ri.us
The Rhode Island State Council on the Arts offers grants to Individual Artists, Arts Organizations, and Educational and Nonprofit Organizations. Individual Fellowships are awarded in the amount of $5000, with a $1000 award made to runners up, if there are any in a given category.

Application forms are available online along with relevant information, guidelines and deadlines.

South Carolina
South Carolina Arts Commission
1800 Gervais Street
Columbia, SC 29201
803-734-8696
www.state.sc.us/arts

With almost $2,000,000 in available funding, the South Carolina Arts Commission has many granting programs. Grants include: Annual Support for Organizations; Subgranting for Organizations; Annual Projects for Organizations; Annual Projects for Individuals (with over $50,000 in monies available); Folklife and Traditional Arts; Arts Education; Multicultural Grants; Quarterly Grants; Cultural Vision.

All information and applications are available for download online, although the Commission does not accept electronic applications at this time.

South Dakota

South Dakota Arts Council
Office of Arts
800 Governors Drive
Pierre, SD 57501-2294
605-773-3131
TT/Relay: 1-800-622-1770
www.sdarts.org
Grants available from the South Dakota Arts Council include the following: Artist; Artist Collaboration; Artist Mentorship; Folk Arts Apprenticeship; Arts Challenge; Artist-in- Schools Residency; Interim Funding; Music Residency; Performing Arts Bank; Projects Grants; Statewide Services Program; Touring Arts; Heartland Arts.

Individual Artists' grants are awarded in the amount of $3000. All applications for all the above listed programs are available online, along with all information and guidelines pertaining to them. Deadlines vary depending on the program.

Tennessee

Tennessee Arts Commission
Citizens Plaza
401 Charlotte Avenue
Nashville, TN 37243-0780
615-741-1701
www.arts.state.tn.us
The Tennessee Arts Commission offers granting programs in the following categories: Arts Access (for Artists of Color); Arts Build Communities; Arts in Education; Community Arts; Folklife; Literary Arts; Performing Arts; Visual Arts, Crafts and Media. For the Individual, Fellowships are available in the amount of $5000.

Deadlines for all of the above programs vary, and all information, guidelines and applications are available online.

Texas

Texas Commission on the Arts
P.O. Box 13406
Austin, TX 78711-3406
512-463-5535
TTY: 512-475-3327
www.arts.state.tx.us
The Texas Commission on the Arts has grants available in the following general categories: Administrative and Project Support, (up to $55,000); Artist in Education Residency; Artist in Education Sponsor, (up to $15,000); Arts Basic, ($1500); Arts Education, (up to $25,000); Arts in Education, (up to $1500); County Arts Expansion, (up to $3000 per county per year); Cultural Connections, (up to $3000); Decentralization Program; Developmental Assistance to Minority Organizations,(up to $15,000); Exhibit Preparation, (up to $25,000); Exhibition Support, (up to $25,000); Statewide Services, (up to

$35,000); Subgranting, (up to $25,000); Texas Apprenticeship Program, (up to $5000); Texas Touring, (up to $25,000). All grantees must receive their funding via direct deposit.

Deadlines, information and applications are available online.

Utah

Utah Arts Council
617 East South Temple Street
Salt Lake City, UT 84102
801-533-5895
www.dced.state.ut.us/arts
Programs funded by the Utah Arts Council include: Arts in Education; Individual Artists Services; Community/State Partnership; Support and Assistance Grants (requiring matching funds); Folk Arts; Literature; Utah Public Art; Visual Arts.

Most proposal deadlines are September 1st and October 1st. The Council also strongly recommends a consultation with the program coordinator before application submission. Individual grants are awarded in the amount of $1000, three times annually.

Vermont

Vermont Arts Council
136 State Street
Montpelier, VT 05633-6001
802-828-3291
TT/Relay: 800-253-0191
www.vermontartscouncil.org
The Vermont Arts Council has three general granting categories, Creation, Presentation, and Education. Within each of the above categories there are four types of grants: Standard Grants, (up to $7000 depending on the category); Incentive grants, ($250-$750, all categories); Artist Development Grants, ($250-$500, Creation category); Technical Assistance/Travel Grants, ($250-$500, Presentation category).

All grants require matching funds. Deadlines vary according to program. Applications, guidelines and information are available online.

Virginia

Virginia Commission for the Arts
223 Governor Street
Richmond, VA 23219
804-225-3132
TT: 804-225-3132
www.artswire.org/~vacomm/
The Virginia Commission for the Arts funds programs in the following categories: General Operating Support for Arts Organizations, ($500-$150,000); Projects, ($1000-$10,000); Technical Assistance, ($500-$50,000); Local Government Challenge Grants, (up to $5000); Touring Assistance; Artists Fellowships, (up to $5000, no match required); Writers in Virginia, (up to $250); Arts in Education, ($300-$2500).

All applications, eligibility requirements and guidelines are available online.

Virgin Islands

Virgin Islands Council on the Arts
41-42 Norre Gade, 2nd Floor

P.O. Box 103
St. Thomas, VI 00802
340-774-5984

Washington

Washington State Arts Commission
234 East 8th Avenue
P.O. Box 42675
Olympia, WA 98504-2675
360-753-3860
TT/Relay: 206-554-7400 or 1-800-833-6388
www.wa.gov/art
The Washington State Arts Commission offers grants in five categories:
Project Support, Organizational Support, Institutional Support, Cooperative
Partnerships and Grants to Artists. A separate category funds Arts in
Education with funding available up to $35,000.

Grants to individuals are awarded through the Artist Trust (www.artisttrust.org) which last year awarded $82,000.
Amounts range from $1200-$5500 in the disciplines of Literature, Media, Visual Arts, Multidisciplinary, and
Performing Arts.

West Virginia

West Virginia Commission on the Arts
1900 Kanawha Blvd. East
Capitol Complex
Charleston, WV 25305-0300
304-558-0220
TT: 304-348-0220
www.wvculture.org/arts/index.html
The West Virginia Commission on the Arts' grants programs include: Touring Programs; Performing Arts; Visual
Arts/Media Arts; Major Institution Support; Planning and Organizational Development; Access and Outreach to the
Arts; Arts in Education Programs; Direct Support to Individuals.

Individual Fellowships are awarded in the amount of $3500 to eight to ten artists annually.

Application deadlines vary according to program. Guidelines and information are available online.

Wisconsin

Wisconsin Arts Board
101 East Wilson Street, 1st Floor
Madison, WI 53702
608-266-0190
TT: 608-267-9629
www.arts.state.wi.us/static
The Wisconsin Arts Board funds in two basic categories: Individual, and Organizational. For Organizational
support, programs are available for Artistic Program Support, Arts Challenge initiative, Community Development
Projects, and Performing Arts network. For the individual, there are fellowships available for $8000 each. Funding
for even-numbered years is given in the disciplines of Literature, Musical Composition, Choreography and
Performance Art. Odd-numbered years are limited to Visual/Media Arts.

Wyoming
Wyoming Arts Council
2320 Capitol Avenue
Cheyenne, WY 82002
307-777-7742
TT: 307-777-5964
http://spacr.state.wy.us/cr/arts
The Wyoming Arts Council has grants in the following categories: Arts Access, (up to $1000); Arts in Education; Community Services ($195,000 granted for the 2000-2001 year); Literature; Performing; Visual Arts; Individual Artists.

Application forms are available online.

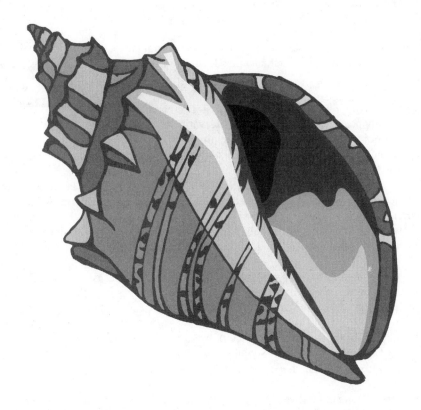

The Humanities

National Endowment for the Humanities

The National Endowment for the Humanities
1100 Pennsylvania Ave, NW
Washington, DC 20506
202-606-8400
info@neh.gov
www.neh.fed.us

Although the National Endowment for the Humanities keeps a lower profile, the National Endowment for the Arts' "sister agency" actually gives away even more grant money. In 2000, the agency awarded $97.8 million in grants, of which just under 30 percent--$29.2 million-will be channeled to state humanities councils. The state councils, in turn, distribute grants to state and local organizations. (See page 501 for a listing of these important funding sources.)

Along with its lower level of recognition, the National Endowment for the Humanities has a bit of an identity crisis. It is often defined in terms of what it does not fund-that is, work in the creative or performing arts. According to an NEH publication, "The humanities are not any one thing. They are all around us and evident in our daily lives. When you visit an exhibition on 'The Many Realms of King Arthur' at your local library, that is the humanities. When you read the diary of a seventeenth-century New England midwife, that is the humanities. When you watch an episode of The Civil War, that is the humanities, too."

The NEH does provide grants to individuals and institutions for research in the humanities, educational opportunities for teachers, preservation of texts and materials, translations of important works, museum exhibitions, television and radio programs, and public discussion and study. Here's a sample of some recent awards:

The Shakers, people whose branch of Christianity led them to build communities that are now known for their exceptional design, settled in Canterbury, New Hampshire about 200 years ago. Canterbury Shaker Village received $500,000 from the NEH, which, along with $2 million from other sources, will allow the organization to construct a visitor center, restore two original buildings and a historic garden, and endow a fund designated for humanities programming.

The NEH awarded the University of Mississippi $75,000 to analyze material excavated from Chickasaw Indian sites in the 1930s. The study will allow scholars to find out more about the changes in the Chickasaws' economic, political and social organizations during the early 1700s, when they first came into contact with Europeans.

The New England Foundation for the Arts received $9,998 from the NEH to consult with scholars and producers on how to develop "The City Game: Basketball and Social Life in 20th-Century America," a public television documentary series on how basketball has shaped urban life.

Twenty-six schoolteachers will spend four weeks of their summer break at the Folger Shakespeare Library in Washington, D.C., learning how to teach Shakespeare plays to students, thanks to a $169,983 grant from the NEH.

Five different NEH sections award grants. As with the National Endowment for the Arts, it's always best to contact the division's office very early in the application process to make sure you're on track. After all, the agency wants the best possible applications and you don't want to waste your time re-doing your request. Here's a listing of each division and an overview of what they fund.

Division of Preservation and Access

The National Endowment for the Humanities
1100 Pennsylvania Ave., NW
Washington, DC 20506
202-606-8570
This office funds projects that involve preserving materials and making them more accessible. Typically these grants go to libraries, archives, museums and historical societies to help them save old books, journals, newspapers, manuscript and archival materials, maps, still and moving images, sound recordings and objects from everyday life. "Access" can entail education and training projects or using technology to make the information these objects contain available to a wider range of people. The Division also funds the United States Newspaper Program, a cooperative national effort among the states and the federal government to locate, catalog, and preserve on microfilm newspapers published in the United States from the 18th century to the present.

Division of Public Programs

The National Endowment for the Humanities
1100 Pennsylvania Ave., NW
Washington, DC 20506
202-606-8267
Typically, nonprofit institutions and organizations including public television and radio stations and state humanities councils receive grants from this division for projects that bring significant insights into the humanities general audiences of all ages. Grants support interpretive exhibitions, radio and television programs, lectures, symposia, multimedia projects, printed materials, and reading and discussion groups.

Division of Research

The National Endowment for the Humanities
1100 Pennsylvania Ave., NW
Washington, DC 20506
202-606-8466 for fellowships for university teachers
202-606-8467 for fellowships for college teachers and independent scholars
202-606-8551 for summer stipends
Through fellowships to individual scholars and grants to support complex, frequently collaborative, research, the Division of Research provides support for scholars to undertake full-time independent research and writing in the humanities.

Division of Education

The National Endowment for the Humanities
1100 Pennsylvania Ave., NW
Washington, DC 20506
202-606-8380
202-606-8463 for seminars and institutes
Public and private elementary and secondary schools, school systems, colleges and universities, nonprofit academic associations, and cultural institutions such as libraries and museums are eligible to apply for these grants, which support curriculum and materials development, faculty study programs within and among educational institutions, and conferences and networks of institutions. The NEH is particularly interested in projects that help teachers use the new electronic technologies to enhance students' understanding of humanities subjects.

Office of Challenge Grants

Office of Challenge Grants
The National Endowment for the Humanities
1100 Pennsylvania Ave., NW
Washington, DC 20506
202-606-8309

Nonprofit post-secondary, educational, or cultural institutions interested in developing new sources of long-term support for educational, scholarly, preservation, and public programs in the humanities may apply for an NEH Challenge Grant. Grantees must raise three or four dollars in new or increased donations for every federal dollar offered. Typically, the money raised goes to establish or increase institutional endowments, giving organizations the financial foundation they need in order to plan and present humanities programs well into the future. However, funds may also be used for limited direct capital expenditures, where such needs are compelling and clearly related to improvements in the humanities.

State Humanities Councils

Before you look to Washington for funds, it's always wise to look in your own backyard first. (As a matter of fact, the voice on the phone at the NEH will probably ask you if you've contacted your state humanities council already.) These state-based organizations will give away almost $30 million this year, primarily to small, local organizations to help pay for teacher training, public lectures, reading and discussion programs, literacy programs for at-risk youth and newly literate adults, film and video projects and traveling exhibitions. Chances are a state-supported humanities program has taken place in your town, since the events funded don't just happen on university campuses. You'll find them in church basements, homes for the elderly, schools, libraries, union halls, and prisons, at historical society sites, public housing projects, and even under the stars on summer nights.

Consider the Ohio Humanities Council, for example. In the first six months of 1999 it gave away more than $120,000 in grants to Ohio organizations. In addition to project support, the OHC offers a speakers bureau, which allows any nonprofit group of adults-be it a service club, library, historical society, church, labor union, professional association or garden club-to engage some of Ohio's best humanities scholars to give a thought-provoking presentation at an organization event for just $25--that's literally hundreds of dollars less than their normal honoraria. The OHC also has revived summer Chautauquas, which now take place all over the state.

Alabama

Alabama Humanities Foundation
1100 Ireland Way, Suite 101
Birmingham, AL 35205-7001
205-558-3980
www.ahf.net

The Alabama Humanities Foundation has grants available in the following categories: Planning and Consulting, (up to $1000); Mini Grants, (up to $2000); Public Discussion, (up to $8500); Teacher Grants, (up to $17,000); Exhibition, (up to $10,000); Media Grants. All grants require matching funds, and are available to nonprofit organizations, including museums, civic groups, social service organizations etc.

Deadlines vary according to program. All forms, guidelines and information are available online or from the address above.

Alaska

Alaska Humanities Forum
421 West First Avenue, Suite 210
Anchorage, AK 99501
907-272-5341

www.akhf.org
Funding categories for the Alaska Humanities Forum include: Media; Oral history; Planning; Public Meeting and Exhibits; Publications; Research. All grants require 1:1 dollar matching funds. Deadlines vary according to program.

Some recent funding recipients include the Anchorage Museum Association ($8000) for Lifting the Fog: Russian Exploration to the North Pole, the Fairbanks Choral Society ($1000) for A History of Music in Alaska, and the National Oral History Association ($5800) for National Oral History Association Conference -1999, Anchorage.

American Samoa
America Samoa Humanities Council
P.O. Box 4074
Pago Pago, AS 96799
684-633-4870

Arizona
Arizona Humanities Council
The Ellis-Shackelford House
1242 North Central Avenue
Phoenix, AZ 85004
602-257-0335
www.azhumanities.org/
Grant awards through the Arizona Humanities Council are limited to $3000. $3000 more may be requested as long as there is a matching gift in place at the time of submission of the application. Grant writing workshops are available to the public quarterly at the office of the Council and at other community locations throughout the state. Deadlines vary according to submission of applications.

Recently funded projects include: Grand Canyon Association ($2300)- A Century of Grand Canyon Art; Museum of Northern Arizona ($3000) - Weaving culture; Old Pueblo Archaeology Center ($6000) - Archaeology Education.

Arkansas
Arkansas Humanities Council
10816 Executive Center Drive, Suite 310
Little Rock, AR 72211-4383
501-221-0091
www.arkhums.org/
The Arkansas Humanities Council offers funding in the following categories: Public Program; Individual Research, (up to $2000); Collaborative Research; Publication, (up to $3500); Media, (up to $25,000); Minigrants, (up to $1000).

Application deadlines vary depending upon the program. All information, guidelines and applications are available online.

California
California Council for the Humanities
312 Sutter Street, Suite 601
San Francisco, CA 94108
415-391-1474
www.calhum.org
The California Council for the Humanities grants are available in the categories of Major Grants (up to $10,000), Planning Grants (up to $750), Film and Speaker Grants, (up to $500), Chautauqua Grants, (up to $700), and Minigrants, (up to $2500).

All application information and program guidelines are available online.

Colorado

Colorado Endowment for the Humanities
1490 Lafayette Street, Suite 101
Denver, CO 80218
303-894-7951
www.ceh.org/

The Colorado Endowment for the Humanities granting programs fall into the categories of Program and Planning Grants, Research Grants and Packaged Program Grants. Program and Planning Grant applicants may request up to $5000, Researchers, up to $1000, and packaged program grantees may receive $50 per speaker, while public radio stations may apply for more in order to fund on air programming.

All grants requiring matching funds in some form or another. Deadlines vary according to program. All information and guidelines are available online.

Connecticut

Connecticut Humanities Council
955 South Main Street, Suite E
Middletown, CT 06457
860-685-2260
www.cthum.org/

Connecticut's Humanities Council offers granting programs within two major categories. The Cultural Heritage Development Fund grants $1,000,000 every year. The Connecticut Collaborations for Teaching the Arts and Humanities was recently created to help improve the quality of teaching of the arts and humanities with the school. This program grants $200,000 each year.

Some recent grantees include: $19,521 in planning funds to the Torrington Historical Society; $25,000 to Stone Soup for Connecticut African American humanities Project; $87,250 in challenge grant funding to the Weir Farm heritage Trust.

Guidelines and applications are available online.

Delaware

Delaware Humanities Forum
100 West 10th Street, Suite 1009
Wilmington, DE 19801
302-657-0650
www.dhf.org

Grants from the Delaware Humanities Forum may be as high as $40,000, with the average being about $5500. Programs available include Regular grants, for funding above $1500, Mini Grants, for funding up to $1500, Program Development Grants, up to $1000 and Rapid Response Book Discussion Grants, for libraries and other organizations wishing to hold a discussion program. $1200 funds any honoraria for leaders and expenses.

The Forum web site states that the odds of obtaining funding (provided there is sufficient humanities content) are about one chance in two. All information, applications and guidelines are available online as well as from the Forum directly.

District of Columbia

Humanities Council of Washington, D.C.
1331 H Street, NW, Suite 902
Washington, DC 20005
202-347-1732
www.humanities-wdc.org/

The Humanities Council of Washington, D.C. is in the process of major restructuring. Currently, they have kicked off a Challenge Grant Campaign, hoping to raise $150,000. Thus far, $22,000 has been raised. According to Interim

Director Joy Austin, the Council seeks to continue with their "unique vision and programming for the 'urban humanities' that has been an inspiration to Councils nationwide".

Florida
Florida Humanities Council
1725 1/2 East Seventh Avenue
Tampa, FL 33605-3708
813-272-3473
www.flahum.org
The Florida Humanities Council has funding available for Major Grants ($2000-$25,000), and Mini Grants (up to $2000) and Scholar/Humanist Fellowships (up to $2000). There is much latitude in topic choice for funding. Matching funds are required except for Scholar/Humanist Fellowships.

Deadlines vary according to program. All applications, information and guidelines are available online.

Georgia
Georgia Humanities Council
50 Hurt Plaza, SE, Room 1565
Atlanta, GA 30303-2915
404-523-6220
www.georgiahumanities.org
Grants from the Georgia Humanities Council fall into the following categories: Planning/Consultant Grants, (up to $1000); Special Grant Programs, (up to $2000); Conference Program Grants, (up to $10,000); Teacher Enrichment Grants, (up to $20,000). All programs require matching funds.

Deadlines vary depending upon the program. All information and guidelines are available online.

Guam
Guam Humanities Council
426 Chalan San Antonio
Center Pointe Bldg., Suite 101
Tamuning, Guam 96911
671-646-4461

Hawaii
Hawaii Council for the Humanities
First Hawaiian Bank Building
3599 Waialae Avenue, Room 23
Honolulu, HI 96816
808-732-5402
www.planet-hawaii.com/hch/
The Hawaii Council for the Humanities Offers grants in the following areas: Mini Grants, (up to $2500); Regular Grants, (over $2500); Planning Grants; Preservation of Hawaii's Heritage Grants, (up to $5000); Publication Assistance or Research Assistance Grant, (up to $2500 for Publication Assistance, up to $1500 for Research Assistance).

Deadlines vary according to program. All information, guidelines and applications are available online for download.

Idaho
Idaho Humanities Council
217 West State Street
Boise, ID 83702
208-345-5346

www2.state.id.us/ihc/
Six categories of grants are available from the Idaho Humanities Council. Major grants are in amounts exceeding $2000 and generally limited to $10,000. Mini Grants are in amounts of $2000 or less with the same basic application procedure followed as with Major Grants. Planning Grants, for planning and Development are available up to $1000. Research Fellowships are awarded to four individuals annually in the amount of $3500 each. Teacher Incentive grants, for classroom enrichment, are funded for up to $1000. Finally, there is a Speaker's Bureau available to groups wishing to host a speaker in their community. Support is available.

All application information and guidelines are available online.

Illinois
Illinois Humanities Council
203 N. Wabash Avenue, Suite 2020
Chicago, IL 60601-2417
312-422-5580
www.prairie.org/
In the last year the Illinois Humanities Council made 115 grants, totaling more than $685,000. Grants ranged from $450-$60,500. There are two categories of funding through the Illinois Humanities Council, Mini Grants, (up to $2000) and Major Grants, (from $2000 -$10,000). All grants require matching funds. Application materials and guideline information are available online.

Some recent grantees include: Rockford Art Museum: $10,830 - African American Heritage, Hager Collection of African American Contemporary Folk Art; Uptown Merchants Association: $1500 - Lincoln Festival; Stories On Stage: $1875 - An Evening of Stories by Illinois Authors; Viet Nam Veterans Against the War: $10,000 - Citizen Soldier: The Story of the VVAW.

Indiana
Indiana Humanities Council
1500 North Delaware Street
Indianapolis, IN 46202
317-638-1500
www.ihc4u.org/
The four categories of grants of the Indiana Humanities Council are: International Understanding Grants, (up to $10,000); Humanities Initiative Grants (Mini Grants offered up to $1000); Historic Preservation Education Grants, (up to $2000); Indiana Heritage Research Grants, (up to $3000). All information, guidelines and application materials are available online. You may submit your application electronically as well.

Some recent awards include: South Bend Regional Museum of Art: $8000 - Witness & Legacy: Contemporary Art About the Holocaust (International Understanding Grant); Operation S.O.A.R, Perry Meridian Middle School: $4367 - Eight -week Unit on the Civil War, Civil War Day (Humanities Initiative Grant); Ferdinand Historical Society: $1100-Ferdinand, Preserve Your Past! (Historic Preservation Education Grant); Friends of the College Football Hall of Fame: $2500 - Oral History Collection of College Football Hall of Fame Indiana Members (Indiana Heritage Research Grant).

Iowa
Humanities Iowa
100 Oakdale
Campus Northlawn
University of Iowa
Iowa City, IA 52242-5000
319-335-4153
www.humanitiesiowa.org/
Humanities Iowa offers four basic grant types: Mini Grants, (up to $1000); Regular Grants, (up to $5000); Major Grants, ($5001-$10,000); Media Grants, (up to $5000).

Deadlines vary according to program. All information and application materials are available to download from the Humanities Iowa web site.

Kansas

Kansas Humanities Council
112 SW Sixth Avenue, Suite 210
Topeka, KS 66603
785-357-0359
www.ukans.edu/kansas/khc/
The Kansas Humanities Council grant categories fall into either Major Grants (over $3500) or Mini Grants (up to $3500). Most grants will not exceed $10,000. There are also Heritage Program Grants, which is a separate funding program dedicated to cultural and historical interests of the state of Kansas.

The applicant puts applications together, with very specific instructions from the Council (available online). Deadlines vary according to program

Kentucky

Kentucky Humanities Council
206 East Maxwell Street
Lexington, KY 40508
606-257-5932
www.kyhumanities.org
The Kentucky Humanities Council offers funding in the following categories: Minigrants, (up to $1000, awarded monthly); Major Grants, (over $1000, awarded annually); Media Grants, (over $1000, awarded annually); Consultation grants, (up to $500, awarded any time). Kentucky also has a grant-matching program. The Council will award $.50 for every privately funded dollar.

Larger grant application deadlines are in August, with notification in December. To request applications, information and guidelines, contact the Kentucky Humanities Council at the above address.

Louisiana

Louisiana Endowment for the Humanities
225 Baronne Street, Suite 1414
New Orleans, LA 70112
504-523-4352
www.leh.org/
Seven categories of grants are available from the Louisiana Endowment for the humanities: General Grants, (no monetary limit, usually @ $10,000); Louisiana Publishing Initiative Grants; Media Grants; Outreach Grants, (up to $2500); Our Town Community History Grants, (up to $25,000); Publication and Photodocumentation Grants, (up to $2500); Resource Grants, ($300); Summer Teacher Institute Grants.

All applications and guidelines are available online. Deadlines vary according to program.

Maine

Maine Humanities Council
371 Cumberland Avenue
P.O. Box 7202
Portland, ME 04112
207-773-5051
www.mainehumanities.org/
The Maine Humanities Council offers six types of grants: Discretionary, ($100-$500); Outreach, ($501-$1000);

Community History, ($501-$1000); Major: Level I, ($1001-$3000); Major: Level II, ($3001-$6000); Arts and Heritage, (up to $2000). Deadlines vary according to program. All application materials and information are available online.

Maryland
Maryland Humanities Council
Executive Plaza One, Suite 503
11350 McCormick Road
Hunt Valley, MD 21031-1002
410-771-0650
www.mdhc.org/
The Maryland Humanities Council has funding available in the categories of Regular Grants ($1200-$10,000), and Mini Grants (up to $1200). Proposals for Regular Grants are due twice a year, in January and in September. Mini Grants may be applied for at any time of the year, but must be submitted at least six weeks prior to a projects beginning.

Massachusetts
Massachusetts Foundation for the Humanities
One Woodbridge Street
South Hadley, MA 01075
413-536-1385
www.mfh.org
Mini Grants (up to $2500) and Major Grants (up to $15,000 or $25,000 with Challenge Grants) are available from the Massachusetts Foundation for the Humanities. Applications consist of a variety of information that must be submitted, including a project summary, budget, statements from scholars involved in the project and resumes. There is no form per se. Deadlines vary, but all information is available online.

Michigan
Michigan Humanities Council
119 Pere Marquette Drive, Suite 3B
Lansing, MI 48912-1270
517-372-7770
http://mihumanities.h-net.msu.edu/
The Michigan Humanities Council offers the following granting programs: Mini Grants, (up to $3000); Collaborative Projects in Communities grants, (up to $12,000, 25% match required); Touring Program Grants; Humanities Resource Grants.

Some recently funded projects include Millennium Oral History Project- sponsored by the Michigan Disability Rights Coalition-$10,000; Our Village: Detroit's West Side, 1920-1950 -sponsored by The Westsiders -$10,000; A Look at Change in the Past Millennium- sponsored by Iron County Museum of Caspian -$2000.

Applications and all guideline information are available online.

Minnesota
Minnesota Humanities Commission
987 East Ivy Avenue
St. Paul, MN 55106
651-774-0105
www.thinkmhc.org/
The Minnesota Humanities Commission offers grants in the following categories: Project Grants - [Mini-Grants, (up to $300); Small Grants, ($300-$1000); General Grants, (up to $3000)]; Media Grants: Works in Progress Scholar Grants, (up to $2500).

All information, guidelines and applications are available online.

Mississippi

Mississippi Humanities Council
3825 Ridgewood Road, Room 311
Jackson, MS 39211
601-432-6752
www.ihl.state.ms.us/mhc/index.html
Categories for the Mississippi Humanities Council grants are the following: Regular Grants, (up to $2000, deadlines 1/15 and 8/15 annually); Mini Grants, (up to $2000); Media Grants. The Council also has an extensive Speaker's Bureau.

Mini Grants deadlines for application submission are six weeks prior to the program date. Regular Grants may be submitted twice a year. All information and application materials are available for download at the MHC web site.

Missouri

Missouri Humanities Council
543 Hanley Industrial Court, Suite 201
St. Louis, MO 63144
314-781-9660
www.umsl.edu/community/mohuman/
The Missouri Humanities Council's granting categories are: Consultant grants, (up to $500); Program Grants, (up to $2500); Program Grants, (up to $5000).

Deadlines vary according to program, with "letters of intent" required prior to applying. All materials, guidelines and applications are available online.

Montana

Montana Committee for the Humanities
311 Brantly Hall
University of Montana
Missoula, MT 59812-8214
406-243-6022
www.humanities-mt.org
The Montana Committee for the Humanities granting programs are in the following categories: Opportunity Grants, (up to $500); Museum Grants; Oral History Grants; Fellowships, (up to $4000, three awards made annually); Tribal Voices; Media Grants, (up to $8000, up to four awards annually).

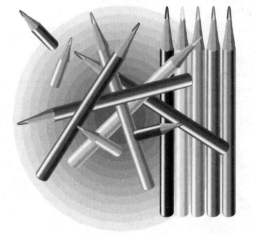

All information and guidelines are available online with the exception of the application forms themselves.

Nebraska

Nebraska Humanities Council
Suite 225 Lincoln Center Building
215 Centennial Mall South
Lincoln, NE 68508
402-474-2131
www.lincolnne.com/nonprofit/nhc/
The Nebraska Humanities Council funding falls into three categories. Available are: Major Grants, ($1500 or more, cash match of 10-25% required); Mini Grants, (up to $1500, cash match of 10% required); Media Grants, ($1500 or more).

Application submission deadlines vary according to program. The Council is clear that their staff is available to help with the application process, and to review all materials. Guidelines and forms are all available online.

Nevada

Nevada Humanities Committee
P.O. Box 8029
Reno, NV 89507
775-784-6587
www.unr.edu/nhc/
The Nevada Humanities Committee awards $125,000 annually to nonprofit organizations, in a range of a few hundred dollars, up to $10,000. Categories for funding include: Mini Grants, (up to $1000, ongoing submission); Media Grants, (up to $10,000, March application deadline); Research Grants, ($1000 research stipends, applications due in March); Publication Subvention Grants, (up to $4000); Planning Grants.

There is an Application Cover Sheet available online as well as downloadable guidelines. However, there is no formal application form and proposals are to be put together by the applicant.

New Hampshire

New Hampshire Humanities Council
19 Pillsbury Street
P.O. Box 2228
Concord, NH 03302-2228
603-224-4071
www.nhhc.org/
Three categories of funding are available from the New Hampshire Humanities Council. With a Human Resource Center providing listings of pre-approved speakers and exhibits, a simple application, and quick approval, the Council offers an easy one-step avenue for non-profit groups wishing to host a program. Other more traditional grant categories are Mini Grants and Project Grants. Mini Grants fund small projects up to $1500, and Project Grants fund those more expansive programs over $1500.

Deadlines vary according to program, and all application and guideline materials are available online.

New Jersey

New Jersey Council for the Humanities
28 West State Street, 6th Floor
Trenton, NJ 08608
609-695-4838
www.njch.org/
Granting programs from the New Jersey Council for the Humanities are available in amounts up to $10,000, and $15,000 for Media Grants. Mini Grants are also available for funds up to $3000. The NJHC also has a Resource Center with a program called Ready grants. This quick and easy process allows funding of loans of humanities materials like books, films and videotapes. It also has a variety of Reading and Discussion groups.

Some recently funded projects include: Forgotten Gateway: The Abandoned Buildings of Ellis Island (photographic exhibit) - $10,000- The Ellis Island New Jersey Foundation; Holocaust Collection Access - $1852 - Beth Israel Community Library.

New Mexico

New Mexico Endowment for the Humanities
Onate Hall, Room 209
University of New Mexico
Albuquerque, NM 87131
505-277-3705
www.nmeh.org/
The New Mexico Endowment for the Humanities offers two grant types, Regular Grants, (over $2000), and Mini Grants, (up to $2000). The NMEH awards direct grants and challenge grants, which require a dollar for dollar match from other funding sources.

Mini Grant applications are due by the 1st of February, April, August, October or December. Regular Grant applications are accepted twice a year, by the 1st of February and October. Contact the address above for further information.

New York

New York Council for the Humanities
150 Broadway, Suite 1700
New York, NY 10038
212-233-1131
www.culturefront.org/
The New York Council for the Humanities offers the following granting programs: Mini Grants, (up to $1500); Major Project Grants, ($2500-$15,000); October Event Grants, (up to $1000); October Program Grants, ($1000-$5000).

Since October is State Humanities Month in New York, the October grants must be utilized for programs and events that take place in October. Major Grant applications are due March and November 1st, and Mini Grant applications are accepted on a rolling basis.
All information, guidelines and applications are available on the Council's web site for download.

North Carolina

North Carolina Humanities Council
200 South Elm Street, Suite 403
Greensboro, NC 27401
336-334-5325
www.nchumanities.org/
Grants available from the North Carolina Humanities Council include: Planning Grants, (up to $750); Mini Grants, (up to $1200); Large Grants, (more than $1200); Media Grants, (up to $5000).

Deadlines vary according to program. All application materials and guidelines are available for viewing or download at the Council's web site.

North Dakota

North Dakota Humanities Council
2900 Broadway East, Suite 3
P.O. Box 2191
Bismarck, ND 58502
701-255-3360
www.nd-humanities.org/
In the past, the North Dakota Humanities Council has had annual funds of approximately $150,000 to put up for general award categories. Application deadlines are the 1st of February, May and September, the months before the Council holds its meetings three times a year. The Council is clear that the first step in applying for any type of humanities grant is to call its office and get some helpful tips and guidance on how to put together a formal application successfully. Contact the Council directly for more information.

Northern Mariana Islands

Northern Mariana Islands Council for the Humanities
AAA-3394, Box 10001
Saipan, MP 96950
670-235-4785
http://cnmi.humanities.org.mp/

Ohio

The Ohio Humanities Council
695 Bryden Road
P.O. Box 06354

Columbus, OH 43206-0354
614-461-7802
www.ohiohumanities.org/
The Ohio Humanities Council grants categories are as follows: Major Grants, ($5000-$20,000); Regular Grants, ($2000-$5000); Mini Grants, (up to $2000); Planning Grants, (up to $2000).

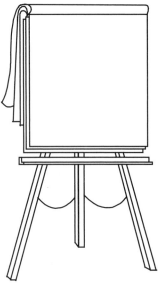

Major Grant proposals are accepted three times annually, with deadlines the 1st of the months of February, September, and November. Regular Grants submission may be made the first business day of any month and Mini Grant applications are accepted any time, with a requested lead-time of five weeks.

All information, guidelines and application requirements are available online.

Oklahoma

Oklahoma Humanities Council, Inc.
Festival Plaza
428 West California, Suite 270
Oklahoma City, OK 73102
405-235-0280
www.okhumanitiescouncil.org/
Grants available from the Oklahoma Humanities Council include: Territory Speakers, ($175); Quick Grants, ($350); Scholar Research Grants, ($500); Mini-Grants, ($1000); Let's Talk About It, Oklahoma, ($1000); Major Grants, ($7500); Challenge Grants; Local Affiliates.

All the above grants require some type of matching funds with the exception of the Local Affiliates Grant. Deadlines vary according to program. Application materials are available online.

Oregon

Oregon Council for the Humanities
812 SW Washington Street, Suite 225
Portland, OR 97205
503-241-0543
www.oregonhum.org/
The Oregon Council for the Humanities was established in 1971 to help provide access to humanities resources for the residents of Oregon. All program information is available by contacting the Council directly. The Council's web site is under construction as of this printing.

Pennsylvania

Pennsylvania Humanities Council
325 Chestnut Street, Suite 715
Philadelphia, PA 19106
215-925-1005
www.pahumanities.org
The Pennsylvania Humanities Council grants are in the following categories: Quick Grants, (up to $500, available any time); Planning Grants, (up to $1000, applications due the first day of every other month starting January 1); Small Grants, (up to $2000, due the first day every other month starting January 1); Large Grants, (up to $10,000, applications due on April 1st and October 1st); Visiting Scholar, (up to $10,000, due on April 1st and October 1st).

All application forms and guidelines are available online for download. The Council also makes a point to note that they will help in any possible way to make the application process easier for applicant, and they consider it to be an interactive process.

Puerto Rico
Fundación Puertorriqueña de las Humanidades
109 San Jose St., 3rd Floor
Box 9023920
San Jose, PR 00902-3920
787-721-2087
www.fprh.org/

*Spanish

Rhode Island
Rhode Island Committee for the Humanities
60 Ship Street
Providence, RI 02903
401-273-2250
www.uri.edu/rich/
The Rhode Island Committee for the Humanities grants categories are the following: Public Project Grants; Early Response Grants, (up to $1000); Media Production Grants; Script Development Grants; Humanities Resource Grants. Deadlines vary depending upon the program, but a letter of intent is required prior to proposal submission. At that time, a Committee staff member will assist the applicant with the rest of the process.

South Carolina
South Carolina Humanities Council
P.O. Box 5287
Columbia, SC 29250
803-691-4100
www.schumanities.org/
Funding from the South Carolina Humanities Council is granted in the following categories: Mini-Grants, (up to $1200); Major Grants, (more than $1200); Resource Grants, (up to $500); Planning Grants, (up to $1200).

Mini Grant and Planning Grant applications are accepted the 1st of each month, while other applications are due twice a year.

South Dakota
South Dakota Humanities Council
Box 7050, University Station
Brookings, SD 57007
605-688-6113
http://web.sdstate.edu/humanities/
The South Dakota Humanities Council offers the following funding programs: Humanities Discussion Program; Humanities Institutes for Schoolteachers; Media Program; Research Program for Humanities Scholars.

Deadlines vary according to program, with all guidelines and application materials available online. Applicants also have the option of applying electronically.

Tennessee
Tennessee Humanities Council
1003 18th Avenue South
Nashville, TN 37212
615-320-7001
http://tn-humanities.org/
The granting programs for the Tennessee Humanities Council fall into ten categories. Speaker Grants, (up to $750); Book and Film Discussion Grants; Community Research Project Grants; Conference and Workshop Grants;

Interpretive Exhibit Grants; Consultant Grants, (up to $1500); Planning Grants, (up to $2500); Media Grants; K-12 Teaching Material Grants, (up to $5000); K-12 Teacher Institute/Workshop Grants.

Guidelines and samples for each category are available at the Council's web site.

Texas
Texas Council for the Humanities
Banister Place A
3809 South Second Street
Austin, TX 78704
512-440-1991
www.public-humanities.org/
Basically, the Texas Council for the Humanities has three distinct categories of funding, but they also have a variety of other programs. Listed are: Packaged Program and Speaker Grants, (up to $1000); Community Projects Grants, ($3500-$7500, with some going higher); Media Grants, ($7500-$10,000, with some going higher).

Deadlines vary according to program. All information and guidelines are available online. Contact the above address for application materials.

Utah
Utah Humanities Council
202 West 300 North
Salt Lake City, UT 84103-1108
801-359-9670
www.utahhumanities.org/
The Utah Humanities Council offers grants in five categories: Mini Grants, (up to $1500, reviewed 3 times/year); Major grants, ($1500-$5000, reviewed once/year); Quick Grants; Teacher Incentive Program, (up to $500); Research fellowship, ($3000, one awarded annually).

All information, guidelines and application materials are available for download from the Council's web site.

Vermont
Vermont Council on the Humanities
200 Park Street
Morrisville, VT 05661
802-888-3183
www.vermonthumanities.org/
The Vermont Council on the Humanities breaks its categories by dollar amount more than by subject. For proposals requesting $2000-$7500, applications are accepted twice a year, proposals of $7500-$15,000 are accepted once a year, and those up to $2000 are accepted three times a year.

The Council clearly says that application materials are not available online because they very much want to discuss any proposal with applicants prior to beginning the application process.

Virginia
Virginia Foundation for the Humanities
145 Ednam Drive
Charlottesville, VA 22903-4629
804-924-3296
www.virginia.edu/vfh/
The granting programs from the Virginia Foundation for the Humanities are categorized a little differently than some of the other state programs. Most grants fall into a very open general category and can be applied for despite topic or funding requirements. Matching funds are a prerequisite. Most of the grants range from $2000-$10,000. Other more specific areas within which an organization may apply include, Film and Video Grants, Teacher Institute

Grants, Digital Media Grants, and Fellowships. The Foundation also has a small amount of mini-grant funding available from time to time.

Application and guideline materials are all available online. The staff is also available to help with the application process.

Virgin Islands
Virgin Islands Humanities Council
5-6 Kongens Gade, Corbiere Complex
Suites 200B and 201B
St. Thomas, VI 00802
340-776-4044

Washington
Washington Commission for the Humanities
615 Second Avenue, Suite 300
Seattle, WA 98104
206-682-1770
www.humanities.org/
The Washington Commission for the Humanities awarded over $102,000 in 1999, funding 21 different projects. Awards ranged from $1600-$8000. Along with Project Grants, the Commission offers some Planning Grants, up to $500. Project Grants are accepted twice a year with Letters of Intent due in March or July and final applications due in April or August. The staff welcomes consultations from applicants for help with proposal writing.

Some recent grantees include: Animal Farm: Public Forum and Resource Guides-$4000-Seattle Children's Theatre; The Mother Tongue Stage-$5000-Northwest Bookfest; People of the Water(Squaxin Island Tribe)-$6400-Squaxin Island Tribe.

West Virginia
West Virginia Humanities Council
723 Kanawha Blvd. East, Suite 800
Charleston, WV 25301
304-346-8500
www.wvhc.com/
The West Virginia Humanities Council funding categories are as follows: Major Grants, ($1500-$20,000, deadlines 2/1 and 9/1); Mini Grants, (up to $1500, deadlines 2/1, 4/1, 6/1, 8/1, 10/1, and 12/1); Media Grants, ($1500-$20,000, deadline 9/1); Fellowships, (up to $2500, deadline 2/1).

All information and guidelines are available online, including downloadable application cover sheets.

Wisconsin
Wisconsin Humanities Council
222 South Bedford Street
Suite F
Madison, WI 53703-3688
608-262-0706
www.danenet.org/whc/
Grants offered by the Wisconsin Humanities Council fall into four basic categories: Planning Grants, (up to $5000, awarded 6 times/year); Mini Grants, (up to $2000, awarded 6 times/year); Major Grants, ($2000-$10,000, awarded 3 times/year); Mega Grants, ($10,000-$20,000, awarded 3 times/year).

The Council's web site is full of information that is all downloadable, with program specific instructions as well as application forms.

Wyoming

Wyoming Council for the Humanities
Box 3643, University Station
Laramie, WY 82071-3643
307-721-9243
www.uwyo.edu/special/wch/
The two basic types of grants available from the Wyoming Council for the Humanities are Regular grants, ($2000-$10,000), and Mini Grants, (up to $2000). Within these two funding groups, monies are allotted for Public Programs, Local and Regional Heritage Programs, Education Grants, Proposal Planning Grants and Special Projects Grants.

Deadlines vary according to programs. All application and guideline materials are available online at the Council's web site.

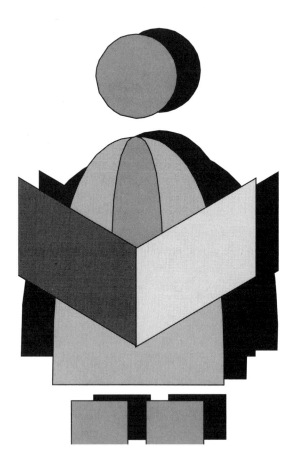

Private Arts Organizations

Not only do federal, state, and local arts organizations support artists, but many private foundations do as well. Although this is not a complete listing, these are some good starting places for artists in search of grants. Don't forget to check out the *How To Find A Nonprofit* chapter to learn how to uncover other resources.

Financial Assistance for Writers

The Llewellyn Miller Fund is part of the American Society of Journalists and Authors. It was established to help established professional writers who are sixty years old or older or disabled. The grant can also be used by writers who are undergoing an "extraordinary professional crisis." The grant is not to be used to fund works in progress, but more to provide needy financial assistance. Your initial contact concerning the grant should be in the form of a letter describing your situation. For more information contact American Society of Journalists and Authors Charitable Trust, 1501 Broadway, Suite 302, new York, NY 10036; 212-997-0947; {www.asja.org}.

Travel Money For Musicians

If you are a talented musician and feel that traveling abroad would be beneficial, then you may find the Frank Huntington Beebe Fund for Musicians is for you. This fund provides up to four grants of up to $12,000 each which is to cover the cost of travel. You must come up with a plan on how the study period would be used. For more information contact Frank Huntington Beebe Fund for Musicians, 290 Huntington Ave., Boston, MA 02115; 617-585-1267.

Money for Vocalists and Instrumentalists

The Leni Fe Bland Foundation provides grants to vocalists and instrumentalists who will use the money to further their training. Many grants are given out each year and the amount of the award does vary. For more information contact Leni Fe Bland Foundation, 2059 Boundary Dr., Santa Barbara, CA 93108.

Grants For Projects

The Ella Lyman Cabot Trust offers grants for financial support for proposed projects that are a unique endeavor for the individual, as well as contributing in some way to society. Grants range up to $20,000. For more information on how to apply contact Ella Lyman Cabot Trust, Inc., 98 River St., Dedham, MA 02026.

Grants For Architecture

The Graham Foundation offers grants to support activities that focus on architecture. Projects include research, exhibitions, and sometimes to support publications. The average grant is less the $10,000. Specific application guidelines are available on the website or by writing the foundation. The Foundation also offers the Carter Manny Award which provides $15,000 to support doctoral thesis work in the field of architecture. For more information contact Graham Foundation, 4 W. Burton Pl., Chicago, IL 60610; 312-787-4071; {www.grahamfoundation.org}.

Grants For Artists in Their Mature Phase

The Adolph and Esther Gottlieb Foundation provides grants to artists who are currently working in their mature phase of their art for at least 20 years. Financial need is also a requirement and a financial disclosure document will need to be provided. They also provide emergency grants to cover unforeseen or catastrophic events. Application forms are only provided by writing to the Foundation. For more information contact Adolph and Ester Gottlieb Foundation, 380 W. Broadway, New York, NY 10012; 212-226-0581; {www.gottleibfoundation.org}.

Fellowships For The Arts

The Guggenheim Fellowships are grants made to individual artists that last for a period of six to twelve months. These grants are designed to provide artists with unrestricted time to explore their creativity. There are no requirements about how the time or money should be spent. The average grant is $34,884. For more information on the application procedures contact the Guggenheim Memorial Foundation, 90 Park Ave., 33rd Floor, New York, NY 10016; 212-687-4470; {www.gf.org}.

Grants For Television, Film, and Video Artists

The independent Television Service awards grants for proposals on projects that will increase the diversity on public television. They was to present a range of subjects and viewpoints that push the envelope of public television offerings. The application form is on the website. For more information contact Independent Television Service, P.O. Box 78008, San Francisco, CA 94107; 415-356-8383; {www.itvs.org}.

Money For Artists And Writers

The Lannan Foundation provides grants each year through three programs: The Art Program, the Literary Program, and the Indigenous Communities Program. The Art Program provides grants to support the creation of new work and looks at the impact of the work on the educational benefit to the public. The Literary Program supports the writing of new literature in poetry, fiction, and nonfiction. The Indigenous Communities Program supports Native people and their attempts to revitalize their communities and their traditions. Money is given to organizations for these projects. Instructions are given on the website as to what information is necessary for the letters of inquiry. For more information you may contact Lannan Foundation, 313 Read St., Santa Fe, NM 87501; 505-986-8160; {www.lannan.org}.

Money For Musicians In Need

The Musicians Foundation provides grants to musicians who are having trouble meeting current living, medical, and other associated expenses. An application is available on the website where the financial need and musical history information are required. For more information contact Musicians Foundation, 875 6th Ave., Suite 2303, new York, NY 10001; 212-239-9137; {www.musiciansfoundation.org}.

More Money For Musicians In Need Or Older Musicians

Sweet Relief is a non-profit organization that provides assistance to musicians who have high medical expenses, or need help with the costs of substance abuse treatment, prescriptions, and other living expenses if they are unable to work. There is also a fund to assistance retired or semi-retired older musicians. For more information contact Sweet Relief Musicians Fund, Box 39666, Los Angeles, CA 90039; 888-955-7880; {www.sweetrelief.org}.

Grants And Fellowships For Artists

The National Foundation for Advancement In The Arts provides grants, fellowships, and scholarships to artists in a variety of disciplines. They provide funding for new, emerging artists, as well as those that are in need of career development. They also offer two Music For Youth Awards. For more information contact the National Foundation ·for Advancement in the Arts, 800 Brickell Ave., Suite 500, Miami, FL 33131; 800-970-ARTS; {www.nfaa.org}.

Money For Sculptors

The National Sculpture Society offers a variety of prizes, grants and scholarships to sculptors and students. Many of the prizes are part of the National Sculpture Competition. They offer $1,000 to students of figurative or representation sculpture, as well as a grant to a realist sculptor who is doing outstanding work. For further information about the awards, grants, or scholarships, send a self-addressed stamped envelop to National Sculpture Society, 1177 Avenue of the Americas, New York, NY 10036; 212-764-5646; {www.nationalsculpture.org}.

Money for Artists

The Pollock-Krasner Foundation provides grants to artists based on the artist's work and their financial need. The Foundation does not offer scholarships. Grants are for a one-year period of time. You must send a letter requesting an application form. The form will require financial report, an artist bio, slides of work, and a resume. For more information contact The Pollock-Krasner Foundation, 863 Park Ave., New York, NY 10021; 212-517-5400; {www.pkf.org}.

Money For Playwrights, Theater, Dance, and Film

The Princess Grace Foundation provides young artists in theater, dance, and film with grants to help them succeed in their field. There are specific deadlines for applicants in each area, and most require that you be age 30 or under. Scholarships, apprenticeships, and fellowships are available. To learn more regarding specific requirements contact Princess Grace Foundation, 150 E. 58th St., 21st Floor, New York, NY 10155; 212-317-1470; {www.pgfusa.com}.

Money For Creativity And Culture

The Rockefeller Foundation provides grants to support the arts and humanities in a variety of ways. The Humanities Fellowships are offered through institutions to support scholars and writers. The Multi-Arts Production Fund offers grants for the creation of new work for live audiences with awards being made to organizations who have commissioned the work. The Film/Video/Multimedia Fellowship Program is offered through a nomination process. The Creative Capital Fund offers audience development, marketing, and other types of assistance to artists exploring new avenues. For more information on the grant process contact The Rockefeller Foundation, 420 5th Ave., New York, NY 10018; 212-869-8500; {www.rockfound.org}.

Money To Travel Overseas

If your work has been accepted at an international festival or exhibition, then the Fund for U.S. Artists and International Festivals may be for you. Supported by two federal agencies and two private foundations, this Fund provides grants to individual artists and organizations, so that they can present their work overseas. For more information contact Arts International, 251 Park Avenue South, 5th Floor, new York, NY 10010; 212-674-9744; {www.artsinternational.org}.

$20,000 For Photojournalists

The W. Eugene Smith Memorial fund provides grants to photojournalists who have a proposal for a photographic project. One grant of $20,000 is available each year. For more information contact W. Eugene Smith Memorial Fund, International Center for Photography, 1130 Fifth Ave., New York, NY 10128; 212-860-1777.

Money For Older Women Artists

The Thanks Be To Grandmother Winifred Foundation offers grants to women age 54 and older, whose projects would enhance the lives of women. The project requirements are broad, and include literary, artistic, musical, or other talents. Grants range from $500 to $5,000. For more information contact The Thanks Be To Grandmother Winifred Foundation, P.O. Box 1449, Wainscott, NY 11975; 631-725-0323; {www.gwfoundation.org}.

$5,000 For Comic Book Writers

The Xeric Foundation offers up to $5,000 for self-publishing comic book creators. The Foundation will not fully support the artist, but they will assist in the cost of publishing the comic book. The most important qualification for this grant is the creativity of the comic book. For more information and the application process contact Xeric Foundation, PMB 214, 351 Pleasant St., Suite 214, Northampton, MA 01060; 413-585-0671; {www.xericfoundation.com}.

Residencies For Women Artists

The Women's Studio Workshop provides Fellowship Grants to women artists and offer studios in intaglio, silkscreen, hand papermaking, photography, letterpress, and clay. Women can apply for residencies from two to six weeks in length and are offered on-site housing an unlimited studio time. Recent college graduates are encouraged to apply for the Emerging Artists Program that provides a two-week residency to get them started on their new work. For more information contact Women's Studio Workshop, P.O. Box 489, Rosendale, NY 12474; 914-658-9133; {www.wsworkshop.org}.

Fellowships For Scholars

The Getty Grant Program offers fellowships for scholars, artists and writers so that the can pursue their work free from obligations and other requirements. There are both residential and non-residential grants, some having requirements as to the area of study. For more information on the Fellowships contact The Getty Grant Program, 1200 Getty Center Dr., Suite 800, Los Angeles, CA 90049; 310-440-7374; {www.getty.edu}.

$3,000 To Perform In New York City

The Franklin Furnace Fund For Performance Art awards ten grants each year of $3,000 each. The money is to be used to produce new work in New York City. The focus is on emerging performance artists. Artists from the United States and the world are encouraged to apply. To learn more about the application process contact Franklin Furnace Archive, 45 John St., Room #611, New York, NY 10038; 212-766-2606; {www.franklinfurnace.org}.

$5,000 For Art In Public Places

The Gunk Foundation supports the production of art that is shown out in public spaces that can be seen by those that do not frequent museums or galleries. Some of the settings can be at places of work, on city streets, or even in public transportation areas. The Foundation likes work that catches people by surprise. For more information contact The Gunk Foundation, P.O. Box 333, Gardiner, NY 12525; 914-255-8252; {www.gunk.org}.

$2,500 For Emerging Artists

The Puffin Foundation awards grants to artists in the areas of art, music, theater, and literature. Their goal is to help the arts world continue to grow and develop. The grants average between $1,000 to $2,500. For more information contact The Puffin Foundation Ltd., 20 East Oakdene Ave., Teaneck, NJ 07666; 201-836-8923; {www.angelfire.com/nj/PuffinFoundation}.

HELP FOR INVENTORS
Patents, Trademarks, and Copyrights

Most inventors realize that it's vitally important to protect their idea by copyrighting it and obtaining the necessary patents and copyrights, but did you know that it's also important to look around for loans and other grants to support your business while working on your invention? If you want an idea to become an actual product, you have to invest an awful lot of your time into its research, and not just on a part time basis. Loans and grants programs for inventors help you do just that. For example, Hawaii offers low cost loans to inventors, as do other states around the country. First, let's talk about getting the necessary information concerning trademark and patent procedures.

Patent and Trademark Office

United States patent and trademark laws are administered by the Patent and Trademark Office (PTO). States also have trade secret statutes, which generally state that if you guard your trade secret with a reasonable amount of care, you will protect your rights associated with that secret. The PTO examines patent and trademark applications, grants protection for qualified inventions, and registers trademarks. It also collects, assembles, and disseminates the technological information patent grants. The PTO maintains a collection of almost 6 million United States patents issued to date, several million foreign patents, and more than 2.2 million trademarks, together with supporting documentation. Here's how to find out what you need to do to patent your idea.

What a Great Idea

To help you get started with patenting your invention, the Patent and Trademark Offices will send you a free booklet upon request called General Information Concerning Patents. There are three legal elements involved in the process of invention: the conception of the idea, diligence in working it out, and reducing it to practice - i.e., getting a finished product that actually works. If you have a great idea you think might work, but you need time to develop it further before it is ready to be patented, what should you do? For answers to general questions on patent examining policies and procedures, contact the Patent Assistance Center at 800-PTO-9199 or 703-308-HELP. They will not answer legal questions or opinions. Applications, forms, and part or all of pamphlets are at their website; {www.uspto.gov}. To order them through the mail write to:

Superintendent of Documents
U.S. Government Printing Office
P.O. Box 371954   202-512-1800
Pittsburgh, PA 15250-7954   Fax: 202-512-2250
www.access.gpo.gov/su_docs

What is a Patent

A patent is a grant of a property right to the inventor for an invention. It lasts for 20 years from the date that the application is filed. United States patent grants are effective within the US, its territories and its possessions. By the language of the grant it is "the right to exclude others from making, using, offering for sale, or selling" the invention

---

in the US or "importing" the invention into the US. It is not the right of the inventor to do so himself that is granted. It is personal property and can be sold or mortgaged, bequeathed or transferred and that person then has the same rights as the original grantee.

What Can Be Patented

A patent can be received for an invention or discovery of any new and useful process, machine, manufacture, or composition of matter, or any new and useful improvement to the original. A design patent is the invention of any new and non-obvious ornamental design for an article of manufacture. Its appearance is protected, not its structural or functional features. A plant patent is the invention or discovery and asexually reproduction of any distinct and new variety of plant. This includes cultivated sports, mutants, hybrids, and newly found seedlings, other than a tuber-propagated plant or a plant found in an uncultivated state. Physical phenomena, abstract ideas, and laws of nature can not be patented. There must be a complete description and not just an idea or suggestion of a subject. It must also do what it claims to do; it must work.

> **A patent can be received for an invention or discovery of any new and useful process**

If an invention has been described in a publication anywhere in the world, or has been used publicly, or put up for sale, a patent must be applied for before one year passes, or the right to a patent is lost.

Who May Apply

There are only a few situations where a person other than the inventor may apply for a patent application.
- a representative if the inventor has died
- a guardian if the inventor is insane
- a joint inventor or a person that has ownership interest if the inventor refuses to apply or can not be found

If two or more persons are the inventors, they may file jointly. However, someone who contributed only financially, is not a joint inventor and cannot be included on the application.

Non-Provisional Application

The application must include:
1)   a written document consisting of the specifications of the invention, and an oath or declaration
2)   a drawing where it is necessary
3)   the filing fee.

It must be in English, legible and written on only one side of white paper with a typewriter or its equivalent. The applicant will be notified if all the requirements are not met. The date that the completed application is filed will then become the filing date. Specifications must include a written description of the invention and the method and process of how it was made and is to be used. It must be in clear, concise, and exact terms to allow any skilled person related to the area of the invention to make and use the same discovery. The oath or declaration is a statement made by the inventor that he/she is the original and first inventor of the subject matter, as well as various other statements, made in front of a notary. The filing fee, excluding design and plant inventions, is a basic fee and additional fees. The basic fee covers 20 claims, including not more than 3 in independent form. There is an additional fee for each claim over 20, whether independent or dependent. The filing fees are cut in half for applicants that file a verified statement claiming small entity status; independent inventor, small business or non-profit. The drawing must show every feature of the invention specified in the claim. Generally, photographs are not accepted. Applications have legal requirements and must be followed precisely.

Provisional Application

These applications create an early effective filing date and the term "Patent Pending" can be applied to the invention. There must be a written description of the invention, any necessary drawings and the name of the inventor(s). Claims and oath or declarations are not required. Also needed, is a cover sheet that states it is a provisional application and a filing fee. The filing date is the date that the PTO receives the application. This type of application can not be filed for design inventions. A non-provisional application must be filed within 12 months or else it will be discarded.

Protect Your Idea for $10

You can file a Disclosure Document with the Patent and Trademark Office, and they will keep it in confidence as evidence of the date of conception of the invention or idea.

> Disclosure Document
> Assistant Commissioner of Patents
> Box DD
> Washington, DC 20231
> Disclosure Office: 800-786-9199
> www.uspto.gov/web/offices/pac/ disdo.html   703-308-HELP

Send an 8 1/2 x 11" drawing, a copy, signed disclosure, SASE, and a check or money order for $10 to file. Upon request, the above office will also send you a free brochure on Disclosure Documents.

This is the best way to keep the idea you are working on completely secret and yet document the date you conceived the idea. You can file the Disclosure Document at any time after the idea is conceived, but the value of it will depend on how much information you put into it - so put as much detail into this statement as you can.

The Purpose of Documenting The Date of Conception

If someone else should try to patent your idea, filing a Disclosure Document shows that you thought of it first, although filing this statement does not legally protect your invention. Documentation of the conception date gives you time to patent your invention, and is invaluable if you need to prove when you thought of your idea if a dispute should arise. (Note that filing a Disclosure Document gives you limited defensive legal protection only if you follow it up with a patent in two years. Unlike a patent, it cannot be used offensively, to stop someone else from patenting the same idea.) When you go to file for a patent, if you and a competitor get into a dispute as to who was the first to invent it, the Patent and Trademark Office (PTO) will hold an Interference Proceeding. If you thought of the idea first, your Disclosure Document will go a long way towards establishing that you were the first inventor and should therefore receive the patent for it.

Examining the Application

They look to see that the application follows the legal requirements and also that the invention is new, useful and non-obvious and meets all requirements. It is not unusual for some, or all, of the claims to be rejected on the first examination. Few are accepted as filed. The applicant will be notified in writing of any errors found. Then the inventor must request reconsideration, specifically pointing out and addressing any errors found and amend any claims that need to be revised. The second examination will generally be made final. Patents are granted in about every 2 out of 3 applications that are filed.

Patent Electronic Business Center

This is the center where you can do business electronically with the USPTO. In order to check the status of your patent application and also find general patent information, you can access the Patent Application Information Retrieval (PAIR). You will also be able to search for specific patents or applications by their number. The Electronic Filing System (EFS) accepts electronically filed applications, but you must have a digital certification and meet other requirements first. This program is only open to select number of people at this time because it is in the beginning stages of operation. Contact the office to see if you may participate!

Research Resources That Can Help You Turn Your Idea Into Reality

While diligently working out the details of your invention you can use the extensive resources of over 190,000 scientific and technical journals, articles, and books at the Scientific and Technical Information Center in Arlington, VA.

Facilitating public access to the more than 25 million cross-referenced United States patents is the job of PTO's Technology Assessment and Forecast Program (TAF); 703-306-2600. It has a master database which covers all United States patents, and searches are available free. An TAF search will not result in an in-depth patent search. (More on that, and how to find classifications in the Conducting Your Own Patent Search section below.) TAF extracts information from its database and makes it available in a variety of formats, including publications, custom patent reports, and statistical reports. The purpose of most of the reports generated by an TAF search is to reveal statistical information.

Copies of the specifications and drawings of all patents are available from PTO. Design patents and trademark copies are $3 each. Plant patents not in color are $10 each, while plant patents in color are $20 each. To make a request, you must have the patent number. For copies, contact:

Office of Public Records (OPR)   800-972-6382
Crystal Gateway 4, Suite 300   703-308-9726
Arlington, VA 22202   Fax: 703-305-8759

Assistant Secretary and Commissioner
P.O. Box 9
ATTN: PTCS
Washington, DC 20231
Public Information Line   703-305-8716

Conducting Your Own Patent Search

Before investing too much time and money on patenting your idea, you will want to see if anyone has already patented it. You may conduct the search yourself on the PTO website at {http://www.uspto.gov} or hire someone to do it for you. If you wish to hire a professional to do your patent search, consult the local yellow pages or again, search the PTO website for a roster of patent attorneys. Even if your search is not as in-depth as that of a patent attorney or a patent agent, you may still find the information that you need. You may also conduct your patent search at the Patent and Trademark Office Search Room.

Patent and Trademark Office (PTO)
Patent and Trademark Search Room
Crystal Plaza 3, 1A01
2021 Jefferson Davis Highway
Arlington, VA 22202   703-305-4463

For information about the Patent and Trademark Depository Library, contact the office listed below.

Patent and Trademark Depository Library (PTDL)
U.S. Patent and Trademark Office
Crystal Park 3, Suite 461   703-308-5558
Washington, DC 20231   Fax: 703-306-2654

You may also conduct your patent search at any of the 83 Patent Depository Libraries (PDLs) throughout the country as listed below.

Patent and Trademark Depository Libraries

Alabama
Ralph Brown Draughon Library, Auburn University, 321 Mell Street, Auburn, AL 36849-5606; 334-844-1747; {www.lib.auburn.edu/scitech/faq/ patent.html}.

Birmingham Public Library, 2100 Park Place, Birmingham, AL 35203; 205-226-3620; {www.bham.lib.al.us/GovDocs/govdocs.html}.

Alaska
Z.J. Loussac Municipal Library, 3600 Denali Street, Anchorage, AK 99503-6093; 907-343-2975; {www.ci.anchorage.ak.us/Services/Departments/ Culture/Library/index.html}.

Arizona
Daniel F. Noble Science and Engineering Library, Arizona State University, P.O. Box 871006, Tempe, AZ 85287-1006; 480-965-7010; {www.asu.edu/ lib/noble/ptdl/ptdl.htm}.

Arkansas
Arkansas State Library, One Capitol Mall, Little Rock, AR 72201; 501-682-2053; {www.asl.lib.ar.us/patents/index.html}.

California
Los Angeles Public Library, 630 West Fifth Street, Los Angeles, CA 90071; 213-228-7220; {www.lapl.org/central/science.html}.

California State Library, Library & Courts Building I, 914 Capitol Mall, Sacramento, CA 95814; {www.library.ca.gov/index.html}.

San Diego Public Library, 820 E Street, San Diego, CA 92101-6478; 619-236-5813; {www.ci.san-diego. ca.us/public-library/index.shtml}.

San Francisco Public Library, 100 Larking Street, San Francisco, CA 94102; 415-557-4500; {http://206.147.53/gic/ptdl.htm}.

Sunnyvale Center for Innovation, Invention & Ideas, 465 South Mathilda Avenue, Suite 300, Sunnyvale, CA 94086; 408-730-7290; {www.sci3.com}.

Colorado
Denver Public Library, 10 West 14th Avenue Parkway, Denver, CO 80204; 303-640-6220; {www.denver.lib.co.us}

Connecticut
Hartford Public Library, 500 Main Street, Hartford, CT 06103; 860-543-8628; {www.hartfordpl.lib.ct.us}.

New Haven Free Public Library, 133 Elm Street, New Haven, CT 06510; 203-946-8130; {www.nhfpl.lib.ct.us/patent.htm}.

Delaware
University of Delaware Library, 181 South College Avenue, Newark, DE 19717-5267; 302-831-2965; {www.lib.udel.edu}.

District of Columbia
Founders Library, Howard University, 500 Howard Place, NW, Washington, DC 20059; 202-806-7252; {www.founders.howard.edu}.

Florida

Broward County Main Library, 100 South Andrews Avenue, Fort Lauderdale, FL 33301; 954-357-7444; {www.co.broward.fl.us/bclblg.htm}.

Dade Public Library, 101 West Flagler Street, Miami, FL 33130; 305-375-2665; {www.mdpls.org}.

University of Central Florida Libraries, 4000 Central Florida Blvd., Orlando, FL 32816; 407-823-2562; {http://library.ucf.edu/GovDocs/PAT_TRAD.htm}.

Tampa Campus Library, 4202 East Fowler Avenue, Tampa, FL 33620-5400; 813-974-2729; {www.lib.usf.edu/virtual/govdocs}.

Georgia

Library and Information Center, Georgia Institute of Technology, 2nd Floor-East Building, Atlanta, GA 30332; 404-894-4508; {http://gtel.gatech.edu/patents}.

Hawaii

Hawaii State Library, 478 South King Street, 2nd Floor, Honolulu, HI 96813-2994; 808-586-3477; {www.hcc.hawaii.edu/hspls/fd/fdmore.html}

Idaho

University of Idaho Library, Rayburn Street, Moscow, ID 83844-2350; 208-885-6235; {www.lib.uidaho.edu/gov/index.htm}

Illinois

Chicago Public Library, 400 South State Str., 4th Floor, Chicago, IL 60605; 312-747-4450; {www.chipublib.org/008subject/009scitech/patents.html}

Illinois State Library, 300 South 2nd Street, Springfield, IL 62701-1796; 217-782-5659; {www.library.sos.state.il.us/isl/collect.html}

Indiana

Indianapolis-Marion County Public Library, 40 E. St. Clair St., Indianapolis, IN 46206; 317-269-1741; {www.imcpl.lib.in.us/bst_patents.htm}.

Siegesmund Engineering Library, Purdue University, 1530 Stewart Center, Potter Room 160, W. Lafayette, IN 47907; 765-494-2869; {www.lib.purdue.edu/engr/patent.html}.

Iowa

State Library of Iowa, 1112 East Grand Avenue, Des Moines, IA 50319; 515-281-4118; {www.silo.lib.ia.us}.

Kansas

Ablah Library, Wichita State University, 1845 Fairmont, Wichita, KS 67260-0068; 316-978-3622; {www.twsu.edu/library/gov/doc/patents.html}.

Kentucky

Louisville Free Public Library, 301 York Street, Louisville, KY 40203; 502-574-1611; {http://lfpl.org/govdoc.htm}.

Louisiana

Troy H. Middleton Library, Louisiana State University, Baton Rouge, LA 70803; 225-388-5652; {www.lib.lsu.edu/sci/eng/int-prop.htm}.

Maine

University of Maine, 5729 Raymond H. Fogler Library, Orono, ME 04469-5729; 207-581-1678; {http://libraries.maine.edu/oroptdl}.

Maryland

Engineering and Physical Sciences Library, University of Maryland, College Park, MD 20742-7011; 301-405-9152; {www.lib.umd.edu/UMCP/ENGIN/patents.html}.

Massachusetts

Physical Sciences and Engineering Library, Lederle Graduate Research Center, University of Massachusetts, Amherst, Amherst, MA 01003-4630; 413-545-1370; {www.library.umass.edu/subject/science/scieng8.htm}.

Boston Public Library, 700 Boylston St., Copley Sq., Boston, MA 02117; 617-536-5400, ext. 267; {www.bpl.org/WWW/science/patent_trademark.html}.

Michigan

Media Union Library, University of Michigan, 2281 Bonisteel Boulevard, Ann Arbor, MI 48109-2094; 734-647-5735; {www.lib.umich.edu/ummu/nwpatentstmstds.html}.

Abigail S. Timme Library, Ferris State University, Big Rapids, MI 49307-2747; 231-591-3730; {www.ferris.edu/library}.

Great Lakes Patent and Trademark Center, Detroit Public Library, 5201 Woodward Avenue, Detroit, MI 48202; 313-833-3379, 800-547-6619; {www.detroit.lib.mi.us/glptc}.

Minnesota

Minneapolis Public Library, 300 Nicollet Mall,

Minneapolis, MN 55401-1992; 612-630-6120;
{www.mpla.lib.mn.us}.

Mississippi
Mississippi Library Commission, 1221 Ellis Ave.,
Jackson, MS 39289-0700; 601-961-4120, 877-
KWIK-REF; {www.mlc.lib.ms.us/
patent_trademark.htm}.

Missouri
Linda Hall Library, Science, Engineering, &
Technology, 5109 Cherry Street, Kansas City, MO
64110-2498; 816-363-4600, 800-662-1545;
{www.lindahall.org}.

St. Louis Public Library, 1301 Olive Street, St. Louis,
MO 63103; 314-241-2288, ext. 390;
{www.slpl.lib.mo.us/library.htm}.

Montana
Montana Tech Library, 1300 West Park Street, Butte,
MT 59701; 406-496-4281; {www.mtech.edu/library/
patents.htm}.

Nebraska
Engineering Library, Nebraska Hall, 2nd Floor West,
City Campus 0516, Lincoln, NE 68588-0410; 402-
472-3411; {www.unl.edu/libr/libs/engr/engr.html}.

Nevada
Clark County Library, 1401 East Flamingo Road, Las
Vegas, NV 89119; 702-733-7810; {www.lvccld.
lib.nv.us/ccl/cl/shtml} - they will be operational soon.

Getchell Library, University of Nevada, 2nd Floor,
Reno, NV 89557; 775-784-6500 ext. 309;
{www.library.unr.edu/~bgic/patent.html}.

New Hampshire
New Hampshire State Library, 20 Park Street,
Concord, NH 03301; 603-271-2143;
{www.state.nh.us/nhsl/patents/index.html}.

New Jersey
Newark Public Library, 3rd Floor, Main Library, 5
Washington St., Newark, NJ 07101; 973-733-7779;
{www.npl.org/Pages/Collections/bst.html}.

Library of Science and Medicine, Rutgers University,
165 Bevier Road, Busch Campus, Piscataway, NJ
08854-8009; 732-445-2895; {www.libraries.rutgers.
edu/rul/libs/lsm_lib/lsm_lib.shtml}.

New Mexico
Centennial Science and Engineering Library, The
University of New Mexico, Albuquerque, NM
87131; 505-277-5327; {http://elibrary.unm.
edu/csel/patents}.

New York
New York State Library, Cultural Education Center,
Empire State Plaza, Albany, NY 12230; 518-474-
5355; {www.nysl.nysed.gov/patents.htm}.

Buffalo and Erie County Library, 1 Lafayette Square,
Buffalo, NY 14203-1887; 716-858-7096;
{www.buffalolib.org/cl_scibusdetails.html}.

Science Industry and Business Library, New York
Public Library, 188 Madison Avenue, New York, NY
10016; 212-592-7000; {www.nypl.org/research/sibl/
pattrade/pattrade.htm}.

Central Library of Rochester & Monroe County, 115
South Ave., Rochester, NY 14604-1896; 716-428-
8110; {www.rochester.lib.ny.us/central}.

Science & Engineering Library, SUNY at Stony
Brook, Stony Brook, NY 11794; 631-632-7148;
{www.sunysb.edu/sciencelibs/patents.htm}.

North Carolina
D.H. Hill Library, North Carolina State University,
2205 Hillsborough Street, Raleigh, NC 27695-7111;
919-515-2935; {www.lib.ncsu.edu/risd/govdocs}.

North Dakota
Chester Fritz Library, University of North Dakota,
University Station, Grand Forks, ND 58202; 701-
777-4888; {www.und.nodak.edu/dept/library/
Collections/Govdocs/govdocs.htm}.

Ohio
Akron-Summit County Public Library, 55 South
Main Street, Akron, OH 44326; 330-643-9000;
{http://ascpl.lib.oh.us/pat-tm.html}.

Public Library of Cincinnati and Hamilton County,
800 Vine Street, 2nd Floor, North Building,
Cincinnati, OH 45202-2071; 513-369-6971;
{http://plch.lib.oh.us/main/pd}.

Cleveland Public Library, 325 Superior Avenue, NE,
Cleveland, OH 44114-1271; 216-623-2800;
{www.cpl.org/Index.asp}.

Science and Engineering Library, Ohio State University, 175 West 18th Avenue, Columbus, OH 43210-1150; 614-292-3022; {www.lib.ohio-state.edu/OSU_profile/phyweb}.

Toledo-Lucas County Public Library, 325 Michigan Street, Toledo, OH 43624; 419-259-5212; {www.library.toledo.oh.us/index4.html}.

Oklahoma
Oklahoma State University, 206 CITD, Stillwater, OK 74078-8085; 405-744-7086; {www.library.ok.state.edu/dept/patents}.

Oregon
Paul L. Boley Law Library, Northwestern School of Law Lewis and Clark College, 10015 SW Terwilliger Boulevard, Portland, OR 97219; 503-768-6786; {www.lclark.edu/~lawlib/ptointro.html}.

Pennsylvania
The Free Library of Philadelphia, 1901 Vine Street, Philadelphia, PA 19103; 215-686-5331; {www.library.phila.gov/central/gpd/pat/fpat.htm}.

Carnegie Library of Pittsburgh, Science and Technology Department, 4400 Forbes Avenue, 3rd Floor, Pittsburgh, PA 15213; 412-622-3138; {www.clpgh.org/clp/Scitech/PTDL/index.html}.

Schreyer Business Library, 301 Paterno Library, 3rd Floor, University Park, PA 16802; 814-865-6369; {www.libraries.psu.edu/crsweb/business/patents}.

Puerto Rico
General Library, University of Puerto Rico at Mayaguez, Mayaguez, PR 00681; 787-832-4040, ext. 2022; {www.uprm.edu/library/patents}.

General Library, Bayamon Campus, #170 Road 174 Minillas Industrial Park, Bayamon, PR 00959; 787-786-2885; {www.cutbupr.clu.edu}.

Rhode Island
Providence Public Library, 225 Washington Street, Providence, RI 02903-3283; 401-455-8027; {www.provlib.org}.

South Carolina
R.M. Cooper Library, Clemson University, Clemson, SC 29634-3001; 864-656-3024; {www.lib.clemson.edu/ptdl/newpat.htm}.

South Dakota
Devereaux Library, 501 East Saint Joseph Street, 2nd Floor, Rapid City, SD 57701; 605-394-1264; {www.sdsmt.edu/services/library/library.html}.

Tennessee
Memphis/Shelby County Public Library & Information Center, 1850 Peabody Avenue, Memphis, TN 38104; 901-725-8877; {www.memphislibrary.lib.tn.us/ftsbc/pttr.htm}.

Stevenson Science & Engineering Library, 3200 Stevenson Center, Nashville, TN 37240; 615-322-2717; {www.library.vanderbilt.edu/science/patents.html}.

Texas
McKinney Engineering Library, University of Texas at Austin, ECJ 1.300, Austin, TX 78713; 512-495-4500; {www.lib.utexas.edu/Libs/ENG/uspat.html}.

Evans Library, Texas A&M University, College Station, TX 77843; 409-845-5745; {http://library.tamu.edu/govdocs/intprop.html}.

Dallas Public Library, 1515 Young Street, 6th Floor, Dallas, TX 75201; 214-670-1468; {www.lib.ci.dallas.tx.us/cgi/cgi.htm}.

Fondren Library, MS225 Rice University, Houston, TX 77251-1892; 713-348-2587; {www.rice.edu/Fondren/PTDL}.

Texas Tech University Libraries, 18th and Boston, Lubbock, TX 79409-0002; 806-742-2282; {www.lib.ttu.edu/govdocs/index.htm}

San Antonio Public Library, 600 Soledad, 2nd Floor, San Antonio, TX 78205; 210-207-2500; {www.st.lib.tx.us/central/govdocs.htm}.

Utah
Marriott Library, University of Utah, 295 South 1500 E, Salt Lake City, UT 84112; 801-581-8394; {www.lib.utah.edu/govdocs}.

Vermont
Bailey/Howe Library, University of Vermont, Burlington, VT 05405; 802-656-2542; {http://bailey.uvm.edu.govdocs.vptdl.html}.

Virginia
James Branch Cabell Library, Virginia

Commonwealth University, 901 Park Avenue, 1st Floor, Richmond, VA 23284-2033; 804-828-1104; {www.library.vcu.edu/sbc/govdocs/govhome.html}.

Washington
Engineering Library, University of Washington, Box 352170, Seattle, WA 98195; 206-543-0740; {www.lib.washington.edu/Engineering/ptdl}.

West Virginia
Evansdale Library, West Virginia University, P.O. Box 6105, Morganstown, WV 26506; 304-293-4696; {www.libraries.wvu.edu/evansdale/patents.htm}.

Wisconsin
Wendt Library, University of Wisconsin, 215 North Randall Ave., Madison, WI 53706; 608-262-6845; {www.wisc.edu/wendt/patent/patent.html}.

Milwaukee Public Library, 814 West Wisconsin Avenue, Milwaukee, WI 53233; 414-286-3051; {www.mpl.org/files/central/science/science.htm}.

Wyoming
Natrona County Public Library, 307 East 2nd Street, Casper, WY 82601; 307-237-4935, ext. 23; {www-wsl.state.wy.us/natrona/ptdl.htm}.

The Patent and Trademark Library Program distributes the information to the 83 PDLs. The information is kept on CD-Rom discs, which are constantly updated, and you can use them to do a patent search. CD-Rom discs have been combined to incorporate CASSIS (Classification and Search Support Information System). CD-Rom discs do not give you online access to the PTO database. Online access is available through APS (Automated Patent Systems), and is presently available to public users of the PTO Search Room and to the 83 Patent Libraries. Each PDL with the online APS has its own rules regarding its use. To use the online APS at the PTO Search Room, you must first sign up and take a class at the Search Room. This class is held for 3 consecutive 1/2 days and is given once per month for a cost of $25. Online access costs $40 per connect hour, and the charge for paper used for printouts is an additional $.25 per sheet.

If you do not live near a PDL, several CD-Rom discs are available through subscription. You may purchase the Classification disc, which dates back to 1790, for $300; the Bibliography disc, which dates back to 1969, for $300; and the ASIST disc, which contains a roster of patent attorneys, assignees, and other information for $200. You can also conduct your patent search and get a copy of it through commercial database services such as:

MeadData Central, Nexis, Lexis: 1-800-843-6476. Patent searches are done for $25. If found, there is a charge of $5 per page of printout and $5 more if there is a drawing. Abstracts are $3. For Trademarks, the charge is $50 and $5 for the drawing. If you intend on doing many searches over time, Nexis Lexis will customize a package for you as a subscriber for approximately $250 per month.

Derwent, 1725 Duke St., Suite 250, Alexandria, VA 22314; 1-800-336-5010, 1-800-523-7668, Fax: 1-800-457-0850. Patent searches are free, but the printouts range from $3.95 to $29.50 per page plus shipping.

If you are going to do your own patent search at your local Patent Depository Library, begin with the Manual and Index to U.S. Patent Classifications to identify the subject area where the patent is placed. Then use the CD-Rom discs to locate the patent. CD-Rom discs enable you to do a complete search of all registered patents but do not enable you to view the full patent, with all its specific details. Lastly, view the patent, which will be kept on microfilm, cartridge, or paper. What information there is to view varies by library, depending on what they have been able to purchase. If the library you are using does not have the patent you want, you may be able to obtain it through inter-library loan.

Copies of patents can be ordered from the PTO at 703-308-9726, for $3 per copy.

To obtain a certified copy of a patent, call 703-308-9726 (Patent Search Library at the PTO). The fee is $25 and you must have the patent number. For a certified copy of an abstract of titles, the fee is $25. For a certified copy of patent assignments, with a record of ownership from the beginning until present, call 703-308-9726. The cost is $25, and to request specific assignments you must have the reel and frame number.

Now You Have Got Your Patent

Once a Notice of Allowance stating that your application for patents approved, you have 3 months to pay another filing fee. If not, the application will be deemed abandoned. There are also maintenance fees due at 31/2, 71/2, and 111/2 years after the original grant. After it has expired, anyone may make, use, offer for sale, or sell or import the invention without the patentee's approval. A patent is personal property.

Tips

* Most importantly, do not reveal the details of your invention to anyone! If you need to do so, establish a confidential relationship with them by law or regulation, or a written agreement. Your plans and information you have gathered can be trade secrets and you must protect them.
* Record your discovery in detail as soon as possible and keep a record as you go. Have it witnessed by two reliable persons with a confidentiality agreement.
* Developing a new product is time consuming and expensive. Determine how much of your time, money, and effort you can invest. Know your personal limitations and when to get professional help.
* Twenty percent of patents issued each year are to private inventors. They must be effective business people to also research business concepts.
* Read articles by successful inventors for tips on what it took for them to market their product. Talk to potential customers to see what they would look for in the type of product that you are discovering.
* Remember, if a product similar to yours exists, you can still patent an improvement that is significant.
* Lastly, many times it is not the first try at inventing a product that is successful, it gets better as you go.

What Are Trademarks and Servicemarks?

A trademark is a word, name, symbol or device used in trade with goods to indicate the source of the goods and to set them apart from the goods of others. A servicemark is used to distinguish the source of a service instead of a product. Trademark or mark is generally the term used to refer to both trademarks and servicemarks. They are to keep others from using a confusingly similar mark, but not to keep others from making or selling the same goods or services under a clearly different mark. The Trademark Assistance Center will provide general information about the registration process and will respond to questions concerning the status of a specific trademark application and registration. They are available Monday through Friday from 8:30am to 5pm at 703-308-9000.

Trademarks

Registering a trademark for your product or service is the way to protect the recognition quality of the name you are building. The PTO keeps records on more than 2.2 million trademarks and records. Over 500,000 active trademarks are kept on the floor of the library, while "dead" trademarks are kept on microfilm. Books contain every registered trademark ever issued, starting in 1870. You can visit the Patent and Trademark Office to research a trademark using the US Trademark Electronic Search System (TESS). You can access TESS at http://tess.uspto.gov. You can then conduct your search manually for no charge or use their Trademark Search System (T-Search) for $40 per hour, plus $.25 cents per page.

Assistant Commissioner of Trademarks
Trademark Search Library
2900 Crystal Dr.
Second Floor, Room 2B30
Arlington, VA 22202   703-308-9800/9805

If you can't do it yourself, you can hire someone to do the search for you. For an agent to do this, consult the local yellow pages under "Trademark Agents/Consultants" or "Trademark Attorneys". You can also locate an agent by calling your local bar association for a referral.

To conduct your own search at a Patent Depository Library, use the CD-Rom disc on trademarks. It is available for purchase. The CD-Rom discs deliver patent and trademark information including full-text facsimile images and searchable text records. Images can be found in the Official Gazette, which contains most current and pending trademarks. The price for an annual subscription to the Official Gazette for trademarks is $766, and for the Gazette for patents, it is $1,061. Both are issued every Tuesday and can be ordered from the U.S. Government Printing Office. You can also purchase an image file which contains pending and registered trademarks and corresponding serial or registration numbers through Thomson and Thomson by calling 1-800-692-8833. The information contained in it dates back to April 1, 1987 and is updated by approximately 500 images weekly. However, the PDL you use is likely to have an image of the trademark on microfilm or cartridge, and also have copies of the Official Gazette. If not, and you have the registration number, you may obtain a copy of the trademark you want for $3 from the PTO. Contact:

Assistant Commissioner of Trademarks
2900 Crystal Dr.
Second Floor, Room 2B30
Arlington, VA 22202   703-308-9800

There are also several commercial services you can use to conduct trademark searches.

Trademark Scan produced by Thomson and Thomson. It can be purchased by calling 1-800-692-8833 (ask for online services), or accessed directly via Saegis. Trademark Scan is updated three times per week, and includes state and federal trademarks, foreign and domestic. To access Trademark Scan you must already have Dialog or Saegis. Many online options are free. The Internet address is {www.thomson-thomson.com}.

Derwent, 1-800-336-5010, is a commercial service that will conduct patent searches only. The cost ranges from $100 and up with a turnaround time of 2-5 days. The Internet address is {www.derwent.com}.

Online services and database discs for both patents and trademarks are constantly being expanded. For information on an extensive range of existing and projected products, call the PTO Office of Electronic Information at 703-306-2600 and ask for the U.S. Department of Commerce, PTO Office of Information Systems' Electronic Products Brochure. For example, there is a Weekly Text File, containing text data of pending and registered trademarks. Information can be called up by using almost any term. It can be purchased from AvantIQ and Thomson & Thomson. You can reach AvantIQ at 1-800-320-6366, 610-584-4380, or online at {http://www.avantiq.lu/}. You can reach Thomson & Thomson at 1-800-692-8833 or online at {www.thomson-thomson.com}.

How to Register a Trademark

The right of a trademark comes from either the actual use of the mark, or by filing the correct application. There are two types of rights in a mark, the right to register it and the right to use the mark. The right to register is given to the first party that uses a mark in commerce, or who files an application at the PTO. The right to use a mark can be a complicated matter. For example, in the case where two people who do not know each other, start to use the same or similar marks without a registration. A court will have to decide who has the right to use the mark. Trademark rights last indefinitely if the owner continues its use. The registration last 10 years with 10 year renewal periods. You can order a free copy of Basic Facts about Trademarks from the U.S. Government Printing Office, or by calling the Trademark Search Library at 703-308-9000.

Types of Applications

The "use" application is for an applicant that already has been using their mark in commerce. The "intent-to-use" application is for those who have a bona fide intention of using the mark in commerce. These offer protection only in the US and it territories. Applications must be filed in the name of the owner of the mark.

For automated information about the status of a trademark application and registration, call 703-305-8747.

The Trademark Electronic Center

The Trademark Electronic Application System (TEAS) has step-by-step instructions for filling out forms and also contains information about the USPTO's procedures and practices. It also allows you to fill out the trademark forms, check them to be sure they are complete, and using e-TEAS, submit it on-line. You must be able to attach either a black-and-white GIF or JPG file to apply for a stylized or design mark. If a sample of actual use in commerce is needed, a scanned image or digital photo in GIF or JPG format must be attached. The final requirement is payment with a credit card or from an account already set up with the PTO. One mark can be filed with each application for a fee of $325, except for Class 9 and Class 25, where there is a $650 fee. E-TEAS will not accept applications from 11pm Saturday to 6am Sunday. Also, if you prefer to send the forms by mail, you can use PrinTEAS to print out your completed forms. You can send check, money order, or make arrangements for payment through a USPTO account. This system can be accessed 24 hours a day, 7 days a week.

You can check the status of marks using TARR-Trademark Applications and Registrations Retrieval at {http://tarr.uspto.gov}.

Symbols

Anyone who claims rights in a mark can use the symbols, TM (trademark) or SM (servicemark) to show that right. However, the registration symbol, an r in a circle (r), can not be used until the mark is registered.

The Right Way to Get a Copyright

Copyrights are filed on intellectual property. A copyright protects your right to control the sale, use of distribution, and royalties from a creation in thought, music, films, art, or books. It is an automatic form of protection for authors of published and unpublished "original works of authorship." The concrete form of expression as opposed to the subject matter is what is protected. Since a copyright is automatic when a work is created, registration is not required for protection. However, there are advantages to registration. If it is registered within 5 years of publication of the work, it establishes prima facie evidence of its validity and can be helpful in case of a court action. Generally the work is protected for the author's life plus 70 years after death.

For more information, contact:

Library of Congress
Copyright Office
101 Independence Avenue SE
Washington, DC 20559
Public Information Office   202-707-3000
Email: copyinfo@loc.gov   TTY: 202-707-6737
www.loc.gov
http://lcweb.loc.gov/copyright

If you know which copyright application you require, you can call the Forms Hotline, open 7 days per week, 24 hours per day at 202-707-9100. The fee is $30 for each registration. Information on all of the different types of copyrights and their applications can be found at their web site.

The Library of Congress provides information on copyright registration procedures and copyright card catalogs that cover several million works that have been registered since 1870. The Copyright Office will research federal copyrights only for varying fees. Requests must be made in writing and you must specify exactly what information you require. If a work does not show any elements of copyright notice, you can search the Copyright Office's catalogs and records. The records from January 1, 1978, to the present can be searched on the Internet through the Library of Congress Information System (LOCIS). That web site address is {www.loc.gov/copyright/rb.html}.

Contact the Copyright Office, Reference and Bibliography, Library of Congress, 101 Independence Ave., SE, Washington, DC 20559; 202-707-6850, Public Information 202-707-3000.

What is Not Protected by Copyright

Works that have not been notated, recorded, or written can not be protected by copyright. Here are some others:

★   titles, short phrases, and slogans; familiar symbols or designs; variations of ornamentation, lettering or coloring, listings of ingredients or contents
★   concepts, methods, systems, principles, or devices, as opposed to description, explanation, and illustration
★   works that are entirely made of information that is common property and don not contain any original authorship

Invention Scams: How They Work

Fake product development companies prey on amateur inventors who may not be as savvy about protecting their idea or invention as experienced inventors might be. Most of the bogus/fake companies use escalating fees.

The following is a description of how most of them operate:

1) The inventor is invited to call or write for free information.

2) The inventor is then offered a free evaluation of his idea.

3) Next comes the sales call. The inventor is told he has a very good potential idea and that the company is willing to share the cost of marketing, etc. Actual fact, there is no sharing with these companies. Most times the inventor has to come up with the money (usually several hundred dollars or more) for a patent search and a market analysis. Neither of these are worth anything.

4) Then the inventor receives a professional/ impressive looking portfolio which contains no real information at all. All the paper crammed into this portfolio looks topnotch, but it's all computer generated garbage.

5) Upon receiving this portfolio, the inventor is lured into signing a contract that commits him to giving the company thousands of dollars to promote/license the product. The company sends some promotional letters to fulfill their obligation, but large manufacturers simply toss them into the trash.

After all this, the inventor has spent thousands of dollars, wasted a lot of time, and gotten nowhere with his product.

How To Avoid Losing a Fortune

According to the experts, the inventor should:

- Beware of the come-ons offered by these unethical companies. Avoid using the invention brokers who advertise on TV late in the evening; in public magazines; those who offer 800 numbers; and those on public transit display signs.

- When upfront money is required, look out. There are very few legitimate consultants who insist on a retainer or hourly fee.

- Don't allow the enthusiasm of your idea to take over your inherent common sense. Talk to your patent attorney and see if he knows anything about this company. Plus, check with inventors associations in the state, and see what they have to say about this particular company.

- Demand to know what percentage of ideas the company accepts. Legitimate brokers might accept 2 ideas out of every 100. The fake companies tend to accept about 99 out of 100.

- Find out their actual success rate. Any corporation/ company that will not give you their success rate (not licensing agreements) is a company to stay away from.

- Get an objective evaluation of your invention from reputable professionals. This will save you plenty of money on a bad idea.

A number of highly recommended programs are listed in the next section.

Free Help for Inventors

If you have a great idea and want to turn it into reality, don't rush out and spend what could be thousands of dollars for a private invention company and a patent attorney. You can get a lot of this help for free or at a fraction of the cost. There is a lot of help out there; university-sponsored programs, not-for-profit groups, state affiliated programs, profit-making companies, etc. Depending on the assistance and the organization, some services are free, others have reasonable fees.

Many of the inventors' organizations hold regular meetings where speakers share their expertise on topics such as licensing, financing and marketing. These groups are a good place for inventors to meet other inventors, patent attorneys, manufacturers, and others with whom they can talk and from whom they can get help.

If the listings in the state-by-state section of this chapter do not prove to be useful, you can contact one of the following organizations for help.

1. Small Business Development Center
    Washington State University
    Parkplace Building
    1200 6th Ave., Suite 1700
    Seattle, WA 98101
    206-553-7328
    Fax: 206-553-7044
    www.sbdc.wsu.edu/franz.htm

This service will evaluate your idea for a fee. They also provide counseling services and can assist you with your patent search.

2. Wisconsin Innovation Service Center/Technology
    Small Business Development Center
    Ms. Debra Malewicki, Director
    University of Wisconsin - Whitewater
    402 McCutchan Hall
    Whitewater, WI 53190
    414-472-3217
    Fax: 414-472-1600

The only service that is guaranteed is the evaluation. However, efforts are made to match inventors with exceptional high evaluation scores with manufacturers seeking new product ideas. (Do not offer direct invention development or marketing services). WISC charges a $495 flat fee for an evaluation. The goal is to keep research as affordable as possible to the average independent inventor. Most evaluations are completed within 30 - 45 days. Those inventions from specialized fields may require more time. WISC also provides preliminary patent searches via on-line databases to client.

3. Drake University
    Small Business Development Center
    Mr. Benjamin C. Swartz, Director
    Drake Business Center
    2507 University
    Des Moines, IA 50311-4505
    515-271-2655
    1-800-532-1216
    Fax: 515-271-1899
    www.iabusnet.org

INVENTURE is a program of the Drake University Business Development and Research Institute designed to encourage the development of valid ideas through the various steps to becoming marketable items. INVENTURE has no paid staff. The entire panel is made up of volunteers. The administration of the program is handled by existing staff from the Small Business Development Center and the College of Business and Public Administration. They will review items from any person regardless of their place of residence. They will review a product idea and check it for market feasibility. INVENTURE may link individuals with business and/or financial partners.

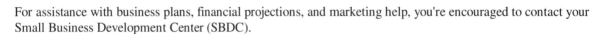

INVENTURE screens every product submitted, but will not consider toy/game or food items. Products are evaluated on 33 different criteria, (factors related to legality, safety, business risk, and demand analysis, to market acceptance/ competition). It normally takes up to 6 weeks to receive results of the evaluation. Evaluators are experienced in manufacturing, marketing, accounting, production, finance and investments.

INVENTURE acts in a responsible manner to maintain confidence of an idea, but cannot guarantee confidentiality.

For assistance with business plans, financial projections, and marketing help, you're encouraged to contact your Small Business Development Center (SBDC).

4.   U.S. Department of Energy
     Mail Stop EE-24
     1000 Independence Ave., SW
     Washington, DC 20585
     202-586-1478
     Fax: 202-586-7114
     www.oit.doe.gov/inventions/
Financial assistance is available at 2 levels: up to $40,000 and up to $200,000 by the Inventions and Innovations program as stated by the Office of Industrial Technologies (OIT) Department of Energy (DOE) for ideas that significantly impact energy savings and future commercial market potential. Successful applicants will find technical guidance and commercialization support in addition to financial assistance.

DOE has given financial support to more than 500 inventions with nearly 25% of these reaching the marketplace bringing in nearly $710 million in cumulative sales.

5.   U.S. Environmental Protection Agency
     Center for Environmental Research Information
     Cincinnati, OH 45260
     513-569-7562
     www.epa.gov
Directory Description: Environmental Protection Agency, Office of Research and Development, 401 M Street, SW, Washington, DC 20460; 202-260-7676, Fax: 202-260-9761.
The Office of Research and Development conducts an Agency wide integrated program of research and development relevant to pollution sources and control, transport and fate processes, health/ecological effects, measurement/monitoring, and risk assessment. The office provides technical reviews, expert consultations, technical assistance, and advice to environmental decision-makers in federal, state, local, and foreign governments.

Center for Environmental Research Information
26 W. ML King Drive, Cincinnati, OH 45268, Calvin O. Lawrence, Director; 513-569-7562; Fax: 513-569-7566.
A focal point for the exchange of scientific/ technical information both within the federal government and to the public.

Office of Research and Development
Is responsible for working with laboratories, program offices, regions to produce information products that summarize research, technical, regulatory enforcement information that will assist non-technical audiences in understanding environmental issues. Contact Office of Research and Development, U.S. Environmental Protection Agency, 401 M St., SW, Washington, DC 20460; 202-260-5767.

Office of Exploratory Research
Robert Menzer, Acting Director, 401 M Street, SW, Washington, DC 20460; 202-564-6849, Fax: 202-260-0450.
The Office of Exploratory Research (OER) plans, administers, manages, and evaluates the Environmental Protection Agency's (EPA) extramural grant research. It supports research in developing a better understanding of the environment and its problems. Main goals are: to support the academic community in environmental research; maintain scientific/technical personnel in environmental science/technology; to support research for the identification/solution of emerging environmental problems.

Goals are accomplished through four core programs:

1. The Research Grants Program:
    Supports research initiated by individual investigators in areas of interest to the agency.

2. The Environmental Research Centers Program:
    Has two components: The Academic Research Center Program (ARC) and the Hazardous Substance Research Centers Program (HSRC).

3. The Small Business Innovation Research (SBIR) Program:
    Program supports small businesses for the development of ideas relevant to EPA's mission. Focuses on projects in pollution control development. Also receives 1.5% of the Agency's resources devoted to extramural Superfund research.

4. The Visiting Scientists Program:
    Components are an Environmental Science and Engineering Fellows Program and a Resident Research Associateship Program. The Fellows Program supports ten mid-career post-doctoral scientists and engineers at EPA headquarters & regional offices. The Research Associateship Program attracts national and international scientists and engineers at EPA research laboratories for up to 3 years to collaborate with Agency researchers on important environmental issues.

Other programs available are:
    A Minority Fellowship Program
    A Minority Summer Intern Program
    The Agency's Senior Environmental Employment Program (SEE)
    The Federal Workforce Training Program
    An Experimental Program to Stimulate Competitive Research (EPSCoR).

To learn more, contact Grants Administration, U.S. Environmental Protection Agency, 401 M St., SW, 3903E, Washington, DC 20460; 202-564-5315. The best way, though, is to search for the word "grant" at the EPA's website, {www.epa.gov}.

State Sources for Inventors

Free Money For Inventors

People pay good money for good ideas, especially, the government. There is even government grant money available to work on ideas, either your own or the ones that the government has. Here is how some state governments give money to inventors:

☺ North Dakota gives inventors up to $100,000 to work on new ideas through Technology Transfer, Inc.

☺ Rhode Island offers grant money to develop new products using the ocean, (how about seaweed cereal), through the Ocean Technology Center.

☺ Pennsylvania offers grants from $5,000 to $100,000 for entrepreneurs to work on new ideas through the Ben Franklin Challenge Grant Program.

☺ Delaware offers inventors up to $25,000 in venture capital to write business plans and get patents, and then up to $250,000 to do marketing, as part of the Delaware Innovation Fund.

☺ North Carolina grants up to $25,000 to develop ideas to eliminate wood waste through the Solid Waste Reduction Assistance Grant.

☺ Wisconsin gives out grants for new ways of recycling in their Recycling Early Planning Grant Program.

☺ Ohio and Indiana have grants for inventors who have new ideas on what to do with old tires.

Contact your local state Office of Economic Development listed in the Appendix to investigate what your state has to offer inventors.

Other Inventing Grants

Some states also offer grant money to inventors who are working on getting government grants for their ideas. The largest source of these grants is the Small Business Innovative Research Grants that offer over $1 billion from 10 different agencies. The Small Business Administration acts as a clearinghouse for this information.

Other federal grant programs for inventors include:

✪ The Inventions and Innovation Program, managed by the U.S. Department of Energy, provides grants for ideas that result in the more efficient use of energy.

✪ The Advanced Technology Program gives $200 million a year in grants for developing new technology from the U.S. Department of Commerce's National Institute of Standards and Technology.

✪ The U.S. Department of Energy's National Industrial Competitiveness through Energy, Environment and Economics (NICE3) offers grants up to $400,000 to develop ideas that save energy.

You can find these programs in a government book in your library called *The Catalog of Federal Domestic Assistance* or by contacting your local Federal Information Center at 800-688-9889; {http://fic.info.gov}.

Below is a listing of a variety of inventors groups, listed state by state. Some organizations listed under the state where they are located are regional or national in scope. In states where there is no specific program for inventors, the Small Business Development Centers (under the U.S. Small Business Administration) can often be of help. They are usually found at the colleges and universities. The Small Business Development Center office is located at 409 Third St., SW, Suite 4600, Washington, DC 20416; 202-205-6766; {www.sba.gov}.

Alabama
Office for the Advancement of Developing Industries
University of Alabama - Birmingham
2800 Milan Ct.   205-934-6560
Birmingham, AL 35211   205-934-6563
www.uab.edu/oadi/index.htm
Inventors can receive help on the commercialization and patent processes and critical reviews of inventions in this office. Assessments can be made on an invention's potential marketability and assistance is available for patent searches. There is a charge for services.

Small Business Development Center
University of Alabama at Birmingham
9015 15th St.   205-934-6760
Birmingham, AL 35294   Fax: 205-934-0538
www.business.uab.edu/SBDC/Index.htm
The center offers counseling for a wide range of business issues and problems.

U.S. Small Business Administration
Business Development
2121 8th Avenue, N, Suite 200   205-731-1338
Birmingham, AL 35203-2398   Fax: 205-731-1404
www.sba.gov
This office offers counseling for a wide range of business issues and problems.

Alabama Technology Assistance Program
University of Alabama at Birmingham
1717 11th Avenue S, Suite 419   205-934-7260
Birmingham, AL 35294   Fax: 205-934-7645
This program provides general assistance/funding information. Inventors meet other inventors and investors.

Alaska
UA Small Business Development Center of Alaska
430 W. 7th Ave., Suite 110   907-274-7232
Anchorage, AK 99501   Fax: 907-274-9524
www.scob.alaska.edu/CENTERS/sbdc.html
The SBDC provides general assistance, including free counseling to inventors on commercialization and patent processes, and arranging meetings between inventors, investors, manufacturers, and others who can be of help.

Alaska Inventors and Entrepreneurs Association
P.O. Box 241801
Anchorage, AK 99524
907-563-4337 (phone and fax)
www.artic.net/~inventor
Email: inventors@artic.net
They provide access to the tools and resources needed in order to empower inventors to bring their product to market. The InventorNet Resource Directory lists professional service providers, agents, designers, and much more.

There are also monthly meetings, magazine subscription discounts, free access to the Internet and other benefits. There is a membership fee.

Arizona
Arizona SBDC Network
2411 West 14th Street   480-731-8720
Tempe, AZ 85281   Fax: 480-731-8729
www.dist.maricopa.edu/sbdc
The center offers counseling for a wide range of business issues and problems.

Inventors Association of Arizona   520-721-2840
P.O. Box 12217   888-299-6787
Tucson, AZ 85732   Fax: 520-722-2840
www.azinventors.org/iaainfo.htm
Email: linxmail@flash.net
Their goal is to guide the creativity of the members through experience, support and confidentiality so that they will be able to market their new invention or idea. Some of the areas they offer assistance in are, patent, trademark, and copyrights, manufacture, finance, and obtaining a product license. Benefits include discounts for legal services, Trade Magazine subscriptions, and consulting, as well as comprehensive information concerning the steps from concept to market. There is a membership fee.

Arkansas
Small Business Development Center
University of Arkansas at Little Rock
100 S. Main, Suite 401   501-324-9043
Little Rock, AR 72201   Fax: 501-324-9049
www.ualr.edu/~sbdcdept
The center offers counseling for a wide range of business issues and problems.

California
Small Business Development Center
1410 Ethan Way   916-563-3210
Sacramento, CA 95825   Fax: 916-563-2366
www.sbdc.net
The center offers counseling for a wide range of business issues and problems.

Inventors' Alliance
P.O. Box 281764   415-468-5156
San Francisco, CA 94120-1764   Fax: 415-967-0720
www.inventorsalliance.org
Email: 74123.1221@compuserve.com
They have monthly meeting with guest speakers on topics such as marketing and product development. These meetings are designed to increase the inventors knowledge and create contacts for a successful production of a product.

Inventors Forum
P.O. Box 8008   714-540-2491
Huntington Beach, CA 92606   Fax: 714-253-0951
www.inventorsforum.org
Email: infor@inventorsforum.org
This nonprofit group teaches inventors about the invention process. Some of the products and services they provide

are, the Invention Showcase, a listing of service providers for a number of different services, and an inventors message base with a range of topics.

Redwood Empire Small Business
Development Center   888-346-SBDC
606 Healdsburg Avenue   707-524-1773
Santa Rosa, CA 95401   Fax: 707-524-1772
www.santarosa.edu/sbdc/general.shtml
Email: sbdc@santarosa.edu
They have a Patent Information Network where inventor clients perform initial patent searches to help in forming an assessment of an idea or design. They also offer one-on-one professional business consulting. There is no charge for these services.

Colorado

Affiliated Inventors Foundation, Inc.
1405 Porter St., #107   719-380-1234
Colorado Springs, CO 80909   Fax: 719-380-1144
To order free Info Kit   800-525-5885
www.affiliatedinventors.com
This foundation counsels inventors on commercialization and patent processes, and provides detailed information on the steps needed to reach commercialization. Preliminary appraisals, evaluations and other services are available for a fee.

Small Business Development Center
Office of Economic Development
1625 Broadway, Suite 1710   303-892-3809
Denver, CO 80202   Fax: 303-892-3849
www.state.co.us/gov_dir/oed/sbdc.html
The center offers counseling for a wide range of business issues and problems.

Rocky Mountain Inventors & Entrepreneurs
Congress (RMIC)
P.O. Box 36233   303-670-3760
Denver, CO 80236   Fax: 303-674-5338
www.RMinventor.org
Email: info@RMinventor.org
Their mission is to help people with new ideas to fulfill their greatest potential. Their members include new and established inventors, prototypers, manufactures, marketers, patent attorneys and others connected to the invention process. Besides dinner and round table meetings, they have networking sessions, monthly educational meetings and an annual conference. They offer information on the invention process, the tools needed and advice on what to do with the invention. Three is a dinner meeting fee.

Connecticut
Small Business Development Center
University of Connecticut
2 Bourn Place, U-94   860-486-4135
Storrs, CT 06269-1594   Fax: 860-486-1576
www.sbdc.uconn.edu
Email: CSBDCinformation@sba.uconn.edu
The center offers counseling for a wide range of business issues and problems.

The Inventors Guild
2 Worsen Avenue
Danbury, CT 06810   203-790-8235
www.thehooktek.com/innovators.html
Email: rfaulkner@snet.net
This is a nonprofit organization for inventors and entrepreneurs for the purpose of introducing inventing, marketing and business methods. They mainly do this through a monthly meeting with a guest speaker and socialization and a network hour. There is a modest membership fee.

Inventors Association of Connecticut
9-B Greenhouse Road   203-866-0720
Bridgeport, CT 06606-2130   Fax: 781-846-6448
www.inventus.org
Email: IACTWinventus.org
This is a nonprofit group who has members that include inventors, designers, engineers, attorneys, and business people. They look to nurture, stimulate creativity and advance the image of independent inventors by education, promotion and sharing of member resources. They have monthly meeting with pre-meeting session, and a newsletter to accomplish this goal. There is a monthly fee.

Delaware

Small Business Development Center
University of Delaware
One Innovation Way, Suite 301   302-831-1555
Newark, DE 19711   Fax: 302-831-1423
www.delawaresbdc.org
The office offers management counseling and seminars on various topics, and can counsel inventors on areas such as the commercialization and patenting processes. Services are by appointment only.

Delaware Economic Development
99 Kings Highway   302-739-4271
Dover, DE 19901   Fax: 302-739-5749
www.state.de.us/dedo/departments/finance/sbir.htm
Assistance is available to any applicant located in Delaware or relocating to Delaware, who has been granted a phase I SBIR award and has submitted a Phase II SBIR application.

District of Columbia

U.S. Department of Commerce
U.S. Patent and Trademark Office   800-PTO-9199
Washington, DC 20231   703-308-4357

District of Columbia Small Business Development Center
Howard University
2600 6th St., NW, Suite 128   202-806-1550
Washington, DC 20059   Fax: 202-806-1777
The center offers counseling for a wide range of business issues and problems.

U.S. Small Business Administration
2328 19th St., NW   202-606-4060
Washington, DC 20009   Fax: 202-205-7064
www.sba.gov
This office provides general assistance and information on funding.

Florida
Small Business Development Center
1531 NW 6th St.
Gainesville, FL 32606   352-377-5621
The center offers counseling for a wide range of business issues and
problems.

Small Business Development Center
University of West Florida
1170 Martin L. King, Jr. Blvd.   850-595-5480
Fort Walton Beach, FL 32547   Fax: 850-595-5487
www.sbdc.uwf.edu
The center offers counseling for a wide range of business issues and problems.

Florida SBDC Network
19 W. Garden St., Suite 300   850-595-6060
Pensacola, FL 32501   Fax: 850-595-6070
www.floridasbdc.com
The network provides general assistance; conducts market/ technical assessments; offers legal advice on patents and
licensing; provides funding information; and assists in building a prototype. Inventors get to showcase their
inventions and meet with other inventors and investors.

University of Central Florida
Small Business Development Center
P.O. Box 161530   407-823-3073
Orlando, FL 32816-1530   Fax: 407-823-3073
www.bus.ucf.edu/sbdc
The center provides general assistance, funding information and conducts market assessments. Inventors meet other
inventors.

Edison Inventors Association
P.O. Box 07398   941-275-4332
Ft. Meyers, FL 33919   Fax: 941-267-9746
Email: drghn@aol.com
They are a non-profit group whose goal is to aid creativity and assistance inventors and entrepreneurs to be
successful. They have monthly meetings.

Inventors Society of South Florida
P.O. Box 4306
Boynton Beach, FL 33424   954-486-2426
They consider themselves a non-profit educational society. The guest speakers include patent agents, attorneys,
government sources, engineers, technicians and more. You will be able to ask questions of the guest and also
network with other inventors at monthly meetings.

Tampa Bay Inventors' Council
P.O. Box 1620
St. Petersburg, FL 33731-1620   727-866-0669 (phone/fax)
http://patent-faq.com/tbichome.htm
Email: KIEWIT@patent-faq.com
This non-profit organization educates its members and others about invention product development and marketing.
The meetings are a public forum for people who have information for inventors and for inventors that have
questions. Members also get a monthly newsletter, a current member directory and reference materials. There is a
membership fee.

INVENTIONS
AND
INNOVATIONS

Emerald Coast Inventors Society
1221 Pine Tree Drive
Indian Harbour Beach, FL 32937   321-773-4031
They accept the challenge to help people in the development of an idea so they can present for a patent. The monthly meetings are open to the public and there is no charge to attend.

Georgia

Small Business Development Center
University of Georgia
Chicopee Complex
1180 East Broad Street   706-542-7436
Athens, GA 30602   Fax: 706-542-6803
www.smallbizplanet.com/uga
The center offers counseling for a wide range of business issues and problems.

Inventor Associates of Georgia
1608 Pelham Way
Macon, GA 31220   912-474-6948 (phone/fax)
www.geocities.com/iaggroup/
Email: jrmiq@mindspring.com
A group of experts and novices that assist independent inventors with the process of developing their ideas so that they can be marketed. Partly, this is accomplished by Q&A with members and impartial evaluations of inventions. There are monthly meetings with roundtable discussions afterwards. There is a membership fee.

Hawaii

Small Business Development Center
University of Hawaii at Hilo
200 West Kawill Street   808-974-7515
Hilo, HI 96720   Fax: 808-974-7683
http://hawaii-sbdc.org
The center offers counseling for a wide range of business issues and problems.

Idaho

Idaho Research Foundation, Inc.
University of Idaho
Morrill Hall 103   208-885-4550
Moscow, ID 83844   Fax: 208-885-0105
Email: Ersatterf@uidaho.edu
This foundation counsels inventors on commercialization and patent processes, and provides critical reviews on inventions. Computerized data searching and marketing service is available. It takes a percentage of intellectual property royalties.

Small Business Development Center
Boise State University
1910 University Drive
Boise, ID 83725   208-426-1640
The center offers counseling for a wide range of business issues and problems.

Idaho Small Business Development Center
P.O. Box 1238
315 Falls Ave.   208-733-9554

Twin Falls, ID 83303-1238   Fax: 208-733-9316
www.csi.cc.id.us - click on community services
The center conducts market assessments and provides funding information.

Idaho Small Business Development Center
Lewis-Clark State College
500 8th Ave.
Lewiston, ID 83501   Fax: 208-799-2831
www.idbsu.edu/isbdc
The center provides general assistance and funding information. They also conduct market assessments.

Idaho State University
Small Business Development Center
2300 N. Yellowstone   208-523-1087
Idaho Falls, ID 83401   Fax: 208-528-7127
The center provides general assistance and funding information, and conducts technical assessments. Inventors meet with other inventors and investors.

Illinois

Small Business Development Center
Department of Commerce and Community Affairs
620 East Adams St., 3rd Floor   217-524-5856
Springfield, IL 62701   Fax: 217-785-6328
www.commerce.state.il.us
The center offers counseling for a wide range of business issues and problems, including commercialization and patent processes.

Small Business Development Center
Evanston Business Investment Corp.
1840 Oak Avenue   847-866-1817
Evanston, IL 60201   Fax: 847-866-1808
The center provides general assistance and funding information.

Western Illinois University
Technical Center and Small Business Development Center
Seal Hall 214
Macomb, IL 61455   Fax: 309-298-2520
www.wiu.edu/sbdc
The center provides general assistance; conducts market/technical assessments; provides investment and funding information; and aids in building a prototype. Inventors meet with other inventors and investors, and get the chance to showcase their inventions.

Illinois Innovators and Inventor's Club
P.O. Box 623
Edwardsville, IL 62025   618-656-7445
They are a non-profit group created to exchange useful information and ideas. Membership fees cover monthly meetings, newsletters, and events.

Inventors' Council
431 South Dearborn, Suite 705   312-939-3329
Chicago, IL 60605   Fax: 312-922-7706
www.donmoyer.com
Email: patent@donmoyer.com

There is a multitude of information and links to information at this web site. Patent searching tools, how to get a free patent application if you are eligible, technology information, science facts, where to look for money, and so much more is available. Mostly, their workshops are in virtual reality on the web, but they still hold some of them in person, and they are free! They list tips from them, such as The Fool Rule, The secrets Rule and other basics. Mr. Moyer cannot answer questions over the phone, but he will do so through Email.

Indiana
Small Business Development Center
One North Capitol, Suite 1275   317-246-6871
Indianapolis, IN 46204   Fax: 317-264-6855
www.isbdcorp.org
The center offers counseling for a wide range of business issues and problems.

Indiana Inventors Association
P.O. Box 2388
Indianapolis, IN 46206   765-674-2845
Email: arhumbert@busprod.com
This is an informal non-profit group. Their members include inventors, engineers, educators and more. They are concerned with the innovation process and look to answer questions and solve problems at the monthly meetings. There is no fee.

Iowa
Small Business Development Center
Administrative Office
Iowa State University
137 Lynn Avenue   515-292-6351
Ames, IA 50014   Fax: 515-292-0020
www.iowasbdc.org
The center offers counseling for a wide range of business issues and problems.

Drake Small Business Development Center and
Inventure Program
2429 University Avenue   515-271-2655
Des Moines, IA 46204   Fax: 515-271-1899
The Inventure Program is a program within the Small Business Development Center. In the program, they will evaluate a product so that the inventor can decide if it is feasible to go to market. There is a fee of $125 and it is open to all people in the nation. The Small Business Development Center offers counseling on commercialization and other business aspects. There is no charge for this and it is only open to residents of Iowa.

Kansas
Small Business Development Center
Wichita State University
Campus Box 148
1845 Fairmont   316-978-3193
Wichita, KS 67260-0148   Fax: 316-978-3647
www.twsu.edu/~ksbdc
The center offers counseling for a wide range of business issues and problems.

Inventors' Association of South Central Kansas
2302 Amarado
Wichita, KS 67205   316-721-1866

www2.southwind.net/~rlfreid/iasck
Email: rlfreid@southwind.net
They have monthly meetings with a guest speaker who takes questions after finishing the speech. Reports of important information concerning the group, discussions and workshops are included. Guests and members must sign a non-disclosure agreement to protect the ideas that are discussed. There is a membership fee.

Kentucky

Small Business Development Center
University of Louisville
Burhans Hall, Room 137
Shelby Campus   502-852-7854
Louisville, KY 40292   Fax: 502-852-8573
This center counsels inventors on commercialization and patent processes and provides critical reviews of inventions. It provides assistance in technically refining inventions. There are no fees.

Small Business Development Center
Kentucky Small Business Development Center
Center for Business Development
College of Business and Economics Building
225 Business and Economics Building
University of Kentucky   606-257-7668
Lexington, KY 40506   Fax: 606-323-1907
The center offers counseling for a wide range of business issues and problems.

Kentucky Transportation Center
176 Oliver H. Raymond Bldg.   606-257-4513
Lexington, KY 40506   Fax: 606-257-1815
www.engr.uky.edu/ktc
The center works closely with various federal, state and local agencies, as well as the private sector to conduct research supported by a wide variety of sources.

Central Kentucky Inventors & Entrepreneurs
117 Carolyn Drive   606-885-9593
Nicholosville, KY 40356   Fax: 606-887-9850
Email: nashky@IBM.net
This is a nonprofit group that helps each other with patents, analysis, and a business plan so that their products can be marketed. Membership fees cover monthly meetings and a newsletter.

Louisiana

Small Business Development Center
Northeast Louisiana University
College of Business Administration
700 University Avenue   318-342-5506
Monroe, LA 71209   Fax: 318-342-5510
The center offers counseling for a wide range of business issues and problems.

Louisiana Department of Economic Development
P.O. Box 94185
Baton Rouge, LA 70804-9185   225-342-3000
www.lded.state.la.us
The department provides general assistance.

Maine

Department of Industrial Cooperation
5717 Corbet Hall, Room 480
Orono, ME 04469-5711
www.umaine.edu/dic

207-581-2200
Fax: 207-581-1479

On March 15, 1984, the Inventors Forum of Maine, Inc. (IFM), was formed and became a nonprofit corporation in the state of Maine. It was organized to stimulate inventiveness and entrepreneurship, and to help innovators and entrepreneurs develop and promote their ideas. It allows inventors and entrepreneurs to join together, share ideas and hopefully improve the chance for success. It gives encouragement, professional expertise, evaluation assistance, confidentiality and moral support of the University of Maine's Network and the University of Southern Maine's Small Business Development Center.

The Inventors Forum of Maine generally meets on the first Tuesday evening of each month at the University of Southern Maine, Campus Center, Room A, B & C on Bedford Street in Portland. Membership is open to all. For information regarding the Inventors Forum of Maine, contact Jake Ward, 207-581-1488.

Portland Inventors' Forum
5717 Corbett Hall, Room 480
University of Maine
Orono, ME 04469-5717
www.umaine.edu/DIC/Invent/IFM.htm
Email: DIC@umit.maine.edu

207-581-1488
Fax: 207-581-1479

This group of inventors and business people offer encouragement, professional expertise, confidentiality and evaluation assistance to its members. At the monthly meeting they have Show & Tell, speakers and open discussions. There is not a membership fee.

Maryland

Inventions and Innovations
Department of Energy
Forrestal Building
1000 Independence Ave., SW
Washington, DC 20585
www.oit.doe.gov/inventions

202-586-2079

The office evaluates all promising non-nuclear energy-related inventions, particularly those submitted by independent inventors and small companies for the purpose of obtaining direct grants for their development from the U.S. Department of Energy.

Small Business Development Center
MMG, Inc.
Baltimore, MD 21202
www.mmggroup.com

410-333-4270
Fax: 410-333-2552

The center offers counseling for a wide range of business issues and problems.

Massachusetts

Massachusetts Small Business Development Center
Salem State College
352 Lafayette St.
Salem, MA 01970

978-542-6345

The center offers counseling for a wide range of business issues and problems.

Small Business Development Center
205 School of Management

University of Massachusetts
Amherst, MA 01003
The center provides general assistance and funding information.

413-545-6301
Fax: 413-545-1273

Smaller Business Association of New England
252 2nd Ave.
Waltham, MA 02451
www.sbane.org
The association provides general assistance and funding information.

781-890-9070
Fax: 781-890-4567

Inventors Association of New England (IANE)
P.O. Box 577
Pepperal, MA 01463
www.gis.net/~starco/iane
Email: crholt@aol.com
At the monthly meetings, they discuss things such as patent protection, licensing, manufacturing and avoiding scams. They also have guest speakers and free workshops. Their inventor shows and exhibits showcase member's inventions. Membership dues cover meetings, a monthly newsletter, and discounts to trade shows, and some publications.

978-433-2397
Fax: 978-433-3516

Inventors Resource Network
P.O. Box 137
Shutesbury, MA 01072-0137
www.patentcafe.com/inventor_orgs/irn.html
Email: pelham@patentcafe.com
The center of this group of inventors and business people have either created successful businesses with their invention, or they have been licensed. They focus on getting the product to market. Monthly meeting alternate between public and private. They involve networking, announcements, assistance and a guest speaker.

413-259-2006

Worcester Area Innovators
132 Sterling Street West
Boylston, MA 01583
This group has monthly meetings with informal networking and guest speakers. There are no summer meetings. They put out a monthly newsletter and there is a minimal membership fee.

508-835-6435

Michigan
Small Business Development Center
2727 Second Avenue
Detroit, MI 48201
The center offers counseling for a wide range of business issues and problems.

313-226-7947
Fax: 313-577-4222

Inventors Club of America
524 Curtis Road
East Lansing, MI 48823
They meet monthly where a roll call is kept. They have an open quorum and look to help each other with past experiences.

517-332-3561

Inventor's Council of Mid-Michigan (ICMM)
519 South Saginaw Street, Suite 200
Flint, MI 48502
www.rjriley.com/icmm
Email: ICMM@bigfoot.com

810-655-8830
Fax: 810-655-8832

The goal is to help members with patents, trademarks, and copyrights and to get their inventions to market without a large cost. The monthly dues cover meetings and a 2 year subscription to Inventors Digest.

Minnesota

Minnesota Project Innovation, Inc.
111 3rd Ave. S., Suite 100   612-338-3280
Minneapolis, MN 55401-2551   Fax: 612-349-2603
www.mpi.org
This project is affiliated with the Minnesota Dept. of Energy and Economic Development, U.S. Small Business Administration, and private companies. It provides referrals to inventors for sources of technical assistance in refining inventions.

Minnesota Inventors Congress (MIC)
P.O. Box 71   507-637-2344
Redwood Falls, MN 56283   Fax: 507-637-8399
www.invent1.org   800-INVENT1

The Minnesota Inventors Congress (MIC) is a nonprofit organization established in 1958 to promote creativity, innovation, entrepreneurship by assisting the inventor and entrepreneur with education, promotion and referral. It's a professional organization composed of private individuals and corporations, who are creating and developing useful technologies. MIC is for inventors at every development stage - the novice and experienced; male or female; young and old; and supporters of invention and innovation. Workshops are also available. These are for individuals with ideas or inventions not yet successfully on the market; for companies, entrepreneurs looking for such inventions or new products.

"World's Oldest Annual Invention Convention," promotes the spirit of invention and innovation. Each year a 3 day convention presents more than 200 inventions and attracts some 10,000 visitors from around the world. The MIC provides a meeting place for:

1. Inventors to showcase their new products, connecting with manufacturers/investors, product test market, educational seminars, publicity, inventors network, and $1,500 in cash awards.

2. Manufacturers, marketers, investors and licenses seeking new products.

3. Inventors, viewers and exhibitors, seeking free counsel and literature on the invention development process.

4. Public to view the latest inventions, by adults and students, purchase MarketPlace products and meet global inventors.

Small Business Development Center
1125 Harmon Pl.   651-962-4500
St. Paul, MN 55403   Fax: 651-962-4508
The center offers counseling for a wide range of business issues and problems.

Society of Minnesota Inventors
20231 Basalt Street
Anoka, MN 55303   612-753-2766
Email: paulparis@uswest.net
With two meetings a month, this group aims to educate inventors. They have inventor question and answer, discussion sessions, and conduct general business. There is a small monthly fee.

Mississippi

Mississippi State University
Small Business Development Center
P.O. Box 5288   601-325-8684
Mississippi State, MS 39762   Fax: 601-325-4016
The center provides general assistance; conducts market assessments; and provides funding information.

Small Business Development Center
Meridian Community College
910 Highway 19 North   601-482-7445
Meridian, MS 39307   Fax: 601-482-5803
The center provides general assistance and funding information; conducts market/technical assessments; and offers legal advice on patents and licensing. Inventors meet with other inventors and investors.

Society of Mississippi Inventors
216 Old Chemistry Building   800-725-7232 (MS)
University of Mississippi   601-232-5001
University, MS 38677   Fax: 601-232-5650
www.olemiss.edu/depts/msbdc/invnet.html
Email: msbdc@olemiss.edu
This Small Business Development Center specializes in assisting inventors. They help inventors to get started with an idea, give them sources for evaluation, patents, trademarks, finance, and specialized assistance. There are also seminars and workshops.

Missouri

Missouri Innovation Center
5658 Sinclare Rd.   573-446-3100
Columbia, MO 65203   Fax: 573-443-3748
This group provides communications among inventors, manufacturers, patent attorneys and venture capitalists, and provides general consultations. It is sponsored by the state, city of Columbia, and the University of Missouri. There are fees for some services.

Inventors Association of St. Louis
P.O. Box 410111
St. Louis, MO 63141   314-432-1291
The group holds monthly meetings, provides communications among inventors, manufacturers, patent attorneys, and venture capitalists. It publishes a newsletter. There are annual dues.

Small Business Development Center
University of Missouri - Columbia
1205 University Ave.
Suite 1800 University Pl.
Columbia, MO 65211   573-882-0344
                                                        Fax: 573-882-4297
www.mo-sbdc.org
The center offers counseling for a wide range of business issues and problems.

Montana

Small Business Development Center
Montana Department of Commerce
1424 Ninth Avenue   406-444-4780
Helena, MT 59620   Fax: 406-444-1872
www.commerce.state.mt.us
The center offers counseling for a wide range of business issues and problems.

Montana Inventors Association
5350 Love Lane
Bozeman, MT 59715
406-586-1541
Fax: 406-585-9028
They have a yearly 2 day meeting for inventors. The guest speaker is a known inventor or a patent officer. They will answer questions and have discussions and some of the inventors talk about the process they used to market their product. They also have a member directory.

Nebraska

University of Nebraska - Lincoln
W 191 Nebraska Hall
Lincoln, NE 68588-0525
402-472-5600
www.engext.unl.edu/engext.html
Upon request, the University will send a packet of information so that the individual may go to the location and conduct their own Patent and Trademark search.

Small Business Development Center
University of Nebraska at Omaha
60th and Dodge Street
CBA, Room 407
Omaha, NE 68182
402-554-2521
Fax: 402-554-3473
The center offers counseling for a wide range of business issues and problems.

Association of SBDCs
3108 Columbia Pike, Suite 300
Arlington, VA 22204
703-271-8700
www.asbdc-us.org
Organization's name and address may be given to individual inventors for referrals.

Nevada

Nevada Small Business Center
University of Nevada - Reno
College of Business Administration/032
Reno, NV 89557-0100
775-784-1717
www.nsbdc.org
Fax: 775-784-4337
The center provides general assistance and funding information. Inventors meet with other inventors and get to showcase their inventions.

Nevada Small Business Center
3720 Howard Hughes Pkwy.
Suite 130
Las Vegas, NV 89109
702-734-7575
Fax: 702-734-7633
www.nsbdc.org
The center provides general assistance and funding information. Inventors meet with other inventors.

Inventors Society of Southern Nevada
Las Vegas, NV 89121
702-435-7741
Email: InventSSN@aol.com
Here inventors will learn the process from A to Z. The group will answer questions and send its members in the correct direction to accomplish their goals. They host different speakers from the field at monthly meetings which are open to the public. All ideas are kept confidential. There are yearly dues that cover all of this plus a newsletter.

Nevada Inventors Association
P.O. Box 11008
Reno, NV 89506
www.greatbasin.net/~inventors
Email: inventors@greatbasin.net

702-677-4824
Fax: 702-677-4888

They offer education, assistance, and networking to their members. Anywhere from one to nine guests will show up at the monthly meetings. They also put together a monthly newsletter.

New Hampshire

Small Business Development Center
University of New Hampshire
108 McConnell Hall
Durham, NH 03824
www.nhsbdc.org

603-862-2200
Fax: 603-862-4876

The center offers counseling for a wide range of business issues and problems.

Small Business Development Center
OEI-MMC
1001 Elm Street
Manchester, NH 03101
www.nhsbdc.org

603-624-2000
Fax: 603-647-4410

The Small Business Development Center provides general assistance and funding information, and offers legal advice on patents and licensing. Inventors meet with other inventors.

New Hampshire Inventors Association
P.O. Box 2772
Concord, NH 03302
www.nhinventor.com
Email: infor@nhinventor.com

603-228-3854

It is their mission to encourage and assist inventors in evaluating, patenting and commercializing their products. They teach them about the patent process and supply them with information and resources. There are speakers at the monthly meetings, workshops, and seminars. Inventors will be able to learn from others through networking. The membership fee covers all of this and a newsletter.

New Jersey

Small Business Development Center
Rutgers University
43 Bleeker St.
Newark, NJ 07102-1913
www.nj.com/smallbusiness

973-353-5621
Fax: 973-353-1030

The Small Business Development Center offers counseling for a wide range of business issues and problems.

Jersey Shore Inventors Club
416 Park Place Avenue
Bradley Beach, NJ 07720
Email: 2edeilmcclain@msn.com

732-776-8467
Fax: 732-776-5418

They have monthly meetings where inventors can learn from each other.

National Society of Inventors
P.O. Box 1661
Livingston, NJ 07039

973-994-9282
Fax: 973-535-0777

This group is "Inventor Friendly". They are inventors helping each other in the New Jersey area. They offer meetings that either have speakers or round table discussions that are open to the public. There is a minimal membership fee.

New Mexico

Albuquerque Invention Club
P.O. Box 30062
Albuquerque, NM 87190   505-266-3541
The contact is Dr. Albert Goodman, president of the club. The club meets on a monthly basis for speakers and presentations by different inventors. Members include patent attorneys, investors, and manufacturers.

Small Business Development Center
Santa Fe Community College
6401 Richards Ave.   505-428-1343
Santa Fe, NM 87505   Fax: 505-428-1469
www.nmsbdc.org
The center offers counseling for a wide range of business issues and problems.

New York

Small Business Development Center
State University Plaza
41 State St.   518-443-5398
Albany, NY 12246   Fax: 518-443-5275
www.nys-sbdc.suny.edu
The center offers counseling for a wide range of business issues and problems.

New York State Energy Research and Development Authority
Corporate Plaza West
286 Washington Ave. Ext.   518-862-1090
Albany, NY 12203-6319   Fax: 518-862-1091
www.nyserda.org
The office provides general assistance and investment and funding information. It assists in building a prototype.

SUNY Institute of Technology
Small Business Development Center
P.O. Box 3050   315-792-7546
Utica, NY 13504   Fax: 315-792-7554
www.sbdc.sunyit.edu
The center provides general assistance and funding information; conducts market/technical assessments; offers legal advice on patents and licensing, and assists in building a prototype. Inventors meet with other inventors.

Small Business Technology Investment Fund
New York State Science and Technology Foundation
30 Pearl St.
Albany, NY 12210   518-473-9741
www.empire.state.ny.us/
The program provides financing assistance for technology-based start-up companies with initial investment as much as $300,000.

Inventors Alliance of America-Rochester Chapter
97 Pinebrook Drive   716-225-3750
Rochester, NY 14616   Fax: 716-225-2712

Email: InventNY@aol.com
This non-profit group helps inventors by educating them to develop their business and offer support and recognition.
The members and guest speakers offer useful information and contacts at the monthly meetings.

New York Society of Professional Inventors
Box 216
Farmingdale, NY 11735   516-798-1490
They are a networking group that meets once a month. Speakers that are experts on different areas of inventing
attend. There is a membership fee.

North Carolina
Small Business Development Center
University of North Carolina
333 Fayetteville Street Mall, #1150   919-715-7272
Raleigh, NC 27601   Fax: 919-715-7777
The center offers counseling for a wide range of business issues and problems.

North Dakota
Center for Innovation
University of North Dakota
4300 Dartmouth Drive   701-777-3132
Grand Forks, ND 58202   Fax: 701-777-2339
www.innovators.net
This center conducts occasional seminars and workshops with speakers; counsels on the commercialization and
patenting process; provides communications among inventors, manufacturers, and patent attorneys. There are fees
for services, but the first consultation is free.

Small Business Development Center
118 Gamble Hall
University of North Dakota
Box 7308   701-777-3700
Grand Forks, ND 58202-7308   Fax: 701-777-3225
www.und.nodak.edu/dept/collegeb/bpa/sbdc.htm
The center offers counseling for a wide range of business issues and problems.

Ohio
Inventors Council of Dayton
Mr. George Pierce, President
P.O. Box 611
Dayton, OH 45409   937-224-8513
www.xec.com/invent/index.html
email: geopierce@earthlink.net
This association meets on a regular basis and provides communication among inventors, manufacturers, patent
attorneys, etc., and often publishes newsletters.

Docie Marketing
73 Maplewood Drive   740-594-5200
Athens, OH 45701   Fax: 740-594-4004
http://docie.com
Docie Marketing provides assistance to inventors worldwide, including free educational material, free referrals to
legitimate invention service providers, commission-based brokerage, and fee-based services for inventors.

Small Business Development Center
Department of Development
30 East Broad Street, 23rd Floor
P.O. Box 1001   614-466-2711
Columbus, OH 43226   Fax: 614-466-0829
www.ohiosbdc.org
The center offers counseling for a wide range of business issues and problems.

Inventors Connection of Greater Cleveland, Inc.
P.O. Box 360804
Strongsville, OH 44136   216-226-9681
http://members.aol.com/icgc/index.htm
Email: icgc@usa.com
This is a non-profit organization of inventors helping inventors that help to make ideas into marketable products.
They provide information on patent developments, educate them on things pertaining to the inventing process, and
identify needs for those inventions that have a possible market. Monthly meetings cover many topics, but stress the
introduction of ideas into the marketplace.

Inventors Council of Canton
303 55th Street, NW
North Canton, OH 44720   330-499-1262
Email: fleisherb@aol.com
The Council provides an opportunity for inventors to meet and share ideas. They hold monthly meetings to further
this goal.

Inventors Network
1275 Kinnear Road
Columbus, OH 43212   614-470-0144
Email: 13832667@msn.com
This is a non-profit group with members in varying occupations. Entrepreneurs and inventors are educated on the
invention process and production. They meet monthly to network and question various guest speakers. They cover
topics like manufacturing, prototyping, and marketing. They also have a yearly seminar.

Oklahoma
Small Business Development Center
Southeastern Oklahoma State University
517 University   580-924-0277
Durant, OK 74701   Fax: 580-924-7071
The center offers counseling for a wide range of business issues and problems.

Inventors Assistance Program
395 Cordell South   405-744-8727
Stillwater, OK 74078   Fax: 405-744-7399
http://www.ceat.okstate.edu/
This is a service to help inventors navigate the process from idea to marketplace using information, education and
referrals. The service itself is free.

Oklahoma Inventors Congress
3212 NW 35th Street   405-947-5782
Oklahoma City, OK 73112   Fax: 405-947-6950
Email: w.baker@cwix.com
They are a self-help group that shares knowledge and experience with each other in order to help in the invention
process. They hold monthly meetings.

Oregon

Eastern Oregon University
Small Business Development Center
1410 L Ave.   541-962-3391
La Grande, OR 97850   Fax: 541-962-3668

Oregon Institute of Technology
Small Business Development Center
3201 Campus Dr., South 314   541-885-1760
Klamath Falls, OR 97601   Fax: 541-885-1855

Southern Oregon University
Small Business Development Center
332 W. 6th St.   541-772-3478
Medford, OR 97501   Fax: 541-734-4813
Small Business Development Centers (SBDCs) at three state colleges and the community colleges can counsel inventors and direct them where to go for patent process, etc.

Oregon Small Business Development Center
44 W. Broadway, Suite 501   541-726-2250
Eugene, OR 97401   Fax: 541-345-6006
The center provides general assistance and funding information.

Small Business Development Center
2701 NW Vaughn St.   503-978-5080
Portland, OR 97210   Fax: 503-222-2570
www.sbdc.citysearch.com
The center provides general assistance and funding information.

Oregon State Library
State Library Building
250 Winter St., NE   503-378-4277
Salem, OR 97310   Fax: 503-588-7119
www.osl.state.or.us
Organization's name and address may be given to individual inventors for referrals.

Southern Oregon Inventors Council
Southern Oregon University
332 West 6th Street   541-772-3478
Medford, OR 97501   Fax: 541-734-4813
http://members.delphi.com/smartly2/index.html
Email: smartly2@aol.com
This is a group that supports each other through the sharing of ideas. They learn the process of going about developing an invention and answer each others' questions at monthly meetings. They also have guest speakers who cover topics such as, marketing, on-line marketing, and manufacturing. The meetings are open to the public. There is a small membership fee.

Pennsylvania

Small Business Development Center
Bucknell University
Dana Engineering Bldg., 1st Floor   570-524-1249
Lewisburg, PA 17837   Fax: 570-524-1768
www.departments.bucknell.edu/sbdc/
The center offers counseling for a wide range of business issues and problems.

Pennsylvania Small Business Development Center
Vance Hall, 4th Floor
3733 Spruce Street   215-898-4861
Philadelphia, PA 19104   Fax: 215-898-1063
www.pasbdc.org
The center provides general assistance and funding information. It also conducts market and technical assessments.
It also oversees all centers in Pennsylvania.

American Society of Inventors
(ATTN:Henry H. Skillman)
P.O. Box 58426
Philadelphia, PA 19102   215-546-6601
www.americaninventor.org
This group offers members legal, technical, and business information. Some of the services that they have are, the
Information Index, the Inventors Notebook, and the Invention Conception, all provided to help the member become
creative and successful. They have bi-monthly meetings and newsletters. At the Board Meeting, 2 members will be
allowed to have their inventions evaluated.

Pennsylvania Inventors Association
2317 East 43rd
Erie, PA 16510   814-825-5820
www.pa-invent.org
Email: dhbutler@velocity.net
"What we are able to conceive, we are meant to create", is the motto of this group. They bring together people with
ideas, link inventors to industry, and get support for inventors. Meetings are open to local inventors and others
interested in promoting creativity.

Rhode Island
Service Corps of Retired Executives (SCORE)
c/o U.S. Small Business Administration
380 Westinghouse, Room #511
Providence, RI 02903   401-528-4571
Volunteers in the SCORE office are experts in many areas of business management and can offer advice to
inventors in areas including marketing and the commercialization process.

Small Business Development Center
7 Jackson Walkway
Providence, RI 02903   401-831-1330
The center offers counseling for a wide range of business issues and problems.

Small Business Development Center
Bryant College
1150 Douglas Pike   401-232-6111
Smithfield, RI 02917   Fax: 401-232-6933
www.risbdc.org
The center provides general assistance and conducts market and technical assessments.

South Carolina
Small Business Development Center
South Carolina State University
School of Business
300 College St.

Campus Box 7176   803-536-8445
Orangeburg, SC 29117   Fax: 803-536-8066
The center offers counseling for a wide range of business issues and problems.

South Carolina Small Business Development Center
University of South Carolina
College of Business Administration   803-777-4907
Columbia, SC 29208   Fax: 803-777-4403
The center provides general assistance and funding information.

South Dakota

Small Business Development Center
University of South Dakota
School of Business
414 East Clark St.   605-677-5287
Vermillion, SD 57069-2390   Fax: 605-677-5427
www.usd.edu/brbinfo
The center offers counseling for a wide range of business issues and problems.

Tennessee

Jackson State Community College
Small Business Development Center
2046 North Parkway Street   901-424-5389
Jackson, TN 38301   Fax: 901-425-2641
The center offers counseling for a wide range of business issues and problems.

Tennessee Inventors Association
P.O. Box 11225   865-539-4466
Knoxville, TN 37939-1225   Fax: 865-869-8138
www.uscni.com/tia
Email: bealaj@aol.com
Their main goal is the advancement of technology through Tennessee by providing guidance, information, and encouragement. They have a TIA Inventor's Guide that has topics such as the Inventors Log, how to market your product yourself, prototypes, and licensing. Their members include inventors, small business developers, research scientist and more to network with. There is a lot more information available with this group.

Texas

North Texas-Dallas Small Business Development Center
Dallas Community College District
1402 Corinth Street   214-860-5850
Dallas, TX 75215   Fax: 214-565-5815
The center offers counseling for a wide range of business issues and problems.

Texas Tech University
Small Business Development Center
2579 S. Loop 289, St. 114   806-745-3973
Lubbock, TX 79423   Fax: 806-745-6207
www.nwtsbdc.com
The center provides general assistance and funding information.

Amarillo Inventors Association
7000 West 45th Street, Suite 2
Amarillo, TX 79109 806-352-6085
They have monthly meetings in order to inform inventors of steps that they can take to enhance their invention.

Houston Inventors Association
2916 West T.C. Jester Boulevard
Suite 105 713-686-7676
Houston, TX 77018 Fax: 713-686-7676
www.inventors.org
Speakers at monthly meeting discuss their success stories, technical areas, and share tips on making money from inventions. There are also monthly workshops on patent fundamentals, injection moldings and more. They will put together members having a problem with members who can help them.

Network of American Inventors &Entrepreneurs
P.O. Box 667113
Houston, TX 77266 713-523-3923 (voice/fax)
www.naie.org
Email: info@naie.org
NAIE is dedicated to the independent inventor. They educate them from the concept stage and through the protection of the idea to the development. They meet twice a month to network and brainstorm. They also offer a variety of services such as patent search, patent applications, filing and more for a fee. There is also a membership fee.

Utah
Utah Small Business Development Center
1627 S. State St. 801-957-5203
Salt Lake City, UT 84115 Fax: 801-957-5300
www.slcc.edu/schools/cce/atc/cad/sbac.html
The center provides general assistance and funding information, and conducts market research and strategy.

Vermont
Economic and Development Office
State of Vermont
National Library Bldg. 802-828-3211
Montpelier, VT 05620-0501 Fax: 802-828-3258
www.state.vt.us/dca
Inventors will be given references to businesses that can assist with the commercialization and marketing process.

Small Business Development Center
60 Main St., Suite 103 802-658-9228
Burlington, VT 05401 Fax: 802-860-1899
www.vermont.org
The center offers counseling for a wide range of business issues and problems.

Virginia
Virginia Small Business Development Center
707 E. Main St.
P.O. Box 446
Richmond, VA 23288-0446 804-371-8258
www.dba.state.va.us
The center offers counseling for a wide range of business issues and problems.

Small Business Development Center
1001 E. Market St.   804-295-8198
Charlottesville, VA 22903   Fax: 804-295-7066
http://monticello.avenue.org/Market/SBDC
The center provides general assistance, conducts market studies, and refers inventors to companies that conduct market and technical assessments.

U.S. Department of Commerce
Patent and Trademark Office   1-800-PTO-9199
Washington, DC 20231   703-308-4357
www.uspto.gov
The office provides general assistance on patents and licensing.

Blue Ridge Inventor's Club
P.O. Box 6701   804-973-3708
Charlottesville, VA 22906-6701   Fax: 804-973-2648
The purpose of this club is to help people protect their innovations, provide information on patents, trademarks, and copyrights, and inform them how the US Patent and Trademark Office operates.

Washington
Innovation Assessment Center
180 Nickerson St., Suite 207   206-464-5450
Seattle, WA 98109   Fax: 206-464-6357
www.sbdc.wsu.edu/innovate.htm
Part of the Small Business Development Center, this center performs commercial evaluations of inventions, counseling and provides assistance with patentability searches. There are fees for services.

Small Business Development Center
Washington State University
Spokane, WA 99201   509-358-7765
www.sbdc.wsu.edu
The center offers counseling for a wide range of business issues and problems.

Small Business Development Center
Western Washington University
308 Parks Hall   360-650-3899
Bellingham, WA 98225   Fax: 360-650-4831
The center provides general assistance, and investment and funding information.

Inventors Network
P.O. Box 5575
Vancouver, WA 98668   503-239-8299
This is a nonprofit inventor's self-help club whose goal it is to make an invention a reality. They will not do it for you, but rather help you to do it yourself. There is an annual membership fee.

West Virginia
Small Business Development Center
West Virginia University
912 Main St.   304-465-1434
Oak Hill, WV 25901   Fax: 304-465-8680
The center offers counseling for a wide range of business issues and problems.

West Virginia Small Business Development Office
2000 7th Ave.   304-696-6798
Huntington, WV 25703-1527   Fax: 304-696-4835
www.marshall.edu
The center provides information on investment and funding.

Wisconsin

Center for Innovation and Development
University of Wisconsin - Stout
278 Jarvis Hall
Menomonie, WI 54751   715-232-5026
http://nwmoc.uwstout.edu
The center counsels inventors on the commercialization and patent processes;
provides critical reviews of inventions; assists inventors on technically refining inventions; and provides prototype
development. There are fees for services.

Wisconsin Innovation Service Center
402 McCutchan Hall
UW-Whitewater   262-472-1365
Whitewater, WI 53190   Fax: 262-472-1600
http://academics.uww.edu/BUSINESS/innovate/innovate.htm
Provides early stage market research for inventors. There is a flat fee of $495 for services.

Small Business Development Center
University of Wisconsin
432 North Lake Street, Room 423   608-263-7794
Madison, WI 53706   Fax: 608-263-7830
cf.uwex.edu/sbdc
The center offers counseling for a wide range of business issues and problems.

Wisconsin Department of Commerce
P.O. Box 7970   608-266-9467
Madison, WI 53707   Fax: 608-267-2829
www.commerce.state.wi.us
The office provides information on investment and funding.

Central Wisconsin Inventors Association
P.O. Box 915
Manawa, WI 54949   920-596-3092
Email: dr.heat@mailexcite.com

Inventors Network of Wisconsin
1066 St. Paul Street
Green Bay, WI 54304   920-429-0331
Email: jhitzler@greenbaynet.com
This group holds monthly meetings to advance the knowledge of its members. They do this through speakers,
networking, and other resources.

Wyoming

Small Business Development Center
111 W. 2nd St., Suite 502
Casper, WY 82601   307-234-6683

www.uwyo.edu/sbdc
Dr. Leonard Holler, who works in the office, is able to help inventors on a wide range of issues including patenting, commercialization and intellectual property rights. There are fees for services.

Canada
Innovative Center
156 Columbia Street W.
Waterloo, Ontario NN 26363   519-885-5870
www.innovationcentre.ca
Provides inventors with market research, idea testing, and helps guide inventors up to the patent stage.

Government Buys Bright Ideas From Inventors: Small Business Innovative Research Programs (SBIR)

The Small Business Innovative Research Program (SBIR) stimulates technological innovation, encourages small science and technology based firms to participate in government funded research, and provides incentives for converting research results into commercial applications. The program is designed to stimulate technological innovation in this country by providing qualified U.S. small business concerns with competitive opportunities to propose innovative concepts to meet the research and development needs of the Federal government. Eleven federal agencies with research and development budgets greater than $100 million are required by law to participate: The Departments of Defense, Health and Human Services, Energy, Agriculture, Commerce, Transportation, and Education; the National Aeronautics and Space Administration; the National Science Foundation; the Nuclear Regulatory Commission; and the Environmental Protection Agency.

Businesses of 500 or fewer employees that are organized for profit are eligible to compete for SBIR funding. Nonprofit organizations and foreign owned firms are not eligible to receive awards, and the research must be carried out in the U.S. All areas of research and development solicit for proposals, and the 1995 budget for SBIR is $900 million. There are three phases of the program: Phase I determines whether the research idea, often on high risk advanced concepts, is technically feasible; whether the firm can do high quality research; and whether sufficient progress has been made to justify a larger Phase II effort. This phase is usually funded for 6 months with awards up to $50,000. Phase II is the principal research effort, and is usually limited to a maximum of $500,000 for up to two years. The third phase, which is to pursue potential commercial applications of the research funded under the first two phases, is supported solely by nonfederal funding, usually from third party, venture capital, or large industrial firms. SBIR is one of the most competitive research and development programs in the government today. About one proposal out of ten received is funded in Phase I. Generally, about half of these receive support in Phase II. Solicitations for proposals are released once a year (in a few cases twice a year). To assist the small business community in its SBIR efforts, the U.S. Small Business Administration publishes the Pre-Solicitation Announcement (PSA) in December, March, June, and September of each year. Every issue of the PSA contains pertinent information on the SBIR Program along with details on SBIR solicitations that are about to be released. This publication eliminates the need for small business concerns to track the activities of all of the federal agencies participating in the SBIR Program. In recognition of the difficulties encountered by many small firms in their efforts to locate sources of funding essential to finalization of their innovative products, SBA has developed the Commercialization Matching System. This system contains information on all SBIR awardees, as well as financing sources that have indicated an interest in investing in SBIR innovations. Firms interested in obtaining more information on the SBIR Program or receiving the PSA, should contact the Office of Technology, Small Business Administration, 409 3rd St., SW, MC/6470, Washington, DC 20416, 202-205-6450.

SBIR representatives listed below can answer questions and send you materials about their agency's SBIR plans and funding:

Department of Agriculture
Dr. Charles Cleland, Directory SBIR Program, U.S. Department of Agriculture, Stop 2243-Room 328 Aerospace Building, 1400 Independence Avenue, SW, Washington, DC 20250-2243; 202-401-4002, Fax: 202-401-6070; Email: Ccleland@reeusda.gov

Department of Commerce
Dr. Joseph Bishop, Department of Commerce, 1315 East-West Highway (SSMC3 # 153421), Silver Springs, MD 20910, 301-713-3565, Fax: 301-713-4100, Email: Joseph.Bishop@NOAA.GOV

Department of Defense
Jon Baron, SBIR/STTR Program Manager, Office Under Secretary of Defense, U.S. Department of Defense, 1777, North Kent Street, Rosslyn Plaza North, Suite 9100, Arlington, VA 22209, 800-382-4634, Fax: 703-588-7561, Email: Baronj@acq.osd.mil

Department of Education
Lee Eiden, SBIR Program Coordinator, Department of Education, Room 588 D-Capitol Place, 555 New Jersey Avenue, NW Washington DC 20208, 202-219-2004, Fax: 202-219-1407, Email: Lee_Eiden@ed.gov

Department of Energy
Dr. Robert E. Berger, SBIR/STTR Program Manager, US Department of Energy, SC-32 19901 Germantown Road, Germantown, MD 20874-1290, 301-903-1414, Fax: 301-903-5488, Email: Robert.Berger@science.doe.gov

Department of Health and Human Services
Mr. Verl Zanders, SBIR Program Manager, Office of the Secretary, U.S. Department of Health and Human Services, Washington, DC 20201; 202-690-7300.

Department of Transportation
Joseph D. Henebury, SBIR Program Director, DTS-22, US Department of Transportation, 55 Broadway, Kendall Square, Cambridge, MA 02142-1093, 617-494-2051.2712, Fax: 617-494-2497/2370, Email: Henebury@volpe.dot.gov

Environmental Protection Agency
James Fallup, Office of Research and Development, US Environmental Protection Agency, ORD/NCERQA/EERD (8722R), 401 M Street SW, Washington DC 20460, 202-564-6823, Fax: 202-565-2447, Email: Gallup.James@epa.gov

National Aeronautics and Space Administration
Dr. Robert L. Norwood, SBIR Program, National Aeronautics Space Administration, 4201 Wilson Boulevard, Room 590, Arlington, VA 22230, 703-306-1390, Fax: 703-306-0337, Email: knarayanb@nsf.gov

Small Business Administration
Daniel O. Hill, US Small Business Administration, 409 3rd Street, SW, Mail Code:6470, Washington, DC 20416, 202-205-6450, Fax: 202-205-7754, Email: Daniel.Hill@sba.gov

FEDERAL MONEY FOR HOUSING AND REAL ESTATE

Always dreamed of owning your own home or rehabbing an historic one? These dreams are not impossible to achieve thanks to a wide variety of federal and state programs. You can get money to fix up your house in the country, emergency assistance for natural disasters, weatherization and heating assistance, and much more. Most states have programs for first-time homebuyers that may provide assistance with lower interest rates or help with the closing costs. You may even be considered a first-time homebuyer if you have not owned a home in the previous three years! In addition, don't forget to check out county and city community development organizations that may have programs to help you on your way to home ownership. Many of these programs take advantage of the Community Development and Block Grant Program from the federal government that allows cities and states to help improve the housing situation.

Now don't forget to read the first part of this book, "Types of Assistance and Grants Sources," as well as "More Help In Finding a Grant." These sections provide some great starting places for your money hunt. In addition, the U. S. Department of Housing and Urban Development has a quite extensive site that provides a wealth of information for those interested in buying a home. The website {www.hud.gov} has everything from how to choose a real estate agent; to calculating your mortgage payments; to finding homes for sale that the government is selling for cheap. There are also links to local HUD offices that can assist you in locating other resources in your area. You can also check out the federal government's {www.consumer.gov} for a listing of publications and other helpful information regarding your home and community.

Other resources to check out include:

- National Association of Housing and Redevelopment Officials, 630 I St., NW, Washington, DC 20001; 202-289-3500; Fax: 202-289-8181; {www.nahro.org}.
- Information Center, Office of Community Planning and Development, P.O. Box 7189, Gaithersburg, MD 20898; 800-998-999; Fax: 301-519-5027; {www.comcon.org}.
- National Association of Community Action Agencies, 1100 17th St., NW, Washington, DC 20036; 202-265-7546; Fax: 202-265-8850; {www.nacaa.org}.

The sections that follow outline the Federal money programs available for housing, followed by each state's programs. Again, don't forget to check out your city or county's programs as well. There is also a section on grants and tax credits to renovate historic homes and buildings, and then a mix of other sources of assistance and help for the homeowner. All that is left for you to do is pack the boxes and you are on your way!

The following is a description of the federal funds available to renters, homeowners, developers, and real estate investors for housing assistance in urban and rural areas. This information is derived from the *Catalog of Federal Domestic Assistance* which is published by the U.S. Government Printing Office in Washington, D.C. The number next to the title description is the official reference for this federal program. Contact the office listed below the caption for further details. The following is a description of some of the terms used for the types of assistance available:

Loans: money lent by a federal agency for a specific period of time and with a reasonable expectation of repayment. Loans may or may not require a payment of interest.

Loan Guarantees: programs in which federal agencies agree to pay back part or all of a loan to a private lender if the borrower defaults.

Grants: money given by federal agencies for a fixed period of time and which does not have to be repaid.

Direct Payments: funds provided by federal agencies to individuals, private firms, and institutions. The use of direct payments may be "specified" to perform a particular service or for "unrestricted" use.

Insurance: coverage under specific programs to assure reimbursement for losses sustained. Insurance may be provided by federal agencies or through insurance companies and may or may not require the payment of premiums.

Money for Conserving the Water and Soil During an Emergency
(10.054 Emergency Conservation Program (ECP))
U.S. Department of Agriculture
Farm Service Agency, Stop 0513
1400 Independence Avenue, SW
Washington, DC 20250
202-720-6221
Objectives: To enable farmers to perform emergency conservation measures to control wind erosion on farmlands, or to rehabilitate farmlands damaged by wind erosion, floods, hurricanes, or other natural disasters and to carry out emergency water conservation or water enhancing measures during periods of severe drought. Types of assistance: direct payments for specified use. Estimate of annual funds available: (Direct payments) $90,853,016.

Money to Improve Your Water and Soil
(10.069 Conservation Reserve Program (CRP))
U.S. Department of Agriculture
Farm Service Agency, Stop 0513
Washington, DC 20250
202-720-6221
Objectives: To protect the Nation's long-term capability to produce food and fiber; to reduce soil erosion; to reduce sedimentation; to improve water quality; to create a better habitat for fish and wildlife; to curb production of some surplus commodities; and to provide some needed income support for farmers. Types of assistance: direct payments for specified use. Estimate of annual funds available: $1,689,893,000.

Money to Change Your Country Property Into a Wetlands
(10.070 Colorado River Basin Salinity Control Program (CRBSCP))

National Resources
Conservation Service
U.S. Department of Agriculture
P.O. Box 2890
Washington, DC 20013
202-720-1873
Objectives: To provide financial and technical assistance to: (1) Identify salt source areas; (2) develop project plans to carry out conservation practices to reduce salt loads; (3) install conservation practices to reduce salinity levels; (4) carry out research, education, and demonstration activities; (5) carry out monitoring and evaluation activities; and (6) to decrease salt concentration and salt loading which causes increased salinity levels within the Colorado River and to enhance the supply and quality of water available for use in the United States and the Republic of Mexico. Types of assistance: direct payments for specified use. Estimate of annual funds available: (Direct payments) $776,966.

Loans to Help Your Country Property Recover From an Emergency
(10.404 Emergency Loans)
Loan Making Division
U.S. Department of Agriculture
Farm Service Agency
AG Box 0520
Washington, DC 20250
202-720-1632
Objectives: To assist established (owner or tenant) family farmers, ranchers and aquaculture operators with loans to cover losses resulting from major and/or natural disasters, which can be used for annual farm operating expenses, and for other essential needs necessary to return disaster victims' farming operations to financially sound bases in order that

they will be able to return to private sources of credit as soon as possible. Types of assistance: direct loans. Estimate of annual funds available: $572,000,000.

Money to Build Houses for Your Employees

(10.405 Farm Labor Housing Loans and Grants (Labor Housing))
Multifamily Housing Processing Division
Rural Housing Service
U.S. Department of Agriculture
Washington, DC 20250
202-720-1604
Objectives: To provide decent, safe, and sanitary low rent housing and related facilities for domestic farm laborers. Types of assistance: project grants; guaranteed/insured loans. Estimate of annual funds available: (Loans) $30,000,000. (Grants) $15,000,000.

Money to Buy, Fix Up or Build Houses in Small Towns

(10.410 Very Low to Moderate Income Housing Loans (Section 502 Rural Housing Loans))
Director
Single Family Housing
Direct Loan Division
U.S. Department of Agriculture
Washington, DC 20250
202-720-1474
Or
Direct Single Family Housing Guaranteed Loan Division
Rural Housing Service
U.S. Department of Agriculture
Washington, DC 20250
202-720-1452
Objectives: To assist lower income rural families through direct loans to buy, build, rehabilitate, or improve decent, safe, and sanitary dwellings and related facilities for use by the applicant as a permanent residence. Subsidized funds are available only on direct loans for low and very low income applicants. Nonsubsidized Funds (loan making) are available for very low and low income applicants who are otherwise eligible for assistance, but based on the amount of the loan requested, the interest credit assistance formula results in no interest credit. Nonsubsidized funds (loan servicing) are available to very low, low and moderate income applicants/ borrowers who do not qualify for interest credit assistance for: (1) Subsequent loans for repair and rehabilitation; and (2) subsequent loan part only

(repair or rehabilitation or the payment of equity) in connection with transfers by assumption or credit sales. Loan guarantees are also available to assist moderate income rural families in home acquisition. Types of assistance: direct loans; guaranteed/insured loans. Estimate of annual funds available: (Direct Loans) $1,300,883 (for subsidized low or moderate income loans for servicing and repairs). (Guaranteed loans) $3,700,000,000.

Money to Develop a Group Practice

(14.116 Mortgage Insurance-Group Practice Facilities) (Title XI)
Office of Business Products
U.S. Department of Housing and Urban Development
Washington, DC 20110
202-708-0624
Objectives: To help develop group practice facilities. Types of assistance: insured loans. Estimate of annual funds available: (Mortgages insured) Reported under Program 14.128.

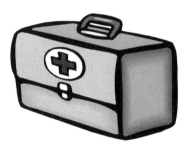

Money to Help Low Income Rural Families Get Housing

(10.441 Technical and Supervisory Assistance Grant)
Rural Housing Service (RHS)
USDA
14th Street and Independence Ave., SW
Washington, DC 20250
202-720-1474
Objectives: To assist low-income rural families in obtaining adequate housing to meet their families needs and/or to provide the necessary guidance to promote their continued occupancy of already adequate housing. These objectives will be accomplished through the establishment or support of housing delivery and counseling projects run by eligible applicants. This program is intended to make use of any available housing program that provides the low-income rural resident access to adequate rental properties or homeownership. Types of assistance: project grants. Estimate of annual funds available: $2,034,000

Money for Nonprofits to Build Rental Houses in Small Towns

(10.415 Rural Rental Housing Loans)
Multi-Family Housing Processing Division
Rural Housing Service
U.S. Department of Agriculture
Washington, DC 20250
202-720-1604
Objectives: To provide economically designed and constructed rental and cooperative housing and related facilities suited for independent living for rural residents. Types of assistance: direct loans. Estimate of annual funds available: (Direct Loans) $120,000.

Loans and Grants to Fix Up Your House in the Country ($5,000 Grants)

(10.417 Very Low Income Housing Repair Loans and Grants (Section 504 Rural Housing Loans and Grants)
Single-Family Housing Processing Division
Rural Housing Service
U.S. Department of Agriculture
Washington, DC 20250
202-720-1474
Objectives: To give very low income rural homeowners an opportunity to make essential repairs to their homes to make them safe and to remove health hazards to the family or the community. Types of assistance: direct loans; project grants. Estimate of annual funds available: (Loans) $40,000,000. (Grants) $30,000,000.

Money for Needy Families to Keep Their Homes

(10.420 Rural Self-Help Housing Technical Assistance) (Section 523 Technical Assistance)
Director, Single-Family Housing Processing Division
Rural Housing Service (RHS)
U.S. Department of Agriculture
Washington, DC 20250

202-720-1474
Objectives: To provide financial support for programs of technical and supervisory assistance that will aid needy and very low and low-income individuals and their families in carrying out mutual self-help housing efforts in rural areas. Types of assistance: project grants. Estimate of annual fund available: (Grants and Contracts) $40,000,000

Help for Low-Income Families to Reduce Their Rent

(10.427 Rural Rental Assistance Payments) (Rental Assistance)
Director, Multi-Family Housing Portfolio Management Division
Rural Housing Service
U.S. Department of Agriculture
Washington, DC 20250
202-720-1600
Objectives: To reduce the tenant contribution paid by low-income families occupying eligible Rural Rental Housing (RRH), Rural Cooperative Housing (RCH), and Farm Labor Housing (LH) projects financed by the Rural Housing Service (RHS) through its sections 515, 514 and 516 loans and grants. Types of assistance: direct payment for specified use. Estimate of annual funds available: $680,000,000

Application Assistance for Low-Income Rural Residents

(10.442 Housing Application Packaging Grants) (Section 509 Grants)
Director, Single Family Housing Processing Division
Rural Housing Service
Department of Agriculture
Washington, DC 20250
202-720-1474
Objectives: To package single family housing applications for very low and low-income rural residents into colonials and designated counties who wish to buy, build, or repair houses for their own use and to package applications for organization wishing to develop rental units for lower income families. Types of assistance: project grants. Estimate of annual funds available: (Grants) $495,000

Money for Emergency Assistance for Natural Disasters

(10.444 Direct Housing-Natural Disaster Loans and Grants) (Section 504, Rural Housing Loans and Grants)
Director, Single Family Housing Processing Division

Rural Housing Service
Department of Agriculture
Washington, DC 20250
202-720-1474
Objectives: To assist qualified recipients to meet emergency assistance needs resulting from natural disaster. Funds are only available to the extent that funds are not provided by the Federal Emergency Management Agency (FEMA) for the purpose of administering these funds, natural disaster will only include those counties identified by a Presidential declaration. Types of assistance: project grants, direct loans. Estimate of annual funds available: (Loans) $15,620,000 (Grants) $11,592,000, Funds under this program are based on supplemental funding provided by Congress in response to a natural disaster.

Money to Improve Housing After a Natural Disaster

(10.445 Direct Housing-Natural Disaster) (Section 502 Very Low and Low Income Loans)
Director
Single Family Housing Processing Division
Rural Housing Service
Department of Agriculture
Washington, DC 20250
202-720-1474
Objectives: To assist qualified lower income rural families to meet emergency, assistance needs resulting from natural disaster to buy, build, rehabilitate, or improve dwelling in rural areas. Funds are only available to the extent that funds are not provided by the Federal Emergency Management Agency (FEMA) for the purpose of administering these funds, natural disaster will only include those counties identified by a Presidential declaration. Types of assistance: direct loans. Estimate of annual funds available: (Loans) $60,717. Funds under this program are based on supplemental funding provided by Congress in response to a natural disaster.

Money to Conserve Soil and Water in Small Towns

(10.900 Great Plains Conservation)
Deputy Chief
National Resources Conservation Program
National Resources Conservation Service
U.S. Department of Agriculture
P.O. Box 2890
Washington, DC 20013
202-720-1873
Objectives: To conserve and develop the Great Plains soil and water resources by providing technical and financial assistance to farmers, ranchers, and others in planning and implementing conservation practices. Types of assistance: direct payments for specified use; advisory services and counseling. Estimate of annual funds available: (Grants) $617,595. (Salaries and expenses) $0.

Money to Fix Up an Abandoned Coal Mine

(10.910 Rural Abandoned Mine Program (RAMP))
Deputy Chief for Programs
Natural Resources Conservation Service
U.S. Department of Agriculture
P.O. Box 2890
Washington, DC 20013
202-720-2847
Objectives: To protect people and the environment from the adverse effects of past coal mining practices, and to promote the development of soil and water resources of unreclaimed mined lands. Types of assistance: direct payments for specified use; advisory services and counseling. Estimate of annual funds available: (Grants) $393,087. (Salaries and expenses) $102,587.

Money for Farmers and Ranchers to Improve Water and Soil

(10.912 Environmental Quality Incentives Program EQIP)
Deputy Chief for Natural Resources
Conservation Programs
Natural Resources Conservation Service
U.S. Department of Agriculture
P.O. Box 2890
Washington, DC 20013
202-720-1845
Objectives: Technical, education and finance assistance to eligible farmers and ranchers to address soil, water and related natural resource concerns on their lands in an environmentally beneficial and cost-effective manner. This program provides assistance to farmers and rancher in complying with Federal, State and tribal environmental laws and encourage environmental enhancement. The purpose of this program is achieved through the implementation of structural, vegetative, and land management practices eligible land. This program is funded through the Commodity Credit Corporation (CCC). NRCS provides overall program management and implementation leadership for conservation planning and implementation. The Farm Service Agency provides leadership for administrative processes and

procedures for the program. Types of assistance: direct payment and specified use. Estimate of annual funds available: (Direct payments) $136,940,000 (Salaries and Expenses) $$37,060,000 (Education Assistance) $4,000,000.

Loans to Fix Up Houses That Are More Than One Year Old

(14.108 Rehabilitation Mortgage Insurance (203(k)))
Contact your State Homeownership Center or local HUD office
Objectives: To help families repair or improve, purchase and improve, or refinance and improve existing residential structures more than one year old. Types of assistance: guaranteed/insured loans. Estimate of annual funds available: (Loans insured) Reported under program 14,133.

Loans to Buy Trailers

(14.110 Manufactured Home Loan Insurance-Financing Purchase of Manufactured Homes as Principal Residences of Borrowers (Title I))
Chief
Home Improvement Branch
451 7th Street, SW, Room 8272
U.S. Department of Housing and Urban Development
Washington, DC 20410
202-708-6396
Objectives: To make possible reasonable financing of manufactured home purchases. Types of assistance: guaranteed/insured loans. Estimate of annual funds available: (Loans insured) $8,000,000.

Loans to Co-op Investors

(14.112 Mortgage Insurance for Construction or Substantial Rehabilitation of Condominium Projects (234(d) Condominiums))
Office of Business Products
U.S. Department of Housing and Urban Development
Washington, DC 20410
202-708-2866
Objectives: To enable sponsors to develop condominium projects in which individual units will be sold to home buyers. Types of assistance: guaranteed/insured loans. Estimate of annual funds available: (Mortgages insured) $0.

Loans to Homeowners Anywhere With 1 to 4 Family Units

(14.117 Mortgage Insurance-Homes (203(b)))
Contact your State Homeownership Center or local HUD office.

Objectives: To help people undertake home ownership. Types of assistance: guaranteed/insured loans. Estimate of annual funds available: (Mortgages insured) $149,883,000,000.

Loans to Buy Single Family Homes for Disaster Victims

(14.119 Mortgage Insurance-Homes for Disaster Victims (203(h)))
Contact your State Homeownership Center or local HUD office.
Objectives: To help victims of a major disaster undertake homeownership on a sound basis. Types of assistance: guaranteed/insured loans. Estimate of annual funds available: (Mortgages insured) reported under Program No. 14.117.

Money for Low to Moderate Income Families Hurt by a Disaster or Urban Renewal

(14.120 Mortgage Insurance-Homes for Low and Moderate Income Families (221(d)(2)))
Director
Single Family Development Division
Office of Insured Single Family Housing
U.S. Department of Housing and Urban Development
Washington, DC 20410
202-708-2700
Objectives: To make homeownership more readily available to families displaced by a natural disaster, urban renewal, or other government actions and to increase homeownership opportunities for low income and moderate income families. Types of assistance: guaranteed/insured loans. Estimate of annual funds available: (Mortgages insured) Reported under Program 14.133.

Money for Homes in Outlying Areas

(14.121 Mortgage Insurance-Homes in Outlying Areas (203(i)))
Contact your State Homeownership Center or local HUD office.

Objectives: To help people purchase homes in outlying areas. Types of assistance: guaranteed/insured loans. Estimate of annual funds available: (Mortgages insured) reported under program No. 14.117.

Money for Homes in Urban Renewal Areas
(14.122 Mortgage Insurance-Homes in Urban Renewal Areas (220 Homes))
Contact your State Homeownership Center or local HUD office.
Objectives: To help families purchase or rehabilitate homes in urban renewal areas. Types of assistance: guaranteed/insured loans. Estimate of annual funds available: (Mortgages insured) Reported under Program 14.113.

Money for Homes in Older Areas of Town
(14.123 Mortgage Insurance-Housing in Older, Declining Areas (223(e)))
Contact your State Homeownership Center or local HUD office.
Objectives: To assist in the purchase or rehabilitation of housing in older, declining urban areas. Types of assistance: guaranteed/insured loans. Estimate of annual funds available: (Mortgages insured) Reported under Program 14.113.

Money to Buy a Co-op Apartment
(14.126 Mortgage Insurance-Cooperative Projects (213 Cooperatives))
Office of Business Products
U.S. Department of Housing and Urban Development
Washington, DC 20410
202-708-2866
Objectives: To make it possible for nonprofit cooperative ownership housing corporations or trusts

to develop or sponsor the development of housing projects to be operated as cooperatives and to allow investors to provide good quality multifamily housing to be sold to such nonprofit corporations or trusts upon completion of construction or rehabilitation. Types of assistance: guaranteed/insured loans. Estimate of annual funds available: (Mortgages insured) Reported under Program 14.135.

Money to Buy a Trailer-Home Park
(14.127 Mortgage Insurance-Manufactured Home Parks (207(m)
Manufactured Home Parks))
Office of Business Products
U.S. Department of Housing and Urban Development
Washington, DC 20410
207-708-2866
Objectives: To make possible the financing of construction or rehabilitation of manufactured home parks. Types of assistance: guaranteed/insured loans. Estimate of annual funds available: (Mortgages insured) Reported under Program No. 14.135.

Money to Buy a Hospital
(14.128 Mortgage Insurance-Hospitals (242 Hospitals))
Office of Insured Health Care Facilities
U.S. Department of Housing and Urban Development
or
Division of Facilities Loans
U.S. Department of Health and Human Services
Rockville, MD 20857
301-443-5317
Objectives: To facilitate the affordable financing of hospitals for the care and treatment of persons who are acutely ill or who otherwise require medical care and related services of the kind customarily furnished only or most effectively by hospitals. Types of assistance: guaranteed/insured loans. Estimate of annual funds available: (Mortgages insured) $1,030,000,000.

Money to Buy a Nursing Home
(14.129 Mortgage Insurance-Nursing Homes, Intermediate Care Facilities and Board and Care Homes (232 Nursing Homes))
Office of Business Products
U.S. Department of Housing and Urban Development
Washington, DC 20412
202-708-2866
Objectives: To make possible financing for construction or rehabilitation of nursing homes,

intermediate care facilities and board and care homes, to allow purchase or refinancing with or without repairs of projects currently insured by HUD, but not requiring substantial rehabilitation, and to provide loan insurance to install fire safety equipment. Types of assistance: guaranteed/insured loans. Estimate of annual funds available: Reported under Program 14.135.

Money to Buy Your House if It is in a Long Term Ground Lease

(14.130 Mortgage Insurance-Purchase by Homeowners of Fee Simple Title From Lessors (240))
Contact your State Homeownership Center or local HUD office.
Objectives: To help homeowners obtain fee-simple title to the property that they hold under long-term leases and on which their homes are located. Types of assistance: guaranteed/insured loans. Estimate of annual funds available: (Mortgages insured) $0.

Money to Buy Your Co-op

(14.132 Mortgage Insurance-Purchase of Sales-Type Cooperative Housing Units (213 Sales))
Contact your State Homeownership Center or local HUD office.
Objectives: To make available, good quality, new housing for purchase by individual members of a housing cooperative. Types of assistance: guaranteed/insured loans. Estimate of annual funds available: (Mortgages insured) Reported under program 14.135.

Money to Buy a Condominium

(14.133 Mortgage Insurance-Purchase of Units in Condominiums (234(c)))
Contact your State Homeownership Center or local HUD office.
Objectives: To enable families to purchase units in condominium projects. Types of assistance: guaranteed/insured loans. Estimate of annual funds available: (Mortgages insured) $9,476,000,000.

Housing Money for Middle Income Families

(14.134 Mortgage Insurance-Rental Housing) (207)
Office of Business Projects
Department of Housing and Urban Development
Washington, DC 20410
202-708-2866
Objectives: To provide good quality housing for middle income families. Types of assistance:

mortgages insured. Estimate of annual funds available: Reported under Program 14.135.

Money to Invest in Apartment Buildings for Middle Class Families

(14.135 Mortgage Insurance-Rental and Cooperative Housing for Moderate Income Families and Elderly, Market Interest Rate (221(d)(3) and (4) Multifamily - Market Rate Housing))
Office of Business Products
U.S. Department of Housing and Urban Development
Washington, DC 20410
202-708-2866
Objectives: To provide good quality rental or cooperative housing for moderate income families and the elderly and handicapped. Single Room Occupancy (SRO) may also be insured under this section (see 14.184). Types of assistance: guaranteed/insured loans. Estimate of annual funds available: (Mortgages insured excluding coinsurance) $5,449,000,000.

Money to Invest in Rental Housing for the Elderly

(14.138 Mortgage Insurance-Rental Housing for the Elderly (231))
Office of Business Products
U.S. Department of Housing and Urban Development
Washington, DC 20410
202-708-2866
Objectives: To provide good quality rental housing for the elderly. Types of assistance: guaranteed/insured loans. Estimate of annual funds available: (Mortgages insured) $0.

Money to Invest in Rental Housing in Urban Renewal Areas

(14.139 Mortgage Insurance-Rental Housing in Urban Renewal Areas (220 Multifamily))

Office of Business Products
U.S. Department of Housing and Urban Development
Washington, DC 20410
202-708-2866
Objectives: To provide good quality rental housing in urban renewal areas, code enforcement areas, and other areas designated for overall revitalization. Types of assistance: guaranteed/insured loans. Estimate of annual funds available: (Mortgages insured) Reported under Program 14.135.

Money to Fix Up Your Home

(14.142 Property Improvement Loan Insurance for Improving All Existing Structures and Building of New Nonresidential Structures (Title I))
Contact your State Homeownership Center or local HUD office.
Objectives: To facilitate the financing of improvements to homes and other existing structures and the building of new nonresidential structures. Types of assistance: guaranteed/insured loans. Estimate of annual funds available: (Loans insured including funding for programs 4.110 and 14.162) $464,000,000.

Money to Fix Up Multifamily Projects

(14.151 Supplemental Loan Insurance-Multifamily Rental Housing (241(a)))
Policies and Procedures Division
Office of Insured Multifamily Housing Development
U.S. Department of Housing and Urban Development
Washington, DC 20411
202-708-2556
Objectives: To finance repairs, additions and improvements to multifamily projects, group practice facilities, hospitals, or nursing homes already insured by HUD or held by HUD. Major movable equipment for insured nursing homes, group practice facilities or hospitals may be covered by a mortgage under this

program. Types of assistance: guaranteed/insured loans. Estimate of annual funds available: (Loans insured) Reported under Program 14.135.

Money to Investors to Purchase or Refinance Multifamily Housing

(14.155 Mortgage Insurance for the Purchase or Refinancing of Existing Multifamily Housing Projects (Section 223(f) Insured Under Section 207))
Office of Business Products
U.S. Department of Housing and Urban Development
Washington, DC 20410
202-708-2866
Objectives: To provide mortgage insurance to lenders for the purchase or refinancing of existing multifamily housing projects, whether conventionally financed or subject to federally insured mortgages at the time of application for mortgage insurance. Types of assistance: guaranteed/insured loans. Estimate of annual funds available: (Mortgages Insured) Reported under Program 14.135.

Money to Build Housing for the Elderly That Also Provides Support Services

(14.157 Supportive Housing for the Elderly (202))
Office of Business Products
U.S. Department of Housing and Urban Development
Washington, DC 20410
202-708-2866
Objectives: To expand the supply of housing with supportive services for the elderly. Types of assistance: direct payment for specified use. Estimate of annual funds available: $1,355,000,000.

Money to Buy a House With Graduated Mortgage Payments

(14.159 Section 245 Graduated Payment Mortgage Program)
Contact your State Homeownership Center or local HUD office.
Objectives: To facilitate early home ownership for households that expect their incomes to rise. Program allows homeowners to make smaller monthly payments initially and to increase their size gradually over time. Types of assistance: guaranteed/insured loans. Estimate of annual funds available: Reported under Program 14.117.

Money to Buy a Trailer and Trailer Lot

(14.162 Mortgage Insurance-Combination and Manufactured Home Lot Loans (Title I))
Chief

Home Improved Branch
U.S. Department of Housing and Urban Development
451 7th Street, SW, Room 9272
Washington, DC 20410
202-708-6396
Objectives: To make possible reasonable financing for the purchase of a manufactured home and a lot on which to place the home. Types of assistance: guaranteed/insured loans. Estimate of annual funds available: (Mortgages insured) Reported under program No. 14.110.

Money to Finance Coop Buildings

(14.163 Mortgage Insurance-Single Family Cooperative Housing (203(n)))
U.S. Department of Housing and Urban Development
Washington, DC 20410
202-708-6396
Objectives: To provide insured financing for the purchase of the Corporate Certificate and Occupancy Certificate for a unit in a cooperative housing project. Ownership of the corporate certificate carries the right to occupy the unit located within the cooperative project. Types of assistance: guaranteed/insured loans. Estimate of annual funds available: (Mortgages Insured) Reported under program No. 14.117.

Money to Developers in Financial Trouble

(14.164 Operating Assistance for Troubled Multifamily Housing Projects (Flexible Subsidy Fund) (Troubled Projects))
Office of Portfolio Management
U.S. Department of Housing and Urban Development
Washington, DC 20420
202-708-3730
Objectives: To provide loans to restore or maintain the physical and financial soundness, to assist in the management and to maintain the low to moderate income character of certain projects assisted or approved for assistance under the National Housing Act or under the Housing and Urban Development Act of 1965. Types of assistance: direct payments for specified use. Estimate of annual funds available: (Reservations) $17,684,000.

Money to Buy Houses in Areas Hurt by Defense Cuts

(14.165 Mortgage Insurance-Homes-Military Impacted Areas (238(c)))
Contact your State Homeownership Center or local HUD office.
Objectives: To help families undertake home

ownership in military impacted areas. Types of assistance: guaranteed/insured loans. Estimate of annual funds available: (Mortgages Insured) Reported under Program 14.133.

Loans to Developers in Trouble During Their First Two Years of Operation

(14.167 Mortgage Insurance-Two Year Operating Loss Loans, Section 223(d) (Two Year Operating Loss Loans))
Office of Business Products
U.S. Department of Housing and Urban Development
Washington, DC 20410
202-708-2866
Objectives: To insure a separate loan covering operating losses incurred during the first two years following the date of completion of a multifamily project with a HUD-insured first mortgage. Types of assistance: guaranteed/insured loans. Estimate of annual funds available: (Loans insured) Reported under Program 14.135

Money to Buy a Home Using Increased Equity Payments

(14.172 Mortgage Insurance-Growing Equity Mortgages (GEMs))
Contact your State Homeownership Center or local HUD office.
Objectives: To provide a rapid principal reduction and shorter mortgage term by increasing payments over a 10-year period, thereby expanding housing opportunities to the homebuying public. Types of assistance: guaranteed/insured loans. Estimate of annual funds available: (Mortgages insured) Reported under program 14.117.

Money to Buy a Home Using an Adjustable Rate Mortgage

(14.175 Adjustable Rate Mortgages (ARMS))
Contact your State Homeownership Center or local HUD office.
Objectives: To provide mortgage insurance for an adjustable rate mortgage which offers lenders more

assurance of long term profitability than a fixed rate mortgage, while offering consumer protection features. Types of assistance: guaranteed/insured loans. Estimate of annual funds available: (Mortgages Insured) Reported under 14.117.

Money to Invest in Houses for Those With Disabilities

(14.181 Supportive Housing for Persons with Disabilities (811))
Housing for Elderly and Handicapped People Division
Office of Elderly and Assisted Housing
U.S. Department of Housing and Urban Development
Washington, DC 20410
202-708-2730
Objectives: To provide for supportive housing and related facilities for persons with disabilities. Types of assistance: direct payments for specified use. Estimate of annual funds available: Reported under program 14.157

Money to Help Elderly Homeowners Convert Their Equity into a Monthly Income

(14.183 Home Equity Conversion Mortgages (255))
Director
Insured Family Development Division
Office of Single Family Housing
U.S. Department of Housing and Urban Development
Washington, DC 20410
202-708-2700
Objectives: To enable elderly homeowners to convert equity in their homes to monthly streams of income or lines of credit. Types of assistance: guaranteed/insured loans. Estimate of annual funds available: (Mortgages insured): Reported under program 14.133.

Money to Help Rid Low-Income Housing of Drug Related Crime

(14.193 Federally Assisted Low-Income Housing Drug Elimination)

Office of Portfolio Management
Department of Housing and Urban Development
451 7th Street, SW, Room 6160
Washington, DC 20410
202-708-3944 x2487
Objectives: The purposes of the Assisted Housing Drug Elimination program are to reduce/eliminate drug-related crime and related problems in and around the premises of federally assisted low income housing; encourage owners of such housing to develop a plan for addressing the problem of drug-related crime in and around the premises of federally assisted low income housing proposed for funding under this part; and make available Federal grants to help the owners of federally assisted low-income housing to carry out their plans. Types of assistance: project grants. Estimate of annual funds available: (Grants) $35,004,739

Money for Supportive Housing for the Homeless

(14.235 Supportive Housing Program) (Transitional Housing; Permanent Housing for Homeless Persons with Disabilities; Innovative Supportive Housing; Supportive Services for Homeless Persons not in Conjunction with Supportive Housing; and Safe Housing)
Director
Office of Special Needs Assistance Programs
Community Planning and Development
Department of Urban Development
451 7th Street, SW
Washington, DC 20410
202-708-4300
Objective: The Supportive Housing Program is designed to promote the development of supportive housing and supportive services to assist homeless persons in the transition from homelessness and to enable them to live as independently as possible. Program funds may be used to provide:(I) transitional housing within a 24 month period as well as up to six months of follow-up services to former residents to assist their adjustment to independent living, (ii) permanent housing provided in conjunction with appropriate supportive services designed to maximize the ability of person with disabilities to live as independently as possible; (iii) supportive housing that is, or is part of, a particularly innovative project for, or alternate method of, meeting the immediate and long-term needs of homeless individuals and families; (iv) supportive services for homeless individuals not provided in conjunction with

supportive housing, and (v) safe havens for homeless individuals with serious mental illness currently residing on the streets who may not yet be ready for supportive services. Types of assistance: project grants, direct payment for specified use. Estimate of annual funds available: (Grants) $630,840,000.

Money to Rid Low-Income Housing of Crime
(14.312 New Approach Anti-Drug Grants)
Application materials:
Super-NOFA Information Center
800-HUD-8929
TTY:800-HUD-2209
Program policy and guidelines:
Henry Colonna
HUD Virginia State Office
3600 West Broad Street
Richmond, VA 23230
804-278-4504 x3027
Objectives: to use a comprehensive, coordinated neighborhood/community based approach to eliminate drug-related and other crime problems on the premises and in the vicinity of low-income housing, which may be privately or publicly owned and is financially supported or assisted by public or nonprofit private entities. To emphasize and facilitate the partnership of owners/operators of eligible housing with Federal and local law enforcement as well as other units of general local government and other stake holders to address crime in an assisted project or in an entire neighborhood which may have more than one assisted housing project. Types of assistance: project grants. Estimate of annual funds available: (Grants) $49,084,096

Rent Supplements to Building Owners With Tenants That Have Low Incomes
(14.856 Lower Income Housing Assistance Program-Section 8 Moderate Rehabilitation (Section 8 Housing Assistance Payments Program for Very Low Income Families-Moderate Rehabilitation))
Office of the Deputy Assistant Secretary for Public Assisted Housing Development
Real Estate and Housing Performance Division
U.S. Department of Housing and Urban Development
Washington, DC 20410
202-708-0477
Objectives: To aid very low income families and homeless individuals in obtaining decent, safe and sanitary rental housing. Types of assistance: direct payments for specified use. Estimate of annual funds available: (Outlays) not separately identifiable.

Money to Have Your State Buy Your Old Farm and Turn It into a Park
(15.916 Outdoor Recreation-Acquisition, Development and Planning (Land and Water Conservation Fund Grants))
Chief, Recreation Programs
National Park Service (2225)
U.S. Department of the Interior
1849 C Street, NW, Room 3622
Washington, DC 20240
202-565-1200
Objectives: To provide financial assistance to the States and their political subdivisions for the preparation of Statewide Comprehensive Outdoor Recreation Plans (SCORPs) and acquisition and development of outdoor recreation areas and facilities for the general public, to meet current and future needs. Types of assistance: project grants. Estimate of annual funds available: (Grants) $40,000,000.

Grants to Build Houses on Indian Reservations
(15.141 Indian Housing Assistance)
Division of Human Services
Office of Tribal Services
Bureau of Indian Affairs
MS 4641 MIB
1849 C Street, NW
Washington, DC 20240
202-208-3667
Objectives: To use the Indian Housing Improvement Program (HIP) and Bureau of Indian Affairs resources to substantially eliminate substandard Indian housing. This effort is combined with the Indian Health Service (Department of Health and Human Services). Types of assistance: project grants (contracts); dissemination of technical information. Estimate of annual funds available: (Total amount of award: Self-determination contracts and direct grants) $28,000,000.

Appalachian Local Development District Assistance
(23.009 Appalachian Local Development District Assistance CLDD)
Inquiries and proposals for projects submitted first to:
Appalachian State Office designated by the Governor (See Appendix IV of the Catalog)
Other inquiries:
Executive Director
Appalachian Regional Commission

1666 Connecticut Avenue, NW
Washington, DC 20235
202-884-7700
Objectives: To provide planning and development
resources in multi county areas; to help develop the
technical competence essential to land development
assistance; and to meet the objectives stated under the
program entitled Appalachian Regional Development
(23.001). Types of assistance: project grants.
Estimate of annual funds available: (Grants)
$5,965,000

Physical Disaster Loans

(59.008 Physical Disaster Loans) (7 (b) Loans (DL))
Office of Disaster Assistance
Small Business Administration
409 3rd Street, SW
Washington, DC 20416
202-205-6734
Objectives: To provide loans to the victims of
declared physical type disasters for uninsured losses.
Types of assistance: direct loans. Estimate of annual
funds available: (Loans) $1,100,000,000 (Obligations
include funds for 59.002 and 59.008).

Homeless Providers Grant

(64.24 VA Homeless Providers Grant and Per Diem
Program)
Program Manager
VA Homeless Providers Grant and Per Diem
Program
Mental Health Strategic Healthcare Group (116E)
Department of Veteran Affairs
810 Vermont Avenue, NW
Washington, DC 20420
202-273-8966
Objectives: To assist public and nonprofit private

entities in establishing new programs and service
centers to furnish supportive services and supportive
housing for homeless veterans through grants that
may be used to acquire, renovate, or alter facilities,
and to provide per diem payments, or in-kind
assistance in lieu of per diem payments, to eligible
entities which established programs after November
10, 1992 that provide supportive services and
supportive housing for the homeless veterans. Types
of assistance: project grants. Estimate of annual fund
available: $31,653,000.

Paraplegic Housing

(64.106 Specially Adapted Housing for Disabled
Veteran) (Paraplegic Housing)
Department of Veteran Affairs
Washington, DC 20420
202-273-7355
Objectives: To help certain severely disabled veteran
acquire a home which is suitable adapted to meet the
special needs of their disability. Types of assistance:
direct payment for specified use. Estimate of annual
funds available: (Direct Payments) $21,065,000

Money for Veterans Who Want to Buy a House

(64.114 Veterans Housing-Guaranteed and Insured
Loans (VA Home Loans))
U.S. Department of Veterans Affairs
Washington, DC 20420
202-273-7390
Objectives: To assist veterans, certain service
personnel, and certain unremarried surviving spouses
of veterans, in obtaining credit for the purchase,
construction or improvement of homes on more
liberal terms than are generally available to non-
veterans. Types of assistance: guaranteed/insured
loans. Estimate of annual funds available: (Closed
Loans Guaranteed) $32,115,917,000.

Loans for Disabled Veterans to Buy a House

(64.118 Veterans Housing-Direct Loans for Disabled
Veterans)
U.S. Department of Veterans Affairs
Washington, DC 20420
202-273-7390
Objectives: To provide certain severely disabled
veterans with direct housing credit in connection with
grants for specially adaptive housing with special
features or movable facilities made necessary by the
nature of their disabilities. Types of assistance: direct
loans. Estimate of annual funds available: (Loans)
$33,000.

Money for Veterans to Buy Mobile Homes

(64.119 Veterans Housing-Manufactured Home
Loans)
U.S. Department of Veterans Affairs
Washington, DC 20420
202-273-7390
Objectives: To assist veterans, servicepersons, and
certain unremarried surviving spouses of veterans in
obtaining credit for the purchase of a manufactured
home on more liberal terms than are available to non-
veterans. Types of assistance: guaranteed/insured
loans. Estimate of annual funds available:
(Guaranteed Loans) $0.

Loans for Native American Veterans to Buy or Build a Home

(64.126 Native American Veteran Direct Loan
Program (VA Native American Home Loan
Program))
U.S. Department of Veterans Affairs
Washington, DC 20420
202-273-7377
Objectives: To provide direct loans to certain Native
American veterans for the purchase or construction of
homes on trust lands. Types of assistance: direct
loans. Estimate of annual funds available: (Loans):
$1,768,000.

Grants for Storm Windows or to Weatherize Your Home

(81.042 Weatherization Assistance for Low Income
Persons)
Director
Office of State and Community Programs
Mail Stop EE-44
Office of Energy Efficiency and Renewable Energy
U.S. Department of Energy
Forrestal Building
Washington, DC 20585
202-586-4074
Objectives: To insulate the dwellings of low income
persons, particularly the elderly and handicapped low
income, in order to conserve needed energy and to
aid those persons least able to afford higher utility
costs. Types of assistance: formula grants. Estimate
of annual funds available: $154,100,000.

Government Subsidized Flood Insurance to Homeowners

(83.100 Flood Insurance)
Edward T. Pasterick
Federal Insurance Administration

Federal Emergency Management Agency
Washington, DC 20472
202-646-3443
Objectives: To enable persons to purchase insurance
against losses from physical damage to or loss of
buildings and or contents therein caused by floods,
mudflow, or flood-related erosion in the United States
and to promote wise flood plain management
practices in the Nation's flood-prone and
mudflow-prone areas. Types of assistance: insurance.
Estimate of annual funds available: $1,380,161,000.

Individual and Family Grants

(83.543 Individual and Family Grants)
Director
Human Services Division
Response and Recovery Directorate
Federal Emergency Management Agency
Washington, DC 20472
202-646-3685
Objectives: To produce funds for the necessary
expenses and serious needs of disaster victims which
cannot be met through other forms of disaster
assistance or through other means such as insurance.
Types of assistance: project grants. Estimate of
annual fund available: (Grants) Not separately
identifiable.

Disaster Housing Program

(83.545 Disaster Housing Program)
Directorate
Federal Emergency Management Agency
Washington, DC 20472
202-646-3685
Objectives: To provide assistance to households
affected by a disaster to assist with their disaster
created housing needs. Types of assistance: direct
payment for specified use; provision of specialized
services. Estimate of annual funds available:
(Housing Assistance) Not separately identifiable.

Grants for Renovation or Construction of Non-Acute Health Care Facilities

(93.887 Project Grants for Renovation or
Construction of Non-Acute Health Care Facilities and
Other Facilities) (1610 (b) Program)
Program:
Acting Director
Division of Facilities Compliance and Recovery
Office of Special Programs
Health Resources and Services Administration
Department of Health and Human Services

Parklawn Building
5600 Fishers Lane, Room 10C-16
Rockville, MD 20857
301-443-5656
Grants:
Management Specialist
Grants Management Branch
Office of Program Support
HIV/AIDS Bureau
Health Resources and Services Administration
5600 Fishers Lane, Room 7-27
Rockville, MD 20857
301-443-5906
Objectives: To renovate, expand, repair, equip, or modernize non-acute health care facilities. Types of assistance: project grants. Estimate of annual funds available: (Grants) $0

Money For Nonprofits to Provide Rural Housing Site Loans

(10.411 Rural Housing Site Loans and Self-Help Housing Land Development Loans (Section 523 and 524 Site Loans))
Director
Single-Family Housing Processing Division
Rural Housing Service
U.S. Department of Agriculture
Washington, DC 20250
202-720-1474
Objectives: To assist public or private nonprofit organizations interested in providing sites for housing, to acquire and develop land in rural areas to be subdivided as adequate building sites and sold on a cost development basis to families eligible for low and very low income loans, cooperatives, and broadly based nonprofit rural rental housing applicants. Types of assistance: direct loans. Estimate of annual funds available: (Loans) $5,009,000.

Money to Fix Up Your Home in the Country (10.433 Rural Housing Preservation Grants)

Multiple Family Housing Processing Division
Rural Housing Service
U.S. Department of Agriculture
Washington, DC 20250

202-720-1660
Objectives: To assist very low and low income rural residents individual homeowners, rental property owners (single/multi-unit) or by providing the consumer cooperative housing projects (co-ops) the necessary assistance to repair or rehabilitate their dwellings. These objectives will be accomplished through the establishment of repair/rehabilitation, projects run by eligible applicants. This program is intended to make use of and leverage any other available housing programs which provide resources to very low and low income rural residents to bring their dwellings up to development standards. Types of assistance: project grants. Estimate of annual funds available: (Grants) $8,000,000.

Money for Homes for Low Income Indian Families

(14.850 Public and Indian Housing)
Assistant Secretary for Public and Indian Housing
U.S. Department of Housing and Urban Development
Washington, DC 20410
202-708-0950
Objectives: To provide and operate cost-effective, decent, safe and affordable dwellings for lower income families through an authorized local Public Housing Agency (PHA) or Indian Housing Authority (IHA). Types of assistance: direct payments for specified use. Estimate of annual funds available: (Includes obligations for 14.851, 14.852, 14.853 and 14.854) $0. Indian Development: $3,192,000,000.

Loans for Families With Bad Credit Histories

(14.140 Mortgage Insurance-Special Credit Risks)
Contact your State Homeownership Center or local HUD office.
Objectives: To make homeownership possible for low and moderate income families who cannot meet normal HUD requirements. Types of assistance: guaranteed/insured loans. Estimate of annual funds available: (Mortgages insured) $0.

Money to Provide Affordable Rental Housing for Low-Income Families

(14.239 HOME Investment Partnerships Program)
Gordon McKay, Director
Office of Affordable Housing Programs
Community Planning and Development
U.S. Department of Housing and Urban Development
451 7th St., SW, Room 7164
Washington, DC 20410
202-708-2470

Objectives: (1) To expand the supply of decent and affordable housing, particularly rental housing, for low and very low income Americans; (2) To strengthen the abilities of State and local governments to design and implement strategies for achieving adequate supplies of decent, affordable housing; (3) To provide both financial and technical assistance to participating jurisdictions, including the development of model programs for developing affordable low income housing and; (4) To extend and strengthen partnerships among all levels of government and the private sector, including for-profit and nonprofit organizations, in the production and operation of affordable housing. Types of assistance: formula grants. Estimate of annual funds available: (Grants) $1,595,780,000.

Money to Invest in Rental Housing for Lower Income Families

(14.856 Lower Income Housing Assistance Program-Section 8 Moderate Rehabilitation)
Office of the Deputy Assistant Secretary for Public Assisted Housing Delivery
Real Estate and Housing Performance Division
U.S. Department of Housing and Urban Development
Washington, DC 20410
202-708-0477
Objectives: To aid very low income families in obtaining decent, safe and sanitary rental housing. Types of assistance: direct payments for specified use. Estimate of annual funds available: (Outlays) not separately identifiable.

Loans to Investors, Builders, Developers of Affordable Housing

(14.189 Qualified Participating Entities QPE Risk Sharing Pilot Program)

Business Products Division
U.S. Department of Housing and Urban Development
Washington, DC 20410
202-708-2866
Objectives: Under this program HUD will provide reinsurance on multifamily housing projects whose loans are originated, underwritten, serviced, and disposed of by qualified participating entities (QPEs) and/or its approved lenders, up to 15,00 units through fiscal year 1994. The program is a pilot designed to assess the feasibility of risk-sharing partnerships between HUD and QPEs, including Government Sponsored Enterprises, State and local housing finance agencies, financial institutions and the Federal Housing Finance Board, in providing affordable housing for the nation. Types of assistance: guaranteed/insured loans. Estimate of annual funds available: (Loans insured) Reported under Program 14.135.

Money for Developers, Investors, and Builders of Low Income Housing

(14.188 HFA Rick Sharing Pilot Program)
Policies and Procedures Division
Office of Insured Multifamily Housing Development
U.S. Department of Housing and Urban Development
Washington, DC 20412
202-708-2556
Objectives: Under this program, HUD will provide credit enhancement for mortgages for multifamily housing projects whose loans are underwritten, processed, serviced, and disposed of by HFAs, HUD, and the Housing Finance Agencies share in the risk of the mortgage. Types of assistance: guaranteed/insured loans. Estimate of annual funds available: (Loans Insured) Reported under program 14.135.

State Money for Housing and Real Estate

State Initiatives

While affordable housing has long held an important place on the Federal government's policy agenda, budget cutbacks in recent years have forced the government to turn over many housing responsibilities to the states. Housing finance

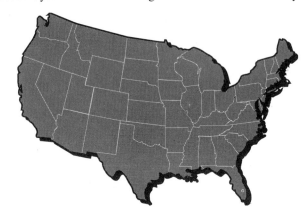

agencies (HFAs) have been created by states to issue tax-exempt bonds to finance mortgages for lower income first-time home buyers and to build multifamily housing.

States are involved in a host of initiatives throughout the broad spectrum of housing finance and development. Interim construction financing programs which can reduce the basic costs of lower income housing projects have been initiated in a number of states, together with innovative home ownership programs and programs directed toward rehabilitation and improved energy conservation.

States are also venturing into areas which have not received as much public sector attention until recently. By encouraging non-traditional types of housing, such as accessory units, shelters, and single room occupancy housing, states are addressing important elements of the housing market.

In Colorado, the state Housing and Finance Authority (CHFA) has issued more than $2.6 billions of bonds and notes since its establishment in 1973, providing housing for more than 47,000 families and individuals of low and moderate income; 27,200 first-time home buyers and over 20,500 rental housing units. In recent years the state has broadened CHFA's authority to allow it to develop finance programs to assist the growth of small business, help exports with insurance on goods sold overseas, and similar projects.

Colorado has done more than simply help its citizens find housing: the programs have resulted in construction employment of more than 20,000 jobs, with wages estimated at almost $20 million in new local real estate taxes and an indirect gain of $1.6 billion for the state.

Wisconsin, Maine and New York each have between 18 and 20 programs including special ones for women and minorities, for disabled persons, and for environmental hazard removal.

Maryland operates 26 programs, including those to help people with closing costs and settlement expenses. It also has special funds available for the elderly and is developing an emergency mortgage fund to help people who have fallen behind in their payments. Nonprofit developers can also tap the state for money to build low cost rental units.

Among Michigan's 29 programs and Minnesota's 25 are several for neighborhood revitalization. Minnesota also offers programs targeting the needs of urban Indians and migrant farm workers. Alaska, Oregon and Vermont offer financing for tenant acquisition of mobile home parks.

Funds are also available for persons who take steps to make their homes more energy efficient, for homeowners and landlords who remove lead paint from dwelling units, for houses without plumbing or those with plumbing that is dysfunctional, for handicapped persons, and to help landlords defray the costs of bringing low income housing into compliance with state and local housing codes. There are also funds for nonprofit organizations to acquire or renovate existing houses and apartments for use as group homes for special needs such as the mentally retarded.

In many states, elderly homeowners can look to the HFA to obtain financing and/or support services they need to remain in their homes and avoid institutionalization. Some of the states have more than one agency dedicated to housing and we have attempted to list them all here. Also, many cities and counties have quasi-federal/quasi-local "housing authorities" with additional programs. Check your local government listings for these.

The following is a complete listing of state housing programs.

Housing Offices

Alabama
Alabama Housing Finance Authority
PO Box 230909
Montgomery, AL 36123-0909
334-244-9200
800-325-2432
www.ahfa.com
E-mail:webmaster@ahfa.com
1. Mortgage Revenue Bond Program: low-rate loans for income-eligible first-time homebuyers.
2. Downpayment Assistance Program: matching funds for lower income home buyers.
3. Access Alabama: financial assistance for lower-income homebuyers that are disabled with the down payment and costs of making the home accessible; in connection with the Bond Program.
4. Low Income Housing Tax Credit Program: federal tax credits for owners of low income rental housing.
5. HOME Program: provides additional opportunities for the production of affordable housing for low income families.
6. Building Blocks to Homeownership: free seminars for new and prospective home buyers.
7. Multifamily Mortgage Revenue Bonds: lower-than-market interest rates for developers of multi-family housing that reserve some of their units for very-low income renters.
8. Alabama Multifamily Loan Consortium: long-term financing for affordable multifamily housing development and rehabilitation.

Alaska
Alaska Housing Finance Corporation
P.O. Box 101020
Anchorage, AK 99510
907-338-6100
800-478-AHFC (AK)
Email: ssimmond@ahfc.state.ak.us
www.ahfc.state.ak.us
1. Mobile Home Program: low downpayment for affordable homes.
2. Veteran Mortgage Program: low interest loans to qualified veterans.
3. Refinance Program: reduce monthly payments on existing loans.
4. Non-Conforming Program: homes which cannot be financed through traditional financing.
5. Rural Nonowner-Occupied Loan Program: financing to qualified borrowers for the purchase, construction, or rehabilitation of housing with up to 8 units in "small communities" in rural Alaska.
6. Multifamily, Congregate and Special Needs Housing Loans: assists qualified nonprofit housing providers and for-profit companies in financing multifamily complexes for low and moderate income housing.
7. Senior Housing Plan: potential borrowers may apply for financing to purchase, construct, rehabilitate or improve various kinds of housing that would meet the needs or person 60 or older.
8. Energy Efficiency Interest: Rate Reduction Participants of an AHFC loan may qualify for an interest-rate reduction depending on the energy efficiency of their home.
9. Affordable Housing Enhanced Loan Program: first-deed-of-trust loan where lower rates/cost secondary

financing is provided by other agencies' programs for low to moderate income people.

10. Assistance Provider Interest Rate Reduction: subsidized interest rates for housing with a live-in care providers for the physically or mentally disabled occupants.

11. Association Loan Program: funds to Homeowners' Associations for common-area improvements if they threaten the health and safety of the residents.

12. Conventional Loan Program: loans for borrowers that do not meet the criteria of other special AHFC programs for eligible property.

13. Multifamily Federally Insured Loan Program: up to 85% of financing for the acquisition, rehabilitation, or refinance of existing multifamily properties.

14. First Time Homebuyer Program: loan programs for income eligible first item homebuyers.

15. Interest Rate Reduction for First Time Homebuyers: interest rate subsidy for low income borrower.

16. Loans to Sponsors: funding to sponsors of affordable housing for low to moderate income people or those living in remote, underdeveloped, or blighted areas of the state.

17. Multi Family Loan Purchase Program: loans for the acquisition, rehabilitation, and refinance of multifamily properties with at least 5 units.

18. Public Service Rental Program: higher loan-to-value and lower interest rate loans for qualified borrowers in areas designated as "very small" communities.

19. Rural Initiative Housing Pilot Program: lower interest rates and relaxed financing requirements to buyers that purchase homes in the selected Pilot Communities of Bethel and Aniak.

20. Rural Owner-Occupied Loan Program: financing for the construction or rehabilitation of a primary residence to qualified borrowers that live in "small communities" in rural Alaska.

21. Second Mortgage for Health and Safety Repair: home improvements loans to qualified borrowers for home improvements; purchase of a home subject of an existing first deed of trust; funding for health and safety repairs to a financed property of AHFC.

22. Second Mortgage Program: funds to qualified borrowers for home improvements or for the purchase of a home subject to an exiting first mortgage.

23. Small Building Material Loan Program: financing for qualified borrowers to purchase materials to rehabilitate primary residences in areas that are defined as "small communities".

24. Streamline Refinance Program: applicants can get financing secured by property that is currently financed by AHFC without income, credit, or appraisal qualifications.

Arizona

Arizona Department of Commerce
Office of Housing and Infrastructure Development
3800 North Central, Suite 150070
Phoenix, AZ 85012
602-280-1300
TDD: 602-280-1301
Fax: 602-280-14
Email: webmaster@az.commerce.com
www.commerce.state.az.us/housing%20infrastructure.htm

1. Low Income Housing Tax credits: federal income tax credits for owners of low income housing units.

2. Arizona Housing Trust Fund: construction, housing rehabilitation, down payment, and closing cost assistance for low/moderate income home buyers.

3. HOME Program: provides help for low income families with various housing needs from rehabilitation to rental assistance.

4. Community Development Block Grant Program: develop viable communities by providing housing and a suitable living environment for low to moderate income people.

5. Special Needs Housing Program: grants to provide planning, technical assistance, and services to groups that serve low-income special needs groups.

6. Section 8 Vouchers and Certificates Program: rental subsidies to income eligible rural tenants.

Arkansas

Arkansas Development Finance Authority
100 Main Street, Suite 200
Little Rock, AR 72201
501-682-5900
www.state.ar.us/adfa

1. HOME Program: funds are used for a variety of activities to develop and support affordable housing for low income. Eligible activities include: Tenant Based Rental Assistance, Rental Rehabilitation, and New Construction and Assistance for Homebuyers and Home Buyers.
2. Low Income Housing Tax Credit Program: federal tax credits for owners of low income rental housing.
3. Home To Own (Mortgage Revenue Bond Program): low-interest rate loans to low and moderate income first time home buyers.
4. Down Payment Assistance Program: closing cost assistance for low- to moderate-income first time home buyers.
5. Tax-Exempt Multi-Family Housing Bonds: below market rate loans for developers that agree to set affordable rental rates for low to moderate income families.

California

California Housing Finance Agency
1121 L Street, 7th Floor
Sacramento, CA 95814
916-322-3991
Email: webmaster@chfa.ca.gov
www.chfa.ca.gov

1. Self-Help Building Assistance Program: loans to nonprofit developers to provide temporary funding for assistance with land acquisition, site development and construction.
2. Tax-Exempt Affordable Mortgage Program: permanent financing for developers and builders of newly constructed or acquired and rehabilitated multifamily units where at least 20% of the occupants have an income of 50% or less of the county median income.
3. Special Needs Affordable Housing Lending Program: loans for all multifamily housing projects that serve at risk tenants that need special services.
4. Preservation Financing Program: financing in order to preserve affordable rental housing for very low and low-income tenants.
5. Bridge Loan Program: tax-exempt bridge loans for multifamily housing projects receiving 4% tax credits.
6. Pre-development Loan Program: funding to help developers with land acquisition and pre-development costs of affordable multi-housing projects with CHFA.
7. Single Loan Process: no fee to lock in an interest rate, on any date, for a loan to be delivered in the next 90 days.
8. First-Time Homebuyers: loans for first time homebuyers for new or existing single family homes.

California Department of Housing and Community Development
PO Box 952054
Sacramento, CA 94252-2050
916-322-1560
www.hcd.ca.gov

1. California Indian Assistance Program: assists tribal organizations to obtain and administer housing, infrastructure community and economic development projects funds provided by federal and state agencies.
2. HOME Program: assist communities and community housing development organizations (CHDOs) in activities that create or retain affordable housing.
3. Mobile Home Park Resident Ownership Program: loans to mobile home park resident organizations, nonprofit housing sponsors, or local public agencies that are purchasing the park.
4. Emergency Housing Assistance Program: grants to provide emergency shelters, transitional housing and services for the homeless.
5. Farmworker Housing Grant Program: grants to provide owner-occupied and rental units for year-round, low

income agricultural workers and to rehabilitate those damaged by natural disaster.

6. State (CBDG) General, Native American, and Colonial Allocations: funding for housing, community, and economic development projects serving lower income people in rural communities.

7. California Self-Help Housing Program: assists low and moderate income families to build and rehabilitate their homes with their own labor.

8. Federal Emergency Shelter Grant Program: grant to fund emergency shelters, services and transitional housing for the homeless.

9. Families Moving to Work Program: loans to Cal WORKS welfare reform program recipients for limited-term housing assistance, childcare, employment assistance and other services.

10. Housing Assistance Program: rent assistance for extremely-low and very-low income households in rural counties without housing authorities.

11. Multifamily Housing Program: loans for new construction, rehabilitation preservation of permanent and transitional rental housing for lower income households.

12. Office of Migrant Services: loans and grants to provide safe, decent and affordable seasonal rental housing and support services for migrant rental housing and support services for migrant farm worker families during peak harvest season.

13. Rural Pre-development Loan Program: short-term loans for pre-development costs of low income housing projects in rural areas.

14. Urban Pre-development Loan Program: short-term loans for the initial cost of preserving existing affordable housing developments for the existing tenants.

15. Child Care Facilities Finance Program: loan guarantees and direct loans for the development and or expansion of child care facilities, child development facilities and family child care homes.

16. The Factory Built Housing Program: provide buyers of Factory Built Homes protection by ensuring that construction standards are met by overseeing their implementation and correcting variances in a fair manner.

17. The Manufactured Housing Program: to ensure the health and safety of person occupying, purchasing, renting or leasing manufactured homes, and commercial coaches.

18. Mobile Home Parks Program: assures the health, safety and general welfare of mobile home park residents and provides them a decent living environment, and to protect their homes.

Colorado

Colorado Housing and Finance Authority
1981 Blake Street
Denver, CO 80202
303-297-2432
800-877-2432
TDD: 303-297-7305
www.colohfa.org

1. Mortgage Credit Certificate Program: reduction of federal income tax for home buyers to pay their monthly mortgage.

2. Rural Development Loan Program: loans for businesses in rural areas of Colorado.

3. Mortgage Revenue Bond Program: below market interest rate loan and cash assistance to help with downpayment and closing expenses for low to moderate-income people.

4. Forward Commitment Program: below market interest rate loan for clients of participating non-profits and Housing Authorities.

5. Down Payment Assistance: low-interest 2nd mortgage loans to help eligible home buyers with down payment and closing costs; only available to those who get CHFA Forward Commitment Loans.

6. Taxable Bond Program: first mortgages at competitive interest rates including cash assistance for low to medium-income home buyers.

7. Housing Opportunity Fund: a flexible loan pool available to 501(c) organizations and government entity sponsors to assist their very-low income homeowner clients.

8. Rental Housing Loan Programs: Provides construction and/or permanent financing for the acquisition, rehabilitation, construction, or in certain cases, refinancing of rental housing.

9. Small Affordable Rental Transaction (SMART): provides long term financing for small rental housing projects; also minimizes the paperwork, document costs and the time it takes to close the loan.
10. RENEW Colorado: financing to businesses that include waste diversion or recycling activities in their business.
11. Quality Investment Capital Program: long-term fixed-rate financing for small businesses.
12. Quality Agricultural Loan Program: financing for land, equipment and machinery to farm and ranch operations.

Connecticut
Connecticut Housing Finance Authority
999 West Street
Rocky Hill, CT 06067
860-721-9501
1. Home Buyer Mortgages: below market interest rates for first time low or moderate income homebuyers that purchase moderate priced homes.
2. Rehabilitation Mortgage Loan Program: loans to income eligible first time home buyers that purchase a home that needs to be repaired; refinancing of a home in need of repair for income eligible homeowners.
3. Homeownership Program: mortgages for public housing tenants and certain public assisted housing residents that meet income requirements; a home buyer education seminar must be attend.
4. Police Homeownership Program: low-interest rate mortgages to police officers that purchase a home in certain communities; must not have owned a home within the past 3 years unless they purchase in targeted areas.
5. Downpayment Assistance Program: downpayment assistance to eligible home buyers; closing costs assistance to low income buyers in the Homeownership Program.
6. Apartment Conversion for the Elderly: funding for elderly homeowners so they can renovate or add an addition on their home to create an accessory apartment to provide rental income.
7. Reverse Annuity Mortgage Program: elderly low income homeowners can use the equity in their home as tax-free income which can be repaid after their death or when they no longer occupy the home.
8. Community Development and Preservation Loan Fund: financing for developers to acquire, rehabilitate, and/or construct one to four family housing for income eligible buyers.
9. Multifamily Rental Housing Program: construction and permanent first mortgages to developers that build or rehabilitate affordable housing where some units are set aside for low income residents.
10. Common Interest Community Common Element Repair Program: financing for repairs to common elements of condominiums and housing cooperatives where other financing is not available.
11. Mobil Manufactured home Parks Pilot Program: financing for resident associations and certain non-profits to purchase mobile home park land to convert it to condominium or cooperative ownership.
12. Low-Income Housing Tax Credit: federal tax credits for developers of rental housing for low income tenants.
13. Employer Assisted Housing Tax Credit Program: state tax credits to employers that create loan funds for low and moderate income employees so they can purchase or rent a home.
14. Housing Tax Credit Contribution Program: tax-credits to non-profits that develop, sponsor or manage housing for very low, low, and moderate income individuals or families.

Delaware
Delaware State Housing Authority
Division of Housing and Community Development
18 The Green
PO Box 1401
Dover, DE 19901
302-739-4263
TDD: 302-739-7428
Fax: 302-739-6122
www2.state.de.us/dsha
1. Single-Family Mortgage Revenue Bond Program: low interest loans to first-time home buyers with low and moderate income.
2. Housing Development Funds: loans to developers of housing for low and moderate income persons and families.

3. Housing Rehabilitation Loan Program: loans to low- to moderate-income homeowners or landlords who rent to low-income tenants of $35,000 for ten years at 3% for repairs or handicapped accessibility modifications.
4. Subsidized Rental Housing Assistance Programs: money to provide subsidies for low and moderate income rental housing in specified counties.
5. Community Development Block Grants: funding to maintain or improve housing of low/moderate income households.
6. Family Assisted Interest Rate Loans: first time homebuyers mortgage assisted at below market interest rates.
7. Second Mortgage Assistance Loan Program: downpayment and closing costs assistance for first time homebuyers.
8. Emergency Shelter Grant Program: federal funds for local communities to rehabilitate, expand and operate emergency shelters.
9. HOME Program: designed to expand affordable housing through tenant and homebuyer assistance, rehabilitation, and new construction.
10. Delaware Housing Partnership Program: second mortgages for settlement assistance to low to moderate income families purchasing homes in targeted new construction subdivisions.
11. Acquisition/Rehabilitation Loan Program: loans for low-and moderate-income first time buyers to purchase homes that are in need of repairs and then get a 3% interest loan to make the repairs all with one application.
12. Neighborhood Revitalization Fund: low-interest loans to help entire communities restore their homes to State Housing Code standards.
13. Section 8 New Construction (Sec 8 NC): affordable housing to very low-income people at 30 different sites in the state where participants pay about 30% of their income for rent.
14. Low Income Housing Tax Credit: federal income tax credit to owners and investors of affordable rental housing that rent to low-income tenants.
15. Housing Capacity Building Program: a range of assistance to providers of affordable housing to increase their capacity to build and maintain the housing.

District of Columbia

District of Columbia Department of Housing and Community Development
801 North Capitol Street, NE, Room 225A
Washington, DC 20002
202-442-7200
www.dhcd.dcgov.org

1. Home Purchase Assistance Program: low or no interest loans for low and moderate income home buyers.
2. First Right Purchase Assistance Program: low cost loans for low and moderate income individuals and tenant groups to exercise their right to purchase their rental housing that is being offered for sale.
3. Homestead Housing Preservation Program: repossessed properties are sold to eligible District residents at low cost and with deferred payment loans.
4. Distressed Properties Improvement Program: tax incentives to encourage the repair of occupied or vacant rental housing and retain low-income residents.
5. Housing Finance for the Elderly, Dependent and Disables: loans for the development of housing for special needs households.
6. Low Income Housing Tax Credit Program: tax credits for owners of low and moderate income rental housing.
7. Single-Family Housing Rehabilitation Program: low cost financing for the rehabilitation of one to four unit low income housing in designated areas.
8. Handicapped Access Improvements Program: grants to remove barriers and improve accessibility; for homeowners or landlords on behalf of handicapped tenants.
9. D.C. Employer Assisted Housing Program: grants and deferred loans to first-time home buyers that are employees of the District of Columbia government.
10. D.C. Metropolitan Police Housing Assistance Program: assistance to members of the Metropolitan Police Department for down payment and closing costs.
11. Homeownership Developer Incentive Fund: grant to development entities to lower the development costs so that they are affordable to low and moderate income residents.

12. Senior Citizen Home Repair and Improvement Program: loans to senior citizens so that they can make emergency repairs to their home that would otherwise threaten their health and safety.
13. Apartment Improvement Program: technical assistance to rental housing owners to make comprehensive property improvement plans that involve a cooperative effort between owners, renters and financial institutions.
14. Construction Assistance Program: assistance to nonprofit land trusts to develop acquired lands and buildings to create low and moderate income housing.
15. Community Land Acquisition Program: assistance to nonprofits to acquire land and building to create low and moderate income housing.
16. Housing Production Trust Fund Program: financial assistance to developers for the planning and production of low to moderate-income housing and related facilities; there are a wide range of housing initiatives concerning housing production and preservation.

Florida

Florida Housing Finance Corporation
227 North Bronough St., Suite 5000
Tallahassee, FL 32301-1329
850-488-4197
Fax: 850-488-9809
Email: infor@floridahousing.org
www.floridahousing.org

1. First-Time Homebuyer Mortgage Revenue Bond Program: below-market rate financing for first-time home buyers with low/moderate income.
2. State Apartment Incentive Loan Program (SAIL): low rate financing for developers who build or rehabilitate rental housing that is affordable to very low-income people.
3. HOME Program: provides states their opportunity to administer federally funded homeownership housing programs.
4. State Housing Initiatives Partnership Program (SHIP): funds for the development and maintenance of affordable housing through public/private partnerships.
5. HOME Rental Program: mortgage loans to construct, rehabilitate, or acquire and rehabilitate affordable housing for low-income households.
6. Housing Credit Programs: federal tax reduction to acquire and rehabilitate or construct rental housing units for low and very low-income renters.
7. Florida Affordable Housing Guarantee Program: issues guarantees on obligations of the financing of affordable housing in order to encourage lending activities.
8. Predevelopment Loan Program: financial assistance to non-profits with limited or no experience that develop affordable housing for very low or low-income households.
9. Multifamily Revenue Bonds: below market rate loans to developers who set aside 20% of the units to low-income or 40% of units to very low-income persons.
10. Home Ownership Assistance Program: 0% interest, non-amortized 2nd mortgage loans to low-income families; 3% interest rate loans for nonprofits to developer or substantially rehabilitate affordable housing.

Georgia

Georgia Department of Community Affairs
60 Executive Parkway South, Suite 250
Atlanta, GA 30329
404-679-4940
www.dca.state.ga.us

1. Low Income Housing Tax Credit Program: federal income tax credits to construct or rehabilitate low/moderate income rental housing.
2. Section 8 Existing Rental Housing Assistance Program: rental subsidy payments to landlords of low income individuals or families.
3. Housing Trust Fund for the Homeless: funding for transitional housing and services to homeless individuals and families.

4. Appalachian Regional Commission: grants for site development and technical assistance for low and moderate income housing projects.
5. Emergency Shelter Grant Program: grants to shelter facilities for their operation and for the essential services for the homeless they provide.
6. Community Housing Development Organizations Program: long term financing for the acquisition, rehabilitation, and/or construction of rental and ownership housing developments of 12 or more units for low or moderate income households.
7. Housing Opportunities for Persons with AIDS Program: direct subsidies of Federal funds to nonprofit groups that operate housing and provide supportive services to people with AIDS and related diseases.
8. Home Buyer Program: low interest rate mortgages to qualified first-time home buyers.
9. Own Home Downpayment Program: loan to cover most of the down payment, closing costs and prepaid expenses to first time home buyers.
10. MultiFamily Housing Resource Bank Financing Program: long term low interest rate loans to develop or rehabilitate multifamily rental housing of 12 or more units for low and moderate income households.
11. Appalachian Housing Fund: cash grants for improvements in association with the construction or rehabilitation of affordable housing in a targeted area.
12. Community Development Block Grant Programs: grants programs including those for housing improvement projects, and economic development projects.
13. Immediate Threat and Danger Grant Program: grants for activities to fix existing conditions that pose a serious and immediate threat to the health and welfare of the community.
14. Empowerment Zones/Enterprise Communities: federal funds to support economic, community, housing and social support programs.
15. Next Step Program: provides rental assistance to homeless people.
16. Job Tax Credit Program: tax credits to businesses that create jobs in specified areas.
17. Better Hometown Program: public/private partnership that gives technical assistance and advice to small towns in order to revitalize their downtowns.
18. Best Practices Technical Assistance Program: technical assistance to groups that offer services to homeless people.
19. Local Development Fund: matching grants to fund community improvement projects.
20. Appalachian Region Business Development Fund: revolving loan fund to finance eligible projects that create or save jobs in the Appalachian area.
21. Downtown Development Revolving Loan Fund: loans to eligible applicants to carry out downtown development projects.
22. Regional Assistance Projects: funds to support the development of multi-county and regional development projects.
23. Employment Incentive Program: financing that can be used with private financing for economic development projects that employ low and moderate income people.

Hawaii

Hawaii Housing and Community Development
1002 North School Street
Honolulu, HI 96813
808-832-6020

1. Homeless Program: shelter and social services for homeless families and individuals.
2. State Rent Supplement Program: rent subsidies to tenants in approved projects.
3. Section 8 Housing Voucher Program: rental housing subsidies
4. Hula Mae Single Family Program: low interest loans to first-time home buyers.
5. Mortgage Credit Certificate Program: direct federal tax credit to potential home buyers so that they have more available income to qualify for a loan and to help make payments.
6. Housing Alteration Revolving Loan Fund Program: low interest loans to persons with physical disabilities to adapt their home or rental unit.
7. Lease Rent Renegotiation Program: arbitration of a lease renegotiation for one and two family residences leased

by cooperative housing corporations.

8. Downpayment Loan Program: down payment loans for borrowers that meet certain criteria.
9. Low Income Housing Tax Credit: tax credit for developers that construct or rehabilitate affordable rental housing.
10. Seed Money Loan: loans or grants to help with the costs to initiate a low to moderate-income housing project.

Idaho

Idaho Housing and Finance Association
565 West Myrtle
P.O. Box 7899
Boise, ID 83707-1899
208-331-4882
TDD: 800-219-2285
Email: about@ihfa.org
www.ihfa.org

1. Section 8 Rental Assistance Program: assistance for low income households to meet costs of rental housing.
2. HOME Program : funds used for the construction and rehabilitation of affordable rental housing for low income families across the state.
3. Family Self-Sufficiency Program: recipients get assistance to eventually free themselves of federal and state welfare assistance.
4. Public Housing In Idaho: IHFA operated public housing in target areas where lower income renters pay 30% of their income towards rent.
5. Housing Opportunities for Persons Living with HIV/AIDS: 45 units with rental assistance to people who have a family member with HIV/AIDS.
6. Emergency Shelter Grants Program: grants to improve the quality of emergency homeless shelters.
7. Supportive Housing Program: supportive housing services to help the homeless with the transition to independent living; long-term assisted housing for persons with disabilities; supportive services for hard-to-reach homeless person with severe mental illness.
8. Shelter Plus Care Program: rental and supportive services for seriously mentally ill homeless people.
9. Homeless Program Assistance: technical assistance for participants of Homeless Assistance and Emergency Shelter Programs.
10. First Time Home Buyer Program: low interest rate loans for first time low-to-moderate income home buyers.
11. Finally Home! Program: after completing the education, program participants may be eligible for financial assistance to purchase a home.

Illinois

Illinois Housing Development Authority
401 North Michigan Ave., Suite 900
Chicago, IL 60611
312-836-5200
800-942-8439
TDD: 312-836-5222
www.ihda.org

1. First Time Home Buyer Program: low interest mortgages for first-time income-eligible home buyers.
2. Affordable Housing Trust Fund: grants and loans to profit and nonprofit developers of low income housing projects.
3. HOME Program: this program is designed to expand the availability of affordable housing for low and very low income persons.
4. Mortgage Credit Certificate Program: federal tax credit to first-time income eligible home buyers.
5. Low-Income Housing Tax Credit: tax credit to investors for new construction and rehabilitation of rental housing for low-income families.
6. Multifamily Programs: low interest loans to build or rehabilitate income housing.

Indiana

Indiana Housing Finance Authority
115 West Washington Street
Suite 1350, South Tower
Indianapolis, IN 46204
317-232-7777
800-872-0371
www.state.in.us/ihfa

1. First Time Home Program: loans to first time home buyers below the market rate.
2. Mortgage Credit Certificate Program: tax credits to low and moderate families to purchase a single family residence.
3. Rental Housing Tax Credits: federal tax credit to owners of low income rental housing.
4. Low Income Housing Trust Fund: funds for development of low income housing, permanent or transitional.
5. HOME Program: funds used for a number of different purposes to create affordable housing.
6. First Home 100 Program: works with the First Home and Rural Development Direct Loan programs for further financial assistance to eligible home buyers.
7. First Home/One Down Program: 0% interest forgivable loan to assist qualified first-time home buyers with a down payment.
8. First Home/PLUS Program: a 5%-10% down payment assistance loan at 0% in conjunction with a First Home Loan.
9. Community Development Block Grants: funding to create affordable housing for low and very low income families.
10. Mark-to-Market Program: subsidies to bring rent down to market level.
11. Build-A-Home: grants to non-profit developers for construction or rehabilitation of single-family homes.

Iowa

Iowa Finance Authority
100 East Grand, Suite 250
Des Moines, IA 50309
515-242-4990
800-432-7230
Fax: 515-242-4957
www.ifahome.com

1. Mortgage Credit Certificate Program: tax credits of up to 25% of the interest paid annually on home loans.
2. Low Income Housing Tax Credit Program: federal tax credits for owners of low income rental housing.
3. Housing Assistance Fund Program: funding for multifamily rehab and construction, rent subsidies, group homes, shelters, and other housing projects.
4. Downpayment/Closing Cost Grant Program: matching grant for low and moderate-income families of up to 5% of their mortgage to pay closing costs, down payment or necessary repairs.
5. First-Time Home Buyer Mortgage Loan Program: low interest rate mortgagee loans for first time homebuyers.
6. H.I.R.E. Program: to help developers finance the construction of new homes in rural areas.
7. Rural Home Building Initiative: grants to increase the construction of affordable homes in specified rural areas.
8. Economic Development Loan Program: loans to promote the development and expansion of family farming, soil conservation, housing and business within Iowa.
9. Iowa Comprehensive Petroleum Underground Storage Tank Fund Program: money to help tank owners and operators clean-up leaking underground storage tanks.
10. Iowa Sewage Treatment Works Financing Program: grant to help pay for upgrades to local wastewater treatment facilities.
11. Correctional Facility Program: assistance to finance the construction or renovation of correctional facilities.

Kansas

Kansas Department of Commerce and Housing
700 SW Harrison, Suite 1300

Topeka, KS 66603
785-296-3481
800-752-4422
www.kansascommerce.com

1. Low Income Housing Tax Credit: tax credits for developers who rent to low income families.
2. Emergency Shelter Grant Program: grants to local government agencies to provide emergency shelters for the homeless .
3. Weatherization: a multi-funded program used to increase energy efficiency in low income homes.
4. First Time Homebuyers Down Payment Assistance Program: loans for qualified home buyers for down payments, closing costs, and legal fees associated with the purchase.
5. Kansas Housing Cost Analysis Program: through public-private partnerships, newly constructed home are offered for sale to income eligible families.
6. Homeowner Rehabilitation of Existing Property Program: funds to help homeowners to repair and rehabilitate their property; priority is given to elderly homeowners and families with school-age children.
7. Homeowner Emergency Rehabilitation Opportunities: helps homeowners to make emergency repairs and rehabilitate their property in order to qualify for weatherization assistance.
8. Interim Development Loans: financial assistance to aid difficult-to-develop rental housing projects.
9. Community Housing Development Organizations Program: loans for non-profit developers to construct, purchase or rehabilitate rental housing.
10. Tenant-Based Rental Assistance Program: grants to the owner of a rental unit to help renters with monthly rent payments.
11. Permanent Housing for Homeless Persons with Disabilities: funding for long-term housing facilities with supportive services for disabled homeless persons.
12. Community Services Block Grant: funding for community action agencies to combat the causes and conditions of poverty in the community.
13. Compliance Monitoring: technical assistance for private property managers to maintain the financial and physical integrity of housing properties.
14. Kansas Housing Partners Program: provides information and technical service related to housing for individuals and communities.

Kentucky

Kentucky Housing Corporation
1231 Louisville Road
Frankfort, KY 40601
502-564-7630
800-633-8896
TTY: 800-648-6056
www.kyhousing.org

1. Home Ownership Program: low interest loans to home buyers who currently do not own property and meet income requirements.
2. Kentucky Appalachian Housing Program: site development grants and loans for housing development in 49 eastern KY counties.
3. Rental Deposits Surety Program: assistance with utility and security deposits for low income households.
4. Low Income Housing Tax Credits: federal tax credits for owners of low income rental housing.
5. Down Payment Assistance Program: low-interest loan for downpayment and closing costs to qualified home buyers.
6. Homeownership Trust Fund: low fixed interest rate for very low-income families with special needs.
7. Yes You Can...Own A Home Program: free homeownership education program.
8. Homeownership Counseling Program: homeownership counseling services to eligible potential homebuyers.
9. New Construction/Substantial Rehabilitation Program: funds to create or substantially rehabilitate housing to make it affordable for very low-income residents.
10. Housing Choice Voucher Program: recipients can locate and rent a dwelling that meets the guideline on their

own; provides rental assistance.
11. Family Self-Sufficiency Program: rental assistance and supportive services for very low-income people that are willing to commit to a goal of being free of government assistance.
12. Risk Sharing Program: Low interest, permanent rate financing to developers of new construction or substantial rehabilitation of apartment units.
13. Assisted Living Program: low interest rate financing to developers of housing/service units for the elderly.
14. Mark-to-Market: assistance to owners of properties with expiring Section 8 contracts to achieve market-rate rents and affordable rental units.
15. Small Multi Family Affordable Loan Program: loans to be used for construction and/or permanent financing of rental housing development not exceeding 11 units for lower-income people.
16. Special Needs Assistance Program: loans to non-profits for construction and/or permanent financing of rental housing developments not exceeding 11 units for extremely low and low-income special needs population.
17. HOME Program: programs to fund affordable housing production and rehabilitation.
18. Nonprofit Housing Production and Repair Program: very low-interest loans for the production and repair of lower-income housing.
19. Housing Development Fund: flexible loan terms and low-interest rates to build affordable housing.
20. Repair Affair: assistance to homeowners that do not qualify for other existing programs to complete needed home repairs.
21. Continuum of Care Programs: variety of programs that offer transitional housing, rental assistance, supportive services, and permanent housing for disables homeless persons and operating funds for emergency shelters.
22. Affordable Housing Trust Fund: funds to acquire, rehabilitate and/or build housing for very low-income residents.
23. Housing Opportunities for Person with AIDS: funds to meet the housing needs of people with AIDS or related diseases.
24. Renaissance Kentucky: assists communities to revitalize their downtowns.

Louisiana
Louisiana Housing Finance Agency
200 Lafayette Street, Suite 300
Baton Rouge, LA 70801
225-342-1320
Fax: 225-342-1310
www.lhfa.state.la.us
1. Multifamily Bond Issues: financing available for developers of low and moderate income housing developments.
2. HOME Assistance Program: assistance when purchasing a home for qualified individuals that reduces the downpayment and related costs.
3. Mortgage Revenue Bond Non-Assisted Program: loans to first time income eligible homebuyers of a 1-4 owner occupied home.
4. Mortgage Revenue Bond Assisted Program: loan of 4% of the mortgage to help first time income eligible home buyers with downpayment and closing costs.
5. Low Income Housing Tax Credit: federal tax credits to developer/owners of rental units for low income families.
6. HOME-funded Rental Programs: financing to private owners/developers and nonprofits for construction, acquisition, and/or rehabilitation of small and large rental properties for very low, low, and moderate income families.

Maine
Maine State Housing Authority
353 Water Street
Augusta, ME 04330
207-626-4600

800-452-4668
Fax: 207-626-4678
TTY: 800-452-4603
www.mainehousing.org

1. Homeownership Program: low downpayment and low rate financing for first-time income-eligible home buyers.
2. Purchase Plus Improvement: home improvement loans for borrowers to make immediate repairs.
3. Rental Loan Program: below market rate loans for new or rehabilitated rental housing affordable to low and very low income households.
4. Housing Program: funding to operate or improve shelters.
5. Low Income Energy Assistance Program: offers assistance to fuel vendors to provide heating for low income homeowners and renters.
6. Closing Cost Assistance: a loan of 2% of the mortgage to eligible applicants to cover closing costs.
7. Down Home Loans: allows a minimum cash contribution of $750 or $1,000 in out-of-pocket expenses for income-eligible borrowers.
8. New Neighbors Program: special financing to buy a home in inner-city, low income neighborhoods in specified areas.
9. Great Rate Program: low interest rate for low income applicants; a homebuyer education course must first be completed.
10. Lead Hazard Control Program: grants and loans to low income homeowners and renters with a child under 6 in the household to get rid of lead-based paint problems.
11. Residential Energy Assistance Challenge Program (REACH): program to help low-income households reduce their energy costs.
12. Weatherization/Central Heating Improvement Program: delivers weatherization and central heating repair/replacement to low income homeowners and renters.
13. New Lease Program: reduced interest rate loans for the acquisition and rehabilitation of housing for low and very low income renters.
14. Assisted Housing Management Oversight: assistance to maintain financial and physical viability of subsidized housing to very low and low income elderly, disabled and families.
15. Tenant Assistance Program: federal rent subsidies to very low income elderly, disabled, or families.
16. Supportive Housing Program: reduced interest rate mortgage financing and subsidy funding for nonprofits to create housing for person who need supportive housing and services.

Maryland

Department of Housing and Community Development
100 Community Place
Crownsville, MD 21032-2023
410-514-7700
800-756-0119
TTY: 410-514-7531
www.dhcd.state.md.us

1. Mortgage Program: below-market interest rate mortgage financing for low and moderate income first time home buyers.
2. Housing Rehabilitation Program-Single Family: loans to limited income homeowners and owners of small nonresidential properties to preserve and improve the properties.
3. Group Home Financing Program: low interest, no interest deferred payment loans to nonprofit organizations to purchase and modify housing for use as group homes and shelters.
4. Rental Allowance Program: subsidies to very low income individuals with emergency needs or that are homeless.
5. Multifamily Bond Program: below-market financing for low income multifamily rental housing development.
6. Partnership Rental Housing Program: loans for local governments and housing authorities for development or acquisition of low income rental housing.
7. Accessory, Shared and Sheltered Housing Program: low rate loans to finance additions and improvement to

create accessory, shared or sheltered housing for low income households.
8. Indoor Plumbing Program: low rate loans to provide indoor plumbing.
9. Section 8 Existing Certificate/Voucher Program: rent subsidies for low income households.
10. Low Income Housing Tax Credit Program: federal tax credits to owners of low income rental housing.
11. Shelter and Transitional Housing Facilities Program: provides grants to improve or create transitional housing and emergency shelters.
12. Homeownership Opportunities for Teacher Initiative: 5% interest rate for teachers that teach in Maryland's public schools during the first 3 years of the loan.
13. Downpayment and Settlement Expense Loan Program: borrowers through the Mortgage Program can get a 0% loan to help cover settlement expenses.
14. Live Near Your Work Program: employees that purchase a home near their work in targeted areas receive a grant for costs associate with the purchase of a home.
15. Lead Hazard Reduction Grant and Loan Program: funds to homeowners and landlords to reduce or eliminate lead-based paint hazard.
16. Weatherization Assistance Program: low interest rate loans assist eligible low income households to install energy conservation materials.
17. HOME Program: funds for the construction, acquisition and rehabilitation of rental housing, owner occupied housing, and special needs housing.
18. Housing Capacity Assistance Program: funding for nonprofits to expand technical capacity to produce housing.
19. Office and Commercial Space Conversion Initiative: financing to convert older offices and commercial space downtown into new affordable rental housing.
20. Special Targeted Area Rehabilitated Program (STAR): funds to help single family home owners to bring their property up to code.

Massachusetts
Massachusetts Housing Finance Agency
One Beacon Street
Boston, MA 02108
617-854-1000
TTY: 617-854-1025
www.mhfa.com
1. General Lending: special loans for income eligible first time home buyers.
2. Home Improvement Loan Program: loans for owner-occupied homes for needed repairs and to correct violations.
3. Project TAP (Tenant Assistance Program): training for project residents and management for drug-and alcohol-related problems.
4. Low Income Housing Tax Credit Program: federal tax credits for owners of low income rental housing.
5. Elder Choice Program: fills the gap between independent living and a nursing home by providing a home-like setting coupled with on-site services that support the needs of frail elderly persons.
6. Mortgage Insurance Fund: provides private mortgage insurance on mortgage loan downpayments below 20%.
7. Get the Lead Out Program: provides loans, some at 9% interest for owners of 1 to 4 family homes to remove lead paint.
8. Homebuyer Counseling Program: educates first-time home buyers of the homebuying process.
9. ReOpportunity: below-market-rate mortgages for qualified buyers of MHFA-held foreclosed properties.
10. FreshRate Program: loan of 4% of the loan amount for down payment and closing cost assistance to qualified buyers.
11. Septic Repair Loan Program: financial assistance for income eligible homeowners to repair a failed septic system.
12. 80/20 Program: tax exempt and/or taxable financing to acquire, rehabilitate and/or construction of multifamily rental units that reserve 20% of units for low-income renters.
13. Expanding Rental Affordability Program: assistance for rental housing where at least 20% of the units are set aside for low income renters.

14. Demonstration Disposition Program: funding to renovate developments in specified areas.
15. Resident Relocation Program: assistance for Demonstration Disposition residents to relocate.
16. Options for Independence Program: financing to community based residences for previously mentally institutionalized person, homeless mentally ill, and other special needs persons.
17. Bridge Loan Financing: for developers of low income rental housing in conjunction with construction/permanent financing.
18. 504/ADA Technical Assistance: technical assistance for housing providers, residents, applicants, and service providers.
19. Youth Resident Activities Program: programs and activities for youths that reside in MHFA properties in specified areas.

Massachusetts Department of Housing and Community Development
One Congress Street, 10th Floor
Boston, MA 02114
617-727-7765
www.state.ma.us/dhcd

1. Section 8 Certificate/Voucher Programs: rent subsidies for very low income families, the elderly and the disabled.
2. McKinney Emergency Community Services Homeless Grant: helps homeless individuals and those at risk of becoming homeless through eviction or foreclosure.
3. Weatherization Assistance Program: funds for full scale energy conservation services in low income households.
4. Community Service Block Grant: provides funds for designated community action agencies to enhance the quality of life among the poor.
5. Local Initiative Program: technical assistance to communities and developers that are working together to create housing that sets aside 24% of units for low and moderate income households.
6. Homeownership Opportunity Program (HOP): reduced rate first mortgage loans to buyers of HOP units.
7. Community Enterprise Economic Development Program: assistance for residents and their local community development corporation to revitalize their neighborhoods.
8. Homeless Intercept Program/Housing Services Program: supportive services for people in a housing crisis situation to find housing.
9. Community Food and Nutrition Program: nutrition education activities to unemployed and low-income people.
10. Neighborhood Housing Services program: support for agency or individual housing rehabilitation projects.
11. Heating Emergency Assistance Retrofit Task Weatherization Assistance program (HEARTWAP): provides heating system repair and replacement services to low-income households.
12. Low Income Home Energy Assistance Program: helps low-income households to pay winter heating bills.
13. Low Income Sewer And Water Assistance Program: financial assistance to homeowners that have excessive water and sewer bills.
14. Community Development Block Grant Program: variety of programs that fund housing and/or public facilities and infrastructure programs.
15. Demolition Grant Program: helps communities to destroy abandoned building that pose health and safety risks.

Michigan

Michigan State Housing Development Authority
401 South Washington Square
PO Box 30044
Lansing, MI 48909
517-373-8370
TTY: 800-382-4568
Fax: 517-335-4797

1. Single-Family Home Mortgage: low interest loans for single-family homes and condominiums.
2. Michigan Mortgage Credit Certificates: federal income tax credits that give home buyers more income to qualify for a mortgage.

3. Property Improvement Loans: home improvement loans for owner and non-owner occupied homes over 20 years old at a low interest rate.
4. Section 8 Existing Rental Allowance Program: rent subsidies for very low income people who find their own housing in private homes and apartment buildings.
5. Moderate Rehabilitation: subsidies to landlords for rehabilitation of units with low income families.
6. Rehabilitation Assistance Program: provides loans to very low income families to make improvements on their homes.
7. Low Income Housing Tax Credit Program: federal tax credit for owners/developers of low income rental housing.
8. Contractor's Assistance Program: provides working capital loans to small contractors who have been selected to work on rental housing projects
9. Taxable Bond Program: loans for rental housing where most tenants will have very low incomes.
10. Community Development Block Grants: grants to small communities and counties so that lower income homeowners can upgrade their homes and carry out other housing activities.
11. Habitat for Humanity Housing Grant Fund: grants to Habitat for Humanity to build or rehabilitate homes.
12. Down Payment Assistance Program: no interest loans up to $5,000 for down payment assistance for first mortgages for income eligible people; available through the Single Family Mortgage Program.
13. Homeownership Counseling Network: free counseling for potential MSHDA borrowers.
14. More Independence through HOME: funds to finance nonprofit's projects that provide rental units for disabled people.
15. Tax-Exempt Apartment for MI (TEAM): program for rental units where 25% of the units are for low income people and 20% are for very low income people.
16. One Percent: rent limits established for development with low income people.
17. Neighborhood Preservation Program: assistance for developers of 4-30 unit housing where 20% of renters are low income.
18. Families in Transition: subsidies to developments for low income, homeless, single mothers and their children where supportive services may be available.
19. Housing Resource Funds: funds for nonprofits and local government to create affordable housing projects.
20. Emergency Shelter Grants:
21. Family Self-Sufficiency Program: help for families in assisted housing that contract to be off of government support .

Minnesota

Minnesota Housing Finance Agency
400 Sibley Street, Suite 300
St. Paul, MN 55101
651-296-7608
800-657-3769
Email: mhfa@state.mn.us
www.mhfa.state.mn.us

1. Urban Indian Housing Program: loans at below market interest rates for low to moderate income Indian families buying their first home in an urban area; low interest rate loans for rental housing developments for Indian families that have a low income.
2. HOME Rental Rehabilitation Program: grants to rental property owners to rehabilitate property so that it is safe and affordable for low income people.
3. Rental Rehabilitation Loan Program: low interest loans to rental property owners to rehabilitate the property.
4. Minnesota Mortgage Program: below market rate loans for low/moderate income first-time home buyers.
5. Home Ownership Assistance Fund; downpayment and monthly payment assistance to lower income MHFA mortgage recipients.
6. Great Minnesota Fix-Up Fund: below market home improvement loans for income eligible homeowners.
7. Great Minnesota Fix-Up Home Energy Loan Program: low rate loans for increasing energy efficiency of homes; no maximum income limits.

8. Low and Moderate Income Program: property improvement loans for low/moderate income households who do not qualify for existing programs.
9. Housing Trust Fund: zero interest deferred loans for acquisition, contraction or rehabilitation of a development of low income rental and co-op housing.
10. Affordable Rental Investment Fund: zero interest deferred loans to rehabilitate small family low income rental housing.
11. New Construction Tax Credit Mortgage/Bridge Loan Program: for construction/rehabilitation of rental units for low income households.
12. Home Stretch: homeownership workshops.
13. Rehabilitation Loan Program: loans to low to moderate income homeowners for home improvements directly affecting the safety, habitability, energy efficiency and accessibility of their home.
14. Great Minnesota Fix-Up Fund Accessibility Loan: loans to make a home more accessible to homeowners or residents of the home with permanent mental or physical disability; no maximum income limits.
15. 4d Property Tax Classification: property tax reduction for owners of residential rental property that pledge to comply with 4d requirements for 5 years.
16. Bridges: housing subsidy for low income households that have at least one adult member with a serious and persistent mental illness.
17. Family Homeless Prevention Assistance Program: grants to support or establish support systems relating to homelessness; funds can be used in an existing home, shelters, or with the transition to permanent affordable housing.
18. Housing Opportunities for Persons with AIDS: grants for housing assistance and services to people with AIDS and/or related diseases and their families.
19. Low and Moderate Income Rental Program: funds for the refinance or rehabilitation OR acquisition/rehabilitation or new construction of existing properties for low income people; funds for the acquisition and rehabilitation or new construction/conversion of rental housing for low and moderate income people.
20. Metropolitan Housing Resource Program: funds to acquire, construct, rehabilitate and develop rental housing affordable to low income families in the 7 county metro area.
21. Nonprofit Capacity Building Revolving Loan Program: funds to nonprofits for predevelopment costs of housing projects for low and moderate income people.
22. Publicly-Owned Neighborhood Land Trust Program: no interest deferred loans to cities to acquire, construct, or rehabilitate housing using a land trust model.
23. Rental Assistance for Family Stabilization: rental assistance to families on public service enrolled in self-sufficiency programs that reside in specified counties.
24. Shelter Plus Care: rental housing assistance and supportive services to homeless persons with disabilities and their families.

Mississippi

Mississippi Home Corporation
840 River Place, Suite 605
PO Box 23369
Jackson, MS 39225
601-718-4642
Fax: 601-718-4643
E-mail: emailus@mshc.com
www.mshomecorp.com

1. Housing Tax Credit Program: tax credits for owners of low income rental housing
2. Downpayment Assistance Program: for lower income buyers who can afford mortgage payments but not a downpayment
3. Mortgage Revenue Bond Program: interest rate at or below market rate and 3% downpayment assistance.
4. Mortgage Credit Certificate Program: reduction of the amount of Federal Income Tax paid by income eligible borrowers.

5. HomeRun: loan for downpayment and closing costs to low to moderate income first time homebuyers.
6. Employer-Assisted Housing for Teachers-Program: down payment and closing cost assistance to licensed teachers that teach in a specified area.
7. Mississippi Affordable Housing Development Fund: loans to owners for construction, mortgage, predevelopment costs and rehabilitation of housing for moderate income households.

Missouri

Missouri Housing Development Commission
3435 Broadway
Kansas City, MO 64111
816-759-6600
TDD: 816-756-2477
E-mail:infor@mhdc.com
www.mhdc.com

1. Low Income Housing Tax Credit Program: tax credits for owners of low income rental housing.
2. Section 8 Certificates and Voucher Program: rental assistance for low income tenants.
3. HOME Rental Housing Production Program: provides financing for the acquisition and rehabilitation of housing for low and moderate income families.
4. Mortgage Revenue Bond Program: mortgage financing at interest rates below conventional market rates.
5. MHDC Rental Housing Production Program: funding to developers who acquire rehabilitate and/or construct rental housing for low and moderate income families.
6. Affordable Housing Assistance Program: tax credit for firms that donate cash, services, or property to a non-profit community organization that develops affordable housing.
7. Next Step: down payment assistance up to 20% of the sale price at no interest for income eligible home buyers in a target area.
8. Rural Growth Home Loan Program: loans to developers single family homes in rural areas.
9. MISSOURI Housing Trust Fund: funds for eligible activities to meet the housing needs of very low income families; activities include rental housing production, housing and related services for the homeless, and rental subsidies.
10. Affordable Housing Rental Assistance Program: rental assistance programs for income eligible families, homeless, and others.

Montana

Montana Board of Housing
836 Front Street
Helena, MT 59620
406-444-3040
http://commerce.state.mt.us/Housing

1. Homebuyers Cash Assistance Program: assist those creditworthy, income eligible persons lacking the financial assistance to purchase a home under any other program.
2. Low Income Housing Tax Credit Program: federal tax credits for owners of low income housing.
3. Reverse Annuity Mortgage Loans: home equity loans for lower income senior 68+ homeowners.
4. Recycled Single Family Mortgage Program: assists lower income households who cannot purchase homes through the Single-Family Mortgage Program; grant funds help lower construction costs for developers, reduce home prices, create low interest loans, and assist with downpayments and closing costs.
5. Disabled Accessible Affordable Homeownership Program: assists people with disabilities to acquire affordable architecturally accessible homes enabling them to live independently.
6. Risk Sharing Program: permanent mortgage financing for affordable rental housing to low income people.
7. General Obligation Program: mortgage underwriting, loan management, and financing for affordable rental housing developments that rent to low income families.
8. Single Family Bond Program: assists low and moderate income people in the purchase of a first home; in targeted areas it does not need to be a first time purchase.

9. HOME Program: funds to government and community housing organizations to create affordable housing, and provide financial and technical assistance for low income persons.
10. Section 8 Housing Program: subsidies for rent and utilities to very low income families.

Nebraska
Nebraska Investment Finance Authority
200 Commerce Court
1230 "O" Street
Lincoln, NE 68508
402-434-3900
800-204-NIFA
TDD: 800-833-7352
www.nifa.org/
1. Agricultural Finance Programs: low interest rate loans to farmers and ranchers.
2. Low Income Housing Tax Credit Program: federal tax credits for owners of low income housing
3. Single Family Home Ownership Program: loans for first time homebuyers that are income eligible.
4. Affordable Housing Trust Fund: funds to help low income households obtain affordable housing.
5. Technical Assistance Review Process (TARP): provides technical assistance on financial resources, applications, housing projects and more.
6. Homebuyer Assistance Program: downpayment and closing cost assistance to participants of the Single Family Program Mortgage.
7. Community Empowerment Resource Fund: development of affordable small rental projects in rural areas for low and moderate income people.

Nevada
Nevada Housing Division
1802 North Carson St., Suite 154
Carson City, NV 89701
775-687-4258
800-227-4960
Email: nhd@govmail.state.nv.us
www.state.nv.us/b&i/hd/index.htm
1. Single Family Mortgage Program: loans to moderate income families with no previous home ownership interest in the past 3 years.
2. Down Payment and Closing Cost Loan Program: loans to income qualified people to help with down payment and closing cost.
3. Multi-Family Project Bond Financing Program: funding to developers of affordable housing projects.
4. Federal Tax Credit Program: tax credits to developers of low and very low income housing.
5. HOME Program: federally funded programs to expand the number of rental housing and improve ownership opportunities for low income people.
6. Low Income Housing Trust Fund: provides matching funds for the HOME Program; funding to counties for emergency assistance for needy families and to expand the supply of rental housing and homeownership opportunities.

New Hampshire
New Hampshire Financing Authority
P.O. Box 5087
Manchester, NH 03108
702-687-5747
800-640-7239
TDD: 603-472-2089
Fax: 603-472-8501
www.nhhfa.org

1. Single-Family Mortgage Program: low interest mortgage funds to qualifying individuals and households.
2. Affordable Housing Fund: funds to support rental housing, group homes and manufactured housing co-ops for low income people.
3. Home Keeper/ Home Equity Conversion Program: loans to help seniors meet living and medical expenses while retaining ownership and residence in their own homes.
4. Section 8 Housing Choice Rental Assistance Program: rental assistance for low income households.
5. Low Income Housing Tax Credit Program: tax credits for owners of low income rental housing.
6. Supportive Services Program: technical assistance and training to managers of senior housing complexes so that they can provide quality supportive services for seniors.
7. Home of Your Own Program: provides homeownership opportunities for developmentally disabled people that are income eligible.
8. HOME Rental Housing Production Program: provides funds to support the development of rental housing opportunities for low and very low income households.
9. First-Time Home Buyer Seminars: free seminars on the process of buying a home.
10. HELP Program (Housing Expense Loan Program): closing cost funds to income eligible home buyers.
11. Purchase/Rehab Program: loans to eligible new homebuyers to make improvements to a home in need of repair.
12. Mortgage Assistance Program (MAP): monthly mortgage subsidies to very low income borrowers with minor children in the household.
13. Special Needs Housing: permanent financing for the development of rental housing for low and very low income special needs people that also provide social services.
14. Housing Finance Fund: funds for short-term construction and bridge financing for new or rehabilitated rental housing.
15. Tax Exempt Bond Financing: for multifamily housing that rents to moderate, low and very low income people.
16. Housing to Work Rental Assistance Program: rental assistance to families that either are eligible or are currently receiving TANF funds and sign an employment agreement.
17. Family Self Sufficiency Program: families receiving Section 8 rental assistance that participate in a program to become economically self sufficient.
18. HOPE-EI Program: section 8 rental assistance and supportive services for frail seniors so they can remain in independent living.
19. Section 8 New Construction/Substantial Rehabilitation: rental assistance to eligible persons that live in housing complexes financed by NHFA's tax exempt bonds or other public, private sources.
20. Emergency Housing Program: short term rental assistance to eligible households when municipalities cannot help them.

New Jersey

New Jersey Housing and Mortgage Finance Agency
6375 Clinton Avenue
Trenton, NJ 08650-2085
609-278-7400
800-NJ-HOUSE
www.state.nj.us/dca/hmfa/

1. Home Buyers Program: low interest loans to urban area, income eligible, first-time buyers with a 3% downpayment.
2. Home Plus Program: low rate financing for income-eligible first time home buyers in urban areas that need immediate home improvements.
3. Home Ownership for Performing Employees (HOPE): employer guaranteed below market, fixed rate loans to eligible employees.
4. Mortgage Opportunity Program (MOP): first time income eligible homebuyers or buyers in targeted urban areas, can finance the entire loan including closing costs for newly constructed, fee simple, non-condominium housing.
5. One Hundred Percent Mortgage Program: no down payment of mortgage insurance loans for qualified first time and urban area buyers ate pre-approved single family housing developments.
6. Police and Fireman's Retirement System Mortgage Program: loans for active members of the New Jersey Police

and Fireman's Retirement System with at least 1 year of active duty for purchase or refinancing of a home.

7. Purchase/Rehabilitation Mortgage Program: below market rate financing to qualified first time buyers and urban target area buyers that purchase and rehabilitate a home or rehabilitate a presently owned home.
8. Reverse Mortgage Program: allows senior to access the equity in their home without a monthly repayment schedule; counseling is required.
9. Too Good, But It's True: 5% fixed rate mortgage with 0 points to buyers of homes in designated neighborhoods.
10. Upstairs-Downtown Mortgages: below market rate funds to acquire and rehabilitate, or refinance and rehabilitate residential structures with a store-front commercial component.
11. Urban Home Ownership Recovery Program; construction financing for developers of urban for sale housing.

New Mexico
New Mexico Mortgage Finance Authority
344 4th Street, SW
Albuquerque, NM 87102
505-843-6880
800-444-6880
www.nmmfa.org

1. Help Program: loans to first-time, income eligible home buyers who participate in the Mortgage Saver Home Program for downpayment and closing costs.
2. Helping Hand Program: downpayment and closing cost assistance to low income families where a member has a disability.
3. Mortgage Saver Program: below market loans to first time home buyers.
4. Housing Tax Credit Program: federal tax credits for owners of low income rental housing.
5. Mortgage Saver Plus: buyers that choose the higher rate get credit towards closing costs up to 3.5% of the principal.
6. Payment Saver Program: first time, income eligible, buyers get a below market interest rate and a 2nd 0% interest loan to pay for up-front costs.
7. Building Trust: assistance to Native American families or individuals from federally recognized tribes, to buy, build, or repair a home on trust land.
8. Housing Opportunities for Person with AIDS: provides housing and supportive services to person with AIDS/HIV; funding to enhance and expand housing opportunities for people with AIDS/HIV.
9. Rural Choice Program: assistance to people that have not owned a home in the past 3 years that purchase one in specified rural areas; 0% interest loan for up front costs and downpayments.
10. Section 8 Assisted Housing Program: permanent financing for 5 multi family housing projects in specified areas.
11. State Homeless Assistance Program: assistance to shelters that provide emergency shelter or short term services to homeless people and their families.
12. Weatherization Assistance Program: assistance to low income homeowners to improve the energy efficiency of their homes.
13. 501(c) (3) Bond Program: funds for the acquisition, new construction, rehabilitation, or refinance of residential rental projects of nonprofit corporations.
14. Build It: guaranties of conventional interim loans to nonprofit organizations, tribal, or public agencies to develop affordable housing.
15. Primero Investment Fund: seed money to nonprofits, tribal, and public agencies to develop multifamily rental or special needs housing projects.
16. Rental HOME: gap financing for projects that create low income housing and special needs projects.
17. Risk Sharing: funding for new construction, substantial rehabilitation, refinancing, or acquisition of projects with at least 16 units.
18. Emergency Shelter Grants Program: assistance to improve the quality of emergency shelters, help with operational costs, and of providing essential services to the homeless.
19. Low Income Energy Assistance Program: assistance for low income households to pay their energy bills.
20. Shelter Plus Care Program: funding to service providers to help disables homeless persons through supportive services.

21. Supportive Housing: funding for transitional housing with supportive services enabling the homeless to live more independently.
22. Tenant Based Rental Assistance Program: one time cash assistance for security deposits, utility deposits, and/or first month's rent, and up to 6 months of rent subsidy to low income tenants in order to obtain permanent or transitional housing.
23. Special Needs Rental Program: below market rate loans to develop affordable rental housing projects with a maximum of 20 units where half are set aside for special needs people.

New York

New York State Division of Housing and Community Renewal
Hampton Plaza
38-40 State Street
Albany, NY 12207
518-473-2517
www.dhcr.state.ny.us

1. Low Income Housing Trust Fund: funds to nonprofit sponsors to rehabilitate existing properties into affordable low income housing.
2. Rural Preservation Program: funds to local not-for-profit organizations engaging in a variety of activities for the benefit of low and moderate income persons in rural areas.
3. Neighborhood Preservation Program: funding to defray administrative cots of nonprofit agencies performing neighborhood preservation activities.
4. Section 8 Statewide Programs: rent subsidies for low income households.
5. HOME Program: provides funds for a variety of housing needs for low income families.
6. Disaster Recovery Initiative Grants: grants to help cities, counties, and States recover from declared disasters, especially in low income areas.
7. Farmworker Housing Program: low-cost loans for the improvement of existing housing or construction of new housing for seasonal farmworkers.
8. Homes for Working Families Initiative: substantial rehabilitation or new construction of affordable rental housing.
9. Senior Housing Initiative: funding for projects that substantially rehabilitate or construct rental housing for seniors.
10. Housing Development Fund: loans to nonprofits for development of low-income housing projects.
11. LOW-Income Housing Credit Program: reduction in federal income tax liability for project owners that develop, rehabilitate, and acquire rental housing for low-income families.
12. New York State Low-Income Housing Tax Credit: state tax credit to developers of low-income rental housing.
13. Residential Emergency Services to Offer Repairs to the Elderly (RESTORE) Program; funds to make emergency repairs in order to eliminate hazardous conditions in elderly owned homes when the homeowner cannot afford to make the repairs.
14. Weatherization Assistance Program: services to low-income households include life-saving health and safety tests and fuel consumption analysis to identify the potential to save energy.
15. Anti-Drug Program: Initiatives to control problems in housing projects cause by drug abuse, violence, and crime.
16. Manufactured Homes Park Program: evaluation of complaints off mobile home owners against the mobile home park.
17. Mitchell-Lama Housing Program: low-interest mortgage loans to build affordable housing for middle-income people.

New York Housing Finance Agency
641 Lexington Avenue
New York, NY 10022
212-688-4000
www.nyhomes.org/hfa/hfa.html

1. Infrastructure Development Demonstration Program: grant funds for infrastructure improvements that serve affordable housing projects.

2. Permanent Housing for Homeless Families: funds for the rehabilitation and new construction of permanent housing units for homeless families and for those at risk of becoming homeless.
3. Manufactured Home Cooperative Fund Program: technical and financial assistance to encourage and facilitate cooperative ownership of mobile home parks.
4. Secured Loan Rental Housing Program: funds for the construction, and acquisition and rehabilitation of multifamily rental developments for income eligible residents.

North Carolina

North Carolina Housing Finance Agency
P.O. Box 28066
Raleigh, NC 27611-8066
919-877-5700
E-mail: ksuggs@nchfa.com
www.nchfa.state.nc.us

1. Homeownership Mortgage Loan Program: below-market, fixed-rate loans for first-time home buyers with low/moderate income.
2. Mortgage Credit Certificate Program: federal tax-credit for first-time income eligible homebuyers.
3. Low Income Housing Tax Credit Program: federal tax credit for owners of low income housing.
4. Catalyst Rental Program: funding for nonprofits for front-end costs in the development of low income rental housing.
5. Single Family Rehabilitation Program; rehabilitation funds for owner occupied low income homes mainly in distressed counties.
6. Rental Production Program: financing for the construction of rental hosing for low income households.
7. Affordable Homeownership Program: loans for the purchase of newly constructed, rehabilitated, or existing homes for income-eligible homebuyers.
8. Assisted Independent Living Program: training and consultation services for developer/owners, managers, and service coordinators to promote affordable housing with services for special needs people.
9. Supportive Housing Development Program: loans for the production of transitional and permanent housing and for the rehabilitation of emergency housing for people with special needs.
10. Urgent Repair Program: grants to fix housing conditions that pose a threat to health and safety in low income homes.
11. Duke Home Energy Loan Program: funds to reduce energy costs to income specific homeowners in the Duke Power service area.
12. Lead Abatement Partnership: funds to identify and eliminate lead pain hazards in homes where children have been poisoned; technical assistance.
13. Multifamily Rental Development Program: federal and state tax credits for developers of low-income housing and below market rate loans to develop the housing.

North Dakota

North Dakota Housing Finance Agency
P.O. Box 1535
Bismarck, ND 58502
701-328-8080
800-292-8621
TTY: 800-366-6888
www.ndhfa.state.nd.us

1. Moderate Rehabilitation Program: incentives for rehabilitation of substandard housing for rental to low income tenants qualifying for rent-subsidies.
2. Low Income Housing Tax Credit Program: federal tax credits for owners of low income rental housing.
3. Home Mortgage Finance Program: low interest rate mortgages for first-time income eligible home buyers.
4. Downpayment and Closing Cost Assistance Program: 0% interest loans to participants of a single family mortgage loan from NDHFA for downpayment and closing costs.

5. Start Down Payment Assistance Program: 0% interest loan not in excess of 3% of the purchase price, or $3,000 (whichever is lower) to help first time, income eligible, home buyers with their downpayment; must be a participant in a Home Mortgage Finance Program for a single family dwelling.
6. Rural Real Estate Mortgage Program: creates a secondary market for residential real estate mortgages for purchasers of a single family, owner occupied, nonfarm, principal residence.
7. Habitat for Humanity Loan Purchase Program: Habitat for Humanity builds and sells a home to a selected family, a private lender finances the purchase, and NDHFA purchases the loan from the lender; this allows Habitat for Humanity to use the funds to build more homes.
8. Major Home Improvement Program: low interest rate loans to income eligible borrowers to buy and rehabilitate single family homes or to rehabilitate their existing homes.
9. Homeownership Acquisition and Rehabilitation Program: low-income households receive home owner education, assistance in finding an affordable home, rehabilitation funds to make the property safe and sanitary and if necessary, help in acquiring the home.
10. Homestart-Homebuyer Education Incentive Program: after completion of the course to help first-time home buyers prepare for home ownership, borrowers may receive a $100 reduction in closing costs.
11. Affordable Housing Disposition Program: the agency serves as a clearinghouse and technical assistance advisor to distribute information about available properties.
12. Helping Housing Across North Dakota (Helping HAND): funds to Habitat for Humanities Affiliates, Native American Reservations, and North Dakota Community Action Agencies to support new or existing single family or multi-family housing rehabilitation programs for low-income housing.
13. Rental Rehab Assistance Program: funds for property improvement to rental units that address the needs of physically disabled people.

Ohio

Ohio Housing Finance Agency
77 South High St., 26th Floor
Columbus, OH 43215
614-466-7970
TDD: 614-466-1940
Fax: 614-644-5393
www.odod.state.oh.us/ohfa

1. First-Time Homebuyer Program: below-market financing for low first-time, low- to moderate-income, home buyers.
2. Housing Credit Program: federal tax credits for owners of low income rental housing.
3. Section 8 Rental Assistance Program: rent subsidies on behalf of low-income people and families including the elderly and handicapped.
4. Downpayment Assistance Program: offers up to $2,200 in downpayment assistance for eligible homebuyers to purchase homes.
5. Mortgage Credit Certificate Program: tax credit equally 20%-30% of the mortgage interest for eligible homebuyers.
6. Affordable Housing Loan Program: loans to developers of low-to moderate-income residents.
7. Multifamily Bond Program: financial assistance with the acquisition, construction, and substantial rehabilitation of multifamily dwelling units and single family housing.
8. Loan Guaranteed Program: the OHFA may guarantee the repayment of all or part of a loan for costs of development housing for low-and moderate-income families and the elderly.
9. Supportive Services; provides a link for elderly residents to home and community-based service providers that help with aging-in-place, allowing seniors to control their own care.

Oklahoma

Oklahoma Housing Finance Agency
1140 NW 63rd Street
P.O. Box 26720

Oklahoma City, OK 73126-0720
405-848-1144
800-256-1489
www.state.ok.us/~ohfa
1. Mortgage Revenue Bond Program: low rate loans to first-time home buyers.
2. Section 8 Rental Assistance Program: rent subsidies for low income households who locate their own housing.
3. Housing Tax Credit Program: tax credits for new construction and rehabilitation of existing rental properties.
4. HOME Program: funding for programs that increase the supply of housing and single family new construction.
5. Transitional Housing Pilot Program: pays maintenance and utility bills at transitional homes.
6. Housing Pilot Program: places homeless people and families in transitional housing and provides them with case management services.

Oregon

Oregon Housing and Community Services
1600 State Street
Salem, OR 97301
503-986-2000
TTY: 503-986-2100
Fax: 503-986-2020
www.hcs.state.or.us/#
1. Multi-Family Housing Finance Program: financing for multi-unit rental housing for moderate, low, and very low income families.
2. Low Income Housing Tax Credit: federal income tax credit to developers who construct, rehabilitate, or acquire qualified low income rental housing.
3. Residential Loan Program: below-market interest rate loans to low and moderate income Oregon home buyers.
4. Low Income Rental Housing Fund: rental assistance for very low income families.
5. Low-Income Energy Assistance Program: helps low-income households pay heating bills.
6. Low-Income Weatherization Assistance Program: free weatherization and energy conservation services to income eligible households.
7. Energy Rate Home of Oregon: provides Oregon home-builders and home-buyers with Home Energy Ratings which can be used to qualify for certain mortgages and programs.
8. Emergency Housing Account : assistance to homeless people or those at risk of becoming homeless to pay for emergency shelter, services and housing assistance.
9. Emergency Shelter Grant: money to increase the amount of bed in emergency shelters.
10. State Homeless Assistance Program: funding to emergency shelters and services directly related to them.
11. Commodity Supplemental Food Program: supplies low-income persons at risk for malnutrition with specified nutritional foods.
12. Emergency Food Assistance Program: provides low-income households with food for home use.
13. Food Distribution Program on Indian Reservations: provides USDA commodities on the Umatilla Indian Tribe reservation.
14. ABC's of Homebuying: training course for first-time home buyers.
15. Downpayment and Closing Cost Assistance Program: assistance to low-income, first-time, homebuyers with downpayment and closing costs.
16. HELP Program: financial assistance for the development of housing for very-low-income families.
17. HOME Program: funds that provide for the acquisition, rehabilitation, and construction of rental housing targeting rural areas; home buyers assistance and rental assistance.
18. Housing Development Grant Program: funding for the acquisition, construction, and/or rehabilitation of housing for low and very low-income families.
19. Oregon Affordable Housing Tax Credits: tax credits for housing projects or community rehabilitation projects for low-income people; savings must be passed on to the tenants by reduced rents.
20. Manufactured Dwelling Park Ombudsman Program: assists park owners and residents to resolve conflicts and provides technical assistance.

Pennsylvania

Housing Finance Agency
2101 North Front Street
P.O. Box 8029
Harrisburg, PA 17105
717-780-3800
TDD: 717-780-1869
www.phfa.org

1. Homeowners Emergency Assistance Program: loans to keep delinquent homeowners from losing their homes to foreclosure.
2. PennHOMES Program: provides interim and permanent mortgage financing to developers of low income rental housing
3. Lower Income Home Ownership Program: provides mortgage loans to low income first time homebuyers that have children or a member with a disability and meet income and home purchase price guidelines.
4. Statewide Home Ownership Program: low interest financing for first-time qualified home buyers or buyers of property in targeted areas.
5. Closing Cost Assistance Program: pays up to $2,000 toward closing costs for houses that are bought by participants in the Lower Income Home Ownership Program, qualified participants must have dependent children or be disabled.
6. Hafer HomeBuyer Program: reduced mortgage and title insurance and below market rate mortgages to eligible purchasers.
7. Homestead Second Mortgage Program: non-interest loans from $1,000 to $10,000 to income eligible families with at least one child or a member with a disability, for downpayment and closing costs.
8. Access Home Modification Program: no-interest accessibility improvement loans ranging from $1,000 to $10,000 in conjunction with PHFA first mortgage financing.
9. Joint Financing Program: below-market interest rate loans to first-time buyers in specified areas of the Commonwealth.
10. GHA 203(k) Program: loans to acquire property in need of repair and to finance the improvements.
11. Purchase Improvement Program: in conjunction with a first mortgage loan , a borrower can make up to $15,000 worth of improvements.
12. Penn-Vest: Individual On-Lot Sewage System Loans: very low interest rate loan up to $25,000 for homeowners to repair or upgrade malfunctioning on-lot sewer systems in rural areas.
13. PHIF-Pennsylvania Housing Insurance Fund: provides credit enhancement for the homeownership programs to prospective buyers that would otherwise be ineligible for loans.
14. Taxable and Tax-Exempt Bond Financing: below-market rate loans to build or rehabilitate rental units.
15. Construction Loan Program: construction loans to sponsors of low-income rental housing who have permanent take-out financing from other lenders.
16. Supportive Services Program: provides on-site supportive housing services for residents of PHFA-finance rental developments.
17. Low Income Housing Tax Credit Program: tax credits to owners and investors of affordable rental housing.
18. Future Home Buyer Program: teaches high school students the importance of budgeting, the use of credit and the ramifications of credit abuse and some of the everyday legal issues they may face in the near future.

Rhode Island

Rhode Island Housing and Mortgage Finance Corporation
44 Washington Street
Providence, RI 02903
401-751-5566
TDD: 401-427-9799
www.rihousing.com/rihousing/

1. Home Repair: fixed rate-loans to make needed repairs to owner occupied homes and on 1-4 unit dwellings that meet income requirements.

2. Rental Housing Production Program: a combination of financing programs to construct or rehabilitate affordable housing where a portion of the units are rented to low income people.
3. HOME Program: grants and low interest loans to encourage the construction or rehabilitation of affordable housing.
4. Low Income Housing Tax Credit Program: tax credits for owners of rental housing for low income households.
5. Preservation Loan Program: below-market rate loans to preserve affordability of existing subsidized rental housing.
6. First HOMES: low interest rates with low down payment requirements for first time home buyers; assistance with down payment costs for lower income first time homebuyers.
7. Jump Start Program: low interest rate loans with up to $5,000 in down payment and closing cost assistance.
8. Opening Doors Program: first mortgages from other banks with down payment and closing cost assistance from RIHMFC for minority purchasers; employment and credit history requirements are relaxed.
9. Purchase Plus Program: loans for income-eligible, first time homebuyers to purchase a home and make up to $10,000 worth of repairs or improvements.
10. Buy It/Fix It Program: low-interest mortgage with construction financing to first time income eligible purchasers; current income eligible homeowners can refinance their mortgage providing they make at least $15,000 worth of needed repairs.
11. Zero Down Program: low-interest loans with federal loan guaranties that allow you to borrow up to 100% of the purchase price for downpayment assistance to first-time, income-eligible buyers.
12. Lead Hazard Reduction: loans to income eligible homeowners and landlords who rent to income eligible tenants to make eligible repairs so their homes/units are lead safe.
13. EquiSense Program: low interest rate, second mortgage based on home equity that has no points or application, title, credit report or appraisal fees.
14. Reverse Mortgages Program: elderly income eligible home owners can use their home equity to provide them with tax-free income; no monthly payments and no repayment as long as they own the home.
15. Next Step Program: loans to nonprofit social service agencies for the development of transitional apartments for people in crisis.
16. Targeted Loans Program: loans for the construction or rehabilitation of affordable apartments; generally available only with first mortgage financing.
17. Taxable and Tax-Exempt Bonds: for construction and permanent financing for projects that have at least 12 units.
18. Technical Assistance Program: technical help and short-term loans to individuals, municipalities, and nonprofit groups to help preserve affordable housing.
19. Thresholds Program: grants for the development of housing that introduces person with long-term mental illness into the community.
20. Access Independence Program: low-interest loans and grants for qualified low- and moderate-income owner-occupied single family homes so they can remodel for person with functional disabilities.
21. Family Self-Sufficiency Program: job training, education and other services to Section 8 voucher holders to get off of welfare.
22. Foundations For Senior Health Program: funding for homemaker services to frail elderly and disabled residents of specified Section 8 apartments.
23. Home of My Own Program: low interest loans and grants so that developmentally disabled persons can own their own home.
24. Housing Research Grants: funding to organizations that are planning studies or research projects concerning affordable housing.
25. Youth RAP: funding for tutoring, employment and self-esteem building activities for disadvantaged children living in RIHMFC financed apartments.

South Carolina
South Carolina State Housing Finance and Development Authority
919 Bluff Road
Columbia, SC 29201

803-734-2000

www.sha.state.sc.us

1. MultiFamily Tax-Exempt Bond Financing Program: permanent financing for property being developed for low to moderate income multifamily rental projects.
2. Mortgage Assistance Loan Program: loans for downpayment and /or up-front closing costs not in excess of $1,000 for qualified home buyers that participate in one of the Homeownership Programs.
3. Homeownership Mortgage Purchase Program: below market rate financing for income-eligible home buyers.
4. Home Ownership Mortgage Revenue Bond: below market rate financing for income-eligible home buyers funded through the sale of bonds.
5. Low Income Housing Tax Credit Program: tax credits for developers of low income rental housing.
6. Section 8 Certificates and Vouchers: rental subsidies for low income households.
7. HOME Program: affords state and local governments the flexibility to fund a wide range of low income housing activities.

South Dakota

South Dakota Housing Development Authority

Pierre, SD 57501

605-773-3181

www.sdhda.org

1. Mortgage Assistance Program: provides down payment and closing costs assistance up to $2,000.
2. Single family Homeownership Program: low rate financing for eligible families to buy homes.
3. Multifamily Bond Financing Program: mortgage loans to finance the construction of multifamily housing.
4. Emergency Shelter Grants Program: financing of shelters for homeless people.
5. Step Rate Option Program: provides low interest mortgage loans to eligible first time home buyers in graduating steps.
6. HOME Programs: designed to expand the supply of affordable housing for very low and low income families.
7. Cooperative Housing Improvement Program: low interest loans for up to seven years for the improvement, repair, or addition to the borrower's home.
8. The Governor's House: technical assistance to income eligible seniors that purchase a manufactured home and lot.
9. Services to Aging Residents: services to elderly people that participate in SDHDA financed housing include housekeeping, transportation, meals and service coordination.
10. Housing Tax Credit: tax credits for the construction and rehabilitation of rental housing for low income households.

Tennessee

Tennessee Housing Development Agency

404 James Robertson Parkway, Suite 1114

Nashville, TN 37243-0900

615-741-2400

TDD: 800-228-THDA

www.state.tn.us/thda

1. Housing Choice Voucher Program: subsidy funds to low income households that find their own dwelling.
2. Low Income Housing Tax Credit: tax credits for 10 years to owners of low income housing.
3. Great Rate Mortgage Program: loans for low and moderate income first time homebuyers for homes that meet certain requirements.
4. HOME Program: federal funding to create affordable housing programs for income eligible people.
5. Great Place Program: funding for single family development to benefit eligible households.
6. Tax Exempt Multi Family Bond Authority: loans for development of multifamily housing that sets aside units for certain income households.
7. Family Self Sufficiency Program: provides access to the supportive services families need to become free of public assistance within 5 years.

8. Mark-to-Market Program: owners of multifamily Section 8 properties receive help to maintain affordable housing projects.

Texas

Texas Department of Housing and Community Affairs
P.O. Box 13941
Austin, TX 78711
512-475-3800
800-792-1119
Email: infor@tdhca.state.tx.us
www.tdhca.state.tx.us

1. Single Family Bond Program: low rate financing for very low and low income first time home buyers.
2. Section 8 Housing Assistance Program: rental assistance via subsidies for low income households, elderly, disabled and handicapped people.
3. Multifamily Bond Program: finances below market loans to nonprofit and for profit developers of apartment projects that agree to set aside units for rental to low income families and special needs people.
4. Down Payment Assistance Program: assists low income families with interest free loans to be used for a downpayments and certain closing costs on a home purchased through the First Time Homebuyer Program.
5. First Time Homebuyer Program: low interest revenue bonds channeled through certain Texas lenders to eligible families purchasing their first home.
6. HOME Programs:
   - Owner Occupied Housing Assistance Program: funds to rehabilitate single family, owner occupied, homes where the owner meets income requirements
   - Homebuyer Assistance Program: loan up to $10,000 to income eligible borrowers for downpayment, closing costs and gap financing.
   - Rental Housing Development Program: funds to build, acquire, and/or rehabilitate rental property for mixed income, mixed use, single room occupancy, or transitional housing.
   - Tenant Based Rental Assistance Program: rent subsidies and security deposit payments to tenants that participate in a self-sufficiency program.
7. Housing Trust Fund Program: funds to nonprofits, local government, public housing authorities, community housing developments and income eligible families to acquire, rehabilitate, or construct affordable housing for low and very low income people.
8. Contract for Deed Consumer Education Program: class to teach consumers about contract for deed sales.
9. Texas Youth Work Program: young adults at risk get work on construction sites of housing projects for low and very low income families and also receive educational and work site training, counseling, and job placement assistance.
10. Statewide Homebuyer Education Program: comprehensive homebuyer education seminars.
11. Statewide Architectural Barrier Removal Program: funds to modify homes occupied by person with disabilities.
12. Home of Your Own Coalition: assistance with downpayments and architectural barrier removal to low income homebuyers with disabilities.
13. Texas Bootstrap Owner-Builder Loan Program: loans for the purchase or refinance or real property so that new residential housing can be built, or improve existing residential housing for very low income people.

Utah

Utah Housing Finance Agency
554 South 300 East
Salt Lake City, UT 84111
801-521-6950
Fax: 801-359-1701
Email: maile@uhfa.org
www.uhfa.org

1. CHAMP Program: combines a mortgage loan with a lower interest rate loan for downpayment and closing costs,

equaling 4% of the mortgage amount for lower income homebuyers; free home buyer education.

2. First Home Program: below market rate mortgage loans to qualifying first time home buyers; purchases made in targeted areas do not need to meet the first time homebuyer requirement.
3. Tax-Exempt Bond Apartment Financing; funds from the sale of bonds to finance affordable rental housing for low and moderate income people.
4. Low Income Housing Tax Credit Program: tax credits for developers/owners of rental housing for income eligible people.

Vermont

Vermont Housing Finance Agency
One Burlington Square
P.O. Box 408
Burlington, VT 05402-0408
800-339-5866
802-864-5743
Fax: 802-864-5746
Email: home@vhfa.org
www.vhfa.org

1. Mortgages for Vermontors (MOVE): low interest mortgages for first-time eligible buyers.
2. Low Income Housing Tax Credit Program: tax credits for developers/owners of rental housing for low income households.
3. Homeownership Opportunities Using Shared Equity: loans with stepped interest rates to nonprofit housing organizations that work together to reduce the purchase price and related costs; they agree to keep the property affordable to future home buyers by sharing any profit when it is sold.
4. Yearly Energy Savings System Program; mortgages with a stepped interest rate to homeowners that make energy improvements resulting in an Energy Rated home.
5. Construction and Permanent Loan Financing Program: financing for the development and preservation of affordable rental housing where at least 51% of the units are rented to low and moderate income people.
6. Nonprofit Housing Predevelopment and Bridge Loan Program: low cost financing to eligible nonprofit housing developers for projects such as transitional Housing, nursing homes, co-op housing, single family homes and more.

Vermont State Housing Authority
One Prospect Street
Montpelier, VT 05602
802-828-3295
www.vsha.org

1. Development Program: assistance for the development and preservation of affordable multi-unit complexes and mobile home parks.
2. Section 8 Rental Assistance Program: rental assistance to eligible person who choose their own housing.
3. Project-Based Certificates and Moderate Rehabilitation Program: a rent subsidy that is attached to the unit and not the tenant.
4. Shelter Care Program: rental assistance to disabled homeless people.
5. Mainstream Housing: rental assistance for disabled families.
6. New Construction/Substantial Rehabilitation Program: creates new and rehabilitated housing in communities without safe and sanitary housing for low income families and the elderly.

Virginia

Virginia Housing Development Authority
601 South Belvidere Street
Richmond, VA 23220
800-968-7837

804-782-1986

www.vhda.com

1. Low Income Housing Tax Credit Program: federal tax credits for owners of low income rental housing.
2. FHA Plus Loan Program: assists qualified borrowers who need down payment assistance.
3. Flexible Alternative Program: optioning for a slightly higher interest rate, allows up to 100% loan-to-value financing without mortgage insurance to eligible buyers.
4. Step Rate Loan Program: lower interest rate for the first 3 years of the loan creating lower mortgage payments for those years.
5. Home Improvement Loans: loans for home improvements with a lower interest rate, low closing costs, and no points for low and moderate income homeowners.
6. Fixed Rate Loans: lower interest fixed rate loans for eligible home buyers.
7. Virginia Housing Fund: low interest rate funds for multifamily projects available to nonprofits, minority, and rural area developers.
8. Bond-Funded Program: funding for multifamily projects that rent to low and very low income tenants.

Washington

Washington State Housing Finance Commission

1000 Second Avenue, Suite 2700

Seattle, WA 98104-1046

206-464-7139

800-767-4663

www.wshfc.org

1. Low Income Housing Tax Credit Program: federal tax credits to developers/owners of low income rental housing.
2. House Key Program: below market rate loans for income eligible first time home buyers and buyers of residences in targeted areas.
3. Home Key Plus Program: loans to income eligible buyers to help pay down payment and closing costs in conjunction with the House Key Program
4. Home Choice Program: downpayment assistance and lower interest rates for low and moderate income people with a disability, or that have a family member with a disability, that are first time buyers or are buying in a targeted area; must complete an education counseling course.
5. House Key Extra: mortgage loan for income eligible first time home buyers with a disability, or a family member with a disability in a rural area and the home is within the specified price range.
6. Mark-to-Market Program: restructuring program for multifamily Section 8 housing that is going to expire so that it remains affordable.
7. Housing for Elderly: below market interest rates for providers of elderly housing.
8. For-Profit Multifamily Developer Program: financing for developers of rental projects or new construction, acquisition and/or rehabilitation, and predevelopment costs.
9. Bonds for Nonprofit Capital Projects: funding to nonprofits for a range or real estate and capital equipment projects.
10. Bonds for Nonprofit Housing: funding to nonprofits for housing projects such as transitional housing, group homes, independent living apartments and more.

West Virginia

West Virginia Housing Development Fund

814 Virginia Street, East

Charleston, WV 25301

304-345-6475

800-933-9843

Email: wvhdf@wvhdf.com

www.wvhdf.com

1. Mortgage Credit Certificate Program: federal tax credit for home buyers.

2. Low Income Housing Tax Credit Program: federal tax credits for developers/owners of low income multifamily housing.
3. Mini-Mod Rehabilitation Program: for upgrading rental units for low income households.
4. HOME Program: funding for housing for low income families.
5. CASH Construction Program: good mortgage loan rates and loans to developers for the construction of lower cost, quality built homes that are affordable.
6. Section 8 Rental Assistance Program: rent subsidies to landlords on behalf of eligible tenants.
7. Development Financing Program: low interest rate financing including economic development endeavors for housing related Initiatives.
8. FAF Mini-Mod Rehabilitation for Existing Section 8 Programs: loans for the rehabilitation of rental units occupied by Section 8 participants.
9. Single Family Mortgage Bond Revenue Program: low interest rate financing for low and moderate income families to buy a home in a specified price range.
10. Closing Cost Assistance Program: assistance with closing costs for participants of a single family loan.
11. Secondary Market Program: below market rate loans or refinancing for eligible home buyers.
12. WVHDF Refinancing Programs: clients of WVHDF can refinance their homes for a lower interest rate or use the equity to pay off large loans.
13. Housing Emergency Loan Program (HELP): funding for structural or construction problems that threaten the health and safety of low income homeowners.

Wisconsin

Wisconsin Housing and Economic Development Authority
201 West Washington
Madison, WI 53701-1728
608-266-7884
800-334-6873
Fax: 608-267-1099
www.wheda.com
Email: info@wheda.com

1. Home Improvement Loan Program: below-market financing for low/moderate income homeowners to make eligible home improvements such as energy-conserving improvements.
2. Small Business Guarantee Program: funding necessary to guarantee conventional loans needed by businesses.
3. HOME Loans: Mortgage loans with low interest rates for low and moderate income people for first time home buyers; homes in targeted areas do not need to meet the first time home buyer requirement.
4. Tax-Exempt Bond Financing: below market rate loans for the development of multifamily rental housing.
5. Tax Credit Development Financing: long term, fixed rate, permanent financing exclusively for tax credit developments.
6. Affordable Housing Tax credits: tax credits to private investors of affordable rental housing.
7. Linked Deposit Loan (LiDL) Subsidy: low interest rate loans to be used for business expenses, including land, buildings, and equipment.
8. Agribusiness Guarantee: loan guarantee to small businesses to develop or expand production of products using Wisconsin's raw commodities.
9. CROP Program: loan guarantees for agricultural production loans.
10. FARM Program: guarantees for agricultural expansion and modernization loans.
11. Beginning Farmer Bond Program: low interest rate funding for the first time purchases of a farm, including land, equipment, livestock, or buildings.

Wyoming

Wyoming Community Development Authority
155 North Beech
Casper, WY 82602
307-265-0603

Email: curry@wyoming.cda.com

www.wyomingcda.com

1. Section 8 Rental Assistance Program: certificates and vouchers to assist low income rental households.
2. HOME Program: funds for the development of affordable housing for low and very low income households.
3. WCDA CDBG Revolving Loan Fund: for housing rehabilitation the benefits low/moderate income households.
4. Low Income Tax credit program: tax credits for owners of rental housing affordable to low income households.
5. Mortgage Revenue Bond Program: lower interest rate mortgage loan for first time, income eligible homebuyers.
6. Housing Trust Fund: financing of non-traditional affordable housing.
7. Low-Rent Public Housing: rental program of single family detached units for very-low income, large families.
8. Qualified Rehabilitation Loan: low interest rate loans for rehabilitation projects from extensive major structural repair to major disrepairs.

Free Grants, Low Interest Loans, and Tax Credits to Renovate Historic Homes and Buildings

Renovating an old house can be very time consuming and expensive. If only there were a way to get someone else to pay

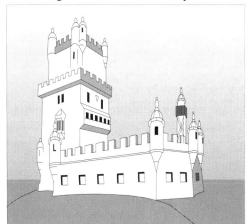

for all that time consuming work...well, there is, if you know where to look. About 20 states offer some kind of grant or loan program for individual homeowners who are renovating historic homes. Here are a few examples:

♦ Iowa offers matching grants for renovation projects
♦ Kansas offers up to $75,000 in matching grants for renovation
♦ South Carolina offers up to $25,000 in matching grants
♦ Maryland offers low interest loans for historic renovation
♦ Tennessee offers 50/50 matching grants for renovation

To qualify for these grant and loan programs, you first need to have your house qualify for the National Register of Historic Places. This isn't as difficult as it might seem. Your house doesn't have to have national significance, such as at one time being George Washington's weekend retreat. It can have local historic or architectural significance to qualify for the National Register. It could be an early example of 18th century Greek Revival style—or have been owned at one time by a locally significant family. You'd be surprised how many older houses have some sort of local significance, and that might be just enough to qualify for these programs. Contact your State Office of Historic Preservation listed below for more information about how to get your property qualified for historic status.

Federal Tax Credits

If you happen to live in one of the 30 states that don't offer renovation grants to individual homeowners, you still may be able to qualify for some types of financial benefits. Under the Federal Tax Credit Program, individuals who have rehabilitated an income producing building used for commercial or industrial purposes can receive a 20% tax credit on expenses incurred during that renovation. To be eligible for funding, buildings must be listed on the National Register of Historic Places or be eligible for membership into that organization.

What this means is that if you renovate your house and use part of it to run your own business, like a gift shop, you may be able to receive a federal tax deduction of 20% of the renovation costs. If you spent $50,000 on renovations, that comes out to a $10,000 tax deduction on next year's taxes. Not bad. Not only would you get the benefit of writing off 20% of your renovation expenses, but you'll also be able to write off part of your mortgage as a business expense.

Nonprofits Get The Breaks

Starting up a nonprofit, or looking to relocate an existing one? Think of moving into an historic building in need of renovation. Most states offer nonprofits matching grant money and low interest loans to buy and renovate historic buildings. Yes, that's right — some states actually offer nonprofits money to buy historic buildings.

Check In Often

The availability of money for historic renovation changes from year to year, depending on the state in which you live. Just because your state isn't awarding grants or loans this year, they may change within the next year or two, so continue to check the resources. Don't forget that some states, like South Dakota and Iowa, allow renovating homeowners of historic places up to 8 years of not having to pay property taxes—in the long run that could be even better for you than getting grant money.

Alabama

Lee Warner
State Historic Preservation Officer
Alabama Historical Commission
468 South Perry
Montgomery, AL 36130-0900
334-230-2654
Fax: 334-240-3477
http://preserveala.org
There are no state grant funds available to individual homeowners. However, owners of commercial property listed in the National Register of Historic Places are eligible for a 50% reduction in property taxes. Nonprofits, local government, and universities are eligible to apply for the Alabama Cultural Resources Preservation Trust Fund, a 50/50 matching grant program. Eligible funding categories include survey and registration, education and public awareness, planning for historic rehabilitation, and planning archaeological project and eligible projects are those encourage good community preservation. The agency also administers the Federal Rehabilitation Tax Credit Program. Individuals who have rehabilitated an income producing building used for commercial or industrial purposes can receive a 20% tax credit on eligible expenses incurred during renovation. To be eligible for funding, buildings must be listed on the National Register of Historic Places or be eligible for membership.

Alaska

Judith Bittner
State Historic Preservation Officer
Alaska Department of Natural Resources
Office of History and Archeology
550 West 7th Avenue, Suite 1310
Anchorage, AK 88501-3565
907-269-8721
Fax: 907-269-8908
www.dnr.state.ak.us/parks/oha_web
Email: oha@alaska.net
There are no funding programs available to individual property owners. Communities can become eligible for matching grant funds for historic preservation activities through Alaska's Historic Preservation Program. In order to qualify, the community must first become a Certified Local Government. As such, they can share in the 10% of federal funds that are passed on to the State Historic Preservation Office. The Federal Tax Rehabilitation Tax Credit is also available, it offers a 20% tax credit on money spent on an eligible rehabilitation of an income producing building that will be used for commercial or industrial purposes. Buildings must be listed on the National Register of Historic Places or be eligible for membership to qualify.

Arizona

James W. Garrison
State Historic Preservation Officer
Arizona State Parks
1300 West Washington
Phoenix, AZ 85007
602-542-4174
Fax: 602-542-4180
www.pr.state.az.us
Although $1.7 million is available in historical renovation grants, funds are not directly awarded to individual property owners. Homeowners must have the support of a sponsoring agency to apply for funding. This may include a certified local government, nonprofit organization, Indian tribe, or a national register listed district or educational institution. Matching funds of 40% are usually required. The office also administers the Federal Investment Tax Credit Program. Through this program, individuals receive a 20% tax credit on expenses they incurred while rehabilitating an income producing building that will be used for commercial or industrial purposes. There is also a State property tax reduction program for non-income producing properties and a State property tax incentive program for commercial or industrial properties. Buildings must be listed on the National Register of Historic Places or be eligible for membership to qualify.

Arkansas

Cathie Matthews
State Historic Preservation Officer
Suite 1500 Tower Buildings
323 Center Street
Little Rock, AR 72201
501-324-9184
Fax: 501-324-9184
www.arkansaspreservation.org
E-mail: infor@arkansaspreservation.org
Owners of historic homes can apply for a 50/50 matching grant from the Historic Preservation Restoration Program. The property must be listed on the Arkansas Register of Historic Places and if the grant will make it eligible for the National Register of Historic Places, the owner must follow through with the listing. The Federal Rehabilitation Tax Credit Program offers a 20% tax credit to individuals who have spent money rehabilitating an income producing building to be used for commercial, industrial, or residential rental purposes. Federal tax deductions can be gained through the donation of a conservation easement of a historic structure. Buildings must be listed on the National Register of Historic Places to qualify for either of these benefits. The Arkansas city governments that participate in the Certified Local Government (CLG) program are eligible for federal pass-through grants. These funds can be used for local historic preservation projects which include the rehabilitation of local historic structures. Individuals that are currently renovating or considering a renovation can receive technical assistance. The agency will provide on-site visits, consultations, and explanations. While cemeteries are not generally included in the National Register of Historic Places, they can be eligible under some circumstances. The Cemetery Preservation Program will consider assistance to those cemeteries where there are a significant amount of older markers and where the graves contain people of historic importance, or if there is a distinctive design feature.

California

Abeyta Daniel
Acting State Historic Preservation Officer
Office of Historic Preservation

Department of Parks and Recreation
P.O. Box 942896
Sacramento, CA 94296-0001
916-653-9824
Fax: 916-653-9824
http://ohp.parks.ca.gov
Email: calshpo@ohp.parkds.ca.gov
There are occasionally state grants available to nonprofit organizations, local governments, and educational organizations. Various cities in California are Certified Local Governments. As such, they are eligible for 10% of the federal funds given to this agency. That money is used for historic preservation actives in each of their communities. The Mills Act provides property tax relief for owners of historic buildings. If the owner pledges to rehabilitate and maintain the historical and architectural character of their building, for a 10 year period they may receive a property tax savings of around 50%. This is not a state program, it is adopted by city and county governments. Another program the agency administers the Federal Historic Preservation Tax Incentive program. Individuals who have rehabilitated an income producing building used for commercial or industrial purposes can receive a 20% tax credit on expenses incurred during renovation. To be eligible for funding, buildings must be listed on the National Register of Historic Places or be eligible for membership.

Colorado

Georgianna Contiguglia
State Historic Preservation Officer
Colorado Historical Society
1300 Broadway
Denver, CO 80203
303-866-3395
Fax: 303-866-4464
www.coloradohistory-oahp.org
The State Historical Fund awards grants to public and non-profit entities. Individuals can obtain funding if they find a public or non-profit organization to apply for and administer funds on their behalf. Eligible categories include acquisition and development, education, and survey and planning projects. Funding is divided into four types: 1) General Grant: Competitive grants from $10,000 or less to multi-year grants.; 2) Preservation Initiative Grants: No dollar amount specified; 3) Historic Structure Assessment Grants: Non-competitive grants of $10,000 or less whose purpose is to prepare a historic building for assessment; 4) Emergency Grants: Non-competitive

grants that generally do not exceed $10,000 for historic properties in danger of being destroyed or seriously damaged. The agency also administers the Colorado Historic Preservation Income Tax Credit. Approved preservation/ rehabilitation projects that cost more than $5,000 and are completed within a 24 month period can receive a 20% credit on state income taxes. Properties must be over 50 years old and listed on the State Register of Historic Places or be landmarked by a Certified Local Government. Another tax savings can be attained through the donation of a preservation easement to this agency. The property must be listed on the National or State Registers of Historic Places to be eligible. There is also the Federal Rehabilitation Tax Credit Program. This is a 20% tax credit on the expenses incurred during the renovation of an income producing building that is used for commercial or industrial purposes. The building must be listed on the National Register of Historic Places or be eligible for a membership.

Connecticut
John W. Shannahan
State Historic Preservation Officer
Connecticut Historical Commission
59 South Prospect Street
Hartford, CT 06106
860-566-3005
Fax: 860-566-5078
There are no state grants or loans for homeowner's renovation projects at this time. There is a state tax incentive program, but it is only available to corporations that purchase homes in certain census tracts. There is however, the Federal Rehabilitation Tax Credit Program. This is a 20% tax credit on the expenses incurred during the renovation of an income producing building that is used for commercial or industrial purposes. The building must be listed on the National Register of Historic Places or be eligible for a membership. Another program available is the federally funded program called the Certified Local Government Program. The CLG's receive 10% of the funds passed on to the Historical Commission to be used for local restoration projects.

Delaware
Daniel R. Griffith
State Historic Preservation Officer
Division of Historical and Cultural Affairs
Hall of Records
P.O. Box 1401

Dover, DE 19903
302-739-5313
Fax: 302-739-6711
www.state.de.us/sos/histcul.htm
There are no funding programs available to individuals. The office does administer the Federal Rehabilitation Tax Credit Program. Through this program individuals receive a 20% tax credit on expenses they incurred while rehabilitating a commercial or industrial building. Buildings must be listed on the National Register of Historic Places or be eligible for membership to qualify. The Certified Local Government Program is a federally funded program. The CLG's receive 10% of the funds passed on to the Department of Consumer and Regulatory Affairs to be used for local restoration projects.

HISTORIC PRESERVATION

District of Columbia
Building and Land Regulation Administration
Historic Preservation Division
614 H Street, NW, Suite 305
Washington, DC 20002
202-442-4570
www.dcra.org/hp/hphome.shtm
At this time there are no funds available from the District of Columbia for individuals to complete restoration projects. However, the agency does administer the Federal Rehabilitation Tax Credit Program. Individuals who have rehabilitated an income producing building used for commercial or industrial purposes can receive a 20% tax credit on expenses incurred during renovation. To be eligible for funding, buildings must be listed on the national Register of Historic Places or be eligible for membership. A federally funded program is the Certified Local Government Program. The CLG's receive 10% of the funds passed on to the Department of Consumer and Regulatory Affairs to be used for local restoration projects.

Florida
George W. Percy
State Historic Preservation Officer
Division of Historical Resources
Department of State
R.A. Gary Building

500 S. Bronaugh Street
Tallahassee, FL 32399-0250
850-487-2333
Fax: 850-488-3353
http://dhr.dos.state.fl.us/index.html
State agencies, units of local government, and
nonprofit organizations are eligible to submit
applications and compete for funding. Funding
categories include acquisition and development,
survey and planning and community education. In
general, grants will provide 50/50 matching
assistance. The agency also administers the Federal
Rehabilitation Tax Credit Program. Individuals who
have rehabilitated an income producing building used
for commercial or industrial purposes can receive a
20% tax credit on expenses incurred during
renovation. To be eligible for funding, buildings must
be listed on the National Register of Historic Places
or be eligible for membership. Another federal
program is the Certified Local Government Program.
With this, the CLG's receive 10% of the funds passed
on to the Division of Historical Resources to be used
for local restoration projects.

Georgia
Ray Luce
State Historic Preservation Officer
156 Trinity Avenue, SW, Suite 101
Atlanta, GA 30303-3600
404-656-2840
www.dnr.state.ga.us/dnr/histpres
There are no state grant programs available to home
owners. However, this office does administer two
federal and one state tax incentive programs. The
Federal Rehabilitation Tax Credit Program allows for
a 20% tax credit on expenses incurred while
rehabilitating an income producing building used for
commercial or industrial purposes. The Historic
Preservation State Tax Incentive Program offers an 8
year freeze on property tax assessments when a
substantial rehabilitation has been done an individual
or business property. There is also a Charitable
Contribution Deduction that gives a one time tax
deduction to the owner of a historic property that
donates a conservation easement. For all of these
programs the building must be listed in the National
Register of Historic Places or be eligible for
membership, have approval for the project to qualify.
There are also cities that are Certified Local
Governments in Georgia. Those cities are eligible for
a portion of the federal funding to be used for their
communities' historic preservation projects and
technical assistance.

Hawaii
Don Hibbard
Department of Land and Natural Resources
State Historic Preservation Division
Kakuhihewa Building
601 Kamokila Boulevard
P.O. Box 621
Honolulu, HI 96809
808-692-8015
Fax: 808-692-8020
www.hawaii.gov/dlnr/
Email: dlnr@pixi.com
A state grant program provides funding, if funds are
available, to local and county governments, nonprofit
organizations and responsible corporations and
individuals. These are 50/50 matching grants,
although there are rarely funds for historic property
renovation. The agency also administers the Federal
Rehabilitation Tax Credit Program Individuals who
have rehabilitated an income producing building used
for commercial or industrial purposes can receive a
20% tax credit on expenses incurred during
renovation. To be eligible for funding, building must
be listed on the National Register of Historic Places
or be eligible for membership. There is also a
property tax exemption available to individuals who
won homes listed on the Historic Register. Local
county tax offices can provide information and
materials. A local government that is deemed a
Certified Local Government becomes eligible for
federal funding to fund historic renovation projects
and technical assistance.

Idaho
Steve Guerber
State Historic Preservation Officer
Idaho State Historical Society
1109 Main Street, Suite 250
Boise, ID 83702
208-334-3861/3847
Fax: 208-334-2774
www2.state.id.us/ishs
There are no funding programs available to
individuals in Idaho. However, this office does
administer the Federal Tax Credit Program. Through
this program individuals receive a 20% tax credit on
expenses they incurred while rehabilitating a building
used for commercial or industrial purposes. Buildings
must be listed on the National Register of Historic
Places or be eligible for membership to qualify. They
also have the Certified Local Government Program in
which CLG's receive 10% of the federal funds passed

on to the Historical Society in the form of matching grants. The funds are used for local preservation projects in the CLG's community.

Illinois

Susan Mogermon, Director
State Historic Preservation Agency
500 East Madison
Springfield, IL 62701-1512
217-785-1511
TDD: 217-524-7128
Fax: 217-785-7937
www.state.il.us/HPA
Email: historicpreservation@yahoo.com
Homeowners must have a sponsoring agency to apply for state grant funding. Sponsoring agencies include nonprofit organizations or Certified Local Governments. The agency administers the Federal Tax Credit Program. Individuals who have rehabilitated a building used for commercial or industrial purposes can receive a 20% tax credit on approved expenses that were incurred. Another tax incentive program for owner-occupied residences is the State Property Tax Assessment Freeze. When at least 25% of the fair market value of the property is spent on a rehabilitation project, the owner can receive a freeze of the assessed valuation of the property at the pre-rehabilitation level for 8 years. After that time, the assessed value will increase in quarter increments for 4 years. Buildings must be listed on the National Register of Historic Places or be eligible for membership to qualify. They also have the Certified Local Government program. With this, a CLG will receive 10% of the federal funds given to the Historic Preservation Agency to be used for historic preservation of their community.

Indiana

Larry D. Macklin, Director
Division of Historic Preservation & Archaeology
402 Washington Street, Room 274
Indiana Government Center South
Indianapolis, IN 46204
317-232-1646
Fax: 317-232-0693
www.state.in.us/dnr/historic/
Email: dhpa_at_dnrlan@ima.isd.in.us
Grants are available to public agencies, nonprofit organizations with a ceiling up to $30,000. These are 50/50 matching grants. The agency also administers the Federal Rehabilitation Tax Credit Program. Individuals who have rehabilitated an income

producing building used for commercial or industrial purposes can receive a 20% tax credit on approved expenses incurred during renovation. To be eligible for funding, the building must be listed on the National Register of Historic Places or be eligible for membership. With the Certified Local Government Program, local communities that have preservation zoning ordinances receive 10% of the federal funds passed on to the Historic Preservation Office. With these matching grants, the CLG's fund local preservation activities in their community.

Iowa

Patricia Ohlarking
State Historic Preservation Officer
State Historical Society of Iowa
Capitol Complex
600 E. Locust Street
515-281-5111
www.iowahisotry.org/
Email: lwessel@max.state.ia.us
The Historic Resource Development Program offers matching grants for work on historic properties, museums and their collections, and documentary collections. The program is open to individuals, nonprofit organizations, Certified Local Governments, businesses, state agencies, school districts and Native American tribes. There is another matching grant available to nonprofits, government bodies and Indian Tribes. For both the buildings must be listed on the National Register of Historic Places or be reviewed by the State Preservation Office to determine eligibility. Local government agencies that become Certified Local Governments receive federal matching grants to fund local preservation planning activities in their communities. This agency also offers a state tax incentive for substantial rehabilitation. This is a combination of a 4 year exemption from any increase of property valuation because of the project and 4 years of decreasing

exemptions. Buildings must be evaluated as eligible for membership on the National Register of Historic Places. There is a Federal Rehabilitation Tax Credit Program for rehabilitated income producing buildings used for industrial or commercial purposes. They will receive a 20% tax credit for approved renovations to the buildings. The property must be listed on the National Register of Historic Places or be eligible for membership to participate in the program.

Kansas

Ramon S. Powers
State Historic Preservation Officer
Kansas State Historical Society
6425 SW Sixth Avenue
Topeka, KS 66615-1099
785-272-8681
TTY: 785-272-8683
Fax: 785-272-8682
www.kshs.org
Email: user@kshs.org
Nonprofit organizations, city or county governments, or individuals may apply for the Heritage Trust Fund Program, an annual grant with a funding ceiling of $75,000. This is a matching grant with 80% provided in grant money and a 20% cash match required on the part of the recipient. The deadline for applications is in February. Eligible properties must be listed on national or state registers of historic places. The agency also administers the Federal Rehabilitation Tax Credit Program. Individuals who have rehabilitated an income producing building used for commercial or industrial purposes can receive a 20% tax credit on approved expenses incurred during renovation. To be eligible for funding, the building must be listed on the National Register of Historic Places or be eligible for membership. With the Certified Local Government Program, local communities that have preservation zoning ordinances receive 10% of the federal funds passed on to the Historic Preservation Office. With these matching grants, the CLG's fund local preservation activities in their community.

Kentucky

David Morgan, Director
Kentucky Heritage Council
300 Washington Street
Frankfort, KY 40601
502-564-7005
Fax: 502-564-5820
www.state.ky.us/agencies/khc/khchome.htm

E-mail: sarah.cunningham@mail.state.ky.us
The State Restoration Grant Program that is available to all owners of historic properties, including individuals. However, nonprofit organizations and government agencies that restore structures for public use generally take precedence. It is a 50/50 matching grant. They have an African American Heritage Grant Program that has funding for projects relating to African American sites. The grants are sometimes used for building restoration, otherwise, it is for research and exhibits. The agency also administers the Federal Tax Credit Program from which individuals may benefit. Individuals who have rehabilitated an income producing building used for commercial or industrial purposes can receive a 20% tax credit on approved expenses incurred during renovation. To be eligible for the credit, buildings must be listed on the National Register of Historic Places or be eligible for membership. With the Certified Local Government Program, local communities that have preservation zoning ordinances receive 10% of the federal funds passed on to the Historic Preservation Office. With these matching grants, the CLG's fund local preservation activities in their community.

Louisiana

Gerri Hobdy
State Historic Preservation Officer
Department of Culture, Recreation & Tourism
Division of Historic Preservation
P.O. Box 44247
Baton Rouge, LA 70804-4247
225-342-8160
Fax: 225-342-8173
www.crt.state.la.us/crt/ocd/hp/ocdhp.htm
At present, state funding is not available to individual property owners. They may however, apply to a Certified Local Government for renovation funding. The CLG's receive a portion of the federal funds given to the Division of Historic Preservation to be used for renovation programs in their communities. These are generally matching grants. The agency does administer the Federal Preservation Tax Credit Program. Individuals who have rehabilitated an income producing building used for commercial or industrial purposes can receive a 20% tax credit on approved expenses incurred during renovation. They also have the Restoration Tax Abatement Program available for business and owner occupied properties that are going to improve, renovate, or create an addition on their buildings. The program creates a freeze on the assessed value and property taxes at the

re-improvement level for 5 years. That can be renewed for an additional 5 years in many parishes. This state program can be used in addition to the Federal Tax Credit Program. To be eligible for funding, the building must be listed on the National Register of Historic Places or be eligible for membership.

Maine

Earle G. Shettleworth, Jr.
State Historic Preservation Officer
Maine Historic Preservation Commission
55 Capitol Street
State House Station 65
Augusta, ME 04333-0065
207-287-2132
http://janus.state.me.us/mhpc
At present, federal and state funding is not available to individual property owners, nonprofit organizations or local county governments. The agency does administer the Federal Historic Preservation Tax Credit Program. Individuals who have rehabilitated an income producing building used for commercial or industrial purposes can receive a 20% tax credit on approved expenses incurred during renovation. To be eligible for funding, the building must be a certified historic structure. With the Certified Local Government Program, local communities that have preservation zoning ordinances receive 10% of the federal funds passed on to the Historic Preservation Office. With these matching grants, the CLG's fund local preservation activities in their community.

Maryland

Rodney Little
State Historic Preservation Officer
Division of Historical and Cultural Programs
Department of Housing and Community
    Development
100 Community Place, 3rd Floor
Crownsville, MD 21032-2023
410-514-7600
www.marylandhistoricaltrust.net
There is a loan and a grant program available to individuals for projects to acquire, rehabilitate or restore eligible properties. The Historic Preservation Grant Fund has awards of $40,000 per year, per project. In order to participate in this program, the owner must give a perpetual historic preservation easement to the Trust before receiving any funds. The Historic Preservation Loan Fund is a low interest

loan. They are available on a first come, first serve basis. A perpetual historic preservation easement must be conveyed for this program also. The agency also administers the Federal Rehabilitation Tax Credit Program. Individuals who have rehabilitated an income producing building used for commercial or industrial purposes can receive a 20% tax credit on approved expenses incurred during renovation. To be eligible for funding, the building must be listed on the National Register of Historic Places or be eligible for membership. The state tax incentive program is the Heritage Preservation Tax Credit Program. The owner of a certified heritage structure can receive a tax credit equal to 25% of the qualified capital costs of the rehabilitation project. It also includes a mortgage credit certificate option. With this, a property owner can choose to transfer the credit to his/her mortgage lender for a reduction in the principal amount or interest rate of the loan. There is also a Certified Local Government Program where those local governments receive a portion of the federal funds given to the Historical Division for historic preservation programs.

Historical Commission

Massachusetts

Judith McDonough
State Historic Preservation Officer
Massachusetts Historical Commission
220 Morrissey Boulevard
Boston, MA 02125-3314
617-727-8470
TDD: 800-392-6090
Fax: 617-727-5128
www.state.ma.us/sec/mhc
At present, state grants are not available to individual property owners. The Massachusetts Preservation Projects Fund will provide approximately $9 million in matching grants over the next 3 years available to municipalities and non-profits.. Money will be used to support the preservation and maintenance of properties and sites listed in the State Register of Historic Places. Eligible categories will include pre-deveopment, development and acquisition projects. Request for pre-development costs range from $5,000 to $30,000; requests for development or acquisition

projects can range from $7,500 to $100,000. Local governments that become Certified Local Governments will receive 10 % of the federal funds given to the Historical Commission for renovation projects in their communities. Individual property owners may benefit from the Federal Rehabilitation Tax Credit Program. Individuals who have rehabilitated an income producing building used for commercial or industrial purposes can receive a 20% tax credit on approved expenses incurred during renovation. To be eligible for funding, the building must be listed on the National Register of Historic Places or be eligible for membership.

Michigan

Kathryn Eckert
State Historic Preservation Office
Michigan Historical Center
Department of State
Lansing, MI 48918
517-373-1630
www.sos.state.mi.us/history/preserve/preserve.html
Email: preservation@sos.state.mi.us
State grants are not available to individual property owners. The agency does, however, administer the Federal Rehabilitation Tax Credit Program. Individuals who have rehabilitated an income producing building used for commercial or industrial purposes can receive a 20% tax credit on expenses incurred during renovation. There is also the Michigan Historic Preservation Tax Incentive. This is an income tax credit of up to 25% for owners of a historical home that are going to start a rehabilitation project. To be eligible for funding, buildings must be listed on the National Register of Historic Places or be eligible for membership. There is a federal funding program for Certified Local Governments. They receive 10% of the State Historical Center's federal appropriation in the form of matching grants. These funds are used for local preservation projects in the CLG's community.

Minnesota

Nina Archabal
State Historic Preservation Officer
Minnesota Historical Society
345 West Kellogg Boulevard
St. Paul, MN 55102-1906
651-296-6126
www.mnhs.org
There is no state funding program available to individual property owners. The agency does, however, offer technical advice concerning restoration projects. They do administer a Federal Rehabilitation Tax Credit Program to individuals that have rehabilitated an income producing building. The credit is for 20% of eligible expenses incurred during renovation and the building must be used for commercial or industrial purposes. In order to be eligible, the building must be listed on the National Register of Historic Places, or be eligible for membership. They also have the Certified Local Government Program. With this program, cities, townships, and counties with qualified local historic preservation ordinances receive federally funded matching grants to be used for local preservation projects.

Mississippi

Elbert Hilliard
State Historic Preservation Officer
Mississippi Department of Archives and History
P.O. Box 571
Jackson, MS 39205-0571
601-359-6940
Fax: 601-359-6975
www.mdah.state.ms.us
Email: msshpo@mdah.state.ms.us
They do have a pending program called the Mississippi Landmark Program. If a property is designated as a Landmark it can be eligible for funding, however, it is not clear if individual property owners will be able to benefit from the grants. They do have the Certified Local Government Program. With this program, cities, townships, and counties with qualified local historic preservation ordinances receive federally funded matching grants to be used for local preservation projects. They also administer a Federal Rehabilitation Tax Credit Program to individuals that have rehabilitated an income producing building. The credit is for 20% of eligible expenses incurred during renovation and the building must be used for commercial or industrial purposes. In order to be eligible, the building must be listed on

the National Register of Historic Places, or be eligible for membership.

Missouri
Stephen Mahfood
State Historic Preservation Officer
State Department of Natural Resources
Division of State Parks
100 East High Street, Lohman Building
Jefferson City, MO 65102
573-751-7858
www.mostateparks.com/hpp
The Historic Preservation Fund Grant is a federal 60/40 matching grant that is open to individuals, state agencies, municipal governments, incorporated organizations, non-profits and educational institutions. The eligible activities for funding are survey, National Register, predevelopment, development and planning. These activities must be directly related to the protection of historical or architectural resources, among other things. The recipient of the grant must fund the entire project and then receive a reimbursement up to the total amount of the grant. The agency also administers the Federal Tax Credit Program. It offers a 20% tax credit on money spent on approved rehabilitation of an income producing building that will be used for commercial or industrial purposes. There is a state investment tax credit for 25% of qualified rehabilitation efforts. Homeowners as well as developers of income producing buildings can qualify for this credit and it can be used in combination with the federal credit for owners of eligible buildings. The Certified Local Government is a federal program administered through local communities. The CLG's receive 10% of the federal funds passed on to the Historical Division to be used for local renovation projects.

Montana
Mark Baumler, Program Manager
State Historic Preservation Office
1410 8th Avenue
P.O. Box 201202
Helena, MT 59620-1202
406-444-7715
www.his.state.mt.us/front.html
There is not any funding available for individual homeowners. The Certified Local Government Program is a federal program administered through local communities. The CLG's receive 10% of the federal funds passed on to the Historical Division to be used for local renovation projects. The agency also

administers the Federal Tax Credit Program. It offers a 20% tax credit on money spent on approved rehabilitation of an income producing building that will be used for commercial or industrial purposes. There is a state investment tax credit for 25% of qualified rehabilitation efforts. Homeowners as well as developers of income producing buildings can qualify for this credit and it can be used in combination with the federal credit for owners of eligible buildings.

Nebraska
Lawrence Sommer
State Historic Preservation Officer
Nebraska State Historical Society
P.O. Box 82554
1500 R Street
Lincoln, NE 68501
402-471-4787
http://nebraskahistory.org
Email: hpnshs@nebraskahistory.org
There are no state grant programs that provide funds for historic preservation to homeowners. Individual property owners may apply for the Federal Tax Credit Program if they have rehabilitated an income producing property used for commercial or industrial purposes. They would receive a 20% tax credit on expenses they incurred during the project. To be eligible, the building must be either listed on the National Register of Historic Places, or be eligible for membership. With the Certified Local Government Program, local communities that have preservation zoning ordinances receive 10% of the federal funds passed on to the Historic Preservation Office. With these matching grants, the CLG's fund local preservation activities in their community.

Nevada
Ronald James
State Historic Preservation officer
Division of Historic Preservation and Archeology
100 Stewart Street
Carson City, NV 89710
775-684-3448
http://dmla.clan.lib.nv.us/docs/shpo
Presently, there are no state grant programs for individuals. They do have a program to rehabilitate buildings that are used for cultural purposes. However, they do have the Certified Local Government Program. With this program, cities, townships, and counties with qualified local historic preservation ordinances receive federally funded

matching grants to be used for local preservation projects. Individuals may be able to become sponsored through the CLG Program for their restoration project. Individual property owners may also apply for the Federal Rehabilitation Tax Credit Program. Rehabilitation of an income producing building that is used for commercial or industrial purposes can receive a 20% tax credit on expenses incurred during renovation. To be eligible for funding, buildings must be listed on the National Register of Historic Places or be eligible for membership.

New Hampshire

Nancy C. Dutton
State Historic Preservation Officer
State Historic Preservation Office
Division of Historical Resources and
    State Historic Preservation Office
19 Pillsbury Street
P.O. Box 2043
Concord, NH 03301-2043
603-271-3483/3558
TDD: 800-735-2964
Fax: 603-271-3433
http://webster.state.nh.us/nhdhr
Email: preservation@mndhr.state.nh.us
Presently, there are no state grants available for individuals or nonprofit organizations. However, they do have the Certified Local Government Program. With this program, cities, townships, and counties with qualified local historic preservation ordinances receive federally funded matching grants to be used for local preservation projects. There is also the Federal Rehabilitation Tax Credit Program that may benefit individual property owners. They can receive a 20% tax credit on eligible expenses incurred during a renovation of an income producing building used for commercial or industrial purposes. To be qualify, the building must be listed on the National Register of Historic Places or be eligible for membership.

New Jersey

Robert C. Shinn
Deputy State Historic Preservation Officer
New Jersey Historic Trust
P.O. Box 457
Trenton, NJ 08625-0457
609-984-0473
Fax: 609-984-7590
www.njht.org/about.htm
The state has both grant and loan programs for nonprofits, government agencies, and educational institutions, however, none for individual homeowners. There are two programs that individuals can use as tax benefits. With the New Jersey Legacies Program, the charitable donation of a historic property allows for reduced estate tax as well as other tax benefits. The Preservation Easement Program gives legal protection to a historic property by the donation of an easement. It also has property and federal tax benefits. The property must be listed on the National Register of Historic Places. There is also the Federal Rehabilitation Tax Credit Program that may benefit individual property owners. They can receive a 20% tax credit on eligible expenses incurred during a renovation of an income producing building used for commercial or industrial purposes. To be qualify, the building must be listed on the National Register of Historic Places or be eligible for membership. With the Certified Local Government Program, local communities that have preservation zoning ordinances receive 10% of the federal funds passed on to the Historic Preservation Office. With these matching grants, the CLG's fund local preservation activities in their community.

New Mexico

Elmo Baca
State Historic Preservation Officer
Historic Preservation Division
Room 320, LaVilla Rivera
228 East Palace Avenue
Santa Fe, NM 87501
505-827-6320
Fax: 505-827-6338
www.museums.state.nm.us/hpd
While there are no state grants currently available, funds from the federal Historic Preservation Fund are being administered by this division through categorical projects. There are ten small grants of up to $2,000 for the promotion of preservation activities available to individuals, local governments, historic and archaeological and preservation groups. The New

Mexico Historic Preservation Loan Fund offers rehabilitation incentives to owners of registered cultural properties. This revolving loan fund combines monies of the state and participating local lenders. To obtain funding, projects must be on the State and/or National Register of Historic Places and reviewed for compliance with the Secretary of the Interior's Standards for Rehabilitation and with the Historic Preservation Division Staff. Borrowers are subject to the lending criteria applied by the participating bank. The maximum principal for a loan is $200,000 with a low interest rate and a term of 5 years. Individual property owners can also apply for the Federal Tax Credit Program. Through this program building owners receive a 20% tax credit on allowed expenses they incurred while rehabilitating a building used for commercial or industrial purposes. Buildings must be listed on the National Register of Historic Places or be eligible for membership to qualify. There is a state tax credit program that is available to homeowners and business owners for expenses incurred during a restoration/rehabilitation project. Those projects that have been approved by the Cultural Properties Review Committee are eligible for a 50% credit for expenditures up to a maximum credit of $25,000. Certified Local Governments get a portion of the federal funding received by the Historic Preservation Division in the form of matching grants. The grants fund local preservation actives in the CLG's community.

New York
Ruth Pierpont
Deputy State Historic Preservation Officer
Field Services Bureau
New York State Parks, Recreation and
    Historic Preservation
Peebles Island
P.O. Box 189
Waterford, NY 12188-0189
518-474-0479
Nyparks.state.ny.us/hist/
There are no state funds available to individual property owners. Funding to nonprofit organizations and local municipal governments made available by the Environmental Protection Act of 1993 and provides up to 50% matching grants fo4r acquisition and restoration. Also, the Historic Barn Tax Credit has established a state income tax credit which provides a reduction in state income tax to barn owners based on the rehabilitation of the barn. This office administers the Federal Rehabilitation Tax

Credit Program. Through this program individuals receive a 20% tax credit on allowable expenses they incurred while rehabilitating a building used for commercial or industrial purposes. Buildings must be listed on the National Register of Historic Places or be eligible for membership to qualify. New York also has two tax abatement programs that allow local municipalities to establish property tax abatement programs for locally designated landmarks. These will allow for the increase in assessed value of a rehabilitated historic building or barn to be phased-in over time. With the Certified Local Government Program, local communities that have preservation zoning ordinances receive 10% of the federal funds passed on to the Historic Preservation Office. With these matching grants, the CLG's fund local preservation activities in their community.

Designated Landmarks

North Carolina
David Brook
Deputy State Historic Preservation Officer
State Historic Preservation Office
Department of Culture Resources
Division of Archives and History
4617 Mail Service Center
Raleigh, NC 27699-4617
919-733-4763
Fax: 919-733-8653
www.hpo.dcr.state.nc.us
Email: hpo@ncsl.dcr.state.nc.us
North Carolina has no state funding program for individual property owners. The Division of Archives and History provides grants to nonprofit organizations and local county governments for historical preservation activities. Individual property owners can, however, benefit from the Federal Tax Credit Program. Through this program individuals receive a 20% tax credit on expenses they incurred while rehabilitating a building used for commercial or industrial purposes. Buildings must be listed on the National Register of Historic Places or be eligible for membership to qualify. Private residences that are going to take on a substantial rehabilitation of their historic home may take advantage of a 30% state tax credit. The project must be certified and the home

must be listed on that National Register or be located within a National Register district. The Certified Local Government Program funds local community preservation activities in communities that have preservation zoning ordinances.

North Dakota
Samuel Wegner
State Historic Preservation Officer
State Historical Society of North Dakota
Archeology & Historic Preservation Division
Heritage Center
612 East Boulevard
Bismarck, ND 58505-0830
701-328-2672
Fax: 701-328-3710
www.state.nd.us/hist
Email: histsoc@state.nd.us
The Restoration Grant Program is available to individuals, but it is offered sporadically. The matching grant comes from federal sources and can be used for approved rehabilitation projects of homes listed on the National Register of Historic Places. The agency also administers the Federal Preservation Tax Credit Program. Individuals who have rehabilitated an income producing building used for commercial or industrial purposes can receive a 20% tax credit on eligible expenses incurred during renovation. To be eligible, the building must be either listed on the National Register of Historic Places, or be eligible for membership. With the Certified Local Government Program, local communities that have preservation zoning ordinances receive 10% of the federal funds passed on to the Historic Preservation Office. With these matching grants, the CLG's fund local preservation activities in their community.

National Register of Historic Places

Ohio
Amos J. Loveday
State Historic Preservation Officer
Ohio Historical Society
Historic Preservation Office
567 East Hudson Street
Columbus, OH 43211-1030
614-297-2300

www.ohiohistory.org/resource/histpres
There is no state funding available to individual property owners. However, they do have the Certified Local Government Program. With this program, cities, townships, and counties with qualified local historic preservation ordinances receive federally funded matching grants to be used for local preservation projects. Individual property owners may benefit from the Federal Tax Credit Program. Individuals who have rehabilitated an income producing building used for commercial or industrial purposes can receive a 20% tax credit on expenses incurred during renovation. To be eligible for funding, buildings must either be listed on the National Register of Historic Places or be eligible for membership. Federal Rehabilitation Tax Credit Program.

Oklahoma
Bob Blackburn
Deputy State Historic Preservation Officer
State Historic Preservation Office
2704 Villa Prom, Shepherd Mall
Oklahoma City, OK 73107
405-521-6249
Fax: 405-521-2918
www.ok-history.mus.ok.us
There is no state or federal funding available to individual property owners at the present time. The agency does, however, administer the Federal Tax Credit Program. Individuals who have rehabilitated an income producing building used for commercial or industrial purposes can receive a 20% tax credit on eligible expenses incurred during renovation. They also have a state tax credit that can be used on top of the federal credit for historic hotels and historic economic development areas. To be eligible for funding for both credits, the buildings must be listed on the National Register of Historic Places, or be eligible for membership. They have another federal program called the Certified Local Government Program. With this program, cities, townships, and counties with qualified local historic preservation ordinances receive federally funded matching grants to be used for local preservation projects.

Oregon
Michael Carrier
State Historic Preservation Officer
State Parks and Recreation
State Historic Preservation Office
1115 Commercial St., NE, Suite 2

Salem, OR 97300-1012
503-378-6305
Fax: 503-378-6447
www.prd.state.or.us/about_shpo.html
Email: shpo.info@state.or.us
They offer competitive grants programs for assistance
to National Register properties when they have
funding available. Currently, there is no funding but
they hope to have it available next year. However,
they do have the Certified Local Government
Program. With this program, cities, townships, and
counties with qualified local historic preservation
ordinances receive federally funded matching grants
to be used for local preservation projects. Individual
property owners may also benefit from the Special
Assessment for Historic Properties Program which
provides a fifteen year tax abatement on increases in
land and improvement. Properties must be listed on
the National Register of Historic Places and be
approved by a State Historic Preservation committee.
This office also administers the Federal
Rehabilitation Tax Credit Program. Income
producing buildings that are used for commercial or
industrial purposes can receive a 20% tax credit for
eligible expenses incurred during a renovation. To be
eligible, the building must be listed on the National
Register of Historic Places, or be eligible for
membership.

Pennsylvania
Brent Glass
Deputy State Historic Preservation Officer
Bureau for Historic Preservation
P.O Box 1026
Harrisburg, PA 17108-1026
717-783-8946
www.phmc.state.pa.us
There are no state funds available to residential
homeowners at the present time. Nonprofit
organizations and public agencies may apply for the
Keystone Historic Preservation Grant to
renovate/restore historic properties that are open to
the public. This is a 50/50 matching grant program.
The agency also administers the Federal Tax Credit
Program. There is also the Certified Local

Government Program. With this program, cities,
townships, and counties with qualified local historic
preservation ordinances receive federally funded
matching grants to be used for local preservation
projects. Individuals who have rehabilitated an
income producing building used for commercial or
industrial purposes can receive a 20% tax credit on
approved expenses incurred during renovation. To be
eligible for funding, buildings must be listed on the
National Register of Historic Places or be eligible for
its membership.

Rhode Island
Frederick C. Williamson
State Historic Preservation Officer
Historical Preservation Commission
Old State House
150 Benefit Street
Providence, RI 02903
401-222-2678
While there are no state grant programs, they do have
a low interest loan program that individual
homeowners can apply to for restoration projects.
The Historical Preservation Loan Fund has an interest
rate of 2% less than prime. The maximum loan is for
$200,000 with a term of 5 years. The agency also
administers the Federal Rehabilitation Tax Credit
Program. Individuals who have rehabilitated an
income producing building used for commercial or
industrial purposes can receive a 20% tax credit on
expenses incurred during renovation. To be eligible
for funding, buildings must be listed on the national
Register of Historic Places or be eligible for
membership. The state's Historic Preservation
Residential Tax Credit Program provides a 10%
income tax credit for eligible rehabilitation and
maintenance costs for homeowners. With the
Certified Local Government Program, local
communities that have preservation zoning
ordinances receive 10% of the federal funds passed
on to the Historic Preservation Office. With these
matching grants, the CLG's fund local preservation
activities in their community.

South Carolina
Roger E. Stroup
Deputy State Historic Preservation Officer
Historic Preservation Office
P.O. Box 11669
Columbia, SC 29211
803-734-8593
www.state.sc.us/scdah

This office administers both federal and state grant programs to support preservation efforts of individuals, organizations, institutions and local governments. Owners of South Carolina properties that are listed in the National Register of Historic Places or determined eligible for membership may apply for State Development Grants and Federal Survey & Planning Grants. Funds from State Development grants assist preservation work on historic structures.. Awards generally range from $5,000 to $20,000. The Federal Survey & Planning Grant assists historic preservation projects in a variety of categories. The work must be done by professionals and must comply with the agencies' guidelines and standards. Both of these are reimbursable 50/50 matching grants. They do also have the Certified Local Government Program. With this program, cities, townships, and counties with qualified local historic preservation ordinances receive federally funded matching grants to be used for local preservation projects. There are two tax incentive programs available. The Special Property Tax Assessments for Rehabilitated Historic Buildings encourages the revitalization of neighborhoods and downtown commercial districts. Municipal and county governments can freeze tax assessments when a property owner finishes a substantial rehabilitation of a historic building and low and moderate income rental properties. The freeze is in effect for up to 2 years if the rehabilitation is completed within those years. For the following 8 years, it will be taxed at the greater of 40% of the post-rehabilitation assessment, or 100% of the pre-rehabilitation assessment.

South Dakota
Jay D. Vogt
Deputy State Historic Preservation Officer
State Historical Society Historic Preservation Center
900 Governor's Drive
Pierre, SD 57501-2217
605-773-3458
Fax: 605-773-6041
www.state.sd.us/state/executive/deca/
      cultural/histpres.htm
There are no state grants available to individual property owners at the present time. However, individuals, public agencies and nonprofits are eligible to apply for the Deadwood Fund which makes loans and grants available to purchase, restore, or develop historic property for residential, commercial, or public purposes. The agency also administers the Federal Rehabilitation Tax Credit Program. Individuals who have rehabilitated an

income producing building used for commercial or industrial purposes can receive a 20% tax credit on expenses incurred during renovation. There is an additional 10% credit for the renovation of buildings that were constructed before 1936. To be eligible for funding, buildings must be listed on the national Register of Historic Places or be eligible for membership. The South Dakota Legislature has also approved and eight year moratorium on property tax assessment for improvements on historical buildings. Buildings must be on the National Register of Historic Places to qualify. There is also the Certified Local Government Program. With this program, cities, townships, and counties with qualified local historic preservation ordinances receive federally funded matching grants to be used for local preservation projects.

Tennessee
Herbert L. Harper
Deputy State Historic Preservation Officer
Tennessee Historical Commission
Clover Bottom Mansion
2941 Lebanon Road
Nashville, TN 37243-0422
615-532-1550
www.state.tn.us/environment/hist/index.htm
The Federal Preservation Grant is open to individuals, local governmental bodies, private organizations or educational institutions. While historic survey projects will be emphasized, funding is also available for other projects that are needed to undertake a restoration. The agency also administers the Federal Renovation Tax Credit Program. Individuals who have rehabilitated an income producing building used for commercial or industrial purposes can receive a 20% tax credit on expenses incurred during renovation. To be eligible for funding, buildings must be listed on the National Register of Historic Places or be eligible for its membership. There is also the Certified Local Government Program. With this program, cities, townships, and counties with qualified local historic preservation ordinances receive federally funded matching grants to be used for local preservation projects

Texas

Lawrence Oaks
Deputy State Historic Preservation Officer
National Register Program
Texas Historical Commission
P.O. Box 12276
Austin, TX 78711-2276
512-463-6100
Fax: 512-475-4872
www.thc.state.tx.us
Email: thc@thc.state.tx.us
The Texas Preservation Trust Fund Grant Program
provides funding to public or private entities in the
form of two for one matching grants. Although
individuals may apply, the large majority of grants
are awarded to nonprofit organizations and municipal
governments. There is also the Certified Local
Government Program. With this program, cities,
townships, and counties with qualified local historic
preservation ordinances receive federally funded
matching grants to be used for local preservation
projects. This agency administers the Federal
Renovation Tax Credit Program. Individuals who
have rehabilitated an income producing building used
for commercial or industrial purposes can receive a
20% tax credit on expenses incurred during
renovation. To be eligible for funding, buildings must
be listed on the national Register of Historic Places or
be eligible for its membership.

Utah

Max Evans
State Historic Preservation Officer
Utah State Historical Society
Office of Preservation
300 South Rio Grande
Salt Lake City, UT 84101-1143
801-533-3501
TDD: 801-533-3502
Fax: 801-533-3503
http://history.utah.org
Email: ushs@history.state.ut.us
At present, there are no state or federal funds directly
available to individual property owners. However,
individuals may be able to apply for funding through
Utah's Certified Local Government Program.
Homeowners qualify if they have support of a
sponsoring agency. Matching funds are usually
required. The agency also administers the State and
Federal Tax Credit Programs. Through these
programs individuals can receive a 20% tax credit on
expenses they incurred while rehabilitating a building

that will be used for residences (state tax credit only),
commercial or industrial purposes. Buildings must be
either listed on the National Register of Historic
Places, or be eligible for membership to qualify.

Vermont

Emily Wadhams
Deputy State Historic Preservation Officer
Vermont Division for Historic Preservation
National Life Building, Drawer 20
Montpelier, VT 05620-0501
802-828-3211
www.uvm.edu/~%7evhnet/hpres/org/vdhp/
     vdhp1.html
Vermont has no state funding for privately owned
properties other than a state grant program that
provides funding for the renovation of old barns.
There is a 50/50 matching grant program available to
nonprofit organizations and municipalities. The
agency also administers the Federal Tax Credit
Program. Individuals who have rehabilitated an
income producing building used for commercial or
industrial purposes can receive a 20% tax credit on
expenses incurred during renovation. To be eligible
for funding, buildings must be listed on the National
Register of Historic Places or be eligible for its
membership. There is also the Certified Local
Government Program. With this program, cities,
townships, and counties with qualified local historic
preservation ordinances receive federally funded
matching grants to be used for local preservation
projects.

Virginia

Alexander Wise, Jr.
State Historic Preservation Officer
Department of Historic Resources
Commonwealth of Virginia
2801 Kensington Avenue
Richmond, VA 23221
804-367-2323
www.dhr.state.va.us
The state grant program is available for local
governments, nonprofit historical associations, and
museum organizations. However, individuals with
state tax liability may benefit from the State
Rehabilitation Tax Credit Program which provides a
25% credit for eligible rehabilitation expenses. The
agency also administers the Federal Tax Credit
Program. Individuals who have rehabilitated an
income producing building used for commercial or
industrial purposes can receive a 20% tax credit on

expenses incurred during renovation. To be eligible for funding, buildings must be listed on the National Register of Historic Places or be eligible for its membership. There is also the Certified Local Government Program. With this program, cities, townships, and counties with qualified local historic preservation ordinances receive federally funded matching grants to be used for local preservation projects.

Washington

Allyson Brooks
State Historic Preservation Officer
Office of Archeology and Historic Preservation
420 Golf Club Road, SE, Suite 201, Lacey
P.O. Box 48343
Olympia, WA 98504-8343
360-407-0752
Fax: 360-407-6217
www.ocd.wa.gov/info/lgd/oahp
At present, state grant funding is not available to individual property owners, nonprofit organizations or local county governments, although, there is the Certified Local Government Program. With this program, cities, townships, and counties with qualified local historic preservation ordinances receive federally funded matching grants to be used for local preservation projects. This agency administers the Federal Rehabilitation Tax Credit Program. Individuals who have rehabilitated an income producing building used for commercial or industrial purposes can receive a 20% tax credit on expenses incurred during renovation. To be eligible for funding, buildings must be either listed on the National Register of Historic Places, or be eligible for membership.

West Virginia

Susan Pierce
Deputy State Historic Preservation Officer
West Virginia Division of Culture and History
1900 Kanawha Boulevard, East
Charleston, WV 25305-0300

304-558-0220
TDD: 304-558-3562
Fax: 301-558-2779
www.wvculture.org/shpo/index.html
State Development Grants are available to individuals who wish to renovate a historical home. Grants range from $1,000 to $20,000 depending upon the scope of the project. There is also the Certified Local Government Program. With this program, cities, townships, and counties with qualified local historic preservation ordinances receive federally funded matching grants to be used for local preservation projects. The Federal Rehabilitation Tax Credit Program is administered by this agency. Individuals who have rehabilitated an income producing building used for commercial or industrial purposes can receive a 20% tax credit on expenses incurred during renovation. In addition, there is a state tax credit program for both residential and commercial property owners that undergo a rehabilitation project. To be eligible for funding, buildings must be either listed on the National Register of Historic Places, or be eligible for membership.

Wisconsin

Jeff Dean
State Historic Preservation Officer
Historic Preservation Division
State Historical Society
Madison, WI 53706-1842
608-264-6500
Fax: 608-264-6504
www.shsw.wisc.edu/ahi/index.html
There are no state or federal grants available to individual homeowners. Individuals can, however, apply for tax assistance under the Federal Tax Credit Program. Individuals who have rehabilitated an income producing building used for commercial or industrial purposes can receive a 20% tax credit on expenses incurred during renovation. To be eligible for funding, buildings must be either listed on the National Register of Historic Places, or be eligible for membership. There is also the Certified Local Government Program. With this program, cities, townships, and counties with qualified local historic preservation ordinances receive federally funded matching grants to be used for local preservation projects.

Wyoming

Wendy Bredehoft

State Historic Preservation Officer
Barrett Building
2301 Central Avenue, 3rd Floor
Cheyenne, WY 82002
307-777-7697
Fax: 307-777-6241
http://spacr.state.wy.us/cr/shpo
There are currently no state or federal grant programs available to individuals. Individuals can, however, apply for tax assistance under the Federal Tax Credit Program. Those who have rehabilitated an income producing building used for commercial or industrial purposes can receive a 20% tax credit on expenses incurred during renovation. To be eligible for funding, buildings must be either listed on the National Register of Historic Places, or be eligible for membership. There is also the Certified Local Government Program. With this program, cities, townships, and counties with qualified local historic preservation ordinances receive federally funded matching grants to be used for local preservation projects.

More Housing Money

Just when you thought there were no other places to turn, we have uncovered even more resources and services you can use for all your housing needs. Need help with your heating bill? What about a new paint job on your house? Is your house a safe place to live? All these questions are answered and more. There are even places you can call if you are falling behind in your mortgage payments!

"WOW!...The Government Will Pay My Mortgage"

You'd never have thought to ask, would you?

There are now programs that will make your mortgage payments for you when you get into financial trouble. For example, Pennsylvania law, 35 P.S. § 1680.401 et seq., states it will provide "*mortgage assistance payments to homeowners who are in danger of losing their homes through foreclosure and through no fault of their own and who have a reasonable prospect of resuming mortgage payments within the prescribed time frame.*" Pennsylvania calls it the ***"Homeowners' Emergency Mortgage Assistance Program."***

One of the best ways to find out if there are programs like this in your area is to contact the local HUD approved Housing Counseling agencies. To find your closest agency, contact your state housing office, the Housing Counseling Center locator at 1-888-466-3487; {www.hud.gov/hsgcoun.html}, or Housing Counseling Clearinghouse, P.O. Box 9057, Gaithersburg, MD 20898; 800-217-6970; Fax: 301-519-6655.

Free Home Owner Calculators at {www.homepath.com/cgi-bin/ WebObjects-4/HomePathWOF/ wa/calculator}

- How Much Is Your Monthly Payment?

- How Much House Can You Afford?

- What Monthly Payment Is Needed for a House with a Specific Sales Price?

- How Much House Can You Afford with a Specific Monthly Payment?

- Is Now A Good Time To Refinance?

If your local agency doesn't have money to pay your mortgage, they will certainly help you work out other arrangements with your mortgage company.

FREE MONEY FOR CLOSING COSTS AND A DOWN PAYMENT

Houston has a program that offers $4,000 in down-payment and closing costs through their First-Time Homebuyers Program. Iowa offers up to $2,750 in grants for a down-payment. You can be earning up to $65,000 a year and still be eligible for the money in their Down Payment/Closing Cost Grant Program. Many cities, like Minneapolis, will offer interest free loans, called Equity Participation Loans, for up to 10% of the cost of the home. You pay back the money when you sell the house.

Programs vary from state to state and city to city. Contact your city government, your county government, and your local community development office to learn about local programs. If you have trouble locating your local community development office, the following organizations may be able to help:

❑ National Association of Housing and Redevelopment Officials, 630 Eye St, NW, Washington, DC 20001; 202-289-3500, 877-866-2476; Fax: 202-289-8181; {www.nahro.org}

❑ Information Center, Office of Community Planning and Development, P.O. Box 7189, Gaithersburg, MD 20898; 800-998-9999, Fax: 301-519-5027; {www.comcon.org}

❑ Also be sure to contact your state housing office listed in the blue pages of your phone book.

Make Money Going To Housing Classes

A HUD-approved housing counseling agency in Philadelphia offers $1,000 in settlement costs to certain people who attend pre-purchase house counseling sessions. A counseling agency in Boston offers new home buyers access to special low down-payment mortgages if they attend pre-housing classes.

There are over 350 HUD-approved counseling agencies that offer free classes and help in housing related issues including:

"The Best Way To Buy And
Finance A Home"
"Is A Reverse Mortgage For You?"
"Foreclosure and Eviction Options"
'The Best Way To Finance A
Home Fix-Up"

Who Qualifies As A First Time Homebuyer?

Most government programs define a first time homebuyer as someone who has not owned a home during the past 3 years or who is legally separated or divorced.

These non-profit agencies are trained and approved by the U.S. Department of Housing and Urban Development (HUD). To find your closest agency, contact your State housing office, the Housing Counseling Center locator at 1-888-466-3487; {www.hud.gov/hsgcoun.html}, or Housing Counseling Clearinghouse, P.O. Box 9057, Gaithersburg, MD 20898; 800-217-6970, Fax: 301-519-6655.

CUT YOUR RENT BY 50%

Studies show that people with less income pay a higher portion of their salary on housing than people in higher income categories. It is not unusual for a single mom to pay 70% of her salary in rent. The government has a program called Section 8 Rental Assistance Program that offers vouchers and direct payments to landlords. This will, in turn, cut your rent down to only 30% of your income.

Of course, there are income requirements for this program. For example, in Arlington Country, VA, a one-person household with an income of $23,000 qualifies for the program. Arlington County also has housing grant rental assistance for low-income elderly, disabled, and working families with children. Some of these programs have waiting lists, but it could be worth the wait.

To apply for these federal programs, contact your state housing authority, your local housing authority, or a community services agency. If you have trouble getting the help you need, you can contact Information Center, Office of Community Planning and Development, P.O. Box 7189, Gaithersburg, MD 20898; 800-998-9999, Fax: 301-519-5027; {www.comcon.org}.

"Get The **Lead** Out"
And Get Your House Or Apartment Painted For Free

If you are living in a house or apartment that was built before 1978, you, or even your landlord, may be eligible for grant money and other assistance to make sure that you do not suffer the effects of lead poisoning from lead-based paint.

Chips or dust from this type of paint can be highly dangerous to humans, especially children. The U.S. Department of Housing and Urban Development spends over $60 million a year helping home owners and apartment owners eliminate the problems that may be caused by lead paint.

Contact your state department of housing to see if your state has money for lead paint removal.

How Lead Paint Can Affect Your Kids

Houses and apartments built before 1978 may contain lead contaminated surface dust and paint chips, which, if consumed by children, can result in reduced intelligence, behavioral problems, learning disabilities, and even permanent brain damage. Government sponsored programs can help you inspect your home for lead paint and even get a blood test for your children for potential problems. To find out more about these programs or the effects of lead-based paint, contact the following:

☞ *National Lead Information Center*, 1025 Connecticut Ave., NW, Suite 1200, Washington, DC 20036; 800-424-LEAD; {www.nsc.org/ehc/lead.htm}.

☞ *Office of Lead Hazard Control*, U.S. Department of Housing and Urban Development, 451 7th Street, SW, Room B-133, Washington, DC 20410; 202-755-1785; Fax: 202-755-1000; {www.hud.gov/lea/leapboff.html}.

Lead Poisoning and Your Children

This publication is free along with three fact sheets, and a list of state and local contacts for additional information. Specific lead questions can be answered by an information specialist at 800-424-LEAD.

For more information, contact National Lead Information Center, 1025 Connecticut Ave., NW, Suite 1200, Washington, DC 20036; 800-424-LEAD; {www.nsc.org/ehc/lead.htm}.

Free Money To Fix Up Your Home

States, cities, and counties, as well as local community development agencies are providing grants, loans, and even supplies and technical assistance for homeowners who want to fix up the inside or outside of their homes. Many of these have income requirements you must meet. Others offer forgivable loans if you stay in the house a certain number of years. Here are some examples of what communities are offering to their residents:

☞ *Sunnyvale, CA*: $2,000 grant for disabled homeowners to fix up anything through the Home Access Grant Program.

☞ *Houston, TX*: loans and grants for major repairs through their Housing Assistance Program for the Elderly and Disabled.

☞ *Tacoma, WA*: Up to $3,500 loan at 0% interest with no monthly payments through the Major Home Repair Program.

☞ *Minneapolis, MN*: $15,000, no interest, and no payments until you sell in their Deferred Rehabilitation Loans.

☞ *Baton Rouge, LA*: $20,000 grant to fix up your home through the Housing Rehabilitation Grant Program.

☞ *Los Angeles, CA*: Free help with roofing, plumbing, electrical and heating work, painting, deadbolt locks, smoke alarms, screens, windows, and yard maintenance for seniors or disabled persons through the Handy Worker Program.

☞ *Michigan*: $1,000 to $10,000 at zero interest, to be paid back when you sell your home through the Rehabilitation Assistance Program.

☞ *Nashville, TN*: $18,000 at 3% to fix up your home.

☞ *Lane County, OR*: offers grants for weatherization assistance for weatherstripping, storm doors and windows, and insulation.

☞ *Des Moines, IA*: offers emergency repair loans.

☞ *Greensboro, NC*: has low interest loans for people with incomes over $30,000 and $8,500 grants for people with incomes up to $20,000.

Programs vary from state to state and city to city. Contact your city government, your county government, and your local community development office to learn about local programs. If you have trouble locating your local community development office, the following organizations may be able to help:

❏ National Association of Housing and Redevelopment Officials, 630 Eye St., NW, Washington, DC 20001; 202-289-3500, 877-866-2476; Fax: 202-289-8181; {www.nahro.org}

*$ & Help To Fix-Up
A Home For A Senior*

*The Home Modification
Action Project at:*

http://www.homemods.org

❑ Information Center, Office of Community Planning and Development, P.O. Box 7189, Gaithersburg, MD 20898; 800-998-9999, Fax: 301-519-5027; {www.comcon.org}
❑ Also be sure to contact your state housing office.

Your Rich Uncle Will Cosign A Loan To Buy or Fix Up a Home

Both the U.S. Department of Housing and Urban Development (HUD) and the Rural Housing Service of the U.S. Department of Agriculture offer loan guarantees to lending agencies around the county. A loan-guarantee assures the lending agency that the government will pay for the loan if you can't. In addition, the Rural Housing Service has a direct loan program that provides loans to lower income families to buy, build, repair, renovate, or relocate their home. This is called the Section 502 Program.

To investigate the programs available in your area, contact your local HUD office listed in the blue pages of your telephone book, or U.S. Department of Housing and Urban Development (HUD), 451 7th Street, SW, Washington, DC 20410; 202-708-1112, 800-245-2691; {www.hud.gov}.

To find your local Rural Housing Service, look in the blue pages of your telephone book, or contact Single Family Housing Programs, USDA Rural Housing Service, Room 5037, South Building, 14th Street and Independence Ave., SW, Washington, DC 20250; 202-720-4323; {www.rurdev.usda.gov/rhs/index.html}. In addition, you may contact your state housing office.

Money For Seniors And Those With A Disability To Buy or Fix Up A Home

The city of Houston offers $5,000 fix up money for the disabled and elderly in their Emergency Repair Program. Minneapolis offers home repair grants of $10,000 to people with disabilities who have incomes under $18,000. Nebraska has a special low interest loan program to help people with disabilities buy a home.

The Rural Housing Service of the U.S. Department of Agriculture offers special grants through their Section 504 program of up to $7,500 if you're over 62, and need to fix up your home. Programs vary from state to state and city to city, and obviously, many have eligibility requirements.

Contact your city government, your county government and your local community development office to learn about local programs. If you have trouble locating your local community development office, contact *National Association of Housing and Redevelopment Officials*, 630 Eye St., NW, Washington, DC 20001; 202-289-3500, 877-866-2476; Fax: 202-289-8181; {www.nahro.org}, or *Information Center, Office of Community Planning and Development*, P.O. Box 7189, Gaithersburg, MD 20898; 800-998-9999, Fax: 301-519-5027; {www.comcon.org}.

To find your local *Rural Housing Service*, look in the blue pages of your telephone book, or contact Single Family Housing Programs, USDA Rural Housing Service, Room 5037, South Building, 14th Street and Independence Ave., SW, Washington, DC 20250; 202-720-4323; {www.rurdev.usda.gov/rhs/index.html}. In addition, you may contact your state housing office.

$4,000 Grant To Paint Your Home

That's what Canton, Ohio offers to very low-income residents — grants to paint their house or put on new siding. They feel that an investment like this improves the value of all the properties in the area.

Sunnyvale, California offers some of their residents $400 in grant money to paint their homes. And if you're over 60 or have a disability, you can get a $1,200 grant.

See if your city or state offers a program like this.

Money To Buy or Fix Up a Mobile Home

The city of Sunnyvale, Ca will lend you up to $7,500 at 0-5% interest for a mobile home. New York State offers loans to help you buy a mobile home park or the land your mobile home sits on through their *Manufactured Home Cooperative Fund Program.* And the U.S. Department of Agriculture has what is called *Section 504 funds* that allow loans of up to $20,000 to fix a mobile home or to move it from one site to another. Here is how to contact the major programs for manufactured (mobile) homes.

◆ VA-Guaranteed Manufactured Home Loan

Contact your local office of the Department of Veterans Affairs, or U.S. Department of Veterans Affairs, 1120 Vermont Avenue, Washington, DC 20420; 800-827-1000; {www.va.gov/about_va/programs.htm}.

◆ FHA Insured Title I Manufactured Home Loan

Contact your local office of Housing and Urban Development listed in the blue pages of your telephone book, or your state housing office, or the Housing Counseling Clearinghouse, P.O. Box 10423, McLean, VA 22102; 800-217-6970; {www.hudhcc.org}

◆ Section 504 Rural Housing Loans and Grants

To find your local Rural Housing Service, look in the blue pages of your telephone book, or contact Single Family Housing Programs, USDA Rural Housing Service, Room 5037, South Building, 14th Street and Independence Ave., SW, Washington, DC 20250; 202-720-4323; {www.rurdev.usda.gov/rhs/index.html}.

HUD-man Goes After The Mobile Home Salesman

If your mobile home is not all that was promised, call HUD. The U.S. Department of Housing and Urban Development regulates the construction of mobile homes and investigates complaints about their performance.

Contact: Manufactured Housing and Standards, Office of Consumer and Regulatory Affairs, U.S. Department of Housing and Urban Development, 451 7th St., SW, Room 9152, Washington, DC 20410; 800-927-2891, Fax: 202-708-4231; Email: {jerrold_h_mayer@ hud.gov}; {www.hud.gov/fha/sfh/mhs/mhshome.html}.

Home Repair Programs

Here are a few *HOME REPAIR* programs we found that were available at the time we were doing research. Things change, but make sure to contact local agencies to see what may be available to you!

City of Sunnyvale
Housing Division
P.O. Box 3707
Sunnyvale, CA 94088
408-730-7444
www.ci.sunnyvale.ca.us/community-dev/ housing/
index.htm

Tacoma Community Redevelopment Authority
747 Market St., Room 1036
Tacoma, WA 98402
253-591-5213
www.ci.tacoma.wa.us/CityHall/cbcdesc.
htm#Redevelopment

Community Development
City of Canton
218 Cleveland Ave., SW
Canton, OH 44702
330-489-3040
www.canton-ohio.com/canton/homerep.html

Minneapolis Community Development Agency
Crown Roller Mill
105 Fifth Ave. S, Suite 200
Minneapolis, MN 55401
612-673-5286

Los Angeles Housing Department
111 N. Hope St.

Los Angeles, CA 90012
213-369-9175; 800-994-4444
www.cityofla.org/LAHD

Dept. of Housing and Community Development
300 W. Washington St.
P.O. Box 3136
Greensboro, NC 27402
336-373-2755
www.ci.greensboro.nc.us/HCD/

Metropolitan Development and Housing Agency
701 S. 6th St.
Nashville, TN 37202
615-252-8530
www.nashville.org/mdha

Department of Community Development
Neighborhood Conservation Services Division
602 E. 1st St.
Des Moines, IA 50309
515-283-4787

Low-Income Weatherization Program
Housing Authority and Community Services Agency
177 Day Island Rd.
Eugene, OR 97401
541-682-3755
www.hacsa.org

Money For Buying a Condo Or Co-op

In 1999 the U.S. Department of Housing and Urban Development will finance about $9 billion for people to buy condominiums. This is almost double the amount financed in 1997. The program is called *Mortgage Insurance — Purchase of Units in Condominiums (234c)*. They also have a special program for units in co-op buildings called *Mortgage Insurance — Single Family Cooperative Housing (203n)*.

Contact your local office of Housing and Urban Development listed in the blue pages of your telephone book, or your state housing office, or the Housing Counseling Clearinghouse, P.O. Box 10423, McLean, VA 22102; 800-217-6970; {www.hudhcc.org}.

Free Houses

Well, maybe they're not free, but they can cost you as little as a few hundred dollars a month. And maybe they're not in good shape, but many of the programs will also offer you a low interest loan to fix up the house. Some states refer to the program as an *Urban Homesteading Act*. The idea of the program is that the government gets you a home for next to nothing and you agree to live there for a certain number of years.

Minnesota has a program. Baltimore had a very active program for many years. Davenport, Iowa purchases homes, completely rehabs them, and then offers the houses in a lottery each May. You must get a mortgage, but your monthly payments are under $400 a month for a completely rebuilt house! There are some states, like Alaska, that still offer wilderness land for homesteading. Because the houses are so cheap, there is usually a lottery for eligible buyers. Contact your city government, your county government and your local community development office to learn about local programs. If you have trouble finding your local community development agency, the following organizations may be able to help:

✦ National Association of Housing and Redevelopment Officials, 630 Eye St., NW, Washington, DC 20001; 202-289-3500, 877-866-2476, Fax: 202-289-8181; {www.nahro.org}

✦ Information Center, Office of Community Planning and Development, P.O. Box 7189, Gaithersburg, MD 20898; 800-998-9999; Fax: 301-519-5027; {www.comcon.org}

✦ You can also contact your state housing office.

Free Legal Help For Renters and Home Buyers

It's illegal for landlords, realtors, bankers and others to discriminate against you because of your race, religion, sex, family status, or handicap. Landlords also have rules to follow in dealing with you as a tenant. With the proper free help you can find out how to:

∗ Stop paying the rent if your toilet doesn't work.
∗ Get the government to sue your landlord for discriminating against your child.
∗ Break a lease and not pay a penalty.
∗ Get your eviction stopped.
∗ Force a bank to give you a loan for a new home.
∗ Get your landlord to widen your doorways to fit your wheelchair.
∗ Get a third party to fight your landlord for you.

To file a complaint or to learn more about your rights in dealing with landlords and people in the housing industry, contact any of the following:

★ Your state housing office
★ Your state Attorney General's office

★ Fair Housing and Equal Opportunity, U.S. Department of Housing and Urban Development, Room 5204, 451 Seventh St, SW, Washington, DC 20410; 800-669-9777; {www.hud.gov/hdiscrim.html}

★ National Fair Housing Advocate Online, Tennessee Fair Housing Council, 719 Thompson Lane, Suite 324, Nashville, TN 37206; 800-254-2166; {www.fairhousing.com}.

Use Your Sweat as a Down Payment and Get a No-Interest Loan

One of the biggest providers of this type of program is the non-profit organization called **Habitat for Humanity**. You've probably seen them in the news with Ex-President Jimmy Carter helping them build houses. They have even received government money to help support their program. The typical arrangement is for people with incomes between $9,000 and $30,000. You and your family work an average of 300 to 500 hours building your home or other people's homes, and in return you get a home with no down-payment and a very low mortgage payment. Because people provide free labor to build the home, you only pay about $60,000 for a $100,000 home, and you get the money interest free. A typical bank loan can cost you over $700 per month, but through this program you pay only about $200 a month.

Other local or national organizations may run similar programs in your area, with or without government financing. To find programs in your area, you can contact:

⇨ Habitat for Humanity International, 121 Habitat Street, Americus, GA 31709; 229-924-6935; {www.habitat.org}. To find a local affiliate, call 229-924-6935, ext. 2551 or ext. 2552

⇨ Information Center, Office of Community Planning and Development, P.O. Box 7189, Gaithersburg, MD 20898; 800-998-9999, Fax: 301-519-5027; {www.comcon.org}.

Free Housing Books

- *A Consumer's Guide to Mortgage Settlement Costs*

- *Home Mortgages: Understanding the Process*

- *A Consumer's Guide to Mortgage Refinancings*

- *Consumer Handbook on Adjustable Rate Mortgages*

For your copies, contact Board of Governors of the Federal Reserve System, Publications Services, MS-127, Washington, DC 20551; 202-452-3244; {www.federalreserve.gov/}.

Staying Clear Of Deadly Radon Gases

Nowadays when you buy a home, you often have a radon level reading taken, but what do the numbers mean? The *National Radon Information Hotline* has a free brochure that explains what radon is, how to test for it, and more.

There is also a Radon FIX-IT Program operated by the Consumer Research Council, a nonprofit consumer organization that provides free guidance and encouragement to consumers who are trying to fix their homes that have elevated radon levels. The Program

FREE HOUSING EXPERTS

The HUD website includes text of over 20 helpful guides, such as: *How To Buy a Home, How to Get A Mortgage,* **and** *Hud-approved Lenders,* **as well as listings of government homes for sale. These are not just HUD homes, but also those from the Department of Veteran Affairs, General Services Administration, and more.**

Although the houses are not steals, you can find some great deals. For housing information, call HUD USER, P.O. Box 6091, Rockville, MD 20850; 800-245-2691; {www.hud.gov}.

operates from noon to 8 p.m. EST and has information on reducing elevated radon levels, referrals to experts, and names of contractors who are qualified to help.

For more information, contact National Radon Information Hotline at 800-767-7236 (SOS-RADON) and the Radon Fix-It Program at 800-644-6999; or Indoor Air Quality Information Clearinghouse, IAQ Info, P.O. Box 37133, Washington, DC 20013; 800-438-4318; {www.epa.gov/iaq/iaqinfo.html}.

Is Your Drinking Water Safe?

According to the National Consumer Water Survey, 75% of those surveyed have concerns about the quality of the water they drink. Many people are purchasing bottled water or water purification devices for drinking water, but is it a wise use of your money?

The *Safe Drinking Water Hotline* can answer any question or concern you may have regarding drinking water, and can provide you with publications such as: *Is Your Drinking Water Safe?, Home Water Testing, Home Water Treatment Units, Bottled Water* fact sheet, and more. Contact Safe Drinking Water Hotline, U.S. Environmental Protection Agency, 401 M St., SW, Washington, DC 20460; 800-426-4791; {www.epa.gov/OGWDW}.

How To Save Up To $650/Year On Fuel Bills

The average family spends close to $1300 a year on their home's utility bills, and a large portion of that energy is wasted. By using a few inexpensive energy efficient measures, you can reduce your energy bills by 10% to 50%.

With the publication, *Energy Savers: Tips on Saving Energy and Money at Home*, you can go step by step through your home to learn energy saving tips. Topics covered include insulation/ weatherization, water heating, lighting, appliances, and more. There is even a major appliance shopping guide that explains the energy labels on appliances and shows you how to choose the best one for you.

The Energy Efficiency and Renewable Energy Clearinghouse can answer your questions on all these topics and has publications and easy to understand fact sheets. Contact the Energy Efficiency and Renewable and Energy Clearinghouse, P.O. Box 3048, Merrifield, VA 22116; 800-363-3732; {www.eren.doe.gov}.

Volunteers Will Fix Up Your
(Or Your Mom's) Home For Free

Many service organizations have begun to organize community service days, where the town is beautified along with certain homes in need of repair. *Christmas in April* is a national organization with over 185 affiliates that gather together volunteers to help rehabilitate the homes of low-income homeowners. The work is done for free with the goal being to provide a safe and secure home for those in need.

An example of a program in the Dallas area is the Volunteer Home Repair and Weatherization Program. This program provides home repairs that improve the health, safety, and energy efficiency of a home for low-income homeowners. Contact your city government, your county government and your local community development office to learn about local programs.

✗ In the Dallas area, contact Volunteer Home Repair and Weatherization Program, Center for Housing Resources, 3103 Greenwood, Dallas, TX 75204; 214-828-4390, Fax: 214-828-4412; {www.chrdallas.org}

GOVERNMENT FORECLOSED HOMES
AT BARGAIN PRICES

No, they are not giving away the kitchen sink, but you may be able to find some good deals nonetheless. The government sells foreclosed homes all across the country, and even in your neighborhood. You don't need to know someone to get in on these deals. All are sold through real estate agents. Contact your agent, ask about government repossessed homes and they can do a search for you. These are not just HUD homes, but also those from the V.A., Fannie Mae, IRS, Federal Deposit Insurance Corporation, and more.

I want to be able to say that they give you these houses at 50% off, but I can't. Most want fair market value, but the government does not want to carry the real estate taxes for all these houses either. You can make a deal that works out best for everyone. For more information, contact HUD USER, P.O. Box 6091, Rockville, MD 20850; 800-245-2691; {www.hud.gov/homesale.html} (Note: this website has links to all the major government home sale programs); U.S. Department of Veterans Affairs, 810 Vermont Ave., NW, Washington, DC 20420; 800-827-1000; {www.va.gov}.

MONEY TO PAY YOUR HEATING BILL

Storm windows, insulation, and even weatherstripping, can help reduce your fuel bill. Families can receive assistance to weatherize their homes and apartments at no charge if you meet certain income guidelines. States allocate dollars to nonprofit agencies for purchasing and installing energy-related repairs, with the average grant being $2,000 per year. The elderly and families with children get first dibs.

Contact your State Energy Office or the Weatherization Assistance Programs Branch, EE44, U.S. Department of Energy, 1000 Independence Ave., SW, Washington, DC 20585; 202-586-4074; {www.eren.doe.gov/EE/buildings-state.html}.

$2,000 GRANTS OR 2% INTEREST LOAN TO FIX UP YOUR HOME

A family of 4 can be making close to $30,000 year and still be eligible for a 2% interest loan from local Community Action Agency. Some agencies also offer grants or are aware of other local organizations that provide grants. There are about 1,000 of them around the country to help neighborhoods.

To find an agency near you, contact National Association of Community Action Agencies, 1100 17th St., NW, Suite 500, Washington, DC 20036, 202-265-7546; Fax: 202-265-8850; {www.nacaa.org}; {www.nemaine.com/whca/housing.htm}.

50% Discount
On a New Heating System

The California Energy Commission offers residences and small businesses up to 50% of the cost of a new heating or air conditioning system if it meets their standards for "emerging renewable technologies," like solar heating, but more. Their program is called Emerging Renewables Buy-Down Program.

To learn more, contact California Energy Commission, Energy Call Center, 1516 Ninth St., MS-25, Sacramento, CA 95814; 800-555-7794; {http://www.energy.ca.gov}. Check with your state utility commission to see if your state offers similar programs.

How To Keep Your Air Clean Of Asbestos, Carbon Monoxide, and Second Hand Smoke

You don't need to hire some high priced consultants to find how to keep the air in your home clean of pollution and other toxic substances. The Indoor Air Quality Information Clearinghouse is the expert on all forms of indoor air pollution. They have publications and information on second hand smoke, asbestos, carbon monoxide, air cleaners, and more.

You can contact them at Indoor Air Quality Information Clearinghouse, IAQ Info, P.O. Box 37133, Washington, DC 20013; 800-438-4318; {www.epa.gov/iaq/iaqinfo.html}.

Free Mortgage Publications

The Federal Trade Commission understands this, so they have compiled several brochures to get you started. Some of the titles include:

Home Financing Primer, Mortgage Servicing, Mortgage Discrimination, and more.

To receive your copies, contact Public Reference, Room 130, Federal Trade Commission, Washington, DC 20580; 202-326-2222, 877-FTC-HELP; {www.ftc.gov}

Free Weatherization, Fuel Bills, and Rent for Incomes Up to $50,000

If you are within a certain income and need help paying your heating bills, need money to make your house more energy efficient, or need funds for urgent repairs, call your local Community Action Agency. There are about 1,000 of them around the country to help neighborhoods. They will also come out and check if your home or apartment needs to be more energy efficient. To find an agency near you, contact National Association of Community Action Agencies, 1100 17th St., NW, Suite 500, Washington, DC 20036; 202-265-7546; Fax: 202-265-8850; {www.nacaa.org}.

$83,000 / YR Income and The Government Considers You Needy?

Many of the government housing programs, especially the grant and low interest programs, may have income requirements. But don't let a good salary stop you from investigating the opportunities. The first time home buyer program in Illinois has income requirements that go up to $83,000.

Also, your local utility can provide you with or refer you to other programs in your area to analyze your energy usage, recommend energy saving measures, provide fuel and utility assistance to retain or restore service, establish payment discounts based on income and usage, or establish affordable payment plans if you are in arrears. Contact your local utility company to take advantage of these services.

FREE NUTRITION COUNSELING AND CLASSES

Nutrition counseling, menu planning, cooking instruction and comparison shopping is available from your local County Cooperative Extension Service. Group instruction is free of charge, but persons requesting individual lessons are asked to pay for the lesson materials.

They also help neighborhoods establish and maintain community gardens, which provide fresh vegetables to area residents. To find an office near you, look in the blue pages of your local telephone book under county government for County Cooperative Extension Service.

Get Money For Down Payments And Closing Costs Here

The following are examples of financial assistance programs offered by states, cities and counties at the time we were doing our initial research for this book. Be aware that these programs are constantly changing and all have some form of eligibility requirements, but don't let that stop you! New ones are added and old ones may be discarded.

To be sure that you are aware of all the programs available in your area, contact your state office on housing, your city housing office, your county housing office, as well as any local community development offices that may be in your area. If you need help locating your community development office, the following may be of assistance: National Association of Housing and Redevelopment Officials, 630 Eye St., NW, Washington, DC 20001; 202-289-3500, 877-866-2476; Fax: 202-289-8181: {www.nahro.org}.

✖ *Houston*: $3,500 to help with a down payment and closing costs in the First-Time Homebuyers Program.

✖ *Iowa*: 5% of your mortgage in grant money for a down payment and closing costs through Down Payment/ Closing Cost Grant Program.

✖ *Minneapolis, MN*: $3,000 at 0% interest due when you sell the home

✖ *Michigan*: $5,000 at 0% interest and no monthly payments

✖ *Baton Rouge, LA*: $10,000 at 0% interest and no payments for 20 years through Home Buyers Assistance Program.

✖ *Georgia*: $5,000 for a down payment at 0% interest through Own HOME Program.

✖ *Hawaii*: $15,000 loans at 3% for down payments, but you only pay interest for the first 5 years in the Down Payment Loan Program.

✖ *Kansas*: You only need $500 and Kansas will assist with down payment, closing costs, and legal fees in First Time Homebuyers Downpayment Assistance Program.

✖ *Maine*: Buy a house with only $750, and finance your down payment at 0% through Down Home Program.

✖ *La Miranda, CA*: 10% loan for down payment for first time homebuyers in the Down Payment Assistance Program.

✖ *Tacoma, WA*: A $5,000 loan for your down payment and settlement costs in Down Payment Assistance Program.

✖ *Indianapolis, IN*: Put 1% down and your closing costs go into a 2nd mortgage in Good Neighbor II Loan Program.

✖ *Los Angeles, CA*: 2% forgivable loan for closing costs money, plus $35,000 loan for repairs with no payments for 30 years or until the house is sold through Home WORKS! Program.

✖ *New York State*: 0% down payment in Low Down Payment, Conventional Rate Program.

✖ *Walnut Creek, CA*: Get a second mortgage for half of the closing costs and 2% of down payment with nothing due until you sell or refinance.

✖ *Washington County, OR*: $19,300 loan with no interest and no payment for the first 5 years in First-Time Home Buyer Program.

✖ *Michigan*: Move into a $60,000 home with only $600 in your pocket in the Down Payment Assistance Program.

✖ *New Hampshire*: $5,000 low interest loan for closing costs through HELP Program.

✖ *Nashville, TN*: Nashville Housing Fund provides down payments, closing costs and low interest loans for first time home buyers.

✖ *Tucson, AZ*: $3,000 loan for down payment and they will pay all closing costs with the Tucson Metropolitan Ministry.

✖ *Oregon*: $500 to $6,000 grant for closing costs, down payment, or minor repairs in their First-Time Homebuyer Program.

Free Furniture

The Community Action Agency in Albany, New York offers free furniture for those with a need because of fire or other hardship reasons. Other agencies offer free furniture if you are moving into a Community Action Agency's affordable housing or housing units operated by the agency. See if your local agency offers free furniture. There are about 1,000 of them around the country to help neighborhoods.

To find an agency near you, contact National Association of Community Action Agencies, 1100 17th St., NW, Washington, DC 20036; 202-265-7546; Fax: 202-265-8850; {www.nacaa.org}; {http://family. knick.net/acoi/}.

x   *Missouri*: Move into a home with only $750 through Down Payment Assistance for Homebuyers.

x   *Canton, OH*: Renters can apply for $5,000 loan for first time home buyers that's forgiven after 5 years through the Down Payment Assistance Program.

x   *South Carolina*: Loans for SINGLE PARENTS for a down payment and closing costs in their Single Parent Program.

NEW HOME HELP

Here's a listing of programs we found that were available at the time we were doing research. Don't forget to contact state and local housing agencies to see what may be available for you.

Nashville Housing Fund
806 S. Sixth St.
Nashville, TN 37202
615-780-7016
janis.nashville.org/mdha/housing_fund.html

Washington County
Department of Housing Services
111 NE Lincoln St.
Suite 200-L
Hillsboro, OR 97124
503-846-4794
www.co.washington.or.us/deptmts/
hse_serv/housemain.htm

Indianapolis Neighborhood Housing Partnership
3550 N. Washington Blvd.
Indianapolis, IN 46205
317-925-1400
www.inhp.org

Department of Community Affairs
60 Executive Parks
Atlanta, GA 30329
800-651-0597
www.dca.state.ga.us

State of New York Mortgage Agency
641 Lexington Ave.
New York, NY 10022
800-382-HOME
www.nyhomes.org/sony/sonyma.html

Housing Hotline
Division of Housing
Kansas Department of Commerce and Housing
700 SW Harrison, Suite 1300

Topeka, KS 66603
800-752-4422
785-296-5865
www.kansascommerce.com

Homes For Houston
P.O. Box 1562
Houston, TX 77251
713-868-8300
www.ci.houston.tx.us/departme/housing/

Iowa Finance Authority
100 E. Grand Ave., Suite 250
Des Moines, IA 50309
515-242-4990
800-432-7230
www.ifahome.com/ home_buyer.htm

MN Housing Finance Agency
400 Sibley St., Suite 300
St. Paul, MN 55101
800-710-8871
651-296-7608
www.mhfa.state.mn.us

Missouri Housing Development Commission
3435 Broadway
Kansas City, MO 64111
816-759-6600
www.mhdc.com

Office of Community Development
P.O. Box 1471
Baton Rouge, LA 70802
225-389-3039
www.ci.baton-rouge.la.us/dept/ocd/
Housing/housing.htm

New Hampshire Housing Finance Authority
32 Constitution Dr.
P.O. Box 5087
Bedford, NH 03110
800-640-7239
www.nhhfa.org

Oregon Housing and Community Services Dept.
1600 State St.
Salem, OR 97301
503-986-2000
www.hcs.state.or.us

Maine State Housing Authority
353 Water St.
Augusta, ME 04330
207-626-4600
800-452-4668
www.mainehousing.org

Community Development Department
1666 N. Main St.
Walnut Creek, CA 94596
925-943-5800
www.ci.walnut-creek.ca.us

South Carolina State Housing Finance and
Development Authority
919 Bluff Rd.
Columbia, SC 29201
803-734-2207
www.sha.state.sc.us

Housing and Community Development Corporation
677 Queen St., Suite 300
Honolulu, HI 96813
808-587-0567
www.hawaii.gov/hfdc.html

MONEY FOR YOUR TRAVELS

If your dream is to become an international jet setter, don't let a little problem like money stand in your way. The Federal government has over 60 programs devoted to travel within the U.S. and abroad, spending over 65 million dollars a year to send you packing. They will even pay to have foreign relatives come and study here. No matter if you are 16 or 65, there is something in these programs for everyone.

You can be like:

- Cowboy artists from the Western Folklife Center of Elko, NV who shared their lore at a festival in Melbourne, Australia with a grant from the National Endowment for the Arts.
- Nancy Friese of Cranston, RI who went to Japan for six months to explore relationships between natural and man-made environments in Japanese landscape gardens through the United States/Japan Artist Exchange Program at the Japan/US Friendship Commission.
- Carl A. Chase, a steel drum maker and tuner from Brooksville, MA who was able to visit Trinidad and Tobago for a residency with one of the islands' foremost steel drum makers through the Travel Grants Program at the National Endowment for the Arts.
- William Ulfelder who spent a year studying the rain forest in Costa Rica as a Fulbright Scholar.
- A police officer from Los Angeles who helped in the creation of D.A.R.E. (Drug Awareness Resistance Education) in several Latin American countries through the U. S. Thematic Programs.
- Piano/violin duo Susan Keith and Laura Kobayashi who toured Latin America and the Caribbean together as Artistic Ambassadors for the U.S. Information Agency.
- Tamara Astor from Northfield, IL who spent a year teaching grades 1-3 in London, England through the Fulbright Teacher Exchange Program at the U.S. Information Agency.
- Central Washington University who sent thirteen K-12 teachers from the state of Washington to Chile for a four-week seminar on the country through the Fulbright-Hays Group Projects Abroad through the U.S. Department of Education.
- Columbia University in New York City acting as the host of seven different humanities seminars for college teachers with grants from the National Endowment for the Humanities.
- Maria Marotti from Santa Barbara, CA who was awarded a $3,000 grant from the National Endowment for the Humanities to study Italian feminism.

Now don't forget to read the first part of this book, "Types of Assistance and Grants Sources," as well as "More Help In Finding a Grant." These sections provide some great starting places for your money hunt. Many of the programs listed below were taken from the *Catalog of Federal Domestic Assistance*. When you see a five digit number like 10.078 after a program title, that refers to the program number in the Catalog. Most libraries have a copy of the Catalog that lists every program the Federal government offers. You can also search the Catalog by number or keyword at {www.cfda.gov}.

Don't forget that you vote for your Senator and your Representative. They want you to vote for them again, so they will do whatever they can to assist you in your cause. You can contact their local office, again by looking in the blue pages of your phone book, or Your Senator, The Senate, Washington, DC 20510; 202-224-3121; {www.senate.gov}; or your Representative, The United States House of Representatives, Washington, DC 20515;

202-224-3121; {www.house.gov}. The federal government has even created a special website called U.S. Consumer Gateway at {www.consumer.gov} that provides links to information by type, topic, current issues, hotlinks, and more. This is a great resource for gathering contacts.

Happy hunting!

High School Students And Teachers Can Visit Russia
(Secondary School Exchange Initiative)
Youth Programs Division
Bureau of Citizen Exchanges
Bureau of Educational and Cultural Affairs
301 4th St., SW
Washington, DC 20547
202-619-6299
Fax: 202-619-5331
http://exchanges.state.gov/education
The program objective is to sponsor the exchange of high school students and teachers between the U.S. and the former Soviet Union through grants to private not-for-profit organizations and public institutions. Grants are awarded to fund projects in two program areas: academic year in the U.S., and short-term exchanges of groups of students and teachers between linked schools. The total amount of money available is $15 million. Contact the office listed above for information on organizations to which you need to apply or for more information on the programs available.

Spend A Year In Europe On A Mid-Career Break
(Hubert Humphrey Fellowship)
Hubert H. Humphrey Fellowship Program
Institute of International Education
1400 K St., NW, Suite 650
Washington, DC 20005-2403
202-619-5289
202-326-7701
Fax: 202-326-7702
www.iie.org/pgms/hhh
The program provides opportunities for accomplished mid-career professionals from developing countries, East and Central Europe, and the former Soviet Union to come to the United States for a year of study and related practical professional experiences. The program provides a basis for establishing lasting ties between citizens of the United States and their professional counterparts in other countries, fostering an exchange of knowledge and mutual understanding throughout the world. Fellows are placed in groups at selected U.S.

universities and design individualized programs of academic coursework and professional development activities. The total amount of money available is $5 million. Applications must be submitted in the candidates' home countries to the United States Information Service Posts or Fulbright Commissions. Applicants must have an undergraduate degree, five years of substantial professional experience, demonstrated leadership qualities, and fluency in English. Contact the office listed above for more information on the application process.

Money For Artists, Filmmakers, Playwrights, And Museum Professionals To Go Overseas
Cultural Programs Division
Bureau of Educational and Cultural Affairs
U.S. Department of State
301 4th St., SW
Washington, DC 20547
202-619-4779
http://exchanges.state. gov/education
The program supports projects by U.S. nonprofit organizations for exchanges of professionals in the arts and museum fields. Priority is given to institutionally-based projects involving artists in the creation of their particular art forms and projects  which will lead to institutional linkages. Two way exchanges are encouraged and cost sharing is required. This exchange program is designed to introduce American and foreign participants to each other's cultural and artistic life and traditions. It also supports international projects in the United States or overseas involving composers, choreographers, filmmakers, playwrights, theater designers, writers and poets, visual artists, museum professionals, and more. The program operates through biannual Federal Register requests for proposals. For more information on the application process and program eligibility, contact the office listed above.

Money For Students, Teachers, Bankers, Lawyers, And Journalists To Travel Overseas

(Fulbright Scholar Program)
Council for International Exchange of Scholars
3007 Tilden St., NW, Suite 5L
Box GBRO
Washington, DC 20008-3009
202-686-4000
Fax: 202-362-3442
www.iie.org/cies

The program provides grants to U.S. students, teachers, and scholars to study, teach, lecture, and conduct research overseas, and to foreign nationals to engage in similar activities in the United States to increase mutual understanding and peaceful relations between the people of the United States and the people of other countries. Fields of study and subjects taught include the arts and humanities, social sciences, and physical sciences. In addition to the exchange of students and scholars, the program includes professional exchanges in journalism, law, management, banking, and public administration. Participants take part in degree programs, nondegree and self-study courses, internships, and professional seminars. The total amount of money available is $108 million. Contact the office listed above for application information.

Money For English, Law, And Journalism Professionals To Go Abroad

Office of Citizen Exchanges
Bureau of Educational and Cultural Affairs
U.S. Department of State
301 4th St., SW, Room 238
Washington, DC 20547
202-619-5348
http://exchanges.state.gov/education

This program sends American academics overseas in response to requests relayed by USIA posts from foreign institutions seeking professional assistance in such academic disciplines as English teaching, law,

and journalism. Experts on the United States can consult with academic and professionals at foreign educational or other relevant institutions about special issues, or to conduct seminars/workshops for professional personnel. The total amount of money available is $1.3 million. Contact the office listed above for guidelines and application information.

Foreign High School Teachers Can Spend Six Weeks In The U.S.

(Study Of The United States)
Study of the US Branch
U.S. Department of State
301 4th St., SW, Room 252
Washington, DC 20547
202-619-4557
http://exchanges.state.gov/education

This program provides grants to foreign secondary school educators for a 4 to 6 week program of academic workshops in U.S. history, culture, and institutions to enhance and update the content of what is taught about the United States abroad. The total amount of money available is $1.6 million. Contact the office listed above for guidelines and application information.

Exchange Program For English Teachers

Office of English Language Programs
U.S. Department of State
301 4th St., SW, Room 304
Washington, DC 20547
202-619-5869
Fax: 202-401-1250
http://exchanges.state.gov/education

The program promotes the study and teaching of English abroad, in host country institutions, and through American educational and binational centers in 140 countries. USIA English teaching programs concentrate on training teachers through seminars, exchanges of foreign and American English specialists, and the development and distribution of curricula and materials for teaching the English language and American culture. The total amount of money available is $915,000. Contact the office listed above for application information.

Teach School Overseas

(Dependent Schools)
U.S. Department of Defense
Teacher Recruitment Section
4040 N. Fairfax Dr.
Arlington, VA 22203-1634

703-696-3068
Fax: 703-696-2695
www.odedodea.edu
The U.S. Department of Defense is responsible for providing schooling to dependent children of military personnel. There are employment positions for elementary and secondary teachers, as well as those that can provide support services. The schools are located in 19 countries around the world, with an enrollment of approximately 100,000 students, and are staffed with 13,000 employees. Contact the office listed above for an application and program information.

Volunteer In The U.S.
(Corporation for National Service
AMERICORPS - 94.006)
Corporation for National Service
1201 New York Ave. NW
Washington, DC 20525
800-942-2677
202-606-5000
http://www.cns.gov
The objective of this program is to supplement efforts of private, nonprofit organizations and federal, state, and local government agencies to eliminate poverty and poverty-related problems by enabling persons from all walks of life and all age groups to perform meaningful and constructive service as volunteers throughout the U.S. Americorps volunteers receive a modest subsistence allowance, an end-of-service stipend, health insurance, and money for college. The total amount of money available is $32,250,000. Applications are available through Americorps State Offices or contact the office listed above for additional information.

$30,000 To Study Farming Internationally
(Scientific Cooperation Program 10.961)
U.S. Department of Agriculture
International Collaborative Research Program
USDA/OICD/RSED
Ag Box 4314
Room 3230 South Building
14th and Independence Ave., SW
Washington, DC 20250
202-690-4872
www.fas.usda.gov
This program enables American scientists to work with foreign researchers on projects aimed at potential threats to U.S. agriculture, technology development, and opportunities to enhance trade in foreign markets. Up to $30,000 a year for one to

three years is available for each researcher. Contact the office listed above for an application form. U.S. researchers from USDA agencies, universities, and private nonprofit agricultural research institutions are eligible.

Your Friends In The Ukraine Can Come To The U.S. To Learn Free Enterprise
(Special American Business Internship Training Program (SABIT) 11.114)
U.S. Department of Commerce
International Trade Administration
Special American Business Internship Training Program, Room 3319
Washington, DC 20230
202-482-0073
http://www.ita.doc.gov
This program awards internships in U.S. firms to business managers and scientific workers from the newly independent states of the former Soviet Union. SABIT provides the intern with a hands-on training program in the business skills necessary to operate in a market economy. A counselor is provided to help with cultural adjustments. Companies provide medical insurance, housing, and any other living expenses beyond those covered by the daily stipend provided by the U.S. The amount of money available varies. Apply to the program through the U.S. Department of Commerce which considers applications through a competitive process. A SABIT fact sheet is also available.

Money For Students And Teachers To Travel Together Overseas
(Overseas Group Projects Abroad - 84.021)
International Education and Grants Programs Service
Office of Postsecondary Education
U.S. Department of Education
400 Maryland Ave. SW
Washington, DC 20202-5332
202-401-9772
Fax: 202-205-9489
http://www.ed.gov

This program is designed to contribute to the development and improvement of the study of modern foreign languages and area studies in the United States, and provide opportunities for American teachers, advanced students, and faculty to study in foreign countries. Grants allow groups to conduct overseas group projects in research, training, and curriculum development. Money can be used for international travel, maintenance allowances, rent of instructional materials in the country of study, and more. The total amount of money available is $3.4 million. Contact the office listed above for application information.

Finish Your Doctorate Research Abroad

(Fulbright-Hays Doctoral Dissertation Research Abroad - 84.002)
Higher Education Programs
U.S. Department of Education
1990 K St., NW
Washington, DC 20006
202-502-7700
http://www.ed.gov
This program is designed to provide opportunities for graduate students to engage in full-time dissertation research abroad in modern foreign language and area studies with the exception of Western Europe. This program is designed to develop research knowledge and capability in world areas not widely included in American curricula. Money can be used for a basic stipend, round trip air fare, baggage allowance, tuition payments, local travel, and more. The total amount of money available is $3.1 million. Candidates apply directly to the institutions at which they are enrolled in a Ph.D. program.

Money For College Teachers To Do Research Overseas

(Fulbright-Hays Faculty Research Abroad - 84.019)
Higher Education Programs
U.S. Department of Education
1990 K St., NW
Washington, DC 20006
202-502-7700
http://www.ed.gov
This program is designed to help develop modern foreign language and area studies in U.S. higher educational institutions. This program enables faculty members to maintain expertise in specialized fields through support of research in the non-Western areas of the world. Fellowships of 3 to 12 months are available. The total amount of money available is $911,000.

Candidates should apply directly to their institution. More information is available on this program through the office listed above.

Money For Teachers To Take A Sabbatical Overseas

(Fulbright-Hays Seminars Abroad - 84.018)
Higher Education Programs
U.S. Department of Education
1990 K St., NW
Washington, DC 20006
202-502-7700
http://www.ed.gov
This program is designed to improve modern foreign language and area studies by providing 3 to 8 week summer seminars abroad for high school and elementary school teachers in foreign languages, social sciences and humanities, administrators, and curriculum specialists of state and local education agencies, and college faculty who are primarily responsible for teaching undergraduates in the social sciences, humanities, and international affairs. The total amount of money available is $1,800,000. Contact the office listed above for application information, as well as a listing of the seminars available.

Grants To College Teachers Who Want To Create Programs In International Business

(Business And International Education - 84.153)
Higher Education Programs
U.S. Department of Education
1990 K St., NW
Washington, DC 20006
202-502-7700
http://www.ed.gov
This program is designed to promote innovation and improvement in international business education curricula at institutions of higher education and promote linkages between these institutions and the business community. Institutions must enter into an agreement with a business enterprise, trade organization, or association engaged in international economic activity, or a combination or consortium of the named entities. The total amount of money available is $4,125,000. Contact the office listed above for application information.

Conduct Health Research In Eastern Europe

(U.S.-Central and Eastern European Scientist Exchanges)
Program Officer

U.S.-Central and Eastern European Scientist
Exchanges
Fogarty International Center
Building 31C, Room B2C39
National Institutes of Health
Bethesda, MD 20892
301-496-1653
Fax: 301-402-0779
http://www.nih.gov/fic
This program is designed to promote contacts and
cooperation between well-qualified health professionals
and biomedical scientists in the United States and
participating countries, and to stimulate relations that
show a promise of becoming long-term and self-
supporting. The programs provide support for visits to
conduct short-term collaborative research or to develop
collaborative research activities. Exchanges are with the
countries of Bulgaria, Hungary, Poland, Romania,
Russia, and Mongolia with most requiring an advanced
degree in the health sciences or a related field. Contact
the office listed above for application forms, including
instructions and other requirements.

Visit The U.S. To Do Health Research
(NIH Visiting Program)
International Services Branch
Fogarty International Center
National Institutes of Health (NIH)
Building 16A, Room 101
Bethesda, MD 20892
301-496-20758
http://www.nih.gov/fic/
This program provides talented scientists throughout the
world with the opportunity to participate in the varied
research activities of the National Institutes of Health.
There are three categories of Visiting Program
participants: Visiting Fellows, Visiting Associates, and
Visiting Scientists. Each participant works closely with
a senior NIH investigator who serves as supervisor or
sponsor during the period of award or appointment. The
Visiting Fellow award is for obtaining research training
experience. Fellows must have a doctoral degree, not
more than 3 years of relevant postdoctoral research
experience, and cannot be U.S. citizens. Visiting
Associates and Visiting Scientists are appointed to
conduct health-related research and are considered
employees of NIH, and receive a salary and benefits.
Individuals interested in a Visiting Program fellowship
award or appointment should write to NIH senior
scientists working in the same research field, enclosing
a resume and brief description of his/her particular

research area. Information about the research being
conducted by NIH scientists and their names may be
obtained from the NIH's Scientific Directory and
Annual Bibliography, which can be obtained from the
office listed above.

New Researchers Abroad Can Use U.S. Facilities
(International Research Fellowships)
International Research Fellowship Program
Fogarty International Center
Building 31, Room B2C39
National Institutes of Health
9000 Rockville Pike
Bethesda, MD 20892
301-496-1653
Fax: 301-402-0779
http://www.nih.gov/fic
This program provides
opportunities for foreign
postdoctoral biomedical
or behavioral scientists
who are in the
formative stages of their
career to extend their
research experience in a
laboratory in the United
States. The total amount

of money available is $4.4 million. To learn more about
the requirements and application process, contact the
office listed above.

Get An Invitation To Do Research Overseas
(Foreign Funded Fellowships For U.S. Scientists)
International Research and Awards Branch
Fogarty International Center
National Institutes of Health
Building 31, Room B2C39
Bethesda, MD 20892
301-496-1653
Fax: 301-402-0779
http://www.nih.gov/fic/
This program provides for international opportunities
for research experience and exchange of information in
the biomedical and behavioral science. Under these
programs, U.S. scientists are invited by foreign host
scientists to participate in research projects of mutual
interest. Support for U.S. scientists is offered by 5
countries to conduct research in their laboratories.
Information and application instructions are available
from the office listed above.

Research Internationally

(International Opportunities In The Health Sciences and Biomedical
Research Through The National Institutes Of Health)
International Research and Awards Branch
Fogarty International Center
Building 31, Room B2C39
National Institutes of Health
Bethesda, MD 20892
301-496-1653
Fax: 301-402-0779
http://www.nih.gov/fic
This program provides for a variety of exchange and collaboration programs with specific countries. Length of exchange varies, with each program focusing on a specific area of research such as AIDS, neurology, genome research, and more. Many programs focus on bringing foreign researchers to the U.S. to collaborate with scientists. Contact the office listed above to learn about specific exchanges and fellowships available in your area of expertise and the application procedure. NIH also publishes a Directory Of International Grants And Fellowships In The Health Sciences book.

Money To Study In Japan

(Japan-U.S. Friendship Commission Grants)
Japan-U.S. Friendship Commission
1120 Vermont Ave., NW, Suite 925
Washington, DC 20005
202-418-9800
Fax: 202-418-9802
http://www.jusfc.gov
This program provides grants to institutions and associations to support American studies in Japan, Japanese studies in the United States, exchange programs in the arts, policy-oriented research, and public affairs, and education. In addition, the Commission is interested in sponsoring research on Japan-US economic relations and activities in Asia, with priority given to Japanese investment in Asia and its effect on Japan-US economic, trade and political relations. The total amount of money available is $2.7 million. Contact the office listed above for more information about the various grant programs, as well as a biennial report which lists previous grants recipients and their projects.

Money For Artists and Performers To Travel Overseas

(Fund For U.S. Artists at International Festival and Exhibits)

Arts International
251 Park Ave. S, 5th Floor
New York, NY 10010
202-674-9744
Fax: 202-674-9092
http://www.artsinternational.org
This program provides grants to assist individual U.S. performers of U.S. performing arts groups who have been invited to international festivals abroad, and who need additional support to make their performances possible. Travel, per diem, international communications, shipping, and salary expense related to participation in the international festival are among eligible costs supported through the Fund. The Fund is particularly interested in receiving proposals which reflect the cultural and regional diversity of the United States and which involve events in areas of the world where U.S. work is rarely performed. The total amount of money available is $437,000. Contact the office listed above for guidelines and an application packet.

Go To Japan For 6 Months

(United States/Japan Creative Artists' Program)
Japan-U.S. Friendship Commission
1120 Vermont Ave., NW, Suite 925
Washington, DC 20005
202-418-9800
Fax: 202-418-9802
http://www.jusfc.gov/
The program is designed to allow artists who create original work to pursue their individual artistic goals and interests by living in Japan for six months, observing developments in their field, and meeting with their professional counterparts in Japan. The total amount of money available is $200,000. Contact the office listed above for guidelines and an application packet.

Money For Artists To Work With the Newly Independent States

(Artslink)
CEC International Partners
12 West 31st St.
New York, NY 10001-4415
212-643-1985
Fax: 212-643-1996
http://www.cecip.org
Artslink encourages artistic exchange with the newly independent states in Central and Eastern Europe, the former Soviet Union, and the Baltics by offering

two categories of support: Artslink Collaborative Projects, which provides funding to U.S. artists to work on mutually beneficial projects with counterparts abroad, and Artslink Residencies, which supports U.S. arts organizations wishing to host a visiting artist or arts manager for a five-week residency. The total amount of money available varies. Contact the office listed above for guidelines and an application packet.

Artists Can Travel To Improve Their Art

(Travel Grants Fund For Artists)
Cultural Programs Division
Bureau of Educational and Cultural Affairs
U.S. Department of State
SA-44, 301 4th St., SW, Suite 568
Washington, DC 20547
202-205-2209
Fax: 202-619-6315
http://exchanges.state.gov
This program is designed to enable U.S. artists to pursue opportunities abroad that further their artistic development. Grant decisions will be based on artistic excellence, the applicant's reasons for wanting to travel to a particular country, as well as his or her sensitivity to the culture and country to which he or she wants to travel. The grants will support artists pursuing a wide variety of activities abroad including the development or expansion of relationships with artists and arts organizations and the exploration of significant developments in their field. The total amount of money available is $100,000. Contact the office listed above for guidelines and an application packet.

Summer Seminars For Teachers

(Summer Seminars For Teachers - 45.163)
Division of Fellowships and Seminars
National Endowment for the Humanities
1100 Pennsylvania Ave., NW, Room 316
Washington, DC 20506
Fax: 202-606-8204
202-606-8463
http://www.neh.fed.us
Email: research@neh.fed.us
Schoolteachers, principals, and other educators from kindergarten through 12th grade, along with selected foreign secondary teachers, can engage in intensive study of basic humanities texts and documents and work closely with outstanding scholars for 4 to 6 weeks at colleges, universities, and other appropriate sites, some of which may be located in a foreign country. Contact the office listed above for a list of seminar offerings, as well as an application packet.

Money For Teachers To Study

(Summer Stipends - 45.121)
Division of Fellowships and Seminars
National Endowment for the Humanities
1100 Pennsylvania Ave., NW, Room 316
Washington, DC 20506
202-606-8466
Fax: 202-606-8204
http://www.neh.fed.us
Email: research@neh.fed.us
Grants provide support for college and university teachers; individuals employed by schools, museums, libraries, etc.; and others to undertake full-time independent study and research in the humanities for two consecutive summer months. Applicants whose projects require significant travel to libraries, archives, or other collections may also apply for a travel supplement to the stipend. Contact the office listed above for guidelines and an application packet.

Grants For Humanities Teachers To Travel In The Summer

(Summer Seminars For College Teachers - 45.116)
Division of Fellowships and Seminars
National Endowment for the Humanities
1100 Pennsylvania Ave., NW, Room 321
Washington, DC 20506
Fax: 202-606-8204
202-606-8463
http://www.neh.fed.us
Email: research@neh.fed.us
This program provides teachers at undergraduate colleges and universities and other qualified individuals not affiliated with an academic institution the opportunity to study at major research institutions with eminent scholars in their own or related fields. Contact the office listed above for guidelines and an application packet. They can also provide you with a list of seminar offerings.

$30,000 To Study And Conduct Research

(Fellowships for College Teachers and Independent Scholars)
Division of Research
National Endowment for the Humanities
1100 Pennsylvania Ave., NW, Room 318
Washington, DC 20506
202-606-8210
Fax: 202-606-8204
http://www.neh.fed.us
Email: research@neh.fed.us
Grants provide support for teachers in two-year,

four-year, and five-year colleges and universities that do not grant the Ph.D.; for individuals employed by schools, museums, libraries, etc.; and also for independent scholars and writers to undertake full-time independent study and research in the humanities. The maximum amount of stipend is $30,000 each. Contact the office listed above for guidelines and an application packet.

Become A Humanities Fellow

(Fellowships At Centers for Advanced Study)
Division of Research Programs
National Endowment for the Humanities
1100 Pennsylvania Ave., NW, Room 318
Washington, DC 20506
202-606-8210
Fax: 202-606-8204
http://www.neh.fed.us
Email: research@neh.fed.us
Grants support postdoctoral fellowship programs at independent centers for advanced study which offer scholars opportunities to pursue independent research in the humanities while benefiting from collegial association with scholars in other areas or disciplines of study. Fellowships in this program are awarded and administered by the centers themselves. Tenure of the fellowships may run from six to twelve consecutive months, and stipends vary at the different centers. Eligibility also varies from center to center, but neither candidates for degrees nor persons seeking support for work toward degrees are eligible to apply. Contact the office listed above for more information on theses programs, as well as a list of centers which accept applications.

Fellowships For University Teachers

(Fellowship for University Teachers)
Division of Fellowships and Seminars
National Endowment for the Humanities
1100 Pennsylvania Ave., NW, Room 318
Washington, DC 20506
202-606-8466
Fax: 202-606-8204
http://www.neh.fed.us
Email: research@neh.fed.us
This program offers faculty members (and retirees) of Ph.D.-granting universities the opportunity to undertake 6 to 12 months of full-time independent study and research in the humanities. Fellowships provide opportunities for individuals to pursue advanced work that will enhance their capacities as teachers, scholars, or interpreters of the humanities.

Fellowships are intended for a range of individuals, from those who stand at the beginning of their careers to those who have made significant contributions to the humanities. The maximum stipend is $30,000. Contact the office listed above for guidelines and application information.

Scientific Collaboration

(Research Collaboration Between U.S. and Foreign Scientists and Engineers)
International Programs Division
National Science Foundation
4201 Wilson Blvd., Room 935
Arlington, VA 22230
703-292-5111
http://www.nsf.gov
Email: info@nsf.gov
This program is designed to advance and benefit U.S. interests by enabling U.S. scientists and engineers to avail themselves of research opportunities in other countries. The Division of International Programs supports efforts to initiate international cooperation involving new foreign collaborators, or new types of activities with established partners. Contact the office listed above for guidelines and application information.

Research In The Tropics

(Short-Term Fellowships)
Office of Fellowships and Grants
Smithsonian Institution
955 L'Enfant Plaza, Suite 7302
Washington, DC 20560
202-287-3271
Fax: 202-287-3691
http://www.si.edu
The objective of this program is to enable selected candidates to work in the tropics and explore research possibilities at the Smithsonian Tropical Research Institute. Fellowships are primarily for graduate students, but awards are made occasionally to undergraduate and postdoctoral candidates. Contact the office listed above for guidelines and application procedures.

Teachers Can Study Abroad

(Fulbright Teacher Exchange Program)
Fulbright Teacher Exchange Program
ATTN: NSL
600 Maryland Ave., SW, Suite 320
Washington, DC 20024-2520
202-314-3520
Fax: 202-479-6806
The program is designed to promote mutual
understanding between citizens of the United States and
other countries through educational and cultural
exchanges. It is open to teachers and administrators
from the elementary through the postsecondary levels,
allowing for classroom-to-classroom exchange of
teaching assignments between U.S. teachers and
counterpart teachers from selected countries worldwide.
Exchange grants may include full or partial travel
grants and cost of living supplements, depending on the
country. The total amount of money available is
$527,000. Contact the office listed above for guidelines
and an application packet.

Money To Attend Workshops Overseas

(Citizens Exchanges)
Office of Citizen Exchanges
Bureau of Educational and Cultural Affairs
U.S. Department of State
301 Fourth St., SW
Washington, DC 20547
202-619-5348
Fax: 202-619-4350
http://exchanges.state.gov
This program awards grants to U.S. nonprofit
organizations for projects that link their international
exchange interests with counterpart institutions/groups
in other countries. Subject areas include environmental
protection, trade unionism, education administration
and curriculum reform, civil and human rights
protection, legislative reform, small business
development and management training, and more.
Programs are normally multi-phase and extend over
more than one fiscal year. Programs usually consist of
sending American specialists on 2-3 week visits to a
country for workshops and meetings, followed by a visit
to the U.S. by foreign counterparts. The total amount of
money available is $21 million. The Office of Citizen
Exchanges develops a series of Requests for Proposals
(RFPs) during the course of the fiscal year. Specific
application and review guidelines are available upon
written request to the office listed above. RFPs are also
published in the Federal Register.

Money For Artists To Visit U.S. Embassies Abroad

(Arts America Program)
Cultural Programs Division
Bureau of Educational and Cultural Affairs
U.S. Department of State
301 4th St., SW, Room 568
Washington, DC 20547
202-619-4779
Fax: 202-619-6315
http://www.exchanges.state.gov
This program develops projects in response to
requests from U.S. embassies abroad, selecting
artists, performers and exhibitions on the basis of
artistic evaluations by expert panels drawn from the
U.S. arts community. It also supports privately-
funded arts initiatives abroad by providing
information, referrals, contacts, and other facilitative
assistance. The total amount of money available is
$845,000. This is not organized as a grant
application program from which individuals or
institutions can request financial assistance for
overseas projects, but is in response to a specific
request from embassies overseas. Individuals or
groups that wish to tour for USIA must go through a
screening process where their work is reviewed.
Contact the office listed above for information about
when the peer review panels meet, the work samples
that are required, and more. A brochure describing
the program is available from the office listed above.

Spend Six Weeks In A Foreign Country Working With Art Colleagues

(American Cultural Specialists)
Cultural Programs Division
Bureau of Educational and Cultural Affairs
U.S. Department of State
301 4th St., SW, Room 567
Washington, DC 20547
202-619-4779
Fax: 202-619-6315
http://exchanges.state.gov
Participants in this program spend two to six weeks in
one country working with foreign colleagues. Among
other activities, they may conduct workshops or master
classes, direct a play, rehearse a ballet, or advise on arts
management. The total amount of money available is
$380,000. This is not a grant program from which
individuals can request financial assistance for overseas
projects, but as a response to a specific request from
embassies abroad. To learn more on how to your resume

reviewed so your name can be placed on the Cultural Specialist roster, contact the office listed above.

Eight Week Foreign Tours For Jazz Musicians And Bands

(Jazz Ambassador Program)
Cultural Programs Division
Bureau of Educational and Cultural Affairs
U.S. Department of State
301 4th St., SW, Room 567
Washington, DC 20547
202-619-4779
Fax: 202-619-6315
http://exchanges.state.gov
This program is designed to use the wealth of often undiscovered musical talent in the U.S. to enhance the mission of promoting cross-cultural understanding. Jazz Ambassadors travel to four or five countries for a period of four to eight weeks. In addition to public performances, they may conduct workshops and master classes. The total amount of money available is $169,000. Nominations of classical musicians in various categories are sought from music schools, conservatories, colleges and universities throughout the U.S. Artistic Ambassadors may not be under management and are selected through live auditions on the basis of their musical ability and suitability as "goodwill ambassadors." To learn more about the application process, contact the office listed above.

Foreign Leaders Can Study In The U.S.

(International Visitors Program)
Office of International Visitors
U.S. Department of State
301 4th St., SW, Room 266
ECA/PE/V/C/P
Washington, DC 20547
800-827-0804
202-619-5217
Fax: 202-205-0792
http://exchanges.state.gov
This office arranges programs for foreign leaders and potential leaders designed to develop and foster professional contacts with their colleagues in the United States and provide a broader exposure to American social, cultural, and political institutions. Areas of expertise government, politics, media, education, science, labor relations, the arts, and other fields. The

total amount of money available is $40 million. Participants are nominated by U.S. embassies. For more information on the program contact the office listed above.

Do Your Part To Help The World

(Peace Corps)
Peace Corps
1111 20th St., NW
Washington, DC 20526
800-424-8580
Fax: 202-606-9410
http://www.peacecorps.gov
The program objective is to promote world peace and friendship, to help other countries in meeting their needs for trained manpower, and to help promote understanding between the American people and other peoples served by the Peace Corps. Volunteers serve for a period of 2 years, living among the people with whom they work. Volunteers are expected to become a part of the community and to demonstrate, through their voluntary service, that people can be an important impetus for change. Volunteers receive a stipend and health insurance. Contact the office listed above for information on how to become a Peace Corps volunteer.

Money For Engineering Students To Travel The Country Visiting DOE Laboratories

(University-Laboratory Cooperative Program - 81.004)
Cindy Music
Postsecondary Programs Division
Office of University and Science Education Programs
Office of Science and Technology
U.S. Department of Energy
Washington, DC 20585
202-586-0987
Fax: 202-586-0019
The program objective is to provide college and university science and engineering faculty and students with energy-related training and research experience in areas of energy research at Department of Energy research facilities. Funds can be used to conduct energy research at one of the DOE research facilities, and students will also receive a stipend and a small travel allowance. Students can also participate in energy-related workshops and conferences. The total amount of money available is $5,525,000. Students must apply to a participating laboratory or university. Contact the office listed above for information on laboratories and universities that take part in this program.

Grants To Junior and Senior College Science And Engineering Students To Visit Energy Laboratories

(Science and Engineering Research Semester - 81.097)
Donna Prokop
Postsecondary Programs
Office of University and Science Education Programs
Office of Energy Research
U.S. Department of Energy
Washington, DC 20585
202-586-8949
202-488-2426
Fax: 202-586-0019

The objective of this program is to give juniors and seniors the opportunity to participate in hands-on research at the cutting edge of science at the Department of Energy Laboratories, and to provide training and experience in the operation of sophisticated state-of-the-art equipment and instruments. College juniors and seniors who are majoring in an energy-related field can spend a semester using some of the Federal government's equipment and instruments at many of the Department of Energy's labs. The energy research must be in an area of the laboratory's ongoing research. Students receive a weekly stipend of $225, complimentary housing or a housing allowance, and a round-trip ticket to the lab. The total amount of money available is $2,500,000. Applications may be obtained by writing to Science and Engineering Research Semester, Office of Science and Technology (ST-50), Room 3F-061, U.S. Department of Energy, 1000 Independence Avenue, SW, Washington, DC 20585.

The Military Could Be Your Ticket Overseas

(U.S. Department of Defense)
U.S. Air Force Recruiting Service
550 D St., W, Suite 1
Randolph Air Force Base, TX 78150-4527
800-423-USAF
210-652-5993
www.airforce.com/

Commander
Naval Recruiting Command
801 N. Randolph St.
Arlington, VA 22203
800-USA-NAVY
www.navyjobs.com/

Commanding General
Marine Corps Recruiting Command
2 Navy Annex
Washington, DC 20380-1775
703-614-2901
www.usmc.mil/

Army Opportunities
P.O. Box 3219
Warminster, PA 18974-9845
800-USA-ARMY
www.goarmy.com/

U.S. Coast Guard Information Center
4200 Wilson Blvd., Suite 450
Arlington, VA 22205
800-GET-USCG
http://www.uscg.mil

The Army, Navy, Marine Corps, Air Force, and the Coast Guard (part of U.S. Department of Transportation) are responsible for protecting the security of the U.S. There are 2.1 million men and women on active duty, with 518,000 serving outside the United States. Length of service does vary, as does pay and types of jobs available. You can even earn the chance to go to college. The military has bases all around the country and the world, and your local recruiter can answer all your questions about the opportunities they have to offer.

Join The Foreign Service

(Foreign Service with the Department of State)
Recruitment Branch
Employment Division
U.S. Department of State
HR/REE, SA-1
2401 E St., NW, 5th Floor
Washington, DC 20522
202-261-8888
http://www.state.gov

Professionals in the Foreign Service advance and protect the national interests and security of the United States, both overseas and at home. Foreign Service Officers are generalists who perform administrative, consular, economic and political functions. Foreign Service Specialists

perform vital technical, support, and administrative services overseas and in the United States. You must be a U.S. citizen, between the ages of 21 and 59, a high school graduate, and be available for assignment anywhere in the world. Contact the office listed above for information and application procedures.

Thousands Of Government Jobs In Foreign Countries

(Office of Personnel Management)
Federal Job Information Center
Office of Personnel Management
1900 E St., NW
Washington, DC 20415
202-606-2700
202-619-4557
http://www.usajobs.opm.gov
The Federal government hires personnel to do everything from typing to spying, and there are posts all around the world. Those interested in jobs overseas can contact the Office of Personnel Management to learn current job openings and the skills required. Other government agencies also hire for jobs abroad, and you could contact them directly for information on employment opportunities. Contact the office listed above for more information, or you may contact the Career America Connection at 912-757-3000. Other agencies that hire for overseas employment include:

Agency For International Development
Recruitment Division
320 21st St., NW
Washington, DC 20523
202-647-7284
http://www.info.usaid.gov

U.S. Customs Service
1301 Constitution Ave., NW
Washington, DC 20229
202-927-1250
www.customs.treas.gov

Central Intelligence Agency
Personnel Representative
P.O. Box 12727
Arlington, VA 22209-8727
703-482-1100
800-562-7242
Fax: 703-482-7814
www.cia.gov

U.S. Department of Commerce
U.S. and Foreign Commercial Service
Office of Foreign Service Personnel
14th and Constitution Ave., NW
Room H-3813
Washington, DC 20230
202-482-4701
Fax: 202-482-1629
www.doc.gov

U.S. Department of Agriculture
Foreign Agricultural Service
Personnel Division – Room 5627
14th St. and Independence Ave., SW
Washington, DC 20250
703-812-6339
www.fas.usda.gov

Sell Your Goods Overseas

(U.S. Department of Commerce)
Trade Information Center
U.S. Department of Commerce
Washington, DC 20230
800-USA-TRADE
http://www.doc.gov
The Trade Information Center is a comprehensive "one-stop-shop" for information on U.S. government programs and activities that support exporting efforts. This hotline is staffed by trade specialists who can provide information on seminars and conferences, overseas buyers and representatives, overseas events, export financing, technical assistance, and export counseling. They also have access to the National Trade Data Bank. They offer trade missions to help you find local agents, representatives, distributors, or direct sales. Their Trade Shows promote U.S. products with high export potential. The Agent/ Distributor Service will locate, screen, and assess agents, distributors, representatives, and other foreign partners for your business. Matchmaker Trade Delegations prescreen prospects interested in your product and assist with meetings. If you cannot afford the cost of traveling overseas, the Trade Information Center can refer you to several programs that offer loans to help you start exporting. You can also receive assistance from your own state's Department of Economic Development. Contact the office listed above for more information on exporting in general, and for more specific information on your product or service.

FREE MONEY FOR YOUR COLLEGE EDUCATION

So you know you need more education to get ahead, but you are not sure how to pay for it? Never fear, we are here! There are billions of dollars worth of money just waiting to help you achieve your dreams. You just need to know where to look. The following sections outline all the federal and state money programs for college, as well as scholarship search engines and hundreds of college scholarships offered by various organizations.

Uncle Sam wants you to go to college, so that is why he set up the Federal government's great website {www.students.gov}. Here you can find information on:

* ★ preparing for college
* ★ vocational schools
* ★ study abroad
* ★ distance education
* ★ fellowships and internships
* ★ student job programs
* ★ scholarships, grants, and student loans
* ★ state financial aid
* ★ work-study
* ★ and much more.

Now there is no reason you can't go to college. There is even help choosing a major!

Don't forget to read the first part of this book, "Types of Assistance and Grants Sources," as well as "More Help In Finding a Grant." These sections also provide some great starting places for your money hunt. It is never too early to start thinking ahead.

Happy hunting!

Federal Money for College

Most people have heard of the federal government's largest money programs for students like the Pell Grant Program and the Guaranteed Student Loan program. But did you know that the federal government is the single largest source of money for students — whether they show financial need or not? It's true, but very few people are aware of the many grant programs in place and just waiting to give money to those students smart enough to find out about them. These little known programs provide students with:

* $15,000 to do graduate studies in housing related topics for the Department of Housing and Urban Development
* Money to finance a graduate degree in criminal justice from the Department of Justice
* $14,000 to get a graduate degree in foreign languages from the Department of Education
* $8,800 plus tuition and expenses to be a nurse from the Department of Health and Human Services

How To Apply

Requirements and application procedures vary widely from program to program. Some programs accept applications once a year, while others award money on a year round basis. Some programs require you to apply directly to the main funding office in Washington, DC, while other programs distribute the money to local organizations, which then distribute funds to individuals. Many of the programs give the money directly to the schools, and then the schools distribute it. For those, you need to request a listing of the schools that receive the funds.

All these federal programs are listed in the Catalog of Federal Domestic Assistance, which is available in most libraries. This catalogue lists all the government grant and loan programs available. The program name and number in parenthesis refer to this publication. You can search the catalog easily at {www.cfda.gov}.

Get Loans Directly From Your School
(Federal Direct Loan 84.268)

The Direct Loan Program was begun to provide loans directly to students through schools, rather than through private lenders. Borrowers complete an application, the Free Application for Federal Student Aid (FAFSA), for all Department student financial aid programs. Schools receive the funds and then disburse them to students.

There are four different direct loans: Federal Direct Stafford/Ford Loans are for students who demonstrate financial need; Federal Direct Unsubsidized Stafford/Ford Loans are for students regardless of financial need; Federal Direct PLUS Loans are for parents to pay for their children's education; and Federal Direct Consolidation Loans help combine one or more federal education loans into one loan. The amount one can borrow depends upon dependent/independent status of student and year in school. There are several different repayment options including income contingent repayment plan. Interest rates for loans vary each year.

For your Free Application for Federal Student Aid, contact Federal Student Aid Information Center, P.O. Box 84, Washington, DC 20044; 800-433-3243. Contact: U.S. Department of Education, Direct Loan Payment Center, P.O. Box 746000, Atlanta, GA 30374; 800-557-7394; {www.ed.gov/DirectLoan/fact.html}.

$15,000 For Graduate Students To Study Overseas
(Educational Exchange - Graduate Students 19.400)

Graduate students who would like to spend a year studying overseas can apply for the Fulbright Program, where if accepted, they will receive round trip transportation, tuition, books, maintenance for one academic year in one country, and health insurance. Students apply through the Fulbright program adviser located at their college or university, or they can apply as an at-large applicant by contacting the New York office of the Institute of International Education. Money available: $14,500,000. The average award per student is $21,000, but awards can range anywhere from $1,200 to $40,000.

Contact Institute of International Education, 809 United Nations Plaza, New York, NY 10017; 212-984-5330; {www.iie.org}.

Travel Overseas For Your Doctorate Research
(International Overseas Doctoral Dissertation 84.022)

This program provides opportunities for graduate students to engage in full-time dissertation research abroad in modern foreign language and area studies with the exception of Western Europe. The program is designed to develop research knowledge and capability in world areas not widely included in American curricula. Money available: $3,141,000. Grants average $22,000.

For more information, contact Advanced Training and Research Team, International Education and Graduate Programs Service, Office of Postsecondary Education, U.S. Department of Education, 400 Maryland Ave., SW, Washington, DC 20202; 202-401-9774; {www.ed.gov}.

$4,000 Grants For Students Having Trouble Paying Tuition
(Federal Supplemental Education Opportunity Grants 84.007)

If you are working towards your first undergraduate baccalaureate degree and are having trouble paying the bills, you may qualify for money through the Federal Supplemental Educational Opportunity Grants (FSEOG) program. Grants are for undergraduate study and range from $100 to $4000 per academic year, with the student eligible to receive a FSEOG for the time it takes to complete their first degree.

Students should contact the Financial Aid office of the school they attend or plan to attend for information regarding application. A student *Financial Aid Handbook* is available, as is a list of grantee institutions by contacting the Federal Student Aid Information Center, P.O. Box 84, Washington, DC 20044; 800-433-3243. Money available: $619,000,0900. Estimated average award is $745. Contact Student Financial Assistance Program, Office of the Assistant Secretary for Post-Secondary Education, U.S. Department of Education, 400 Maryland Ave., SW, Washington, DC 20202; 202-708-8242; {www.ed.gov}.

Money For a Foreign Language Degree
(National Resource Centers and Fellowships Program for Language and Area or Language and International Studies 84.015)

In this global world, foreign languages and international studies are becoming increasingly important. The Department of Education has funds to support centers which promote instruction in foreign language and international studies at colleges and universities. In addition, there are graduate fellowships to pursue this course of study in order to develop a pool of international experts to meet our nation's needs. Funds for centers may be used for instructional costs of language and area and international studies programs, administration, lectures and conferences, library resources and staff, and travel. Grants for fellowships include tuition, fees, and a basic subsistence allowance. Students must apply to those institutions that received the money. For a listing of institutions that received money, contact the office listed below. Students can contact these institutions directly. Money available: Grants: $13,719,000.

Contact International Studies Branch, Center for International Education, Office of Postsecondary Education, U.S. Department of Education, Seventh and D Sts., SW, Washington, DC 20202; 202-401-9783; {www.ed.gov/office/OPE/HEP/iegps/flasf.html}

Money For Students And Teachers
To Travel Overseas
(Fulbright-Hays Training Grants - Group Projects Abroad 84.021)

The program objective is to help educational institutions improve their programs in modern foreign language and area studies through overseas study/travel seminar group research, advanced foreign language training, and curriculum development. Funds are available to support overseas study/travel seminar group research and advanced foreign language training. Grant funds may be used for international travel, maintenance allowances, rental of instructional facilities in the country of study, and more. Money available: $2,326,000.

Contact Office of Assistant Secretary for Postsecondary Education, U.S. Department of Education, 600 Independence Ave., SW, Washington, DC 20202; 202-502-7700; {www.ed.gov/offices/OPE/HEP/iegps/ gpa.html}.

Money For Ph.D. Students
To Do Research Overseas
(Fulbright-Hays Training Grants - Doctoral Dissertation
Research Abroad 84.022)

Graduate students now have the opportunity to engage in full time dissertation research abroad in modern foreign language and area studies. This program is designed to develop research knowledge and capability in world areas not widely included in American curricula. The grant includes a basic stipend, round trip airfare, baggage allowance, tuition payments, local travel, and more. Candidates apply directly to the institutions at which they are enrolled. Money available: $2,072,000.

Contact Karla Ver Bryck Block, Advanced Training and Research Branch, Center for International Education, Office of Assistant Secretary for Postsecondary Education, U.S. Department of Education, 600 Independence Ave., SW, Washington, DC 20202, 202-502-7700, {www.ed.gov/offices/OPE/HEP/iegps/ddrap.html}

Loans To Go To School
(Federal Family Education Loans 84.032)

Guaranteed loans for educational expenses are available from eligible lenders such as banks, credit unions, savings and loan association, pension funds, insurance companies, and schools to vocational, undergraduate, and graduate students enrolled at eligible institutions. Loans can be used to pay the costs associated with obtaining a college education. The PLUS program is also available, which allows parents to borrow for their dependent student. More information is available by contacting the lending institution regarding the loans available and the application procedure. Money available: $21,032,000,000.

Contact Division of Policy Development, Policy, Training and Analysis Service Office of Assistant Secretary for Postsecondary Education, U.S. Department of Education, Washington, DC 20202; 202-708-8242; {www.ed.gov/offices/OSFAP/Students/}.

Work-Study Program Pays For School
(Federal Work-Study Program 84.033)

Part-time employment is available to students to help meet education expenses. This program pays an hourly wage to undergraduates. Graduate students may be paid by the hour or may receive a salary. There are Federal Work-Study jobs both on and off campus. Money can be used to help defray the costs of higher education.

Students should contact the educational institution they attend or plan to attend to find out about application procedures. A Student Financial Aid Handbook is available, as is a list of grantee institutions, by contacting Federal Student Aid Information Center, P.O. Box 84, Washington, DC 20044; 800-433-3243. Money available: $900,000,000.

Contact Division of Policy Development, Student Financial Assistance Programs, Office of Assistant Secretary for Postsecondary Education, 400 Maryland Ave., SW, Washington, DC 20202; 202-708-8242; {www.ed.gov/offices/OSFAP/Students}.

Low-Interest Student Loans
(Federal Perkins Loan Program 84.038)

Low-interest loans are available to eligible post-secondary students with demonstrated financial need to help meet educational expenses. Students can borrow money to meet the costs of school. These loans are for students with exceptional financial need. To apply, contact the Financial Aid office of the school you attend or plan to attend. A student Financial Aid Handbook is available, as well as a list of grantee institutions by contacting the Federal Student Aid Information Center, P.O. Box 84, Washington, DC 20044; 800-433-3242. Money available: $60,000,000.

Contact Division of Policy Development Student Financial Assistance Programs, Office of Assistant Secretary for Postsecondary Education, U.S. Department of Education, 600 Independence Ave., SW, Washington, DC 20202; 202-708-8242; {www.ed.gov/offices/OSFAP/Students}.

Get Help To Study
(TRIO Upward Bound 84.047)

This program generates skills and motivation necessary for success in education beyond high school among low income and potential first-generation college students and veterans. The goal of the program is to increase the academic performance and motivational levels of eligible enrollees so that they have a better chance of completing secondary school and successfully pursuing postsecondary educational programs.

Eligible students must have completed the eighth grade and be between the ages of 13 and 19, enrolled in high school, and need such services to achieve their goal of college. The program provides instruction in reading, writing, study skills, and mathematics. They can provide academic, financial, or personal counseling, tutorial services, information on student financial assistance, assistance with college and financial aid applications, and more.

Contact your local Upward Bound project to find out more about this program. For a listing of institutions that received money contact the office listed below. Money available: $243,000,000.

Contact Division of Student Services, Education Outreach Branch, Office of Postsecondary Education, U.S. Department of Education, 600 Independence Ave., SW, Room 5065, Washington, DC 20202; 202-260-1494; {www.ed.gov/offices/ OPE}.

$2,700 Grants To Go To School
(Federal Pell Grant Program 84.063)

Grants are available to students with financial need to help meet education expenses. Grants may not exceed $2,700 per year, and must be used for student's first bachelor's or other professional degree. Once an application is completed, the student's financial eligibility for assistance is calculated and the agency then notifies the student of eligibility. A Free Application for Federal Student Aid is available from the Federal Student Aid Information Center, P.O. Box 84, Washington, DC 20044; 800-433-3243. Money available: $7,594,000,000.

Contact Division of Policy Development, Student Financial Assistance Programs, Office of Postsecondary Education, U.S. Department of Education, 600 Independence Ave., SW, Washington, DC 20202; 202-708-8242; {www.ed.gov/offices/OSFAP/Students/}.

Aid For Students Who Want To Help The Deaf
(Training Interpreters For Individuals Who Are Deaf and Individuals Who Are Deaf-Blind 84.160)

This program supports projects that train new interpreters and improve the skills of manual, oral, and cued speech interpreters already providing services to individuals who are deaf and individuals who are deaf-blind. Grants are awarded for training, classroom instruction, workshops, seminars, and field placements. Ten grants are awarded to colleges and universities that have ongoing sign language/oral interpreter training programs of proven merit.

Programs include training courses connected to degree programs in interpreting; short term practical training leading to interpreter certification; and workshops, seminars, and practices. Students must apply to those institutions that have received the program money. For a listing of institutions that received money contact the office listed below. Money available: $2,100,000.

Contact Deafness and Communicative Disorders Branch, Rehabilitation Services Administration, U.S. Department of Education, 600 Independence Ave., SW, Washington, DC 20202; 202-205-9152; 202-205-8352 TTY; {www.ed.gov/offices/OSERS/RSA/PGMS/RT/scholrsp.html}.

Money For Students Interested In Helping People With Disabilities
(Rehabilitation Training 84.129)

This program supports projects that provide new personnel and improve the skills of existing personnel trained in providing vocational rehabilitation services to individuals with disabilities in areas targeted as having personnel shortages.

Training grants are provided in fields directly related to the vocational and independent living rehabilitation of individuals with disabilities, such as rehabilitation counseling, independent living, rehabilitation medicine, physical and occupational therapy, speech-language, pathology and audiology, and more. Projects include residency scholarships in physical medicine and rehabilitation; teaching and graduate scholarships in rehabilitation counseling; and more.

Students must apply to those institutions that have received the program money. A catalogue of projects is available that provides address, phone number, contact person, and an abstract for each grant awarded. Money available: $17,200,000. Contact Rehabilitation Services Administration, Office of Special Education and Rehabilitation Services, U.S. Department of Education, Washington, DC 20202; 202-205-8926; {www.ed.gov/offices/OSERS/RSA/ PGMS/RT/scholrsp.html}.

$25,400 Per Year For Graduate Study
(Jacob K. Javits Fellowships 84.170)

This program provides fellowships to individuals of superior ability for graduate study in the fields within the arts, humanities, and social sciences. Money can be used to support a student while he or she attends an institution of higher education.

To apply for these fellowships contact the Federal Student Aid Information Center, P.O. Box 84, Washington, DC 20044; 800-4-FED-AID. Money available: $5,931,000. Contact Higher Education Programs, Office of Postsecondary Education, U.S. Department of Education, Washington, DC 20202; 202-502-7700; {www.ed.gov/offices/OPE/HEP/iegps/javits.html}.

$1,500 Per Year For College
(Robert C. Byrd Honors Scholarships 84.185)

Scholarships are available to exceptionally able students who show promise of continued academic achievement. Scholarships for up to four years to study at any institution of higher education are available through grants to the states. The scholarships are awarded on the basis of merit and are renewable.

To apply for this grant award, interested applicants must contact their state educational agency, which administers this program. Money available: $39,288,000. Contact U.S. Department of Education, Office of Student Financial Assistance, Office of the Assistant Secretary for Postsecondary Education, Division of Higher Education Incentive Programs, The Portals, Suite C-80, Washington, DC 20024; 202-502-7700; {www.ed.gov/offices/OPE/HEP/idues/byrd.html}.

Money For Graduate Study
(Graduate Assistance In Areas Of National Need 84.200)

Fellowships are available through graduate academic departments to graduate students of superior ability who demonstrate financial need and are able to enhance the capacity to teach and conduct research in areas of national need.

Designated academic areas change each year and are currently biology, chemistry, engineering, foreign languages, mathematics, and physics. Money can be used to support a student completing a graduate degree program. Students must apply to those institutions that have received the money. For a listing of institutions that received money contact the office listed below. Money available: $26,800,000. Contact International Education and Graduate Programs Service, Office of Postsecondary Education, U.S. Department of Education, 600 Independence Ave., SW, Washington, DC 20202; 202-502-7700; {www.ed.gov/offices/OPE/HEP/ iegps/gaann.html}.

Grants For Those Who Have Trouble Paying Tuition
(Ronald E. McNair Post Baccalaureate Achievement 84.217)

This program provides grants to institutions of higher education to prepare low income, first-generation college students and students underrepresented in graduate education for graduate study. Money can be used to pay the costs for research and other scholarly activities, summer internships, seminars, tutoring, academic counseling, and securing admission and financial assistance for graduate study.

Students must apply to those institutions that have received the money. For a listing of institutions that received money contact the office listed below. Money available: $23,540,000. Contact U.S. Department of Education, Division of Student Services, Office of Postsecondary Education, 600 Independence Ave., SW, Washington, DC 20202; 202-502-7600; {www.ed.gov/offices/OPE/HEP/trio/mcnair.html}.

Grants for the Environment
(Training and Fellowships for the Environmental Protection Agency- 66.607)

The funds for this program are to provide resources to allow for training and fellowships related to environmental issues. Money available $35,000,000. Grants range from $4,000 to $5,000,000. For more information, contact Environmental Protection Agency, Grants Administration Division, 3903R, 401 M St., SW, Washington, DC 20460; {www.epa.gov}.

Money For Public Service Students
(Harry S. Truman Scholarship Program 85.001)

A special scholarship program for college juniors has been established to encourage students to pursue careers in public service. Money can be used to support a student completing his or her undergraduate and graduate studies.

A faculty representative is appointed for each school and is responsible for publicizing the scholarship program; soliciting recommendations on students with significant potential for leadership; conducting a competition on campus; and forwarding the institution's official nomination to the Truman Scholarship Review committee. For more information write to the Foundation listed above. Money available: $3,187,000. Contact Louis Blair, Executive Secretary Truman Scholarship Foundation, 712 Jackson Place, NW, Washington, DC 20006; 202-395-4831; {www.truman.gov}.

Spend A Semester In A
Department Of Energy Lab
(Science and Engineering Research Semester 81.097)

The program objective is to give undergraduate students the opportunity to participate in hands-on research at the cutting edge of science at the Department of Energy laboratories, and to provide training and experience in the operation of sophisticated state-of-the-art equipment and instruments.

Those students majoring in energy related fields can spend a semester at many of the Department of Energy's labs. The energy research must be concentrated in an area of the laboratory's ongoing research. Applications may be obtained by writing to ERULF, ORISE 36, P.O. Box 117, Oak Ridge, TN 37831; 423-576-2478; {www.scied.science.doe.gov}. Money available: $2,500,000. Students receive a weekly stipend of $350.

Contact Sue Ellen Walbridge, Office of Laboratory Management, U.S. Department of Energy, Washington, DC 20585; 202-586-7231.

Money For Minority Students At Junior Colleges Who
Are Energy Majors
(Minority Technical Education Program 81.082)

The program objective is to provide scholarship funding to financially needy minority honor students pursuing training in energy related technologies and to develop linkages with energy industries. Scholarship funds are available to defray costs of tuition, books, tools, transportation, and laboratory fees for minority students attending junior colleges and majoring in energy related field. The students must apply to those institutions that received the money. For a listing of those institutions contact the office listed below. Money available: $382,000.

Contact The Minority Energy Information Clearinghouse, Minority Economic IMPACT, Office of Economic Impact and Diversity, U.S. Department of Energy, Forrestal Building, Washington, DC 20585; 202-586-8383; {www.hr.doe.gov/ed/OMEI/Omei.html}.

Part-Time Jobs In The Government
(Student Temporary Employment Program 27.003)

The program gives students 16 years of age and older an opportunity for part time temporary employment with federal agencies in order to allow them to continue their education without interruptions caused by financial pressures. The money can be used to pay expenses while attending school. Apply for this program through the youth division of the local office of the State Employment Service.

Look in the government section of your phone book to find an office near you, or contact the Main State Employment Service office for referral to a local office. Contact Employment Service, Office of Personnel Management, 1900 E St., NW, Washington, DC 20415; 202-606-0830; {www.usajobs.opm.gov}.

INTERNSHIPS FOR GRADUATE STUDENTS TO WORK AT 54 GOVERNMENT AGENCIES
(Presidential Management Intern Program 27.013)

The PMI Program is a two-year entry-level employment and career development program designed to attract to the federal civil service men and women with graduate degrees from diverse cultural and academic backgrounds. Interns will have demonstrated academic excellence, possess management and leadership potential, and have a commitment to and a clear interest in a public service career. Nominees for the PMI Program undergo a rigorous, competitive screening process.

Being selected as a PMI Finalist is a first step, but does not guarantee a job. Agencies designate positions for the PMIs and each establishes its own procedures for considering and hiring PMIs. Once hired by agencies, PMIs are encouraged to work with their agencies to establish an "individual development plan." PMIs participate in training conferences, seminars, and congressional briefings. Money can be used to pay for expenses.

An application form and more information can be requested by contacting the Career America Hotline at 912-757-3000. Contact Office of Personnel Management, Philadelphia Service Center, Federal Building, 600 Arch St., Philadelphia, PA 19106; 215-597-7136; {www.usajobs.opm.gov}.

Money for Health Profession Students
(Health Professions Student Loans 93.342)

The Health Professions Student Loan Program provides long-term, low interest rate loans to full-time financially needy students pursuing a degree in dentistry, optometry, pharmacy, pediatric medicine, or veterinary medicine. Under this program, funds are made available to schools for the establishment of revolving student loan funds.

To apply for this loan, contact the student financial aid office at the school where you intend to apply for admission or where you are enrolled. Loans can not exceed tuition. The interest rate is 5%. A Health Professions Student Loan Fact Sheet is available from the office listed above. Money available: $5,000,000.

Contact Health Professions Student Loan Program, Division of Student Assistance, Bureau of Health Professions, Health Resources and Services Administration, Public Health Service, U.S. Department of Health and Human Services Administration, Parklawn Building, Room 8-34, 5600 Fishers Lane, Rockville, MD 20857; 301-443-4776; {http://bhpr.hrsa.gov/dsa/}.

Money For Primary Care Students
(Health Professions Student Loans, Including Primary Care Loans 93.342)

The Primary Care Loan Program provides long-term low interest rate loans to full-time financially needy students pursuing a degree in allopathic or osteopathic medicine. Under this program, funds are made to schools to establish revolving student loan funds. Students must agree to enter and complete residency training in primary care and to practice in primary care until the loan is paid in full.

To apply for this loan, contact the student financial aid office at the school where you intend to apply for admission or where you are enrolled. Loans cannot exceed tuition. Money available: $5,000,000. Contact Division of Student Assistance, Bureau of Health Professions, Health Resources and Services Administration, Public Health Service, U.S. Department of Health and Human Services Administration, Parklawn Building, Room 8-34, 5600 Fishers Lane, Rockville, MD 20857; 301-443-4776; {http://bhpr.hrsa.gov/dsa/}.

LOANS FOR DISADVANTAGED HEALTH PROFESSION STUDENTS
(Loans for Disadvantaged Students 93.342)

Loans for Disadvantaged Students Program provides funding to eligible health professions schools for the purpose of providing long-term, low-interest loans to assist full-time, financially needy, disadvantaged students to pursue a career in allopathic or osteopathic medicine, dentistry, optometry, podiatry, pharmacy, or veterinary medicine. To apply for this loan, contact the student financial aid office at the school where you intend to apply for admission or where you are enrolled. Loans For Disadvantaged Students Fact Sheet is available from the office listed below. Money available: $5,000,000.

Contact Division of Student Assistance, Bureau of Health Professions' Health Resources and Services Administration, Public Health Service, U.S. Department of Health and Human Services Administration, Parklawn Building, Room 8-34, 5600 Fishers Lane, Rockville, MD 20857; 301-443-4776; {http://bhpr.hrsa.gov/dsa/}.

Money For Nursing Students
(Nursing Student Loans 93.364)

The Nursing Student Loan program provides for long-term, low-interest loans to full-time and half-time financially needy students pursuing a course of study leading to a diploma, associate, baccalaureate or graduate degree in nursing. Federal funds for this program are allocated to accredited public or nonprofit nursing schools. These schools are responsible for selecting the recipients of loans and for determining the amount of assistance a student requires.

To apply for this loan, contact the student financial aid office at the school where you intend to apply for admission or where you are enrolled. Interest rate is 5%. Money available: $3,000,000. Contact Division of Student Assistance, Bureau of Health Professions, Health Resources and Services Administration, Public Health Service, U.S. Department of Health and Human Services Administration, Parklawn Building, Room 8-34, 5600 Fishers Lane, Rockville, MD 20857; 301-443-4776; {http://bhpr.hrsa.gov/dsa/}.

Money For Faculty Loan Repayments
(Disadvantaged Health Professions Faculty Loan Repayment Program 93.923)

The Faculty Loan Repayment Program provides a financial incentive for degree-trained health professionals from disadvantaged backgrounds to pursue an academic career. The health professional must agree to serve as a member of a faculty of a health professions school, providing teaching services for a minimum of two years, faculty for schools of medicine, nursing, osteopathic medicine, dentistry, pharmacy, pediatric medicine, optometry, veterinary medicine, public health, or a school that offers a graduate program in clinical psychology. The federal government, in turn, agrees to pay as much as $20,000 of the outstanding principal and interest on the individual's educational loans.

To participate in the program, an individual must be from a disadvantaged background, must not have been a member of a faculty of any school at any time during the 18 month period preceding the date on which the program application is received, must have a degree or be enrolled as a full-time student in the final year of training leading to a degree in one of the eligible disciplines, and must have entered into a contract with an eligible health professions school to serve as a full-time faculty member for a minimum of two years. Money available: $1,061,000.

Contact Division of Student Assistance, Bureau of Health Professions, Health Resources and Services Administration, Public Health Service, U.S. Department of Health and Human Services Administration, Parklawn Building, Room 8-34, 5600 Fishers Lane, Rockville, MD 20857; 301-443-1503; 888-275-4772; {http://bhpr.hrsa.gov/DSA/flrp/index.htm}.

Scholarships For Disadvantaged Health Profession Students
(Scholarships For Health Profession Students From Disadvantaged Backgrounds 93.925)

The Scholarships For Disadvantaged Students program provides funds to eligible schools for the purpose of providing scholarships to full-time financially needy students from disadvantaged backgrounds enrolled in health professions and nursing programs. Under this program, funds are awarded to accredited schools of medicine, osteopathic medicine, dentistry, optometry, pharmacy, podiatric medicine, veterinary medicine, nursing (diploma, associate, baccalaureate, and graduate degree), public health, allied health (baccalaureate and graduate degree programs of dental hygiene, medical laboratory technology, occupational therapy, physical therapy, radiologic technology), and graduate programs in clinical psychology.

The schools are responsible for selecting recipients, making reasonable determinations of need and disadvantaged student status, and providing scholarships that cannot exceed the student's financial need. To apply for this scholarship, contact the student financial aid office at the school where you intend to apply for admission or where you are enrolled. Money available: $18,000,000. Contact Division of Student Assistance, Bureau of Health Professions, Health Resources and Services Administration, Public Health Service, U.S. Department of Health and Human Services Administration, Parklawn Building, Room 8-34, 5600 Fishers Lane, Rockville, MD 20857; 301-443-4776; {http://bhpr.hrsa.gov/dsa/}.

Money For American Indians Who Want To Be Health Care Professionals
(Health Professions Recruitment Program For Indians 93.970)

The program objective is to increase the number of American Indians and Alaskan Natives who become health professionals and money has been set aside to help identify students interested in the field and to assist them in enrolling schools. Some of the projects funded include the recruitment of American Indians into health care programs, a variety of retention services once students have enrolled, and scholarship support.

Students should contact their school directly for assistance. Money available: $2,870,700. Contact Indian Health Service, Division of Health Professions Support, 12300 Twinbrook Parkway, Suite 100, Rockville, MD 20852; 301-443-4242; {www.ihs.gov}.

Health Professions Scholarships For American Indians
(Health Professions Pregraduate Scholarship Program for Indians 93.123)

The program objective is to provide scholarships to American Indians and Alaskan Natives for the purpose of completing pregraduate education leading to baccalaureate degree in the areas of pre-medicine or pre-dentistry. Money can be used to support a student while completing their degree.

Contact the Indian Health Service for application information. Money available: $1,702,569. Awards range from $12,283 to $27,217. Contact Indian Health Service, Scholarship Program, 12300 Twinbrook Parkway, Suite 100, Rockville, MD 20852; 301-443-6197; {www.ihs.gov}.

Opportunity To Receive College Tuition From NSA
(Mathematical Sciences Grants Program 12.901)

National Security Agency (NSA) will consider any student who meets the requirements below and who chooses a full-time college major in either computer science, electrical or computer engineering, languages or mathematics. Requirements consist of having a minimum SAT score of 1100 and a minimum composite ACT score of 25. Chosen students can receive college tuition, reimbursement for books, year-round salary, summer work and have a guaranteed job with the NSA after graduation.

Students must work for NSA for one and a half times their length of study, which is usually about five years. Money available: $2,600,000. Contact National Security Agency, Manager, Undergraduate Training Program, Attn: S232R (UTP), 9800 Savage Rd., Suite 6840, Ft. Meade, MD 20755-6840; 301-688-0400; {www.nsa.gov}.

MONEY FOR AMERICAN INDIANS WHO NEED EXTRA STUDIES FOR HEALTH CARE PROGRAM
(Health Professions Preparatory Scholarship Program for Indians 93.971)

The program objective is to make scholarships available to American Indians and Alaskan Natives who need to take some extra courses in order to qualify for enrollment or re-enrollment in a health profession school. Money can be used for up to two years of scholarship support, and the funds can cover tuition, stipends, and books.

Students must apply to the Indian Health Service Office for application information. Money available: $2,000,000. Grants range from $13,182 to $26,019. Contact Indian Health Service, Scholarship Program, 12300 Twinbrook Parkway, Suite 100, Rockville, MD 20852; 301-443-6197; {www.ihs.gov}.

Scholarships For Health Care Professionals
(Health Professions Scholarship Program 93.972)

This program objective is to provide scholarships to American Indians and
Alaskan natives attending health professions schools and who are interested in
serving other Indians. Upon completion, scholarship recipients are obligated to
serve in the Indian Health Service one year for each year of scholarship support,
with a minimum of two years.

The health professions needed are listed annually in the Federal Register. The
money can be used to support a student completing a health profession degree.
Money available: $7,300,000. Grants range from $12,136 to $38,222. Contact
Indian Health Service, Scholarship Program, 12300 Twinbrook Parkway, Suite
100, Rockville, MD 20852; 301-443-6197; {www.ihs.gov}.

Money For Dental Students For Advanced Residency Training
(Residency Training And Advanced Education in General Practice Of Dentistry 93.897)

The program objective is to assist schools of dentistry or dental training to institute residency training and advanced
educational programs in the general practice of dentistry. The grant can be used to support personnel, residents or
trainees who are in need of financial assistance, to purchase equipment, and for other expenses necessary to conduct
the program. Money can be used to support a student while he or she completes a dental training program or
residency. Students must apply to those institutions that have received the money.

For a listing of institutions that received money contact the office listed below. Money available: $3,500,000.
Contact Public Health and Dental Education Branch, Division of Public Health and Allied Health, Bureau of Health
Professions, Health Resources and Services Administration, Public Health Service, U.S. Department of Health and
Human Services, 5600 Fishers Lane, Rockville, MD 20857; 301-443-6880; {http://bhpr.hrsa.gov/
dadphp/dadphp.htm}.

Health Careers Opportunity Program
(Health Careers Opportunity Program 93.822)

The Health Careers Opportunity Program provides assistance to individuals from disadvantaged backgrounds to
obtain a health or allied health profession degree. Grants can be used to identify, recruit, and select individuals from
minority and disadvantaged backgrounds for education and training in a health or allied health professions school;
facilitate entry of eligible students into such schools; provide counseling or other services designed to assist such
individuals in successfully completing their education and training; provide preliminary education for a period prior
to entry into the regular course of health or allied health professions education, designed to assist students in
successfully completing regular courses of education, or refer the appropriate individuals to institutions providing
preliminary education; and provide disadvantaged students with information on financial aid resources.

For a listing of institutions that received money contact the office listed below. Money available: $26,870,000.
Contact Division of Disadvantaged Assistance, Bureau of Health Professions, Health Resources and Services
Administration, Public Health Services, U.S. Department of Health and Human Services, Room 8A-09, 5600
Fishers Lane, Rockville, MD 20857; 301-443-2100; {http://bhpr.hrsa.gov/dhpd/hcophome1.htm}.

Grants for Native Hawaiian Students
(Native Hawaiian Higher Education Program 84.316)

Grants are give to provide full or partial fellowship support for Native Hawaiian students enrolled at two or four year degree granting institutions of higher education. Awards are based on academic potential and financial need. Full or partial support will also be given to support Native Hawaiian students enrolled at post-baccalaureate degree granting institutions. Priority will be given to providing fellowship support for professions that are underrepresented in the Native Hawaiians community. Money available: $2,700,000.

For more information, contact Higher Education Programs, Office of Postsecondary Education, Department of Education, 400 Maryland Ave., SW, Washington, DC 20202; 202-502-7700; {www.ed.gov}.

Money For Nursing Students To Repay Their Loans
(Nursing Education Loan Repayment Agreements For Registered Nurses Entering Employment At Eligible Health Facilities 93.908)

As an incentive for registered nurses to enter into full time employment at health facilities with nursing shortages, this program assists in the repayment of their nursing education loans. The program is designed to increase the number of registered nurses serving designated nurse shortage areas. Nurses can use the money to pay off nursing student loans. An Applicant Information Bulletin For Registered Nurses is available at the address listed below. Money available: $2,183,000.

Contact Loan Repayment Programs Branch, Division of Scholarships and Loan Repayment, Bureau of Primary Health Care, Health Resources and Services Administration, 4350 East-West Highway, Rockville, MD 20857; 301-594-4400; 800-435-6464; {http://bphc.hrsa.gov/bhpc/}.

Money For Health Professionals Who Want To Be In Public Health
(Public Health Traineeships 93.964)

The program objective is to help support graduate students who are studying in the field of public health. Grants are given to colleges and universities offering graduate or specialized training in the public health field. Support is limited to the fields of biostatistics, epidemiology, environmental health, toxicology, public health nutrition, and maternal and child health. Money can be used to support a student completing a public health degree, and includes a stipend, tuition, and fees, and a transportation allowance. Students must apply to those institutions that have received the money.

For a listing of institutions that received money contact the office listed below. Money available: $2,326,000. Contact Division of Associated, Dental, and Public Health Professions, Bureau of Health Professions, Health Resources and Services Administration, Public Health Service, Parklawn Bldg., Room 8C-09, 5600 Fishers Lane, Rockville, MD 20857; 301-443-6041; {http://bhpr.hrsa.gov}.

Scholarships For
National Health Service Corps
(National Health Service Corps Scholarship Program 93.288)

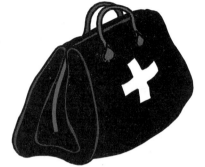

The program objective is to provide service-conditioned scholarships to health professions students to assure an adequate supply of physicians, dentists, certified nurse midwives, certified nurse practitioners, and physician assistants in Health Professional Shortage Areas. The scholarship pays for tuition and required fees, books, supplies, and equipment for the year, plus a monthly stipend to students ($935 per month), and a single annual payment to cover the cost of all other reasonable educational expenses.

Each year of support incurs one year of service, with a two-year minimum service obligation required. Service sites are selected from those listed by the National Health Service Corps one year prior to service in federally designated Health Professional Shortage Areas. Money available: $30,066,400. Contact National Health Service Corps Scholarships, Division of Scholarships and Loan Repayments, Bureau of Primary Health Care, Health Resources and Services Administration, Public Health Service, U.S. Department of Health and Human Services, 4350 East-West Hwy., 10th Floor, Bethesda, MD 20814; 301-594-4410; 800-638-0824; {www.bphc.hrsa.dhhs.gov/nhsc}.

$30,000 TO STUDY THE HUMANITIES
(Promotion of the Humanities - Fellowships and Stipends 45.160)

Fellowships and Summer Stipends provide support for scholars to undertake full-time independent research and writing in the humanities. Grants are available for 6 to 12 month fellowships and two months of summer study. Projects may contribute to scholarly knowledge or to the general public's understanding of the humanities. The proposed study or research may be completed during the grant period or it may be part of a longer project.

Contact the office listed below for application information. Money available: $6,100,000. Stipends are $4,000 for summer; $24,000 for 6-8 months; and $30,000 for 9-12 months. Contact Fellowships and Stipends, Division of Research and Education, National Endowment for the Humanities, Room 318, Washington, DC 20506; 202-606-8466; {www.neh.gov}.

Grants For Graduate Training
In Family Medicine
(Grants For Graduate Training In Family Medicine 93.379)

The program objective is to increase the number of physicians practicing family medicine, particularly to those willing to work in medically under-served communities. Grants are available to cover the cost of developing and operating residency-training programs, and to provide financial assistance to participants in the programs. A grant may be made to a residency program in family practice; an internship program in osteopathic medicine which emphasizes family medicine; or a residency program in osteopathic general practice.

Money can be used to support a student while he or she completes a residency or internship program. Residents must apply to those institutions that have received the money. For a listing of institutions that received money contact the office listed below. Money available: $13,616,136. Contact Division of Medicine, Bureau of Health

Professions, Health Resources and Services Administration, Public Health Service, U.S. Department of Health and Human Services, Room 9A27, 5600 Fishers Lane, Rockville, MD 20857; 301-443-1468; {http://bhpr.hrsa.gov/dm/MEDICINE.HTM}.

Money To Train To Be A Professional Nurse
(Professional Nurse Traineeships 93.358)

The program objective is to prepare individuals who have completed basic nursing preparation as nurse educators, public health nurses, nurse midwives, and nurse practitioners, or as other clinical nursing specialists. Money can be used to support a student while they complete the professional nurse traineeships. Students must apply to those institutions that have received the program money. A fact sheet is available entitled *Program Guide for Professional Nurse Traineeship Program.*

For a listing of institutions that received money contact the office listed below. Money available: $15,666,000. Students may receive stipends up to $8,800 plus tuition and other expenses. Contact Division of Nursing, Bureau of Health Professions, Health Resources and Services Administration, Public Health Service, U.S. Department of Health and Human Services, 5600 Fishers Lane, Rockville, MD 20857; 301-443-5786; {http://bhpr.hrsa.gov/dr/dr.htm}.

Money For Job Safety and Health Training
(Occupational Safety and Health - Training Grants 93.263)

The program objective is to develop specialized professional and paraprofessional personnel in the occupational safety and health field with training in occupational medicine, occupational health nursing, industrial hygiene, and occupational safety. Money can be used to pay for long and short-term training and educational resource centers. Students must apply to those institutions that have received the money.

For a listing of institutions that received money contact the office listed below. Money available: $11,092,000. Contact National Institute for Occupational Safety and Health (NIOSH), Centers for Disease Control and Prevention, Public Health Service, U.S. Department of Health and Human Services, 1600 Clifton Rd., Atlanta, GA 30333; 404-639-3525; {www.cdc.gov/niosh}.

MONEY FOR HEALTH CARE TRAINING IN RURAL AREAS
(Interdisciplinary Training For Health Care For Rural Areas 93.192)

This program is designed to help fulfill the health care needs of people living in rural areas. Money is set aside to recruit and retain health care professionals in rural health care settings. Funds can be used for student stipends, postdoctoral fellowships, faculty training, and the purchase or rental of necessary transportation and telecommunication equipment. Money can be used to support health profession students while they complete their degree or training. Students must apply to those institutions that have received the money.

For a listing of institutions that received money contact the office listed below. Money available: $3,926,000. Contact Division of Associated, Dental and Public Health Professions, Bureau of Health Professions, Health Resources and Services Administration, Room 8C-26, Parklawn Building, 5600 Fishers Lane, Rockville, MD 20857; 301-443-6867; {http://bhpr.hrsa.gov/interdisciplinary/rural.html}.

GRANTS FOR PEDIATRIC TRAINING
(Pediatric Residency in Primary Care 93.181)

Hospitals and schools of pediatric medicine can receive money to support residency programs for primary care pediatric practice. Funds can be used to cover the development and establishment of Pediatric Primary Care Residency programs and to provide resident stipends for those planning to specialize in pediatric primary care. Money can be used to support a resident while he or she completes his or her pediatric primary care residency. Students must apply to those institutions that have received the money.

For a listing of institutions that received money contact the office listed below. Money available: $624,440. Contact Division of Medicine, Bureau of Health Professions, Health Resources and Services Administration, Public Health Service, U.S. Department of Health and Human Services, Room 8C-26, Parklawn Building, 5600 Fishers Lane, Rockville, MD 20857; 301-443-6880; {http://bhpr.hrsa.gov}.

Money For Disadvantaged Students To Study Nursing
(Nursing Education Opportunities For Individuals From Disadvantaged Backgrounds 93.178)

Schools of nursing can receive financial assistance to meet the costs of projects that increase nursing education opportunities for individuals from disadvantaged backgrounds. Money can be used for counseling, preliminary education of students, and to support a student while completing a nursing degree. Students must apply to those institutions that have received the money.

For a listing of institutions that received money contact the office listed below. Money available: $3,779,000. Contact Division of Nursing, Bureau of Health Professions, Health Resources and Services Administration, Public Health Services, U.S. Department of Health and Human Services, Room 8C-26, Parklawn Building, 5600 Fishers Lane, Rockville, MD 20857; 301-443-6880; {http://bhpr.hrsa.gov}.

Money To Repay Loans
(National Health Service Corps Loan Repayment 93.162)

The National Health Service Corps provides for the repayment of educational loans for health professionals who agree to serve in a health manpower shortage area. Priority is given to primary care physicians, dentists, certified nurse midwives, certified nurse practitioners, and physicians' assistants. Money can be used to repay student loans. The amount of money available per professional is up to $25,000 a year during the first two years of practice and $35,000 for each year after that. Health professionals also receive a very competitive salary and benefits package. Money available: $36,000,000.

Contact National Health Service Corps Scholarships, Division of Scholarships and Loan Repayments, Bureau of Primary Health Care, Health Resources and Services Administration, Public Health Service, U.S. Department of Health and Human Services, 4350 East-West Hwy., 10th Floor, Bethesda, MD 20814; 301-594-4410; 800-435-6464; {www.bphc.hrsa.dhhs.gov/nhsc}.

Money For Minorities Pursuing a Health Professions Education
(Programs of Excellence In Health Professions Education For Minorities 93.157)

The program helps health professions schools train minority health professionals. These funds can be used to recruit and retain faculty, improve the facilities and information resources, and improve student performance, student recruitment, and student research. Students must apply to those institutions that have received the money. For a listing of institutions that received money contact the office listed below. Money available: $22,800,000.

Contact Division of Disadvantaged Assistance, Bureau of Health Professions, Health Resources and Services Administration, Public Health Service, U.S. Department of Health and Human Services, Room 8A-09, Parklawn Building, 55600 Fishers Lane, Rockville, MD 20857; 301-443-1348; {http://bhpr.hrsa.gov/dhpd/coehome1.htm}.

Get Your Loans Paid Through Indian Health Service
(Indian Health Service Loan Repayment Program 93.164)

To ensure that there are enough trained health professionals, the Indian Health Service provides for the repayment of loans to those professionals who agree to serve in an Indian Health Service Facility. Money can be used for the repayment of student loans. An application is available by contacting the office listed below. Money available: $11,233,900. The minimum period of participation is two years, and the maximum loan payment is $30,000 per year. Contact Indian Health Service, Loan Repayment Program, 12300 Twinbrook Parkway, Suite 100, Rockville, MD 20852; 301-443-3369; {www.ihs.gov}.

Financial Assistance For Disadvantaged Health Professions Students
(Financial Assistance For Disadvantaged Health Professions Students 93.139)

Health profession students who are of exceptional financial need and are studying for a degree in medicine, osteopathic medicine, or dentistry can receive financial support. Money can be used to support a student while in school. Funds are awarded to accredited schools of medicine, osteopathic medicine, or dentistry. Students should apply to their school for these scholarships. Money available: $6,741,000. The maximum amount available per student is $18,000.

Contact Division of Student Assistance, Bureau of Health Professions, Health Resources and Services Administration, Public Health Service, U.S. Department of Health and Human Services, Room 8-34, 5600 Fishers Lane, Rockville, MD 20857; 301-443-4776; {http://bhpr.hrsa.gov}.

Money To Train To Become A Nurse Anesthetist
(Nurse Anesthetist Traineeships 93.124)

Registered nurses can receive money to become nurse anesthetists through this program that provides funds for a maximum 18-month period of full-time study. Nurses must complete 12 months of study in a nurse anesthetist program. Money can be used to support a student while completing the training program. Students need to apply to those institutions that have received the money. For a listing of institutions that received money contact the office listed below. Student stipend is usually $8,800 plus tuition and other expenses. Money available: $2,717,000.

Contact Division of Nursing, Bureau of Health Professions, Health Resources and Services Administration, Public Health Service, U.S. Department of Health and Human Services, Room 9-36, 5600 Fishers Lane, Rockville, MD 20857; 301-443-6880; {http://bhpr.hrsa.gov}.

Money To Study Food
(Food and Agricultural Science National Needs Graduate Fellowship Grants 10.210)

The program awards grants to colleges and universities that have superior teaching and research competencies in the food and agricultural sciences. These grants are to be used to encourage outstanding students to pursue and complete a graduate degree in an area of the food and agricultural sciences for which there is a national need for development of scientific expertise.

Money can be used to support a student completing a graduate, masters, or doctorate degree. Students must apply to those institutions that received the money. For a listing of institutions that received money contact the office listed below. Money available: $2,910,000.

Contact Grants Program Manager, Office of Higher Education Programs, CSREES, U.S. Department of Agriculture, Administrative Building, Room 338A, 14th and Independence Ave., SW, Washington, DC 20250; 202-720-7854; {www.reeusda.gov/serd/hep/index.htm}.

Money To Help Math Students and Summer Scientists
(Independent Education and Science Projects and Programs 11.449)

This program objective is to increase the number of minority students enrolling in college and majoring in math, science and engineering. Another objective is to recruit scientists and engineers from the Boulder county area to serve as science/math tutors. Money can be used to help high school and middle school students who are part of the Math, Engineering, Science Achievement (MESA) Program in Colorado. It is also for students pursuing a course of study related to oceanic and atmospheric sciences and who are interested in a summer hands-on experience in a laboratory setting. Money can be used for transportation, housing and stipends for students during the summer months where students learn about the laboratories mission and perform hands-on assignments. Money available: $75,000.

Contact Tony Tafoya, NOAA/Environmental Research Laboratories, R/Ex-4, 325 Broadway, Boulder, CO 80303; 303-497-6731; {www.etl.noaa.gov}.

Money To Study Community Planning and Development
(Community Development Work-Study Program 14.512)

The Community Development Work-Study Program makes grants to institutions of higher education to provide assistance to economically disadvantaged and minority students. Students take part in community development work-study programs while they are enrolled full-time in graduate or undergraduate programs with that major. Grants are given to encourage minority and economically disadvantaged students to develop careers in community and economic development, community planning, and community management. Related fields include public administration, urban management, and urban planning.

Student assistance is in the form of work stipends, tuition support, and additional support to cover books and travel related to conferences and seminars. Students must apply to those institutions that received the money. For a listing of institutions that received money contact the office listed below. Money available: $3,000,000. Average grant per student is $30,000. Contact U.S. Department of Housing and Urban Development, Community Planning and Development, Office of University Partnerships, 451 7th St., SW, Room 8130, Washington, DC 20410; 202-708-1537, ext. 218; {www.hud.gov/progdesc/cdwsp.html}.

Money To Study Housing Issues
(Doctoral Dissertation Research Grant Program)

The program objective is to encourage doctoral candidates to engage in policy related housing and urban development research and to assist them in its timely completion. Money can used to support Ph.D candidates while they complete work towards their degree. Students must have a fully developed and approved dissertation proposal that addresses the purpose of this program. Students can request an application package from the address listed below or by calling HUD USER at 800-245-2691. Each student is eligible for up to $15,000 per year.

Contact Division of Budget, Contracts, and Program Control, Office of Policy Development and Research, U.S. Department of Housing and Urban Development, 451 7th St., SW, Room 8230, Washington, DC 20410; 202-708-0544; {www.huduser.org}.

Money For Members Of Indian Tribes
To Go To College
(Indian Education-Higher Education Grant Program 15.114)

The program objective is to provide financial aid to eligible Indian students to enable them to attend accredited institutions of higher education. Members of an Indian tribe may be eligible for these grants to supplement the total financial aid package prepared by their college financial aid officer. Once you have been accepted by a college and have completed their financial aid application, you may request a grant application form from your tribal group. Money available: $20,290,000. The amount of assistance per student ranges from $300-$5000 per year.

Contact Bureau of Indian Affairs, Office of Indian Education Programs, Code 522, Room S 3512-MIB, U.S. Department of the Interior, 1849 C St., NW, Washington, DC 20240; 202-208-3478; {www.oiep.bia.edu}.

Money To Study The Break Up Of The USSR
(Russian, Eurasian, and East European Research and Training 19.300)

The program is designed to sustain and strengthen American expertise on the Commonwealth of Independent States, Georgia, the Baltic countries, and countries of Eastern Europe by supporting graduate training; advanced research; public dissemination of research data, methods, and findings; contact and collaboration among government and private specialists; and first hand experience of the (former) Soviet Union and Eastern European countries by American specialists, including on site conduct of advanced training and research. Graduate students interested in conducting research on the Commonwealth of Independent States, Georgia, the Baltic countries, and the countries of Eastern Europe can receive fellowships which can support a student while conducting research or training.

Funds are given to nonprofit organizations and institutions of higher learning who act as intermediaries for the federal funds by conducting their own competitions to make the awards. Grants in the past include grants for onsite independent short term research; individual exchange fellowships for American graduate students to pursue research in the region; and advanced in-country language training fellowships in Russian, Ukrainian, Hungarian, Polish, and more. Students must apply to those institutions that received the money. For a listing of institutions that received money contact the office listed below. Money available: $4,800,000. Contact Eurasian and East European Research and Training Program, INR/RES, U.S. Department of State, 2201 C St., NW, Room 6841, Washington, DC 20520; 202-736-4851; {www.state.gov/}.

Money For Criminal Justice Majors
(Criminal Justice Research and Development - Grant Research Fellowships 16.562)

The program objective is to improve the quality and quantity of knowledge about crime and the criminal justice system. Additionally, the program seeks to increase the number of persons who are qualified to teach in collegiate criminal justice programs, to conduct research related to criminal justice issues, and to perform more effectively within the criminal justice system. Students can receive a fellowship for a year, plus, two to three months to visit the National Institute of Justice to work with staff as an intern.

This competitive program provides fellowship stipends, major project costs and certain university fees, round trip travel expenses to the Institute, and housing costs. Detailed information can be received by requesting the NIJ Research Plan from the National Criminal Justice Reference Service, Box 6000, Rockville, MD 20850; 800-851-3420. Money available: $150,000. Maximum grant per student $15,000. Contact National Institute of Justice, 633 Indiana Ave., SW, Washington, DC 20531; 202-307-2942; {www.ncjrs.org}.

$3,000 A Year To Be A Merchant Marine
(State Marine Schools 20.806)

The program objective is to train merchant marine officers in State Marine Schools. You can receive $3,000 per year to train to be a merchant marine officer at a designated State Marine School. In exchange for this incentive payment program, you must commit yourself to a minimum of five years duty to the Maritime Administration, which can be satisfied by: serving as a merchant marine officer aboard vessels; as an employee in a U.S. maritime related industry, profession or marine science; or as a commissioned officer on active duty in an armed force of the U.S. or in the National Oceanic and Atmospheric Administration. You must also remain in a reserve unit of an armed force for a minimum of eight years.

Students need to apply to one of the State Marine Schools. Money available: $6,750,000. Contact Office of Maritime Labor and Training, Maritime Administration, U.S. Department of Transportation, 400 7th St., SW, Washington, DC 20590; 202-366-5755; {www.marad.dot.gov}.

ALL EXPENSES PLUS
$558 A MONTH TO BE A MERCHANT MARINE

This program trains merchant marine officers while they attend the Merchant Marine Academy in Kings Point, NY. Students receive training, subsistence, books, quarters, uniforms, medical care, and program travel without cost. In addition, the student will receive a monthly wage from their steamship company employer. Money available: $33,250,000. An allowance is prescribed for all personnel for uniforms and textbooks. During the sea year a midshipman will earn $558.04 per month from the steamship employer.

Contact Office of Maritime Labor and Training, Maritime Administration, U.S. Department of Transportation, 400 Seventh St., SW, Washington, DC 20590; 202-366-5755; {www.marad.dot.gov}.

Money For Social, Behavioral, And Economic Sciences Students
(Social, Behavioral, and Economic Sciences 47.075)

The program objective is to promote the progress of the social, behavioral, and economic science; to facilitate cooperative research activities with foreign scientists, engineers, and institutions and to support understanding of the resources invested in science and engineering in the U.S. Funds are provided for U.S. scientists and engineers to carry out studies abroad, to conduct research, to engage in joint research projects with foreign counterpart organizations, and to support international scientific workshops in the U.S. and abroad.

Money can be used for paying associated costs necessary to conduct research or studies for doctorate students; and more. Students must contact the office listed below for application information. Money available: $150,260,000. Contact Assistant Director, Social, Behavioral, and Economic Research, National Science Foundation, 4201 Wilson Blvd., Arlington, VA 22230; 703-306-1710; {www.nsf.gov}.

Money For Disabled Veterans To Go To College
(Vocational Rehabilitation For Disabled Veterans 64.116)

The program objective is to provide all services and assistance necessary to enable service-disabled veterans and service persons hospitalized pending discharge to achieve maximum independence in daily living and, to the maximum extent possible, to become employable and to obtain and maintain suitable employment. The fund provides for the entire cost of tuition, books, fees, supplies, and other services to help the veteran live with a reduced dependency on others while staying in their homes and communities. The veteran also receives a monthly allowance, a work-study allowance, and more. Enrollment can be in a trade, business, or technical schools, colleges, apprenticeship programs, cooperative farming, special rehabilitation facilities, or at home when necessary.

Students must obtain an application from any Veterans Affairs office or regional office. Money available: Direct payments: $402,907,0000; Loan advances: $2,401,000. Monthly full time allowances per student range from $413 for a single veteran to $604 for a veteran with two dependents, plus $44 for each dependent in excess of two. Contact Department of Veterans Affairs, Central Office, Washington, DC 20420; 800-827-1000; {www.va.gov}.

Money For Spouses And Children Of Deceased Or Disabled Veterans To Go To School
(Survivors and Dependents Educational Assistance 64.117)

The program provides partial support to those seeking to advance their education who are qualifying spouses, surviving spouses, or children of deceased or disabled veterans who, as a result of their military service, have a permanent and total (100 percent) service connected disability, or a service personnel who have been listed for a total of more than 90 days as currently Missing in Action, or as Prisoners of War. Spouse, surviving spouse, or child of a deceased or disabled veteran can receive monthly payments to be used for tuition, books, subsistence, for courses, training, or college. Financial assistance is $485 per month, and there is tutorial assistance, vocational counseling and testing, and a work-study allowance. Benefits may be awarded for pursuit of associate, bachelor, or graduate degrees at colleges and universities, as well as study at business, technical, or vocational schools.

Information on the program and application forms are available from your local or regional Veterans Affairs office. Money available: $108,530,000. Contact Department of Veterans Affairs, Central Office, Washington, DC 20420; 800-827-1000; {www.va.gov}.

Money For Vietnam Veterans To Go To School
(Post-Vietnam Era Veterans' Educational Assistance 64.120)

Post-Vietnam veterans who entered the Armed Services between 1977 and 1985 may be eligible for funds to obtain a college degree or vocational training. Through this program, the government matches $2 for every $1 the serviceman contributes. Some contribution to the fund must have been made prior to April 1, 1987. Contact your local or regional Veterans Affairs office for additional information or application materials. Money available: $54,614,000.

Up to a maximum of $8,100 of basic benefits is available per student, as well as a work-study allowance of minimum wage and tutorial assistance up to a maximum of $1,200. Contact Department of Veterans Affairs, Central Office, Washington, DC 20420; 800-827-1000; {www.va.gov}.

Money For Retired Veterans To Go To School
(All-Volunteer Force Educational Assistance 64.124)

This program helps servicemen readjust to civilian life after their separation from military service, assists in the recruitment and retention of highly qualified personnel in the active and reserve components in the Armed Forces, and extends the benefits of a higher education to those who may not otherwise be able to afford it. Honorably discharged veterans can take advantage of the Montgomery GI Bill Active Duty benefits, which provides funds to pursue professional or vocational education, and even covers correspondence courses.

Veterans can receive a monthly stipend while attending school, with the amount varying depending upon date of entry into the service and length of service. Additional information and application materials are available through any regional Veterans Affairs office. Money available: $816,798,000. A maximum allowance of $19,008 as basic assistance is available per student, as well as a work-study allowance, and up to $1,200 in tutorial assistance. Contact Department of Veterans Affairs, Central Office, Washington, DC 20420; 800-827-1000; {www.va.gov}.

Volunteer And Earn Money To Pay For School
(AmeriCorps 94.006)

AmeriCorps is an initiative designed to achieve direct results in addressing the nation's critical education, human, public safety, and environmental needs at the community level. The program provides meaningful opportunities for people to serve their country in organized efforts, fostering citizen responsibility, building their community, and providing education opportunities for those who make a serious commitment to service.

Stipends can be used to support the person while they volunteer. Health care and childcare benefits may also be provided. Participants will also receive an education award, which may be used to pay for higher education or for vocational training, and may also be used to repay any existing student loans. Contact the Corporation for National Service to locate programs in your area or to apply for programs at the national level. Money available: $256,816,000.

Contact Corporation for National Service, 1201 New York Ave., NW, Washington, DC 20525 202-606-5000, ext. 474; {www.americorps.org}.

Money To Study The Drug Abuse Field
(Drug Abuse National Research Service Awards for Research Training 93.278)

Individual grants are made to fellows seeking predoctoral or postdoctoral support for full time research training in the drug abuse field. It can be used to cover tuition fees, and more. Postdoctoral researchers are obligated to pay back their first year of support through a period of research and/or teaching activities. Predoctoral stipends are $14,688 and postdoctoral awards range from $26,256 to $41,268. Money available: $15,600,000.

Contact National Institute on Drug Abuse, National Institutes of Health, U.S. Department of Health and Human Services, Neurosciences Building, 6001 Executive Blvd., Bethesda, MD 20892; 301-443-6710; {www.nih.gov}.

Fellowships for Creative Writers and Translators
(Promotion of the Arts-Grants to Organizations and Individuals 45.024)

The National Endowment for the Arts provides grants to support Literature Fellowships, Fellowships for Creative Writers, Fellowships awarded to writers of poetry, fiction, and creative nonfiction to allow them to devote time to writing, research, travel, and to advance their writing careers. Money available: $830,000. Fellowships are usually $20,000. For more information, contact National Endowment for the Arts, 1100 Pennsylvania Ave., NW, Washington, DC 20506; 202-682-5400; {http://arts.gov}.

Scholarships for Minorities
(Higher Education Multicultural Scholars Program 10.220)

This program is designed to increase the ethnic and cultural diversity of the food and agricultural scientific and professional work force, and to advance the educational achievement of minority Americans. Money is given to colleges and universities that have a demonstrable capacity to attract, educate, and graduate minority students for careers as agriscience and agribusiness professionals. Funds can be used to support full-time undergraduate students pursuing a baccalaureate degree in an area of food and agricultural sciences. Money available: $1,920,000.

Contact Grants Programs Manager, Education Programs, SCREES, U.S. Department of Agriculture, Room 3912, South Building, Washington, DC 20250; 202-720-7854; {www.reeusda.gov}.

State College Money

After checking out what money programs are available from the federal government, your next task is to find out what's available at the state level. There are close to 400 programs worth almost $3 billion dollars in financial aid available thru all 50 states. Just because you or your parents don't have the money to pay for college, that doesn't mean your dream of a college degree will never happen. Even if you do have the money, financial assistance from one of these programs could make things a little easier for all concerned.

Did you know that there are state money programs which:

Pay for a singing degree?
Give you money to study wildlife?
Give you $2000 to go to vocational school?
Pay for your nursing, teaching or law degree?
Give you $7,000 to study marine sciences?

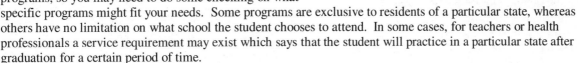

The advantages of many of these programs are that most people don't even know they exist, so your competition will be less. Each state has different requirements for their various programs, so you may need to do some checking on what specific programs might fit your needs. Some programs are exclusive to residents of a particular state, whereas others have no limitation on what school the student chooses to attend. In some cases, for teachers or health professionals a service requirement may exist which says that the student will practice in a particular state after graduation for a certain period of time.

What follows is a concise and comprehensive state-by-state listing of available programs. It will allow you to shop around for the best program to suit your individual needs. By remaining flexible and adjusting your educational goals to fit the program that most appeals to you, chances are you might find yourself pursuing the college education that you always thought was beyond your reach. Using this information might be an important first step in building a successful future for yourself.

STATE AID

Alabama

Alabama Commission on Higher Education
P.O. Box 30200
Montgomery, AL 36130-2000
334-242-1998
Fax: 334-242-0265
www.ache.state.al.us
General requirements: Resident of Alabama and attending an in-state school.

Programs Available:
Grants To Students Who Can't Afford Tuition (Alabama Student Assistance Program)
Grants To Students Attending Private Colleges (Alabama Student Grant Program)
Join The National Guard And Get $1,000 A Year For College (Alabama National Guard Assistance Program)
Grants and Loans To Nursing Students (Alabama Nursing Scholarships)
Tuition, Fees, And Books To Spouses and Children Of Veterans
    (Alabama GI Dependents Educational Benefit Program)

Grants To Children and Grandchildren of Veterans (American Legion Scholarship and
American Legion Auxiliary Scholarship Programs)
Free Tuition If You're Over 60 (Senior Adult Scholarships)
Money For Jocks Going To Junior College (Junior and Community College Athletic Scholarships)
Money For Dancers, Singers, and Actors Attending Junior College
(Junior and Community College Performing Arts Scholarships)
Grants To Children Of The Blind (Alabama Scholarships for Dependents of Blind Parents)
Grants For Dependents Of Fire Fighters And Police Officers Killed In The Line Of Duty (Police Officers and Fire
Fighters Survivor's Educational Assistance Program)
Loans That Guarantee The Price Of Your Future Tuition (Prepaid College Tuition Program)
School Technology Scholarship Program for Alabama Teachers (Two Year College Academic Scholarship Program)
Other Alabama Assistance Awards:
University Station
1600 Eighth Ave., S.
Birmingham, AL 35294
Alabama Board of Dental Scholarship
Alabama Board of Medical Scholarship
Alabama Board of Optometric Scholarship
Alabama State Chiropractic Association

Alaska

Alaska Commission on Postsecondary Education
3030 Vintage Blvd.
Juneau, AK 99801
907-465-2962
Fax: 907-465-5316
www.state.ak.us/acpe
General requirements: Alaska resident and attending an in-state or out-of-state school.

Programs Available:
Free Money To Go To School If You Work In Law Enforcement (Michael Murphy Memorial Scholarship Loan)
Money For 8 Years Of College If You Study Food Or Wildlife (A.W. "Winn" Brindle Memorial Scholarship Loan)
$7,500 A Year and Travel Money If You Study To Be A Teacher In A Small Town
(Teacher Scholarship Loan Program)

Arizona

Arizona Commission for Postsecondary Education
2020 North Central, Suite 550
Phoenix, AZ 85004
602-258-2345
www.acpe.asu.edu
General requirements: Arizona administers a "decentralized" form of student aid in
higher education. Monies are allocated based on a formula to postsecondary schools,
and each college or university sets their own individual funding limits. Students
should contact the Financial Aid office at the college they plan to attend for
applicable scholarship, grant, and loan information. State residency is required for
the programs listed.

Programs Available:
$2,500 Grants For Students Having Trouble Paying Tuition (LEAP)
Money And Help To Educate Students With Physical and Mental Disabilities (Vocational Rehabilitation Assistance)
Reduced Tuition To Take Courses Not Offered In Arizona (Student Exchange Program)
$3,000 For Community College Graduates To Go To Private College

Arkansas

Arkansas Department of Higher Education
114 East Capitol
Little Rock, AR 72201
501-371-2000
Fax: 501-371-2003
www.arkansashighered.com

General requirements: Applicants must be current residents of Arkansas.

Programs Available:
$600 Per Year On First-Come, First-Served Basis (Student Assistance Grants)
$4,000 For High School Graduates With At Least 3.5 Averages (Governor's Scholars)
$2,500 For High School Graduates With At Least 2.5 Averages (Arkansas Academic Challenge Scholarship)
Free Money For School If You Become a Math, Science, or Special Education Teacher, or a Guidance Counselor (Emergency Secondary Education Loan)
Free Tuition, Room, Board, and Fees To Dependents and Spouses of MIA's and POW's (MIA/KIA Dependent's Scholarship)
Grants To Dependents Of Law Enforcement Officers Killed Or Totally Disabled In The Line Of Duty (Law Enforcement Officer's Dependents Scholarship)
$1,000 To Top Ten GED Scorers (Second Effort Scholarship)
Money To Go Out Of State To Study Chiropractic Medicine, Dentistry, Optometry, Osteopathic Medicine, Podiatric Medicine, Or Become A Vet (Arkansas Health Education Grant Program)
$5,000 For Minorities To Get Teaching Certificate (Minority Teachers Scholarship)
Money To Teachers To Take Classes (Teacher and Administrator Program)
$7,500 For Minorities To Study Math, Sciences, Or Foreign Languages (Minority Masters Fellows Program)

California

California Postsecondary Education Commission
1303 J Street, Suite 500
Sacramento, CA 95814
916-445-7933
www.cpec.ca.gov

General requirements: Applicants must be residents of California.

Programs Available:
Grants For Tuition, Living Expenses, and Vocational Training (Cal Grants A, B, and C)
Help To Work Your Way Through College (State Work-Study Program)
$11,000 To Become A Teacher (Assumption Program of Loans for Education (APLE))
Grants To Graduate Students Who Want To Become College Teachers (Graduate APLE)
Grants To Dependents Of Fire Fighters, Police Officers, and Correctional Officials Killed Or Totally Disabled In The Line Of Duty (Law Enforcement Personnel Dependents Scholarship)
$9,700 Grant To Get Teaching Certificate (Cal Grant T)
$4,000 To Study Child Development (Child Development Grant Program)
$1,500 Each Year For Bright Students (Robert C. Byrd Honors Scholarship Program)

Colorado

Colorado Commission on Higher Education
1380 Lawrence Street, Suite 1200
Denver, CO 80204
303-866-2723
www.state.co.us/cche_dir/hecche.html

General requirements: Applicants must be residents of Colorado.

Programs Available:

Grants To Students From Families Who Don't Normally Go To College
    (Colorado Diversity Grants)

Grants To Students Who Are Having Trouble Paying For Tuition (CLEAP)

More Grants To Students Who Are Having Trouble Paying For Tuition
    (Colorado Student Grants (CSG))

Money For Students Going To College Part Time
    (Colorado Part time Grants)

State Jobs For Students Having Trouble Paying Tuition (Colorado
    Work-Study)

Money For Smart Students Going To College In Colorado (Undergraduate
    Merit Awards)

Money For Graduates Who Have Trouble Paying Tuition (Colorado Graduate Grants)

Money For Smart Graduate Students (Colorado Graduate Fellowships)

Grants To Dependents Of POW/MIA's or Fire Fighters, Police Officers, and Correctional Officials Killed Or Totally
    Disabled In The Line Of Duty (Law Enforcement/POW-MIA Dependents Tuition Assistance)

Money To Be A Nurse And Practice In Colorado (Colorado Nursing Scholarship)

100% Tuition For National Guard Members (Colorado National Guard Tuition Assistance Program)

Connecticut

Department of Higher Education
61 Woodland St.
Hartford, CT 06105-2326
860-947-1800
www.ctdhe.org

General requirements: Applicants must be Connecticut residents for in-state and out-of-state schools programs.

Programs Available:

$2,000 A Year If You Are In Top 20% Of Your High School Class (Capitol Scholarship)

$8,548 A Year To Attend A Private College (Connecticut Independent College Student Grant)

Money For Students Who Need Help Paying Tuition At A Public University
    (Connecticut Aid for Public College Students)

Money To Dependents Of Deceased, Disabled, Or MIA Veterans
    (Aid to Dependents of Deceased, Disabled, or MIA Veterans)

Free Tuition To Veterans (Tuition Waiver for Veterans)

$1,500 Each Year For Bright Students (Robert C. Byrd Honors Scholarship Program)

$10,000 For Minorities To Become Teachers (CT Minority Teacher Incentive Program)

Delaware

Commission on Higher Education
Carvel State Office Building, Fifth Floor
820 N. French St.
302-577-3240
Wilmington, DE 19801
Fax: 302-577-6765

General requirements: Applicants must be Delaware residents for in-state or out-of-state colleges.

Programs Available:

Money To Be A Teacher In Delaware (Christa McAuliffe Teacher Scholarship Loan)

$1,250 A Year For Undergraduate Students (Diamond State Scholarship)

Full Tuition, Room and Board To Smart High School Seniors
    (B. Bradford Barnes Scholarship)

Money To Be A Registered Or Practical Nurse And Practice In A State-Owned
Hospital (Delaware Nursing Incentive Program)
$2,220 each Year To Attend College For Financially Needy (Scholarship
Incentive Program-ScIP)
100% Tuition For Dependents Of Deceased Veterans (Education Benefits for
Children of Deceased Veterans and Others)
$1,500 Each Year To Attend College Part-Time (Governor's Workforce
Development Grant)
100% Tuition For Bright Students To Study Humanities Or Social Sciences
(Charles L. Hebner Memorial Scholarship)
100% Tuition To Study at Delaware State University (Herman M. Holloway, Sr.
Memorial Scholarship)
$1,500 Each Year For Bright Students (Robert C. Byrd Honors Scholarship
Program)
$500 To Write An Essay (Legislative Essay Scholarship)
Loan (With Loan Forgiveness Provisions) To Study Optometry (Optometry Scholarship Program)
Loan (With Loan Forgiveness Provisions) To Become Librarian And Archivist
(Librarian and Archivist Incentive Program)
Loan (With Loan Forgiveness Provisions) To Become Speech/Language Pathologist
(Speech/Language Pathologist Incentive Program)
Support For Medical Students To Study At Jefferson Medical College Or Pennsylvania College of Osteopathic
Medicine (Delaware Institute for Medical Education and Research and Delaware State Loan Repayment Program
For Physicians and Dentists)
Lower Tuition To Become Vet At University of Georgia (University of Georgia College of Veterinary Medicine)

District of Columbia

Office of Postsecondary Education
2100 Martin Luther King, Jr., Ave., SE, Suite 401
Washington, DC 20020
202-695-2400
http://dhs.washington.dc.us
General requirements: Applicants must be District of Columbia residents for in-state or out-of-state school programs.

Programs Available:
Money For College Anywhere (D.C. State Student Incentive Program)
D.C. State Student Incentive Program, $700 per student for the academic year. Applications available: March 1.

Florida

Florida Office of Student Financial Assistance
1940 N. Monroe St., Suite 70
Tallahassee, FL 32303-4759
888-827-2004
Fax: 850-488-3612
General requirements: Applicants must be Florida residents for in-state or out-of-state school programs.

Programs Available:
Money For Students Who Have Trouble Paying Their Tuition (Florida Student Assistance Grants (FSAG))
Work Your Way Through College With A Job At A Local Elementary School
(Instructional Aide Scholarship Program)
Jobs For Full Or Part-Time Students Who Need Help Paying Tuition (Florida Work Experience Program (FWEP))
Money For Smart High School Graduates Who Want To Be Teachers In Florida
("Chappie" James Most Promising Teacher Scholarship Loan Program)
Money For College Students Who Want To Be Teachers (Critical Teacher Shortage Scholarship Loan Program)

$3,000 A Year To Smart High School Graduates (Mary McLeod Bethune Scholarship Challenge Grant Fund)
Grants For American Indians To Go To College (Seminole and Miccosukee Indian Scholarship Program)
Money For Dependents Of Deceased or Disabled Veterans And POW/MIA's
     (Scholarships for Children of Deceased or Disabled Veterans)
$2,000 For Hispanic Americans Who Want To Go To College (Jose Marti Scholarship Challenge Grant Fund)
Money For Teachers To Take Part-Time Graduate Courses
     (Critical Teacher Shortage Tuition Reimbursement Program)
Free College Money If You Teach In Florida Public Schools
     (Critical Teacher Shortage Student Loan Forgiveness Program)
Money For Teachers To Get Retrained (Exceptional Student Education Training Grant for Out-of-Field Teachers)
Loan Forgiveness Program For Occupational or Physical Therapist
     (Critical Occupational Therapist or Physical Therapist Shortage Student Loan Forgiveness Program)
Ethics In Business Scholarship
Scholarships For Bright Students (Florida Bright Futures Scholarship Program)
$1,500 Each Year For Bright Students (Robert C. Byrd Honors Scholarship Program)
Grants To Minorities To Go To College Or Vo-Tech Schools (Rosewood Family Scholarship)
Grants To Attend Private College (William L. Boyd, IV Florida Resident Access Grant)

Georgia

Student Finance Commission
2082 E. Exchange Place, Suite 200
Tucker, GA 30084
770-724-9000
770-724-9225
www.gsfc.org

General requirements: Georgia provides no state grants but does offer the merit-based Valedictorian Governors Scholarship Program. This program identifies and recognizes high school seniors who have achieved excellence in school and community life. Requirements include: a minimum score of 1300 on the SAT test; a score of 31 on the ACT; or a ranking in the upper 10% of his or her graduating class. As a recipient of the award, the student may receive a Governor's Scholarship if he or she continues their postsecondary education in an approved public or private college or the University of Georgia, and meets other program requirements. The scholarship is used to defray the cost of tuition for a maximum of four years eligibility. The maximum amount awarded is $1,575.

Programs Available:
Scholarship To Go To College (HOPE-Helping Outstanding Pupils Educationally)
Grants To Attend College Out Of State, But Near The Border (Georgia Tuition Equalization Grant)
Scholarship To Study Engineering (Scholarship For Engineering Education)
$1,500 Each Year For Bright Students (Robert C. Byrd Honors Scholarship Program)
Grants To Attend College For Dependents of Deceased Law Enforcement Officers, Firefighters, or Prison Guards
     (Law Enforcement Personnel Dependents Grant/Public Safety Memorial Grant)
Grants For Low Income Students To Attend College (Leveraging Educational Assistance Program)
100% Tuition To Attend North Georgia College and State University And Participate In Reserve Officers Training
     Corps (ROTC Grant) Or Georgia's Army National Guard (Military Scholarship)
100% Tuition To Attend Georgia Military College (Georgia Military college State Service Scholarship)
Scholarship To Become A Teacher (Charles McDaniel Teacher Scholarship)
Loan To Become Osteopathic Doctor (Osteopathic Medical Loan)

Hawaii

Hawaii State Postsecondary Education Commission
2444 Doic Street, Room 209
Honolulu, HI 96822
808-956-8213
http://doe/k12.hi.us/scholarship.htm

General requirements: Applicants must be Hawaii residents. Money available: $780,000.

Programs Available:
Free Tuition (Hawaii Student Incentive Grants (HSIG))
Free Tuition And Travel To High School Graduates With 3.5 Grade Point Averages
   (Regents Scholarship for Academic Excellence)
Free Tuition And Travel To High School Graduates With 3.7 Grade Point Averages
   (Presidential Achievement Scholarship)
Money For Students Planning To Study Pacific/Asian Studies (Pacific Asian Scholarships)
Robert C. Byrd Honor Scholarship
$2,000 To Major In Art, Geophysics, Music, Oceanography, or Medical Records (Community Scholarship Program)

Idaho

Office of the State Board of Education
P.O. Box 83720
Boise, ID 83720-0037
208-334-2270
www.sde.state.id.us/osbe/board.htm
General requirements: Applicants must be Idaho residents.

Programs Available:
$3,000 For Student Activists (Idaho Governor's Challenge Scholarship)
Disadvantaged High School Students Can Get $2,500 To Go To
   College (Idaho Minority and "At-Risk" Student Scholarship)
Free Money For Students Studying To Be Teachers Or Nurses
   (Education Incentive Loan Forgiveness)
$250 Per Semester To Attend College (Idaho Promise Category B Scholarship)
$5,00 For Financially needy To Attend College
   (Leveraging Educational Assistance State Partnership Program-LEAP)
Subsidy To Study Medicine, Dentistry, Or Veterinary Medicine In Other States
$3,000 For Bright Students To Attend College (Idaho Promise Category A Scholarship)
Attend College In Washington Or Utah At In-State Rates
   (Idaho-Washington Reciprocity Program/ Utah-Idaho Scholarship)
$1,500 Each Year For Bright Students (Robert C. Byrd Honors Scholarship Program)
$2,000 To Attend College For Emmett High School Graduates (Tschudy Family Scholarship)
Attend College In Western United States At Reduced Rates (Western Interstate Commission For Higher Education)
Work Study Program For financially Needy (Atwell J. Parry Work Study Program)

Illinois

Illinois Student Assistance Commission
1755 Lake Cook Drive
Deerfield, IL 60015
847-948-8500
www.isca-online.org
General requirements: Applicants must be Illinois residents.

Programs Available:
Grants Up To $3,500 No Matter What Your Grades Are (Monetary Award Program)
$1,000 For Students In The Top 5% Of Their Class (Illinois Merit Recognition Scholarship Program)
Join The National Guard For Free Tuition For Graduate Or Undergraduate Studies
   (National Guard/Naval Militia Grant Program)
Veterans Living In Illinois Can Get Free Tuition and Fees (Illinois Veteran Grant Program)
Grants To Dependents Of Fire Fighters Or Police Officers Killed In The Line Of Duty
   (Police Officer/Fire Officer Dependent's Grant Program)

Grants To Dependents Of Correctional Officers Killed Or Disabled In The Line Of Duty
    (Correctional Officer's Survivor's Grant Program)
$2,500 To Study IT Industry (Arthur F. Quern Information Technology (Quern IT) Grant)
Enroll or be enrolled, at least half time in an eligible program of undergraduate information technology
$500 To Attend College (Illinois Incentive for Access (IIA) Program (Need-Based))
$5,000 For Minorities to Become Teachers (Minority Teachers of Illinois (MTI) Scholarship Program)
$5,000 For Bright Students To Become Teachers (DeBolt Teacher Shortage Scholarship Program)
$1,500 Each Year For Bright Students (Robert C. Byrd Honors Scholarship Program)
100% Tuition To Become Special Ed Teacher (Illinois Special Education Teacher Tuition Waiver Program)

Indiana

State Student Assistance Commission of Indiana
150 W. Market St., Suite 500
Indianapolis, IN 46204
317-232-2350
Fax: 317-232-3260
www.ai.org/ssaci
General requirements: Applicants must be Indiana residents.

Programs Available:
Indiana College Students Who Have Trouble Paying Tuition (Indiana Higher Education Grant)
$500 For Bright Students To Attend College (Hoosier Scholar Award)
100% Tuition For Financially Needy To Attend State College (Twenty-first Century Scholars Program)
Scholarship To Become A Nurse (Nursing Scholarship Fund Program)
Scholarship For Minorities To Become Teachers or Anyone To Become Special Ed Teacher
    (Minority Teacher/Special Education Scholarship)
$1,500 Each Year For Bright Students (Robert C. Byrd Honors Scholarship Program)
Get A Summer Job (Summer State Work Study Program)
Grant To Go To College For National Guard Members (Indiana National Guard Supplemental Grant)
Grants To Go To School Part-Time (SSACI's Higher Education Award and Freedom of Choice Grant)

Iowa

Iowa College Student Aid Commission
200 Tenth, 4th Floor
Des Moines, IA 50309-3609
515-242-3344
www.state.ia.us/collegeaid
General requirements: Applicants must be Iowa residents.

Programs Available:
Money For High School Graduates In The Top 15% Of Their Class (State of Iowa Scholarship Program)
Grants To Pay For Tuition At Private Colleges (Iowa Tuition Grants)
$650 To Take A Vocational Education Course (Iowa Vocational-Technical Tuition Grants)
Grants To Students Who Need Money For Education (Iowa Grants)

Kansas

Kansas Board of Regents
700 SW Harrison, Suite 1410
Topeka, KS 66603
785-296-3421
Fax: 785-296-0983
www.kansasregents.org
General requirements: Applicants must be Kansas residents.

Programs Available:
$1,500 A Year For Minority Students (Kansas Ethnic Minority Scholarship)
$500 To Take A Vocational Training Course (Vocational Education Scholarship)
$5,000 A Year If You Study To Be A Teacher In Kansas (Kansas Teacher Service Scholarship)
$3,500 A Year To Be A Nurse (Kansas Nursing Scholarship)
$1,000 To High School Graduates Who Have Trouble Paying Tuition (Kansas State Scholarship)
$3,000 For Financially Needy To Go To College (Kansas Comprehensive Grants)
$15,000 To Study Osteopathy (Kansas Osteopathy Medical Service Scholarship)
Subsidy For Optometry Students Who Open Practices in Kansas (Kansas Optometry Service Scholarship)
Subsidy For Dental Students Who Open Practices in Kansas (Kansas Dentistry Assistance)
$2,456 To Study Abroad (James B. Pearson Fellowship)
Grants To Scholars For Graduate Study (Kansas Distinguished Scholarship Program)
Subsidy For Students To Study Out Of State (Midwest Student Exchange Program)

Kentucky

Kentucky Higher Education Assistance Authority502-696-7200
1050 U.S. 127 South
Frankfort, KY 40601
800-928-8926
Fax: 502-696-7496
www.kheaa.com

General requirements: Applicants must attend an eligible Kentucky college; be enrolled in an undergraduate degree program; be state residents; establish financial need; and meet program requirements. Funds are limited, so students who file by April 1 have the best chance of receiving awards. Money available: Approximately $20,100,000.

Programs Available:
Grants To Financially Needy Full-Time and Part-Time Students
    (College Access Program Grants (CAP))
Grants To Students (Kentucky Tuition Grants (KTG))
Scholarships For Good Students (Kentucky Educational Excellence
    Scholarship)
Scholarship To Become A Teacher (KHEAA Teacher Scholarship Program)
Scholarship To Study Child Development (Early Childhood Development Scholarship)
Scholarship To Study Osteopathic Medicine (Osteopathic Medicine Scholarship)
Jobs For Those In College (KHEAA Work-Study Program)

Louisiana

Office of Student Financial Assistance
P.O. Box 91202
Baton Rouge, LA 70821-9202
225-922-1011
800-259-5626
Fax: 225-922-0790
www.osfa.state.la.us

General requirements: Applicants must be Louisiana residents.

Programs Available:
Maximum $7,000 Grant To Study Forestry Or Marine Sciences (Louisiana Rockefeller State Wildlife Scholarship)
Scholarships For Financially needy To Go To College (Leveraging Educational Assistance Partnership-LEAP)
$1,500 Each Year For Bright Students (Robert C. Byrd Honors Scholarship Program)

Maine

Finance Authority of Maine (FAME)
Maine Education Assistance Division
5 Community Drive
Augusta, ME 04332-0949
800-228-3734 (In Maine)
207-623-3263
207-626-2717
Fax: 207-632-0095
www.famemaine.com
General requirements: Applicants must be Maine residents.

Programs Available:
Free Tuition To Dependents Of Law Enforcement Officers And Fire Fighters Killed In The Line Of Duty (Tuition Waiver Program for Children of Fire Fighters and Law Enforcement Officers Killed in the Line of Duty)
Robert C. Byrd Honor Scholarship
Up to $1,250 For Needy To Attend College (Maine State Grant Program)
$12,000 Forgivable Loan Program To Those Who Agree Teach (Educators For Maine Program)
Tuition Waiver For Foster Children (Foster Children Under The Custody of the Department of Human Services)
Tuition Waiver For Spouses And Children Of Deceased EMTs (Children and Spouses of Emergency Medical Services Personnel Killed in the Line of Duty)
Scholarships For Needy Who Attend University of Maine (The University of Maine System Scholarship)
$1,000 For Architectural or Engineering Students (Advancement of Construction Technology Scholarship)

Maryland

Maryland Higher Education Commission
State Scholarship Administration
The Jeffrey Building
16 Francis Street, Suite 209
Annapolis, MD 21401-1781
410-260-4500
Fax: 410-974-5994
www.mhec.state.md.us
General requirements: Applicants must be Maryland residents, unless specified for in-state or out-of-state schools.

Programs Available:
$2,000 To Full- Or Part-Time Students (Senatorial Scholarship Program)
$200 To Full-Time Or Part-Time Students (House of Delegate Award)
$1,500 To Take A Vocational Education Course (Tolbert Grant)
$3,000 A Year For Smart Students (Distinguished Scholar Program)
$4,800 To Get A Degree In Nursing (Maryland State Nursing Scholarship)
$3,000 A Year To Become A Teacher In Maryland (Teacher Education Distinguished Scholar Program)
Grants To Dependents Of POW's, Fire Fighters, Police Officers, and Safety Personnel Killed Or Disabled In The Line Of Duty (Edward Conroy Grant)
Grants To Study Physical Therapy (Physical and Occupational Therapists and Assistants Scholarships)
$7,500 A Year To Study Family Practice Medicine (Family Practice Medical Scholarship)
Grants To Study Law, Dentistry, Medicine, Nursing Or Pharmacy (Professional Scholarship)
Tuition, Fees, Room and Board To Become A Teacher (Sharon Christa McAuliffe Critical Shortage Teacher Scholarship)
$2,000 To Study Child Care, Full or Part Time (Child Care Provider Scholarship)
Free Tuition To Fire Fighters and Rescue Squad Members Who Want To Study Full Or Part Time (Reimbursement of Fire Fighters and Rescue Squad Members)

Student Loans If You Work For A Non-Profit (Loan Assistance Repayment Program (LARP))
$3,000 For Science and Technology Majors (Science and Technology Scholarship)

Massachusetts

Board of Higher Education
One Ashburton Place, Room 1401
Boston, MA 02108-1696
617-994-6950
General requirements: Applicants must be Massachusetts residents.

Programs Available:
Money To Attend Private Colleges In Massachusetts
    (Gilbert Matching Scholarship)
Free Tuition At State Schools (Tuition Waiver Program)
No Interest Loan Program, $10,000,000.
Tuition Wavers For Smart Students (Paul Tsongas Scholarship)
$5,212 For Smart Teachers (Tomorrow's Teachers Scholarship Program)
$12,000 For Computer, Math and Science Majors (Commonwealth Futures Grant Program)
$2,900 Per Year For Needy To Attend College (MASSGrant Program)
Money To Help Pay For Fees (Massachusetts Cash Grant Program)
Money To Go To School Part-Time (Massachusetts Part-Time Grant Program)
Tuition For Spouse or Child Of Person Killed Or Missing In Line Of Public Service
    (Massachusetts Public Service Grant Program)
Up To $2,00 For Needy Students Who Do Well In College (Performance Bonus Grant Program)
Free College Courses For Teachers (Career Advancement Program Tuition Waiver)
Tuition Waivers For Veterans, Seniors, Disabled, Military And Native Americans (Categorical Tuition Waivers)
Tuition Waivers To Teachers Who Mentor (Collaborative Teachers Tuition Waiver)
Tuition Waiver For Foster Care Children (Department of Social Services Tuition Waiver For Foster Care Children)
Tuition Waiver For Adopted Children (DSS Adopted Children Tuition Waiver)
Tuition Waiver For Graduate Students (Graduate Tuition Waivers)
Tuition Waiver For High Technology Majors (High Technology Scholar/Intern Tuition Waiver Program)
Tuition Waiver For Teacher Shortage (Incentive Program For Aspiring Teachers)
1/3 Tuition Waiver For Community College Students Who Attend Four-Year University
    (Joint Admissions Tuition Advantage Program Waiver)
Tuition Waiver For Smart Students (Stanley Z. Koplik Certificate of Mastery Tuition Waiver)
Tuition Waiver For Students To Attend Other Colleges (University of Massachusetts Exchange
    Program Tuition Waiver)
Tuition Waiver For Work/Learning Experiences (Washington Center Program Tuition Waiver)

Michigan

Michigan Higher Education Assistance Authority
Office of Scholarships and Grants
P.O. Box 30462
Lansing, MI 48909
517-373-3394
Fax: 517-335-5984
www.MI-StudentAid.org
General requirements: Applicants must be Michigan residents.

Programs Available:
Money For Smart Kids Who Have Trouble Paying Tuition (Michigan Competitive Scholarships)
Money For Students Attending Private Colleges (Michigan Tuition Grants)
Robert C. Byrd Honor Scholarship
Scholarships For Community College Students (Postsecondary Access Student Scholarship Program)

Minnesota

Minnesota Higher Education Services Office
1450 Energy Park Drive, Suite 350
St. Paul, MN 55108-5227
651-642-0533
www.mheso.state.mn.us

General requirements: Applicants must be residents of Minnesota, unless otherwise specified.

Programs Available:
Money To Pay Half Your College Expenses (State Grant Program)
Money For Part-Time Students (State Part-Time Grant Program)
Money For Child Care While You Go To School Or Work Part Time (Non-AFDC Child Care Grant Program)
$1,000 For High School Students To Take Summer Courses At A College (Summer Scholarships for Academic Enrichment)
Grants To Dependents Of Safety Officers Killed In The Line Of Duty (Safety Officers' Survivor Program)
$1,500 Each Year For Bright Students (Robert C. Byrd Honors Scholarship Program)
$1,850 Per Year For Native Americans To Attend College (Minnesota Indian Scholarship Program)
100% Tuition For Smart Students (MN Academic Excellence Scholarship)
Scholarships For Farm Families
$500 For Student Service Scholars   (MN Service Scholarship Matching Grant)

Mississippi

Mississippi Institution of Higher Education
5825 Ridgewood Rd.
Jackson, MS 39211-6453
601-432-6997
www.ihl.state.ms.us

General requirements: Applicants must be Mississippi residents.
Money available: $2,600,000.

Programs Available:
Money To Pursue Degrees In Another State That Are Not Offered In Mississippi (Academic Common Market Program)
Grants To Full-Time Students Who Have Trouble Paying Tuition (State Student Incentive Grant Program)
Graduate Students Can Make $1,000 A Month As Student Interns (Mississippi Public Management Graduate Internship Program)
Money To Dental Students (State Dental Education Loan/Scholarship Program)
Money To Full-Time Students Who Want To Become Teachers (William Winter Teacher Scholar Loan Program)
$10,000 A Year To African-American Ph.D. Students (African-American Doctoral Teacher Loan/ Scholarship Program)
Money To Study Optometry Or Osteopathic Medicine (Southern Regional Educational Board (SREB) Loan/ Scholarship Program)
Tuition, Room and Board and Fees To Dependents Of Police Officers and Fire Fighters Who Died Or Became Disabled In The Line Of Duty (Law Enforcement Officers and Firemen Scholarship Program)
Tuition, Room and Board and Fees To Dependents Of POW/MIA's (Southeast Asia POW/MIA Scholarship Program)
Money To Professional Students Who Have To Go Out Of State To Get Their Degrees (Graduate and Professional Degree Loan/Scholarship Program)
Money To Professional Students Who Study In Mississippi (State Medical Education Loan/ Scholarship Program)
Money For Registered Nurses Who Want To Go Back And Get A Bachelor's Degree In Nursing (Career Ladder Nursing Loan/Scholarship Program)
Up To $5,000 Per Year For Nursing Students (Nursing Education Loan/ Scholarship Program)
$4,000 For Nursing Students (Special Nursing Education Loan/Scholarship for Study in Baccalaureate Nursing Education Program)

780   *Matthew Lesko, Information USA, Inc., 12081 Nebel Street, Rockville, MD 20852 • 1-800-955-7693 • www.lesko.com*

Money For Studying Psychology, Speech Pathology, Occupational Therapy, and Physical Therapy
    (Health Care Professions Loan Scholarship Program)
Money For Medical Students (Special Medical Education Loan/Scholarship Program)
Mississippi Resident Tuition Grant Program
Mississippi Eminent Scholar Program
Mississippi Nursing Teacher (Stipend) Program

Nursing Education Loans/Scholarship Program:
$1,500 A Year For RN's Going To School To Get A BSN Degree Who Will Be A Nurse In Mississippi
    (RN To BSN Program)
Up To $4,000 For Nursing Students To Get A BSN Degree (BSN Program)
$3,000 Per Year To Study Full-Time For A MSN Degree (MSN Program)
$5,000 Per Year For To Get A DSN Degree And Work In Mississippi For One Year (DSN Program)

Missouri

Missouri Coordinating Board of Higher Education
P.O. Box 1438
3515 Amazonas Drive
Jefferson City, MO 65109
573-751-2361
Fax: 573-751-6635
www.cbhe.mo.us
General requirements: Applicants must be Missouri
residents.

Programs Available:
$2,000 A Year To Students With ACT Scores In The Top 3% (Missouri Higher Education Academic Scholarship
    Program) (Bright Flight)
Tuition For Dependents Of Public Safety Officers Or Department Of Highway Officers Who Were Killed In The Line
    Of Duty (Public Service Officer or Employee's Child Survivor Grant Program)
$10,000 For Biomedical or Information Technology Majors (The Advantage Missouri Program)
$1,500 For Financially Needy To Attend College (Charles Gallagher Student Financial Assistance Program)
Scholarships For Working Students (Marguerite Ross Barnett memorial Scholarship)
Tuition Adjustment For Students Who Attend School Out-Of-State (Midwest Student Exchange Program)
Tuition For Financially Needy (Missouri College Guarantee Program)
Tuition Waiver For Spouses Or Children Of Deceased Vietnam Veterans
    (Vietnam Veterans Survivor Grant Program)

Montana
Board of Regents of Higher Education
P.O. Box 203101
Helena, MT 59620-3101
406-444-6570
www.montana.edu/wwwbor
General requirements: Applicants must be Montana residents.

Programs Available:
Free Tuition For Senior Citizens, Veterans, War Orphans, Etc. (Fee Waivers)
Scholarships For National Merit Semi-Finalists (National Merit Semi-Finalist Scholarship)
First Year of College Free To Smart High School Students (High School Honor Scholarship)
Scholarship For Community College Graduates To Attend Four Year College
    (Community College Honor Scholarship)
Scholarships For Disadvantaged Students (GEAR UP Scholarship)

$600 For Needy Students (Montana Higher Education Grant)
Money To Working Students (MTAP Baker Grant)

Nebraska

Nebraska Coordinating Commission For Postsecondary Education
P.O. Box 95005
Lincoln, NE 68509-5005
402-471-2847
Fax: 402-471-2886
www.ccpe.state.ne.us/PublicDoc/CCPE/Default.asp

General requirements: Nebraska administers a "decentralized" form of student aid in higher education. Monies are allocated based on a formula to postsecondary schools. A limited number of state programs are administered directly through postsecondary schools. Students should contact the Financial Aid Office at the college they plan to attend for scholarship, grant, and loan information. State residency is required.

Nevada

Nevada Department of Education
Student Incentive Grant Program
700 E. 5th Street
Carson City, NV 98701-9050
775-687-9200
www.nde.state.nv.us

General requirements: Nevada has no state scholarships. The Nevada Student Incentive Grant Program is the only source of state grants. It administers renewable, need-based awards of up to $2,500 per year. Students should contact the Financial Aid Office at the college they plan to attend for further information. State residency is required.

Programs Available:
Robert C. Byrd Honor Scholarship

New Hampshire

New Hampshire Postsecondary Education Commission
2 Industrial Park Drive
Concord, NH 03301
603-271-2555
Fax: 603-271-2696
www.state.nh.us/postsecondary

General requirements: Applicants must be New Hampshire residents, for programs involving colleges in and out of state.

Programs Available
Grants To Attend Colleges In The New England States (New Hampshire Incentive Program)
Money For Dependents Of Veterans Who Died In Service (Scholarships for Orphans of Veterans)
Robert C. Byrd Honor Scholarship
Scholarship For Students In Career Shortage Areas (NH Career Incentive Program)
Scholarships For Medical Students At Dartmouth (Dartmouth Medical Education Program)
Scholarships For Nursing Students (Nursing Leveraged Scholarship Loan Program)
Scholarship For Vet Students (Veterinary Education Program)

New Jersey

New Jersey Department of Higher Education
Office of Student Assistance
4 Quakerbridge Plaza, CN 540
Trenton, NJ 08625
609-588-3226
800-792-8670
www.hesaa.org
General requirements: Applicants must be New Jersey residents.

Programs Available:
$4,580 A Year In Grants To Full-Time Students (Tuition Aid Grants)
Grants To Students With High SAT Scores (Edward J. Bloustein Distinguished Scholar Program)
Grants To Smart High School Juniors (Garden State Scholars Program)
$1,000 For Smart City Kids (Urban Scholars Program)
$7,500 For High Achieving Students (OSRP)
Scholarships For Spouses and Dependents Of Deceased Law, Fire, or Emergency Personnel
    (Survivor Tuition Benefits)

New Mexico

New Mexico Commission On Higher Education
1068 Cerrillos Road
Santa Fe, NM 87501
505-827-7383
Fax: 505-827-7392
www.nmche.org
General requirements: Applicants must be New Mexico
residents, unless otherwise stated.

Programs Available:
Free Tuition To Students With "Good Moral Character" (Three Percent Scholarship Program)
Tuition, Books, and Fees For High School Students In Top 5% Of Class (New Mexico Scholars Program)
Part-Time Jobs To Undergraduate and Graduate Students (New Mexico Work-Study Program)
Money For Osteopathic Students Willing To Practice In New Mexico (Osteopathic Medical Student Loan Program)
Grants To Half-Time and Full-Time Students In Financial Need (New Mexico Student Incentive Grant)
Tuition, Books, And Fees To Vietnam Vets (Vietnam Veterans' Scholarship Program)
$12,000 For Nursing Students Willing To Practice In New Mexico (New Mexico Nursing Student Loan for Service
    Program)
$7,500 Per Year For Women And Minorities To Go To Graduate School (Graduate Scholarship Program)
Money For Students Attending Private Colleges (Student Choice)
Money For Medical Students Willing To Practice In New Mexico (New Mexico Physician and Physician Assistant
    Student Loan for Service Program)
$25,000 For Women And Minority Ph.D. Students (Minority Doctoral Assistance Loan for Service Program)
Money For Student Athletes (Athletic Scholarships)
Money For Child Care (Child Care Grants)
Scholarships For Children of Deceased Military and State Police (Children of Deceased Military and State Police
    Personnel Scholarship)
Go To School In New Mexico (Competitive Scholarship For Out Of State Students)
Scholarships For Minority Students (Gates Millennium Scholars)
$2,500 For Financially Needy (Legislative Endowment Scholarships)
100% Tuition Scholarships (Lottery Success Scholarships)
Reduced Tuition For Senior Citizens (Senior Citizens' Reduced Tuition Act)
Loans For Allied Health Students (Allied Health Student Loan-For-Service)

Loan Repayment Program For Health Professionals (Health Professional Loan Repayment Program)
Loans for Minority or Disabled Teaching Majors (Southeastern New Mexico Teachers' Loan-For-Service)

New York

New York Higher Education Services Corporation
Grants and Scholarship Information
99 Washington Ave.
Albany, NY 12255
518-473-7087
Fax: 518-474-2839
www.hesc.com

General requirements: Applicants must be residents of New York. Amounts awarded are determined by the type of school you are planning to attend, your financial status (net taxable income), year in which the award is received, and amount of tuition.

Programs Available:
Grants For Full-Time Students (Tuition Assistance Program (TAP))
Grants For Part-Time Students (Aid for Part-Time Study (APTS))
Money For Accounting, Veterinary, and Students Pursuing 19 Other Professional Careers (New York Regents
	Professional Opportunity Scholarships)
Money for Students Studying Medicine Or Dentistry (New York Regents Health Care Opportunity Scholarships)
Money for Students Studying To Be Dental Hygienists, Midwives, Therapists, And Speech-Language Pathologists
	(New York State Health Service Corps Scholarships)
Money for Native Americans To Attend College (State Aid to Native Americans)
Grants To Dependents Of Deceased Or Disabled Veterans (Regents Award for Children of Deceased or Disabled
	Veterans)
Tuition And Fees For Dependents Of Deceased Police Officers and Fire Fighters (Memorial Scholarships for
	Children of Deceased Police Officers and Fire Fighters)
$1,000 Per Semester For Vietnam Veterans (Vietnam Veterans and Persian Gulf Veterans Tuition Awards)
Robert C. Byrd Honor Scholarship
$4,000 Scholarship (New York State Lottery Scholarship)
$1,500 For Smart High School Students (Scholarships For Academic Excellence)

North Carolina

North Carolina State Education Assistance Authority
P.O. Box 14103
Research Triangle Park, NC 27709
919-549-8614
Fax: 919-549-8481
www.ncseaa.edu

General requirements: Applicants must be residents of North Carolina.

Programs Available:
Grants For Full-Time And Part-Time Students (Appropriated Grants)
$5,000 A Year For Preschool, Elementary, Or Secondary Level Teachers (Paul
	Douglas Teacher Scholarship Program (PDTS))
$3,000 For Smart High School Students Active In Public Service (Incentive Scholarship Program)
Grants For Minorities Studying Part Time Or Full Time (Minority Presence Grant Program)
Grants For Minorities Studying Law, Veterinary Medicine, Or Working On A Ph.D. (Minority Presence Grant
	Program: Doctoral/Law/Veterinary Medicine Program)
Grants For Students Going Part Time To Junior Colleges (North Carolina Community College Scholarship Program)
$1,500 To Full-Time Undergraduate Students (North Carolina Student Incentive Grant)

Grants Given By State Legislators To Students Who Don't Even Need The Money (North Carolina Legislative Tuition Grant Program, Private College).

$8,500 A Year For Undergraduate Or Graduate Students In Health, Science, Or Mathematics (North Carolina Student Loan Program for Health, Science, and Mathematics)

$5,000 A Year To Students Who Want To Be Teachers (North Carolina Teaching Fellows Scholarship Program)

Grants To Dependents Of Deceased Or Disabled Veterans Or POW/MIA's (North Carolina Veterans Scholarship)

Grants To Full-Time Or Part-Time Native American Students (American Indian Student Legislative Grant Program)

Money For Students In 2-Year Or 4-Year Nursing Programs (Nurse Education Scholarship Loan Program)

$6,000 A Year For Nursing Students Willing To Practice In North Carolina (Nursing Scholars Program)

$5,000 Plus Tuition And Fees For Dental Students (Board of Governors Dental Scholarship)

$5,000 Plus Tuition And Fees For Medical Students (Board of GovernorsMedical Scholarship Program)

Free Loans For Studying Psychology, Counseling, Or Speech (Prospective Teacher Scholarship Loans)

Grants To Part-Time Or Full-Time Students Attending Private Colleges (State Contractual Scholarship Program, Private Colleges)

Tuition, Fees, And Day Care For the Physically Or Mentally Disabled (Vocational Rehabilitation Program)

North Dakota

University Systems
600 E. Boulevard Ave., Dept. 215
Bismarck, ND 58505-0230
701-328-2960
www.nodak.edu

General requirements: Applicants must be residents of North Dakota.

Programs Available:
$600 To Students Attending Any College (North Dakota State Student Incentive Grant Program)
100% Tuition Awarded To Top High School Students (North Dakota Scholars Program)
$2,000 For Students With 1/4 Indian Blood (North Dakota Indian Scholarship)
$2,000 For Teacher Training (Teacher Retraining Scholarship Program)
Loan Forgiveness For Teachers (Teacher Shortage Loan Forgiveness Program)

Ohio

Ohio Board of Regents
State Grants and Scholarship Department
P.O. Box 182452
Columbus, OH 43218-2451
888-833-1133
614-466-7420
Fax: 614-752-5903
www.regents.state.oh.us

General requirements: Applicants must be residents of Ohio.

Programs Available:
Grants For Middle Income Families To Pay Tuition (Ohio Instructional Grants)
Grants To Pay Tuition At Private Colleges (Ohio Student Choice Grant Program)
Grants To Dependents Of Deceased Or Disabled Veterans And POW/MIAs (Ohio War Orphans Scholarship Program)

$2,100 A Year To Smart High School Students Who Attend Ohio Colleges
    (Ohio Academic Scholarship Program)
$3,500 A Year For Graduate Students (Regents Graduate/Professional Fellowship Program)
Free Tuition To Dependents Of Fire Fighters And Police Officers Killed In The Line Of Duty
    (Ohio Safety Officers College Memorial Fund)
$3,000 Loan With Loan Forgiveness For Work For Nurses (Nurse Education Assistance Loan Program)
$1,500 For Smart Students (Robert C. Byrd Honors Scholarship Program)
$144 For Career School (Student Workforce Development Grant Program)

Oklahoma

Oklahoma State Regents for Higher Education
655 Research Parkway, Suite 200
Oklahoma City, OK 73104
405-225-9100
www.okhighered.org
General requirements: Applicants must be Oklahoma residents.

Programs Available:
Chiropractic Education Assistance Scholarship
Money For Students Having Trouble Paying Tuition (Oklahoma Tuition Aid Grant Program)
Grants To Top 15% High School Students Who Want To Be Teachers (Future Teachers Scholarship Program)
Robert C. Byrd Honor Scholarship
Scholarships For Smart Students (Academic Scholars Program)
$3,000 For National Merit Students (Regional University Baccalaureate Scholarship)
$500 For Public Works Students (American Public Works Association Scholarship)
$1,000 For Public Service Students (George and Donna Nigh Public Service Scholarship)
$5,500 For Dependent Children Of Oklahoma City Bombing Victims (Heartland Scholarship Fund)
Tuition Waiver For Foster Children (Independent Living Act)
National Guard Tuition Waiver
$2,300 For AmeriCorps (Smart Start For Brain Gain)

Oregon

Oregon Student Assistance Commission
1500 Valley River Dr., Suite 100
Eugene, OR 97401
503-687-7400
www.osac.state.or.us
General requirements: Applicants must be residents of Oregon.

Programs Available:
Grants To College Students In Financial Need (Need Grants)
State Scholarships For High School Seniors, Graduate, and Undergraduate Students

Pennsylvania

Pennsylvania Higher Education Assistance Agency
1200 N. 7th Street
Harrisburg, PA 17102
717-720-2850
www.pheaa.org
General requirements: Applicants must be Pennsylvania residents for in-state schools,
unless otherwise specified.

Programs Available:
Up to $3,300 For Financially Needy Students (Pennsylvania State Grants)
Financial Aid For Veterans
$3,792 For National Guard Members (Educational Assistance Program for the Pennsylvania National Guard)
Tuition Waivers for Dependents of Deceased Police, Firefighters, Rescue Workers, and Others
    (Postsecondary Educational Gratuity Program)
Up To $3,000 For Technology Students (SciTech and Technology Scholarships)
State Work Study Program
Loan Forgiveness For Nursing, Early Childhood and Agriculture Education Students (Loan Forgiveness Programs)

Rhode Island
Rhode Island Higher Education Assistance Authority
560 Jefferson Boulevard
Warwick, RI 02886
401-736-1100
Fax: 401-732-3541
www.riheaa.org
General requirements: Applicants must be residents of Rhode Island.

Programs Available:
Up to $750 For Part-Time And Full-Time Students (Rhode Island State Grant Program)

South Carolina

South Carolina Commission on Higher Education
1333 Main Street, Suite 200
Columbia, SC 29201
803-737-2260
Fax: 803-737-2297
www.che400.state.sc.us
General requirements: Applicants must be residents of South Carolina.

Programs Available:
$3,320 For Students In Financial Need (South Carolina Tuition Grants)
$15,000 For Graduate Students (South Carolina Graduate Incentive
    Scholarship Program)
$1,000 For Minority Students (South Carolina "Other Race" Grant Program)
$5,000 For High School Seniors With High Test Scores (Palmetto Fellows Scholarship)
$10,000 A Year For Medical And Dental Students (South Carolina Medical and Dental Scholarship Fund)
Free Tuition For Students Over 60 Years Old (Tuition Waiver for Senior Citizens)
Free Tuition For Dependents Of Disabled Or Deceased Veterans (Free Tuition for Children of Deceased or Disabled
    South Carolina Veterans)
Free Tuition For Dependents Of Deceased Or Disabled Fire Fighters, Law Officers, and Members Of The Civil Air
    Patrol (Free Tuition for Children of Deceased or Disabled South Carolina Fire Fighters, Law Officers, and
    Members of Civil Air Patrol or Organized Rescue Squad)
Robert C. Byrd Honor Scholarship
$3,000 For Smart Students (LIFE Scholarship Program)

South Dakota
South Dakota Board of Regents
306 East Capitol Ave., Suite 200
Pierre, SD 57051
605-773-3455
www.ris.sdbor.edu
General requirements: Applicants must be residents of South Dakota.

Programs Available:
$600 Per Year For Students In Financial Need (South Dakota State Student Incentive Grant Program)
$300 For Students Attending Private Colleges (South Dakota Tuition Equalization Grant Program)
Robert C. Byrd Honor Scholarship

Tennessee

Tennessee Student Assistance Corporation
404 James Robertson Parkway
Suite 1900, Parkway Towers
Nashville, TN 37243-0820
615-741-3650
Fax: 615-741-6230
www.state.tn.us/tsac
General requirements: Applicants must be residents of Tennessee.

Programs Available:
$1,482 For Financially Needy Students (Tennessee Student Assistance
    Award)
$5,000 A Year For Minorities In The Top 25% Of Class To Become Teachers (Minority Teaching Fellows Program)
Robert C. Byrd Honor Scholarship Program
$6,000 For Smart Students (Ned McWherter Scholars Program)
$1,000 For Teachers (Christa McAuliffe Scholarship Program)
Scholarships For Dependents of Deceased Law, Emergency, Fire and Other Personnel (Dependent Children
    Scholarship Program)
Scholarships For Teachers (Tennessee Teaching Scholars Program)

Texas

Texas Higher Education Coordinating Board
Box 12788, Capitol Station
Austin, TX 78711-2788
512-427-6127
Fax: 512-427-6101
General requirements: Applicants must be residents of Texas, unless otherwise specified.

Programs Available:
Money To Attend Public Colleges In Texas (Texas Public Education Grant)
Money To Attend Private Colleges In Texas (Tuition Equalization Grant)
$1,250 For Half Time Or Full Time Students (LEAP)
Grants To Financially Needy Students (Texas Tuition Assistance Grant)
Money To Study To Be A Nurse
Tuition And Fees For Blind Or Deaf Students
Money For Dependents Of Disabled Or Deceased Firemen, Peace Officers, Custodial Employees of the Department
    Of Corrections, Or Game Wardens
Money For Dependents Of POW/MIAs (Children of Prisoners of War or Persons Missing in Action)
Tuition And Fees For Fire Fighters To Take Science Courses (Fire Fighters Enrolled in Fire Science Courses)
Free Tuition And Fees For Veterans (Veterans and Dependents (The Hazelwood Act))
Money For The Smartest High School Students (Valedictorian Exemption)
Money For Foreign Students From Central America (Students from Other Nations of the American Hemisphere
    (Good Neighbor Scholarship))
Up To $1,500 For Undergraduates (Texas Educational Opportunity Grant)
Robert C. Byrd Honors Scholarship Program
Scholarships for Students Enrolled In Two Colleges (Concurrent Enrollment Waiver)
$1,000 Scholarships For Early High School Graduates (Early High School Graduation Scholarship)

$500 For Educational Aide (Educational Aide Exemption)
Tuition Waiver For High School Students Who Take College Classes (Exemption for Dual-Enrolled Students)
Tuition Waiver For Texas National Guard Members (Texas National Guard Tuition Assistance Program)
Tuition For Children of Deceased Military or National Guard Members (Orphans of Texas Members of the U.S. Armed Forces or National Guard)
Reduced Tuition For Those Who Take More Credit Hours (Reduction in Tuition Charges for Students Taking 15 or More Semester Credit Hours Per Term)
Reduced Tuition for Senior Citizens (Senior Citizen, 55 or Older Tuition Reduction Program)
Tuition Waiver For Foster Care Kids
Tuition Waiver For Children Whose Parents Receive TANF (Temporary Assistance To Needy Families Exemption Program)
$3,000 for Accounting Students (Fifth Year Accounting Student Scholarship)
Scholarship For Needy Students (License Plate Insignia Scholarship)
Scholarships for Rural EMS Training (Rural Emergency Medical Services Scholarship Incentive Program)
$15,000 Stipend For Physicians Willing To Work In Under-served Areas (Texas Health Service Corps Program)
Grants To Needy Community College Students (Toward Excellence, Access & Success Grant II Program)
Scholarships For Smart Students (Toward Excellence, Access, & Success Grant Program)
Grants For Associate's Degree (Toward Excellence, Access, & Success Grant Program)
Scholarships For Vocational Nurses (Vocational Nursing Scholarships)

Utah

Utah System of Higher Education
355 West North Temple
3 Triad, Suite 550
Salt Lake City, UT 84180-1205
801-321-7101
Fax: 801-321-7199
www.utahsbr.edu
General requirements: Utah administers funding to state residents. The state uses a decentralized system. Students should contact the Financial Aid Office at the college they plan to attend.

Programs Available:
Grants For Students In Financial Need (State Student Incentive Grant Program)
75% Tuition Scholarships For Those That Complete Associate Degree While In High School (New Century Scholarship Program)
$2,500 For Needy Students (Leveraging Educational Assistance Partnership (LEAP)
Scholarships For College (Utah Centennial Opportunity Program for Education Grant)
Loan and Loan Forgiveness Program For Students Who Want To Be Teachers (Terrel H. Bell Teaching Incentive Program)

Vermont

Vermont Student Assistance Corporation
P.O. Box 2000
Champlain Mill
Winooski, VT 05404
800-642-3177
802-655-9602
www.vsac.org
General requirements: Applicants must be Vermont residents, unless otherwise stated.

Programs Available:
Grants For Students In Financial Need (Vermont Incentive Grants)

Grants For Part Time Students (Vermont Part Time Student Grants)
$650 Per Course If You're NOT Working Toward A Degree (Vermont
    Non-Degree Student Grant Program)
Extra Loans For College Students (Vermont EXTRA Loans (Supplemental))

Virginia

Virginia State Council of Higher Education
Office of Financial Aid
James Monroe Building
101 North 14th St., 9th Floor
Richmond, VA 23219
804-225-2628
Fax: 804-225-2638
www.schev.edu
General requirements: Applicants must be Virginia residents.

Programs Available:
$5,000 For Students In Financial Need (Virginia College Assistance Program (CSAP))
Grants For Students Even Though They Don't NEED The Money (Virginia Tuition Assistance Grant Program
    (TAGP))
Free Tuition For White Students To Attend Black Colleges (Virginia Transfer Grant Program (VTGP))
Grants To Black Undergraduate Students (Last Dollar Program)
Nursing Students Receive $100 A Month For Every Month They Agree To Work In Virginia (Nursing Scholarship
    Program)
Money For Medical Students Who Agree To Work In Virginia (Medical Scholarship Program)
$5,000 To Dental Students Who Agree To Work In Small Virginia Towns (Rural Dental Scholarships)
$3,720 A Year For Teaching Students For Every Year They Agree To Work In Virginia (Virginia Teaching
    Scholarship)
Free Tuition, Fees, And Room and Board For State Cadets
    (State Cadetships)
Free Tuition For Dependents Of Deceased Or Disabled Veterans (Virginia War Orphan Education Act)
Free Tuition And Fees For Students Who Want To Study Soil Science (Soil Scientist Program)
Free Tuition For Students Over 60 (Senior Citizens Tuition Waiver)
Loans To Middle Class Families Having Trouble Paying For Tuition (EDVANTAGE)
Robert C. Byrd Honors Scholarship Program
Scholarships For Financially Needy Students (Virginia Guaranteed Assistance Program)
Scholarships For Good Students (Virginia Graduate and Undergraduate Assistance Program)

Washington

Higher Education Coordinating Board
917 Lakeridge Way
P.O. Box 43430
Olympia, WA 98504
360-753-7800
Fax: 360-753-7808
www.hecb.wa.gov
General requirements: Applicants must be Washington residents for in-state or out-of-state programs, when specified.

Programs Available:
College Students Who Have Trouble Paying Tuition (Washington State Need Grant Program)
Part Time Employment To Students Who Need Money (Washington State Work-Study Program)
Money to High School Students In The Top 1% (Washington Scholars Program)

Money To Study Optometry In Other States (Western Interstate Commission for Higher Education (WICHE) Professional Exchange Program)

Money To Get A Master's Or Ph.D. In Out-Of-State Schools (Western Interstate Commission for Higher Education (WICHE) Regional Graduate Program)

Robert C. Byrd Honors Scholarship Program

$2,500 For Financially Needy Students (Educational Opportunity Grant)

Scholarships and Loan Repayment for Health Professionals (Health Professional Loan Repayment and Scholarship Program)

Grants For Vocational Education (Washington Award for Vocational Excellence- WAVE)

$1,000 For Native Americans (American Indian Endowed Scholarship)

West Virginia

West Virginia Higher Education Policy Commission
1018 Kanawha Blvd. East, Suite 700
Charleston, WV 25301
304-558-2101
Fax: 304-558-2101
www.hepc.wvnet.edu

General requirements: Applicants must be residents of West Virginia. Money available: $10,995,000.

Programs Available:

Money For Financially Needy Students (West Virginia Higher Education Grant)

Money To Study Teaching At The Graduate Or Undergraduate Level (Underwood-Smith Teacher Scholarship Program)

Money For Medical Students (Central Office of the State College and University Systems Medical Student Loan Program)

Robert C. Byrd Honors Scholarship Program

Scholarships For Good Students (PROMISE- Providing Real Opportunities for Maximizing In-State Student Excellence)

$3,000 For Science and Technology Majors (West Virginia Engineering, Science and Technology Scholarship Program)

Scholarships For Part-Time Students ((Higher Education Adult Part-Time Student (HEAPS) Grant Program))

Wisconsin

State of Wisconsin Higher Educational Aids Board
P.O. Box 7885
Madison, WI 53707-7885
608-267-2206
Fax: 608-267-2808
www.heab.state.wi.us

General requirements: Applicants must be residents of Wisconsin.

Programs Available:

Grants To College Or Vocational Students (Wisconsin Higher Education Grant)

Grants To Students Attending Private Colleges In Wisconsin (Wisconsin Tuition Grant)

Grants For Deaf And Blind Students (Visual and Hearing Impaired Program)

Grants To Blacks, Hispanics, Native Americans, And Former Citizens Of Laos, Vietnam, and Cambodia (Minority Retention Grant)

Grants To Non-Traditional Students (Talent Incentive Program)

$2,200 A Year To Students With At Least 25% Native American Blood (Indian Student Assistance Grant)

Grants To Smart High School Students (Academic Excellence Scholarships)

$1,000 A Year For Every Year You Work As A Nurse In Wisconsin (Nursing Student Stipend Loans)

Cheap Tuition For Attending Minnesota Universities (Minnesota-Wisconsin Reciprocity Program)
Loan and Loan Forgiveness For Minority Teachers (Minority Teacher Loan Program)
$10,000 For Those Who Teach Visually Impaired (Teacher of the Visually Impaired Loan)
Go To Dental School At Marquette (Contract for Dental Education)
$10,000 for Med School (Medical College of Wisconsin Capitation Program)
Loan and Loan Forgiveness Program For Teachers (Teacher Education Loan)

Wyoming

Wyoming Department of Higher Education
Hathaway Building, 2nd Floor
Cheyenne, WY 82002
307-777-7675
www.k12.wy.us/higher_ed.html
General requirements: Applicants must be residents of Wyoming.

Programs Available:
Grants and Loans To Education Majors (Scholarship/Loan Fund for Superior Students in Education)
Grants To Students With 25% Native American Blood (Bureau of Indian Affairs Scholarship and Loan)
Robert C. Byrd Honors Scholarship Program
$500 For First Generation American To Go To College (Douvas Memorial Scholarship)
$600 For Student Leaders (Student Leader Scholarship)
Scholarship For Shoshone Members (Shoshone Tribal Scholarship)
Scholarship for Arapaho Members (Northern Arapaho Tribal Scholarship)
Scholarship For Community College (County Commissioners' Scholarship)

FREE SCHOLARSHIPS

Organizations are continuously initiating, ending or changing scholarship programs. We have attempted to gather information on some scholarships available, but because of the perpetual changes you will want to check directly with the organization for details and the most up-to-date information. When possible, we have included the website of the organization offering the scholarship for your convenience.

Using the Internet!

Half the battle of scholarships is FINDING them! Thanks to the advent of the Internet, it has become increasingly easy to find scholarships and financial aid information. If you have Internet access, you will want to consider exploring the following websites first. All allow free searches of their databases. Some allow you to "save" your search results, others automatically notify you of new or updated scholarship offerings, and some provide excellent advice on how to improve your odds of winning scholarships. To maximize your information, it is recommended to try all of them because each database offers different information and services.

FreSch! The Free Scholarship Information Service
http://www.freschinfo.com

FastWeb: Financial Aid Search through The Web
http://www.fastweb.com

FastAid
http://www.fastaid.com

SallieMae
http://scholarships.salliemae.com

CollegeEdge
http://www.CollegeEdge.com/FA/

GoCollege
http://www.gocollege.com

ExPan Online
http://www.collegeboard.org/fundfinder/bin/ fundfind01.pl

CollegeNet
http://www.collegenet.com

OSAD Scholarship Search for Study Abroad
http://www.istc.umn.edu/study/scholarships.html

IUPUI Scholarship Database
http://www.iupui.edu/~scentral/ scsearchdbase.html

For those of you with AOL access, try RSP Funding by going to **KEYWORD: RSP.**

General Financial Aid Information Websites

FinAid
http://www.finaid.org

The Financial Aid Resource Network
http://www.theoldschool.org

Employers

If you have a job, ask your own human resources department if they offer scholarships or tuition reimbursement programs. If you are still in high school, have your parents ask their employers.

Professional or Social Organizations

Of what professional or social organizations are you or your parents members? 4H, JayCees, Lions Club? Association for Internet Addiction? If you or your parents are a member of an organization, ask them and see if they offer any kind of scholarships. If you are NOT a member of any organizations, the next thing to check with is organizations that represent what you are planning on studying. Many such organizations offer scholarships to students who are studying what they support, even if you are not a member. For example, the American Medical Record Association offers several scholarships for those planning on making a career in medical record administration, but there is no requirement that you be a member. Many organizations that do permit non-members to apply for scholarships, however, do expect you to join the organization after receiving the scholarship.

Labor Unions

Are you or your parents a member of a union? All the major labor unions offer scholarships for members and their dependent children (AFL-CIO, Teamsters, etc.)

Church

Check with your church. Your local parish may or may not have any scholarships for their members, but the diocese or headquarters may have some available. And if you have been very active in your local church, they may be able to help you in other ways.

High School

If you are still in high school, it is very important that you speak with your guidance counselor or administration office and ask about scholarships that are available to students at your school.

College

If you are already attending college, or are planning on attending, the financial aid office at your college can be an excellent resource for scholarships and financial aid. You will also find applications for most of the state and federal level aid programs available at your financial aid office.

Scholarships

$1,000 + Job From Microsoft

Women or minorities studying computers can receive $1,000 scholarships and paid summer internships that allow you to help develop products for Bill Gates. Contact Mary Blain, National Women's Technical Scholarship Application or National Technical Scholarship Application, Microsoft Corporation, One Microsoft Way, Redmond, WA 98052; {www.microsoft.com/}.

$5,000 for Minorities in Science and Engineering

Xerox Technical Minority Scholarship Program provides funding to minorities enrolled in technical science or engineering majors including computer and software engineering, and information management. $4,000 for undergraduates and $5,000 for graduate students. Contact: Xerox Corp., Corporate Employment and College Relations, Technical Minority Scholarship Program, 800 Phillips Rd., Webster, NY 14580; {www.xerox.com/}.

Women In Science and Engineering Scholarship

Program Intel offers a Minority Engineering Scholarship Program for undergraduates interested in computer science or engineering and a Women in Science and Engineering Scholarship Program. They also provide internships and mentors to scholarship recipients. Scholarships are only available at selected colleges and universities, and Intel does not accept applications directly from students. Students must be nominated by their school for a scholarship. For more information, contact {www.intel.com/ intel/community/}.

Scholarships For Mature Women

The Women's Opportunity Award's intent is to assist mature women who need additional skills, training and education to upgrade their employment status in order to enter or return to the job market. Applicant should be the head of her household with financial responsibility for her dependents, indicate that specific training is necessary to enter or re-enter the job market, demonstrate financial need and be entering vocational or technical training, or be completing an undergraduate degree. Contact Women's Opportunity Award Soroptimist International of the Americas, Two Penn Center Plaza, Suite 1000, Philadelphia, PA 19102.

Scholarships for Smart Business Majors

Fifty Exceptional Student Fellowships, consisting of $3000 each to be used for educational expenses during the academic year following the competition, are given each year. Applicants must be full time junior or senior college students majoring in a business-related field, demonstrate significant leadership in extra-curricular activities, have a minimum 3.6 GPA, be nominated by a dean, department head, professor or academic advisor, currently attend an accredited college or university in the U.S. and be of U.S. citizenship. Contact the Foundation for current application deadlines. Contact State Farm Companies Foundation, One State Farm Plaza, SC-3, Bloomington, IL 61710; 309-766-2039/2161; Nancy.Lynn.gr3o@statefarm.com; {www.statefarm.com}.

Scholarships for Composers

Young composers and musicians may apply for a variety of different awards, some of which include the John Lennon Scholarship that is awarded for excellence in vocal/instrumental composition and has been established by Yoko Ono Lennon; the Annual Student Composer Awards ($500-$2,500) for which young composers of concert music may compete; and the Jerry Harrington Jazz Composition Award to encourage composition of new large-ensemble jazz works.

Contact BMI Foundation, 320 West 57th Street, New York, NY 10019; 212-586-2000.

Scholarships Available For Family Of Fleet Reserve

This association offers four different scholarships. In order to be eligible, the applicant must either be a daughter/granddaughter of Naval, Marine Corps, and Coast Guard personnel, active Fleet Reserve, Fleet Marine Corps Reserve, and Coast Guard Reserve, retired with pay or deceased. Children/grandchildren of deceased FRA members or persons who had eligibility for FRA membership at the time of death, plus children/grandchildren of members of LA FRA are also eligible for these scholarships. Awarding of scholarships is based on financial need, scholarship proficiency and character.

Contact Fleet Reserve Association, Ladies Auxiliary, LA FRA Scholarship Administrator, c/o Fleet Reserve Association, 125 N. West Street, Alexandria, VA 22314-2754; 703-683-1400; 800-FRA-1924.

$1000 Scholarships For Smart Women Pursuing Science Majors

The Dr. Vicki L. Schechtman Scholarship awards $1000 to an undergraduate woman pursuing scientific studies. Preference is given to applicants pursuing research. Applicant must have a minimum GPA of 3.0 and be a U.S. citizen. Graduate opportunities include four awards: Amy Lutz Rechel Award for plant biology students; Luise Meyer-Schutzmeister Award for women students in physics; Ruth Satter Memorial Award for women who have had to interrupt their education for 3 or more years in order to raise a family; The Diane H. Russel Award for graduate students in the biochemistry of pharmacology fields. Additionally, there are approximately 10 Citations of Merit given each year ranging from $250-$500.

Contact Association For Women In Science (AWIS), AWIS National Headquarters, 1200 New York Ave., NW, Suite 650, Washington, DC 20005; 202-326-8940; 800-886-AWIS; {Email: awis@awis.org}.

$1500 SCHOLARSHIPS FOR CHILDREN OF AIR FORCE MEMBERS

This successful program has been awarding grants since 1988. The AFAS provides $1500 grants for undergraduate study to selected daughters and sons of active duty, retired or deceased Air Force members, stateside spouses of active duty members and surviving spouses of deceased personnel. The Society considers family income and education cost factors for its awards. Contact the AFAS for the current deadline.

Contact Air Force Aid Society (AFAS), Education Assistance Department, 1745 Jefferson Davis Hwy., Suite 202, Arlington, VA 22202-3410; 202-692-9313.

$2000 For Library Science Graduate Students

This association offers a variety of scholarships and grants, most in the amount of $2000. Each year the MLA awards money to qualified students in graduate library science programs. Money is also available to practicing health science librarians in order to enable them to continue to develop professionally. Contact Medical Library Association (MLA), 6 North Michigan Ave., Suite 300, Chicago, IL 60602-4805; 312-419-9094.

Garden Club Awards Up To $4000/Year

In order to stimulate knowledge of gardening and to restore, protect and improve the environment, this club offers a variety of scholarships and fellowships. Undergraduate and graduate students are eligible for awards up to $4000/year. Each scholarship varies in its focus and student eligibility. Contact the GCA for details and deadlines. Over $24,000 is available each year. Contact The Garden Club Of America (GCA), 14 East 60th Street, New York, NY 10022; 212-753-8287; {www.gcamerica.org}.

Money For Physical Therapy Doctoral Students

Physical therapist doctoral students pursuing scientific and clinical research are eligible for scholarships from this organization. Awards are based on the distinct phases of education and funding may vary from year to year depending on available resources. Contact the Foundation for details and deadlines. Contact Foundation For Physical Therapy, 1111 North Fairfax Street, Alexandria, VA 22314-1488; 706-684-5984; 800-875-1378; {Email: foundation@apta.org}.

Up To $1500 For Federal Employees And Dependents

Civilian federal and postal employees, with a minimum of three years of federal service, and their dependent family members are eligible for scholarships from FEEA. Applicants may be high school seniors or students who are continuing their college education and have a minimum GPA of 3.0. Awards range from $500-$1500 and are based on merit. Academic achievement, community service, a recommendation and a two-page essay are included in criteria for selection of recipients. A total of $250,000 is given out annually in scholarships. Contact Federal Employee Education And Assistance Fund, 8441 W. Bowles Ave., Suite 200, Littleton, CO 80123-3245; 303-933-7580; 800-323-4140; {www.feea.org}.

Up To $4000 For A Health And Nutrition Major

Odwalla's Femme Vitale Scholarship awards are granted annually to women in pursuance of a degree in health and nutrition. Full time women students in a qualified field of study are eligible to apply for the scholarship. Up to $4000 may be awarded and may be used at any institution of higher learning that offers accredited undergraduate or graduate courses. The applicant must be a resident of or studying in one of the states where Odwalla juice products are sold. Products are sold in California, Washington, Utah, New Mexico, Arizona, Oregon, Texas, Colorado, Nevada, Illinois, Wisconsin, Michigan, Minnesota, Louisiana, New Jersey, Virginia, Maryland, Pennsylvania and Washington, DC. Contact ODWALLA, 120 Stone Pine Road, Half Moon Bay, CA 94019; 650-726-1888; {www.odwallazone.com}.

$1500 For Women Over 35 Years Of Age Pursuing Below Graduate Level Education

The Foundation offers twenty-five awards of $1500 each to U.S. female citizens over the age of thirty-five years of age who are enrolled or accepted in either a certified program of technical/vocational training or an undergraduate program. This is not for graduate work or to pursue a second degree. Send a self-addressed stamped business envelope with your sex, age, level and/or year of study written on the envelope. Contact Jeanette Rankin Foundation, PO Box 6653, Athens, GA 30604; 404-543-8733; {www.wmst.unt.edu/}.

Up To $5000 For Health Information Management

AHIMA offers a variety of scholarships ranging from $1000-$5000 to members. Field of study must be in health information management or health information technology. Applicant must be a full time student in a program accredited by the Commission on Accreditation of Allied Health Education Programs (CAAHEP). Scholarships are available for undergraduate and graduate study. Contact American Health Information Management Association (AHIMA), 919 N. Michigan Ave., Suite 1400, Chicago, IL 60611-1683; 312-787-2672, ext. 302.

Money For Female Artists And Writers

This organization gives small grants that are designed to support feminists who are active in art, fiction, non-fiction and poetry. For more information, contact the organization. Grants range from $250-$1000. Contact Money For Women, P.O. Box 630125, Bronx, NY 10463.

Up To $10,000 For RN's To Pursue Graduate Nursing Education

Scholarships ranging from $2500-$10,000, with the amount varying each year depending on contributions to the organization, are available to U.S. registered nurses. The RN must be a member of a national, professional nursing, enrolled in or applying to a National League for Nursing accredited masters program in nursing, or at the doctoral level. The applicant must also be either a full time master's student or full or part time doctoral level student. The first criteria considered is academic excellence. Contact Nurses Educational Fund, Inc., 555 West 57th Street, New York, NY 10019; 212-399-1428.

$1000 For Students Interested In Medical Assisting

The AAMA offers the Maxine Williams Scholarship of $1000 for one school year. High school graduates who are enrolled in or soon to be enrolled in a post-secondary medical assisting program which is accredited by the Commission on Accreditation of Allied Health Education Programs are eligible. Scholarships are awarded based on interest, need, and aptitude.

Contact American Association Of Medical Assistants (AAMA), 20 North Wacker Drive, Suite 1575, Chicago, IL 60606-2903; 312-899-1500; 800-228-2262.

Scholarships For Medical And Dental Assistant Studies

High school graduates interested in pursuing studies in medical technology, medical laboratory technician, medical assisting, dental assisting, phlebotomy or office laboratory technician may apply for a scholarship with this organization. Applicants must plan on studying at an accredited college or university in the United States. There is an April 1 deadline for submitting applications. Call for an application. Contact American Medical Technologists, 710 Higgins Road, Park Ridge, IL 60068-5765; 847-823-5169.

$1000 For A Woman In Surveying And Mapping

The Porter McDonnell Memorial Award of $1000 is given annually to a woman displaying potential leadership in surveying and mapping. This award is intended to assist with educational expenses of the Bachelor's degree. The Caddy McDonnell Memorial Scholarship Award of $1000 recognizes a woman enrolled in the surveying field who is a legal resident of one of the following western states: Montana, Idaho, Washington, Oregon, Wyoming, Colorado, Utah, Nevada, California, Arizona, New Mexico, Alaska, and Hawaii. This organization also offers a variety of other awards ranging from $500-$2000 and according to level of education.

Contact American Congress On Surveying And Mapping, 5410 Grosvenor Lane, Suite 100, Bethesda, MD 20814; 301-493-0200; {Email: lillym@mindspring.com}.

Money For Law Librarians

If you are in library school to get your law librarian degree, or are already a librarian and getting your law degree, then the American Association of Law Libraries has scholarships for you. The Association provides scholarships in ten different focus areas to help further the profession of law librarianship. For more information contact American Association of Law Libraries, 53 W. Jackson, Suite 940, Chicago, IL 60604; 312-939-4764; {www.aallnet.org}.

$500 Available For Masters And Doctoral Level Health Education

The AAHE has scholarships available in the amount of $500. There are separate awards for doctoral and masters level students who are currently enrolled in a health education programs. Applicants must have a minimum 3.0 GPA on a 4.0 scale and prior AAHE scholarship recipients may not apply. Contact American Association For Health Education (AAHE), 1900 Association Drive, Reston, VA 20191-1599; 703-476-3437.

Money For Women Builders

This foundation awarded over $75,000 to worthy recipients in 1998! Applicants must be in a construction related degree program for a bachelor's or associate degree. You must have at least a 3.0 grade point average and be enrolled full-time in school. Application forms are available through www.fastweb.com or you can send a self-addressed stamped envelope to the address listed below.

Contact National Association Of Women In Construction (NAWIC), 327 South Adams, Fort Worth, TX 76104; 817-877-3943; {www.nawic.org}.

Creative Mothers Can Win Money!

This organization's goal is to assist mothers in educating their children. The American Mothers Cultural and Creative Arts Awards program grants monetary prizes to mothers in three different categories: arts and crafts, literature and vocal music. The intent of the program is to encourage mothers to develop talents that will uplift, teach and share with children. Financial awards are given to the winners in the contests.

Contact American Mothers Inc., The Waldorf Astoria, 301 Park Avenue, New York, NY 10022; 212-755-2539; {www.americanmothers.org}.

$1500-$5000 Available For Civil Engineers

The ASCE has many different scholarships available. Undergraduate freshmen, sophomores, or juniors who are National ASCE Student members are eligible for the Samuel Fletcher Tapman Scholarship, 12 awards of $1500 given annually, or are also eligible for the Charles Tiney Memorial Student Scholarship where $2000 is awarded annually.

The Arthur S. Tuttle Scholarship is for undergraduates in their senior year. $3000-$5000 is awarded to the recipient for the first year of formal graduate civil engineering education tuition. Membership applications may be submitted with scholarship application.

Contact American Society Of Civil Engineers (ASCE), Member Scholarships and Awards, 1801 Alexander Bell Drive, Reston, VA 20191-4400; 800-548-2723; {www.asce.org/peta/ed/cssf_hm.html}.

$500 For Full Time Food Majors

The Worthy Goal Scholarship Fund awards $500 scholarships for those interested in food service. Applicant must be a full time student who is either enrolled in or accepted in a food service related major or vocational training program for the fall following the award. In addition, local scholarships are available through IFSEA Senior branches.

Information regarding Senior branches may be obtained by calling IFSEA headquarters. A total of $100,000 in scholarships is available. Contact International Food Service Executives Association, OFSEA Headquarters, 1100 S. State Road 7, Suite #103, Margate, FL 33368-4033; 954-977-0767.

Creative Women Over 35 Are Eligible For $1000 Award

Women artists, photographers, writers and composers who are 35 years or older are eligible for scholarships of $1000. The intent of the scholarship is to support professional development. A portfolio of work is required with entry. Contact The National League Of American Pen Women, Scholarship Chairman-Mrs. Mary Jane Hillery, 66 Willow Road, Sudbury, MA 01776-2663.

Bright Broadcasters Eligible For $1250-$5000 In Scholarships

College juniors, seniors and graduate students attending a BEA Member university and preparing for a career in broadcasting are eligible for a variety of awards offered by BEA. Fifteen scholarship awards, which range from $1250-$5000, are awarded to full time students to be used exclusively for tuition, student fees, books, and university dorm room and board. Applicants must possess evidence of high integrity and have a strong academic record.

Contact Broadcast Education Association, 1771 N St., NW, Washington, DC 20036-2891; 202-429-5354; {www.beaweb.org} or {Email: fweaver@nab.org}.

$1000 For Women In Advanced Agriculture Or Horticulture Study

The Association offers the Sarah Bradley Tyson Memorial Fellowship to properly qualified women for advanced study in agriculture, horticulture, and allied subjects. The $1000 award is to be used for advanced study at an educational institution of recognized standing within the U.S.A. A letter of application should be sent to the chairman, Mrs. Elmer Braun. Contact Women's National Farm And Garden Association, Inc., Mrs. Elmer Braun, 13 Davis Drive, Saginaw, MI 48603; 517-793-1714.

Up To $1500 For Veterinarian Students

The AAEP has two scholarships available. Fourth-year veterinary students are eligible for The AAEP/American Livestock Insurance Company Scholarship, which awards six $1500 scholarships each year. AAEP student members attending colleges of veterinary medicine either in the US or Canada are eligible. The second scholarship, The AAEP/United States Pony Club Scholarship, awards one $1000 to a current or graduate Pony Club member who is entering veterinary school.

Contact American Association Of Equine Practitioners, 4075 Iron Works Pike, Lexington, KY 40511; 606-233-0147.

$2500 AVAILABLE FOR TECHNICAL COMMUNICATION STUDENTS

STC awards fourteen $2500 scholarships each year toward school tuition and expenses. Applicants must be full time students, either graduate students pursuing a master's or doctor's degree or undergraduate students pursuing a bachelor's degree. They should be studying communication or information about technical subjects such as technical writing, editing, graphical design, interface design, and web design. Awards are made to the school for the benefit of the selected student.

Contact Society For Technical Communication (STC), 901 N. Stuart Street, Suite 904, Arlington, VA 22203-1854; 703-522-4114; {www.stc.org}.

Money Available For Business Majors

The Kemper Foundation offers its scholarships to students enrolled in one of seventeen different colleges and universities. Contact the Foundation for a list of participating schools, as you apply for the scholarships through the schools. Eligibility consists of students interested in pursuing a career in business and is based on financial need.

The Foundation also awards a limited number of merit scholarships, $1500 per academic year, to scholars who show no financial need. The current maximum annual scholarship awarded is $7000. Those who obtain scholarships agree to work for pay during their summers for Kemper Insurance Companies in a variety of capacities and offices. Sixty to seventy scholarships are awarded each year. Contact Kemper Foundation, 1 Kemper Drive, Long Grove, IL 60049-0001.

Scholarships Starting At $2000 For Physician Assistants Students

The Foundation has awarded over 290 scholarships in the past nine years, totaling over $720,000. Student members of the AAPA who are currently enrolled in an accredited PA program are eligible to apply. Awards, which start at $2000, are intended to help students complete their education. Contact American Academy Of Physician Assistants, 950 N. Washington St., Alexandria, VA 22314-1552; 703-836-2272; {Email:aapa@aapa.org}.

Creative Kids Can Win Up To $20,000 In U.S. Savings Bonds

This competition which is sponsored by Duracell North Atlantic Group and administered by the National Science Teachers Association is offered to 6th through 12th grade students. The entrants are divided into two groups; grades 6-9 and grades 10-12 with many awards granted. Each group has one first place winner receiving a $20,000 U.S. Savings bond, two second place prizes of $10,000 savings bond, five third place prizes of $3000 savings bond, 12 fourth place prizes of $1000 savings bond and 30 fifth place prizes of $500 savings bond. Students entering must create and build a working device that is powered by Duracell batteries.

Contact DURACELL/NSTA Scholarship Competition, 1840 Wilson Boulevard, 3rd Floor, Arlington, VA 22201-3000; 888-255-4242; {Email: duracell@nsta.org}.

$500-$2500 Available For Architectural Students

A variety of scholarships, ranging from $500-$2500, are available to architectural students who are pursuing a professional degree in architecture. The scholarship applied for depends upon the student's level of education, starting from those just entering and proceeding to postgraduates and professionals.

The AIA/AAF Minority/Disadvantaged Scholarship program offers college freshmen and others twenty-five scholarships of $500-$2,500 based on financial need for bachelor or master of architecture majors. The AIA/AAF Scholarship Program for First Professional Degree Candidates awards $500-$2,500 for the final two years of a professional architecture degree program. The RTKL Traveling Fellowship offers one $2,500 award to a student who is almost finished with their program to encourage foreign travel to further their education.

Contact The American Institute Of Architects and The American Architectural Foundation, 1735 New York Ave., NW, Washington, DC 20006-5292; 202-626-7511.

Many Opportunities For Orthopedic Nurses

NAON offers a variety of grant and scholarship opportunities to NAON members, ranging from $1000-$5000 in value. Scholarships support attendance at NAON programs and continuing college education in the field of orthopedic nursing. Contact National Association Of Orthopedic Nurses (NAON), NAON Foundation, East Holly Avenue, Box 56, Pitman, NJ 08071-0056; 609-256-2310.

BETA SIGMA PHI MEMBERS AND FAMILY MEMBERS ELIGIBLE FOR SCHOLARSHIPS

Scholarships are available to Beta Sigma Phi members, or the child or grandchild of a member in good standing. If you meet that eligibility, please contact to request one of the scholarship applications. Contact BETA SIGMA PHI, 1800 West 91st Place, Kansas City, MO 64114; 816-444-6800; {Email: bspintl@aol.com}.

$1500 Available For Students
Pursuing Critical Care

The American Association of Critical Care Nurses offers scholarships of $1500 to promote nursing professionalism and to advance the science of critical care nursing. Students completing a generic baccalaureate-nursing program, as well as AACN members who are registered nurses completing a baccalaureate or graduate degree program in nursing, are eligible. The funds may be used for tuition, books, supplies and or fees while the student is enrolled in a baccalaureate program accredited by the National League for Nursing or a graduate program.

Contact American Association Of Critical Care Nurses, Educational Advancement Scholarship, AACN, 101 Columbia, Aliso Viejo, CA 92656-1491; 800-899-2226; {www.aacn.org}.

$500-$1500 Scholarships Available To Court Reporting Students

The NCRA has three scholarships available to students attending an NCRA approved court reporter education program. Lists of schools are available from NCRA on request. Applicants must be nominated by their program and are required to submit an essay on a predetermined subject. The awards range from $500-$1500.

The NCRA also awards six $500 tuition grants to student members of the Association who are chosen by a drawing. Contact National Court Reporters Association (NCRA), 8224 Old Courthouse Road, Vienna, VA 22182-3808; 703-556-6272; 800-272-6272.

Up To $5000 In Grants
Available For English Teachers

Grants up to $5000 are awarded by the Research Foundation for pre-K-12 classroom teachers. Grants are intended for teachers to explore questions related to teaching English/Language Arts. Research questions should be related to work, and have arisen due to questions, concerns or ideas in the classroom. Members of NCTE may apply.

Contact National Council Of Teachers Of English (NCTE), 1111 W. Kenyon Road, Urbana, IL 61801-1096; 217-328-3870.

Opportunity To Receive
College Tuition From NSA

NSA will consider any student who meets the requirements below and who chooses a full-time college major in either computer science, electrical or computer engineering, languages or mathematics. Requirements consist of having a minimum SAT score of 1100 and a minimum composite ACT score of 25. Chosen students can receive college tuition, reimbursement for books, year-round salary, summer work and have a guaranteed job with the NSA after graduation. Students must work for NSA for one and a half times their length of study, which is usually about five years. Contact National Security Agency, Manager, Undergraduate Training Program, Attn: S232R (UTP), 9800 Savage Rd., Suite 6840, Ft. Meade, MD 20755-6840; 800-669-0703; {www.nsa.gov}.

Opportunity For An RN To Win $3000 Toward Occupational Health Education

The AAOHN offers a $3000 award. Applicant must be a registered nurse who is either a full-time or part-time student in a nationally accredited school of nursing baccalaureate program and demonstrate an interest in occupational and environmental health. The Association also offers a variety of research grants for environmental and health registered nurses. Contact the Association for details.

Contact American Association Of Occupational Health Nurses (AAOHN), AAOHN Foundation, Suite 100, 2920 Brandywine Road, Atlanta, GA 30341-4146; 770-455-7757; {www.aaohn.org}.

Opportunity For $600-$12,000 For Manufacturing Engineering Students

The SME Education Foundation offers scholarships based on degree of education. High school students in their senior year are eligible to apply for scholarships ranging from $600-$2500 if they are planning to enroll full-time in a manufacturing engineering or manufacturing engineering technology program. Full-time college students with 30 completed hours and a minimum GPA of 3.5 who are pursuing a career in manufacturing engineering, manufacturing engineering technology, automated systems or robotics may apply for scholarships ranging from $900-$3500.

Graduate fellowships are available to eligible applicants accepted in a manufacturing engineering or industrial engineering graduate program with a minimum GPA of 3.5. New this year is a program offered by SME for grandchildren and children of SME members providing up to $20,000 annually for graduating high school seniors. Contact Society Of Manufacturing Engineers (SME), Education Foundation, One SME Drive, PO Box 930, Dearborn, MI 48121-0930; 313-271-1500; {www.sme.org/foundation}.

$3,000 For Audio Engineers

The Audio Engineering Society provides scholarships to those college graduates who are entering graduate studies in the field of audio engineering. Award recipients are allowed to renew the scholarship for a second year. For information on how to apply, contact Audio Engineering Society, 60 East 42nd St., New York, NY 10165; 212-661-8528; {www.aes.org}.

$200-$5000 Available For Smart Women Engineers

The SWE administers over 90 scholarships per year ranging from $200-$5000. Women majoring in engineering or computer science in a college or university with an ABET-accredited program or in a SWE approved school are eligible. There are a variety of scholarships available. Applicants for sophomore, junior, senior and graduate scholarships must have a minimum GPA of 3.5.

SWE also offers re-entry scholarships to assist women, who have been out of the engineering job market as well as out of school for a minimum of two years, in obtaining the credentials necessary to re-enter the job market as engineers. Contact Society Of Women Engineers (SWE), 120 Wall Street, 11th Floor, New York, NY 10005-3902; 212-509-9577; {www.swe.org}; {Email: hq@swe.org}.

Money Available For Therapists

AMBUCS offers scholarships ranging from $500-$1500 annually to students in their junior/senior year in a bachelor's degree program, or a graduate program leading to a master's or doctoral degree. There is also one two-year award in the amount of $6000 offered. Applicants must be accepted in an accredited program in physical therapy, occupational therapy, speech language pathology, and hearing audiology. Applications available through www.fastweb.com. Contact AMBUCS Scholarship Committee, P.O. Box 5127, High Point, NC 27262; 336-869-2166; {www.ambucs.com}.

Funeral Service Scholarships Opportunities Available

The NFDA provides a list of State Funeral Directors Associations, National Funeral Service Organizations and Mortuary Colleges that offer scholarships to funeral service students. The list provided has over 60 associations, organizations and colleges listed and provides amounts of scholarships available. Contact National Funeral Directors Association (NFDA), 13625 Bishop's Drive, Brookfield, WI 53005-6607; 414-789-1880; {www.nfda.org}; {Email: nfda@nfda.org}.

Opportunity For Pharmacy Students To Get $250-$5000 Scholarships

The ASHP has compiled a listing of a variety of scholarships ranging from $250-$7500. Applicants must either be entry-level B.S. or Pharm.D. program student, in the last three years of a B.S. of Pharm.D. program and planning to pursue the Ph.D. in a college of pharmacy graduate program, or in the final year of a pharmacy college B.S. or Pharm.D. program or have completed a pharmacy degree, depending on the scholarship.

Each scholarship offered may have additional requirements. Contact ASHP for a listing. College loans and residencies information is also available. Contact American Society Of Health-System Pharmacists (AHSP), 7272 Wisconsin Ave., Bethesda, MD 20814; 301-657-3000; {www.ashp.org}.

$2500 Scholarship Opportunity For School Librarian Media

The AASL /School Librarian's Workshop Scholarship offers $2500 for the professional education of persons who are pursuing school library media specialist standing at the preschool through high school levels in public or private educational settings. Applicants are required to have received bachelor's degree with proven academic excellence and to have the intention to pursue full-time graduate level education in an ALA accredited library school program. Contact the Association for details.

Contact Graduate Education, American Library Association, AASL/Scholarship Recommendation, 50 E. Huron St., Chicago, IL 60611-2795; 312-280-4386.

$4000 Scholarship For Communication Science Graduate Student

The Foundation offers full-time graduate students in communication sciences and disorders programs who demonstrate outstanding academic achievement the opportunity to compete for $4,000 scholarships.

Graduate students with disabilities and minority students, who are enrolled in a communication sciences or disorders program, can compete for a $2,000 scholarship. Contact the Foundation for application availability and due dates. Contact American Speech-Language-Hearing Foundation, 10801 Rockville Pike, Rockville, MD 20852; 301-897-5700.

Women Music Majors Eligible For $300 Scholarship

WBDI offers five annual scholarships to women who are currently enrolled in a music education program and are pursuing a career as a band director. Each award is a non-renewable $300 scholarship. Contact Women Band Directors International (WBDI), Linda Moorhouse, Department of Bands, School of Music, Louisiana State University, Baton Rouge, LA 70803.

National Security Related Careers Eligible For Scholarship

The Horizon Foundation offers scholarships valued at no less than $500 to encourage women to pursue careers related to the national security interests of the U.S. Applicants must be currently enrolled at an accredited university/college either full or part-time. Undergraduate (at least junior level status) and graduate students are eligible. Applicants must also have a minimum GPA of 3.25 and be a U.S. citizen. Women in engineering, computer science, physics, mathematics, business, law, international relations, political science, operations research, and economics fields have preference.

Contact Horizons Foundation Scholarship Program, WID Horizons Foundation, c/o National Defense Industrial Association (NDIA), 2111 Wilson Boulevard, Suite 400, Arlington, VA 22201-3061; 703-247-2552; {http://wid.ndia.org}; {Email: william_j_lee@ raytheon.com}.

$1000 Scholarship Opportunity For Women In Business or Economic Education

The Foundation generally grants three $1000 scholarships per year. Women students who are pursuing a career in the business and/or economics field of study are eligible to apply. Applicants must be a full-time student at an approved college/university in the U.S. in pursuit of a business and/or economics degree and must have completed at least one semester or two quarters of college level study. Selection is based on scholastic achievement, leadership potential, motivation and financial need. Contact Phi Chi Theta Foundation Scholarship Committee, 8656 Totempole Dr., Cincinnati, OH 45249.

DAUGHTERS OF A CAREER OFFICER ELIGIBLE FOR SCHOLARSHIPS

This program is for seniors in high school who are the daughters of a career officer commissioned in the regular Army, Navy, Air Force, Coast Guard, or Marine Corps (active, retired or deceased). Selection is based on merit and need. Awards are for up to four years and are granted at the college of the candidate's choice. Contact Daughters Of The Cincinnati, Scholarship Program, 122 East 58th Street, New York, NY 10022; 212-319-6915.

$5000 Grant Opportunity For Midwifery Students

The MCA Foundation offers the Hazel Corbin Grant to provide financial assistance to an individual who demonstrates academic excellence, financial need and a commitment to a family-centered maternity care and who is enrolled in an ACNM accredited midwifery program. The grant is in the amount of $5000.

Contact Maternity Center Association (MCA), 281 Park Avenue South, 5th Floor, New York, NY 10010; 212-777-5000; {www.maternity.org}; {Email: macbirth@ AOL.com}.

Money To Study The Earth And Sky

The AMS offers an array of graduate fellowships and undergraduate scholarships to help further the education of outstanding graduate and undergraduate students. Students must plan to pursue careers in the atmospheric or related oceanic and hydrologic sciences. The amount of the award depends on education level, with a range from $300-$15,000. Contact American Meteorological Society (AMS), 45 Beacon Street, Boston, MA 02108; 617-227-2426 #235; {www.ametsoc.org/AMS}; {Email: armstrong@ametsoc.org}.

Scholarship Of $2500 Available To High School Seniors With Inter-Scholastic Sports

This program offered by ESPN is not an athletic scholarship program. ESPN presents awards to eight graduating seniors, one male and one female in each of the four regions of the U.S.A., each year. The one time $2,500 grants are made to defray the cost of tuition, room and board at an accredited college/university. Selection criteria includes academic achievement, service to school and community, and leadership in interscholastic sports. Applicants must be legal U.S. citizens. Employees of ESPN, Inc., Walt Disney Co., the Hearst Corp. or their respective subsidiaries are not eligible. Contact Sports Leadership, ESPN Sportsfigures Scholarship, P.O. Box 630, Hartford, CT 06142-0630.

Scholarships From Zeta Phi Beta Sorority, Inc.

The Foundation offers nine different scholarships, two of which only Zeta Phi Beta Sorority members are eligible for. The general graduate scholarship is available to graduate women working on a professional degree, masters, doctoral or enrolled in post-doctoral study and is not to exceed $2500 per year. The general undergraduate scholarship is available to high school seniors and undergraduate students and ranges from $500-$1000.

The Deborah Partridge Wolfe International Fellowship is available to graduate and undergraduate U.S. students studying abroad and/or foreign students studying in the U.S. Amount varies from $500-$1000. The S. Evelyn Lewis Memorial Scholarship in Medical Health Sciences is available to graduate or undergraduate women enrolled in a program leading to a medicine or health science degree. Amount $500-$1000. The Lullelia W. Harrison Scholarship in Counseling is available to graduate or undergraduate students enrolled in a counseling degree program and awards $500-$1000. The Isabel M. Herson Scholarship in Education is available to graduate or undergraduate level students enrolled in either an elementary or secondary education degree program. Amount of $500-$1000.

The Zora Neal Hurston Scholarship is available to graduate students pursuing a degree in anthropology or related fields. Amount $500-$1000. The Nancy B. Woolridge McGee Graduate Fellowship and the Mildred Cater Bradham Social Work Fellowship are available to Zeta Phi Beta Sorority members only and each offers $500-$1000. Contact Zeta Phi Beta Sorority, Inc., National Education Foundation, 1734 New Hampshire Avenue, NW, Washington, DC 20009.

Scholarships For Licensed Radio Amateurs, Females Preferred

The FAR will be administering 67 scholarships, ranging from $500-$2500, for the coming academic year. FAR offers 28 different scholarships, which may have different requirements. Unless otherwise specified, all licensed amateurs meeting the specific requirements may compete for the awards if they are now enrolled or have been accepted for enrollment in an accredited university, college or technical school to pursue a full-time course of studies. Contact Foundation For Amateur Radio (FAR), P.O. Box 831, Riverdale, MD 20738.

$500-$1000 Offered To AMVETS Auxiliary And Family

AMVETS Auxiliary provides aid to members and sons/daughters or grandchildren of members in order to recognize and reward need, academic achievement, and potential. Applicants of the Career Start Scholarship must be AMVETS Auxiliary members who have completed at least one semester at an accredited technical school, business school, college, or university.

The AMVETS Auxiliary Scholarship applicants may either be members or a son/daughter, or grandchild of a member and be in at least his/her second year of undergraduate study at an accredited college or university. Scholarships range from $500-$1000. Contact AMVETS Auxiliary National Headquarters, 4647 Forbes Boulevard, Lanham, MD 20706; 301-459-6255.

$300 Available For Geographic Education

The National Council for Geographic Education Committee for Women in Geographic Education offers a $300 scholarship to an undergraduate or graduate woman enrolled in a program leading to a career in geographic education. Applicants must have an overall GPA of 3.0 and a geography GPA of 3.5 and submit a 200 word essay. Contact NCGE for details.

Contact Women In Geographic Education Scholarships, NCGE Central Office, Indiana University of Pennsylvania, Leonard Hall, Room 16A, 421 North Walk, Indiana, PA 15705; 724-357-6290.

$2,000 For High School Female Golfers

The Foundation provides undergraduate scholarships which awards grants in the amount of $2000 per year and are renewable each year for four years if the student has continued financial need and maintains a minimum GPA of 3.0.

Applicant must be a high school senior girl intending to graduate in the year of application, a U.S. citizen and meet the requirements of and plan to enroll at an accredited college/university. Selection is based on academic achievement, financial need, excellence of character and an involvement in the sport of golf, although skill or excellence in the sport of golf is not required. Contact Women's Western Golf Foundation, Director of Scholarship, Mrs. Richard W. Willis, 393 Ramsay Road, Deerfield, IL 60015.

$3000-$5000 For Family And Consumer Science Students

The AAFCS awards national and international fellowships annually to support graduate study in the family and consumer sciences field. The array of scholarships offered supports different aspects of the family and consumer sciences (formerly known as home economics) field and range from $300-$5000. Recipients of AAFCS fellowships, grants and awards must be current members of the Association. Membership must be applied for prior to applying for an award. Contact American Association Of Family And Consumer Sciences, 1555 King Street, Alexandria, VA 22314-2752; 703-706-4600; {www.aafcs.org}; {Email: staff@aafcs.org}.

Daughters Of The US Army Offers Scholarships

DUSA provides one-year, renewable awards of no more than $1000 for financial assistance for undergraduate education to daughters and granddaughters of active, retired or deceased Army officers. Applicants must be a daughter, stepdaughter, adopted daughter, or granddaughter of a career warrant officer or commissioned officer of the United States Army. Selection criteria includes personal record, financial need and a minimum GPA of 3.0 in academic work to date. Contact Society Of Daughters Of The United States Army, c/o Janet B. Otto, Chairman, DUSA Memorial & Scholarship Funds, 7717 Rockledge Court, Springfield, VA 22151-3854.

Scholarships To Students
Who Have Hearing Impairment Or Loss

The organization sponsors scholarships as prizes for contests. Enter contests through local Optimist Clubs. The International essay contest is for grades 10-12 (11-13 in Jamaica only) who attend school in the U.S., Canada or Jamaica. Topics change each year and prizes awarded range from medallions to a $5000 college scholarship. An all-expense paid Freedoms Foundation in Valley Forge, Pennsylvania trip is awarded to all district level winners. The Communication Contest for the Deaf and Hard of Hearing is for people up to the 12th grade in the U.S., Canada or Jamaica identified as having hearing loss/ impairment. Sign language, oral presentation or a combination of both may be used. Prizes range from medallions to a $1500 college scholarship. The Oratorical Contest is for U.S., Canadian or Jamaican students under the age of 16. Applicants are required to give a 4-5 minute speech. Topics vary every year. Each boy and girl winner progress to the next level. Prizes range from medallions to a $1500 college scholarship for each boy and girl district winner. Contact Optimist International, 4494 Lindell Blvd., St. Louis, MO 63108; 314-371-6000.

SCHOLARSHIPS FOR YOUNG BLACK WOMEN

The Association provides financial assistance to young Black women interested in pursuing post-secondary education. Applicants must be graduating high school seniors or enrolled in an accredited college or university and have a minimum GPA of 2.5. All recipients must be full-time students and be either citizens of the U.S. or enrolled in an accredited college in the U.S.

Contact National Association Of Negro Business & Professional Women's Clubs, Inc., 1806 New Hampshire Avenue, Washington, DC 20009-3298; 202-483-4206.

$2000 Scholarships
For Spouses And Children Of Blind Veterans

The Blinded Veterans Association offers its Kathern F. Gruber Scholarship Program to dependent children and spouses of blinded veterans of the U.S. Armed Forces. The veteran must be legally blind, but the blindness need not be service-connected. There are eight $2000 scholarships and eight $1000 scholarships available. Applicants must either be already enrolled in or accepted for admission, as a full-time student in an accredited institution of higher education, or business, secretarial or vocational school. Contact Blinded Veterans Association, 477 H Street, Northwest, Washington, DC 20001-2694; 202-371-8880.

Junior Miss Competition Rewards Winners
With College Scholarships

This nationwide scholarship program's purpose is to recognize, reward and encourage excellence while promoting self-esteem in young women. Winners of local competition advance to state competition and all 50 state winners will travel to Mobile, AL to compete for the title of America's Junior Miss. The recipient of the America's Junior Miss title will receive a $30,000 college scholarship. State, local and national scholarships awarded annually total approximately $5 million. High school girls who are U.S. citizens are eligible to take part in the competition if they have never been married, however it is advisable to inquire during her sophomore year because the local competition may take place prior to her senior year. Contact America's Junior Miss, P.O. Box 2786, Mobile, AL 36652-2786; 334-438-3621.

$4000 Scholarship For Industrial Engineering

The Institute supports the advancement of engineering education and research through a variety of scholarships and awards. The United Parcel Service Scholarship for Female Students awards $4000 annually. Applicants must be undergraduate students pursuing an industrial engineering degree enrolled in any school in the U.S., Canada and Mexico which is accredited by an agency recognized by IIE. Applicants must be full-time students with an overall minimum 3.4 GPA who are active Institute members and have at least five full quarters or three full semesters of school remaining from the date of nomination. Please contact the Institute for details and other scholarship and award programs not limited to females only. Contact United Parcel Service Scholarship For Female Students, Institute of Industrial Engineers, 25 Technology Park/Atlanta, Norcross, GA 30092-2988; 770-449-0461; 800-494-0460.

$300-$1000 Scholarship For Chemistry Students

This National Honor Society for Women in Chemistry offers scholarships for women pursuing a chemistry degree in an accredited college or university. Scholarships vary depending on educational level and amounts awarded. The nominee may be, but need not be, a member of Iota Sigma Pi, depending on the scholarship. The Society also offers professional awards. Awards range from $300 to $1000. Please contact the address listed below for details. Contact Iota Sigma Pi, c/o Dr. Lily Ng, Chemistry Dept., Cleveland State University, Cleveland, OH 44115; {http://chem-faculty.ucsd.edu/sawrey/ Iota_Sigma_Pi/}; {Email: I.ng@popmail.csuohio.edu}.

Legally Blind Eligible For $300-$10,000

The National Federation of the Blind is able to offer a broad array of scholarships to applicants who are legally blind and studying full-time in a post-secondary institution in the United States. One scholarship is available to a full-time employee also attending school part-time. 1 scholarship for $10,000 and 3 scholarships for $3000 have no additional restrictions. Twenty-two scholarships are awarded for $3000. Some have no additional restrictions, although some have female only restrictions and some have field of study restrictions. Contact National Federation Of The Blind, 805 Fifth Ave., Grinnel, IA 50122; 515-236-3366.

Fellowships And Grants For Advancement Of Women In Society

The AAUW provides funds through grants and fellowships to advance education, research, and self-development for women, and to foster equity and positive societal change. Applicants are not required to be members of AAUW. Applicants must demonstrate scholarly or professional excellence and preference is given to women whose interests show a commitment to advancing the welfare of women and girls. Grants to individuals go up to $27,000, and include education, community action, and career development grants. A booklet is available that describes the various programs. Contact American Association Of University Women Education Foundation (AAUW), 2201 N. Dodge Street, Dept. 148, Iowa City, IA 52243-4030; 319-337-1716; {www.aauw.org}.

SCHOLARSHIPS FOR LUTHERAN WOMEN

Women of the Evangelical Lutheran Church in America (Women of the ELCA) offers scholarships in three different categories. Scholarships for Lutheran Lay Women provides assistance to women of the ELCA in a variety of fields as they return to school after experiencing at least a two year interruption. The Arne Administrative Leadership Scholarship provides assistance to Lutheran women who are pursuing an education to prepare for an administrative position. The Herbert W. and Corrine Chilstrom Scholarship provides assistance to Lutheran women who are second-career students at ELCA seminaries and preparing for the ordained ministry in the ELCA.

Contact Women Of The Evangelical Lutheran Church In America, 8765 W. Higgins Road, Chicago, IL 60631-4189; 773-380-2730; 800-638-3522, ext. 2730; {Email: womnelca@elca.org}.

Musicians Eligible For Awards

The National Federation Of Music Clubs (NFMC) is dedicated to finding and fostering young musical talent. The Federation conducts annual Junior Festivals and offers more than a quarter of a million dollars in state and national competitions.

The awards NFMC offers are numerous. Age limits and categories vary greatly per award. Many awards include performance bookings. Almost all awards require NFMC membership. Contact the NFMC for a chart of competitions and awards. Contact National Federation Of Music Clubs (NFMC), 1336 North Delaware Street, Indianapolis, IN 46202-2481; 317-638-4003.

Scholarships For Female Jocks

Women's Sports Foundation offers scholarships to provide female high school student-athletes with a means to continue their athletic participation as well as their college education. The three scholarships offered for this purpose are The Linda Riddle/SGMA Scholarship, Mervyn's California/Women's Sports Foundation Scholarship and Gart Sports/Women's Sports Foundation College Scholarship. The Dorothy Harris Scholarship is offered to provide female graduate students in physical education, sports management, sports psychology or sports sociology with a means to attend graduate school. Contact Women's Sports Foundation, Eisenhower Park, East Meadow, NY 11554; 800-227-3988; {www.womenssportsfoundation.org}; {Email: WoSport@aol.com}.

Smart Science Majors Scholarships

The Clare Boothe Luce Program is intended "to encourage women to enter, study, graduate, and teach" in fields where there have been many obstacles to their advancement. These fields include physics, chemistry, biology, meteorology, engineering, computer science, and mathematics. Undergraduate scholarships are generally awarded for two years to a highly qualified female and solely based on merit. Graduate fellowships are awarded to highly qualified women who are doctoral candidates. Contact the Foundation for details. The Clare Boothe Luce Program, The Henry Luce Foundation, Inc., 111 West 50th Street, New York, NY 10020; 212-489-7700; {www.hluce.org}.

$1500 For Engineering Students

Information Handling Services/SAE Women Engineers Committee Scholarship was established to encourage young women and minority students who are graduating from high school to enter the field of engineering. Applicants must have a minimum 3.0 GPA and be accepted into an ABET accredited engineering program. This $1500 award will be given for the freshman year only.

In addition, the Society offers over $27,000 worth of scholarships to engineering students at any accredited engineering programs. They also offer scholarships for use at over 50 specific universities. Contact the Society for more information and application deadlines. The Society Of Automotive Engineers, 400 Commonwealth Drive, Warrendale, PA 15096-0001; 724-772-8534.

Up to $5000 for Aspiring Journalists

The NAHJ Scholarship Fund was established to assist aspiring minority journalists pursuing a career in journalism. Applicants need not be a member of NAHJ, but must be a student enrolled full-time in a college for the entire academic year. Selection is based on academic excellence, a demonstrated interest to pursue a career in journalism and financial need.

High school seniors, college undergraduate or graduate students majoring in print or broadcast journalism are eligible for a $1000-$2000 NAHJ Scholarship. College juniors or seniors are eligible for the $5,000 Newhouse Scholarship Program. Contact National Association Of Hispanic Journalists, 1193 National Press Building, Washington, DC 20045-2100; 888-346-NAHJ; {www.nahj.org}.

$1000-$5000 For
Broadcast Journalism Majors

The Foundation sponsors seven different scholarships for students seeking a career in electronic journalism. One of the seven awards is for graduate students only. Award amounts range from $1000-$5000. Applicants must be full-time students who have at least one year of college remaining and are officially enrolled in a college. Several of the awards are specific to minorities. The Foundation also offers a variety of internship programs. Contact Radio And Television News Directors Foundation, RTNDF Scholarships, 1000 Connecticut Ave., NW, Suite 615, Washington, DC 20036; {www.rtndf.org}.

$6000 For Women Pursuing Sports Administration

The NCAA offers 12 scholarships to women and 12 scholarships to ethnic minorities who are college graduates and will be entering the first semester of their initial postgraduate studies. Applicants must be accepted into a sports administration or related program. Applicants must be pursuing a career in intercollegiate athletics such as coaching, sports medicine, athletics administration and other careers that provide a direct service to intercollegiate athletics. Each award is for $6000.

The Degree Completion program is for student athletes who have completed their eligibility for athletics-related aid at a Division I school and be within 30 hours of obtaining their degree. They can be funded five semesters part-time or two semesters full-time. They also offer eight $3,000 scholarships to college juniors majoring in sports journalism. Each year more than $1.7 million in scholarships is awarded. The NCAA also awards a variety of postgraduate scholarships.

Please contact Stanley D. Johnson, staff liaison. Contact The National Collegiate Athletic Association, 6201 College Boulevard, Overland Park, KS 66211-2422; 913-339-1906.

$1500 FOR MEDICAL AND DENTAL STUDENTS

The CAMS awards scholarships to help qualified candidates, especially of Chinese descent, with financial hardship, to complete their study of research or teaching in the medical science field. This includes either undergraduate study in medical or dental schools in the U.S.A. or post-graduate medical study or research in schools participating in teaching in medical schools or helping Chinese people abroad. Four to six scholarships are awarded ranging from $1,000-$1,500. Contact Chinese-American Medical Society, Dr. H.H. Wang-Executive Director, 281 Edgewood Ave., Teaneck, NJ 07666; 201-833-1506; {www.camsociety.org}; {Email: hw5@columbia.edu}.

Women Pursuing CEO Or CFO Positions Eligible For Scholarships

The Foundation offers scholarships to women majoring only in finance or economics who are planning for a corporate business career in the private sector. They are targeting women who they believe are most likely to become tomorrow's CEO's or CFO's of major manufacturing companies. Applicants may range from high school seniors to Ph.Ds. The college of attendance must already be determined and that institution informed. The number of awards, as well as the amount, varies from year to year.

Contact The Karla Scherer Foundation, 737 North Michigan Avenue, Suite 2330, Chicago, IL 60611; 312-943-9191; {http://comnet.org/kschererf}.

$500-$1500 FOR PRESBYTERIAN CHURCH MEMBERS

The Presbyterian Church Higher Education Program provides $2 million dollars in grants, loans, and scholarships to students, both undergraduates and graduates, who belong to the Presbyterian Church. Grants range from $500-$2000 for studies.

One program is for students enrolled full-time and pursuing a medical profession. Other programs are for general studies. Applicants must be members of the Presbyterian Church (U.S.A.), U.S. citizens or permanent residents of the U.S., demonstrate financial need and be recommended by an academic advisor at the institution and by a church pastor. A booklet is available which lists the programs or you may check their website for more information.

Contact Presbyterian Church (U.S.A.), 100 Witherspoon Street, Louisville, KY 40202-1396; 502-569-5776; {www.horeb.pcusa.org/highered/}.

$1000 For Females With A Love Of Flying

This wonderful fund is offered in remembrance of Nancy Horton who loved to fly! One award of $1000 is given to the recipient to further the student's flight training. Applicants must be at least 18 years old, have a minimum 3.0 GPA if in school, at least a private pilot, high recommendation from flight instructor, extra flight related activities and, an essay portraying one's love of flight. Contact Nancy Horton "Touch The Face Of God" Scholarship, 4466 N.E. 91st Ave., Portland, OR 97220.

$1000-$2500 For Students Studying Real Estate

IREM offers the Brooker scholarship to increase participation of minorities in the real estate management industry. One graduate level award of $2500 and two undergraduate-level awards in the amount of $1000 are given. Applicants must be minority students who are U.S. citizens who have declared a major in real estate or in a related field and have a minimum GPA of 3.0. Students should have completed at least two courses in real estate at the time of application.

Contact George M. Brooker Collegiate Scholarship For Minorities, Institute of Real Estate Management, Attn: Brooker Scholarship, 430 N. Michigan Ave., Chicago, IL 60611-4090; 312-329-6008; {Email: gohlson@irem.org}.

$5000 For Students With Disabilities

EIF has established a scholarship which awards $5000 each to students with disabilities who are pursuing or about to pursue undergraduate or graduate studies directly related to the electronics industry. Selection is based on GPA, relevance of major, planned studies, career goals, outside activities, and essay questions on the scholarship. Contact Electronic Industries Foundation (EIF), Scholarship Award Committee, 2500 Wilson Boulevard, Suite 210, Arlington, VA 22201-3834; 703-907-7408.

Up To $4000 for Female Medical Students

AMWA Student Members are eligible for a variety of awards from the AMWA. The Wilhelm-Frankowski Scholarship of $4000 is offered to medical students attending an accredited U.S. medical or osteopathic medical school. The Janet M. Glasgow Essay Award of $1000 is presented for the best essay identifying a woman physician who has been a significant mentor and role model. The Carroll L. Birch Award of $500 is presented for the best original research paper written by a student member of the AWMA.

Loans are also available. Contact American Medical Women's Association Foundation (AMWA), 801 North Fairfax Street, Suite 400, Alexandria, VA 22314; 703-838-0500; {Email: mglanz@amwa-doc.org}.

$750 For Geoscience Thesis Work

The Association offers a scholarship program for women who require financial assistance to complete their thesis and to complete a masters or Ph.D. degree in a geoscience field. Applicant must be a woman whose education has been interrupted for at least one year, a candidate for an advanced degree in a geoscience field, and completing their thesis during the current academic year. The scholarship is to be used for typing, drafting, childcare or whatever it takes to finish the thesis. Two $750 scholarships will be awarded. Contact The Association For Women Geoscientists, Chrysalis Scholarships, G&H Production Company, LLC, #930, 518-17th Street, Denver, CO 80202; 303-534-0708; {Email: leete@macalstr.edu}.

$5000 For Training In Field Of Water Supply And Treatment

The American Water Works Association offers The Holly A. Cornell Scholarship to encourage and support outstanding female and/or minority students pursuing advanced training in the field of water supply and treatment. Current master's degree students or students who have been accepted into graduate school are eligible. The scholarship provides a one-time grant of $5000 to the most outstanding eligible candidate.

The Lars Scholarship is open to any student in a master's or doctorate program in science or engineering. There is a $5,000 scholarship for an M.S. student and a $7,000 scholarship for Ph.D. student. Contact American Water Works Association, 6666 W. Quincy Avenue, Denver, CO 80235; 303-347-6206.

SCHOLARSHIPS FOR JOINING AFROTC

Air Force ROTC offers scholarships to high school seniors and high school graduates. Applicants must have a minimum GPA of 2.5 and minimum SAT scores of 1100, ACT scores of 24. The 2 or 3-year scholarships are offered to in-college students in all majors, but the highest concentration is in science and engineering fields. To qualify, applicants must have a minimum 2.65 GPA for science and engineering majors and a 3.0 GPA for all other majors and must hold an AFROTC Professional Officer Course allocation. If accepted for scholarship, students must pass a physical exam and a physical fitness test. Recipients must later serve on active duty to repay obligation. Contact AFROTC for more details. Contact Air Force ROTC, Headquarters AFROTC Scholarship Action Section, 551 E. Maxwell Blvd., Maxwell AFB, AL 36112-6106; 334-953-2091.

$1000 For Women Statisticians

The Gertrude Cox Scholarship is open to women who have been accepted into a graduate statistical program. Masters and doctorate students are encouraged to apply for the scholarship. Contact American Statistical Association, 1429 Duke St., Alexandria, VA 22314; 703-684-1221; 888-231-3473; {www.amstat.org}.

Scholarships For Spouse Or Children Of EOD Officer Or Technician

The EOD Memorial Scholarship Application can be viewed at the website below. Applicants must be an unmarried child under the age of 23 years, a widowed spouse who has never been remarried, or a spouse of an EOD officer or enlisted EOD technician of the Army, Marine Corps, Navy, or Air Force who have successfully completed NAVSCOLEOD. Applicants must also be a graduate of an accredited high school and be enrolled in or accepted for enrollment in a full-time undergraduate course of study at an accredited college/university or technical school beyond the high school level.

Money can be used for tuition, books, room, board, and other fees. The amount of the award varies each year. Contact EOD Memorial Scholarship Fund, Naval School, Explosive Ordnance Disposal, 309 Strauss Avenue, Indian Head, MD 20640-5040; 703-317-0635; {www.erols.com}.

Money For Grandmas

If you are fifty-four or older and have an idea for a project or program dealing with women, then this program is for you. The grants range from $500-$5,000. The projects cannot involve men or children. The projects need to be designed to enhance a skill or talent or produce a report or product that somehow involves women. Call for application guidelines. Contact The Thanks Be To Grandmother Winifred Foundation, P.O. Box 1449, Wainscott, NY 11975; 516-725-0323.

MONEY FOR MIDWIVES TO-BE

The American College of Nurse-Midwives provides scholarships to students in good standing who are enrolled in an accredited midwifery program. For application information contact the office listed below, or use their fax-on-demand system at 202-728-9898 and request document #9001. Contact American College of Nurse-Midwives, 818 Connecticut Ave., NW, Suite 900, Washington, DC 20006; 202-728-9860; {www.midwife.org}.

$500-$2500 For Ohio Engineering Majors

The Engineers Foundation of Ohio provides a variety of grants ranging from $500-$2500 for Ohio residents who meet a minimum grade point and SAT/ACT score. These grants are for students who have been accepted into engineering programs. For specific information about the grants and an application, please contact the office listed below. Contact Engineers Foundation of Ohio, 236 East Town St., Suite 210, Columbus, OH 43215; 614-228-8606.

UP TO $2,500 FOR RESPIRATORY CARE MAJORS

The American Respiratory Care Foundation awards grants ranging from $1,000 to $2,500 for students in respiratory therapy programs, both associate and baccalaureate degree programs. Awards generally include travel and registration to the annual conference. One award, the Morton B. Duggan, Jr. Memorial gives a preference to students from Georgia and South Carolina. Contact American Respiratory Care Foundation, 1030 Ables Lane, Dallas, TX 75229; 972-243-2272; {www.aarc.org}.

Add Up Your Money Women Accountants

The Educational Foundation for Women in Accounting supports women in the accounting profession. They offer a variety of scholarships ranging from $1,250-$5000. The Laurels Fund Scholarships are one-year scholarships targeting women who are pursuing advanced accounting degrees.

Women in Transition Scholarship is for $4,000 and is given to women pursuing an accounting degree. This is for a woman who is in "transition" and was formerly called Displaced Homemaker Scholarship. Contact The Educational Foundation for Women in Accounting, Administrative Office, P.O. Box 1925, Southeastern, PA 19399; 610-407-9229; {www.efwa.org}.

A TOTAL OF $15,000 FOR WOMEN ACCOUNTING MAJORS

Each year the American Society of Women Accountants awards $15,000 in scholarships to women pursuing either a master's or bachelor's degree in accounting. The student can be attending full or part-time. Contact the office listed below for application information. Contact American Society of Women Accountants, 60 Revere Dr., Suite 500, Northbrook, IL 60062; 800-326-2163; {www.aswa.org}.

Money For Human Resource Majors

The Society of Human Resource Management offers a variety of scholarships to undergraduate and graduate human resource majors. Awards range from $1,000-$5,000. Students must maintain a "C" average. Several of the awards are competitions in a research project or essay writing. Contact the office listed below for application information.

Contact Society for Human Resource Management, 1800 Duke St., Alexandria, VA 22314; 703-548-3440; {www.shrm.org}.

Money For Latinas

MANA, a national Latina organization, provides scholarships to Latinas who have good academic records and financial need. They offer a variety of scholarships. Contact the office listed below for application information. Contact MANA: A National Latina Organization, 1725 K St., NW, Suite 501, Washington, DC 20006; 202-833-0060; {www.hermana.org}.

$1000 For Real Estate Appraisers

The Appraisal Institute offers scholarships to minority students interested in the real estate appraisal field. The scholarship award of $1000 is for undergraduate or graduate degrees in the field. Contact Appraisal Institute, 875 North Michigan Ave., Suite 2400, Chicago, IL 60611; 312-335-4121; {www.appraisalinstitute.org}.

Confederates Unite

If you are a lineal descendant of worthy confederates, you may be eligible for scholarships through this organization. You must have certified proof of Confederate Military Record of one ancestor, and information on how to obtain this information is available. You also need recommendations, a 3.0 grade point average and more. There are several four-year scholarships without restrictions as to schools, major, or state of residency, and others that have some type of restriction. Send a self-addressed stamped envelope to the address listed below for information and application requirements. Contact United Daughters of the Confederacy, 3202 Superior Lane, Bowie, MD 20715.

Count On Accounting

The National Society of Public Accountants awards 30 scholarships per year, approximately $1,000 each. Students must have a 3.0 grade point average and major in accounting at a 2-year or 4-year college. Scholarships are awarded based upon academic excellence and financial need. Contact the Society for application information. National Society of Public Accountants, 1010 North Fairfax St., Alexandria, VA 22314; 703-549-6400; {www.nsacct.org}.

AT&T Labs Fellowship Program for Women & Minorities in Science & Tech

Outstanding minority and women students who plan to pursue Ph.D. studies in computers, engineering, and other communications-related fields are eligible to apply for the AT&T Fellowships. The students chosen as fellows will have a mentor assigned to them to help guide them through their studies. The fellowships cover most education expenses, an annual living stipend and more for up to five years of graduate studies.

For more information contact AT&T Labs Fellowship Administrator, Room C103, 180 Park Ave, Florham Park, NJ 07060; {www.research.att.com/academic/}.

$500-$1,500 FOR SMART BUSINESS WOMEN

The American Business Women's Association offers a variety of scholarships to undergraduate and graduate business majors, and to students pursuing professional degrees. Awards range from $500-$1,500. Students must be female. Some awards are limited to residents of Anne Arundel County, Maryland. Contact American Business Women's Association, 9100 Ward Parkway, P.O. Box 8728, Kansas City, MO 64114-0728; 301-255-1067; {www.abwahq.org}.

Up to $1000 for Legally Blind Women

The American Foundation for the Blind offers various support services and scholarships to undergraduate students who are legally blind. Some scholarships are restricted to specific majors; others require a short essay. They also offer several scholarships to students pursuing a Classical Music career. All are based on academic achievement. Contact American Foundation for the Blind, 15 W. 16th St., New York, NY 10011; {www.afb.org}.

Money for Smart Business Women

The Business and Professional Women's Association offers a variety of scholarships to women over the age of 25 who are returning to college after a break/delay in their education and plan on pursuing a business career. Some scholarships are intended for use during your junior and senior year only.

The Association considers financial need, academic achievement, recommendations and a personal statement in their decisions. The $1000 Kelly Services Second Career Scholarship is for women returning to or starting their education due to the death of a spouse or divorce, and is for use during any undergraduate year. The Association may also have loans available. Contact Business and Professional Women's Association, 2012 Massachusetts Ave., NW, Washington, DC 20036; 202-293-1200.

$500 for Meteorologists and Atmospheric Science Majors

Interested in a career in the Atmospheric Sciences? The American Geophysical Union offers undergraduate women a chance at $500! Contact American Geophysical Union, American Geophysical Union, 2000 Florida Ave., NW, Washington, DC 20009; 202-462-6903 {earth.agu.org or www.agu.org}.

Up to $3000 for
Nuclear Scientists and Nuclear Engineers

The American Nuclear Society has a large variety of scholarships and research grants available to women who plan to pursue a career in the nuclear sciences. One scholarship awarded each year is reserved for women who are returning to school after a break/delay in their education. All scholarships can be applied for using one application form, which is available on their website. Contact American Nuclear Society, 555 N. Kensington Ave., La Grange Park, IL 60525; {www.ans.org}.

$500-$3,500 for Smart New York Women

The Foundation has various programs for Jewish female undergraduate students who live in New York, NY. Please write for further information, include a SASE. Contact Jewish Foundation for the Education of Women, 330 W. 58th St., New York, NY 10019.

$1,000 for Engineering, Math and Science Students

The Brookhaven Institute's Women in Science program targets women who have had their education interrupted due to financial, family, or other problems. Financial need is the primary consideration. Intended for use during your junior or senior year, the scholarship converts to a loan if you do not maintain good academic standing for two consecutive semesters. Contact Brookhaven Women in Science, P.O. Box 183, Upton, NY 11973; 516-344-7226.

$5,000 for SCUBA Divers

Our World Underwater Scholarship Society provides a scholarship to a SCUBA diver who wants to experience a year of field studies. The Scholarship award provides for a year of travel so the recipient can have a variety of underwater experiences. You can learn about underwater photography, biology, scientific expeditions and more. For more information contact Our World Underwater Scholarship Society, P.O. Box 4428, Chicago, IL 60608; 312-666-6525; {www.owuscholarship.org}.

$2000 for Smart Engineering Women

The National Society of Professional Engineers offers several scholarships to graduating high school seniors who are in the top 25% of their class and intend on pursuing a career in engineering. The scholarship is renewable, and requires a minimum GPA of 3.0. Contact National Society of Professional Engineers, 1420 King St., Alexandria, VA 22314; 703-684-2858; {www.nspe.org}.

Money for Smart Jewish Women in Massachusetts

Priority is given to those who are returning to school after a five year or longer absence. Financial need is the primary consideration, the awards may be used during any undergraduate field of study. A strong desire for financial independence is a plus. Contact National Council of Jewish Women, 75 Harvard Ave., Allston, MA 02134.

$1,000 FOR CALIFORNIA CONSTRUCTION WOMEN

The El Camino Real Chapter of the National Association of Women in Construction offers $1,000 to women entering their junior or senior year of study. Must be attending a college in California. Academic achievement is the primary consideration.

Women studying architecture, architectural engineering, civil engineering or any construction-related major are welcome to apply. Contact National Association of Women in Construction, El Camino Real Chapter 158, 333 W. Santa Clara St., Suite 110, San Jose, CA 95113; 408-998-4646.

$1,000 for Smart Journalism Women

The National Federation of Press Women offers several different scholarships, most paying around $1000, to high school seniors and college undergraduates pursuing a career in journalism. The Federation considers academic achievement, financial need, and potential for success in their decisions. Contact National Federation of Press Women, 4510 W. 89th St., Prairie Village, KS 66207-2282; 913-341-0165.

Up to $500 for Activists at CUNY

For women attending any campus of the City University of New York. The Astraea Foundation offers two $500 awards annually to women who demonstrate political and social commitment to actively fighting for gay and lesbian civil rights. For use during any undergraduate year, lesbian sexual orientation is not a requirement - just commitment to lesbian civil rights. Financial need is considered but not required. Contact Astraea National Lesbian Action Foundation, 116 E. 16th St., 7th Floor, New York, NY 10003; 212-529-8021; {www.astraea.org}.

UP TO $2000 FOR WOMEN IN BROADCASTING

For undergraduate women planning on a career in radio or television broadcasting. Contact Opportunities for Women in Broadcasting, c/o The Citizen's Scholarship Foundation of America, 326 S. Minnesota Avenue, St. Peter, MN 56082; 507-931-1682; 507-931-8034.

$1000 for Daughters of Penelope

The Daughters of Penelope offers to members or children of members three different awards ranging from $1000 to $1500 for use during your undergraduate years. Academic achievement, financial need and an essay are required. Members of The Maids of Athena are also eligible to apply. For application and information, check with your local chapter first, or the address below. Contact The Daughters of Penelope, 1909 Q St., NW, Suite 500, Washington, DC 20009; 202-234-9741.

Up to $1000 for Landscape Architects

The Foundation offers ten different programs assisting landscape architecture students. Some programs require written papers on the subject of landscape architecture, others require photos or slides of work you have done. Please contact the Foundation for details. Landscape Architecture Foundation, 4401 Connecticut Ave., NW, Suite 500, Washington, DC 20008; 202-686-0068.

UP TO $1,000 FOR MEDICAL WOMEN

For undergraduate women interested in pursuing a career in clinical healthcare or health administration. Contact American College of Medical Practice Executives, 104 Inverness Terrace East, Englewood, CO 80112; 303-799-1111; {www.ache.org}.

$500-$1000 for Kappa Kappa Gamma Women

If you are a member of Kappa Kappa Gamma and studying social work, special education, or rehabilitation, KKG has money for you!! For application and information, please check with your college's chapter or send a SASE to the address below. Contact Kappa Kappa Gamma, 530 E. Town St., Columbus, OH 43216; 614-228-6515.

$500-$5,000 for
Daughters of the Railroad

The Foundation offers 150 scholarships yearly to daughters of deceased employees of any railroad company. Preference is given to women who are about to graduate high school. Contact John Edgar Thomson Foundation, The Rittenhouse Claridge, Suite 318, Philadelphia, PA 19103; 215-545-6083.

$1,000 for Smart California Women

For undergraduate women studying in any college in California. Must have graduated from a high school in California. Based on financial need, academic achievement, community service, references. Contact Amaranth Fund Awards, California Mason Foundation, 1111 California St., San Francisco, CA 94109.

$1,000 for the Top Ten College Women

Each year, Glamour Magazine looks for the Top Ten College Women in America. Applications are taken during your junior year. Academic achievement, extracurricular activities, community service, personal statement, references and an essay are all considered — looking fantastic helps but isn't necessarily required. For full-time college juniors. Information for next year's contest will be available at the 800 number below.

Contact Glamour Magazine, 350 Madison Ave., New York, NY 10017; 800-244-4526; {www.glamour.com}; {Email: ttcw@glamour.com}.

Lots of Money for
All Kinds of Women in El Paso, TX

The El Paso Community Foundation handles scholarships for a large variety of foundations, with many different restrictions — some with none! But all are restricted to residents of El Paso, TX. Some are restricted to current high school seniors. Some can only be used at colleges in Texas. Most are based on academic achievement and require full-time student status. For detailed information, contact The El Paso Community Foundation, 201 E. Main St., Suite 1616, El Paso, TX 79901.

Lots of Money for All Kinds of Women in
Santa Barbara, CA

The Santa Barbara Foundation handles scholarships for a large variety of foundations, with many different restrictions — some with none! But all are restricted to residents of Santa Barbara, CA. Some are restricted to current high school seniors. Most are based on academic achievement and require full-time student status. For detailed information, contact Santa Barbara Foundation, 16 E. Carrillo St., Santa Barbara, CA 93101.

$6,000 for Graduate Women

The Amelia Earhart Fellowship, awarded annually by the Zonta International Foundation, is for women pursuing graduate level studies in aerospace, aeronautics, engineering and related studies. Academic achievement is the primary consideration. Contact Zonta International Foundation, 557 W. Randolph St., Chicago, IL 60661; 312-930-5848.

Up to $3000 for California Golfers

For women who are residents of southern California, this renewable award is based primarily upon academic achievement and financial need. Must have an interest in golfing, however actual skill in golfing is not a consideration. Must be attending or planning on attending a four-year college or university full-time. Contact Gloria Fecht Memorial Scholarship Foundation, 402 W. Arrow Highway, Suite 10, San Dimas, CA 91773; {www.womensgolf.org}.

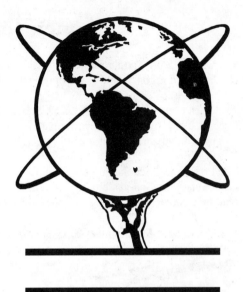

A CALL TO ACTION — FOR MONEY!

The Call to Action Essay Contest is for undergraduate women who live in California and are studying business, education, health care, law enforcement or social service. Up to $5,000 is awarded to the winning essay, topic changes yearly. Please write or contact your financial aid office for information. Contact Governor's Conference for Women, A Call To Action, Office of the Governor, 300 S. Spring St., 16th Floor, Los Angeles, CA 90013.

Up to $10,000 for Young Women

Girls Incorporated offers several scholarships and contests to its members, including a national academic scholarship contest worth $10,000. Must be a high school student in grades 10 through 12, under age 19, and a member of Girls Incorporated. Contact Girls Incorporated, 120 Wall St., New York, NY 10005.

Money for Women Ministers

For undergraduate women attending college full-time who are preparing for the ministry. Please include SASE with requests for information. Contact Disciples of Christ Church, P.O. Box 1986, Indianapolis, IN 46206.

MONEY FOR AMATEUR ATHLETES

The Amateur Athletic Union provides scholarship from $500-$3,000 to high school seniors who participate in at least one high school sport. You must write an essay on the goals you achieved and the obstacles you overcame in order to reach those goals. For more information contact Amateur Athletic Union, c/o Walt Disney World Resort, P.O. Box 10000, Lake Buena Vista, FL 32830; 407-934-7200; {www.aausports.org}.

Money for Women in Oregon

The Oregon State Scholarship Commission manages a large variety of scholarship offers for women who are residents of Oregon. Some of the opportunities for undergraduate women include:

The Agricultural Women-in-Network Scholarship for college sophomore and junior students attending college in Oregon, Washington, or Idaho. Primarily based on financial need and academic achievement, you must be planning on pursuing an agricultural-related career.

The Private 150 Scholarship Program, for current college juniors and seniors studying business. The Professional Land Surveyors Scholarship, for use during your junior or senior year. Must be attending any college in Oregon and plan on a career in surveying, cartography, or related careers.

Contact Oregon State Scholarship Commission, 1500 Valley River Dr., Suite 100, Eugene, OR 97401-7020.

Over $1 Million Available for Farmers

Over 300 different scholarship programs are available to members of the Future Farmers of America. Some programs are available to non-members who are pursuing agricultural-related degrees. Details and applications are available at the website. Contact Future Farmers of America, Inc., Scholarship Office, P.O. Box 68960, Indianapolis, IN 46268-0960; {www.ffa.com}.

$250 for Teaching in Oregon

This renewable scholarship is for undergraduate students who plan on teaching in Oregon upon completion of their education degree. Preference is given to those who plan on teaching at the elementary or secondary school levels. Contact Oregon PTA, 531 SE 14th Ave., Room 205, Portland, OR 97214.

$3,500 for Broadcasting in Oregon or Washington

For current undergraduate students attending any college in Oregon or Washington who intend on pursuing a career in broadcasting. Academic achievement is the primary consideration. Contact Oregon Association of Broadcasters, P.O. Box 20037, Portland, OR 97220.

UP TO $1000 FOR SHEEP

For undergraduate students who are studying agriculture, animal science, veterinary medicine, or animal husbandry and intend on pursuing a career in the Sheep industry. Must be a resident of Oregon. Contact Oregon Sheep Growers Association, 1270 Chemeketa St., NE, Salem, OR 97301; 503-364-5462.

Tuition and up to $13,500 for Smart Graduate Students

The A.W. Mellon Fellowship in Humanistic Studies is designed to encourage and prepare students of exceptional academic promise for teaching and scholarship careers in humanistic studies. Students majoring in American studies, art history, the classics, comparative literature, cultural anthropology, english literature, foreign language, history, the philosophy of science, and related majors are welcome to apply. For use at the graduate level of study, this highly competitive and prestigious award grants tuition, fees, and a stipend of up to $13,500 to 80 people yearly. Contact The A.W. Mellon Fellowship in Humanities, Woodrow Wilson National Fellowship Foundation, CN 5329, Princeton, NY 08543-5329; 609-452-7007.

Money for Dietetic Technicians

The American Dietetic Association offers various scholarships to students who are studying dietetics or nutrition, and plan on a career in dietetics. Must be entering your first year of study in an ADA-accredited dietetic technician program. Financial need and academic achievement are the primary considerations. Contact American Dietetic Association, 216 W. Jackson Blvd., Suite 800, Chicago, IL 60606-6995; 312-899-0040; {www.eatright.org}.

Up to $1,500 for Dental Hygienists

The Association offers a large variety of scholarships to students who plan on a career as a dental hygienist. Most awards are limited to current college juniors, however some are open to all undergraduate students. Some of their programs target students studying for a certificate in dental hygiene, others target minority students. Applications and information are available at their website. Financial need and academic achievement are the primary considerations. Contact American Dental Hygienists Association, 444 N. Michigan Ave., Suite 3400, Chicago, IL 60611; 312-440-8944; {www.adha.org}.

Money for Internet Teams

Teams of kids can gather together to work on an Internet Project together. College scholarships totaling over $1,000,000 are awarded to students, as well as monetary awards to project team coaches and schools. Elementary and secondary students are eligible. For more information check out the website {www.thinkquest.org}.

$2,500 FOR NURSES

The Eight and Forty Scholarship, offered by the American Legion, was established to assist current registered nurses (RN's) who wish to advance their career for positions in supervision, administration or teaching. Students are to have prospects of being employed in specific positions in hospitals, clinics, or health departments on completion of their education and the position must have a full-time and direct relationship to lung and respiratory control.

For more information, contact the address listed below. Contact The American Legion, Attn: Eight and Forty Scholarships, P.O. Box 1055, Indianapolis, IN 46206; {www.legion.org/}.

Up to $10,000 for Handicapped Musicians

This music competition is open to students who are blind, deaf, learning disabled, or physically disabled. An audition tape is required. Check with your local Very Special Arts Organization, or the address below for further information. Contact Very Special Arts and the Panasonic Electronics Company, 1300 Connecticut Ave., NW, Washington, DC 20036; 800-933-8721; {www.vsarts.org}.

Up to $9,000 for Women from Developing Countries

Five awards are available, each up to $9,000 for female students from developing countries. Must show service to women and/or children. Must be 25 years of age or older. Must be planning on returning to your home country within two years. Contact Margaret McNamara Memorial Fund, World Bank, Q-5-080, 1818 H Street, NW, Washington, D.C. 20433; 202-473-5804; {www.erols.com/prlinn/ mmmf.html}, {Email: wservices1@worldbank.org}.

UP TO $5,000 FOR FOOD SERVICE EXPERIENCE

The National Restaurant Association has two different programs available. The Industry Assistance Grants offer up to $1000 to further the education of those who have at least three years experience in food service. The Undergraduate Scholarships Program offers up to $5,000 to current college sophomores and juniors who have at least a 3.0 GPA. You must also have at least 1000 hours of work experience in the food service industry. Contact National Restaurant Association Educational Foundation, 250 S. Wacker Drive, Suite 1400, Chicago, IL 60606-5834; 800-765-2122, ext. 760.

$6,000 For The Health Therapy Profession

AMBUCS offers scholarships to students who are in their junior or senior year of a bachelor's program or in graduate school studying physical therapy, occupational therapy, speech language pathology, or hearing audiology. Awards range from $500 to $1,500 annually, with one two-year award of $6,000 being offered. The total amount awarded each year is $225,000. You must fill out the application form online. Check out AMBUS Scholarship Committee, P.O. Box 5127, High Point, NC 27262; 336-869-2166; {www.ambucs.com}.

Up to $2,000 for Essays!

Applicants must research and write an essay on a topic to be determined by The Foundation. Applicants must contact The Heritage of America Scholarship Foundation to receive an application form and essay question. Open to current high school seniors, current undergraduate and graduate students. Essays and application forms must be postmarked on or before April 30.

Please include SASE with requests for information! Requests without SASE will not be responded to! Contact Heritage of America Scholarship Foundation, 8222 Thetford Lane, Houston, TX 77070.

$1,000 for Oregon High School Students

Five awards of $1,000 are available through the annual Cascade Policy Essay Competition. Based on an essay, the topic changes yearly. Private, public and homeschooled students are all encouraged to enter. All high-school age students are eligible to apply, not just college-bound seniors. Contact Cascade Policy Institute, 813 SW Alder, Suite 450, Portland, OR 97205; 503-242-0900; {www.CascadePolicy.org/essay.asp}, {Email: Essay@ CascadePolicy.org}.

Over $200,000 Available for Students with Norwegian Interests!

The Sons of Norway has several programs available. King Olav V Norwegian American Heritage Fund Students from Norway are also eligible to apply. For U.S. students, you must demonstrate a keen and sincere interest in the Norwegian heritage. For Norwegian students, you must demonstrate a strong interest in American heritage. Students at the high school senior, college undergraduate and college graduate level are eligible to apply. Most awards are in the range of $250-$3,000.

Nancy Lorraine Jensen Memorial Scholarship Fund for women under the age of 35, who are either members of the Sons of Norway, or employees of NASA/Goddard Space Flight Center. Daughters and granddaughters of members or employees area also eligible to apply. Must be studying chemistry, chemical engineering, mechanical engineering, electrical engineering, or physics. For undergraduate study only, must have completed at least one semester of studies at time of application.

Contact King Olav V Norwegian American Heritage Fund, Sons of Norway Foundation, 1455 W. Lake St., Minneapolis, MN 55408; {www.sofn.com}.

Up to $1,500 for Returning Students

The P.E.O. Program for Continuing Education provides grants to women whose education has been interrupted and who find it necessary to resume studies due to changing demands in their lives. There must be a need for financial assistance with their educational expenses to improve their marketable skills. Must have been out of school for at least a year, must be within the last two years of finishing your degree, must be a citizen of either the United States or Canada. Apply directly with a local P.E.O. Sisterhood chapter. Contact P.E.O. Sisterhood, 3700 Grand Avenue, Des Moines, IA 50312-2899, Attn: Executive Office.

Money for Graduate Students

Delta Sigma Theta has various programs available to graduate students who have demonstrated a commitment to serving their community. Must have at least a 3.0 GPA. Contact Century City Alumnae Chapter, Delta Sigma Theta Sorority, P.O. Box 90956, Los Angeles, CA 90009; 213-243-0594.

Up to $3.5 Million for Young Women

The American Young Woman of the Year, a talent and scholarship contest, is for current high school seniors. It's based on SAT or ACT scores, GPA, transcript, interview, physical fitness, talent, poise, and appearance. Contact American Young Woman of the Year Program, P.O. Box 2786, Mobile, AL 36652.

$1,000 for Young Feminists

Spinster's Ink offers an essay contest on "What Feminism Means to Me," for current female high school seniors. Winning essays will also be published in a national magazine. Contact Spinster's Ink, ATTN: Claire Kirch, 32 East First St. #330, Duluth, MN 55802; 218-727-3222; 800-301-6860; {www.spinsters-ink.com}.

Money for Texas Women Returning to School

The Ajay Castro Scholarship for Re-Entering Women provides financial assistance to women from Bexar County, Texas, who have been out of school for at least three years. Must be pursuing your first undergraduate degree, and must be studying a communications-related major. Contact Association for Women in Communications, San Antonio Professional Chapter, P.O. Box 780382, San Antonio, TX 78278; 210-231-5799; {Email: jones@texas.net}.

Up to $2,500 for Nevada Women

The Nevada Women's Fund offers a large variety of programs to assist women in Nevada who wish to pursue a college education. Women studying at any academic level are welcome to apply, all programs are based primarily on academic achievement, financial need, and community service. Preference is given to women who are returning to school after a few years break and to single mothers. Most programs are renewable. Must attend college in Nevada. Contact Nevada Women's Fund, P.O. Box 50428, Reno, NV 89513; 775-786-2335.

Money for Arkansas Single Parents

The Arkansas Single Parent Scholarship Fund is open to single parents (of either gender) who wish to begin or continue their higher education. Applicants must reside in a county where a Single Parent Scholarship Fund has been established — you can get a list of counties with this program by contacting the address below or your school's financial aid office. Contact Arkansas Single Parent Scholarship Fund, 614 East Emma Avenue, Suite 119, Springdale, AR 72764; 501-927-1402.

Money for Palo Alto, California Women

Young women who are graduating from any high school in Palo Alto with a 3.0 or higher GPA are eligible to apply. Must be planning on attending a 4-year college or university, must be planning on studying science or a related major. Primary considerations for this award are athletic activities, community service, academic achievement and financial need. Please contact your high school's guidance counselor office or the address below for further information. Contact Peninsula Community Foundation, 1700 South El Camino Real, Suite 300, San Mateo, CA 94402-3049; 650-358-9369.

Up to $750 for Nursing or Teaching Women from Maine

This program is open to young women in Knox County, Maine, who wish to pursue an education in nursing or education. Students with financial need are given preference. Contact Barbara Thorndike Wiggin Fund, c/o Trust Department, Fleet Bank of Maine, P.O. Box 1280, Portland, ME 04104; 207-874-5232.

Up to $1,000 for Journalism Women in Washington

Women journalism majors entering their junior or senior year at any university in the state of Washington are eligible to apply. Contact Bobbi Mccallum Memorial Scholarship, Seattle Post-Intelligencer, 101 Elliott Avenue West, Seattle, WA 98119-4220; 206-448-8316.

$100 FOR FOLK WOMEN

The Elli Kongas-Maranda Student Prize awards undergraduate and graduate students who submit papers or productions on women's traditional, vernacular, and local culture and/or work on feminist theory and folklore.

Contact American Folklore Society, Women's Folklore Section, c/o Clover Williams, Indiana University, Folklore Institute, 504 North Fess, Bloomington, IN 47405.

$1,000 for Danish Sisterhood of America Women

Danish Sisterhood of America members, and their immediate families, are eligible to apply for a variety of programs offered by the Sisterhood. The awards can be used for either undergraduate or graduate work. You must have been a member for at least one year and have at least a 3.0 GPA. This award can also be used for studying in Denmark! Contact Danish Sisterhood of America, 8004 Jasmine Boulevard, Port Richey, FL 34668-3224; 813-862-4379.

Up to $1,000 for Alpha Chi Omega Women

Undergraduate members of Alpha Chi Omega are eligible to apply for a variety of different programs offered, ranging from $400 to $1000. Some programs are based on financial need, others on academic achievement, most consider service to the sorority. Please contact your local chapter first for further information.

Contact Alpha Chi Omega Foundation, 5939 Castle Creek Parkway North Drive, Indianapolis, IN 46250-4343; 317-579-5050; {www.alphachiomega.org}.

$1,000 for Texas Communication Women

Any woman attending any college or university in Texas who is studying journalism and has an interest in sports journalism is eligible to apply. Programs are available for both undergraduate and graduate level study. Contact Texas Professional Communicators, P.O. Box 173, Denison, TX 75021-0173; 903-465-8567.

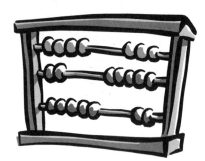

Money for Mathematical Woman

The American Mathematical Society has a variety of programs to reward outstanding undergraduate and graduate women in mathematics. Women in both the United States and Canada are eligible to apply. Contact American Mathematical Society, Attn: Executive Director, P.O. Box 6248, Providence, RI 02940-6248; 401-455-4000; 800-321-4AMS; {www.ams.org}, {Email: ams@ams.org}.

$3,000 FOR SPORTS JOURNALISM

The Sports Journalism Scholarship Program is open to students entering their senior year who are interested in a career in sports journalism. Women and minorities are particularly encouraged to apply. Contact Freedom Forum, 1101 Wilson Boulevard, Arlington, VA 22209; 703-284-2814; {www.freedomforum.org/}, {Email: gpolicinski@ freedomforum.org}.

Money for Rochester Women

High school students in and around the Rochester, New York area are eligible to apply. Over sixty different programs are available; requirements vary by program. Details on the various scholarships are available on the website. Applications are only available through your high school guidance office, please do NOT write directly to the Foundation for information. Contact Rochester Area Community Foundation, 500 East Avenue, Rochester, NY 14607-1912; 716-271-4100; {www.racf.org}.

3M ENGINEERING AWARDS

The National Action Council for Minorities in Engineering offers a variety of programs to minority women who have outstanding academic achievement, community service, and display a strong interest in math, sciences, and engineering areas. Programs are available at the high school, undergraduate and graduate level.

For most programs, students do not apply directly to NACME. Consult with your guidance counselor, program director, dean's office, financial aid officer or advisor to get information on the nomination process at your school or for applications. The application period for most

Money for Navy Wives

The Mary Paolozzi Membership Scholarship is open to women who are wives of Navy personnel and have been members of the Navy Wives Club for at least two years. Financial need is considered. Contact Navy Wives Club of America, P.O. Box 6971, Washington, DC 20032.

programs is November through February. Contact National Action Council for Minorities in Engineering, 350 Fifth Avenue, Suite 2212, New York, NY 10118-2299; 212-279-2626; {www.nacme.org}.

UP TO $2,500 FOR HAWAIIAN WOMEN

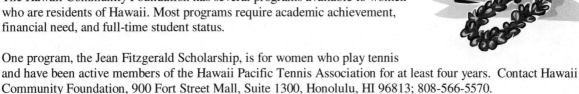

The Hawaii Community Foundation has several programs available to women who are residents of Hawaii. Most programs require academic achievement, financial need, and full-time student status.

One program, the Jean Fitzgerald Scholarship, is for women who play tennis and have been active members of the Hawaii Pacific Tennis Association for at least four years. Contact Hawaii Community Foundation, 900 Fort Street Mall, Suite 1300, Honolulu, HI 96813; 808-566-5570.

Money for Jewish Women for Jesus

The Hazel Stone Memorial Scholarship is available to Jewish women who have committed their life to Jesus, plan on or are attending a Bible college or seminary, and are committed to an evangelistic career after graduation. Financial need is a primary consideration. Contact Jews for Jesus, 60 Haight Street, San Francisco, CA 94102; {www.jewsforjesus.org}.

Up to $1,000 for Women in Hunterdon County, New Jersey

The Mildred Preen Mortimer Woman-In-Transition Award is intended to provide financial aid to women in Hunterdon County, New Jersey, who are either returning to school after a break or who wish to pursue a second career. Financial need and desire for financial independence are the primary considerations. Contact Hunterdon Women's Fund, P.O. Box 183, Flemington, NJ 08822.

MONEY FOR BEAUTIFUL AFRICAN AMERICAN WOMEN

This annual competition is open to all African American women, including those who are married and/or have children, are eligible to enter this competition. The competition begins at the state level, winners move on to the national levels. Winners are chosen based on beauty, talent, and personality. There is a $40 application fee and a $550 sponsorship fee. The fees can be paid for by sponsors, fundraising, or by selling subscriptions to "Black America" magazine. Contact Miss Black America Pageant, P.O. Box 25668, Philadelphia, PA 19144; 215-844-8872.

MONEY FOR WOMEN

Open to women from ages 3 to 20 (and men from ages 18-20), the purpose of this program is to "recognize and reward girls who could become tomorrow's leaders." Contestants must never have been married or have a child. In addition to appearance, academic achievement and community service are considered. Pageants are first held on the state level, winners then move on to the national competition. There is a $15 registration fee, and a $350 sponsor fee (which can be paid for by an individual's sponsors, family, friends, or through fund-raising.) Contact American Co-ed Pageants, 3695 Wimbledon Drive, Pensacola, FL 32504; 850-432-TEEN; {www.americanpageants.com/pageant.html}.

Up to $2,500 for Music Women in Massachusetts

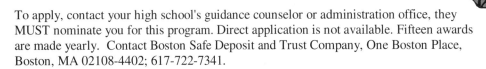

The Madelaine H. Soren Trust Scholarship is available to women music students who have graduated from a Massachusetts high school and wish to pursue their college education in the Boston area.

To apply, contact your high school's guidance counselor or administration office, they MUST nominate you for this program. Direct application is not available. Fifteen awards are made yearly. Contact Boston Safe Deposit and Trust Company, One Boston Place, Boston, MA 02108-4402; 617-722-7341.

Money for Mennonite Women

The purpose of this program is to provide financial support to train emerging women church leaders around the world. Open to women from any country, this program helps with funding training at any level to prepare women for Mennonite church leadership. Training can include workshops for lay women who have very little education as well as course work for high school or college graduates.

Contact Mennonite Women International Women's Fund, 722 Main Street, P.O. Box 347, Newton, KS 67114; 316-283-5100.

Money For Graphic Communication Majors

Over 300 awards of up to $1,000 are available annually to students who wish to pursue a career in graphic communications. High school seniors and current college students are eligible to apply. All students must be attending or planning on attending college full-time. Academic achievement and career goals are the primary considerations, although references and extracurricular activities are also considered. All awards are renewable provided a 3.0 GPA or above is maintained. Winners also receive a complimentary membership in the Graphic Arts Technical Foundation. Contact National Scholarship Trust Fund of the Graphic Arts, Attn: Scholarship Competition, 200 Deer Run Road, Sewickley PA 15143-2600; 412-741-6860; 800-910-GATF; {www.gatf.org}, {Email: info@gatf.org}.

Money for Talented Deaf Women

Miss Deaf America Pageant Awards. Must be deaf and between the ages of 18 and 28. The main objective of the Miss Deaf America Talent Pageant is "... to help us elevate the image and self-concept of deaf ladies throughout the United States. This is not an ordinary contest...beauty, poise, gracefulness are desirable qualities, but the biggest point is one's cultural talent performance. Talent is no longer the only thing; the women are judged across a broad spectrum of categories including community service, academics, current events, deaf culture, and more."

Contact National Association of the Deaf, 814 Thayer Avenue, Silver Spring, MD 20910-4500; 301-587-1788; TTY: 301-587-1789; {Email: nadinfo@nad.org}; {http://nad.policy.net}.

$2000 for Deaf Graduate Women

The William C. Stokoe Scholarship is an annual award made to a deaf graduate student. The goal of the Stokoe Scholarship is to increase the number of deaf social scientists who are actively involved in research on sign language or the deaf community, whether in linguistics, psychology, anthropology, sociology, or other fields. Limited to deaf students who have graduated from a four-year college program and are pursuing part-time or full-time graduate studies in a field related to sign language or the deaf community, or a deaf graduate student who is developing a special project on one of these topics is eligible. Contact National Association of the Deaf, 814 Thayer Avenue, Silver Spring, MD 20910-4500; 301-587-1788; TTY: 301-587-1789; {http://nad.policy.net}, {Email: nadinfo@nad.org}.

MORE MONEY FOR DEAF WOMEN

Scholarships are awarded to prelingually deaf or hard-of-hearing students who use speech and speechreading to communicate, and who are attending or have been admitted to a college or university program that primarily enrolls students with normal hearing. Applicants must have had a hearing loss since birth or before acquiring language with a 60dB or greater loss in the better ear in the speech frequencies of 500, 1000, and 2000 Hz.

Only the first 500 requests for applications will be accepted. Applications must be requested between November 1st and December 1st. Contact Alexander Graham Bell Association for the Deaf, 3417 Volta Place, N.W., Washington, DC 20007-2778; 202-337-5220 (Voice and TTY); {www.agbell.org/}.

$500 for Communications Women in Maine

This program is open to women of any age who are residents of Maine, and who will be enrolled in a communications or mass communications related college program. Financial need, academic achievement, career goals, and interest in communications are the primary consideration. Contact Maine Media Women, Attn: Katy Perry, Scholarship Committee, 9 Middle Street, Hallowell, ME 04347; 207-626-3242.

$1,000 FOR NAVAL ACADEMY CHILDREN AND WOMEN

Eligible to apply for these scholarships are children of active, retired, or deceased; Navy or Marine Corps officers or enlisted personnel who are or were permanently stationed at the United States Naval Academy complex, children of current full-year members of the Naval Academy Women's Club, children of civilian employees of the Naval Academy and any current member of the Naval Academy Women's Club.

Applicants must be in their senior year of high school, or have graduated from high school, and plan on attending full-time at any 2-year or 4-year college or university, any art school or any technical/trade school. Contact Naval Academy Women's Club, P.O. Box 826, Annapolis, MD 21404-0826.

Up to $5,000 for Desert Shield/Desert Storm Veterans and their Spouses and Children

This program provides financial assistance to Veterans of Desert Storm/Desert Shield. Highest preference is given to the children and spouses of men and women who lost their lives while on active duty in these campaigns. At the time of this writing, the schools participating in this program are: University of Arizona, Baylor University, Florida State University, George Mason University, University of Houston, Loyola University of New Orleans, Norfolk State University, Northeastern University, University of Oklahoma, Rice University, Roosevelt University of Chicago, Saint John's University, San Diego State University, Seton Hall University, Southern Methodist University, Texas A&M University, Texas Christian University, Texas Tech University, University of Texas at Austin, and Villanova University. You MUST apply directly with your school; Mobil Corp. does not accept direct applications for this program. Contact The Mobil Corporation Desert Shield/Desert Storm Scholarship Program, Mobil Corporation, 3225 Gallows Road, Fairfax, VA 22037-0001.

Money for Future Homemakers

The Family, Career, and Community Leaders of America offers members a large variety of scholarship and grant programs. Most are based on a combination of academic achievement, potential for success, community service, volunteer work, service to FCCLA, and career goals. Most programs are applied for directly from your local FCCLA chapter, please check with your local chapter for further information. Contact Family, Career, and Community Leaders of America, Inc., 1910 Association Drive, Reston, VA 20191-1584; 703-476-4900; 800-234-4425; {www.fcclainc.org}; {Email: natlhdqtrs@fcclainc.org}.

Money for Smart Women

American Mensa offers a variety of essay-based competitions and academic-achievement scholarship programs available through local chapters. Most programs are available to non-members. Please contact your local Mensa chapter (a list of chapters is available at the website) for more information. Contact American Mensa, 1229 Corporate Drive West, Arlington, TX 76006-6103; 817-607-0060; {www.us.mensa.org}.

Red River Valley Fighter Pilots Association Scholarships

This scholarship is available to the dependent sons, daughters and spouses of any member of the U.S. Armed Forces who is listed as killed in action, missing in action, or prisoner of war from any combat situation involving our military since August, 1965. Any dependent child or spouse of any military aircrew member who was killed as a result of performing aircrew duties during non-combat missions and the dependents of any current or deceased Red River Valley Association member are also eligible to apply.

The program has paid out over 735 scholarships worth over $1,200,000 total since its inception. Individual awards vary depending upon the financial need of the applicant and the cost of their chosen college or university. Academic achievement, financial need, community service, and extracurricular activities are the primary considerations. Contact Red River Valley Fighter Pilots Association, Red River Valley Association Foundation, c/o Al Bache, P.O. Box 1551, North Fork CA 93643; 209-877-5000, {www.eos.net/rrva/}; {Email: afbridger@aol.com}.

Up to $3,000 for Western Art Women

The Grandma Moses Scholarship Program is for female high school seniors who plan on studying art at a college, university, or art school. Preference is given to women from the western states. Samples of your art work must be submitted, and the work must "manifest a congruence with the work of the famed folk artist, Grandma Moses." Contact Western Art Association, 13730 Loumont Street, Whittier, CA 90601.

Money for Delta Gamma Women

The Delta Gamma Foundation offers scholarships for undergraduate work, fellowships for graduate study, and loans for any form of higher education beyond the sophomore year. They also offer several programs that specifically target blind members of Delta Gamma and members who are pursuing a career in the sciences. Undergraduate members with 3.0 or above GPA's are eligible to apply for grants of up to $1,000. Graduate members are eligible to apply for up to $2,500.

Contact Delta Gamma Foundation, 3250 Riverside Dr., Columbus, OH 43221-0397; 614-481-8169; {www.deltagamma.org/found/scholar.htm}.

Up to $1,000 for Slovenian Women's Union Members

Slovenian Women's Union members, who have been members for at least three years, are eligible to apply for five different scholarships awarded annually. Must plan on attending college full-time. Financial need, academic achievement, community service, and participation in the local organization are the main considerations. Please contact your local chapter for application information. Contact Slovenian Women's Union of America, 52 Oakridge Drive, Marquette, MI 49855.

Up to $8000 for Nebraska Women in English

The Norma Ross Walter Scholarship is offered to current high school seniors and recent high school graduates who live in Nebraska and plan on majoring in English. This scholarship is renewable for four years, and is paid out at $2,000 a year, provided a minimum GPA of 3.0 in English is maintained. Must be graduating or have already graduated from any Nebraska high school. Information on this program should be available at your guidance counselor's office. Contact Willa Cather Foundation, 326 N. Webster, Red Cloud, NE 68970; 402-746-2653.

At least $9,000 for
International Women in Education

The International Teacher Education Scholarship is open to single women under 30 years old who are from countries OTHER THAN the United States, and wish to receive teacher training in the United States. Alpha Delta Kappa members are not eligible for this program.

After receiving the scholarship, the winner is expected to return to their home country to work in education for at least one year, within three years of receiving the scholarship. Contact Alpha Delta Kappa, 1615 W. 92nd St., Kansas City, MO 64114; 816-363-5525.

$1,000 for Jewish Women in Los Angeles

The Women Helping Women program offers up to $1,000 a year to female residents of Los Angeles County who are entering or returning to school. Married or single women are eligible, women who are returning to school after a break and/or have children are given priority. Primary consideration is financial need. Contact National Council of Jewish Women, Los Angeles Chapter, 543 N. Fairfax Ave., Los Angeles, CA 90036-1715; 213-655-3807.

Up to $2,500 for
Geological Women

The Geological Society of America offers a variety of scholarships and research grants to undergraduate students. Both members and nonmembers of the Society are eligible to apply. Preference for women studying at universities in the south-central and midwestern region of the United States. Must be studying geology or earth-science related majors. Contact Geological Society of America, 3300 Penrose Pl., Boulder, CO 80301-0140; 303-447-2020; {www.geosociety.org}.

Up to $300 for
Phi Gamma Nu Women

Members of Phi Gamma Nu are eligible to apply for scholarships of up to $300. Open only to undergraduate students who are studying business or related majors. Also have small loans available (usually around $200 per year). Contact Phi Gamma Nu, 6745 Cheryl Ann Dr., Seven Hills, OH 44131; 216-524-0934.

Money for Washington Accounting Women

The Mary M. Fraijo Scholarship is offered to women who live in the state of Washington and are part-time or full-time undergraduate or graduate students in accounting. Applicants must have completed at least 60 credit hours towards their degree, but do not need to be a member of the American Society of Women Accountants. Primary considerations are academic achievement, financial need and references.

Contact American Society of Women Accountants, Inland Northwest, Chapter No. 4, Attn: Leslie Miller, P.O. Box 2903, Spokane, WA 99220-2903.

Up to $2,000 for Hotel Women

The American Express Scholarship Program is offered to students who are currently working at least 20 hours a week at any AH&MA member hotel or resort. Dependent children of current employees are also eligible to apply. Part-time and full-time students attending either a two-year or four-year college or university are eligible to apply. Must be majoring in hotel or hospitality related majors. Work experience, financial need, academic achievement, community service and career goals are the primary considerations. Contact American Hotel Foundation, 1201 New York Ave., NW, Suite 600, Washington, DC 20005-3931.

Up to $4,500 for African-American Colorado Women

Current African-American high school seniors who plan on attending any college in Colorado are eligible to apply. Must have been a Colorado resident for at least five years and have never enrolled in college. Financial need is the primary consideration, although academic achievement and references are also considered. Contact Sachs Foundation, 90 S. Cascade Ave., Suite 1410, Colorado Springs, CO 80903; {www.frii.com/~sachs}.

$500 for Homeschooled Californians

To be eligible to apply, you must be a resident of California who has been homeschooled for at least 4 years, your parents must be a member of the CHEA. Contact Christian Home Educators Association of California, Inc., Attn: Scholarship Committee, P.O. Box 2009, Norwalk, CA 90651-2009.

Up to $2,000 for California Real Estate Students

For current California students enrolled at any California two-year or four-year degree who plan on a career in real estate. Acceptable majors include but are not necessarily limited to: real estate brokerage, real estate finance, real estate management, real estate law and related areas. Also, current realtors in California who wish to pursue advanced education or degrees are eligible to apply. Contact California Association of Realtors, 525 S. Virgil Ave., Los Angeles, CA 90020; 213-739-8200.

Up to $2,500 for Architectural Women in California

The Association offers California women who are either residents of California or non-residents attending school in California and are studying architecture the opportunity to apply for several scholarships that they offer. Must be a current undergraduate student. Contact Association for Women in Architecture, 2550 Beverly Blvd., Los Angeles, CA 90057; 213-389-6490.

Money for Welding Women

Any student intending to pursue a career in welding technology is eligible to apply for the American Welding Society's District Scholarship program. These renewable scholarship awards may be used at any school in the United States with a welding or materials joining program, including technical/vocational schools. Financial need is the primary consideration. Applications are available at the website. Contact The American Welding Society, 550 NW LeJeune Rd., Miami, FL 33126; 800-443-9353; {www.aws.org}.

MONEY FOR HAM RADIO WOMEN

Do you have an interest in ham radios? Have you an amateur or general radio license? Then you might want to check in with the American Radio Relay League. They offer a large number of different scholarships for amateur radio operators, most of which have very few restrictions! Contact American Radio Relay League, 225 Main St., Newington, CT 06111; 203-666-1541; {www.arrl.org}.

Up To $3,000 If You Live Near A Tyson Food Plant

If you live near a Tyson Foods plant and are a full-time undergraduate student with at least a 2.5 GPA, you may be eligible to apply for up to $3,000! Those majoring in agribusiness, agricultural related majors, computer science, and other majors are eligible for this renewable scholarship. Contact Tyson Foundation, Inc., 2210 W. Oaklawn Dr., Springdale, AR 72762; 501-290-4955.

Up to $2,000 for Connecticut Construction Women

For Connecticut residents pursuing a construction-related career. Primary considerations for this renewable award are academic achievement, personal statement, financial need and an interview. Contact Connecticut Building, Congress Scholarship Fund, 2600 Dixwell Ave., Hamden, CT 06514-1833.

Up to $1,500 for DECA Women

For current members of DECA who are planning on studying marketing, merchandising, or management. Members of the Future Business Leaders of America are also eligible to apply for some of the awards. Contact your local DECA chapter for further information, or the website. Contact DECA - Distributive Education Club of America, 1908 Association Drive, Reston, VA 20191-4013; 703-860-5000; {www.deca.org}.

MONEY FOR PETROLEUM WOMEN

The Desk and Derrick Educational Trust offers women in the United States and Canada who are studying business, engineering, natural resources or technology related majors and intend to pursue a career in the petroleum industry an opportunity to apply for $1,000. Financial need and academic achievement are the primary considerations. For use during your junior, senior, or graduate years. Contact Desk and Derrick Educational Trust, 4823 S. Sheridan, Suite 308A, Tulsa, OK 74145; 918-622-1675.

Up to $10,000 for Executive Women

Executive Women International offers over 100 scholarship awards ranging from $100-$10,000 every year to women who wish to pursue a four-year degree in business or related majors. Must apply while you are still a high school junior and plan on attending a four-year college. Awards are renewable. Contact Executive Women International, 515 S. 700 East, Suite 2E, Salt Lake City, UT 84102; 801-355-2800.

Money for Horse Racers

Have any experience with harness racing? Then the Harness Horse Youth Foundation may have some money you can apply for! They offer several scholarship programs for students pursuing animal sciences, biology, agricultural, and business related majors. For students who are under 24 years of age and have some experience with harness racing. Contact Harness Horse Youth Foundation, 14950 Greyhound Ct., Suite 210, Carmel, IN 46032; 317-848-5132; {www.hhyf.org}.

$500 for Kansas Communications and Journalism Women

Kansas Press Women has several scholarships available to women who are residents of Kansas and are about to enter their senior year in college. Must be a journalism or communications major and studying at a college in Kansas. Preference is given to students with a strong interest in writing. Contact Kansas Press Women, Inc., 115 N. Pinecrest, Wichita, KS 67208; 316-268-6367.

$3,000 for Speaking Women

For current full-time junior, senior and graduate students with a strong interest in public speaking. Applications and information are available at the website. Contact National Speakers Association, 1500 S. Priest Dr., Tempe, AZ 85281; {www.nsaspeaker.org}.

$1,000 for Food Technology

Current junior and senior students in food science, food engineering, and food technology majors with outstanding academic achievement and a strong desire to pursue a career in food science or food engineering are eligible to apply for a variety of scholarships offered by the Institute. Direct application is not available, you must have your department chairman or other school administrator recommend you for an award. Contact Institute of Food Technologists, 221 N. LaSalle St., Suite 300, Chicago, IL 60601; 312-782-8424.

Up to $1,000 for Dental Women

The American Association of Women Dentists has several academic achievement-based scholarships available to current junior and senior dental students who are members of the Association. Contact American Association of Women Dentists, 401 N. Michigan Ave., Chicago, IL 60611; 312-527-6757.

Up to $10,000 for Heating, Refrigerating and Air Conditioning

For students studying electrical engineering, electronics, heating, air conditioning, refrigeration technology, or other majors with intention on pursuing a career in the heating, refrigeration and/or air conditioning industry. Must have at least two years left before graduation, a 3.0 GPA or above, attending a ABET-accredited school, and financial need. Contact American Society of Heating, Refrigerating and Air Conditioning Engineers, Inc., 1791 Tullie Circle, NE, Atlanta, GA 30329-1683; 404-636-8400; {www.ashrae.org}.

$1,500 for Safety Engineers

Two awards annually for student members of the American Society of Safety Engineers. Must be attending college full-time with a minimum GPA of 3.0, studying a safety engineering related major, and plan on pursuing a career in safety engineering. Contact American Society of Safety Engineers Foundation, 1800 E. Oakton, Des Plaines, IL 60018; 847-699-2929.

Money for Lutheran Women in Mental Retardation

Interested in a career in service to the mentally disabled? Bethesda Lutheran Homes offers a large variety of scholarships to students in social services, nursing, legal services, special education, health administration, education, therapy, and related majors. Must be an active, communicant member of a Lutheran church. Must be at least a college sophomore.

Please call or write for more information about available programs. Contact Bethesda Lutheran Homes and Services, Inc., National Christian Resource Center, 700 Hoffman Dr., Watertown, WI 53094-6294; 920-261-3050; {www.blhs.org}.

Up to $1,000 for Black Nurses

Members of the National Black Nurses Association are eligible to apply for several scholarships that average $1,000. Must have completed at least one year of school at time of application and be an African American. Primary considerations are academic achievement, potential for success, references, and involvement in the African American community.

When requesting information, please include a SASE with two stamps on it. Contact National Black Nurses Association, Inc., 1511 K St., NW, Suite 415, Washington, DC 20005.

Money for Michigan Nurses

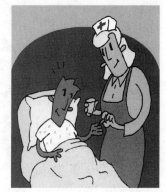

Up to $500 is available for sophomores, juniors, and seniors who are residents of Michigan and are attending a college in Michigan. Must be pursuing a nursing degree and have at least a 2.0 GPA. Preference is given to students who plan on working as a nurse in Michigan upon graduation. Contact Michigan League for Nursing, 33150 Schoolcraft Rd., Suite 201, Livonia, MI 48150-1646.

Up to $2,500 for Oncology Nurses

A variety of scholarships are available to current registered nurses who wish to further their education and pursue careers as oncology nurses. Some awards are specifically for minority students, others are for current oncology nurses who have contributed to the field of oncology nursing. Some of the programs require a $5 application fee. Contact Oncology Nursing Foundation, 501 Holiday Dr., Pittsburgh, PA 15220; 412-921-7373; {www.ons.org}.

Up to $3,000 for Logistics

For full-time undergraduate students pursuing a logistics or related major at any four-year college. Must have at least a 3.0 GPA. Contact SOLE-The International Logistics Society, 8100 Professional Pl., Suite 211, New Carrollton, MD 20785; {www.sole.org}.

Up to $5000 for Composers

The Society offers a variety of contests and competitions for original compositions and musical scores. Some programs are available only to members of the Society. Most require a taped performance of your original music.

Contact American Society of Composers, Authors, and Publishers Foundation, ASCAP Building, One Lincoln Plaza, New York, NY 10023-2399; 212-621-6327; {www.ascap.com}.

Up to $3,000 for Parapsychology Students

For undergraduate and graduate students who can show a very strong and serious interest in parapsychology through coursework, research, essays, term papers and dissertations. Students who have only a minor interest are not eligible. Contact Parapsychology Foundation, 228 E. 71st St., New York, NY 10021; 212-628-1550; {www.parapsychology. org}.

Up to $3,000 for Christians

Several grants are available to undergraduate and graduate students who are pursuing a Master of Divinity degree at any accredited theological or seminary school. Students from midwestern states and those who plan on serving in a local church ministry are given preference. Ph.D. students are not eligible. Must be between the ages of 25 and 55 and have a strong Christian faith. Contact Opal Dancey Memorial Foundation, 45 South St., Croswell, MI 48422; 810-679-4729.

Up to $3,000 for Travel Agents

The American Society of Travel Agents has a large variety of scholarship programs available for undergraduate students pursuing a career in the travel and tourism industry. Some of the scholarships are restricted to women re-entering the work force after a few year's break, some are restricted to members only, others are open to current high school seniors and college undergraduates. Some of the programs are available to students attending an accredited travel school.

Please check the website or write for more information. Contact American Society of Travel Agents, Scholarship Foundation, 1101 King St., Suite 200, Alexandria, VA 22314-2187; 703-739-2782; {www.astanet.com}.

Up to $4,000 for Physical Therapy and Occupational Therapy Women

Allied Resources offers current college juniors, seniors and graduate students who have no more than two years left to complete their physical therapy or occupational therapy degree up to $4,000. All recipients must agree to work through Allied Resources after graduation. Please include a SASE with requests for information. Contact Allied Resources, 810 Regal Drive, Huntsville, AL 35801; 800-217-7870.

Money for Native American Single Parents

The Schuyler Meyer Jr. Scholarship is for single parents who have at least one child under the age of 18, are attending college full-time, and have at least a 2.0 GPA. Must be at least 25% Native American or Alaskan American (Inuit) and have tribal recognition. Open to students studying any major. Financial need is a primary consideration. Contact American Indian Science and Engineering Society, 5661 Airport Blvd., Boulder, CO 80301-2339; 303-939-0023.

Up to $2,500 for Marine Veterans

The Fifth Marine Division Scholarship is available to current high school seniors and college undergraduate students who are children of any Fifth Marine Division veteran. The veteran must be a member of the Fifth Marine Division Association. Financial need is the primary consideration — total family income must be below $45,000 in order to be considered, although academic achievement is also considered. Contact Marine Corps Scholarship Foundation, P.O. Box 3008, Princeton, NJ 08543-3008; 800-292-7777; {www.marine-scholars.org}.

Money for Civitan Members

Members of Civitan who are current college juniors, seniors or graduate students are eligible to apply for a variety of local and national scholarships offered through Civitan. Most programs are based primarily on academic achievement and community service.

Please check with your local chapter for information, or the website below. When writing for information, please include a SASE with three stamps on it. Contact Civitan International Foundation, P.O. Box 130744, Birmingham, AL 35213-0744; {www.civitan.org}.

MONEY FOR DEMOLAY MEMBERS

Current and former members of DeMolay are eligible to apply. There are no restrictions on what major you are studying. Scholarships are based primarily upon financial need, academic achievement, character and community service. Award amounts vary, but on average are $800. DeMolay members should also check with their local chapter for local scholarships. Contact DeMolay Foundation, 10200 N. Executive Hills Blvd., Kansas City, MO 64153; {www.demolay.org}.

Money for Non-Commissioned Officers Association Members

The Non-Commissioned Officers Association offers a variety of programs to its members and their children. Of particular interest is the Betsy Ross Educational Fund, which awards $250 to members who wish to take classes to improve their job skills. Other scholarships are available to spouses and children of members.

Please include a SASE with requests for information. Contact Non Commissioned Officers Association, P.O. Box 33610, San Antonio, TX 78265-3610; 610-653-6161.

Money for Girl's Club Members

Teenagers between the ages of 14 and 18 who are members of the Girl's Club for at least one year are eligible to apply for scholarships ranging between $2,000 and $8,000. Must apply for this scholarship through your local Girl's Club chapter — direct application is not available. Must have at least a 3.0 GPA in high school. Academic achievement, community service, and leadership potential are the primary consideration. Contact Reader's Digest Foundation, 1230 W. Peachtree St., NW, Atlanta, GA 30309.

Up to $1,000 for Jewelry and Gems

The Gemological Institute of America offers students over the age of 17 a variety of different scholarship programs. All require that the applicant be pursuing a gemology-related major and plan on pursuing a career in the gemology field. Must be attending or planning on attending a school with a Gemological Institute accredited program of study. Contact Gemological Institute of America, 5345 Armada Dr., Carlsbad, CA 92008-4698; 760-603-4005.

Money for Royal Neighbors

Current high school students who have been members of the Royal Neighbors of America are eligible to apply for a variety of scholarships offered worth up to $2,000. Must be under 20 years of age. Primary considerations are academic achievement, service to Royal Neighbors, and community service. Contact Royal Neighbors of America, 230 16th St., Rock Island, IL 61201-8645; 309-788-4561.

$1,000 for Sculpture

For students who have created figurative or representational sculpture. Must include up to 10 photos of your work with application. Please include a SASE with requests for information. Contact National Sculpture Society, 1177 Avenue of the Americas, 15th Floor, New York, NY 10036; 212-764-5645.

Money for Maine Women

The Maine Community Foundation has a variety of programs available to current high school seniors and college undergraduates who are residents of Maine. Most require that you attend school in Maine. Applications are sent to local high schools and colleges every year, so check with your guidance counselor or financial aid office first for information. Contact Maine Community Foundation, P.O. Box 148, Ellsworth, ME 04605; 207-667-9735.

Up to $10,000 for Non-Traditional Michigan Women

Michigan women who have been out of school for at least four years and plan on attending any campus of the University of Michigan are eligible to apply. Each year, they offer up to 35 scholarships ranging from $1,000 to $10,000. Financial need is the primary consideration. Contact Center for the Education of Women, 330 E. Liberty St., Ann Arbor, MI 48104-2289; 734-998-7210.

More Money for Hawaiian Women

Female college juniors, seniors, and graduate students who are residents of Hawaii and have a strong interest in women's studies and commitment to serving women are eligible to apply. Must be attending a four-year college. Contact Kilohana United Methodist Church, 1536 Kamole St., Honolulu, HI 96821.

Money for Vermont Women

The Vermont Student Assistance Corporation manages a large variety of scholarship offers for women (and men) who are residents of Vermont. Awards range from $500 to over $5,000. Requirements vary greatly for individual programs, please contact them and request their free scholarship booklet for Vermont residents. Contact Vermont Student Assistance Corporation, P.O. Box 2000, Winooski, VT 05404-2000; 802-655-9602; {www.vsac.org}.

Money for Louisiana Residents

A variety of scholarships and loans are available for Louisiana residents who are attending college or university in Louisiana. For undergraduate students only. Academic achievement is the primary consideration. Contact Willis and Mildred Pellerin Foundation, P.O. Box 400, Kenner, LA 70063-0400.

Money for Non-Traditional Native Americans

The Association offers several programs to assist Native American single parents or displaced homemakers. Awards are intended to assist with the costs of child care, transportation, and basic living expenses while finishing your education. Primary consideration is financial need. Must have either a certificate of degree of Indian blood or a Tribal enrollment card. Contact Association on American Indian Affairs, Inc., P.O. Box 268, Sisseton, SD 57262; 605-698-3998.

Up to $1000 for Lutheran Women

The Adult Degree Completion Scholarship Program is available to Lutheran women who are over age 25, full members of the Aid Association, and have an insurance policy or annuity in their name through the Association. Must be pursuing your first associate's or bachelor's degree. Part time students are eligible to apply, however the award will be reduced. Contact Aid Association for Lutherans, 4321 N. Ballard Rd., Appleton, WI 54919-0001; 414-734-5721; {www.aal.org}.

MONEY FOR FLIGHT ATTENDANTS

Members and their dependent children are eligible to apply for this scholarship program. Must write an essay, topic changes yearly. Also considered is academic achievement and financial need. Contact Association of Flight Attendants, P.O. Box 212, Warrenton, VA 22186.

Money for New Hampshire Women

Residents of New Hampshire are eligible to apply for a large variety of programs offered through the Foundation. Only one application needs to be filled out for consideration of all programs that you may be eligible for. Some programs are restricted to handicapped students, others to those entering the Protestant ministry. For all programs, academic achievement and financial need is considered. Must sign an affidavit certifying that you do not smoke or drink alcohol. Undergraduate and graduate students at both 2 and 4 year vocational schools, colleges and universities are eligible to apply. Contact New Hampshire Charitable Foundation, 37 Pleasant St., Concord, NH 03301-4005; 603-225-6641; {www.nhcf.org}.

Money for Asian Pacific Women in Los Angeles

The Asian Pacific Women's Network offers a variety of scholarship and support services to Asian Pacific women who live in the Los Angeles area and surrounding counties and wish to increase their job skills and educational background. Women returning to school after a break due to child rearing or financial difficulties, immigrant women, and refugees are especially encouraged to apply. Financial need is the primary consideration. Contact Asian Pacific Women's Network, P.O. Box 86995, Los Angeles, CA 90086; 213-891-6040; 909-596-5331.

Up to $1,500 for Chinese American Women

Current college juniors, seniors and graduate students of Chinese-American background who have at least a 3.0 GPA are eligible to apply for this scholarship. Please include a SASE with requests for information. Contact Chinese-American Educational Foundation, P.O. Box 2217, Sunnyvale, CA 94087-0217.

MONEY FOR SOUTHERN CALIFORNIAN WOMEN

Current sophomore, junior or senior women with a 3.0 or above GPA and are attending any college in southern California are eligible to apply. Application is done through your financial aid office — you must have your financial aid officer nominate you. Direct application is not available.

Contact College Women's Club of Pasadena, Scholarship Foundation, P.O. Box 452, Pasadena, CA 91102.

Up to $2,000 for Short People

Students who are less than 4 feet 10 inches tall, along with their parents and children (regardless of height), are eligible to apply for several different scholarship programs offered by the Foundation. Current high school seniors and college undergraduates are eligible. Academic achievement, financial need, and leadership abilities or potential are the primary considerations. Contact Billy Barty Foundation, 929 W. Olive Avenue, Suite C, Burbank, CA 91506; 800-891-4022; 818-953-5410.

Money for Baptist Acteens

Female high school seniors who are Southern Baptists and active in Acteens are eligible to apply. Primary considerations are character, church service, academic achievement, an essay and references. Amount awarded varies depending upon funding availability. Contact Woman's Missionary Union Foundation, P.O. Box 11346, Birmingham, AL 35202-1346; 205-408-5525.

$1,000 for African American Church of Christ Women

Undergraduate and graduate African American women who are members of the Church of Christ and are residents of southern California are eligible to apply. Priority is given to non-traditional women who are returning to college after a break, making a mid-life career change, or starting their college career after age 25. Contact United Church of Christ, Southern California Conference, 2401 N. Lake Ave., Altadena, CA 91001; 626-798-8082.

Up to $5,000 for
Rhode Island Women

Rhode Island residents who are current college sophomores and juniors are eligible to apply for the Michael P. Metcalf Memorial Grants. These grants are to support or subsidize non-traditional educational opportunities, such as traveling for educational purposes, public service programs, etc., so long as the experience's primary purpose is to expand your horizons, perspective, and personal growth. Financial need must be established. Primary considerations are thoughtfulness of the proposal, creativity and motivation, and initiative. Contact Rhode Island Foundation, 70 Elm St., Providence, RI 02903; 401-274-4564.

Money for New Mexico Women

The Albuquerque Community Foundation offers a variety of scholarships. Current high school seniors and undergraduate students who are residents of New Mexico are eligible to apply. For all programs available, financial need is the primary consideration. Amount awarded is based upon need. Contact Albuquerque Community Foundation, P.O. Box 36960, Albuquerque, NM 87176-6960; 505-883-6240.

$2,500 FOR HOME AND WORKSHOP WRITERS

Current high school seniors, college undergraduates, and graduate level students who have a strong interest in pursuing a career in the "do-it-yourself" market as a writer or journalist are eligible to apply, regardless of declared major.

Contact National Association of Home and Workshop Writers, c/o Frank Brugmeier Company, 7501 Woodstream Terrace, North Syracuse, NY 13212-1921; 315-458-0291.

$1000 for Lesbians in Louisiana

Louisiana residents who are affirmed and open Lesbians or Gays and over the age of 17 are eligible to apply. Must be attending any college or university at least three-quarter time. Community service, service to the Gay and Lesbian community, activism, leadership ability or potential and financial need are the primary considerations.

Contact Parents, Families and Friends of Lesbians and Gays, New Orleans Chapter, ATTN: Scholarship Committee, P.O. Box 15515, New Orleans, LA 70175; 504-895-3936; {www.gayneworleans.org/pflag/ scholar.htm}.

Money for Massachusetts Baptist Women

Women who are residents of Massachusetts and members of an American Baptist Church in Massachusetts are eligible to apply. Must intend on rendering Christian Service in their chosen major or career, although there is no restriction on what major you may be studying. Primary considerations are academic achievement, financial need, dedication, character and values.

Contact American Baptist Women's Ministries of Massachusetts, 20 Milton St., Dedham, MA 02026-2967; 617-320-8100.

Money for African American Women

African American women who have completed at least one semester or two quarters of undergraduate studies with at least a 2.0 GPA are eligible to apply. Financial need is the primary consideration. Direct application is not available, you must be nominated by a member of the National Association of Colored Women's Clubs. Contact your local Club chapter for further information and to find a potential sponsor to nominate you.

NOTE: This award is offered only during even-numbered years. Contact National Association of Colored Women's Clubs, 5808 16th St., NW, Washington, DC 20011-2898; 202-726-2044.

$1,500 for New York Women in Communications

Full-time undergraduate and graduate level women who are residents of New York and are studying communications, journalism, speech, broadcasting, and marketing are eligible to apply. Must have at least a 3.0 GPA and be attending a college or university in the New York City region and surrounding counties. Primary consideration is academic achievement and potential for success. Contact New York Women in Communications, Inc., 355 Lexington Ave., 17th Floor, New York, NY 10017-6603; 212-661-4737.

Up to $1,500 for Theater Women

Women who have outstanding dramatic talent and need financial assistance to continue their education are eligible to apply. Although preference is given to residents of Massachusetts, there is no restriction on residency. Applications must include recommendations from member(s) of the theatrical profession. Only applications from serious theater arts students of the highest talent will be considered — those with only a passing interest in dramatic arts and theater are not eligible. Contact Lotta M. Crabtree Trusts, 11 Beacon St., Suite 1110, Boston, MA 02108; 617-742-5920.

$1000 for Sigma Alpha Iota Women

Sigma Alpha Iota, a national organization for women musicians, offers a variety of scholarships and other support programs to its members. The Undergraduate Performance Scholarship is for outstanding performances in vocal and instrumental music, the String Performance Scholarship is for outstanding string performances, and the Scholarship for the Visually Impaired is for members of the organization who are legally blind and are enrolled full-time in a music-related major. Contact Sigma Alpha Iota Philanthropies, Inc., 34 Wall St., Suite 515, Asheville, NC 28801-2710; 828-251-0606; {www.sai-national.org}.

Up to $2,000 for Jewelry Women

Women who are pursuing a jewelry-related career and are enrolled in a program that will enable them to achieve this goal are eligible to apply. Selection is based primarily upon skill in designing or creating unique pieces of jewelry, as determined by submitted photos or drawings of your work. Academic achievement, work experience, recommendations and financial need are also considered. Contact Women's Jewelry Association, 333B Route 46 W., Suite B201, Fairfield, NJ 07004; 201-575-7190.

$1,500 for Minnesota Nurses

College juniors and seniors who are either residents of Minnesota or attending college in Minnesota are eligible to apply for these scholarships which are funded by the American Cancer Society. Selection is based on an essay related to the nurse's role in caring for patients with cancer, research or public education on cancer, or a cancer-related subject of your choice. To apply, you do not need to be actually involved in oncology nursing or necessarily plan on a career as an oncology nurse. Contact Minnesota League for Nursing, P.O. Box 24713, Edina, MN 55424; 612-829-5891.

Money for Holistic Women

Nursing students and currently licensed nurses already in the workforce who have a strong interest in furthering their education in holistic health care or alternative health techniques are eligible to apply. Must have been a member of the Association for at least six months. Current nursing students must have at least a 3.0 GPA, financial need and career goals are also considered. Nurses who are already in the workforce are considered primarily on their work experience and interest in holistic health. Contact American Holistic Nurses Association, 2733 E. Lakin Dr., P.O. Box 2130, Flagstaff, AZ 86003-2130; 520-526-2196.

$1,000 for California Nurses

Women who are already licensed Registered Nurses working in California and wish to return to school to pursue a B.S.N or graduate degree program are eligible to apply. Must attend school at least half-time and plan on finishing the degree within five years. If the winner doesn't finish their degree within five years, the scholarship reverts to a loan and must be repaid. References, commitment to nursing, work experience and financial need are the primary considerations. This award is renewable yearly depending upon academic achievement. Contact California Nurses Association, 1145 Market St., Suite 1100, San Francisco, CA 94103; 415-864-4141.

MONEY FOR HISPANIC NURSES

Hispanic members of the Association who are pursuing diploma or certificate programs in nursing or associate or bachelor's degrees in nursing are eligible to apply. Academic achievement and financial need are the primary considerations. Contact National Association of Hispanic Nurses, 1501 16th St., NW, Washington, DC 20036; 202-387-2477.

Money for Wisconsin Nurses

Residents of Wisconsin who are currently enrolled in any college in Wisconsin and have completed at least half of the requirements needed for their degree are eligible to apply. Applications are available from the financial aid offices at all Wisconsin colleges, please do not write to the address below requesting an application as they do not send applications directly to students. Contact Wisconsin League for Nursing, 2121 E. Newport Ave., Milwaukee, WI 53211; 414-332-6271.

UP TO $2,000 FOR TRAVEL AND TOURISM WOMEN

The Foundation offers a variety of scholarships to travel and tourism students. For all programs, you must be enrolled full-time in a two or four-year school, have at least a 3.0 GPA, and be majoring in travel and tourism, hotel management, restaurant management, or a related major. You must be intending to pursue a career in the travel or tourism industry. Contact National Tourism Foundation, 5546 E. Main St, P.O. Box 3071, Lexington, KY 40596-3071; 606-226-4444.

$1,000 or More for Women Grocers

Members of the Women Grocer's of America, along with their children, spouses, employees, and grandchildren are eligible to apply. Must be a college sophomore or above with at least a 2.0 GPA enrolled in a food marketing, food service technology, business administration, business management, agribusiness or related major and plan on pursuing a career in the grocery industry. Hotel/restaurant management and public health majors are not eligible to apply. Contact Women Grocers of America, 1825 Samuel Morse Dr., Reston, VA 20190-5317; 703-437-5300.

$2,500 for Diabetes Women

Women (and men!) who have Type 1 Diabetes and are planning on attending full-time any public or private undergraduate school in the United States are eligible to apply. The primary considerations for this award are outstanding service to the diabetes community, promotion of diabetes awareness in the community, or having overcome personal obstacles related to your diabetes, academic achievement, essays, and recommendations. Contact Lilly For Learning, Diabetes Scholarship Program, Eli Lilly and Company, Lilly Corporate Center, Drop Code 1625, Indianapolis, IN 46285; 800-88LILLY; {www.lillydiabetes.com}.

Up to $2,500 for Jewish Women in Washington, DC

The Irene Stambler Vocational Opportunities Grant Program is open to Jewish women who are residents of the Washington metropolitan area and need to improve their earning power because of divorce, separation or death of their spouses. Grants may be used to complete an educational or vocational program or start or expand a small business. Contact Jewish Social Service Agency Of Metropolitan Washington, 6123 Montrose Road, Rockville, MD 20852; 301-881-3700.

UP TO $10,000 FOR GOVERNMENT AND Public Policy WOMEN

This year-long fellowship program places women graduate students in Congressional offices to encourage more effective participation by women in policy formation at all levels. Preference is given to women who are studying government, public policy, women's issues or social sciences. Must be a U.S. citizen or legal resident. Send self-addressed, stamped business-sized envelope for information. Contact Women's Research And Education Institute, Congressional Fellowships for Women and Public Policy, 1750 New York Ave., NW; Suite 350, Washington DC 20006; 202-628-0444.

Money for Grand Rapids, Michigan Women

Various scholarship programs are available to female residents of Grand Rapids, Michigan. Preference is given to students currently attending or planning on attending Grand Rapids Community College and intend on transferring to the University of Michigan upon graduation from GRCC. Contact The Grand Rapids Foundation, 209-C Waters Bldg., 161 Ottawa Ave. NW, Grand Rapids MI 49503-2703; 616-454-1751.

Money for Chiropractic Women

The Association offers several programs to student members who are college juniors or above. Awards are only available at colleges and universities where ICA student chapters are located. Please check with your local chapter for information. Contact International Chiropractors Association, 1110 N. Glebe Rd., Suite 1000, Arlington, VA 22201; 703-528-5000.

$2000 for Graduate Historical Women

The Alice E. Smith Fellowship is open to any woman doing graduate level research in American history. Preference will be given to graduate research on history of the midwest or Wisconsin. Transcripts, work samples and references are not required nor sought. Four copies of a 2-page letter of application should describe in detail the applicant's current research. Send to State Historian at address below. Contact State Historical Society Of Wisconsin, 816 State St., Madison, WI 53706; 608-264-6464.

$2,000 FOR WOMEN IN MASSACHUSETTS

Open to women who have lived in Massachusetts for at least five years. For graduate study in specific fields which change each year. Letter of endorsement from president of your local Women's Club is required. They also have a $600 scholarship program available for undergraduate women attending Mt. Ida College or Fisher College. Contact your local club or write to address below for complete information. Enclose self-addressed stamped envelope. Contact General Federation Of Women's Clubs Of Massachusetts, Box 679, Sudbury, MA 01776-0679; 508-443-4569.

Up to $5,000 in
No-Interest Loans for Jewish Women

Special no-interest-charged scholarship-loans available to active Jewish women women pursuing any undergraduate, graduate or professional degree. Must repay loan within ten years. Write for complete information. Contact Samuel Lemberg Scholarship Loan Fund Inc., 60 East 42nd St., Suite 1814, New York, NY 10165.

Up to $400 for
Jewish Women in Boston

The Amelia Greenbaum/Rabbi Marshall Lifson Scholarship Program is open to undergraduate Jewish women who are residents of Boston (or vicinity) and are attending any Massachusetts college or university. Primary consideration is financial need. Priority is given to those returning to school after a five-year or longer break in their education. Contact National Council of Jewish Women, Greater Boston Section, 831 Beacon St., Newton Centre, MA 02159; 617-783-9660.

UP TO $1,000 FOR NEW YORK BUSINESS WOMEN

For women who are permanent residents of NY state. Fellowships for graduate study (master or doctorate) at an accredited NY state college or university. U.S. citizenship required. Applications available Oct. 1 through Jan. 31. Send a business-size, self-addressed stamped envelope for complete information.

Contact Business and Professional Women's Clubs, New York State Chapter, 7509 State Route 5, Clinton, NY 13323-3632; 315-735-3114.

$4000 for Bowling Women

Open to women under the age of 23 who are amateur bowlers and members in good standing with WIBC or YABA. Announcements regarding scholarships are sent to all member bowling alleys annually and also available from the address below. Please include self-addressed, stamped envelope with requests for information. Contact Young American Bowling Alliance, 5301 S. 76th St., Greendale, WI 53129.

$500 for San Mateo County, California Women

Awards for young women, age 16 to 26, who have attended a high school in San Mateo County, California. Must need financial support to re-enter a post-secondary school, community college, university, or vocational school. Award is to help young women who have dropped out of school for reasons beyond their control or have undergone unusual hardships to remain in school. Contact Peninsula Community Foundation, 1700 S. El Camino Real #300, San Mateo, CA 94402; 650-358-9369.

Up to $5,000 for Physically Disabled Women

Awards for physically disabled women in need of further education who are between 15 and 40 years old. Venture Club is an organization for young business and professional women sponsored by Soroptimist International of the Americas. Primary considerations are financial need and the capacity to profit from further education. Applicants should contact the nearest Venture Club or Soroptimist Club for application or send self-addressed, stamped envelope to the address below. Contact Venture Clubs Of The Americas, Two Penn Center Plaza, Suite 1000, Philadelphia, PA 19102-1883; 215-557-9300; Fax: 215-568-5200; {Email: siahq@voicenet.com}.

Money for Delta Phi Epsilon Women

Scholarships for women students who are members of Delta Phi Epsilon Sorority. Daughters or granddaughters of members are also eligible to apply. Applications available in January. Write or Email Ellen Alper, Executive Director, at address below. Contact Delta Phi Epsilon Educational Foundation, 734 West Port Plaza, Suite 271, St. Louis, MO 63146; 314-275-2626; {Email: ealper@conentric.net}; {www.dphie.org }.

Money To Study Women Education Issues

One award for a graduate student, and one award for a postgraduate or non-student. Research project on any topic relevant to the education and personal and professional development of women and girls. Each submission is to have a single author. All entries must be original and not previously published or under review elsewhere. Contact National Association For Women In Education, 1325 18th St., NW, Suite 210, Washington, DC 20036-6511; 202-659-9330.

Money for Behavioral Science Women

Scholarships and grants open to women who are post-graduates, graduate students, and professionals in the behavioral sciences. Awards support study and/or research projects. Preference (but not limited) to organizational behavior and business ethics. Contact National Chamber Of Commerce For Women, 10 Waterside Plaza, Suite 6H, New York, NY 10010; 212-685-3454.

$250 for Writing about Christian Women

$250 to the author of the best essay published during the previous calendar year on any aspect of the role of women in the history of Christianity. Please include self addressed, stamped envelope with requests for information. Contact American Society Of Church History, P.O. Box 8517, Red Bank, NJ 07701.

$1,000 for African American Writing Women

Scholarships for African-American women pursuing careers in writing and/or journalism. Must major in English or journalism in a four-year university, have at least a 2.5 GPA, and demonstrate financial need. Contact Women On Books, 879 Rainier Ave. N., Suite A105, Renton, WA 98055; 206-626-2323.

Up to $1,500 for Public Service Women

COMPA offers two academic scholarships, five travel grants, and a $1,000 gift to the college that has the largest number of student registrants at its annual conference. Travel grants are for attending the conference. For minority women pursuing full-time education in the public administration, public service or public policy and are committed to excellence in public service

Money for Louisiana Women

Student loans for college-bound young women who are residents of Louisiana. Contact Agnes T. Maguire Trust, c/o Premier Bank, Trust Department, P.O. Box 91210, Baton Rouge, LA 70821-9210; 504-332-4011.

and administration in city, county, state, and federal governments. Contact Conference Of Minority Public Administrators, P.O. Box 3010, Fort Worth, TX 76113; 817-871-8325; {www.compa.org}.

Up To $5,000 for Minority Women in Technology

The Association offers several scholarship awards to minority women studying science, mathematics, engineering and applied technology who intend to pursue a technology-related career. Local chapters may also have scholarships available. Contact National Technical Association, Inc., 6919 North 19th St., Philadelphia, PA 19126-1506; 215-549-5743; {www.ntaonline.org}.

Money for Flying Women

Open to women whose goal is to fly the world's airlines. Award is intended to assist with achieving advanced pilot ratings, such as the U.S. FAA ATP certificate or equivalent; they also have other scholarship awards available to women studying any major but planning on an aviation career. Applicants must have a U.S. FAA Commercial Pilot Certificate with an Instrument Rating and a First Class medical or equivalent and a minimum of 750 flight hours. Contact International Society Of Women Airline Pilots, 2250 E. Tropicana Ave., Suite 19-395, Las Vegas, NV 89119-6594.

$2,000 for Opera Women in Connecticut

The Jenny Lind Competition for Sopranos is open to women between 18 and 25 years of age who have had formal training in operatic or concert singing but have not reached professional status. Only residents or students in Connecticut may apply. Contact Barnum Festival, 1070 Main St., Bridgeport, CT 06604.

$3,500 for Medical Women

Women who have already achieved their bachelor's degree from any American university and are attending or planning on attending any accredited medical school are welcome to apply. Must be studying medicine and be intending on pursuing a general practice career (but not in psychiatry.) Contact Cartland Shackford Medical Fellowships, c/o Wellesley College, Secretary, Graduate Fellowships, Career Center, Wellesley MA 02181; 617-283-3525.

Up to $4,000 for Medical Women in Illinois

Medicine-leading to an M.D.degree for U.S. citizens who are residents of Illinois and either accepted to or already attending any accredited medical college. Must be a legal resident of Illinois. Preference given to women who have lived in Dekalb County. Contact Nesbitt Medical Student Foundation, c/o National Bank & Trust Co., 230 West State St., Sycamore, IL 60178.

Money for Native American Women in the Humanities

Open to women of Native American heritage who are pursuing academic programs at the graduate level in the humanities or social sciences. Contact D'arcy McNickle Center for American Indian History, Attn: Cynthia Soto, 60 West Walton St., Chicago, IL 60610-3380; 312-255-3564.

MONEY FOR MENTAL HEALTH WOMEN

Open to holders of a Ph.Ds, M.D.s, or equivalent degrees who are interested in pursuing careers in mental health services research. Minorities and women are especially encouraged to apply. Fellows will improve their knowledge of public mental health systems and services and increase their theoretical, methodological, and analytic skills during the two-year program. Contact National Association of State Mental Health Program Directors Research Institute, Noel A. Mazade Ph.D, Exec Director, 66 Canal Center Plaza, Suite 302, Alexandria, VA 22314; 703-739-9333.

MONEY FOR CHESS PLAYERS

High school juniors and seniors who excel in academics, chess play and sportmanship are eligible to apply. Primary considerations are an essay regarding how chess has had a positive influence on your life, academic achievement, and recommendations. Contact U.S. Chess Federation, c/o Sharon Brunetti, 3054 NYS Route 9W, New Windsor, NY 12553; 914-562-8350; {www.uschess.org}.

$2,500 for Peaceful Women

The Nuclear Age Peace Foundation awards two scholarships to undergraduate or graduate ethnic minority students. Primary consideration is a three-page essay on ways to achieve peace in the Nuclear Age, and how you hope to contribute to peace. Financial need and academic achievement are also considered.

Contact Nuclear Age Peace Foundation, Lena Chang Scholarship Awards, 1187 Coast Village Rd, Suite 123, Santa Barbara, CA 93108; 805-965-3443; {www.napf.org}; {Email: wagingpeace@napf.org}.

Up to $5,000 for Environmental Public Policy Women

College sophomores and juniors pursuing a career in environmental public policy are welcome to apply for this highly competitive scholarship award. Direct application is not available. Application and nomination forms are sent to colleges annually, if your department chairman or financial aid office does not have information on this program, have your financial aid officer contact the Foundation for information. They also have a highly regarded internship opportunity available. Contact The Morris K. Udall Foundation, 803/811 E. 1st St., Tucson, AZ 85719; 520-670-5529; {www.udall.gov}.

Money for Women in Sports Journalism

Must be studying journalism or communications and intend on pursuing a career in sports journalism. Open to current college juniors only. Scholarships include a six to ten week internship. Minorities are especially encouraged to apply. Contact Sports Journalism Institute, Sports Illustrated, 1271 Avenue of the Americas, New York, NY 10020-1393; 212-522-6407.

Money for Political Science Women in Maryland

Undergraduate women who are residents of Montgomery County, Maryland and studying political science, government, or public administration and attending any college in Maryland are eligible to apply. Send self-addressed stamped envelope for application and complete information. Contact Lavinia Engle Scholarship Foundation, c/o Judith Heimann, 6900 Marbury Rd., Bethesda, MD 20817; 301-229-4647.

Money for Unitarian Women

Limited funding available for active, involved Unitarian women at both the Undergraduate and Graduate level. Some funds are set aside specifically for children of Unitarian ministers. One program, the Ministerial Education Fund, is specificallly for students enrolled in a Masters of Divinity degree program intending on pursuing a career as a Unitarian minister. Contact Unitarian Universalist Association, 25 Beacon St., Boston, MA 02108, 617-742-7025; {www.uua.org}.

$1000 for Aviation Women in Los Angeles

Three scholarships available to women living in the greater Los Angeles area who wish to pursue a career in aviation. Must be at least 18 years old at time of application. Please include a self-addressed, stamped envelope with requests for information. Contact San Fernando Valley Ninety-Nine's, P.O. Box 8160, Van Nuys, CA 91409; 818-989-0081.

Up to $10,000 for Texas Women

Several hundred scholarships worth more than $1,000,000 are awarded annually to outstanding high school seniors in the Houston, Texas area. Some funds are also available to students in Texas but living outside of Houston. Most programs are available to students pursuing any major. Must plan on attending college full-time. Contact Houston Livestock Show and Rodeo, P.O. Box 20070, Houston, TX 77225-0070; 713-791-9000; {www.rodeohouston.com}.

Up to $2,000 for Nursing

The Aliene Ewell Scholarship Program offered by Chi Eta Phi is for undergraduate women planning on a career in nursing. Must be recommended by a current member of Chi Eta Phi. Primary considerations are financial need, academic achievement, and potential for success. Contact Chi Eta Phi Sorority, 3029 13th St., NW, Washington, DC 20009; 202-232-3858.

Up to $5000 for Ethics Women

Scholarship essay contest open to full time juniors and seniors in an accredited 4 year college or university. Essay must be on a ethics-based topic, such as "Why are we here and how are we to meet our ethical obligations" or reflecting on an ethical aspect of a public policy issue. The prizes are 2 at $500, 1 at $1500, 1 at $2500 and 1 at $5000. Please write for more information. Include a self-addressed stamped envelope with requests. Contact Elie Wiesel Prize In Ethics Essay Contest, Elie Wiesel Foundation for Humanity, 380 Madison Avenue, 20th Floor, New York, NY 10017.

Up to $3000 for Women in Technology

The AFCEA offers several scholarship programs for students. For all scholarships, you must be a full-time student attending a 4-year college or university, a U.S. citizen, studying electrical engineering, aerospace engineering, electronics, computer science, computer engineering, physics, or mathematics, and must have a GPA of 3.4 on 4.0 scale or better.

The General John A. Wickham Scholarship accepts applications from current college juniors and seniors. The Ralph W. Shrader Scholarship is for postgraduate students working towards a master's degree in any of the above majors, or communications technology, communications engineering, or information management. At least one scholarship award is set aside specifically for a woman candidate, provided all eligibility criteria is met.

Please include a self-addressed and stamped envelope with information on field of study when writing to request information and application. Contact AFCEA Educational Foundation, 4400 Fair Lakes Ct., Fairfax, VA 22033-3899; 703-631-6149; 800-336-4583, ext. 6149; {www.afcea.org}; {Email: scholarship@afcea.org};.

At least $750 for
Pennsylvania Journalism Women

The Pennsylvania Women's Press Association offers a competitive scholarship of at least $750. To be eligible, one must be a Pennsylvania resident, a print journalism major in a four-year or graduate-level program in a Pennsylvania college or university, and be classified as a junior, senior or graduate student for Fall term. The winner will be selected on the basis of proven journalistic ability, dedication to journalism and general merit. Contact PWPA Scholarship Committee, c/o Teresa Spatara, P.O. Box 152, Sharpsville, PA 16150; {www.pnpa.com/pwpa/index.htm}.

$1,000 for Communications
Women in New York

Women who are residents of New York, studying communications, and members or a child of a member of the American Legion Auxiliary, the American Legion Juniors, or the American Legion, any New York chapter. Graduates of Girls State are also eligible to apply. Must be attending or planning on attending an accredited four-year college. Contact New York State Legion Press Association, P.O. Box 1239, Syracuse, NY 13201-1239.

Up to $10,000 for
Education Women in Delaware

This is a renewable scholarship loan program. Current high school seniors or undergraduate college students who are Delaware residents, studying education, and attending any Delaware university are eligible to apply. Must have at least a 2.75 GPA. Must agree to teach in Delaware one year for each year the award was received or pay back the loan. Contact Delaware Higher Education Commission, 820 North French Street, Fourth Floor, Wilmington, DE 19801.

$1000 for Vocational Women in Minnesota

Applicant must be a Minnesota high school senior planning to go to vocational school. Selection is based upon financial need, academic achievement, promise of leadership ability, and good character. Students planning on attending a two-year or four-year college are not eligible to apply. Contact Minnesota Federation of Teachers, Scholarship Committee, 168 Aurora Avenue, St. Paul, MN 55103.

Up to $4,000 for Journalism Women

High school seniors who show an interest in a career in the newspaper business, broadcasting, and journalism are eligible to apply. Primary considerations are financial need, academic achievement, character, and potential for success. Contact F. Ward Just Scholarship Foundation, c/o Kennedy, 805 Baldwin Ave, Apt. 308, Waukegan, IL 60085-2359.

$1000 for Clinical Laboratory Technology Women

The Society offers several scholarships to both undergraduate and graduate members. Check with your local chapter first for information. Contact International Society for Clinical Laboratory Technology, 917 Locust St., Suite 1100, St. Louis, MO 63101-1413.

Up to $13,000 for Scuba Diving Women

Open to undergraduate women who are certified SCUBA divers and between the ages of 21 and 25. Academic achievement is also considered. Contact Our World Underwater Scholarship Society, P.O. Box 4428, Chicago, IL 60608; 312-666-6525; {www.owuscholarship.org}.

$1000 for Lesbian Women

Each year, after a highly competitive application process, Legacy awards several $1000 scholarships to outstanding lesbian undergraduate and graduate full-time students. Must have at least a 3.0 grade point average, and demonstrate a commitment or contribution to the lesbian community. Other considerations are financial need, academic performance, honors, personal or financial hardship, and most especially, service to the lesbian community. Further information and applications are available at the website.

Contact An Uncommon Legacy Foundation, Inc., Scholarship Committee, 150 West 26th St., Suite 602, New York, NY 10001; 212-366-6507; {www.uncommonlegacy. org}; {Email: uncmlegacy@aol.com}.

Up to $10,000 for Women with Community Service

The Target All-Around Scholarship program is available to both men and women who are current high school seniors and legal U.S. residents. Must be planning on attending any vocational/technical, two-year, or four-year school full-time. Primary consideration is the amount and quality of time you have spent in service to your community as a volunteer. Applications are available every September at all Target stores. Contact Target All-Around Scholarship, c/o Citizens' Scholarship Foundation of America, Inc., 1505 Riverview Rd., P.O. Box 297, St. Peter, MN 56082; 800-537-4180.

Money for Connecticut Women

Current high school seniors who are residents of Waterbury, Connecticut are eligible to apply. Financial need is the primary consideration. Check with your high school counselor or administration office for application and information, or at the address below. Contact Elisha Leavenworth Foundation, 35 Park Pl., Waterbury, CT 06702.

Money for Operating Room Nurses

Scholarship awards covering tuition and fees are available to current Registered Nurses who are members of AORN and wish to return to college to continue or advance their education. Must have at least a 3.0 GPA and attend a four-year college. Graduate students are welcome to apply.

Contact Association of Operating Room Nurses Foundation, Credentialing Division, 10170 E. Mississippi Ave., Denver, CO 80231; 303-755-6300; 800-755-2676, ext. 8229; {www.aorn.org}; {Email: tbarlow@aorn.org}.

$1,000 To Study Farming

Current college sophomores and juniors who are members of or children of members of the Society and plan on studying any agricultural-related major, agricultural engineering, or biological engineering are eligible to apply. Primary consideration is financial need, although academic achievement is also considered. Contact American Society of Agricultural Engineers, 2950 Niles Rd., St. Joseph, MI 49085; 616-428-6336; {www.asce.org}.

$1000 for Seattle Women in Service to the Homeless

Seven scholarships are available to high school seniors who are residents of Seattle and plan on attending college full-time. Must have a committed interest to the plight of the homeless and have demonstrated community service to the homeless. Financial need, recommendations and an essay are also considered. Contact Windermere Foundation Scholarship, College Planning Network, Attn: Vicki Breithaupt, Campion Tower, 914 E. Jefferson, Seattle, WA 98112-5366; 206-323-0624; {www.collegeplan.org}.

Up to $1,500 for Wives of
Overseas Active Duty Service Members

Open only to spouses residing with an active duty service member stationed overseas. A grant of up to 50% of tuition for on-base education programs, up to a maximum of $300 per undergraduate term, or $350 per graduate term, and $1,500 per academic year is available. Do not need to be a full-time student. Contact Navy-Marine Corps Relief Society, Education Division, 801 N. Randolph St., Suite 1228, Arlington, VA 22203-1978; 703-696-4960.

$500 for Graduate Women in Lesbian Studies or Jewish Women Studies

The Graduate Scholarship in Lesbian Studies awards $500 to a student who will be doing research for or writing a master's thesis or Ph.D. dissertation in lesbian studies. The Scholarship in Jewish Women's Studies awards $500 to a graduate student who is enrolled full-time for the fall semester and whose area of research is Jewish Women's Studies. Contact National Women's Studies Association, University of Maryland, 7100 Baltimore Blvd., Suite 500, College Park, MD 20740; 301-403-0525; {www.nwsa.org/ scholarship.htm}.

Money For Delaware Women Over Age 20

Young women who are at least 20 years old, have graduated high school or achieved a GED, have been accepted to any Delaware two year or four year college, and are residents of Delaware are eligible to apply. Financial need is the only consideration. Contact Wilmington Women in Business, Inc., P.O. Box 2310, Wilmington, DE 19899; Attn: Scholarship Committee; {www.wwb.org/fresh.htm}.

Money for Washington, DC Women in Communications

Current junior or senior female students studying communications, advertising, journalism, public relations, marketing, graphic arts, or a related field are eligible to apply. Must have at least a 3.0 GPA, work experience in communications or related field, active in extra-curricular activities including family obligations, volunteer work, club and organization involvement that show versatility and commitment.

Contact Association of Women in Communications, Washington DC Chapter, Attn: Maralee Csellar, Vice President of Student Affairs, 1754 Westwind Way, McLean, VA 22102-1606; {www.awic-dc.org}.

Money for Saginaw, Michigan Women

Each year, the Saginaw Community Foundation awards over 100 scholarships worth over $200,000 to area high school students and college students. Please check with your high school guidance counselor, college financial aid officer, or the address below for further information.

Contact Saginaw Community Foundation, 100 S. Jefferson, Suite 501, Saginaw, MI 48607; 517-755-0545.

$1000 for Culinary Women in Maine

The Maine Restaurant Association offers scholarships to current high school seniors who are residents of Maine and plan on pursuing a career in the restaurant business. Culinary arts majors are also eligible to apply. Primary considerations are financial need and academic achievement. Contact Maine Restaurant Association, P.O. Box 5060, Augusta, ME 04330.

Up to $1,500 for Georgia Women

Renewable scholarships available to undergraduate women who are residents of Georgia and studying anything except law, theology, or medicine (although nursing students may apply). Primary considerations are financial need and academic achievement. Preference given to women who live in Chatham County, Georgia.

Contact William F. Cooper Scholarship, c/o First Union National Bank-CMG, P.O. Box 9947, Savannah, GA 31412; 912-944-2154.

Up to $2,000 for Northern Virginia Women

Open to undergraduate women who are 23 years old or over and attending or planning on attending an accredited college or university in northern Virginia. If your planned course of study is not available at any northern Virginia schools, this award may be used at institutions outside of northern Virginia. Primary consideration is financial need.

Contact Junior League of Northern Virginia, 7921 Jones Branch Dr., Suite 320, McLean VA 22102; 703-893-0258.

Scholarships Help Graduate Nursing Students Continue Education

Educational assistance is available to financially needy graduate nursing students residing in the U.S. through the Foundation of the Alumnae Association of the Mount Sinai Hospital School of Nursing, Inc. Contact Foundation of the Alumnae Association of Mount Sinai Hospital School of Nursing, Inc., 1 Gustave L. Levy Pl., New York, NY 10029; 212-289-5566.

FREE MONEY TO SEND YOUR CHILD TO PRIVATE KINDERGARTEN THRU HIGH SCHOOL

- -
Private Voucher Clearinghouse
- -

CEO (Children's Educational Opportunity Foundation) serves as a national clearinghouse for privately funded voucher programs that provide everything from support services to new programs on videotapes for K-12 grades. These private tuition grants and tax funded options give families the power to choose the K-12 school that will best accomplish their needs.

The website has a map of the U.S. Just click on the area of the program that is located near or in your hometown. For example, click on Phoenix, AZ and the next screen will pop up indicating who is the contact person for AZ, the total amount invested in the voucher program, as well as other information. The website also gives you a history about school choice legislation, school choice research, and some testimonies on how you can make a difference in the program.

Contact: CEO America, P.O. Box 330, Bentonville, AR 72712; 501-273-6957; Fax: 501-273-9362; {www. ceoamerica.org}.

TUITION ASSISTANCE FOR BLACK STUDENTS

The Black Student Fund has provided financial assistance and support services to African American students and their families in the Washington, DC area for over 34 years. All financial assistance is based on a sliding scale. During the last several years, their scope has broadened to provide services to families in the greater Washington, DC area and the nation.

Contact them at Black Student Fund, 3636 16th Street, NW, 4th Floor, Washington, DC 20010; 202-387-1414; {www.blackstudentfund.org}; {E-mail: mail@ blackstudentfund.org}.

40,000 Scholarships For Kids From K to 8th Grade

That's how many scholarships were given out in 1999 by the Children's Scholarship Fund, but at press time it was not clear when the scholarships will be available again. The scholarships averaged $1,100 for children from K through 8th grade to attend private schools. There were income requirements, but the income level can go up to $44,415 for a family of 4. The awards are based on a lottery process.

To keep in touch to see when this program will be available again, contact Children's Scholarship Fund, 7 West 57th St. 3rd Floor, New York, N Y 10019; 212-751-8555; {www.scholarshipfund. org}.

$1,400 FOR ELEMENTARY STUDENTS IN NEW YORK CITY

The School Choice Scholarships Foundation provides funds to cover the annual tuition costs up to $1,400 maximum per child and it is guaranteed for at least three years.

Scholarships are only for elementary school children who are currently enrolled in a New York City's public schools, and meet the income levels requirements. Students are selected by a lottery drawing with priority given to children who attend the lowest performing schools.

Contact: School Choice Scholarships Foundation, Inc., 730 Fifth Avenue, 9th Floor, New York, NY 10019; 212-338-8711; Fax: 212-307-3230; {www.nygroup.com}; {E-mail: scsf@ nygroup.com}.

Dentist Offers Scholarships for Elementary School Children

For several years Dr. Albert Landucci has sponsored awards and scholarships to the less fortunate. Scholarships are based on academic excellence, community service, volunteering, science and mathematics excellence and dental assisting.

Scholarships are offered in the San Mateo Elementary School District at:

Abbott	Laurel
Audubon	Laurel's Highly Gifted Program
Bayside	Meadow Heights
Baywood	Nesbit
Beresford	North Shoreview
Borel	Notre Dame
Bowditch	Park
Brewer Island	Parkside
Central Elementary	Ralston
Cipriani	St. Gregory
Fiesta Gardens International	St. Matthew
Foster City	St. Timothy
Fox	Sandpiper
George Hall	Sunnybrae
Highlands	Turnball Learning Academy
Horrall	All the high schools in San Mateo
Immaculate Heart of Mary	County College of San Mateo

For more information about the awards, scholarships and to see if your school is in the district, visit Dr. Landucci's website. Contact: Albert O. J. Landucci, D.D.S, 2720 Edison Street, San Mateo, CA 94403-2495; 650-574-4444; 650-574-4441 (voice mail); {www.drlanducci.com}; {E-mail: E@DrLanducci.com}.

Free Private Schools For Kids of Color

A Better Chance's mission is work with minority students from the 6th grade through college to open opportunity doors that otherwise would not be open without a helping hand. There are several programs that include helping students receive financial aid for attending private local schools, boarding schools, or summer programs to help prepare for college.

Contact: A Better Chance, 88 Black Falcon Ave., Suite 250, Boston, MA 02210-2414; 800-562-7865; 617-421-0950; Fax: 617-421-0965; {www.abetterchance.org}.

$1,700 Washington Scholarship Fund, Inc.

The Washington School Fund provides financial assistance for children to attend either private or parochial schools in the Washington, D.C. area for grades K through 8th. The maximum amount received per child is $1,700, and families of 4 with incomes up to $35,802 are eligible to apply.

Contact: Washington Scholarship Fund, Inc., 1133 15th Street, NW, Suite 580, Washington, DC 20005; 202-293-5560; Fax: 202-293-7893; {www.wsf-dc.org}.

MONEY FOR FUTURE WRITERS

For those future award-winning writers, Amelia Magazine awards $200 for a high school student's first publication. First publications can be a previously unpublished poem, a nonfiction essay or a short story. Deadline for the contest is May 15.

Write or call for further information. Amelia Student Award, Amelia Magazine, 329 East Street, Bakersfield, CA 93304; 805-323-4064.

$2,000 FOR CHILDREN IN ARIZONA

Arizona children in K-12, with incomes up to $29,693 (for family of 4) can receive up to $2,000 per child per school year with a minimum three-year commitment to qualified children.

Contact: Arizona Scholarship Fund, P.O. Box 2576, Mesa, AZ 85214; 602-497-4564; Fax: 602-832-8853; {E-mail: ChamBria@ Azscholarships. org}; or Arizona Scholarship Fund, P.O. Box 31354, Tucson, AZ 85751-1354; 502-886-7248; {E-mail: ChamBria@ Azscholarships. org}; {www. azscholarships. org}.

EDUCATION LOANS UP TO $20,000
FOR GRADES K THRU 12

As with college loans, there are many financial institutions that provide loans for families to send their children to private or parochial schools at the elementary and secondary school levels. Listed below are some of the organizations that are providing these types of loans. Be sure to be aware that you can always contact your state banking commissioner by calling your state capitol operator listed in the Appendix.

1) **Key Education Resources**
   745 Atlantic Ave., Suite 300
   Boston, MA 02111
   800-225-6783 (toll free)
   617-348-0010
   Fax: 617-348-0020
   {www.petersons.com/graduate/keylink.html}}

2) **USA Group Tuition Payment Plan**
   P.O. Box 7039
   Indianapolis, IN 46207-7039
   800-824-7044
   Fax: 317-951-5889
   {www.usagroup.com}

3) **The Education Resources Institute (TERI)**
   800-255-TERI
   {www.teri.org}

4) **First Marblehead Corporation**
   30 Little Harbor
   Marblehead, MA 01945
   781-639-2000
   Fax: 781-639-4583
   {http://gateloan.com}

5) **FACTS SCHOLAR Loan Program**
   P.O. Box 67037
   100 N. 56th Street
   Suite 306
   Lincoln, NE 68504
   800-624-7092
   402-466-1063
   Fax: 402-466-1136
   {www.factsmgt.com}

$10,000 for a 7th Grade Essay

The 53-year-old contest is open to parochial, private and home schooled 7th and 8th graders. Students should submit a 300-400 word, typed essay based on a patriotic theme established by VFW.

Contact your school counselor or principal to apply, or contact the VFW listed and they will tell you where your local chapter is located. First place national winners receive a $10,000 savings bond, 2nd place winners receive a $6,000 savings bond and 3rd place winners receive $5,000 savings bond.

Contact: VFW Voice of Democracy Essay Contest, Veterans of Foreign Wars of the United States, VFW Building, 406 West 34th Street, Kansas City, MO 64111; 816-756-3390; Fax: 816-968-1149; {www.vfw.org}; {E-mail: info@vfw.org}.

$3,000 for Artists

Any high school students that need help with furthering their education can enter the VFW Ladies Auxiliary National Patriotic Creative Art Competition. Students should submit their entry through the VFW Ladies Auxiliary Local Chapter first.

Finalists from the local chapters are selected for the grand prize competition. First place grand prize winners receive $3,000, and an all expense paid trip to the VFW Ladies Auxiliary Conference for Community Service in Washington, DC. Second place winners receive $2,000, 3rd place winners receive $1,500, 4th place winners receive $1,000 and 5th place winners receive $500.

Contact: VFW Ladies Auxiliary National Patriotic Creative Art Competition, Ladies Auxiliary to the VFW National Headquarters, 406 West 34th Street, Kansas City, MO 64111; 816-561-8655; Fax: 816-931-4753; {www.ladiesauxvfw.com}.

Money For Young Writers

Contestants receive a cash award for writing a short story that promotes brotherhood and is 4,000 words maximum. The money can be used for anything. For more information, contact Aim Magazine Short Story Contest, 7308 S Eberhart, Chicago, IL 60619.

$1,500 For Young Science Types

Each year General Learning Communication with Dupont sponsors a science essay contest for children in grades 7-12. First place winners of each division receive $1,500, and an expense paid trip to Space Center Houston with their parents. This trip includes airfare, hotel and an allowance. Second place winners receive a $750 prize, 3rd place winners a $500 prize and honorable mentions receive $50. The deadline for the contest is January 29. Write or visit the website to obtain the entry application and mail first class in a 9x12 envelope.

Contact: Dupont Science Challenge, Science Essay Awards Program , c/o General Learning Communications, 900 Skokie Blvd, Suite 200, Northbrook, IL 60062; 847-205-3000; Fax: 847-564-8197; {www.glcomm.com/dupont}.

$150 For Young Artists

American Automobile Association (AAA) awards prizes up to $150 for children in K to 12th grade and $5,000 for college students in their *School Traffic Safety Program*. In the K-12 division, children submit posters. In the senior high division, students can submit essays, brochures, and even creative videos.

Contact your local AAA office and ask for the School Traffic Safety Division. You may also contact AAA School Traffic Safety Poster Program, Poster Program Manager, American Automobile Association (AAA), 1260 Fair Lakes Circle, Fairfax, VA 22033; 407-444-7916; Fax: 407-444-7956.

Students in Grades 6-12
Can Win $20,000

Each year the **NSTA (National Science Teachers Association)** sponsors a scholarship competition for students in grades 6-12, who compete either individually or in pairs. The first place winner in the grades 6-9 receive a $20,000 savings bond, two 2nd place winners receive one $10,000 savings bonds each, and each 3rd place winner (5) receives one $3,000 savings bonds. The same awards disbursement will be done for grades 10-12. Deadline for the competition is in January.

Six teachers from the 1st and 2nd place winners will receive a $2000 gift certificate towards computer equipment. Ten teachers from the third place winners will receive a $200 certificate for NSTA publications. Contact: Duracell/NSTA Scholarship Competition, 1840 Wilson Blvd., Arlington, VA 22201; 888-255-4242 (toll free); {www.nsta.org}.

$1,000 FOR 13-21 YEAR OLDS

Seventeen Magazine's writing contest offers first place winners $1,000, 2nd place winners $500, and 3rd place winners $250. Honorable Mentions receive $50. Writers must be between the ages of 13-21. Contestants should submit a double-spaced manuscript copy of their fiction writing and the copy should be no more than 4,000 words, which is approximately 16 pages. Deadline date is April 30. Contact: Seventeen Magazine, 850 3rd Avenue, New York, NY 10020; 212-407-9700.

$10,000 For Young Inventors

Craftsman sponsors a program where students either invent or modify a tool independently. Two winners from grades 3-5 and 6-8 will receive a $10,000 savings bond. Ten finalists, five from each grade will receive a $5,000 savings bond. The teachers of these winners and their schools will receive prizes from Sears. Every contestant will receive a gift and certificate of appreciation.

Contact: Craftsman/NSTA Young Inventors Awards Program, National Science Teachers Association, 1840 Wilson Boulevard, Arlington, VA 22201; 888-494-4994 (toll free); {E-mail: younginventors@ nsta.org}.

$1,000 For Writing About Technology

Students in K-12 from the U.S. and Canada can use their imagination and creative writing and illustrating skills to compose a ten page or less essay to indicate what technology would be like 20 years from now. There are four categories for students to participate: grades K-3, grades 4-6, grades 7-9 and grades 10-12. Final first place winners receive a $10,000 savings bond, second place winners receive a $5,000 savings bond, and teachers receive Toshiba prizes.

Contact: Toshiba/NSTA Explora Vision Awards Program, 1840 Wilson Boulevard, Arlington, VA 22201; 800-397-5679 (toll free); 703-243-7100; {E-mail: exploravision@ nsta.org}.

$1,000 a Year for 3 Years In Kentucky

School Choice Scholarships Inc. (SCSI) in Jefferson County, Kentucky awards its kids with 100 new partial-scholarships per year in addition to the 325 scholarships awarded just last year! If your Jefferson County child is in K-6 and your family meets the Federal School Lunch regulations, you can be awarded 50%-60% of all tuition (up to $1000) for THREE YEARS! SCSI is willing to make a three-year commitment to making sure your child can enjoy the freedom of school choice! Contact: SCSI, P.O. Box 221546, Louisville, KY 40252-1546; 502-254-7274.

$1,250 FOR 4 YEARS IN CONNECTICUT

CEO Connecticut offers your K-5 child, living in either Hartford or Bridgeport, CT, the extra help needed to attend any chosen private school in the area. Just meet the Federal School Lunch Program guidelines, apply, and you could be awarded up to half the tuition for four years (up to $1250). Just last year, CEO Connecticut awarded 200 four-year scholarships in Hartford and another 106 in Bridgeport! Plus, they're happy to help families stay together by making use of a sibling policy! Contact: CEO Connecticut, P.O. Box 6364, Bridgeport, CT 06606; 203-334-3003; Fax: 203-334-7358.

Up to $1,800 in Michigan

The Educational Choice Project assist K-8 students eligible for the Federal School Lunch Program by offering to pay half of the tuition needed to attend the child's school of choice (up to $1800). Last year alone, 149 students from Calhun County gladly accepted this generous opportunity! Contact: The Educational Choice Project, 34 W. Jackson, One River Walk Center, Battle Creek, MI 49017-3505; 616-962-2181; Fax: 616-962-2182.

$1,200 in Arizona

Arizona School Choice Trust (coupled with the Childrens Scholarship Fund) will grant 25%-75% towards your child's choice of educational institution (up to $1200). If you live in Maricopa County, meet the Federal School Lunch Program guidelines, and your child is in a grade from K-8, you are eligible to apply!

The Arizona School Choice Trust has awarded more than 500 four-year awards and through tax-deductible donations adds more students to the program each year. To ensure your child's success in the program, ASCT requires that while enrolled, your student must maintain a 90% attendance rate. Contact: Arizona School Choice Trust, Inc., 3737 E. Broadway Rd., Phoenix, AZ 85040-2966; 602-454-1360; Fax: 602-454-1362; {www.asct.org}.

$1,450 For Families In TEXAS

The Childrens Educational Opportunity Foundation is a private scholarship program that will pay one-half of a child's tuition at any private school or out-of-district public school in Harris County (up to $1450). If your Harris County, TX family meets the Federal School Lunch Program requirements, your child enrolled in 1st to 8th grade may apply. This year, the Foundation hopes to award 550 students with the ability to practice school choice!

Contact: The Childrens Educational Opportunity Foundation, 952 Echo Lane, Suite 350, Houston, TX 77024; 713-722-8555; Fax: 713- 722-7442; {www.hern.org/ceo/index.html}.

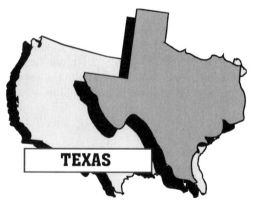

TEXAS

Over $5 Million More For Texas Children

The Today Foundation of Dallas, Texas joins with the Childrens Education Fund and the Childrens Scholarship Fund (CSF) to be able to grant Dallas students in grades K-8 with help to attend their schools of choice. Just recently, the CSF agreed to donate 5 million dollars (over four years) to help these students (who must also be eligible for the Federal School Lunch Program).

Already, the Today Foundation has been able to award 500 students with half of their school choice tuition and due to this amazing gift from the CSF, many more students will be given a very special opportunity. For more information, contact Children's Education Fund, P.O. Box 225748, Dallas, TX 75222-5748; 972-298-1811; Fax: 972-296-6369; {E-mail: today@todayfoundation.org); {www.TodayFoundation.org}.

$2,000 For Elementary Students In Colorado

Educational Options for Children offers your K-6 Denver student the opportunity to get up to 65% of private school tuition paid for four years! (You must also meet the criteria of the Federal School Lunch Program.) Every 2 years, another 50-60 four year partial-tuition opportunities (up to $2000) are available!

EOC is a non-profit organization. For more information, contact Linda Tafoya, Executive Director or Sheryl Glaser, Program Administrator at c/o Adolph Coors Foundation, 3773 Cherry Creek North Dr., Denver, CO 80209; 303-380-6481; Fax: 303-477-9986.

Save 50% On Elementary School Tuition

Gateway Educational Trust offers to pay half of your child's tuition (up to $1000) for up to three years to elementary school children. Your child must be entering K-4, live or attend school in St. Louis, and meet the regulations of the Federal Reduced Price Lunch Program. That's it! Simple!

If you'd like an application mailed to you, call 314-771-1998 and leave your name and address. For more information, you may contact Irene Allen, the Executive Director at Gateway Educational Trust, 7716 Forsyth Blvd., St. Louis, MO 63105-1810; 314-721-1375; Fax: 314-721-1857; {E-mail: ager2@aol.com}.

JOB TRAINING THROUGH UNCLE SAM

Uncle Sam wants you — to be working that is. The Federal government has developed several different programs to help you find a new career, get the training you need to move up in your present job, or find a new skill if you lost your old job. Many of these programs will cover childcare, transportation, and relocation costs to get you on your way up the job ladder.

Become A Journeyman

Getting a good job does not always mean that you must attend college or trade school, but no one will readily admit that. There are apprenticeship programs all over the country that will provide free on-the-job training — and you will learn while you earn.

Apprentices learn each skill of a job by carrying it out step by step under the close supervision of a skilled craft worker. An apprenticeship involves planned, day-by-day supervised training on the job, combined with technical instruction. Length of training varies depending on the job and is determined by standards adopted by a particular industry. The minimum term of apprenticeship is one year, but can be as long as four. Currently there are over 800 apprenticeable occupations, including cook, air craft mechanic, electrician, computer programmer, tool maker, and welder.

For more information, look in the blue pages of your phone book for the Bureau of Apprenticeship located in your state, or you may contact Bureau of Apprenticeship and Training, U.S. Department of Labor, 200 Constitution Ave., NW, Room N4649, Washington, DC 20210; 202-219-5921; {www.doleta.gov/indiv/apprent.htm}.

State Contacts

Alabama
U.S. Department of Labor
Bureau of Apprenticeship and Training
950 22nd St., North
Birmingham, AL 35203
205-731-1308

Alaska
U.S. Department of Labor
Bureau of Apprenticeship and Training
3301 C St., Suite 201
Anchorage, AK 99503
907-271-5035

Arizona
Department of Economic Security
438 W. Adams St.

Phoenix, AZ 85003
602-252-7771 Ext. 114

U.S. Department of Labor
Bureau of Apprenticeship and Training
Suite 302
3221 North 16th St.
Phoenix, AZ 85016
602-640-2964

Arkansas
U.S. Department of Labor
Bureau of Apprenticeship and Training
700 West Capitol St.
Little Rock, AR 72201
501-324-5415

California

Division of Apprenticeship Standards
Department of Industrial Relations
45 Freemont St., Suite 1040
San Francisco, CA 94105
415-975-4251

U.S. Department of Labor
Bureau of Apprenticeship and Training
Suite 1090-N
1301 Clay St.
Oakland, CA 94612
510-637-2951

Colorado

U.S. Department of Labor
Bureau of Apprenticeship and Training
721 19th St., Room 469
Denver, CO 80202
303-844-4826

Connecticut

Apprenticeship Program Manager
Connecticut Labor Department
200 Folly Brook Blvd.
Wethersfield, CT 06109
860-566-2450

U.S. Department of Labor
Bureau of Apprenticeship and Training
135 High St., Room 367
Hartford, CT 06103
203-240-4311

Delaware

Apprenticeship and Training Section
Division of Employment and Training
4425 N. Market St.
Station 313
P.O. Box 9828
Wilmington, DE 19809
302-761-8121

U.S. Department of Labor
Bureau of Apprenticeship and Training
844 King St.
Wilmington, DE 19801
302-573-6113

District of Columbia

D.C. Apprenticeship Council
500 C St., NW, Suite 241
Washington, DC 20001
202-724-7246

Florida

Apprentice Section
Bureau of Job Training
Department of Labor
1320 Executive Center Dr.
Atkins Building, Suite 200
Tallahassee, FL 32399
850-488-9250

U.S. Department of Labor
Bureau of Apprenticeship and Training
227 North Bronough St.
Tallahassee, FL 32301
850-942-8336

Georgia

U.S. Department of Labor
Bureau of Apprenticeship and Training
61 Forsyth St., SW
Atlanta, GA 30303
404-562-2323

Hawaii

Apprenticeship Division
Department of Labor and Industrial Relations
830 Punchbowl St.
Room 334
Honolulu, HI 96813
808-586-8877

U.S. Department of Labor
Bureau of Apprenticeship and Training
300 Ala Moana Blvd.
Honolulu, HI 96850
808-541-2519

Idaho

U.S. Department of Labor
Bureau of Apprenticeship and Training
3050 North Lakeharbor Lane
Boise, ID 83703
208-334-1013

Illinois

U.S. Department of Labor
Bureau of Apprenticeship and Training
230 South Dearborn St., Room 708
Chicago, IL 60604
312-353-4690

Indiana

U.S. Department of Labor
Bureau of Apprenticeship and Training
46 East Ohio St., Room 414

Indianapolis, IN 46204
317-226-7592

Iowa
U.S. Department of Labor
Bureau of Apprenticeship and Training
210 Walnut St., Room 715
Des Moines, IA 50309
515-284-4690

Kansas
Apprenticeship Director
Department of Human Resources
401 S.W. Topeka Blvd.
Topeka, KS 66603
785-296-4161

U.S. Department of Labor
Bureau of Apprenticeship and Training
444 SE Quincy St., Room 247
Topeka, KS 66683
785-295-2624

Kentucky
Apprenticeship Director
Division of Employment Standards and Mediation
Kentucky Labor Cabinet
1047 U.S. 127 South, Suite 4
Frankfort, KY 40601
502-564-2784

U.S. Department of Labor
Bureau of Apprenticeship and Training
600 Martin Luther King Place
Louisville, KY 40202
502-582-5223

Louisiana
Director of Apprenticeship
Louisiana Department of Labor
1001 North 23rd St.
P.O. Box 94094
Baton Rouge, LA 70804
504-342-7820

U.S. Department of Labor
Bureau of Apprenticeship and Training
501 Magazine St.
New Orleans, LA 70130
504-589-6103

Maine
Apprenticeship Standards
Department of Labor

Bureau of Employment Services
55 State House Station
Augusta, ME 04333
207-624-6431

U.S. Department of Labor
Bureau of Apprenticeship and Training
68 Sewall St., Room 401
Augusta, ME 04330
207-622-8235

Maryland
Apprenticeship and Training Council
1100 North Eutaw St., Sixth Floor
Baltimore, MD 21201
410-767-2968

U.S. Department of Labor
Bureau of Apprenticeship and Training
300 West Pratt St., Room 200
Baltimore, MD 21201
410-962-2676

Massachusetts
Division of Apprentice Training
Department of Labor and Workforce
100 Cambridge St., Room 1107
Boston, MA 02202
617-727-3488

U.S. Department of Labor
Bureau of Apprenticeship and Training
Room E-370
JFK Federal Building
Boston, MA 02203
617-565-2288

Michigan
U.S. Department of Labor
Bureau of Apprenticeship and Training
Room 304, 801 South Waverly
Lansing, MI 48917
517-377-1746

Minnesota
Division of Apprenticeship
Department of Labor and Industry
443 Lafayette Rd., 4th Floor
St. Paul, MN 55155
651-296-2371

U.S. Department of Labor
Bureau of Apprenticeship and Training
316 Robert St., Room 134

St. Paul, MN 55101
651-290-3951

Mississippi
U.S. Department of Labor
Bureau of Apprenticeship and Training
100 West Capitol St.
Jackson, MS 39269
601-965-4346

Missouri
U.S. Department of Labor
Bureau of Apprenticeship and Training
1222 Spruce St.
St. Louis, MO 63103
314-539-2522

Montana
Apprenticeship and Training Program
Montana Department of Labor
715 Front St.
Helena, MT 59620
406-447-3210

U.S. Department of Labor
Bureau of Apprenticeship and Training
301 South Park Ave.
Room 396 - Drawer #10055
Helena, MT 59626
406-441-1076

Nebraska
U.S. Department of Labor
Bureau of Apprenticeship and Training
Room 801, 106 South 15th St.
Omaha, NE 68102
402-221-3281

Nevada
Labor Commissioner
Nevada Apprenticeship Council
555 E. Washington Ave., Suite 4100
Las Vegas, NV 89101
702-486-2660

U.S. Department of Labor
Bureau of Apprenticeship and Training
301 Stewart Ave., Room 311
Las Vegas, NV 89101
702-388-6396

New Hampshire
Director of Apprenticeship
State Office Park South

95 Pleasant St.
Concord, NH 03301
603-271-6297

U.S. Department of Labor
Bureau of Apprenticeship and Training
143 North Main St., Room 205
Concord, NH 03301
603-225-1444

New Jersey
U.S. Department of Labor
Bureau of Apprenticeship and Training
Parkway Towers
Building E- 3rd Floor
485 Route #1, South
Iselin, NJ 08830
908-750-9191

New Mexico
Apprenticeship Director
New Mexico Department of Labor
501 Mountain Rd., NE
Albuquerque, NM 87102
505-841-8989

U.S. Department of Labor
Bureau of Apprenticeship and Training
505 Marquette, Room 830
Albuquerque, NM 87102
505-766-2398

New York
Apprentice Coordinator
NYS Department of Labor
State Campus Building #12
Room 140
Albany, NY 12240
518-457-4391

U.S. Department of Labor
Bureau of Apprenticeship and Training
Leo O'Brien Federal Building
North Pearl & Clinton Ave.
Room 809
Albany, NY 12207
518-431-4008

North Carolina
Apprenticeship Division
Department of Labor
4 West Edenton St.
Raleigh, NC 27601
919-733-7540

U.S. Department of Labor
Bureau of Apprenticeship and Training
Somerset Park, Suite205
4407 Bland Rd.
Raleigh, NC 27609
919-790-2801

North Dakota
U.S. Department of Labor
Bureau of Apprenticeship and Training
New Federal Building
304 East Broadway, Room 332
Bismarck, ND 58501
701-250-4700

Ohio
Director of Apprenticeship
State Apprenticeship Council
Bureau of Apprenticeship Services
145 S. Front St.
Columbus, OH 43215
614-644-2242

U.S. Department of Labor
Bureau of Apprenticeship and Training
Room 605, 200 North High St.
Columbus, OH 43215
614-469-7375

Oklahoma
U.S. Department of Labor
Bureau of Apprenticeship and Training
1500 South Midwest Blvd., Suite 202
Midwest City, OK 73110
405-732-4338

Oregon
Apprenticeship and Training Division
Bureau of Labor and Industry
800 NE Oregon St., Room 32
Portland, OR 97232
503-731-4891

U.S. Department of Labor
Bureau of Apprenticeship and Training
1220 SW 3rd Ave.
Portland, OR 97204
503-326-3157

Pennsylvania
Apprenticeship and Training Council
Labor and Industry Building
7th and Forster St., Room 1301
Harrisburg, PA 17120
717-787-4763

U.S. Department of Labor
Bureau of Apprenticeship and Training
Federal Building
228 Walnut St., Room 773
Harrisburg, PA 17108
717-221-3496

Rhode Island
Apprenticeship Training Programs
Department of Labor
610 Manton Ave.
Providence, RI 02909
401-457-1859

U.S. Department of Labor
Bureau of Apprenticeship and Training
Federal Building
100 Hartford Ave.
Providence, RI 02909
401-528-5198

South Carolina
U.S. Department of Labor
Bureau of Apprenticeship and Training
Strom Thurmond Federal Building
1835 Assembly St., Room 838
Columbia, SC 29201
803-765-5547

South Dakota
U.S. Department of Labor
Bureau of Apprenticeship and Training
Oxbow I Building, Room 204
2400 West 48th St.
Sioux Falls, SD 57105
605-330-4326

Tennessee
U.S. Department of Labor
Bureau of Apprenticeship and Training
1321 Murfreesboro Rd., Suite 541
Nashville, TN 37210
615-781-5318

Texas
U.S. Department of Labor
Bureau of Apprenticeship and Training
2320 LaBranch St.
Houston, TX 77004
713-750-1696

Utah
U.S. Department of Labor
Bureau of Apprenticeship and Training

1600 West 2200 South, Suite 101
Salt Lake City, UT 84119
801-975-3650

Vermont
Apprenticeship and Training
Department of Labor and Training
5 Green Mountain Dr.
P.O. Box 488
Montpelier, VT 05620
802-828-5082

U.S. Department of Labor
Bureau of Apprenticeship and Training
11 Elmwood Ave., Room 612
Burlington, VT 05401
802-951-6278

Virginia
Apprenticeship Director
Department of Labor and Industry
13 South 13th St.
Richmond, VA 23219
804-786-2381

U.S. Department of Labor
Bureau of Apprenticeship and Training
700 Centre, Suite 546
704 East Franklin St.
Richmond, VA 23219
804-771-2488

Washington
Apprenticeship Program Manager
Department of Labor and Industries
P.O. Box 44530
46 Legion Way S.E.

Olympia, WA 98504
360-902-5320

U.S. Department of Labor
Bureau of Apprenticeship and Training
1400 Talbot Rd. South
Renton, WA 98055
206-277-5214

West Virginia
U.S. Department of Labor
Bureau of Apprenticeship and Training
1108 Third Ave., Suite 203
Huntington, WV 25301
304-528-7540

Wisconsin
Dept of Workforce Develp
Division of Workforce Excellence
Bureau of Apprenticeship Standards
7201 E. Washington Ave., Room 211
P.O. Box 7972
Madison, WI 53707
608-266-3133

U.S. Department of Labor
Bureau of Apprenticeship and Training
212 East Washington Ave., Room 303
Madison, WI 53703
608-264-5377

Wyoming
U.S. Dept. of Labor Bureau of Apprenticeship and
Training
1912 Capitol Ave.#508
Cheyenne, WY 82001
307-772-2448

Free Training If You Are Laid Off

If you have found yourself on the losing end of a plant closing or mass
layoff, apply for money and re-training under the Economic Dislocation and
Worker Adjustment Assistance Act. The program is administered by each
state, and because of that, the program differs from state to state. Under
certain circumstances, states may also authorize service for displaced
homemakers.

Workers can receive classroom, occupational skills, and/or on-the-job
training to qualify for jobs in demand. Basic and remedial education,
entrepreneurial training, and instruction in literacy or English-as-a-second-
language may be provided. For more information contact your state Department of Labor in the blue pages of your
phone book, or you may contact Office of Worker Retraining and Readjustment Programs, U.S. Department of

Labor, Room N-5426, 200 Constitution Ave., NW, Washington, DC 20210; 202-219-5577; {www.doleta.gov/ programs/factsht/edwaa.htm}.

State Dislocated Worker Contacts

Alabama
Workforce Development Division
Alabama Dept. of Economic and Community Affairs
401 Adams Ave.
P.O. Box 5690
Montgomery, AL 36103
334-242-5300
800-562-4916

Alaska
Division of Community and Rural Development
Department of Community and Regional Affairs
333 West 4th Ave., Suite 220
Anchorage, AK 99501
907-269-4658

Arizona
Dislocated Worker Coordinator
Job Training Partnership Act
1789 West Jefferson
Site Code 920Z
Phoenix, AZ 85005
602-542-2484

Arkansas
Arkansas Employment Security Department
P.O. Box 2981
Little Rock, AR 72203
501-682-3137

California
Displaced Worker Services Section
Job Training Partnership Division
Employment Development Department
P.O. Box 826880
Sacramento, CA 94280
916-654-8275

Colorado
Dislocated Worker Unit
Governor's Job Training Office
720 South Colorado Blvd., Suite 550
Denver, CO 80222
303-620-4200
800-388-5515

Connecticut
CT Department of Labor
Dislocated Worker Unit
200 Folly Brook Blvd.
Wethersfield, CT 06109
203-566-4290

Delaware
Division of Employment and Training
Delaware Department of Labor
4425 North Market St.
Wilmington, DE 19809
302-761-8117

District of Columbia
Dislocated Worker Unit
Department of Employment Services
500 C St., NW
Washington, DC 20001
202-724-7130

Florida
Bureau of Workforce Program Support
Division of Labor, Employment and Training
1320 Executive Center Dr.
Atkins Building, Room 200
Tallahassee, FL 32399
850-488-9250
800-633-3572

Georgia
Georgia Department of Labor
Sussex Place
148 International Blvd., NE
Suite 440
Atlanta, GA 30303
404-656-6336

Hawaii
Workforce Development Division
Department of Labor and Industrial Relations
830 Punchbowl St., Room 329
Honolulu, HI 96813
808-586-8812

Idaho
Dept. of Employment
317 Main St.
Boise, ID 83735
208-334-6298

Illinois
Job Training Division
Department of Commerce and Community Affairs
620 East Adams St.
Springfield, IL 62701
217-785-6006

Indiana
Indiana Department of Employment and Training
Services
Program Operations Division
10 North Senate Ave.
Indianapolis, IN 46204
317-232-7461
800-437-9136

Iowa
Division of Workforce Development
Iowa Department of Economic Development
1000 East Grand Ave.
Des Moines, IA 50319
515-281-5365
800-562-4692

Kansas
Job Training Director
Department of Human Resources
Division of Employment and Training
401 SW Topeka Blvd.
Topeka, KS 66603
785-296-7876

Kentucky
Office of Training and Reemployment
Workforce Development Cabinet
275 East Main
3 Floor West
Frankfort, KY 40601
502-564-5360

Louisiana
Special Programs Section Office of Labor Federal
Training Program
P.O. Box 94094
Baton Rouge, LA 70804
504-342-7637

Maine
Dislocated Worker Unit
Hallow/Annex Central Building
55 State House Station
2nd Floor
Augusta, ME 04330
207-624-6390

Maryland
Department of Labor, Licensing and Regulations
Office of Employment and Training
1100 North Eutaw St.
Room 310
Baltimore, MD 21201
410-767-2803

Massachusetts
Corporation for
Business, Work and Learning
The Schrafft Center
529 Main St., Suite 400
Boston, MA 02129
617-727-8158 ext. 319

Michigan
Dislocated Worker Unit
Michigan Jobs Commission
201 N. Washington Square
Lansing, MI 48913
517-373-6234

Minnesota
State Dislocated Worker Unit
Minnesota Department of Jobs and Training
390 North Robert St.
First Floor
St. Paul, MN 55101
651-296-7918
800-438-5627

Mississippi
Employment and Training Division
Mississippi Department of Economic and
Community Development
301 West Pearl St.
Jackson, MS 39203
601-949-2234
800-762-2781

Missouri
Division of Job Development and Training
Department of Economic Development
P.O. Box 1087
Jefferson City, MO 65102
314-751-7796
800-877-8698

Montana
Dislocated Worker Unit
State Job Training Bureau
Montana Department of Labor and Industry
P.O. Box 1728

Helena, MT 59624
406-444-4500

Nebraska
Job Training Program Division
Nebraska Department of Labor
550 South 16th St.
Lincoln, NE 68509
402-471-9903

Nevada
State Job Training Office
Capitol Complex
400 West King St.
Suite 108
Carson City, NV 89710
702-687-4310
800-900-4614

New Hampshire
New Hampshire Job Training
Coordinating Council
64-B Suncock Rd.
Concord, NH 03301
603-228-9500

New Jersey
Rapid Response Team
Labor Management Committee
New Jersey Department of Labor, CN 058
Trenton, NJ 08625
800-343-3919

New Mexico
EDWAA Coordinator
P.O. Box 4218
Santa Fe, NM 87502
505-827-6866

New York
Dislocated Worker Unit
NY State Department of Labor
State Office Campus, Bldg. 12
Albany, NY 12240
518-457-3101

North Carolina
Division of Employment and Training
NC Department of Commerce
441 N. Harrington St.
Raleigh, NC 27603
919-733-6383 Ext. 212
800-562-6333

North Dakota
Job Training Division
Job Service North Dakota
1000 E. Divide Ave.
P.O. Box 5507
Bismarck, ND 58502
701-328-2843
800-247-0981

Ohio
Dislocated Worker Unit
Ohio Bureau of Employment Services
145 South Front St.
P.O. Box 1618
Columbus, OH 43215
614-466-3817

Oklahoma
Oklahoma Employment Security Commission
Will Rogers Bldg., Room 408
2401 North Lincoln Blvd.
Oklahoma City, OK 73104
405-557-7294

Oregon
Dislocated Worker Unit
Economic Development Department
255 Capitol St., NE
3rd Floor
Salem, OR 97310
503-373-1995

Pennsylvania
Dislocated Worker Unit
Labor and Industry Building
12th Floor
7th and Forester Sts.
Harrisburg, PA 17120
717-772-0781

Rhode Island
EDWAA Coordinator
Department of Employment and Training
109 Main St.
Pawtucket, RI 02860
401-828-8283

South Carolina
Manpower Training Unit
P.O. Box 1406
Columbia, SC 29202
803-737-2601
800-922-6332

South Dakota
Job Training Partnership Act Administrator
South Dakota Department of Labor
Kneip Building
700 Governors Dr.
Pierre, SD 57501
605-773-5017
800-952-2316

Tennessee
Tennessee Dept. of Labor
Gateway Plaza
710 James Robertson Parkway, 4th Floor
Nashville, TN 37243
615-741-1031
800-255-5872

Texas
Work Force Development Division
Texas Workforce Commission
211 East 7th St., Suite 1000
Austin, TX 78701
512-936-0474
888-562-7489

Utah
Utah Department of Workforce Services
140 East 300 South, Suite 500
Salt Lake City, UT 84114
801-526-4312
888-848-0688

Vermont
Dislocated Worker Unit
Department of Employment and Training
P.O. Box 488
Montpelier, VT 05602
802-828-4177

Virginia
Virginia Employment Commission
P.O. Box 1358
Richmond, VA 23218
804-786-3037

Washington
Dislocated Worker Unit
Employment Security Department
Employment Security Bldg.
P.O. Box 9046
Olympia, WA 98507
360-438-4629

West Virginia
Governor's Administered Programs
Bureau of Employment Programs
Job Training Programs Division
112 California Ave.
Charleston, WV 25305
304-558-1847

Wisconsin
Department of Labor, Industry and Human Relations
201 E. Washington Ave.
P.O. Box 7972
Madison, WI 53707
608-266-0745
888-822-5246

Wyoming
Job Training Program
Department of Employment
100 West Midwest
P.O. Box 2760
Casper, WY 82601
307-235-3601
800-730-9725

Free Training If You Lose Your Job From Increased Imports

Ever notice how so many products have gotten less expensive over the last ten years? Shirts that once cost $30 are now sold for $15. Televisions and VCRs — not to mention computers — have never been cheaper.

Almost everything we now buy in the U.S. is being made overseas. If you lost your job because of imports, you can get help looking for a new job or get paid to get more training. The Trade Adjustment Assistance program will help you learn more marketable job skills, so you can move to greener employment pastures. You can receive up to 104 weeks of on-the-job and classroom training; you can receive 52 weeks of benefits after your unemployment expires if you are part of a job training program; you can receive $800 to travel for job hunting purposes; $800 to relocate for a job; and transportation expenses to job training programs.

For more information, contact your local employment services office in the blue pages of your phone book, or Office of Trade Adjustment Assistance, Employment and Training Assistance, U.S. Department of Labor, Room C4318, 200 Constitution Ave., NW, Washington, DC 20210; 202-219-5555; {www.doleta.gov}. For a listing of state contacts, see the list located after the next item.

Free Training For Those Who Lose Their Jobs Because Of Increased Trade With Mexico or Canada

NAFTA is not a dirty word, but a lot of U.S. workers swear it is a plan to put them out of work and ship their jobs where labor costs are cheaper — Canada, but more significantly to Mexico and other Latin American countries. In a dog-eat-dog global economy, there are no real borders.

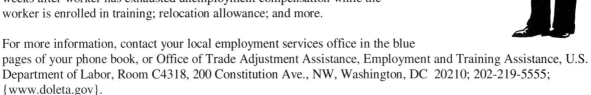

If you were laid off or lost your job because of the North American Free Trade Agreement (NAFTA), the government wants to help you find a new one, and probably one that pays you more than your last job. The NAFTA Transitional Adjustment Assistance Program is like a job skills and retraining SWAT team geared to provide rapid and early response to the threat of unemployment. The program includes on-site services to let workers know they are eligible; assessment of skills; financial and personal counseling; career counseling; job placement assistance; child care; transportation; income support for up to 52 weeks after worker has exhausted unemployment compensation while the worker is enrolled in training; relocation allowance; and more.

For more information, contact your local employment services office in the blue pages of your phone book, or Office of Trade Adjustment Assistance, Employment and Training Assistance, U.S. Department of Labor, Room C4318, 200 Constitution Ave., NW, Washington, DC 20210; 202-219-5555; {www.doleta.gov}.

State TAA-NAFTA Contacts

Alabama
Department of Industrial Relations
649 Monroe St., Room 330A
Montgomery, AL 36131
334-242-8635

Alaska
Employment Security Division
P.O. Box 25509
Juneau, AK 99802
907-465-5954

Arizona
Department of Employment Security
P.O. Box 6666

Phoenix, AZ 85005
602-495-1861

Arkansas
Arkansas Employment Security Department
P.O. Box 2981
Little Rock, AR 722-3
501-682-3747

California
Employment Development Department
P.O. Box 826880
Attn: MIC40
Sacramento, CA 94280
916-654-9305

Colorado
Department of Labor and Employment
Two Park Central, Suite 400
1515 Arapahoe St.
Denver, CO 80202
303-620-4201

Connecticut
Connecticut Department of Labor
Employment Security Division
200 Folly Brook Blvd.
Wethersfield, CT 06109
860-566-2424

Delaware
Division of Employment and Training
P.O. Box 9828
4425 North Market St.
Wilmington, DE 19809
302-761-8117

District of Columbia
Office of Unemployment Compensation
D.C. Department of Employment Services
500 C St., NW, Room 515
Washington, DC 20001
202-724-7274

Florida
Department of Labor and Employment Security
1320 Executive Center Dr.
Room 200, Atkins Building
Tallahassee, FL 32399
850-488-9250

Georgia
Georgia Department of Labor
148 International Blvd.
Room 440
Atlanta, GA 30303
404-656-6336

Hawaii
Department of Labor and Industry
830 Punchbowl St., Room 329
Honolulu, HI 96813
808-586-8820

Idaho
Idaho Department of Labor
317 Main St.
Boise, ID 83735
208-334-6314

Illinois
Department of Employment Security
401 South State St., 7th Floor
Chicago, IL 60605
312-793-6805

Indiana
Department of Workforce Development
10 North Senate Ave.
Indianapolis, IN 46204
317-232-7186

Iowa
Department of Workforce Development
1000 E. Grand Ave.
P.O. Box 10332
Des Moines, IA 50306
515-281-4981

Kansas
Department of Human Resources
512 S.W. 6th Ave.
Topeka, KS 66603
785-291-3470

Kentucky
Department of Employment Services
2nd Floor West
CHR Building
275 E. Main St.
Frankfort, KY 40621
502-564-5334

Louisiana
Louisiana Department of Labor
1001 N. 22nd St.
P.O. Box 94094
Baton Rouge, LA 70804
504-342-8753

Maine
Maine Department of Labor
Bureau of Employment Services
55 State House Station
Augusta, ME 04330
207-624-6390

Maryland
Department of Labor, Licensing and Regulations
Division of Employment and Training
1100 N. Eutaw St.
Baltimore, MD 21201
410-767-2832

Massachusetts
Corporation for Business, Work and Learning
Schrafft Center
529 Main St.
Boston, MA 02129
617-727-8158

Michigan
Employment Security Agency
7310 Woodward Ave.
Detroit, MI 48202
313-876-5374

Mississippi
Employment Security Commission
P.O. Box 1699
Jackson, MS 39215
601-961-7544

Missouri
Department of Labor and Industrial Relations
Division of Employment Security
P.O. Box 59
Jefferson City, MO 65104
573-751-3784

Montana
Department of Labor and Industry
Job Service Division
P.O. Box 1728
Helena, MT 59624
406-444-3351

Nebraska
Department of Labor
P.O. Box 94600
Lincoln, NE 68509
402-471-3406

New Hampshire
New Hampshire Employment Security
P.O. Box 9505
Manchester, NH 03108
603-656-6608

New Jersey
Department of Labor
Central Regional Office
506 Jersey Ave.
New Brunswick, NJ 08901
732-937-6249

New Mexico
Department of Labor
P.O. Box 1928

Albuquerque, NM 87103
505-841-8452

New York
Department of Labor
State Office Building
Campus #12, Room 156
Albany, NY 12240
518-457-3101

North Carolina
Employment Security Commission
Workforce Development Division
P.O. Box 26988
Raleigh, NC 27611
919-733-6745

North Dakota
Job Service of North Dakota
1000 East Divide Ave.
P.O. Box 5507
Bismarck, ND 58506
701-328-2817

Ohio
Bureau of Employment Services
145 South Front St.
P.O. Box 1618
Columbus, OH 43216
614-644-2706

Oklahoma
Employment Security Commission
Will Rogers Memorial Office Building
2401 North Lincoln
P.O. Box 52003
Oklahoma City, OK 73152
405-557-7274

Oregon
Job Training Administration
Attn: DWU
255 Capitol St.
Salem, OR 97310
503-947-1665

Pennsylvania
Dept. of Labor and Industry
7th and Forster Sts., Room 1100
Harrisburg, PA 17120
717-783-8050

Rhode Island
Department of Labor and Training
175 Main St.

Pawtucket, RI 02860
401-277-3450

South Carolina
Employment Security Commission
P.O. Box 1406
Columbia, SC 29202
803-737-3096

South Dakota
Department of Labor
Kniep Building
700 Governors Dr.
Pierre, SD 57501
605-773-5017

Tennessee
Dept. of Employment Security
Davy Crockett Building, 11th Floor
500 James Robertson Parkway
Nashville, TN 37245
615-741-1948

Texas
Texas Workforce Commission
101 E. 15th St.
Austin, TX 78778
512-305-9638

Utah
Department of Workforce Services
140 East 300 South
P.O. Box 45249
Salt Lake City, UT 84145
801-526-4309

Vermont
Department of Employment Security

P.O. Box 488
5 Green Mountain Dr.
Montpelier, VT 05602
802-828-4177

Virginia
Virginia Employment Security
703 East Main St., Room 308
Richmond, VA 23219
804-786-8825

Washington
Employment Security Department
P.O. Box 9046
Mail Stop 6000
Olympia, WA 98507
360-438-4645

West Virginia
Division of Employment Service
Bureau of Employment Programs
112 California Ave.
Charleston, WV 25305
304-558-2850

Wisconsin
Department of Workforce Development
201 E. Washington
P.O. Box 7946
Madison, WI 53707
608-266-0745

Wyoming
Department of Employment
200 West Midwest
P.O. Box 2760
Casper, WY 82602
307-235-3284

Free Training For Teens and Unemployed Adults

The Job Training Partnership Act (JTPA) provides job training services for disadvantaged adults and youth, dislocated workers, the elderly, and others who face significant employment barriers. Free services include an assessment of an unemployed individual's needs and abilities and a strategy of services, such as classroom training, on-the-job training, job search assistance, work experience, counseling, basic skills training, and support services, such as transportation and child care.

There are hundreds of JTPA sites across the U.S. To locate your nearest one, look in the blue pages of your phone book or contact Office of Employment and Training Programs, U.S. Department of Labor, 200 Constitution Ave., NW, Room N4469, Washington, DC 20210; 202-219-6236; {www.doleta.gov}.

State JTPA Contacts

Alabama
Job Training Division
Alabama Department of Economic and Community
Affairs
401 Adams Ave.
P.O. Box 5690
Montgomery, AL 36103
334-242-530

Alaska
Division of Community and Rural Development
Department of Community and Regional Affairs
333 W. 4th Ave.
Suite 220
Anchorage, AK 99501
907-269-4520

Arizona
Division of Employment and Rehabilitation Services
1789 W. Jefferson
P.O. Box 6123
Suite 901A
Phoenix, AZ 85005
602-542-4910

Arkansas
Arkansas Employment Security Department
Two Capitol Mall, Room 506
Little Rock, AR 72203
501-683-2121

California
Employment Development Department
800 Capitol Mall, MIC 83
P.O. Box 826880
Sacramento, CA 95814
916-654-8210

Colorado
Governor's Job Training Office
720 S. Colorado Blvd.
Suite 550
Denver, CO 80222
303-758-5020

Connecticut
Connecticut Department of Labor
200 Folly Brook Blvd.
Wethersfield, CT 06109
203-566-4280

Delaware
Employment and Training
Delaware Department of Labor
P.O. Box 9828
Newark, DE 19809
302-761-8110

District of Columbia
District of Columbia Department of
Employment Services
500 C St., NW, Suite 600
Washington, DC 20001
202-724-7130

Florida
Department of Labor and Employment Security
2012 Capital Circle, Southeast
Suite 303
Tallahassee, FL 32399
850-922-7021

Georgia
Georgia Department of Labor
148 International Blvd., NE
Atlanta, GA 30303
404-656-3011

Hawaii
Department of Labor and Industrial Relations
830 Punchbowl St., Room 329
Honolulu, HI 96813
808-586-8844

Idaho
Idaho Department of Employment
317 Main St.
Boise, ID 83735
208-334-6110

Illinois
Department of Commerce and Community Affairs
620 E. Adams St.
Springfield, IL 62701
217-785-6454

Indiana
Indiana Department of Workforce Development
10 N. Senate Ave., Room SE 302
Indianapolis, IN 46204
317-233-5661

Iowa
Iowa Department of Economic Development
Division of Workforce Development
100 E. Grand
Des Moines, IA 50319
515-281-5365

Kansas
Kansas Department of Human Resources
401 SW Topeka Blvd.
Topeka, KS 66603
913-296-7474

Kentucky
Office of Training and Reemployment
Workforce Development Cabinet
275 E. Main St., 2 West
Frankfort, KY 40621
502-564-5360

Louisiana
Office of Labor
P.O. Box 94094
Baton Rouge, LA 70804
504-342-7693

Maine
Department of Labor
20 Union St.
P.O. Box 309
Augusta, ME 04332
207-287-3788

Maryland
Labor, Licensing and Regulations
1100 N. Eutaw St.
Room 600
Baltimore, MD 21201
410-767-2400

Massachusetts
Corporation for Business, Work, and Learning
The Schrafft Center
529 Main St.
Suite 400
Boston, MA 02129
617-727-8158

Michigan
Michigan Jobs Commission
201 N. Washington Square
Lansing, MI 48909
517-373-6227

Minnesota
Minnesota Department of Economic Security
390 N. Robert St., 1st Floor
St. Paul, MN 55101
651-296-3700

Mississippi
Department of Economic and Community
Development
Employment Training Division
301 W. Pearl St.
Jackson, MS 39203
601-949-2234

Missouri
Department of Economic Development
2023 St. Mary's Blvd.
Jefferson City, MO 65102
573-526-8229

Montana
Department of Labor and Industry
State Job Training Bureau
P.O. Box 1728
Helena, MT 59624
406-444-2416

Nebraska
Department of Labor
P.O. Box 94600
550 S. 16th St.
Lincoln, NE 68509
402-471-9792

New Hampshire
New Hampshire Job Training
Coordinating Council
64-B Old Suncook Rd.
Concord, NH 03301
603-228-9500

New Jersey
State of New Jersey
Department of Labor
CN 055
Trenton, NJ 08629
609-292-2323

New Mexico
New Mexico Department of Labor
P.O. Box 1928
Albuquerque, NM 87103
505-841-8409

New York
New York State Department of Labor
State Office Campus
Building 12
Albany, NY 12240
518-457-2741

North Carolina
Division of Employment and Training
Department of Commerce
111 Seaboard Ave.
Raleigh, NC 27604
919-733-7979

North Dakota
Governor's Employment and Training Forum
P.O. Box 5507
Bismarck, ND 58502
701-328-2836

Ohio
Ohio Bureau of Employment Services
145 S. Front St., 4th Floor
Columbus, OH 43215
614-466-3817

Oklahoma
Security Commission
2401 N. Lincoln
Will Rogers Bldg.
Room 408
Oklahoma City, OK 73152
405-557-5329

Oregon
Oregon Economic Development Department
255 Capitol St., NE, Suite 399
Salem, OR 97310
503-373-1995

Pennsylvania
Employment Security and Job Training
Pennsylvania Department of Labor and Industry
7th and Forster Sts.
Room 1700
Harrisburg, PA 17120
717-787-3907

Rhode Island
Department of Employment and Training
101 Friendship St.
Providence, RI 02903
401-277-3600

South Carolina
South Carolina Employment Security Commission
1550 Gadsden St.
P.O. Box 995
Columbia, SC 29202
803-737-2617

South Dakota
Department of Labor
Kneip Bldg.
700 Governor's Dr.
Pierre, SD 57501
605-773-3101

Tennessee
Department of Labor
710 James Robertson Pkwy. 4th Floor
Nashville, TN 37243
615-741-3031

Texas
Workforce Development Division
Texas Workforce Commission
101 E. 15th St.
Austin, TX 78778
512-436-2654

Utah
Department of Worforce Services
140 East 300 South
Salt Lake City, UT 84111
802-531-3780

Vermont
Vermont Department of Employment and Training
P.O. Box 488
Five Green Mountain Dr.
Montpelier, VT 05601
802-828-4325

Virginia
Governor's Employment and Training Division
701 E. Broad St.
Richmond, VA 23219
804-786-2315

Washington
Employment and Training Division
605 Woodland Square Loop
P.O. Box 9046
M/S 6000
Olympia, WA 98507
360-438-4611

West Virginia
Bureau of Employment Programs
Job Training Programs Division
112 California Ave., Room 610
Charleston, WV 25305
304-558-2630

Wisconsin
Division of Jobs, Employment and Training Services

P.O. Box 7972
Madison, WI 53707
608-266-2439

Wyoming
Employment Resources Division
P.O. Box 2760
Casper, WY 82602
307-235-3254

Free Training for Workers Laid Off Because Their Factories Complied With Air Pollution Laws

Federal air pollution laws on the books are certainly better than none at all. Look at Mexico City's respiratory fatalities due to industrial smoke.

Even though the government has shut down your factory because of pollution or environmental questions, Uncle Sam will help you get back on your feet with free training programs and unemployment services. Those eligible for this program include dislocated workers who are unlikely to return to their previous industries or occupations, and who have been terminated or laid off due to a decision to reduce employment as a result of a company's compliance with the requirements of the Clean Air Act.

For more information, contact your state job training office, check the State Dislocated Worker Contacts on page 799, or Office of Worker Retraining and Adjustment Programs, Employment and Training Administration, U.S. Department Labor, Room N5426, 200 Constitution Ave., NW, Washington, DC 20210; 202-219-5577; {www.doleta.gov}.

Free Training If You Are Laid Off Due To Defense Cutbacks

Thousands of communities around the country have felt the fallout of the end of the Cold War. And the fallout has been economic, not nuclear. Base closings mean no jobs — pure and simple. Fortunately, the Defense Conversion Adjustment (DCA) Program provides retraining and other assistance for workers hurt by defense cutbacks.

The DCA Program offers retraining and readjustment services tailored to meet each individual participant. Long-term training, including educational and occupational, is encouraged. Those eligible include workers who lose their jobs because of plant closings or mass layoffs due to reduced U.S. defense expenditures or closed military facilities.

For more information contact your state job training office, check the State Dislocated Worker Contacts on page 799, or Office of Worker Retraining and Adjustment Programs, Employment and Training Administration, U.S. Department Labor, Room N5426, 200 Constitution Ave., NW, Washington, DC 20210; 202-219-5577; {www.doleta.gov}.

Free Training If You Are Laid Off
By A Defense Contractor

If you have been laid off or fired because the company you worked for was on the wrong end of cutbacks at the U.S. Department of Defense, you may qualify to be retrained for another job. The Defense Diversification Program (DDP) provides retraining and readjustment assistance to workers and military personnel dislocated by defense cutbacks and base closings, as well as career planning support and assistance. Those eligible for the program include civilian employees of the Department of Defense, Department of Energy, and defense contractors who have been terminated or laid off, or have a notice of termination or layoff.

For more information contact your state job training office, check the State Dislocated Worker Contacts on page 799, or Office of Worker Retraining and Adjustment Programs, Employment and Training Administration, U.S. Department Labor, Room N5426, 200 Constitution Ave., NW, Washington, DC 20210; 202-219-5577; {www.doleta.gov}.

How To Make A
High School Diploma Worth More

The School-to-Work program provides money to States and local partnerships of business, labor, government, education, and community organizations to develop school-to-work systems.

School-to-Work is based on the concept that education works best and is most useful for future careers when students apply what they learn to real life, real work situations. School-to-Work has three core elements: School-based learning, Work-based learning, and Connecting Activities. School-to-Work looks different in each state and locality. Contact your state office to learn more. State offices can be contacted from the list below; or National School-To-Work Learning and Information Center, 400 Virginia Ave., SW, Room 210, Washington, DC 20024; 800-251-7236; {www.stw.ed.gov}.

School-to-Work Grantees

Alabama
Center for Commerce
Room 424
401 Adams Ave., Suite 380
Montgomery, AL 36103
334-242-5300
www.noicc.gov

Alaska
Alaska Department of Education
801 W. 10th St., Suite 200
Juneau, AK 99801
907-465-8726
E-mail: {Sally_Saddler@ educ.state.ak.us}.

Arizona
Arizona Department of Commerce
STW Division
3800 North Central Ave., Building D
Phoenix, AZ 85012
602-280-8130
www.state.az.us/commerce

Arkansas
Arkansas Career Opportunities Initiative
Department of Workforce
3 Capitol Mall, Room 506D
Little Rock, AR 72201
501-682-1579

California
Department of Education High School Division
Assistant Superintendent and Director
721 Capitol Mall, 4th Floor
Sacramento, CA 94244
916-657-2532

Colorado
Colorado School-to-Career Partnership
1580 Logan St., Suite 410
Denver, CO 80203
303-894-2060
www.state.co.us/gov_dir/ltgov/schooltowork/
index.html

Connecticut
Connecticut State Department of Education
Acting Associate Commissioner of Education
25 Industrial Park Rd.
Middletown, CT 06457
860-807-2005

Delaware
Delaware Department of Public Instruction
Vocational-Technical Education & STW Transition
Townsend Building
Federal & Lockerman Streets
Dover, DE 19901
302-739-4638

District of Columbia
DC Public Schools
Corporation and Community Relations
825 N. Capitol, NE
8th Floor, Room 8144
Washington, DC 20002
202-442-5155

Florida
Florida Department of Education
325 West Gaines St., Unit 754
Tallahassee, FL 32399
850-488-7394

Georgia
Workforce Development Initiatives
Georgia Department of Technical & Adult Education
1800 Century Place, Suite 400
Atlanta, GA 30345
404-679-1658

Hawaii
Hawaii School-to-Work Opportunities
State Executive Director

874 Dillingham Blvd.
Honolulu, HI 96817
808-845-9432
www.hdo.k12.hi.us/stwo

Idaho
Idaho School-to-Work
Executive Director
650 W. State St., Suite 300
P.O. Box 83720
Boise, ID 83720
208-332-6928
http://netnow.micron.net/~stw/index.html

Illinois
Office of the Governor
107 Stratton Building
Springfield, IL 62706
217-782-1145

Indiana
Department of Workforce Development
State STW Director
10 N. Senate Ave., SE
Room 302 Indiana Government Center
Indianapolis, IN 46204
317-232-1832
www.dwd.state.in.us

Iowa
Workforce Development Administrative Center
Grimes State Office Building, 3rd Floor
Des Moines, IA 50319
515-242-5611

Kansas
Kansas State Department of Education
Coordinator, School-to-Careers
120 SE 10th Ave.
Topeka, KS 66612
785-296-3915

Kentucky
Executive Director
Berry Hill Annex
700 Louisville Rd.
Frankfort, KY 40601
502-564-5901
www.state.ky.us/agencies/
wforce/

Louisiana
Office of Lifelong Learning
School-to-Work Liaison

P.O. Box 94004
Baton Rouge, LA 70804
504-342-2094
www.leeric.lsu.edu/stw

Maine
Department of Education
Workforce Education and School-to-Work
Opportunities
23 State House Station
Augusta, ME 04333
207-287-5854

Maryland
Department of Education
Assistant State Superintendent
200 West Baltimore St.
Baltimore, MD 21201
410-767-0157

Massachusetts
Massachusetts Office for School-to-Work Transition
350 Main St.
Malden, MA 02148
781-388-3300 ext. 311
www.stw.bssc.org

Michigan
Michigan Jobs Commission
Office of Workforce Development
201 North Washington Square
Victor Office Center, Fifth Floor
Lansing, MI 48913
517-335-5858
www.mjc.state.mi.us

Minnesota
Minnesota Dept. of Children, Families and Learning
Office of Lifework Development
1500 Highway 36 West
Roseville, MN 55113
651-582-8427
http://children.state.mn.us

Mississippi
Mississippi Department of Education
Central High School Building
359 North West St.
Jackson, MS 39205
601-359-1737

Missouri
Missouri Department of Elementary and Secondary
Education

Assistant Director
School-to-Work
P.O. Box 480
Jefferson City, MO 65102
573-751-4192

Montana
Office of the Commissioner of Higher Education
Director for Workforce Development
2500 Broadway
Helena, MT 59620
406-444-0316
www.montan.edu/wochesw/
docs/webpage.html

Nebraska
Nebraska Alliance for Learning
STW Director
301 Centennial Mall South
Lincoln, NE 68509
402-471-3741
www.ded.state.ne.us/stw/
stw.html

Nevada
Nevada Dept. of Education
State School-to-Careers Coordinator
700 E. Fifth St.
Carson City, NV 89701
775-687-9243

New Hampshire
Department of Education
Educational Consultant
101 Pleasant St.
Concord, NH 03301
603-271-3729

New Jersey
New Jersey Department of Education
Office of School-to-Work Initiatives
100 Riverview Plaza
Trenton, NJ 08625
609-633-0665
www.state.nj.us.gov.educ

New Mexico
Office of the Governor
Governor's Education Policy Advisor/STW
Coordinator
State Capitol Bldg., Suite 400
Santa Fe, NM 87503
505-827-3078
www.edd.state.nm.us/ST

New York
New York State Education Department
Assistant Commissioner, Workforce Preparation and
Continuing Education
89 Washington Ave.
Room 319 EB
Albany, NY 12234
518-474-8892
www.nysed.gov/workforce/work.html

North Carolina
Commission on Workforce Preparedness
School-to-Work Transition
116 West Jones St.
Raleigh, NC 27603
919-715-3300

North Dakota
North Dakota/STW Opportunities System
State Capitol, 15th Floor
Bismarck, ND 58505
701-328-3074

Ohio
Ohio School-to-Work
131 North High St., Suite 500
Columbus, OH 43215
614-728-4630
www.ohio-stw.com

Oklahoma
Department of Vocational and Technical Education
State Coordinator
1500 West Seventh Ave.
Stillwater, OK 74074
405-743-5158
www.okvotech.org

Oregon
Oregon Department of Education
Coordinator, School-to-Work Teams
255 Capitol St., NE
Salem, OR 97310
503-378-3584 Ext. 350

Pennsylvania
Pennsylvania Department of Education
School-to-Work Opportunities Liaison
333 Market St., 5th Floor
Harrisburg, PA 17126
717-772-4177

Rhode Island
Rhode Island School-to-Work Director
610 Manton Ave., 3rd Floor

Providence, RI 02909
401-222-4922

South Carolina
Office of the Governor
STW Coordinator
1429 Senate St., Room 912A
Columbia, SC 29201
803-734-8410

South Dakota
Department of Labor
STW Coordinator
700 Governors Dr.
Pierre, SD 57501
605-773-5017
www.state.sd.us/dol/jtpa/stw.htm

Tennessee
Department of Education
Executive Director
710 James Robertson Parkway, 6th Floor
Nashville, TN 37243
615-532-5942
www.state.tn.us/education/ stchpage.html

Texas
Texas Workforce Commission
Research Specialist III
STW Coordinator
1117 Trinity St., Room 326T
Austin, TX 787778
512-936-3267

Utah
Utah State Office of Education
Coordinator, School to Careers
250 East 500 South
Salt Lake City, UT 84111
801-538-7850

Vermont
Vermont Department of Employment and Training
5 Green Mountain Dr.
P.O. Box 488
Montpelier, VT 05601
802-828-4301
www.det.state.vt.us

Virginia
Virginia Business-Education Partnership
100-101 North 9th St., Fifth Floor
Richmond, VA 23219
804-692-0244
www.state.va.us/vbep

Washington
Office of Superintendent of Public Instruction
Secondary Education and Career Preparation
Old Capitol Building
600 Washington St., SE
Olympia, WA 98504
360-753-2062
www.wa.gov/wtb

West Virginia
Director
1900 Kanawha Blvd., East
Building 6, Room 235
Charleston, WV 25305
304-558-2389

Wisconsin
Department of Workforce Development, Connecting
Education & Work
Division Administrator
201 East Washington Ave.
Room 231X
Madison, WI 53702
608-266-0223

Wyoming
Office of Workforce Development
Herschler Building
122 W. 25th St.
Cheyenne, WY 82002
307-777-7639

Free Training For Dead Beat Dads

No one likes a deadbeat dad, but Uncle Sam understands that many fathers fall behind in child support not because they're evil, wicked, mean, and nasty. Some just don't have a job and not much training to make them qualified for many jobs.

The Parents Fair Share Program was a demonstration program of the Administration for Children and Families (part of the U.S. Department of Health and Human Services), and was designed to help parents get the training they need to get a paycheck to help with child support. The demonstration program has since ended, but many of the sites continue to provide job readiness and job skills training.

For more information, contact one of the sites below:

California
Los Angeles County Fair Share, Bureau of Family Support Operations, 5770 South Eastern Ave., Commerce, CA 90024; 323-889-2954.

Florida
Duvall County Parents' Fair Share, Employment and Training Security, Department of Labor, 421 W. Church St., Jacksonville, FL 32202; 904-798-4720.

Massachusetts
Massachusetts JOBS Parents' Fair Share Project, Springfield Employment Resource Ctr., Inc., 140 Wilbraham Ave., Springfield, MA 01109; 413-737-9544.

Michigan
Non-Custodial Parent Program, 385 Leonard NE, Grand Rapids, MI 49503; 616-458-6350.

New Jersey
Operation Fatherhood, Union Industrial Home For Children, 4 N. Broad St., Trenton, NJ 08608; 609-695-3663.

Ohio
Options for Parental Training and Support, Montgomery County Department of Human Services, 14 W. Fourth St., Dayton, OH 45402; 937-225-4077.

Triple Your Salary With
Job Training For Migrant And Farm Workers

Migrant workers and seasonal laborers are some of the hardest working people in America. Yet when the crops are all picked or the economy sags, they are some of the first to be out of a job. And most of these people live just at the poverty level to begin with.

Fortunately, the government has a special job training program to help them find less backbreaking work. Participants can receive a weekly allowance at the current minimum wage and learn new work skills in classroom and on-the-job training programs, work experience in new employment areas, job development and placement services, relocation and education assistance, and more.

For more information contact your local job training office, or U.S. Department of Labor, Office of Special Targeted Programs, Division of Migrant and Seasonal Farmworker Programs, Room N-4641, 200 Constitution Ave., NW, Washington, DC 20210; 202-219-5500; {www.wdsc.org/msfw}.

Migrant and Seasonal Farmworker Programs

Alabama
Alabama Dept. of Economic and Community Affairs
401 Adams Ave.
Montgomery, AL 36103
334-242-5100

Alabama Opportunity Program
224 Church St., Suite D
Huntsville, AL 35801
205-536-8218

Arizona
Portable Practical Educational Preparation, Inc.
806 East 46th St.
Tucson, AZ 85713
520-622-3553

Arkansas
Arkansas Human Development Corporation
Suite 800, 300 S. Spring St.
300 Spring Building
Little Rock, AR 72201
501-374-1103

California
Employers Training Resource
County of Kern

2001 28th St.
Bakersfield, CA 93301
805-861-2495

Center for Employment Training
701 Vine St.
San Jose, CA 95110
408-287-7924

Proteus, Inc.
4612 West Mineral King Ave.
P.O. Box 727
Visalia, CA 93279
559-733-5423
www.proteusinc.org

Central Valley Opportunity Center, Inc.
1748 Miles Court
P.O. Box 2307
Merced, CA 95348
209-383-2415
www.elite.net/~cvocplan/

Colorado
Rocky Mountain Ser/
Jobs for Progress, Inc.
3555 Pecos St.
P.O. Box 11148

Denver, CO 80211
303-480-9394

Connecticut
New England Farm Workers' Council, Inc.
191 Franklin Ave.
Hartford, CT 06114
860-296-3518

Delaware
Telamon Corp.
504 North Dupont Highway
Dover, DE 19901
302-734-1903

Florida
Adult Migrant and Seasonal Farm Workers Program
Suite 200, 3801 Corporex Park Dr.
Corporex Plaza Two
Tampa, FL 33619
813-744-6303

Georgia
Telamon Corporation
Suite 140, Building D
2720 Sheraton Dr.
Macon, GA 31204
912-750-7134
www.telamon.org

Hawaii
Maui Economic Opportunity, Inc.
189 Kaahumanu
P.O. Box 2122
Kaului, HI 96732
808-871-9591

Idaho
Idaho Migrant Council
104 North Kimball
P.O. Box 490
Caldwell, ID 83606
208-454-1652

Illinois
Illinois Migrant Council
16th Floor, 28 East Jackson Blvd.
Chicago, IL 60604
312-663-1522

Indiana
Transition Resource Corporation
Suite 0-2, 2511 East 46th St.
Indianapolis, IN 46205

317-547-1924
www.telamon.org

Iowa
Proteus, Inc.
175 NW 57th Place
Des Moines, IA 50313
515-244-5694
www.netins.net/showcase/proteus

Kansas
SER Corporation of Kansas/SER Rural Initiatives
709 East 21st
Wichita, KS 67214
316-264-5372

Kentucky
Kentucky Farmworker Programs, Inc.
1844 Lyda St., Suite 210
P.O. Box 51146
Bowling Green, KY 42102
502-782-2330

Louisiana
Motivation, Education and Training, Inc.
1055 Laurel St.
Baton Rouge, LA 70802
504-343-0301

Maine
Training and Development Corporation
14 High St.
Ellsworth, ME 04605
207-667-7543

Maryland
Telamon Corp.
237 Florida Ave.
Salisbury, MD 21801
410-546-4604

Massachusetts
New England Farm Workers' Council, Inc.
1628-1640 Main St.
Springfield, MA 01103
413-781-2145

Michigan
Telamon Corp.
6250 West Michigan Ave.
Suite C
Lansing, MI 48917
517-323-7002

Minnesota
Motivation Education and Training Inc.
1900 Highway 294, NE, Suite 2040
Wilmar, MN 56201
320-231-5174

Mississippi
Mississippi Delta Council for Farm Workers
Opportunities, Inc.
1005 State St.
Clarksdale, MS 38614
601-627-1121

Missouri
Rural Missouri, Inc.
1014 Northeast Dr.
Jefferson City, MO 65109
573-635-0136

Montana
Rural Employment Opportunities, Inc.
25 South Ewing St., 5th Floor
P.O. Box 831
Helena, MT 59624
406-442-7850

Nebraska
NAF Multicultural Human Development Corp.
416 East 4th St.
P.O. Box 1459
North Platte, NE 69103
308-534-2630

Nevada
Center for Employment Training
520 Evans Ave.
Reno, NV 89512
702-348-8668

New Hampshire
Farm Workers' Council, Inc.
370 Union St.
Manchester, NH 03103
603-622-8199

New Jersey
New Jersey Rural Opportunities
510-12 E. Landis Ave.
Vineland, NJ 08360
609-696-1000

New Mexico
Home Education Livelihood Program, Inc.
5101 Copper NE

Albuquerque, NM 87017
505-265-3717

New York
Rural Opportunities, Inc.
400 East Ave., Suite 401
Rochester, NY 14604
716-546-7180

North Carolina
Telamon Corp.
3937 Western Blvd.
P.O. Box 33315
Raleigh, NC 27636
919-851-7611
www.telamon.org

Telamon Corp.
Suite 200, 4917 Waters Edge Dr.
Raleigh, NC 27606
919-851-6141
www.telamon.org

North Dakota
Midwest Farmworker Employment and Training Inc.
Suite D, 1323 South 25th St.
Fargo, ND 58106
701-241-8442

Ohio
Rural Opportunities Inc.
320 West Gypsy Lane Rd.
P.O. Box 186
Bowling Green, OH 43402
419-354-3552

Oklahoma
ORO Development Corp.
Suite 204, 5929 North May Ave.
Oklahoma City, OK 73112
405-840-7077

Oregon
Oregon Human Development Corp.
Suite 110, 9620 SW Barbur Blvd.
Portland, OR 97219
503-245-2600
www.1stop.org/washco/ohdc/

Pennsylvania
Rural Opportunities, Inc.
1300 Market St., 2nd Floor
Lemoyne, PA 17043
717-731-8120

Puerto Rico
Commonwealth of Puerto Rico
Department of Labor and Human Resources
505 Munoz Rivera Ave., 21st Floor
Hato Rey, PR 00918
809-472-6620

South Carolina
Telamon Corp.
1413 Calhoun St.
P.O. Box 12217
Columbia, SC 29211
803-256-8528
www.telamon.org

South Dakota
Midwest Farmworker Employment and Training, Inc.
121 W. Dakota St.
Pierre, SD 57501
605-224-0454

Tennessee
Tennessee Opportunity Program For Seasonal Farm Workers, Inc.
1370 Hazelwood Dr., Suite 207
P.O. Box 925
Smyrna, TN 37167
615-459-3600

Texas
Motivation, Education and Training, Inc.
307 North College
P.O. Box 1749
Cleveland, TX 77328
281-592-6483

Utah
Private Industry Council, Inc.
Futures Through Training, Inc.
533 26th St., Suite 204
Ogden, UT 84401
801-394-9774

Vermont
Central Vermont Community Action Council, Inc.
195 US Rt. 302-Berlin

Barre, VT 05641
802-479-1053

Virginia
Telamon Corp.
4915 Radford Ave., Suite 202A
Richmond, VA 23220
804-355-4676
www.telamon.org

Washington
Director of Employment Training
Washington State Migrant Council
105-B South 6th St.
Sunnyside, WA 98944
509-837-5443

West Virginia
Telemon Corp.
100 Williamsport Ave.
Martinsburg, WV 25401
304-263-0916

Wisconsin
DILHR- Employment and Training
Room 231-X
201 East Washington Ave.
P.O. Box 7972
Madison, WI 53707
608-267-7273
www.dwd.state.wi.us

United Migrant Opportunity Services
929 West Mitchell St.
P.O. Box 04129
Milwaukee, WI 53204
414-671-5700

Wyoming
Northwestern Community Action Programs of Wyoming, Inc.
1922 1/2 Robertson Ave.
P.O. Box 158
Worland, WY 82401
307-347-6185

FREE JOBS AND TRAINING FOR DROPOUTS INTERESTED IN CONSTRUCTION CAREERS

Bottom line: most construction jobs pay really well. If you like the work, training in the construction industry can fatten the paycheck even further. If you get the itch, you might even want to become an engineer, or — better yet — become someone who gets to use the wrecking ball.

Young men and women can get experience in the construction trades, while helping to build housing for the homeless under the Youthbuild program. Participants get hands-on training in the rehabilitation and construction of housing, as well as valuable off-site education. Low income kids between the ages of 16 and 24 are eligible to participate.

For more information about sites across the country check out the list below, or contact Office of Economic Development, Community Planning and Development, U.S. Department of Housing and Urban Development, Washington, DC 20410; 202-708-2035.

Youthbuild Sites

Alabama
Birmingham Enterprise Community, Inc.
1200 Tuscaloosa Ave., West
Birmingham, AL 35211
205-322-3117

Arizona
City of Phoenix
200 West Washington
Phoenix, AZ 85003
602-262-4032

Town of Guadalupe
9050 S. Avenida Del Yaqui
Guadalupe, AZ 85283
602-730-8030

California
Century Center for Economic Opportunity
17216 S. Figueroa St.
Gardena, CA 90248
310-255-3070

Community Services And Employment Training
2150 S. Mooney Blvd.
Visalia, CA 93277
209-732-4194

Excelsior Education Center
14564 7th St.
Victorville, CA 92392
760-245-4264, ext. 22

Neighborhood Housing Services of the Inland Empire, Inc.
390 North D St.
San Bernardino, CA 92405
909-884-6891

Pacific Asian Consortium In Employment
1541 Wilshire Blvd.
Los Angeles, CA 90017
213-353-3982

Sonoma County People for Economic Opportunity
555 Sebastopol Ave.
Santa Rosa, CA 95401
707-544-6911

Venice Community Housing Corp.
318 Lincoln Blvd., Suite 225
Venice, CA 90291
310-399-4100

Connecticut
Co-Opportunity Inc.

117 Murphy Rd.
Hartford, CT 06114
860-236-3617

District of Columbia
Arch Training Center, Inc.
2427 Martin Luther King, Jr. Ave., SE
Washington, DC 20012
202-889-6344

Latin American Youth Center
3045 15th St., NW
Washington, DC 20009
202-483-1140

Sasha Bruce Youthwork, Inc.
741 8th St., SE
Washington, DC 20003
202-675-9340

Florida
City of Jacksonville
117 W. Duval St.
Jacksonville, FL 32202
904-630-6440

Gainesville Housing Authority
1900 SE 4th St.
Gainesville, FL 32602
352-371-3180

Illinois
Youthbuild McLean County
1312 W. Monroe
Bloomington, IL 61701
309-827-7505

Louisiana
Louisiana Technical College-Tallulah
Old Highway 65 South
Tallulah, LA 71282
318-574-4820

Maine
Portland West Neighborhood Planning Council
155 Brackett St.
Portland, ME 04102
207-775-0105

Maryland
Southern Area Youth Services, Inc.
4710 Auth Place, Suite 620
Suitland, MD 20746
301-702-9730

Massachusetts
Massachusetts Job Training, Inc.
332 Main St., Suite 601
Worcester, MA 01608
508-753-2991

Nueva Esperanza inc.
401 Main St.
Holyoke, MA 01040
413-533-9442

Old Colony Y Services Corp.
320 Main St.
Brockton, MA 02301
508-584-1100 ext. 21

People Acting in Community Endeavors, Inc.
P.O. Box 5626
New Bedford, MA 02742
508-999-9920

Youthbuild Boston, Inc.
504 Dudley St.
Roxbury, MA 02119
617-445-8887

Michigan
Neighborhood Information and Sharing Exchange
200 Paw Paw
Benton Harbor, MI 49022
616-925-3948

Oakland Livingston Human Service
196 Oakland Ave.
Pontiac, MI 48343
248-209-2622

Washtenaw County
220 North Main St.
Ann Arbor, MI 48105
734-994-2435

Missouri
Youth Education and Health in Soulard
1921 South 9th St.
St. Louis, MO 63014
314-436-1400

Montana
Human Resource Development Council of District
IX, Inc.
321 East Main, Suite 300
Bozeman, MT 59715
406-587-4486

Nebraska
Chadron Community Development Corp.
P.O. Box 978
Chadron, NE 69337
308-432-4346

New Hampshire
Odyssey House, Inc.
P.O. Box 780
Hampton, NH 03843
603-929-3038 Ext. 341

New Jersey
Atlantic City Youthbuild
1 South Carolina Ave.
Atlantic City, NJ 08401
609-345-4575

Isles, Inc.
10 Wood St.
Trenton, NJ 08618
609-393-5656 ext. 14

New Jersey Community Development Corp.
13 1/2 Van Houten St.
Paterson, NJ 07505
973-225-0555

Paterson Coalition for Housing, Inc.
262 Main St.
Paterson, NJ 07505
973-684-5998

New Mexico
Youthbuild New Mexico Coalition, Inc.
115 Second St., SW
Albuquerque, NM 87102
505-244-9505

New York
New York Housing Authority
250 Broadway
New York, NY 10007
212-306-8424

The Urban League of Rochester, NY, Inc.
265 N. Clinton Ave.
Rochester, NY 14605
716-325-6530

Youth Action Programs and Homes, Inc.
218 East 106th St.
New York, NY 10029
212-860-8190

North Carolina
Housing Authority of the City of High Point
500 East Russell Ave.
High Point, NC 27260
336-887-2661

River City Community Development Corp.
501 E. Maine St.
Elizabeth, NC 27909
252-331-2925

UDI Community Development Corp.
P.O. Box 1349
631 United Dr.
Durham, NC 27702
919-544-4597

Ohio
Community Action Commission of Fayette County
324 E. Court St.
Fayette County, OH 43160
740-335-7282

Cuyahoga County Youthbuild
112 Hamilton Court
Cleveland, OH 44114
216-443-8160

Improved Solutions for Urban Systems, Inc.
100 N. Jefferson St., Suite 602
Dayton, OH 45402
937-223-2323

Private Industry Council of Trumbull County, Inc.
815 Youngstown Warren Rd.
Niles, OH 44446
330-652-2095

Oklahoma
Housing Authority of the City of Tulsa
415 E. Independence
Tulsa, OK 74148
918-581-5777

Oregon
City of Portland
808 SW Third Ave.
Portland, OR 97204
513-286-9350

Pennsylvania
Crispus Attucks Community Development Corp.
605 S. Duke
York, PA 17403
610-921-6997

Housing Authority City of Pittsburgh
200 Ross St.
Pittsburgh, PA 15219
412-456-5085

Philadelphia Youth for Change Charter School
619 Catherine St.
Philadelphia, PA 19147
215-627-8671

Youthbuild Pittsburgh, Inc.
7129 Hamilton Ave.
Pittsburgh, PA 15208
412-242-7709

South Carolina
Telamon Corp.
P.O. Box 12217
Columbia, SC 29211
803-256-7411

Tennessee
Tennessee Technology Center at Memphis
550 Alabama Ave.
Memphis, TN 38105
901-527-9617

Texas
American Institute for Learning
422 Congress Ave.
Austin, TX 73701
512-472-3395

Community Development Corporation of
Brownsville
1150 East Adams St.
Brownsville, TX 78520
956-541-4955

Gulf Coast Trades Center
P.O. Box 515
New Waverly, TX 77358
409-344-6677

Harlingen Community Development Corp.
518 East Harrison
Harlingen, TX 78550
956-421-2351

Harris County Youthbuild
1310 Prairie
Houston, TX 77002
713-755-4766

Vermont
King Street Youth Center
14 South Williams St.
Burlington, VT 05401
802-862-6736

Randolph County Housing Authority
1200 Harrison Ave.
Elkins, WV 26241
304-636-6495

Southern Appalachian Labor School
P.O. Box 127
Kincaid, WV 25119
304-442-3157

Wisconsin
809 N. Broadway, 3rd Floor
Milwaukee, WI 53202
414-286-2034

Milwaukee Community Service Corps.
Milwaukee Christian Center
1150 E. Beady St.
Milwaukee, WI 53202
404-276-6272

Operation Fresh Start Inc.
1925 Winnebago St.
Madison, WI 53704
608-244-4721

Free Job Training and More For Foster Care Teens

All kinds of free help is out there for teenagers in foster care — and young adults who have been raised in foster homes — to get the job skills they need to make a good life on their own. The Independent Living program helps foster care youth between the ages of 16 and 21, in getting a GED or a driving permit and provides assistance in filling out college applications. Those who live out in the country can even get free transportation to job training programs that can assure them of a good paying career track.

For more information, contact your foster care worker, or to learn your state contact for the Independent Living program contact Division of Child Welfare, Children's Bureau, Administration for Children and Families, P.O. Box 1182, Washington, DC 20013; 202-205-8740; {www.acf.dhhs.gov/programs/cb/programs/index.htm}.

Independent Living State Coordinators

Alabama
Alabama Department of Human Resources
1050 Government St.
Suite 201
Mobile, AL 36604
334-433-4456

Alaska
Alaska Division of Family and Youth Services
P.O. Box 110630
Juneau, AK 99811
907-465-2145

Arizona
Arizona Department of Economic Security
1717 W. Jefferson, 3rd Floor
Phoenix, AZ 85007
602-542-5120

Arkansas
Arkansas Division of Children and Family Services
P.O. Box 1437, Slot 819
Little Rock, AR 72203
501-682-8453

California
California Department of Social Services
744 P St.
MS 19-78
Sacramento, CA 95814
916-324-9084

Colorado
Colorado Department of Human Services
1575 Sherman St., 2nd Floor
Denver, CO 80203
303-866-3228

Connecticut
DCYS
505 Hudson St.
Hartford, CT 06106
860-550-6471

Delaware
Division of Child Protective Services
1825 Faulkland Rd.

Wilmington, DE 19805
302-633-2659

District of Columbia
Department of Human Services
Independent Living Programs
65 I St., SW, Room 219
Washington, DC 20024
202-727-1534

Florida
Florida Department of Health and Rehabilitative Services
1317 Winewood Blvd.
Tallahassee, FL 32399
850-921-1883

Georgia
Division of Family and Children Services
2 Peachtree St., NW
Atlanta, GA 30303
404-657-3459

Hawaii
Hawaii Department of Human Services
Family and Adult Services
810 Richards St., Suite 400
Honolulu, HI 96809
808-586-5668

Idaho
Idaho Department of Health and Welfare
P.O. Box 83720
Boise, ID 83720
208-334-38000

Illinois
Illinois Department of Children and Family Services
406 E. Monroe Station, #75
Springfield, IL 62701
217-785-2467

Illinois Department of Children and Family Services
Research and Demonstration Unit
1921 S. Indiana
Chicago, IL 60616
312-808-5240

Indiana

Indiana Department of Public Welfare
Children and Family Services
402 W. Washington St., Room W364
Indianapolis, IN 46204
317-232-4631

Iowa

Division of Adults, Children, and Family Services
Hoover State Office Building
Des Moines, IA 50319
515-281-6786

Kansas

Youth and Adult Services
Docking State Office Building
9155 SW Harrison, 5th Floor
Topeka, KS 66606
913-368-8165

Kentucky

Kentucky Department of Social Services
Children and Youth Services, 6W
275 E. Main St.
Frankfort, KY 40621
502-564-2147

Louisiana

Louisiana Department of Social Services
Office of Community Services
P.O. Box 3318
Baton Rouge, LA 70821
504-342-2279

Office of Community Services
P.O. Box 61210
New Orleans, LA 70161
504-342-2268

Maine

Maine Department of Human Services
11 State House Station
Augusta, ME 04333
207-287-5060

Maryland

Maryland Department of Human Resources
Independent Living Coordinator
311 W. Saratoga St., Suite 572
Baltimore, MD 21201
410-767-7634

Massachusetts

Massachusetts Department of Social Services
24 Farnsworth St.

Boston, MA 02110
617-727-0900

Michigan

Michigan Department of Social Services
235 S. Grand, Suite 511
Lansing, MI 48909
517-373-2083

Minnesota

Minnesota Department of Human Services
444 Lafayette Rd.
St. Paul, MN 55155
651-296-7635

Mississippi

Department of Human Services
Office of Social Services
P.O. Box 352
Jackson, MS 39205
601-359-4982

Missouri

Missouri Division of Family Services
P.O. Box 88
Jefferson City, MO 65103
314-751-4319

Montana

Department of Family Services
P.O. Box 8005
Cogswell Bldg. 1
1400 Broadway
Helena, MT 59620
406-444-5900

Nebraska

Nebraska Department of Social Services
301 Centennial Mall South
State Office Building
Lincoln, NE 68509
402-471-9434

Nevada

Nevada State Welfare/ Department of Human Resources
Division of Child and Family Services
6171 W. Charleston Blvd., Bldg. 15
Las Vegas, NV 89158
702-486-6014

New Hampshire

New Hampshire Division for Children, Youth, and Family

Bureau of Children
6 Hazen Dr.
Concord, NH 03301
603-271-4706

New Jersey
Division of Youth and Family Services
1 S. Montgomery St.
CN 717- Fifth Floor
Trenton, NJ 08625
609-292-0887

New Mexico
Department of Children, Youth and Family
707 Broadway NE, #500
Albuquerque, NM 87102
505-841-9500

New York
NYS Department of Social Services
40 N. Pearl St., Floor 11-A
Albany, NY 12243
518-474-9586

North Carolina
Care Program
North Carolina Division of Social Services
325 N. Salisbury St.
Raleigh, NC 27603
919-733-4622

North Dakota
North Dakota Department of Human Services
600 E. Boulevard Ave.
Bismarck, ND 58505
701-328-4934

Ohio
Ohio Department of Human Services
Family Enhancement Services
65 East Sate St., 5th floor
Columbus, OH 43215
614-728-4733

Oklahoma
Oklahoma Department of Human Services
P.O. Box 25352
Oklahoma City, OK 73125
405-521-4364

Oregon
Oregon Children's Service Division
Program Development Grant Support
500 Summer St., NE

Salem, OR 97310
503-945-6619

Pennsylvania
Pennsylvania Department of Public Welfare
DPW-OCYF
P.O. Box 2675
Harrisburg, PA 17105
717-783-3984

Rhode Island
Rhode Island Department of Children and Families
610 Mt. Pleasant Ave., Bldg. 10
Providence, RI 02908
401-457-4503

South Carolina
South Carolina Department of Social Services
P.O. Box 1520
Columbia, SC 29202
803-734-3515

South Dakota
Department of Social Services
Office of Child Protection Services
700 Governor's Dr.
Pierre, SD 57501
605-773-3227

Tennessee
Tennessee Department of Human Services
Social Services Policy Development
400 Deaderick St., 14th Floor
Nashville, TN 37248
615-532-5644

Texas
Texas Department of Protective and Regulatory
Services
P.O. Box 149030, MC E-558
Austin, TX 78714
512-438-5442

Utah
Utah Dept. of Social Services
120 N. 200 W.
P.O. Box 45500
Salt Lake City, UT 84103
801-538-4070

Vermont
Vermont Department of Social Services
103 S. Main St.
Waterbury, VT 05676
801-241-2131

Virginia
Independent Living Program Coordinator
Virginia Department of Social Services
730 E. Broad St.
Richmond, VA 23219
804-692-1293

Washington
Division of Children and Family Services
4045 Delridge Way Southwest, Suite 400
Seattle, WA 98106
206-933-3538

Wisconsin
Wisconsin Department of Health and Social Services
One W. Wilson St.

P.O. Box 8916, Room 465
Madison, WI 53708
608-266-5330

West Virginia
West Virginia University
Independent Living Program Manager
955 Harman Run Rd.
Morgantown, WV 26505
304-558-7980

Wyoming
Department of Family Service
324 Hathaway Bldg.
Cheyenne, WY 82001
307-777-5878

Free Job Training, GED Courses, And Guaranteed Jobs For High School Kids And Poverty Zone Drop Outs

Growing up in poverty today isn't what it was earlier this century. In years past, a life of poverty was much harder. There was no government assistance, no food stamps, no volunteer organizations willing to spend time helping anyone out.

Youth Fair Chance is a new community based program that gives money directly to areas where problems for kids are greatest — high poverty zones. The purpose of Youth Fair Chance is to serve kids who just aren't getting what they need from traditional job training and placement programs. Some of the special kinds of help kids can receive include: employment and training, help staying in school, assistance in dealing with drug and gang involvement, participation in sports and recreation, family support, and more. Kids and young adults between 14-30 years of age who reside in rural and urban communities are eligible.

For more information on the program or to locate the site nearest you, contact Office of Policy and Research, Employment and Training Administration, U.S. Department of Labor, 200 Constitution Ave., NW, Washington, DC 20210; 202-219-8668; {www.doleta.gov}.

Need Money But Out Of Work

If you have been laid off or your company has downsized you out of your job through no fault of your own, then help is out there for you. Unemployment compensation is the government's first line of defense against the ripple effects of unemployment. By cash payments made directly to laid off workers, the program ensures that at least a significant proportion of the necessities of life, such as food, shelter, and clothing, can be met while a search for work takes place. There are no federal standards for benefits, in terms of qualifying requirements, benefit amounts, or duration of the regular benefits. All states do require that a person work a certain amount of time or earn a specified amount of wages to qualify for the program. Unemployment benefits can often be extended in certain circumstances.

To learn more contact your local Unemployment Office that can be found by looking in the blue pages of your phone book. If you need more information, you may also contact the main office at Unemployment Insurance Service, Employment and Training Administration, U.S. Department of Labor, 200 Constitution Ave., NW, Washington, DC 20210; 202-219-5200; {www.doleta.gov}.

Want Your High School Diploma?

People drop out of or fail to complete high school for many different reasons. But one thing is clear; getting your high school diploma or GED is the key to advancement. GED stands for General Educational Development. When you take a GED test, it tests your knowledge and ability in five different areas: writing skills, social studies, science, interpreting literature and the arts, and mathematics. GED tests are given at sites all across the United States. There are several ways to learn where the nearest GED test site is located. You can contact your local Board of Education, which may also know about free or cheap preparation classes. You can also contact your State Department of Adult Education, which you can locate by looking in the blue pages of your phone book. The GED Information Hotline is operated by the American council on Education, One Dupont Circle, NW, Suite 250, Washington, DC 20036; 800-62-MY-GED; {www.acenet.edu/calec/ged/home.html}.

Free Help For Migrant Workers
Who Want To Get Their GEDs

Migrant farm workers who missed out completing high school because of the demands of seasonal work schedules now qualify for a little known program called the Migrant Education High School Equivalency Program.

Over 25 different nonprofit groups receive money to offer free help to migrant workers who want to earn their GEDs. The program provides transportation to and from classes, a weekly stipend, GED preparation, housing for those in the residential programs, tutorial assistance, assistance in applying to higher education institutions, and more. Many programs will pay expenses to get students to their sites. Many are residential programs, where you can live while you are studying to complete your GED. You even get your meals there!

For more information or to locate a site near you contact Office of Migrant Education, U.S. Department of Education, 600 Independence Ave., SW, Room 4100, Washington, DC 20202; 202-260-1124; 800-234-8848; {www.ed.gov/offices/OESE/MEP}.

Free Tutoring And Financial Counseling For Migrant
Workers Who Want To Go To College

Migrant workers who are attending college for the first time experience a number of difficulties that are unique to them. To help these workers make a smooth transition into the academic environment of college, the government created the College Assistance Migrant Program (CAMP). CAMP provides intensive services during students' first year in college including campus tours, application assistance, housing orientation, academic advising, tutoring, financial aid, health services, and more. For more information or to locate a site near you, contact Office of Migrant Education, U.S. Department of Education, 600 Independence Ave., SW, Room 4100, Washington, DC 20202; 202-260-1124; 800-234-8848; {www.ed.gov/offices/OESE/MEP}.

Free Tutors and Other Services To Help Low-Income School Dropouts Reach College

Talent Search is a special program that provides funding to help youth from disadvantaged backgrounds re-enter the educational system, complete high school, and go on to the college of their choice. Program services include academic, financial and personal counseling, career exploration and aptitude testing, financial aid application assistance, preparation for college entrance exams, and more. Talent Search programs are sponsored by colleges, public or private agencies or organizations, with candidates between the ages of 11 and 27 years.

To find a site near you contact Division of Student Services, Education Outreach Branch, Division of Postsecondary Education, U.S. Department of Education, 600 Independence Ave., SW, Washington, DC 20202; 202-708-4804; {www.ed.gov/offices/OPE/HEP}.

Free Help In Getting A College Degree

Upward Bound helps disadvantaged high school students prepare for college entrance by helping them improve pre-college performance, locating financial aid and other services, including preparation for entrance exams. It also provides these services for students from families where neither parent holds a college degree and for first-generation military veterans.

Program services include instruction in reading, writing and study skills, academic, financial and personal counseling, tutoring, assistance in completing college entrance and financial aid applications, and more. Those eligible must have completed the 8th grade and be between the ages of 13 and 19 and demonstrate a need for support.

To learn more or to locate an Upward Bound program near you contact Division of Student Services, Division of Postsecondary Education, U.S. Department of Education, 600 Independence Ave., SW, Room 5065, Washington, DC 20202; 202-708-4804; {www.trioprograms.org}.

Free Training For Parents To Make Them Better At Doing Homework

We all want to be better parents, and the U.S. Department of Education wants that too. It gives money to hundreds of programs across the country that shows parents how to become more involved in their children's education. The program is called Even Start, and it focuses on parents of children up to seven years old.

Even Start is a family literacy program that integrates early childhood education and adult literacy training. It provides adult basic education, including helping parents learn to read or teach English as a second language. It also integrates parenting education with early childhood education. For more information or to find a site near you contact Even Start, U.S. Department of Education, 600 Independence Ave., SW, Room 4400, Washington, DC 20202; 202-260-0958; {www.ed.gov/offices/OESE/CEP}.

Free Job Training And Education For Kids And High School Dropouts

Are you or someone you love a high school drop out? Need some help sticking with a program? Job Corps may be for you. This is the nation's largest residential education and training program for disadvantaged youth. There are 111 centers in 46 states, the District of Columbia and Puerto Rico. It is a full-time year-round residential program that offers a comprehensive array of training, education and supportive services, including supervised dormitory housing, meals, medical care, and counseling. The job training covers a variety of occupational trades and more.

To learn about Job Corps, contact Office of Job Corps, U.S. Department of Labor, 200 Constitution Ave., NW, Room N4510, Washington, DC 20210; 202-219-8550, 800-733-JOBS; {www.jobcorps.org}.

State Job Corps Listings

Alabama
Montgomery Job Corps
1145 AirBase Blvd.
Montgomery, AL 36109
334-262-8883
Fax: 334-265-2339

Gadsden Job Corps
Region: IV
P.O. Box 286
Gadsden, AL 35902
205-547-6222
Fax: 205-547-9040
Special Features: Vocational offerings are being taught by Gadsden State Community College
Job Training: Advanced Word Processing, Secretary, Home Health Aide, Carpentry, Auto Repair Technician, Electrician

Alaska
Alaska Job Corps Center
Region X
750 Cope Industrial Way
Palmer, AK 99645
907-746-8800
Fax: 907-746-8810

Job Training: Carpentry, Building and Apartment Maintenance, Heavy Equipment Operator, Food Service, Painter, Health Occupations, Clerical

Arizona
Fred G. Acosta Job Corps
Region: IX
902 South Campbell Ave.
Tucson, AZ 85719
520-792-3015
Fax: 520-628-1552

Special Feature: ESL for Hispanic and Asian students
Job Training: Clerical, Sales Cl Ret Tr, Auto Repair Technician, Electronics Assembler, Auto Body Repair, Electrician, Plumber, Building and Apartment Maintenance

Phoenix Job Corps
Region: IX
518 South Third St.
Phoenix, AZ 85004
602-254-5921
Fax: 602-340-1965
Special Features: ESL for Hispanic, Asian and Eastern European students

Job Training: Off-center Programs, Clerical, Sales Person, Nurses Aide, Electronics Assembler, Painter, Plasterer, Cement Mason, Carpenter, Bricklayer, Building and Apartment Maintenance

Arkansas

Cass Civilian Conservation
Region: VI
USDA, Forest Service
HCR 63, Box 219
Ozark, AR 72949
501-667-3686
Fax: 501-667-3689
Job Training: Food Service, Welder, Building and Apartment Maintenance, Cement Mason, Operating Engineer, Carpenter, Bricklayer, Painter

Little Rock Job Corps
Region: VI
2020 Vance St.
Little Rock, AR 72206
501-376-4600
Fax: 501-376-6152
Special Feature: Handicapped accessible
Job Training: Clerical, Food Service, Nurses Aide, Building and Apartment Maintenance, Plumber

Ouachita Civilian Conservation
Region: VI
USDA
Forest Service
570 Job Corps Rd.
Royal, AR 71068
501-767-2707
Fax: 501-767-2768
Job Training: Welder, Building and Apartment Maintenance, Painter, Plasterer, Cement Mason, Carpenter, Bricklayer

California

Inland Empire Job Corps
Region: IX
3173 Kerry St.
San Bernardino, CA 92405
909-887-6305
Fax: 909-887-8635
Special Feature: ESL for Asian students
Job Training: Clerical, Bookkeeper, Building and Apartment Maintenance, Carpenter, Tilesetter, Sales Cl Ret Tr, Food Service, Machinist, Surveyor Assist I, Landscaping, Welder, Off-center Programs

Long Beach Job Corps
1903 Santa Fe Ave.
Long Beach, CA 90810
562-983-6304
Fax: 562-983-6393

Los Angeles Job Corps
Region: IX
1106 South Broadway
Los Angeles, CA 90015
213-748-0135
Fax: 213-746-4549
Special Feature: ESL for Hispanic, Asian and Ethiopian students
Job Training: Nurse Licensed Practical, Clerical, Food Service, Offset Duplicating Machine Operator, Electronics Tech, Computer Programmer, Radiology Cl Technician, Accounting Clerk, Ward Clerk, Teacher Aide, Machinist, Welder, Auto Repair Tech, Data Entry, Building and Apartment Maintenance

Sacramento Job Corps
Region: IX
3100 Meadowview Rd.
Sacramento, CA 95832
916-393-2880
Fax: 916-424-2872
Special Features: Handicapped accessible, ESL for Hispanic and Asian students
Job Training: Clerical, Building and Apartment Maintenance, Sales Cl Ret Tr, Food Service, Security Guard, Painter, Plasterer, Cement Mason, Surveyor Assist I, Landscaping, Operating Engineer, Carpenter

San Diego Job Corps
Region: IX
1325 Iris Ave.
Imperial Beach, CA 92154
619-429-8500
Fax: 619-429-3909
Special Features: ESL for Hispanic, Asian and Ethiopian students, child care for non-residential students
Job Training: Clerical, Bookkeeper, Sales Cl Ret Tr, Food Service, Nurses Aide, Grounds Keeper, Auto Repair Technician, Electronics Assembler, Welder, Painter, Plasterer, Cement Mason, Carpenter, Bricklayer, Tilesetter, Solar Installer, Nursery School Attendant

San Jose Job Corps
Region: IX
3485 E. Hills Dr.
San Jose, CA 95127
408-937-3200
Fax: 408-254-5663

Special Features: ESL for Hispanic, Asian and Ethiopian students, child care for non-residential students
Job Training: Building and Apartment Maintenance, Food Service, Electronics Technician, Drafter Assist, Computer Programmer, Off-center Programs, Clerical, Teller, Computer Operator, Accounting Clerk Landscape Gardener, Machinist, Auto Repair Technician, Offset Duplicating Machine Operator, Electronics Tester, Welder, Electrician, Carpenter, Dental Assist, Nursing Assist, Clerical

Treasure Island Job Corps
Region: IX
National Maritime Union
Job Corps Training
Bldg. 363 Treasure Island
San Francisco, CA 94130
415-362-4436
415-362-4458
Fax: 415-395-4219
Job Training: Deckhand, Advanced Food Service

Colorado
Collbran Civilian Conservation
Region: VIII
USDI, Bureau of Reclamation
Route 1, 5760
Highway 33
Collbran, CO 81624
303-487-3576
Fax: 303-487-3823
Job Training: Clerical, Food Service, Welder, Painter, Dental Asst, Carpentry, Cement Mason

Connecticut
Connecticut Job Corps Center
455 Wintergreen Ave.
New Haven, CT 06515
203-397-3775
Fax: 203-392-0299

District of Columbia
Potomac Job Corps
Region: III
No. 1 DC Village Lane, SW
Washington, DC 20032
202-574-5000
Fax: 202-563-7069
Special Feature: Childcare for non-residential students
Job Training: Clerical, Data Entry, Bookkeeper, Nurses Aide, Security Guard, Landscape Gardener,

Electrician, Painter, Plasterer, Cement Mason, Carpenter, Bricklayer, Plumber, Train Clerk

Florida
Gainesville Job Corps
Region: IV
5301 NE 40th Terrace
Gainesville, FL 32609
352-377-2555
Fax: 352-374-8257
Special Features: Handicapped accessible, ESL for Hispanic students, alternative learning program, National Honor Society.
Job Training: Clerical, Cashier Checker, Food Service, Nurses Aide, Auto Repair Technician, Electronics Assembler, Building and Apartment Maintenance, Auto Body Repair, Painter, Carpenter, Tilesetter, Plasterer

Jacksonville Job Corps
Region: IV
205 West Third St.
Jacksonville, FL 32206
904-353-5904
Fax: 904-359-4747
Job Training: Clerical, Secretary, Terminal Operator, Cosmetologist, Nursery School Attendant, Food Service, Auto Body Repair, Auto Repair Technician, Small Engine Mechanic, AC Refrigerator Mechanic, Machinist, Offset Duplicating Machine Operator, Welder, Electronics Assembler Diesel Mechanic, Medical Assist, Nurse Licensed Practical, Surgical Technician, Home Health Aide, Cement Mason, Carpenter, Bricklayer, Electrician, Plumber, Pipefitter Marine

Miami Job Corps
Region: IV
3050 NW 183rd St.
Miami, FL 33055
305-626-7800
Fax: 305-626-7857
Special Features: ESL for Hispanic and Creole students, National Honor Society
Job Training: Clerical, Data Entry, Food Service, Accounting Clerk, Hotel Clerk, Sales Cl Ret Tr, Building and Apartment Maintenance, Welder

Georgia
Atlanta Job Corps Center
Region: IV
239 West Lake Ave., NW
Atlanta, GA 30314
404-794-9512

Fax: 404-794-8426
Special Features: ESL for Amerasians, off-center
college programs
Job Training:, Clerical, Center Food Service, Nurses
Aide, Building and Apartment Maintenance, Data
Entry, Off-center programs

Brunswick Job Corps
Region: IV
4401 Blynco Parkway
Brunswick, GA 31520
912-264-8843
Fax: 912-267-7192
Job Training: Clerical, Food Service, Welder, Auto
Body Repair, Nurses Aide, Horticulture Wkr I,
Electrician, Painter, Carpenter, Plumber, Building
and Apartment Maintenance

Turner Job Corps
Region: IV
2000 Schilling Ave.
Albany, GA 31708-7501
912-883-8500
Fax: 912-434-0383
Special Feature: BSA Explorer Post
Job Training: Clerical, Sales Cl Ret Tr, Food Service,
Nurses Aide, Horticulture Wkr I, Auto Repair
Technician, Offset Duplicating Machine Operator,
Welder, Electrician, Painter, Carpenter, Bricklayer,
Building and Apartment Maintenance, Cement
Mason, Plasterer, Brick Masonry, Carpentry,
Painting, Cement Masonry, Computer Specialist,
Construction Estimator

Hawaii
Hawaii Job Corps
41-467 Hihimanu St.
Waimanalo, HI 96795
808-259-6001
Fax: 808-259-7907

Idaho
Centennial Job Corps
3201 Ridgecrest Dr.
Nampa, ID 83687
208-442-4500
Fax: 208-442-4506

Illinois
Joliet Job Corps
Region: V
1101 Mills Rd.
Joliet, IL 60433
815-727-7677

Fax: 815-723-7052
Job Training: Clerical, Food Service, Health
Occupations, Auto Repair Technician, Dispensing
Optician, Painter, Building and Apartment
Maintenance, Tilesetter

Golconda Civilian Conservation
Region: V
USDA, Forest Service
Route 1
Box 104A
Golconda, IL 62938
618-285-6601
Fax: 618-285-3121
Job Training: Building and Apartment Maintenance,
Food Service, Welder, Painter, Carpenter, Bricklayer,
Clerical, Electrician

Chicago Job Corps
3348 S. Kedzi
Chicago, IL 60623
773-847-9820
Fax: 773-847-9823

Indiana
Atterbury Job Corps Center
Region: V
P.O. Box 187
Edinburg, IN 46124
812-526-5581
Fax: 812-525-9551
Special Feature: ESL for Hispanic and Asian students
Job Training:, Clerical, Food Service, Health
Occupations, Auto Repair Technician, Building and
Apartment Maintenance, Welder, Plasterer, Cement
Mason, Carpenter, Bricklayer, Painter, Glazier, Retail
Sales, Heavy Equipment Operator, Sign Painter,
Heavy Equipment Mechanic

Independence JCC
Region: V
17 West Washington St.
Indianapolis, IN 46204
317-684-2555
Fax: 317-231-2375
Job Training: Computer Service Technician, Medical
Records Transcriptionist, Aviation, Clerical

Iowa
Denison Job Corps
Region: VII
Highway 30 East
P.O. Box 608
Denison, IA 51442

712-263-4192
Fax: 712-263-6910
Job Training: Clerical, Security Guard, Food Service, Nurses Aide, Building and Apartment Maintenance, Welder, Painter, Carpenter, Bricklayer, Nurse Licensed Practical, Plumber, Rental Equipment, Electrician

Kansas
Flint Hills Job Corps
Region: VII
P.O. Box 747
Manhattan, KS 66502-0007
785-537-7222
Fax: 785-537-9517
Job Training: Clerical, Food Service, Health Occupations, Plumber, Building and Apartment Maintenance, Carpenter, Cement Mason

Kentucky
Carl D. Perkins Job Corps
Region: IV
Box G-1
Goble Roberts Rd.
Prestonsburg, KY 41653
606-886-1037
Fax: 606-886-6048
Job Training: Food Service, Electrician, Carpenter, Bricklayer, Building and Apartment Maintenance, Health Occupations, Retail Sales

Earl C. Clements Job Corps
Region: IV
2302 US Highway 60 East
Morganfield, KY 42437
502-389-2419
Fax: 502-389-1134
Special Feature: ESL for Hispanic and Asian students
Job Training: Auto Body Repair, Bricklayer, Building and Apartment Maintenance, Carpenter, Secretary, Electrician, Food Service, Home Health Aide, Landscape Technician, Offset Duplicating Machine Operator, Computer Service Technician, Telephone Station Installer, Painter, Plumber, Welder, Auto Repair Technician, Heavy Equipment Operator, Diesel Mechanic, Auto Parts Clerk

Great Onyx Civilian Conservation
Region: IV
USDA, National Park Service
Mammoth Cave National Park
3115 Ollie Ridge Rd.
Mammoth Cave, KY 42259
502-286-4514

Fax: 502-286-8824
Job Training: Clerical, Cement Mason, Food Service, Auto Repair Technician, Welder, Painter, Carpenter, Bricklayer, Building and Apartment Maintenance

Frenchburg Civilian Conservation
Region: IV
USDA
Forest Service
Box 935
Mariba, KY 40345
606-768-2111
Fax: 606-768-3080
Job Training: Clerical, Food Service, Auto Repair Technician, Painter, Cement Mason, Carpenter, Bricklayer

Pine Knot Civilian Conservation
Region: IV
USDA, Forest Service
Pine Knot, KY 42635
606-354-2176
Fax: 606-354-2170
Job Training: Food Service, Auto Repair Technician, Welder, Painter, Cement Mason, Carpenter, Bricklayer

Whitney Young Job Corps
Region: IV
P.O. Box 307
Simpsonville, KY 40067
502-722-8862
Fax: 502-722-8719
Special Feature: National Honor Society
Job Training: Secretary, Food Service, Home Health Aide, Welder, Building and Apartment Maintenance, Carpenter, Bricklayer

Louisiana
New Orleans Job Corps
Region: VI
3801 Hollygrove St.
New Orleans, LA 70118
504-486-0641
Fax: 504-486-0823
Special Feature: National Honor Society
Job Training: Secretary, Hotel Clerk, Sales Cl Ret Tr, Food Service, Home Health Aide, Building and Apartment Maintenance, Auto Repair Technician, Welder, Carpenter, Cosmetology

Shreveport Job Corps
Region: VI
2815 Lillian St.

Shreveport, LA 71109
318-227-9331
Fax: 318-222-0768
Job Training: Clerical, Food Service, Nurses Aide, Security Guard, Building and Apartment Maintenance, Welder, Painter, Cement Mason, Carpenter, Off-center Programs

Maine
Penobscot Job Corps
Region: I
1375 Union St.
P.O. Box 8148
Bangor, ME 04401
207-990-3000
Fax: 207-942-9829
Special Feature: Handicapped accessible
Job Training: Secretary, Clerical, Bookkeeper, Food Service, Nurses Aide, Welder, Building and Apartment Maintenance, Wastewater Treatment

Loring Job Corps
RR #1, Box 1727
Limestone, ME 04750
207-328-4212
Fax: 207-328-4219

Maryland
Woodstock Job Crops
Region: III
10900 Old Court Rd.
Randallstown, MD 21133
410-461-1100
Fax: 410-461-5794
Job Training: Clerical, Bookkeeper, Food Service, Nurses Aide, Welder, Plasterer, Cement Mason, Carpenter, Landscape Gardener, Electrician, Painter, Bricklayer, Cosmetology, Retail Sales, Building and Apartment Maintenance

Woodland Job Corps
Region: III
3300 Fort Meade Rd.
Laurel, MD 20724
301-725-7900
Fax: 301-497-8978
Special Features: Moderate hearing and sight impaired accessible. ESL classes
Job Training: Clerical, Data Entry, Bookkeeper, Food Service, Nurses Aide, Plasterer, Painter, Carpenter, Building and Apartment Maintenance, Cement Mason

Massachusetts
Grafton Job Corps
Region: I
P.O. Box 575
Route 30
North Grafton, MA 01536
508-839-6904
Fax: 508-839-9781
Special Feature: Solo Parent Program in conjunction with Rhode Island Dept. of Health and Human Services
Job Training: Clerical, Food Service, Nurses Aide, Painter, Data Entry, Teacher Aide, Janitor I (Building Service), Cement Mason, Landscape Gardener, Plumber, Electrician, Building and Apartment Maintenance

Westover Job Corps
Region: I
16 Johnson Dr.
Westover Air Force Base
Chicopee, MA 01022
413-593-5731
Fax: 413-593-5170
Special Features: ESL for Hispanic and Asian students, evening program with child care for non-residential students
Job Training: Clerical, Computer Operator, Food Service, Nurses Aide, Auto Repair Technician, Welder, Painter, Carpenter, Bricklayer, Hotel Clerk, Sign Painter, Plumber, Glazier, Electrician, Landscape Technician

Fort Devens Job Corps
192 MacArthur Ave.
Devens, MA 01432
978-784-2600
Fax: 978-784-2721

Michigan
Detroit Job Corps
Region: V
10401 East Jefferson Ave.
Detroit, MI 48214
313-821-7000
Fax: 313-821-7126
Job Training: Clerical, Health Occupations, Welder, Building and Apartment Maintenance, Computer Operator, Visual Arts

Grand Rapids Job Corps
Region: V
110 Hall St. SE
Grand Rapids, MI 49507

616-243-6877
Special Feature: BSA Explorer Post
Job Training: Clerical, Food Service, Health
Occupations, Auto Repair Technician, Welder,
Carpenter, Building and Apartment Maintenance,
Data Entry

Flint-Genessee Job Corps
2400 N. Saginaw St.
Flint, MI 48505
810-232-1131
Fax: 810-232-6835

Minnesota
Hubert H. Humphrey Job Corps
Region: V
1480 North Snelling Ave.
St. Paul, MN 55108
612-642-1133
Fax: 612-642-0123
Job Training: Clerical, Food Service, Health
Occupations, Data Entry, Welder, Building and
Apartment Maintenance, Auto Repair Technician,
Carpenter

Mississippi
Batesville Job Corps Center
Region: IV
Route 3, Box 2J
Batesville, MS 38606
601-563-4656
Fax: 601-563-1644
Job Training: Clerical, Retail Sales, Food Service,
Auto Repair Technician, Welder, Building and
Apartment Maintenance, Lithograph Painter, Health
Occupations

Gulfport Job Corps
Region: IV
3300 20th St.
Gulfport, MS 39501
601-864-9691
Fax: 601-865-0154
Job Training: Medical Assistant, Secretary, Home
Health Aide, Welder, Electrician, Carpenter,
Bricklayer, Plumber, Building and Apartment
Maintenance, Data Entry, Advanced Career Training

Mississippi Job Corps
Region: IV
P.O. Box 817
Crystal Springs, MS 39059
601-892-3348
Fax: 601-892-3719

Special Feature: National Honor Society
Job Training: Bricklayer, Plumber, Building and
Apartment Maintenance, Clerical, Health
Occupations, Landscape Technician, Retail Sales,
Food Service, Welder, Electrician, Carpenter,
Advanced Career Training

Missouri
Excelsior Springs Job Corp
Region: VII
701 St. Louis Ave.
Excelsior Springs, MO 64024
816-637-5501
Fax: 816-637-1806
Job Training: Food Service, Clerical, Nurses Aide,
Welder, Building and Apartment Maintenance,
Painter, Cement Mason, Carpenter, Data Entry, Word
Processing, Geriatric Nurse Assistant, Advanced
Career Training

Mingo Civilian Conservation
Region: VII
USDI
Fish and Wildlife Service
Route 2, Box 133
Puxico, MO 63960
573-222-3537
Fax: 573-222-3801
Special Feature: BSA Explorer Post
Job Training: Clerical, Food Service, Nurses Aide,
Auto Repair Technician, Welder, Painter, Operating
Engineer, Carpenter, Bricklayer, Building and
Apartment Maintenance

St. Louis Job Corps
Region: VII
4333 Goodfellow Blvd.
St. Louis, MO 63120
314-679-6200
Fax: 314-679-6244
Special Feature: Child care for non-residential
students
Job Training: Clerical, Data Entry, Food Service,
Nurses Aide, Security Guard, Welder, Painter, Train
Clerk, Plasterer, Cement Mason, Carpenter, Building
and Apartment Maintenance, Advanced Career
Training

Montana
Kicking Horse Job Corps
Region: VIII
2000 Mollman Pass Trail
Ronan, MT 59864
406-644-2217

Fax: 406-644-2343
Job Training: Clerical, Food Service, Forester Aide, Diesel Mechanic, Operating Engineer, Carpenter, Building and Apartment Maintenance, Dental Assist, Medical Assist

Trapper Creek Civilian Conservation
Region: VIII
USDA
Forest Service
5139 West Fork Rd.
Darby, MT 59829
406-821-3286
Fax: 406-821-4730 Ext.179
Job Training: Clerical, Food Service, Welder, Electrician, Painter, Cement Mason, Carpenter, Stock Clerk, Building and Apartment Maintenance

Anaconda Civilian Conservation Center
Region: VIII
USDA, Forest Service
1407 Foster Creek Rd.
Anaconda, MT 59711
406-563-3476
Fax: 406-563-8243
Job Training: Welder, Clerical, Painter, Carpenter, Operating Engineer, Construction Equipment Mechanic, Bricklayer, Food Service

Nebraska
Pine Ridge Civilian Conservation
Region: VII
USDA, Forest Service
Star Route #1, Box 39F
Chadron, NE 69337
308-432-3316
Fax: 308-432-4145
Job Training: Clerical, Food Service, Welder, Painter, Plasterer, Cement Mason, Carpenter, Bricklayer

Nevada
Sierra Nevada Job Corps
Region: IX
5005 Echo Ave.
Reno, NV 89506
702-972-5627
Fax: 702-972-6480
Special Features: ESL for Hispanic and Asian students
Job Training: Medical Assistant, Clerical, Food Service, Security Guard, Janitor I, Landscape Gardener, Auto Repair Technician, Welder, Painter, Plasterer, Cement Mason, Carpenter, Bricklayer,

Electrician, Plumber, Building and Apartment Maintenance, Advanced Career Training

New Jersey
Edison Job Corps
Region: II
500 Plainfield Ave.
Edison, NJ 08817-2587
732-985-4800
Fax: 732-985-8551
Special Features: ESL for Hispanic, Asian and East Indian students, 22-24 year of age pilot program, accessible for hearing and sight impaired students
Job Training: Carpenter, Bricklayer, Tilesetter, Building and Apartment Maintenance, Plumber, State of NJ Auto Repair Technician, Security, Electrician, Horticulture, Clerical, Health Occupations, Painter, Food Service, Bookkeeper

New Mexico
Roswell Job Corps
Region: VI
P.O. Box 5970
Roswell, NM 88201
505-347-5414
Fax: 505-347-2243
Special Feature: ESL for Hispanic students
Job Training: Secretary, Food Service, Home Health Aide, Building and Apartment Maintenance, Electrician, Painter, Carpenter, Plumber, Clerical, Health Occupations, Advanced Career Training

Albuquerque Job Corps Center
Region: VI
1500 Indian School Rd., NW
Albuquerque, NM 87104
505-842-6500
Fax: 505-247-3262
Special Feature: English as a Second Language for Hispanic students
Job Training: Clerical, Data Entry, Sales Clerk, Food Service, Nurses Aide, Security Guard, Welder, Appliance Repair, Electrician, Carpenter, Plumber, Building and Apartment Maintenance, Security Guard, Welder, Cosmetology

New York
South Bronx Job Corps
Region: II
1771 Andrews Ave.
Bronx, NY 10453-6803
718-731-7700
Fax: 718-731-3543

Special Features: ESL for Hispanic students, day care for non-residential students
Job Training: Clerical, Bookkeeper, Ward Clerk, Food Service, Carpenter, Plumber, Building and Apartment Maintenance, Nurses Aide

Cassadaga Job Corps
Region: II
Glascow Rd.
Cassadaga, NY 14718
716-595-8760
Fax: 716-595-3963
Job Training: Interior Design, Clerical, Food Service, Painter, Carpenter, Plumber, Building and Apartment Maintenance, Off-center Programs, Nurses Aide

Delaware Valley Job Corps
Region: II
P.O. Box 325
Callicoon, NY 12723-4762
914-887-5400
Fax: 914-887-4762
Special Feature: ESL for Hispanic students
Job Training: Clerical, Food Service, Auto Repair Technician, Electronics Assembler, Auto Body Repair, Electrician, Painter, Hotel Clerk, Health Occupations, Building and Apartment Maintenance, Retail Sales, Security Guard

Glenmont Job Corps
Region: II
P.O. Box 993
Route 144
Glenmont, NY 12077-0993
518-767-9371
Fax: 518-767-2106
Job Training: EKG Technician, Medical Assistant, Clerical, Food Service, Building and Apartment Maintenance, Nurses Aide, Auto Repair Technician, Auto Body Repair, Data Entry, Cosmetologist

Iroquois Civilian Conservation
Region: II
USDI, National Park Service
11780 Tibbits Rd.
Medina, NY 14102
716-798-7000
Fax: 716-798-7046
Special Feature: National Honor Society
Job Training: Clerical, Welder, Electrician, Painter, Plasterer, Carpenter, Bricklayer

Oneonta Job Corps
Region: II
Box 51A, Rd. No. 4

Oneonta, NY 13820-9325
607-433-2111
Fax: 607-433-1629
Special Feature: Solo Parent dorm and Day Care center for mothers and 30 children
Job Training: Clerical, Food Service, Nurses Aide, Auto Repair Technician, Auto Body Repair, Welder, Electrician, Plumber, Tile Setter, Nursery School Attendant, Hotel Clerk

North Carolina
Oconaluftee Civilian Conservation
Region: IV
USDI, National Park Service
200 Park Circle
Cherokee, NC 28719
828-497-5411
Fax: 828-497-4417
Job Training: Plasterer, Cement Mason, Carpenter, Bricklayer, Food Service, Auto Repair Technician, Welder, Painter, Building and Apartment Maintenance

Kittrell Job Corps
Region: IV
Kittrell College
P.O. Box 278
Kittrell, NC 27544
252-438-6161
Fax: 252-492-9630
Job Training: Clerical, Sales Cl Ret Tr, Food Service, Nurses Aide, Painter, Carpenter, Bricklayer, Building and Apartment Maintenance

Schenck Civilian Conservation
Region: IV
USDA, Forest Service
98 Schenck Dr.
Pisgah Forest, NC 28768
828-877-3291
Fax: 828-877-3028
Job Training: Food Service, Auto Repair Technician, Welder, Painter, Carpenter, Bricklayer, Building and Apartment Maintenance, Forester Aide, Landscape Technician

Lyndon Johnson Civilian Conservation
Region: IV
466 Job Corps Dr.
Franklin, NC 28734
828-524-4446
Fax: 828-369-7338

Job Training: Food Service, Welder, Building and Apartment Maintenance, Cement Mason, Carpenter, Bricklayer, Clerical, Painter

North Dakota
Burdick Job Corps Center
Region: VIII
1500 University Ave., W
Minot, ND 58701
701-838-9976
Fax: 701-838-9979
Job Training: Auto and Farm Machinery Parts, Auto and Farm Equipment Mechanic, Food Service, Clerical, Building and Apartment Maintenance, Health Occupations, Carpenter

Ohio
Cincinnati Job Corps
Region: V
1409 Western Ave.
Cincinnati, OH 45214
513-651-2000
Fax: 513-651-2004
Job Training: Clerical, Food Service, Building and Apartment Maintenance, Auto Repair Technician, Welder, Carpenter

Cleveland Job Corps
Region: V
10660 Carnegie Ave.
Cleveland, OH 44106
216-795-8700
Fax: 216-795-1109
Job Training: Clerical, Retail Sales, Data Entry, Operator, Health Occupations, Data Entry, Building and Apartment Maintenance

Dayton Job Corps
Region: V
3849 Germantown Pike
Dayton, OH 45418
937-268-6571
Fax: 937-268-5339
Special Feature: National Honor Society
Job Training: Clerical, Hotel Clerk, Food Service, Health Occupations, Painter, Electronics Assembler, Carpenter, Building and Apartment Maintenance

Oklahoma
Guthrie Job Corps
Region: VI
P.O. Box 978
600 Academy Rd.
Guthrie, OK 73044-0978
405-282-9930

Fax: 405-282-4977
Job Training: Drafter Clerical, Food Service, Nurses Aide, Security Guard, Offset Duplicating Machine Operator, Welder, Electrician, Floor Layer, Painter, Carpenter, Plumber, Building and Apartment Maintenance, Word Processing, Physical Therapy, EKG Technician, Medical Lab Assistant, Respiratory Therapy, Phlebotomist, Nurse Licensed Practical

Talking Leaves Job Corps
Region: VI
P.O. Box 948
Tahlequah, OK 74465
918-456-9959
Fax: 918-456-3508
Special Feature: Child care for non-residential students
Job Training: Clerical, Food Service, Auto Body Repair, Building and Apartment Maintenance, Health Occupations, Cosmetology, Front End Mechanic, Auto Repair Technician, Welder, Electrician, Carpenter, Diesel Mechanic

Treasure Lake Civilian Conservation
Region: VI
USDI
Fish and Wildlife Service
Route 1, Box 30
Indiahoma, OK 73552
405-246-3203
Fax: 405-246-8222
Special Feature: Child care for non-residential students
Job Training: Food Service, Health Occupations, AC Refrigeration Mechanic, Electrician, Painter, Plasterer, Cement Mason, Carpenter, Bricklayer

Tulsa Job Corps
Region: VI
1133 N. Lewis Ave.
Tulsa, OK 74110
918-585-9111
Fax: 918-592-2430
Special Features: Vision and hearing impaired accessible, BSA Explorer Post, child care for non-residential students
Job Training: Clerical, Nurses Aide, Security Guard, Food Service, Cosmetologist, Electronics Assembler, Carpenter, Building and Apartment Maintenance, Painter, Barber

Oregon
Springdale Site
Region: X

31224 E. Crown Point Hwy.
Troutdale, OR 97060
503-695-2245
Fax: 503-695-2254
Special Feature: Child care
Job Training: Clerical, Food Service, Nurses Aide,
Auto Body Repair, Building and Apartment
Maintenance, Sign Painting

Timber Lake Civilian Conservation
Region: X
USDA, Forest Service
59868 E. Highway 224
Estacada, OR 97023
503-834-2291
Fax: 503-834-2333
Job Training: Food Service, Forester Aide, Welder,
Painter, Plasterer, Carpenter, Building and Apartment
Maintenance

Tongue Point Job Corps
Region: X
Astoria, OR 97103
503-325-2131
Fax: 503-325-5375
Job Training: Building and Apartment Maintenance,
Landscape Gardener, Food Service, Electronics
Assembler, Welder, Painter, Plasterer, Cement
Mason, Carpenter, Glazier, Seamanship, Electrician,
Lithographic Printer, Nursing Assist, Dental Assist,
Accounting Clerk, Clerical

Angell Civilian Conservation Center
Region: X
USDA
Forest Service
335 NE Blogett Rd.
Yachats, Oregon 97498
503-547-3137
Fax: 503-547-4236
Special Features: English as a Second Language for
Asian, Micronesian, and Hispanic
Job Training: Clerical, Food Service Center, Forester
Aide, Auto Repair Technician, Welder, Painter,
Carpenter, Bricklayer

Wolf Creek Civilian Conservation
Region: X
USDA
Forest Service
2010 Opportunity Lane
Glide, OR 97443-9733
541-496-3507
Fax: 541-496-0015

Job Training: Food Service, Forester Aide, Welder,
Painter, Plasterer, Cement Mason, Carpenter,
Building and Apartment Maintenance, Clerical

Pivot Job Corps
2508 NE Everett
Portland, OR 97232
503-916-6170
Fax: 503-916-6168

Pennsylvania
Keystone Job Corps
Region: III
#1 Foothills Dr.
P.O. Box 37
Drums, PA 18222
570-788-1164
Fax: 570-788-1119
Special Features: ESL for Asian, Ethiopian and
Hispanic students, off-center training at Tobyhanna
Army Depot
Job Training: Clerical, Food Service, Nurses Aide,
Floor Layer, Carpentry, Electrician, Building and
Apartment Maintenance, Plumbing, Painting,
Bricklayer, Cement Masonry, Plasterer

Philadelphia Job Corps
Region: III
4601 West Market St.
Philadelphia, PA 19139
215-471-9689
Fax: 215-747-8552
Job Training: Clerical, Food Service, Nurses Aide,
Building and Apartment Maintenance

Pittsburgh Job Corps
Region: III
Highland Dr.
Pittsburgh, PA 15206
412-441-8700
Fax: 412-441-1586
Special Feature: Child care for non-residential
students
Job Training: Electronics, Drafter Assist, Surveyor
Assist I, Nurse General Duty, Radiological
Technician, Med-Lab Assist, Respiratory Therapy,
Medical Assistant, Program Aide, Legal Secretary,
Secretary, Stenographer, Computer Operator,
Medical Records Clerk, Teacher Aide, Food Service,
Nursery School Attendant, Hotel Clerk, Auto Body
Repair, Diesel Mechanic, Building and Apartment
Maintenance, Independent Truck Operator, Clerical,
Nurses Aide

Red Rock Job Corps
Region: III
P.O. Box 218
Lopez, PA 18628
570-477-2221
Fax: 570-477-3046
Job Training: Clerical, Bookkeeper, Nurses Aide, Landscape Gardener, Auto Repair Technician, Carpenter, Bricklayer, Plumber, Electrician, Painter, Building and Apartment Maintenance, Cosmetologist

Puerto Rico
Ramey Job Corps
Region: II
P.O. Box 643
Ramey, PR 00604-0463
787-890-2030/2505
Fax: 787-890-4749
Job Training: Nurse Licensed Practical, Clerical, Food Service, Front End Mechanic, Electrician, Cement Mason, Carpenter, Plumber, Home Health Aide

Arecibo Job Corps Center
Region: II
P.O. Box 544
Garrochales, PR 00652-0540
787-881-2300
Fax: 787-881-7243
Job Training: Nurse Licensed Practical, Clerical, Home Health Aide, Auto Body Repair, Electrician, Building and Apartment Maintenance

Barranquitas Job Corps Center
Region: II
P.O. Box 68
Barranquitas, PR 00794
787-857-5200
Fax: 787-857-2262
Job Training: Nurse Licensed Practical, Clerical, Furniture Upholsterer, Electrician, Cement Mason, Building and Apartment Maintenance

South Carolina
Bamberg Job Corps Center
Region: IV
P.O. Box 967
200 South Carlisle St.
Bamberg, SC 29003
803-245-5101
Fax: 803-245-5915
Job Training: Clerical, Food Service, Nurses Aide, Auto Body Repair, Welder, Cement Mason,

Carpenter, Plumber, Building and Apartment Maintenance, Retail Sales

South Dakota
Boxelder Civilian Conservation
Region: VIII
USDA, Forest Service
P.O. Box 110
Nemo, SD 57759
605-348-3636
Fax: 605-348-3636
Job Training: Clerical, Food Service, Auto Repair Technician, Welder, Carpenter, Bricklayer, Building and Apartment Maintenance, Painter

Tennessee
Memphis Job Corps
1555 McAlister Dr.
Memphis, TN 38116
901-396-2800
Fax: 901-396-2892

Jacobs Creek Civilian Conservation
Region: IV
USDA, Forest Service
Drawer W-Route No. 1
Bristol, TN 37620
423-878-4021
Fax: 423-878-7034
Job Training: Food Service, Construction Equipment Mechanic, Welder, Painter, Cement Mason, Operating Engineer, Carpenter, Bricklayer

Texas
David L. Carrasco Job Corps
Region: VI
11155 Gateway West
El Paso, TX 79935
915-594-0022
Fax: 915-591-0166
Special Feature: ESL for Hispanic students
Job Training: Clerical, Cosmetology, Food Service, Health Occupations, Auto Repair Technician, Electronics Tester, Welder, Building and Apartment Maintenance

Gary Job Corps
Region: VI
P.O. Box 967
San Marcos, TX 78667-0987
512-396-6652
Fax: 512-396-6666
Special Feature: ESL for Asian, Ethiopian and Hispanic students

Job Training: Clerical, Accounting Clerk, Construction Equipment Mechanic, Retail Sales, Building and Apartment Maintenance, Food Service, Meat Cutting, Auto Repair Technician, Auto Body Repair, Auto Parts Clerk, Carpentry, Electrician, Bricklayer, Cement Mason, Tile Setter, Painter, Heavy Equipment Operator, Machinist, Welder, Lithographic Printer, Material Handler, Health Occupations, Dental, Advanced Training, Automotive Diagnostic, Peripheral Equipment Operator, Environmental Control

Laredo Job Corps
Region: VI
P.O. Box 1819
101 Island St.
Laredo, TX 78044-1819
956-727-5147
Fax: 956-727-1937
Special Features: ESL for Hispanic students, Advance Vocational Training (AVT), horses on center
Job Training: Clerical, Bookkeeper, Food Service, Welder, Electrician, Carpenter

McKinney Job Corps
Region: VI
P.O. Box 750
McKinney, TX 75069-8003
972-542-7941
Fax: 972-542-8870
Job Training: Clerical, Food Service, Health Occupations, Lithographic Printing, Material Handler, Electrician, Painter, Plasterer, Cement Mason, Carpenter, Bricklayer, Plumber, Building and Apartment Maintenance, Security/Correctional Officer, Desktop Publishing, Bookkeeper, Data Entry, Word Processing

Utah
Clearfield Job Corps
Region: VIII
P.O. Box 160070
Clearfield, UT 84016
801-774-4000
Fax: 801-773-8906
Special Feature: ESL for Hispanic and Asian students
Job Training: Clerical, Welder, Building and Apartment Maintenance, Offset Duplicating Machine Operator, Auto Body Repair, Auto Repair Technician, Food Service, Nurses Aide, Machinist, Bookkeeper, Auto Parts Clerk, Auto Repair Technician, Diesel Mechanic, Auto Body Repair, Off-center Programs

Weber Basin Civilian Conservation
Region: VIII
USDI
Bureau of Reclamation
Rural Free Delivery (RFD) No. 6
Ogden, UT 84405
801-479-9806
Fax: 801-476-5985
Job Training: Clerical, Food Service, Welder, Painter, Carpenter, Bricklayer, Health Occupations, Building and Apartment Maintenance

Vermont
Northlands Job Corps
Region: I
100-A MacDonough Dr.
Vergennes, VT 05491
802-877-2925
Fax: 802-877-2699
Job Training: Clerical, Bookkeeper, Food Service, Nurses Aide, Auto Repair Technician, Auto Body Repair, Welder, Building and Apartment Maintenance

Virginia
Blue Ridge Job Corps Center
Region: III
245 West Main St.
P.O. Box 425
Marion, VA 24354
540-783-7221
Fax: 540-783-1751
Job Training: Medical Assist, Medical Secretary, Clerical, Bookkeeper, Ward Clerk, Accounting Clerk, Nurses Aide, Sales Cl Ret Tr, Food Service, Teacher Aide, Diesel Mechanic, Building and Apartment Maintenance, Welder, Machinist

Flatwoods Civilian Conservation
Region: III
USDA, Forest Service
Rt. 1 Box 2111
Coeburn, VA 24230
703-395-3384
Fax: 703-395-2043
Job Training: Welder, Painter, Plasterer, Cement Mason, Carpenter, Bricklayer, Plumber, Electrician

Old Dominion Job Corps
Region: III
P.O. Box 278
Monroe, VA 24574
804-929-4081
Fax: 804-929-3511

Job Training: Clerical, Bookkeeper, Sales Cl Ret Tr, Food Service, Nurses Aide, Auto Repair Technician, Electrician, Painter, Carpenter, Bricklayer, Plumber, Building and Apartment Maintenance, Landscape Gardener

Washington
Cascades Job Corps
Region: X
2267 Northern State Rd.
P.O. Box 819
Sedro Woolley, WA 98284
360-856-3400
Fax: 360-856-3419
Special Feature: Handicapped designated for hearing and sight impaired
Job Training: Dental Assist, Clerical, Food Service, Building and Apartment Maintenance, Landscape Technician, Cable TV Installer, Painter, Plasterer, Cement Mason, Carpenter, Nurses Aide

Columbia Basin Civilian Conservation
Region: X
USDI
Bureau of Reclamation
Building 2402
6739 24th St.
Moses Lake, WA 98837
509-762-5581
Fax: 509-762-9540
Job Training: Dental Assist, Building and Apartment Maintenance, Food Service, Painter, Plasterer, Cement Mason, Carpenter, Tilesetter, Welder, Nurses Aide

Curlew Civilian Conservation
Region: X
USDA, Forest Service
Star Route, Box 100
Wauconda, WA 98859
509-779-4611
Fax: 509-779-4328
Special Feature: High School Diploma Program
Job Training: Clerical, Food Service, Forester Aide, Auto Repair Technician, Construction Worker, Welder, Painter, Carpenter, Bricklayer, Building and Apartment Maintenance

Fort Simcoe Civilian Conservation
Region: X
USDI

Bureau of Reclamation
40 Abella Lane
White Swan, WA 98952
509-874-2244
Fax: 509-874-2342
Job Training: Food Service, Auto Repair Technician, Truck Driver, Auto Body Repair, Painter, Plasterer, Carpenter, Bricklayer, Heavy Equipment Operator, Heavy Equipment Mechanic, Clerical, Dental

West Virginia
Charleston Job Corps
Region: III
1000 Kennawa Dr.
Charleston, WV 25311
304-925-3200
Fax: 304-925-7127
Job Training: Clerical, Computer Operator, Food Service, Nurses Aide, Offset Duplicating Machine Operator, Drafter, Cosmetologist, Cashier Checker, Nurse Licensed Practical, Stenographer, Diesel Mechanic, Welder, Electrician, Auto Body Repair, Auto Repair Technician, Nursery School Attendant, Commercial Artist, Carpenter, Building and Apartment Maintenance

Harpers Ferry Civilian Conservation
Region: III
USDI
National Park Service
P.O. Box 237
Harpers Ferry, WV 25425
304-725-2011
Job Training: Painter, Plasterer, Cement Mason, Carpenter, Bricklayer, Building and Apartment Maintenance, Clerical

Wisconsin
Blackwell Civilian Conservation Center
Region: V
USDA
Forest Service
Route 1 Box 233A
Laona, WI 54541
715-674-2311
Fax: 715-674-4305
Special Feature: Handicapped accessible
Job Training: Food Service, Building and Apartment Maintenance, Electrician, Welder, Painter, Carpenter, Bricklayer, Clerical

STATE AND NATIONAL
JOB TRAINING PROGRAMS

Not only does the Federal Government offer job training programs, but state, national, and local organizations do so as well. Here is a listing to get you started.

To give you an idea of what is available, The Single Parent/Homemaker Project Services in Greensburg, IN and the Center for Displaced Homemakers in Shreveport, LA provide vocational education, job training, career counseling, job placement and life management training, as well as support groups for single parents. The Institute of Social and Economic Development in Iowa City, IA and the Grand Rapids Opportunities for Women in Grand Rapids, MI want to encourage self-sufficiency through the growth of a small business and will provide services to help you begin your endeavor. Hard Hatted Women in Cleveland, OH and Tradeswomen of Purpose in Philadelphia, PA allow women to learn the construction trades through various apprenticeship and training programs.

Don't forget to also contact your local One-Stop Career Center and your state Department of Labor office listed at the beginning of each state to learn more about job training programs near you.

National

The following is a list of national associations and agencies available to guide you in finding resources in your local area.

America's Learning eXchange

The American Association of Community Colleges has partnered with the U.S. Department of Labor to support learners, employers, and training suppliers. The vehicle is the web-based America's Learning eXchange. ALX can connect you with the training and education you need. It is intended to be a breakthrough resource for workers entering the job force, people interested in lifelong learning, and employers looking for enhanced performance. Their website is like a one-stop electronic marketplace for lifelong learning resources. The links there will lead you to tens of thousands of training offerings and providers— everything from continuing education courses to Internet-based training, from traditional classroom-based courses to CD-ROM and video instruction. Check out {www.alx.org/}.

Help For The Homeless

The International Union of Gospel Missions is made up of over 250 member organizations. They are located primarily in North America, with other member missions in South Africa, India, South America, and Australia. Many member organizations offer job training as a part of their mission though programs vary by location. Most of those holding Organizational Membership follow the traditional "rescue mission model," providing meals, housing, and spiritual help for the homeless. Many offer other innovative services aimed at the addicted, urban youth, the mentally ill, and other needy people in their communities.

To find a service provider near you, refer to the website below or contact International Union Of Gospel Missions, 1045 Swift Ave., Kansas City, MO 64116-4127; 816-471-8020; {www.iugm.org/missions.html}.

Training With Goodwill

Along with offering many services, Goodwill Industries is also one of the world's largest nonprofit providers of employment and training services for people with disabilities and other disadvantaging conditions. Their goal is to equip people with the skills they need to find and sustain competitive employment by overcoming any obstacles that may be preventing them from working.

Goodwill's job training and placement programs are designed to meet the needs of local communities so programs tend to vary by location. Typical services offered include vocational evaluation, work adjustment, career counseling, job placement and transitional employment opportunities. Workshops covering stress management, personal finance, responsible parenting and other "life skills " are also common. Examples of career-specific job training that may be offered in your area include careers in banking, customer service, health care, and adaptive technology among others.

There are 187 Goodwill organizations in the United States and Canada. To locate one near you, call 800-664-6577 or contact their headquarters at Goodwill Industries International, Inc., 9200 Rockville Pike, Bethesda, MD 20814; 301-530-6500; TTD: 301-530-9759; {www.goodwill.org/home.html}.

Learn Skills Online

Does your lifestyle or location prevent you from entering a conventional learning center? This one is a cyber university for women! Women's International Electronic University promotes the empowerment of women online by facilitating access to training in skills such as information technology, health promotion and living skills. They have no physical address, so visit their website to learn more at {www.wvu.edu/~womensu/}.

Economic Independence For Women

Women In Community Service (WICS) is dedicated to reducing the number of young women living in poverty by promoting self-reliance and economic independence. The organization actively addresses critical national issues surrounding employment, job training, welfare reform, poverty, and cultural diversity. Each year, WICS volunteers and staff help more than 150,000 low-income women and young adults by providing support services, mentoring and workforce preparation programs nationwide.

With service centers located throughout the country, contact the national office to locate one near you. Women In Community Service, 1900 N. Beauregard St., Suite 103, Alexandria, VA 22311; 703-671-0500; 800-442-9427; Fax: 703-671-4489; {www.wics.org/}; {Email: WICSNatl@aol.com}.

Considering a Non-traditional Career?

The Institute for Women in Trades, Technology & Science (IWITTS) is dedicated to integrating women into the full range of trades, technology and science careers in which they are underrepresented: from engineer to police officer, pilot, automotive technician, electrician and web master, to name just a very few. To accomplish this mission, IWITTS serves as a resource nationally to the education and job-training systems and employers.

Contact them at Institute for Women in Trades, Technology & Science (IWITTS), 3010 Wisconsin Ave. NW, Suite E-10, Washington, D.C. 20016; 202-686-7275, {www.serve.com/iwitts}; {Email: iwitts@aol.com}.

Christian Programs

Ursuline Companions in Mission is a Christian association of lay women and men who seek to make a difference in the lives of the poor through a variety of programs including job training. They have service delivery sites in Delaware, Illinois, Kentucky, Minnesota, Missouri, New Mexico, and Ohio. Programs vary from location to location.

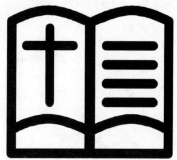

For more information, contact Ursuline Companions In Mission, Sr. Jane Quinlan, College of New Rochelle, College Center, Room 155, New Rochelle, NY 10805; 914-654-5270; Fax: 915-654-5290; {www.theursulines. org}; {Email: ursulinecomp@hotmail.com}.

The Old Reliable

The YWCA has long been committed to providing women and girls with the education, training, and support they need to provide for themselves and their families. The YWCA's spectrum of offerings in this area include basic lifeskills training, English courses, GED courses, adult education, welfare to work programs, structured training curricula, training for non-traditional employment, career counseling, entrepreneurial workshops, job clubs and more.

Local YWCAs tailor their programs and services to meet the needs of the women, families and employers in their local communities. To find the YWCA in your area contact: YWCA of the USA, Empire State Building, Suite 301, 350 Fifth Avenue, New York, NY 10118; 212-273-7800; Fax: 212-465-2281; {www.ywca.org/index.html}.

Networking For Hi-Tech Women

Webgrrls International provides a web-based forum for women in or interested in new media and technology to network, exchange job and business leads, form strategic alliances, mentor and teach, intern and learn skills needed to succeed in an increasingly technical workplace and world. They offer ongoing workshops focusing on enhancing business and communication such as refining negotiating skills. The original chapter was founded in New York City and many new branches continue to be added around the country. For more information, contact 212-642-8012; {www.webgrrls.com/ny}; {Email: nyc@webgrrls.com}.

Training On An International Level

The Centre for Development and Population Activities (CEDPA) is a women-focused non-profit international organization founded in 1975. CEDPA's mission is to empower women at all levels of society to be full partners in development. All CEDPA activities are designed to advance gender equity. Working with partner non-governmental organizations and networks in more than 37 countries, CEDPA designs, implements, monitors, and evaluates projects in family planning and reproductive health, family life education, women's participation in empowerment, youth services, and international advocacy for women and girls.

The Women in Management (WIM) leadership training workshop is CEDPA's flagship capacity-building initiative. During this five-week tuition-based workshop, WIM participants from around the world hone leadership and management skills with peers for a dynamic dialogue. This training program is designed for women working in government, non-governmental, and community-based organizations who design, manage, and evaluate gender-equitable development programs and women working in a wide range of professions who have demonstrated leadership potential in areas related to gender-equitable development. The goal of the Women in Management program is to enhance women's leadership capacity for managing strategic responses to health, economic, education, and other development challenges.

For more information, contact Workshops Coordinator, CEDPA, 1717 Massachusetts Avenue, NW, Suite 200, Washington, DC 20036; 202-667-1142; Fax: 202-332-4496; {www.cedpa.org/}; {Email: ketty@cedpa.org}.

Displaced Homemakers

Are you forced to go into the work world suddenly? Do you need help getting your job skills upgraded? Women Work! can help you. They have over 1400 sites across the country to help women from diverse backgrounds achieve economic self-sufficiency through job readiness, education, training and employment. Women Work! provides these services through a network of programs in every state. Women Work! also takes on the toughest women's employment issues and fights for them in Congress and in state legislatures.

For more information on Women Work! or to find a location near you contact Women Work!, 1625 K Street NW, Suite 300, Washington, DC 20006; 800-235-2732; 202-467-6346; Fax: 202-467-5366; {www.womenwork. org/}; {Email: womenwork@womenwork.org}.

Help for Southwestern Low-Income Young Women

Job Corps is a school to work program that gives low-income young women, ages 16-24, a chance at a fresh start and a promising future. At Job Corps, young women receive the educational, vocational and social skills training they need to compete in today's challenging job market. Since 1964, over 1.5 million youth have participated in the program and have found the independence they've been looking for. The training is free for the trainee and there is an exciting variety of training programs. Job Corps Centers are located in Arizona, California, Nevada, and Utah. Contact René E. Nutter, 582 Market St. Suite #719, San Francisco, CA 94104; 415-981-821; Fax: 415-981-8433; {http://proudofit.org/}; {Email: r9desi00@jcdc.jobcorps. org}.

Resources for Women Business Owners

The National Foundation for Women Business Owners (NFWBO) is a central source of information and statistics on women business owners and their businesses providing non-profit research, leadership development and entrepreneurial training. Their website has a large collection of related links. Contact National Foundation for Women Business Owners, 1100 Wayne Avenue, Suite 830, Silver Spring, MD 20910-5603; 301-495-4975; Fax: 301-495-4979; {www.nfwbo.org/index.htm}; {Email: NFWBO@worldnet.att.net}.

Grow Your Business With Expert Advice

The Women's Network for Entrepreneurial Training (WNET) links seasoned entrepreneurs with women whose businesses are ready to grow. In a year-long program, experienced women business owners provide technical business advice and training to women with lesser skills and experience. For more information please contact the local SBA District Office in your area. Go to the Small Business Administration's Home Page and click on the SBA Resources icon to find the office nearest you.{www.sbaonline.sba.gov/} .

Network With Other Businesswomen

The mission of the American BusinessWomen's Association is to bring together businesswomen of diverse occupations and to provide opportunities for them to help themselves and others grow personally and professionally through leadership, education, networking support and national recognition. ABWA believes education and training are key to helping women grow personally and professionally. The Association supports education by providing continuing education programs and products, which enhance members business skills.

Members receive discounts on a variety of products and services, including career-focused books and audiotapes, seminars by national seminar providers and computer application classes. For more information, contact American Business Women's Association, 9100 Ward Parkway, PO Box 8728, Kansas City, MO 64114-0728; 816-361-6621; Fax: 816-361-4991; {www.abwahq.org/}; {Email: abwa@abwahq.org}.

Train For Well Paid Work

Wider Opportunities for Women (WOW) has worked for more than 30 years both nationally and in its home community of Washington, DC to achieve economic independence and equality of opportunity for women and girls. WOW can help you learn to earn, with programs emphasizing literacy, technical and non-traditional skills, welfare-to-work transition, and career development. Since 1964, WOW has trained more than 10,000 women for well paid work. The location of their national office is WOW, 815 15th Street, NW, Suite 916, Washington, DC 20005; 202-638-3143; Fax: 202-638-4885; {www.w-o-w.org/ default.htm}; {Email: info@w-o-w.org}.

Network with Professional Women of Color

Professional Women of Color (PWC) is a nonprofit organization that provides workshops, seminars, group discussions as well as networking sessions to help women of color more effectively manage their personal and professional lives. There is a $50 annual Membership Fee to join PWC. Contact Professional Women of Color, PO Box 5196, New York, NY 10185; 212-714-7190; {Email: www.pwconline.org/}.

Entrepreneurial Training For Women of Color

If you would like to become more self-sufficient, check out the economic entrepreneurial centers run by the National Council of Negro Women (NCNW). For more information, contact National Council of Negro Women, Christine Toney, Executive Director, Lucenia Dunn, Director of Programs, 633 Pennsylvania Avenue, NW, Washington, DC 20004; 202-737-0120; Fax: 202-737-0476; {www.ncnw.com}; {Email: ncnwbpdc@erols.com}.

Online Training For Women Business Owners

You can receive information, training, and opportunities for online networking to women business owners wherever you are at any time of the day. The Online Women's Business Center (OWBC) provides these services through an Internet site.

This "virtual" women's business center works in unison with, and as an extension of, more than 54 Women's Business Centers (WBC) throughout the United States that have contributed actively to its creation. The combined efforts of the WBCs and OWBO create unlimited possibilities for reaching women who want instant access to information, personal guidance and insight into business management skills, particularly if they do not have a WBC nearby or if their current employment prevents them from visiting a WBC during operating hours. OWBC was developed on behalf of the U. S. Small Business Administration's (SBA) Office of Women's Business Ownership (OWBO) and several corporate sponsors who joined forces in a unique public/private partnership.

For more information, contact Online Women's Business Center, Paula Aryanpur, Project Director, Bill J. Priest Institute for Economic Development, 1402 Corinth Street, Suite 209, Dallas, TX 75215-2111; 214-565-0447; Fax: 214-565-7883; {www.onlinewbc.org}; {Email: virtual@ onramp.net}.

Free Job Training and Part-Time Jobs For Those Age 55 And Over

The Senior Community Service Employment Program offers part-time training and employment opportunities for eligible low-income persons 55 years of age and older in a variety of public or private non-profit community service settings, such as senior centers, nutrition programs, social service agencies, libraries, environmental projects, and many others. The program provides seniors with income and the opportunity to learn new skills or improve the ones they already have. There are sites in every state that offer training and employment.

To learn about the site nearest you contact Division of Older Worker Program, Employment and Training Administration, U.S. Department of Labor, 200 Constitution Ave., NW, Room 4641, Washington, DC 20210; 202-219-5904; {www.wdsc.org/owprog/ index.html}.

States

The following is a state-by-state listing of resources and contacts providing services and programs to meet your needs.

Alabama

One-Stop Career Centers
A network of One-Stop Career Centers throughout the state offers a wide range of employment related services including job training. Services vary by location. To find a location near you, please refer to the website {www.adeca.state.al.us }. To learn more about the services they offer, contact your state coordinator. Mr. Mickey Hutto, One-Stop Coordinator Workforce Development Division, Alabama Department of Economic and Community Affairs, P.O. Box 5690, 401 Adams Avenue, Montgomery, AL 36103-5690; 334-242-5300; Fax: 334-242-5855.

Job Service Offices
A system of Employment Service/Job Service offices is located within every state with the goal of assisting millions of job seekers and employers. While services may vary from location to location, many provide job training, skills assessment and related services. With approximately 1,800 Employment Service/Job Service offices nationwide there is bound to be one near you. To learn more about the services offered in your area, contact your state administrator. Alice McKinney, Director, Department of Industrial Relations, 649 Monroe Street, Room 2813, Montgomery, AL 36130; 334-242-8003; Fax: 334-242-8012; {www.dir.state.al.us/es/default.htm).

Career Center
The Shoals Career Center, part of Alabama Career Center System is now open. The vision of the career center is to utilize all equipment and training resources to develop a well-trained, qualified, and diverse workforce for Alabama. The center strives to serve as the primary connection between employers and qualified workers. For more information, contact Shoals Career Center, Town Plaza Shopping Center, 500 South Montgomery Ave., Suite 102, Sheffield, AL 35660; 256-381-0611; Fax: 256-381-9972; {www.dir.state.al.us/es}; {Email: ccshoals@ADECA.state.al.us}.

Assistance For Your New or Existing Business
The Women's Business Assistance Center (WBAC) provides training seminars and one-on-one counseling for the south Alabama and northwest Florida area. It is located in the Center for Entrepreneurial Excellence, a former school campus that was purchased and renovated by the City of Mobile and Mobile County. It is now a business incubator and training center. Their physical address is Women's Business Assistance Center, Kathryn Cariglino, Director, 1301 Azalea Road, Suite 201A, Mobile, AL 36693 (Mailing Address: P.O. Box 6021, Mobile, AL 36660); 334-660-2725; 800-378-7461; Fax: 334-660-8854; {http://ceebic.org/~wbac}; {Email: wbac@ ceebic.org}.

Women Work!
Find yourself suddenly in need of employment? Get the training and support you need to make the transition into the workforce. Women Work! is a national membership organization dedicated to helping women from diverse backgrounds achieve economic self-sufficiency through job readiness, education, training and employment. Alabama Women Work!, Linda Waide, President, Northwest Shoals Community College, P.O. Box 2545, Muscle Shoals, AL 35662; 256-331-5321.

Welfare-to-Work Program
The Welfare-to-Work Program is an employment and training program for welfare recipients that have notable employment barriers. The goal of this program is to provide resources and support to the participants, generally those with poor education, low skills, and little job experience, to find and keep jobs. To find out more about the

program, contact Alabama Department of Economic and Community Affairs, Department of Workforce Development, 401 Adams Avenue, P.O. Box 5690, Montgomery, AL 36103; 334-242-5525; {www.adeca.state.al.us}.

Migrant and Seasonal Farm Worker Program

The Migrant and Seasonal Farm Worker Program was created to help farm workers and their dependents to find and keep work. Their services are provided for free and include job training , job search assistance, and other supportive assistance. Eligible participants are those with chronic seasonal unemployment and underemployment in the agricultural industry. For more information, contact Alabama Department of Economic and Community Affairs, Department of Workforce Development, 401 Adams Avenue, P.O. Box 5690, Montgomery, AL 36103; 334-242-5525; {www.adeca.state.al.us}.

Alabama Industrial Development Training

Alabama Industrial Development Training recruits and trains skilled workforce in order to attract new industries to the state as well as increase the income of the residents. They work with businesses to train their employees as well as individuals. The program includes a full range of customized technical training and assessment programs at no cost to the trainees. Job-specific pre-employment and on-the-job training programs are provided. For information, contact Development Office, 401 Adams Avenue, Suite 670, Montgomery, AL 36130-4106; 800-248-0033; {www.ado.state.al.us}; {Email: idinfo@www.ado.stat.al.us}

Alaska

One-Stop Career Centers

A network of One-Stop Career Centers throughout the state offers a wide range of employment related services including job training. Services vary by location. To find a location near you, please refer to the website {www.jobs.state.ak.us/}. To learn more about the services they offer, contact your state coordinator.

Mr. Remond Henderson, DCRA, Division of Administration and Finance, P.O. Box 112100, Juneau, AK 99811-2100; 907-465-4709; Fax: 907-465-8760.

Ms. Ann Spohnholz, Alaska Job Center Network Project Manager, Alaska Job Center Network Division of Community and Rural Development, 3890 University Lake, Bldg # 110, Anchorage, AK 99508; 907-786-1399; Fax: 907-786-1396; {Email: aspohnholz@ comregaf.state.ak.us}.

Job Service Offices

A system of Employment Service/Job Service offices is located within every state with the goal of assisting millions of job seekers and employers. While services may vary from location to location, many provide job training, skills assessment and related services. With approximately 1,800 Employment Service/Job Service offices nationwide there is bound to be one near you. To learn more about the services offered in your area, contact your state administrator. Rebecca Nance, Director, Alaska Department of Labor, Employment Security Division, P.O. Box 25509, Juneau, AK 99802-5509; 907-465-2712; Fax: 907-465-4537; {www.labor.state.ak.us/esd/esd.htm}.

Unemployment Program

The state of Alaska wants to help you get back to work. That's why they created the State Training and Employment Program (STEP). They offer you training or retraining for new or emerging industries and technologies. Persons are eligible who are unemployed and receiving unemployment insurance benefits, or who have exhausted their UI benefits; are employed but likely to lose their job within six months due to the job's elimination, or due to obsolescence of their job skills; or have worked in a job covered by unemployment insurance during the last three years but are ineligible for benefits because the job was seasonal, temporary, part-time, or wage contributions were insufficient, or due to underemployment. For more information, contact Department of Labor and Workforce Development, Employment Security Division, Job Training and Work Readiness Unit, P.O. Box 25509, Mail Stop 0509, Juneau, AK 99802-5509; 907-465-4863; Fax: 907-465-3212; {www.ajcn.state.ak.us/jt/step.html} {Email: katherine_brown@labor.state.ak.usb}.

Prepare for Work
The Department of Health and Human Services offers a program called JOBS - Job Opportunities and Basic Skills. If you are an AFDC recipient, they can help you prepare for and find employment. Through aptitude and interest testing, they help identify your strength areas to match you with appropriate employers. Contact Jobs Program, Val Horner, Program Manager, 350 Main Street, Room 310, P.O. Box 110640, Juneau, AK 99811-0640; 907-465-3349; 907-465-5154; {http://health.hss.state.ak.us/htmlstuf/pubassis/jobs/job.htm}.

Help for Women-owned Microenterprises
WOMEN$ Fund is a microenterprise training and microlending program for women entrepreneurs in Anchorage, AK. They provide training classes in entrepreneurship, technical assistance, individual mentoring and seed money for your women-owned small businesses, helping you to gain economic self-sufficiency. For more information, WOMEN$ Fund, A Program of the YWCA of Anchorage, Kathryn J. Maieli, Program Director, Sharon Richards, YWCA Executive Director, 245 West Fifth Avenue, P. O. Box 102059, Anchorage, AK 99510-2059; 907-274-1524; Fax: 907-272-3146; {Email: ywcaak@alaska.net}.

Network With Alaskan Women Online
The Alaska Women's Network's purpose is to further the empowerment of Alaskan women through sharing of information, education and support and through encouraging the development of skills which will enable women to assume leadership roles in building a better world. To achieve this purpose, they maintain a statewide communications network between Alaskan women and women's organizations, through electronic means that can be a valuable resource in helping you identify job-training opportunities. Point your browser to {www.junequ.com/akwomen} or contact Alaska Women's Network, Barbara Belknap, President, 4481 Abby Way, Juneau, AK 99801; 907-780-8602; Fax: 907-780-4203; {Email: nringland@touch-alaska.com}.

Assistance for Women in Construction
Alaskan Tradeswomen Network reaches out to all women involved in construction and related trades. They provide a support network, mentoring, aid/assistance, and continuing education. Contact: Alaskan Tradeswomen Network, P.O .Box 240712, Anchorage, AK 99524-0712; 907-566-2200; {Email: cacurtis@ Alaska.net}.

Networking and Training for Women Environmental Professionals
Alaska Women's Environmental Network creates networking opportunities and leadership training programs for Alaskan women working in the environmental field. AWEN members include women from state and national conservation groups, state and federal land management agencies, Alaskan businesses, educators and artists. They can improve your leadership and communications skills, help you pursue leadership positions in environmental fields, link you to like-minded women through a diverse, statewide network and support system, and find a mentor for you to improve professional and personal skills and lessen isolation. They also publish a directory of Alaskan women in environmental fields. Contact: Martha Levensaler, 750 W. 2nd Ave. #200, Anchorage, AK 99501; 907-258-4810; Fax: 907-258-4811; {Email: levensaler@nwf.org}.

Employment Education And Training Programs
The Alaska Human Resource Investment Council is the lead state planning and coordinating entity for federal, state, and local employment and training and human resource programs. They can provide you with employment education, training programs, and services to insure you have the skills and opportunities necessary to earn a living wage. Contact the AHRIC at 550 West Seventh Avenue, Suite 1830, Anchorage, AK 99501; 907-269-7489; Fax: 907-269-7489; {www.gov.state.ak.us/ahric/ahric.htm}.

Basic Skills Education
Participants in the Adult Basic Education (ABE) Program will receive reading, writing and math basic skills, and GED preparation. This will prepare them for employment, higher academic, or vocational training. Also, supportive services offered, such as transportation ,child care resources, help with the transition from the ABE program to work, pre and post assessments and more. The Life Skills Workshops cover topics such as resume writing and budgeting. They also work with employers to develop workplace literacy training activities. The goal is to help each adult learner to reach a higher level of self-sufficiency as an individual, a family member, and a community member. Contact the Employment Security Division at PO Box 25509, Juneau, AK 99802-5509; 907-465-2712; Fax: 907-465-4537; {www.ajcn.state.ak.us/abe}.

Computer Training in Fairbanks
FairNet offers several different computer courses taught by instructors for a small fee. For those who have no experience with computers, there is Intro to Computers which covers the basics like how the computer works, desktop management, and more. For the more experienced user, there is Intermediate Computers covering Word, Excel, and the Internet. Their organizations is currently putting together a resume workshop. It will cover writing a resume, finding jobs online, using on line resumes and profiles, and more. They also are working on other computer programs that will be offered in the future. These, and more courses are posted on their web site for people who can not attend classes, as well as an abundance of other information. Go to {www.fairnet.org} or contact Fairbanks Alaska Internet Resources Network for Education and Training (FairNet), 1620 Washington Drive, Fairbanks, AK 99709; 907-451-6298.

Volunteer for Training
The Family Self-sufficiency (FSS) program is a voluntary program designed to promote economic self-sufficiency for families that live in public housing or that receive a section 8 voucher. It combines housing assistance with education, job training, and support services so that the participants can find full-time work. The Gateway Learning Center houses the FSS program. It provides literacy training, entrepreneurial training, and computer skills in office environment software. To find out more about this program, contact Carol Richards, Gateway Learning Center, PO Box 101020, Anchorage, AK 99510 ;907-277-2450; {Email: crichard@ahfc.state.ak.us}.

Alaska Minority Business Development Center
Alaska Minority Business Development Center is a nonprofit organization that helps minorities to develop or expand their businesses. Their services include: one-on-one counseling; technical and management assistance in the areas of business planning, marketing, financial planning, and more; and the identification, development and leverage of procurement contracting opportunities. All ethnic minority entrepreneurs that operate, or plan to operate, their business in Alaska are eligible. The initial consultation is free and there is a nominal fee for their services, based on the gross receipts of the clients business. Contact the Alaska Minority Business Development Center, Tanana Chiefs Conference, Inc., 1122 First Avenue, Suite 600, Fairbanks, AK 99701-4897; 907-452-8251 ext. 3277; Fax: 907-459-3957; {www.tananachiefs.org/mbdc/default.htm}; {Email: lallen@tananachiefs.org}.

Arizona

One-Stop Career Centers
A network of One-Stop Career Centers throughout the state offers a wide range of employment related services including job training. Services vary by location. To find a location near you, please refer to the website {www.de.state.az.us/oscc/index.htm}. To learn more about the services they offer, contact your state coordinator.

Stan Flowers, One-Stop Coordinator, Arizona Department of Economic Security Division, Site Code 901A, 1789 W. Jefferson, P.O. Box 6123, Phoenix, AZ 85005; 602-542-1250; Fax: 602-542-2273; {Email: onestop@de.state.az.us}.

John L. Clayton, Arizona Department of Economic Security, Site Code 010A, 1717 W. Jefferson, PO Box 6123, Phoenix, AZ 85005-6123; 602-564-5331; Fax: 602-564-7452.

Job Service Offices

A system of Employment Service/Job Service offices is located within every state with the goal of assisting millions of job seekers and employers. While services may vary from location to location, many provide job training, skills assessment and related services. With approximately 1,800 Employment Service/Job Service offices nationwide there is bound to be one near you. To learn more about the services offered in your area, contact your state administrator. John L. Clayton, Director, Department of Economic Security, P.O. Box 6123-010A, Phoenix, AZ 85005; 602-542-5678; Fax: 602-542-5339; {www.de.state.az.us}.

Food Stamp Recipients

If you are using food stamps, the state of Arizona would like to train you for work. Their Food Stamp Employment & Training Policy provides you with skills and training assistance towards gaining the skills and experience which lead to employment and decreased long-term FS dependence. They can assist you with job searching, job readiness, unsubsidized employment, on-the-job training, unpaid work experiences, community service programs, vocational education training, high school/secondary education, remedial education, General Education Diploma (GED), and English for Speakers of Other Languages (ESOL). They provide guidance and support and activities that help build your confidence, recent work history, and enhance skills you already possess. Contact Janice Aragon, Food Stamp Employment & Training Policy Specialist, JOBS/JTPA Administration, 1789 West Jefferson, SC-720A, Phoenix, AZ 85007-3202; 602-542-6542; Fax: 602-542-6310; {www.commerce.state.az.us/afd/oq.pdf}.

Referral Agencies

A great place to begin your search for job training is Arizona's Workforce Development Unit. Through a process called Individual Referral Certification (IRC), the Department of Education has linked together partners in employment and training to meet the customized training needs and employment goals of eligible participants. Acting as a catalyst, the ADE's Workforce Development Unit functions as a liaison among eligible participants, referral agencies, and training facilities. Training and technical assistance is provided to referral agencies. By contacting the Workforce Development Unit, you can join the nearly eight hundred participants each year who are placed into individualized training programs to assist them in becoming gainfully employed. Contact Mike French, Coordinator, Arizona Department of Education, 1535 West Jefferson,  Bin #39, Phoenix, AZ 85007; 602-542-5142; Fax: 602-542-3818; {www.ade.az.gov/arizonaheat}; {Email: mfrench@ade.az.gov}.

Single Parent And Displaced Homemakers Gain New Skills

If you are a single parent or displaced homemaker, Arizona Department of Education's Vocational Equity in Arizona offers you employment preparatory services such as instruction in basic academic and occupational skills. They can assist you in attaining vocational competencies and marketable skills. Due to new funding to the program the list of Displaced Homemaker/Single Parent programs is still in the works. Please refer back to their web site for those contacts in the future. Contact Mike French, Arizona Department of Education, Workforce Development Unit, 1535 West Jefferson Street, Bin #39, Phoenix, AZ 85007; 602-542-4361; 800-352-4558; {www.ade.az.gov}; {Email: mfrench@ade.az.gov}.

The following is a list of regional service providers from their website at {internet.ade.state.az.us/programs/foundations/stw/equity/sph-dh.htm}.

- STEP Program AZ Western CC, PO Box 929, Yuma, AZ 85366-0929; 520-344-7699, ext. 23; Fax: 520-344-7730; Angelica Diaz de Leon & Yolanda Rios.

- Working in New Directions (WIND), Central AZ CC, Superstition Mt. Campus, 273 Old West Hwy., Apache Junction, AZ 85219; 602-288-4033; Fax: 602-288-4038; Sharon Stinard.

- Working in New Directions (WIND), Central AZ CC, Main Campus, 8470 N. Overfield Rd. Coolidge, AZ 85228; 520-426-4422; Fax: 520-426-4234; Barbara Meyer.

- Single Parent Program, Cochise CC, 901 N. Colombo, Sierra Vista, AZ 85635; 520-364-0223; Fax: 520-364-0236; Joanne Darbee.

- Self PRIDE Program, Coconino CC, 3000 N 4th St., #17, Flagstaff, AZ 86004; 520-527-1222, ext. 323; Fax: 520-526-1821; Diana Bedore.

- Single Parents/Homemakers Eastern, AZ CC, 600 Church St., Thatcher, AZ 85552; 520-428-8317; Fax: 520-757-0850; Hopi Fitz-William.

- Re-Entry And Change (REACH), Mohave CC, 1971 Jagerson Ave., Kingman, AZ 86401; 520-757-0850; Fax: 520-757-0896 Jane Barkhurst

- REACH, Mohave CC North Campus, PO Box 980, Colorado City, AZ 86021-0980; 520-875-2799; Fax: 520-875-2831; Peggy Oakleaf.

- REACH, Mohave CC Valley Campus, 3400 Hwy 95, Bullhead City, AZ 86442; 520-758-3926; Fax: 520-758-4436; Patricia Post.

- REACH, Mohave CC Lake Havasu Campus, 1977 W. Acoma Blvd, Lake Havasu, AZ 86403; 520-855-7812; Fax: 520-453-1836; Jackie Binenfeld & Geri DeBellis.

- Women in Progress, WIP Pima CC Downtown Campus, 1255 N. Stone, Tucson, AZ 85709-3000; 520-206-6293, 520-206-6135; Fax: 520-206-6201; Mini Montez.

- WIP Pima CC Community Campus, 1901 N. Stone, Tucson, AZ 85705; 520-206-6408, 520-206-3968; Fax: 520-206-6542; Beth Hunter.

- WIP Pima CC West Campus, 2202 W. Anklam Rd., Tucson, AZ 85709-0001; 520-206-6645; Fax: 520-206-6847; Nadia Villalobos.

- WIP Pima CC Desert Vista Campus, 5901 S. Calle Santa Cruz, Tucson, AZ 85709-6010; 520-295-5099; Fax: 520-295-5055; Karen Engelsen.

- WIP Pima CC East Campus, 8181 E. Irvington Rd., Tucson, AZ 85709-4000; 520-722-7606; Fax: 520-722-7690; Deborah Lloyd.

- New Directions, Yavapai CC, 601 Blackhills, Clarkdale, AZ 86324; 520-634-6528, Fax: 520-634-6549; Barbara Duncan.

- AZ Women's Education & Employment (AWEE), 640 N. 1st Ave., Phoenix, AZ 85003; 602-223-4333; Fax: 602-223-433; Marie Sullivan, Director, Mary Lou Yetman, Pat Gregan.

- AWEE-North, 914 E. Hatcher, #135, Phoenix, AZ 85021; 602-371-1216; Fax: 602-534-2773; Mary Kelly & Pattie Fessler.

- AWEE-Prescott, 161 S. Granite, Suite C, Prescott, AZ 86303; 520-778-3010; Fax: 520-778-0737; Ginger Johnson, Carol Basinger, Ann Balowski.

- Center for New Directions, 1430 N. 2nd St., Phoenix, AZ 85004; 602-252-0918; Fax: 602-253-2628; Yolanda Rohrer, Director, Susan Schmidt, Laura Valadez.

- Center for New Directions East Valley, 943 S. Gilbert, Suite 204, Mesa, AZ 85204; 602-507-8619; Fax: 602-507-8618; Joyce Vidal-Thornburg.

- Center for New Directions West Valley, 6010 W. Northern, #304, Glendale, AZ 85301; 602-435-8530; 602-435-2392; Barbara Estrada.

- Adult Vocational Training Project (AVTP), Pima County AVTP, 1630 S. Alvernon, Suite 104, Tucson, AZ 85711; 520-327-8733; Fax: 520-327-8904; Peg Nash.

- Project for Homemakers in AZ Seeking Employment (PHASE), U of A PHASE, 1230 N. Park Ave., #209, Tucson, AZ 85721; 520-621-3902; Fax: 520-621-5008; Diane Wilson.

- Transition Works, NAU, P.O. Box 6025, Flagstaff, AZ 86011-6025; 520-523-4564; Fax: 520-523-6395; Carol Eastman.

- Career Success Program, Yavapai CC, Prescott Valley Business Center, 6955 Panther Path, Prescott Valley, AZ 86314; 520-772-8368; Fax: 520-772-8861; Kim Ewing.

Learn Construction Skills

The Family Self-Sufficiency Housing Program is a construction/training company created by the Housing Authority of the City of Nogales. If you are interested in learning construction related work skills, they would like to hire you for projects and on-the-job training. Their concept is to eliminate the "mobilization costs" of hiring outside contractors while providing employment and training for the community. For more information, contact Rebecca T. Swanson, Nogales Housing Authority, P.O. Box 777, Nogales, AZ 85628; 520-287-4183; {Email: nha@dakotacom.net}.

Help For Single Parents and Displaced Homemakers Reentering College

The COMPASS program is a college re-entry program for single parents and displaced homemakers located at Cochise Community College in Sierra Vista and Douglas, AZ. The program focuses on the special needs of single parents and displaced homemakers who are looking to upgrade their employment and job readiness skills. They can provide support services while you are enrolled in college and ease your transition into the workforce.

Services can be customized to your individual needs and may include: financial assistance; academic planning; career counseling; summer school sponsorships; personal counseling and support; job-readiness training; academic skills workshops; personal/professional development credit classes; information on non-traditional careers; support groups; new student orientation; life skills workshops; lending library; newsletters mailings; referrals; mentor guidance and support. For more information about this program you can contact Compass, Cochise College, 4190 W. Hwy. 80, Douglas, AZ 85607; 520-364-7943; {www.cochise.org/spp/onestop}; {Email: johnsonk@cochise.cc.az.us}, or Sierra Vista Campus, 901 North Colombo, Sierrra Vista, AZ 85635; 520-515-5410; {Email: chaviral@cochise.cc.az.us}.

Economic Independence

If you are unemployed or underemployed, Arizona Women's Education and Employment can help you move to economic independence and well being through the dignity of work. They can provide job readiness training, job search support, job placement, guidance to keep a job, and support for transportation and child care. The program is a series of classes, workshops, and one on one sessions. Please contact AWEE-AZ Women's Education and Employment, 640 N. 1st Ave., Phoenix, AZ 85003; 602-223-4338.

Self-Employment Training For Women and Minorities

Are you a low-income individual who would like to start or expand a small business? The Self-Employment Loan Fund, Inc. (SELF) is a private non-profit organization that can provide you with training, technical assistance, and loan access. The training sessions are ten to fourteen weeks in length with the outcome of a completed business plan. Upon the completion of the business plan, participants are eligible for SELF's peer lending process, called Borrower's Circles. These circles of three to eight individuals provide an avenue for support, debt repayment, and continuing business education. SELF serves all of Maricopa County and will soon be providing services in Graham and Gila counties. For more information, contact Self-Employment Loan Fund, Inc. (SELF), Jean Rosenberg, Director, Andrea Madonna, Project Manager, 201 North Central Avenue, Suite CC10, Phoenix, AZ 85073-1000; 602-340-8834; Fax: 602-340-8953; {www.selfloanfund.org}; {Email: self@uswest.net}.

Train to Work in Highway Construction

The Pre-Apprentice Training Program is sponsored by the Arizona Department of Commerce Apprenticeship Division and the Arizona Department of Transportation. The program provides training in highway construction crafts. Participants of the program will learn marketable skills that they will be able to use afterwards in a registered apprenticeship program. The 8 hour training days last for six weeks and are designed to build skills and to help the trainees become self-sufficient. The program offers hands on experience in electrical, carpentry, welding, and piping trades. They will participate in strength training, math review, care and use of tools, blueprint reading, and become computer literate. The trainees will be able to meet potential employers on field trips to job and training sites. Graduates will get direct entry into wage paying apprenticeship programs or employment with highway construction contractors. This program is geared toward economically disadvantaged people with a focus on minorities and women. For more information, contact the Department of Commerce, Office of Workforce Development, Apprenticeship Division, 3800 North Central Avenue, Suite 1500, Phoenix, AZ 85102; 602-212-1912; {www.commerce.com/wfd/Pre-Apprenticeship_Program.htm}.

Business Assistance for Seniors

The Office of Senior Industries Development offers different services for new, existing, or relocating senior run businesses. Their goal is to maximize the economic benefits to Arizona's communities and businesses due to the demographic shift to an aging population and greater wealth among older Americans. One of the services they offer to seniors is the Annual Senior Industries Conference, a 2 day conference and business-to-business expo. This event provides almost 30 educational workshops, several key note speakers and important networking activities to more than 500 businesses and community leaders. Information on the latest mature market trends and activities, future projections for Arizona's Senior industries growth, and cutting edge 55+ marketing information is also available. Another service is the Business Development Department's decision-making information available for senior business operators. They will offer assistance with marketplace and demographic data, contract for professional services, and general senior industries information. To find out more, contact the Office of Senior Industries Development, Arizona Department of Commerce, 3800 North Central Avenue, Suite 1500, Phoenix, AZ 85102; 602-280-8197; Fax: 602-280-8142; {www.azcommerce.com/senior_industries.htm}.

GED Preparation

The Arizona Institute of Business & Technology is a non-profit educational institution. It has a GED program open to the general public available at no cost. It has an open entry flexible schedule and smaller classes specifically designed for those that need a brush up before taking the GED. Also, check out some other training programs that they have available. Because they change the topics of those programs regularly, they could not be listed here. However, in the past they have offered a Medical Assistance program and a Business Technology Specialist program. For more information, contact one of the following colleges:

AIBT, 4136 North 75th Avenue, #104, Phoenix, AZ 85033; 623-873-8208
AIBT, 6049 North 43rd Avenue, Phoenix, AZ 85109; 602-242-6265
AIBT, 925 South Gilbert Road, #201, Mesa, AZ 85024; 480-545-8755
AIBT, 1844 South Alvernon Way, Tucson, AZ 85711; 520-748-9799

Seasonal Farmworkers Job Assistance

The Rural Comprehensive Career Centers offers and Employment and Training program for the Migrant and Seasonal Farmworkers population. The no-cost program offers computer classes, construction classes, GED, Commercial Drivers License, On-The-Job Training, Work Experience, Apprenticeship in Landscaping, College, and other training. To be eligible to participate, you must have done farm work within the past 24 months, worked at least 25 days or earned $800, and meet lower living standard income level, and be a legal resident. They are located in Yuma, Maricopa, Pinal, and Cochise couties. For more information contact PPEP, 802 East 46th Street, Tucson, AZ 85713; 520-622-3553; 800-376-3553 (out of town); Fax: 520-622-1480.

Arkansas

One-Stop Career Centers

A network of One-Stop Career Centers throughout the state offers a wide range of employment related services including job training. Services vary by location. To find a location near you, please refer to the website {www.state.ar.us/onestop}. To learn more about the services they offer, contact your state coordinator.

Travis Beebe, One-Stop Lead Arkansas Employment Security Department, #2 Capitol Mall (Zip 72201), P.O. Box 2981, Little Rock, AR 72203; 501-682-5630.

Job Service Offices

A system of Employment Service/Job Service offices is located within every state with the goal of assisting millions of job seekers and employers. While services may vary from location to location, many provide job training, skills assessment and related services. With approximately 1,800 Employment Service/Job Service offices nationwide there is bound to be one near you. To learn more about the services offered in your area, contact your state administrator. Phil Price, Director, Employment Security Department, P.O. Box 2981, Little Rock, AR 72203-2981; 501-682-2121; Fax: 501-682-2273; {www.state.ar.us/esdofffices.html}.

Other State Programs

The Arkansas Department of Labor periodically schedules training seminars on a variety of work related topics. For a schedule, refer to the website {www.state.ar.us/labor/pr02.htm}. For information on the program content, or how to register for a conference, call Bonita Stocks at 501-682-4520; {Email: bonita.stocks@mail.state.ar.us}. For all other information, contact Department of Labor, 10421 West Markham, Little Rock, AR 72205; 501-682-4500; Fax: 501-682-4535; {Email: becky.bryant@mail.state.ar.us}.

Training For Trainers

If you work professionally with those returning to the workforce, the Arkansas Public Administration Consortium can help you further develop your skills. In order to improve the quality of public services in Arkansas, they offer public administration education and management training opportunities for public and non-profit organizations. All APAC courses, while not traditional college courses, are eligible for Continuing Education Units (CEUs). APAC administers the following training programs: Certified Employment Manager (CEMP); Certified Public Manager (CPM); Certified Volunteer Manager (CVM); MPA Internship Placements; Neighborhood Leadership Program (NLP); Volunteer Management 101; TEAM UP! (Training for Employment And Management); Fund Raising Certificate (FRC). Fees are usually $100-$175 for a two-day class. For further information contact Arkansas Public Administration Consortium, Library Room 523, University of Arkansas at Little Rock, 2801 South University Avenue, Little Rock, AR 72204; 501-569-3090; Fax: 501-569-3021; {www.ualr.edu/~iog/APAC.html}; {Email: apacprog@ualr.edu}.

Training for Non-High School or College Graduates

Looking for work without a degree can be a challenge. Conway Adult Education Center's Basic Skills Program can provide you with skills training in technical reading, technical math using work-based materials, or state-of-the-art computer training to meet the challenges of changing technology in the workplace. They also offer a high school equivalency program for adults who do not have a high school diploma, the GED (General Educational Development Testing Program). If language is a barrier, CAEC offers specialized ESL (English as a second language) courses to help non-native speakers communicate more effectively in the English language. Another program, WAGE, is a community-based work force development program that addresses the need to improve the basic skills of the unemployed. For more information, please contact: Karen Mellon, Work Place Coordinator, Conway Adult Education Center, 615 E. Robins Street, Conway, AR 72032; 501-450-4810; Fax: 501-450-4818; {www.caec.org/}; {Email: rawill@conwaycorp.net}.

Arkansas Adult Learning Resource Center

Arkansas Adult Learning Resource Center administers the Work Alliance for Growth in the Economy(WAGE) program. It is a partnership between local employers, city government, employment agencies, industrial development organizations, and educators. Its goal is to improve the basic skills of unemployed-and underemployed individuals so they can become employed and stay successful at their job. They also offer job placement as part of their service. To find out what type of training you can receive, contact Jackie DeBusk, Arkansas WAGE Coordinator, Department of Workforce Education, Adult Education Section, #3 Capitol Mall, 2nd Floor, Little Rock, AR 72201: 501-682-1970; Fax: 501-682-1982; {http://aalrc.org/html/we/wage.html}.

Training To Work in Delta

The Industry Partners Employment Training is a 24 week training program for people that are looking for work in Delta. The services offered assess, educate, job train, job place and provide past employment support. The trainees spend about half of the time learning basic skills for potential employers. They do receive a small stipend for the 20 hours of work they do, and as part of their weekly training schedule. For more information, contact Industry Partners, ETC 301 West 25th, PO Box 936, Stuttgart, AR 72160; 870-672-9765; Fax: 870-672-9715; {Email: pedir@ipa.net} or Industry Partners ETC2, Room 111, T&I Building, c/o BCC/UA, 1000 Campus Drive, P.O. Box 514, Helena, AR 72342; 870-338-3279; Fax: 870-338-8438; {Email: hsitemgr@ipa.net}; {www.arenterprise.org/workforce_development/careers/index.html}.

Business Training

The Good Faith Fund has Entrepreneurial Education Training as well as other training programs for entrepreneurs. The programs are designed to develop or expand the business, financial planing, and management skills. Inexperienced business owners can take advantage of a 7 session training program that will identify and strengthen their skills and complete a feasibility study of their business. There is a special addition of the basic business skills agenda for home-based and center-based child care providers. Contact the Good Faith Fund, 2304 West 29th Avenue, Pine Bluff, AR 71603; 870-535-6233; Fax: 870-535-0741; {Email: bforbus@ehbt.com} or Arkansas Enterprise Group, 605 Main Street, Suite 203, Arkadelphia, AR 71923; 870-246-9739; Fax: 870-246-2182; {Email: nsandage@ehbt.com}; {www.arenterprise.org/workforce_development/careers/index.htm}.

Community College Career Center

Garland County Community College Career Center allows people to develop and enhance their job skills. There, you will be able to have a skills assessment, use up to date materials to help in your job search, career software and a match of career interests with training requirement. They offer workshops and individual instruction in the areas of employability skills, workplace communications, basic skills upgrade, resume and interview skills, and more. Career Services is open to everyone at no charge. To find out how to participate with this program, contact the Garland County Community College Career Center, 101 College Drive, Hot Spring, AR 71913; 501-760-4246; 800-760-1825; Fax: 501-760-4236; {www.gccc.cc.ar.us/CSCE/services.htm}.

California

One-Stop Career Centers

A network of One-Stop Career Centers throughout the state offers a wide range of employment related services including job training. Services vary by location. To find a location near you, please refer to the website {www.sitcc.ca.gov/ SJTCCWEB/ONE-STOP}. To learn more about the services they offer, contact your state coordinator. Ms. Danna Owens, Manager, Employment Development Department, P.O. Box 826880 MIC 77, Sacramento, CA 94280-0001; 916-653-6347; Fax: 916-654-9863; {Email: dowens@edd.ca.gov}.

Job Service Offices

A system of Employment Service/Job Service offices is located within every state with the goal of assisting millions of job seekers and employers. While services may vary from location to location, many provide job training, skills

assessment and related services. With approximately 1,800 Employment Service/Job Service offices nationwide there is bound to be one near you. To learn more about the services offered in your area, contact your state administrator. Contact {www.edd.cahwnet.gov/jsind.htm}.

Victoria L. Bradshaw, Director, Employment Development Dept., P.O. Box 826880, MIC 83, Sacramento, CA 94280-0001; 916-654-8210; Fax: 916-657-5294

Mark Sanders, Dep. Dir. Operations, Employment Development Dept., P.O. Box 942880, MIC 86, Sacramento, CA 94280-0001; 916-654-9047; Fax: 916-653-3440.

Help Is Just A Phone Call Away

Forced to go into the work world suddenly or do you need help getting your job skills upgraded? Women Work! is for you. They have over 1400 sites across the country to help women from diverse backgrounds achieve economic self-sufficiency through job readiness, education, training and employment. Women Work! provides these services through a network of programs in every state. Women Work! also takes on the toughest women's employment issues and fights for them in Congress and in state legislatures. For more information on Women Work! or to find a location near you contact Women Work! Regional Representative, Region IX, Joanne Durkee, Displaced Homemaker Program, Mt. Diablo Adult Education, 1266 San Carlos Avenue, Concord, CA 94518; 510-685-7340, ext. 2786; Fax: 510-687-8217.

Opportunities in San Jose

MetroED is a collaborative education district in San Jose that prepares youth and adults to be sought-after employees and contributing community members who learn and earn for a lifetime. Their network of service providers include the following programs.

Central County Occupational Center Program-CCOC provides a wide variety of technical training options at the CCOC campus, and on high school and other campus locations throughout the county. Courses offered include training in over 32 occupational choices including electronics, manufacturing, business, automotive, construction, and health occupations. CCOC/P training serves high school juniors, seniors and adults. Contact CCOC, 760 Hillsdale Avenue, San Jose, CA 95136; Office: 408-723-6400; Student Services: 408-723-6407; {www.metroed.net/ccoc.htm}.

Metropolitan Adult Education Program-MAEP provides learning opportunities in over 50 locations throughout San Jose and Campbell which serve a combined total of 43,000 adults around the clock in subjects including: English as a Second Language, citizenship preparation (offered in English and 5 other languages), adult basic education-literacy skills in reading, writing, and math, GED preparation, high school diploma program for adult students, short-term vocational certificate programs helping people gain skills to enter, or re-enter, the workforce, educational programs for older adults, childbirth and parenting education, and community interest programs for personal growth and job skills enhancement. For more information, contact Campbell Center (Western Region): 1224 Del Mar Avenue, San Jose, CA 95128; 408-947-2300; or Metropolitan Center (Southern Region): 760 Hillsdale Avenue, San Jose, CA 95136; 408-723-6450; or San Jose Center (Central Region): 1149 E. Julian Street, San Jose, CA 95116; 408-947-2311; {www.metroed.net/maep.htm}.

Training For Low-Income People

The Center for Employment Training (CET) is a private, non-profit, community based organization that provides quality employment training for those who need it most. They offer extensive life skills and workplace know-how instruction through a program that includes job preparedness training, job development and placement. CET keeps students in training until they are placed and conducts follow-up on all placements to ensure stable employment and job growth. CET's primary activity is classroom skill training, which is provided year-round. CET does not screen applicants through testing, but accepts anyone who is willing to do the necessary work. Courses are offered on an open-entry, open-exit basis and students complete training at their own pace.

CET training is intensive, with students attending 5 days and 35 to 40 hours per week for an average of seven months. CET training is competency based, highly individualized, and hands-on. The average training course at CET maintains a 20-1 student/ teacher ratio. CET uses basic skills instruction and human development conducted in a simulated work setting. At least twenty-five job training options are offered at CET nationwide. These include automated office skills, building maintenance, electronic assembly, medical assistant, truck driving, and shipping/receiving. Skill offerings vary from one center to another. A typical CET center offers 4-5 skills and may serve up to 250 persons annually. To locate a service center near you, refer to the list below or contact CET Corporate Offices, 701 Vine St., San Jose, CA 95110; 408-287-7924; 800-533-2519 (for your local center); {www.cet2000.org}.

CET Service Centers in California

- 294 South Third St., El Centro, CA 92243; 760-337-6565; Fax: 760-353-5589.

- 1151 East Washington Ave., Suite A, Escondido, CA 92025; 619-347-4808; Fax: 619-747-8238.

- 7800 Arroyo Circle, Gilroy, CA 95020; 408-842-6484; Fax: 408-842-7158.

- 44105 Jackson Street, Building A, Indio, CA 92201; 619-347-4808 Fax: 619-342-4563.

- 8390 Capwell Drive, Oakland, CA 94621; 510-568-6166; Fax: 510-568-6723.

- 761 South C Street, Oxnard, CA 93030; 805-487-9821; Fax: 805-486-8762.

- 1099 La Cadena Dr., Riverside, CA 92501; 909-680-0238; Fax: 909-680-0125.

- 421 Monterey St., Salinas, CA 93901; 408-424-0665; Fax: 408-424-4743.

- 3925 Market Street, San Diego, CA 92102; 619-233-6829; Fax: 619-233-6350.

- 701 Vine Street, San Jose, CA 95110; 408-287-7924; Fax: 408-294-7849.

- 120 West Fifth Street, Suite 120, Santa Ana, CA 92701; 714-568-1755; Fax: 714-568-1331.

- 509 West Morrison, Santa Maria, CA 93454; 805-928-1737; Fax: 805-928-1203.

- 42066 Avenida Alvarado, Unit A, Temecula, CA 92590; 909-676-7514; Fax: 909-694-0913.

- 10 Blanca Lane, Watsonville, CA 95076; 408-728-4551; Fax: 408-728-1659.

Training Programs in Oakland
The Oakland Private Industry Council offers services to people who need to earn a high school diploma or GED, update skills, or prepare for a new career. They also work with many community based agencies which provide job training and placement services to local residents. PIC administers the following employment and training programs in partnership with the City of Oakland. All training programs include assistance with job search and placement. PIC is an equal opportunity service provider; auxiliary aid is available upon request for persons with disabilities. For more information, refer to the list below and call the program(s) which interest you.

Note: This is not a comprehensive directory of vocational programs, but a list of programs funded by the Oakland PIC. Main address: Oakland Private Industry Council ("The PIC"), 1212 Broadway, Suite 300, Oakland, CA 94612; 510-891-9393; {www.oaklandpic.org/ programs.asp}.

- *American Viet League* - Training in basic skills, English as a second language, and computerized accounting skills. Vickie Nguyen, 255 International Blvd., Oakland, CA 94606; 510-834-7971; Fax: 510-834-7974.

- *Asian Neighborhood Design* - Training in manufacturing technologies (including Auto CAD and CNC), construction-related trades, cabinetmaking, carpentry and basic education. Daniel Duvernay or David Meiland, 1890 Campbell Street, Oakland, CA 94607; 510-433-1370; Fax: 510-433-1375.

- *ASSETS Senior Employment Opportunities Program* - Training in life skills, early childhood development, general office procedures, typing, bookkeeping, computer programs and customer service skills. Also, work experience. Brendalynn Goodall, City of Oakland, 250 Frank Ogawa Plaza, Suite 4353, Oakland, CA 94612; 510-238-3535; Fax: 510-238-7207.

- *Berkeley Adult School* - Training in general clerical, medical clerical, nursing assistant/home health aide, warehouse/forklift, accounting clerk and restaurant occupations. ESL, GED/HS diploma preparation. Contact Berkeley Adult School, 1222 University Avenue, Berkeley, CA 94702; 510-644-8970; Fax: 510-644-8789.

- *Career Resources Development Center* - Training in computer applications, business math and English, 10-key and typing, customer service and cash register use. Career Resources Development Center, 320 13th Street, Oakland, CA 94612; 510-268-8886; Fax: 510- 268-0688.

- *Catholic Charities* - Pre-employment and basic skills training. Vocational ESL, bilingual job counseling and assessment and on-the-job training. Aldric Chau, 707 Jefferson Street, Oakland, CA 94607; 510-465-0642; Fax: 510-465-4044

- *Center for Employment Training* - Training in office skills, shipping/receiving, machine tool operator and building maintenance. Gil Rodriguez, 8390 Capwell Drive, Oakland, CA 94621; 510-568-6166; Fax: 510-568-6723.

- *Cypress Mandela/Women in Skilled Trades Training Center* - Pre-apprentice construction training, lead abatement, hazardous materials and asbestos removal skills. Jeri Robinson, 2229 Poplar Street, Oakland, CA 94607; 510-208-7350; Fax: 510-835-3726.

- *Dislocated Workers Program* - PIC contracts with agencies and institutions to provide training in a variety of growing fields. Revelina Valmores, 1212 Broadway, Suite 200, Oakland, CA 94612; 510-768-4440; Fax: 510-451-4049.

- *English Center for International Women* - Four levels of intensive ESL instruction. Occupational training includes word processing and spreadsheet skills. Deborah Taylor, Mills College, 5000 MacArthur Blvd., Oakland, CA 94613; 510-430-2064; Fax: 510-430-2259.

- *Jobs for Homeless Consortium* - Training in carpentry, janitorial, and clerical occupations. David Lyons or Nina Grotch, 1722 Broadway, Oakland, CA 94612; 510-251-6241; Fax: 510-251-6093.

- *Local 250 Health Care Workers Union* - Pre-employment skills and on-the-job training as certified nursing assistants. Joan Braconi, 560 20th Street, Oakland, CA 94612; 510-251-1250; Fax: 510-763-2680.

- *Oakland Unified School District, Adult Education* - Basic education training, GED preparation and training in nursing assistant, home health aide, clerical, computer operation, security and janitorial skills. Offered at many sites across Oakland. Contact Oakland Unified School District, 1025 2nd Avenue, Portable 15, Oakland, CA 94606; 510-879-8131; Fax: 510-879-1840.

- *Oakland Unified School District, Exceptional Children's Program* - Basic education instruction, workplace education and labor market orientation. On-site job training and job mentoring. Contact Exceptional Children's Program, 4655 Steele Street, Oakland, CA 94619; 510-879-1763; Fax: 510-879-1769.

- *Scotland Youth and Family Center* - Basic and pre-employment skills training, California HS Proficiency Exam preparation/testing, GED preparation and work experience. Hanna McQuinn, 1651 Adeline Street, 2nd Floor, Oakland, CA 94607; 510-832-4544; Fax: 510-832-3521.

- *Spanish Speaking Citizens' Foundation and Lao Family Community Development, Inc.* - Training in dietary aide and dietary clerk fields. Work experience at hospital or public health facility. Rosario Flores, 1470 Fruitvale Avenue, Oakland, CA 94601; 510-261-7839; Fax: 510-261-2968.

- *Stepping Stones Growth Center* - Training in janitorial, grounds maintenance, boat cleaning and detailing, recycling, and utility and stock clerk occupations. Jerry Joseph, 311 MacArthur Boulevard , San Leandro, CA 94577; 510-568-3331; Fax: 510-568-416.

- *Summer Youth Employment and Training Program* - Program starts in June. Offers labor market orientation, job readiness and work experience. Kelly Robinson, Oakland Private Industry Council, 1212 Broadway, Suite 300, Oakland, CA 94612; 510-768-4446; Fax: 510-763-5132.

- *Youth Employment Partnership* - The Career Tryout Program covers pre-employment/work, maturity skills, and leadership development. There is also training in the areas of driver's training, academic enhancement, GED preparation, and individualized work experience. Dennis Smith or Mark Henderson, 1411 Fruitvale Avenue, Oakland, CA 94601; 510-533-3447; Fax: 510-533-3469.

Get The Help You Need To Start Your Own Business

Founded in 1976, the American Woman's Economic Development Corporation is the premier national not-for-profit organization committed to helping entrepreneurial women start and grow their own businesses. Based in New York City, AWED also has offices in southern California, Connecticut and Washington, D. C. Join over 100,000 women who have benefitted from formal course instructions, one-to-one business counseling, seminars, special events and peer group support. AWED's goal is to increase the start-up, survival and expansion rates of small businesses. Contact American Woman's Economic Development Corporation (AWED), Suzanne Tufts, President and CEO, 71 Vanderbilt Avenue, Suite 320, New York, NY 10169; 212-692-9100; Fax: 212-692-9296.

California Branch Offices

- You can benefit from two long-term training modules depending on your stage in owning your own business. The Women's Enterprise Development Corporation was previously known as California AWED which began in 1989 with SBA funding to assist the growing number of women business owners in Los Angeles. The Community Entrepreneurial Program works in partnership with local community organizations. Residents of economically disadvantaged neighborhoods can take advantage of a comprehensive business training and micro-loan program. They also offer other services such as low-cost business assistance, one-on-one business counseling, workshops, and more. Starting Your Own Business ($240) is for beginning business owners. Managing Your Own Business ($525) is for women who have been in business at least one year with gross receipts over $50,000. Courses are in six languages: Chinese, English, Japanese, Khmer, Korean and Spanish. For more information contact Women's Enterprise Development Corporation, Phil Borden, Executive Director, 235 East Broadway, Suite 506, Long Beach, CA 90802; 562-983-3747; Fax: 562-983-3750; {www.wedc.org/}; {Email: wedc1@wedc.org}.

Enhance Your Business Skills Close To Home

If you live in lower-income communities around San Francisco, particularly Fruitvale, San Antonio and Central East Oakland, the Women's Initiative for Self Employment can provide you with training and technical assistance in establishing your own business. The training program consists of an orientation and three workshops. The orientation is a two hour program that covers their services and starts the process of assessing the clients readiness for self-employment. "Making Sense of Your Business" is a 2 week workshop on the planning and research needed to start, stabilize, or expand a business. "Managing Your Small Business" lasts for 14 weeks and teaches marketing and sales, financial management and operations, and personal development. The Business Support Workshops are to be attended at various stages of the training and for the duration of the client's entrepreneurial career. They also have Business Enhancement Services such as Writing Your Business Plan, Business Improvement Seminars, and more. All of their services are available in Spanish.

Contact Women's Initiative for Self Employment (WI), 1390 Market Street, Suite 113, San Francisco, CA 94102; 415-247-9473; Fax: 415-247-9471; {www.womensinitiative.org}, {Email: bjohnson@womensinititative.org}. Spanish Language Program: 415-826-5090; {Email: msansores@womensinititative.org}.

Looking For A Job Or Planning A Career In Sacramento, S.F., L.A. or San Diego?

JobStar is the right place to start your career, plan your job campaign or negotiate a good salary. They have comprehensive listings for programs related to employment in Sacramento, S.F., L.A. or San Diego including job training opportunities.

The listings are too numerous to include here. However, to give you an idea of what is available, the list below includes programs concerned with job training just in the Los Angeles area. Note that the list below does not include programs concerned with job placement and other non-training related services. If you are interested in these services or would like more information, refer to their website below. If the Internet is not readily available to you, don't forget that your local library will probably have access. {http://jobstar.org/index.htm}.

- *Career Encores* is a non-profit program that assists adults age 50 and over with employment opportunities. Job preparation training offered in two Career Transition Centers (Burbank and mid-Wilshire.) Special attention is given to the needs of older persons and their services are free. For more information, contact Career Encores, 3700 Wilshire Blvd., Suite 200, Los Angeles, CA 90010; 800-833-6267; {www.careerencores.org}.

- *Chicana Service Action Center* - Los Angeles offers free job training and placement for low-income people of any nationality. Training in office work, warehousing, and other trades. Must be 18 or older with proper ID, residency and income to qualify. Call for locations in Huntington park and Pomona. For more information, contact Chicano Service Action Center - Los Angeles, 315 West 9th Street, Los Angeles, CA 90015; 213-253-5959.

- *Chinatown Service Center* is a non-profit organization whose free programs include employment training, basic skills remediation, job placement, career planning & referrals to vocational training centers. They serve Asians and other immigrants, refugees and other Americans in the greater L.A. area. Multicultural, multi-lingual staff speak Chinese dialects, Vietnamese, Cambodian, Spanish and English. For more information, contact Chinatown Service Center, 767 N. Hill Street, Suite 400, Los Angeles, CA 90012; 213-808-1700; Fax: 213-680-0787; {http://csc.apanet.org/services.html}.

- *Forty Plus of Southern California* is a non-profit, cooperative membership organization open to executives, managers & professionals seeking new employment or a career change. They offer job search preparation, interviewing assistance, computer training, unadvertised job market and have free orientations. For more information, contact Forty Plus of Southern California, 3450 Wilshire Boulevard, Suite 510, Los Angeles, CA 90010; 213-388-2301; {www.socal.com/40plus}.

- *Jewish Vocational Services* is a non-profit, nonsectarian service organization providing a full range of skills assessment, training, job search & consulting services to job seekers & employers on a sliding fee basis. They have special services for immigrants, disabled, students, downsized workers, outplacement professionals, career changers. Entertainment Networking Group is for persons either in or seeking to enter the entertainment industry. Must be L.A. resident, 18 or older. For more information, contact Jewish Vocational Services, 5700 Wilshire Boulevard #2303, Los Angeles, CA 90036; 323-761-8888; {www.jvsla.org}.

- *Central Job Service* offers free career counseling, vocational testing, job search skills workshops, computerized job matching and placement, job club. EDD Home Page has information on job services, unemployment insurance and locations of 22 offices throughout L.A. County. For more information, contact L.A. Central Job Service, Employment Development Department, 158 W. 14th Street, Los Angeles, CA 90015; 213-744-2244; {www.edd.cahwnet.gov/edd.home}.

- *L.A. Works* provides a free comprehensive system of training, placement and career planning for job seekers throughout southern California. For more information, contact L.A. Works, 5200 Irwindale, Ave., Suite130, Irwindale, CA 91706; 626-960-3964; {www.laworks.org}.

- *Los Angeles County Regional Occupational Programs* is one of 12 Regional Occupational Education Programs throughout L.A. County. Programs are offered at high schools, adult schools, community colleges, private postsecondary schools and community or business facilities. Students learn entry-level skills in a wide variety of occupational fields including animal care, banking, nursing, food service, retail sales and electronics. Applicants must be at least 16 years of age. Call for additional locations. Free to high school students, fees for adults. For more information, contact Los Angeles County Regional Occupational Programs, 20122 Cabrillo Lane, Cerritos, CA 90703; 562-403-7382.

- *Los Angeles Urban League* offers free employment services focused on African Americans and other minorities, but open to anyone age 15 years or older. The League assists job-ready applicants and employers through counseling, workshops and a job bank. Services include pre-employment preparation, job development, on-the-job training and placement in computers, automotive, electronics and other trades. Call for additional Pasadena and Pomona locations. For more information, contact Los Angeles Urban League, 3450 Mount Vernon Drive, Los Angeles, CA 90008; 323-299-9660; {www.laul.org/Programs/programs.htm}.

- *The Maxine Waters Employment Preparation Center* is one of 6 Los Angeles Unified School District Skills Centers offering short-term vocational training designed to get people working. Each site offers training specialties suited to the surrounding community. Services include extensive vocational counseling in addition to job training and placement. Adult Basic Education and GED high school diploma testing are also offered. Programs are adaptable with open entry, open exit and flexible scheduling to meet individual needs. They serve a culturally diversified population throughout L.A. County aged 14 and older and students may enroll concurrently with regular school. There is a small registration fee. For information on additional locations & special community-based programs for particular groups, contact Maxine Waters Employment Preparation Center, Los Angeles Unified School District Skills Centers, 10925 S. Central Avenue, Los Angeles, CA 90059; 323-564-1431.

- *Mexican American Opportunity Foundation* is a non-profit agency offering free services that include job listings, computer training, on-the-job training with partial reimbursement to employers; work experience for preschool teacher's aides, basic skills training in reading and math, limited paid internships for youths 18-21. For anyone that does not qualify for government funded programs. For more information, contact Mexican American Opportunity Foundation, 401 N. Garfield Avenue, Montebello, CA 90640; 213-890-9600; {www.maof.org/maof.htm}.

- *Pacific Asian Consortium in Employment* is a community-based agency offering youth & adult free job training and transitional workshops, job preparation, referral and placement to low-income individuals age 22 and older. Training & technical assistance is available for low-income entrepreneurs, educational/leadership development for high school dropouts and at-risk youth. Call for additional information on Gardena location. For more information, contact Pacific Asian Consortium in Employment (PACE), 1541 Wilshire Blvd., Suite 210, Los Angeles, CA 90017; 213-353-3982; {www.pacela.org}.

- *Southeast LA County Workforce Investment Board* offers one-stop employment and training programs & services for laid-off workers, the unemployed and low-income. They have special services for youth seeking G.E.D. and older workers (over 55). Career Center offers resources, workshops. If eligible, you may qualify for individual or in-depth training programs. Their services are free but some services are only for eligible clients. For more information, contact Southeast L.A. County Private Industry Council, 10900 E. 183rd St., #350, Cerritos, CA 90703; 562-402-9336; {www.selaco.com}.

- *Southern California Indian Center* is a non-profit organization serving the American Indian community. Provides free employment assistance and vocational training to American Indians, Native Alaskans and Native Hawaiians who are unemployed, underemployed or economically disadvantaged. Services include annual job fair, training, resume & job application preparation, job search techniques, job listings and referrals and educational workshops for parents. For more information and additional locations, contact Southern California Indian Center, 3440 Wilshire Blvd., Los Angeles, CA 90010; 213-387-5772.

- *Verdugo Private Industry Council* is one of 6 federally funded Private Industry Councils (PICs) in the greater L.A. area. Applicants may qualify for one or more reasons including layoff, long-term unemployment or income below poverty levels. Their free services include educational, vocational & on-the-job training; job-search skills and placement; dislocated workers program; older workers programs and youth training programs. For more information and additional locations, contact Verdugo Private Industry Council, 706 W. Broadway, Suite 202, Glendale, CA 91204; 818-409-0476.

- *Women at Work* is a non-profit, drop-in career and job resource center serving unemployed and underemployed women (and men) in the greater L. A. area seeking jobs or changing careers. Services include job listings, job market information, career library, career workshops, career counseling, occupational testing, special employment programs, job search support groups, computer classes, self-serve computer lab. Fees are involved and may vary. For more information, contact Women at Work, 50 North Hill Avenue, Suite 300, Pasadena, CA 91106; 626-796-6870; {www.womenatwork1.org}.

Help For Northern CA Small Business Owners

WEST Company serves micro enterprise owners in rural northern California. Through their Build a Better Business training and consulting program, they assist clients in developing a business plan for both start-up and expansion purposes. They make individual and peer loans; assist with the formation of business networks; and have started a cross-generational technology-mentoring program. For more information, contact the website at {www.westcompany.org}, or:

West Company, Sheilah Rogers, Executive Director, 367 North State Street, Suite 201, Ukiah, CA 95482; 707-468-3553; Fax: 707-468-3555; {Email: info@westcompany.org}

West Company, Carol Steele, Loan Fund Manager, 306 E. Redwood Avenue, Suite 2, Fort Bragg, CA 95437; 707-964-7571; Fax: 707-964-7576; {Email: westcofb@mcn.org}.

Learn To Work At A Job Usually Filled By Men

The Job Training Network in Alliance with the Private Industry Council is a successful partnership between public and private sectors, which provides valuable employment and training programs throughout Santa Barbara County. One of their many client services is Non-traditional Options for Women (N.O.W.) that offers women an array of training programs in jobs usually filled by men. Contact Job Training Network, 228 W Carrillo St. # C, Santa Barbara, CA 93101-6159; 805-882-3675; {www.jtnwinjobs.org/}.

Network And Learn From Other Women In Management

Women In Management (WIM) is a non-profit educational corporation for the advancement of women into management positions. Open to everyone, regardless of your place on the career path, WIM's annual membership costs only $65 per person. They host monthly meetings in the southern California area for managers, entrepreneurs, administrative assistants, the self-employed and anyone who would like to make contacts, develop leadership skills, establish rewarding relationships and advance their career. They also offer scholarships for education to their members. WIM does not have a permanent address, since all of their board positions are on a volunteer basis and the people who fill the positions change annually. You can reach them at 800-531-1359, {www.wimworks.com}; {Email: mail@WIMworks.com}.

Nearly Free Job Training Classes
The Norwalk-LaMirada Adult School provides classes and career counseling at practically no cost. While their information is limited on their offerings, according to locals, their program is extremely popular. Contact Norwalk-LaMirada Adult School, Attention: Donatella, 12820 Pioneer Boulevard, Norwalk, CA 90650; 562-868-0431.

I Could Do That Guy's Job
Women In Non-traditional Employment Roles' (WINTER) mission is to encourage and support women's training, employment, and retention in high wage, high skill jobs. The common bond is that all share the goal of opening more doors for women. As a member, you can take advantage of training workshops, job counseling, job search assistance and referrals. Other organizational activities include: educating members on job rights, skill building, safety, and other issues; holding monthly support group meetings; publishing monthly newsletter; publicizing job and apprenticeship openings; advocating for equal employment opportunity; networking with other organizations on labor issues; promoting active involvement of women in  unions; providing technical assistance to employers, unions, community based organizations, and schools; producing videos on women in non-traditional jobs; engaging in research investigating job segregation; organizing speaker's bureau. Contact Ebony Shakoor-Akbar, Women In Non-traditional Employment Roles, P.O. Box 90511, Long Beach, CA 90809-0511; 310-590-2266; {www.ttrc.doleta.gov/research/wanto}.

Training For Virtually Any Job!
Private Industry Council, Inc. offers job training in health/human services; clerical; administration/management; cosmetology; construct/manufacturing; mechanical/repair; agriculture/forestry; transportation; education/child development; legal/law enforcement; technical/computer; and communication/marketing. They also offer a huge variety of job-related services at the following three locations.

Jobtree located in the EDD Office, 2523 S. Mooney Blvd., Visalia, CA 93277; 209-737-4226; Fax: 209-737-4320; {www.climbthejobtree.org}

Tulare County Workforce Development Center, 1249 N. Cherry, Tulare, CA 93274; 209-685-2680; Fax: 209-685-2567; {www.climbthejobtree.org}

Tulare County Workforce Development Center (located in the EDD Office), 61 N. Second St., Porterville, CA 93257; 209-782-4718; Fax: 209-782-4786; {www.climbthejobtree.org}

Training & Employment Center
The Napa County Training and Employment Center (TEC) is a nationally recognized, service-integrated, one-stop career center offering comprehensive career and employer services which are designed to enhance options for job seekers and employers alike. Focusing on solutions and positive outcomes, as well as customer satisfaction, TEC offers responsive services designed to enhance employability and employment options. Their services include: competency-based job readiness skills training; job search workshops; networking opportunities; vocational and career assessment; computerized labor market information; resume preparation; vocational skills training; academic programs including high school diploma and GED preparation; English as a second language and basic literacy courses; immediate employment referral for job seekers with marketable skills; career resource center; retraining for new skills; job development and placement assistance; and personalized support services. For more information, contact Training & Employment Center, 650 Imperial Way, Napa CA 94558; 800-289-1872, 707-253-4291.

A Handful of Other Training Opportunities

- *North Valley Private Industry Council* offers vocational and on-the-job training, counseling, support services, job referrals and placement for youth, seniors, and unemployed, laid-off workers. Contact North Valley Private Industry Council, 505 W. Olive Avenue, #550, Sunnyvale, CA 94086; 408-730-7232; (TDD) 408-730-7501; Fax: 408-730-7643; {www.novapic.org}.

- *Opportunities Industrialization Center West* offers job training for economically disadvantaged, unemployed, or underemployed adults and youth. Contact Opportunities Industrialization Center West (OICW), 1200 O'Brien Drive, Menlo Park, CA 94025; 650-322-8431; Fax: 650-324-3419; {www.oicw.org}, {Email: info@oicw.org}.

- *San Jose Job Corps Center* offers remedial education, recreation, GED preparation, vocational training, and a residential program for youth age 16-24. Contact San Jose Job Corps Center, 3485 East Hills Drive, San Jose, CA 95127; 408-937-3229; Fax: 408-254-5663; {www.nyec.org/pepnet/awardees/sanjcc.htm}.

- *Santa Clara County Office of Education* - Regional Occupational Programs offers career and vocational training for adults, out-of- school youth, and high school students age 16 or over. Contact Santa Clara County Office of Education, 575 W. Fremont Avenue, Sunnyvale, CA 94087; 408-733-0881; {http://isb.sccoe.org/sps_rop.html}.

Verdugo Jobs Center

Verdugo Jobs Center is a full service job and career center. The services they have available include, internet access to job postings boards and resources; workshops; resume, interview and job search assistance; and educational and occupational training assistance. There are eligibility requirements for some of the free services. To find out how to participate with the Center, contact Verdugo Jobs Center, 1255 South Central Avenue, Glendale, CA 91204; 818-409-0476

Career Centers

There are six Career Centers in San Diego County that provide employment and training services to county residents. There are specific services for laid-off and long-term unemployed persons. While each of the centers offers their unique enhanced services, they all offer services that include career assessment, job training and placement. They encourage customers to check out each of the Centers services to see which best suits their needs. Each also has access to Job Bank, electronic resume posting and multimedia resource rooms, referrals to job openings, career counseling, and much more. Contact a Center near you at: {www.workforce.org/career/index.html}.

- San Diego Metro Career Center, 8401 Aero Drive, San Diego, CA 92123-1720; 858-974-7620; Fax: 858-974-9805; {www.workforce.org/career/sdmet_f.html}.

- North County Career Center, 5315 Avenida Encinas, Carlsbad, CA 92008; 760-930-2400; Fax: 760-930-8014; {www.workforce.org/career/north_f.html}.

- South County Career Center, 1111 Bay Boulevard, Suite E, Chula Vista, CA 91911; 619-424-1112; Fax: 619-424-1144; {www.workforce.org/career/south_f.html}.

- South Metro Career Center, 6145 Imperial Avenue, San Diego, CA 92114; 619-266-3600; Fax: 619-266-3605; {www.workforce.org/career/smet_f.html}.

- East County Career Center at the East County Regional Education Center, 924 East Main Street, El Cajon, CA 92021; 619-590-3900; Fax: 619-579-4720; {www.workforce.org/career/east_f.html}.

- Inland North County Career Center, 1935 East Valley Parkway, Escondido, CA 92027; 760-738-0274; Fax: 760-738-8723; {www.workforce.org/career/inlandf.html}.

Colorado

One-Stop Career Centers

A network of One-Stop Career Centers throughout the state offers a wide range of employment related services including job training. Services vary by location. To find a location near you, please refer to the website {www.cdle.state.co.us}. To learn more about the services they offer, contact your state coordinator.

Ms. Ledy Garcia-Eckstein, Executive Director, Workforce Coordinating Council, 1580 Logan Street, Suite 410, Denver, CO 80203; 303-894-2077; Fax: 303-894-2064; {Email: gareckl@ capitol.state.co.us}

Mrs. Judy Richendifer, Director, Office of Employment and Training Programs Colorado Department of Labor and Employment, 1515 Arapahoe Street, Tower 2, Suite 400, Denver, CO 80202-2117; 303-620-4204; Fax: 303-620-4257; {Email: judi.Richendifer@state.co.us}.

Job Service Offices

A system of Employment Service/Job Service offices is located within every state with the goal of assisting millions of job seekers and employers. While services may vary from location to location, many provide job training, skills assessment and related services. With approximately 1,800 Employment Service/Job Service offices nationwide there is bound to be one near you. To learn more about the services offered in your area, contact your state administrator. John J. Donlon, Executive Director, Department of Labor & Employment, Tower 2, Suite 400, 1515 Arapahoe Street, Denver, CO 80202-2117; 303-620-4701; Fax: 303-620-4714; {http://employsvcs.cdle.state.co.us}.

Help For Low-income Latina Women

The Mi Casa Resource Center for Women, Inc. provides quality employment and education services that promote economic independence for low-income, predominantly Latina women and youth. You can receive educational counseling, job readiness and job search training, life skills development, job placement, non-traditional and computer skills training. If you lean towards owning your own business, you can receive training on how to start a business and develop business plans with micro-loans available to program graduates. Other services include: youth development, drop-out prevention, leadership training and responsible decision making, provided through two youth programs - Mi Carrera (My Career) and Fenix (teen-pregnancy, AIDS and STD prevention program). Contact Mi Casa Resource Center for Women, Inc., Agnes Talamantez Carrol, Director of Business, 571 Galapago Street, Denver, CO 80204; 303-573-0333; Fax: 303-607-0872; {www.micasadenver.org}; {Email: acarrol@micasadenver.org}.

Job Training Has Advantages

Hone your job skills at The Training Advantage. They can help prepare you for participation in the labor force by increasing your occupational and educational skills. Their free services include: assessment of job skill level and training needs; job and career counseling; information and training for women in non-traditional jobs; classroom training in occupational skills; academic skills training, including GED preparation, math, English, reading; work experience programs and internships; on-the-job training in an occupational skill; in-house computer training; and supportive services. For more information, contact:

The Training Advantage, 11 South Park, P.O. Box 2146, Montrose, CO 81402; 970-249-2234; {www.montrose.org/hospital/resource/pages/ training_advantage.htm}.

The Training Advantage, Director: Mary Layton; P.O. Box 800, 285 Lakin Street, Ignacio, CO 81137; 970-563-4517; Fax: 970-563-4504; {www.ignacio.co.us/sucap/index.html}.

Contacts for Small Business Training

The Colorado Alliance for Microenterprise Initiatives is a coalition of micro-enterprise development organizations and practitioners. They provide entrepreneurs in under-served communities the opportunities and resources needed to become self-sufficient by connecting them to a variety of organizations that can help. Some of the assistance available is in the area of workshops, technical assistance, training classes, counseling and loan assistance. They do not have a primary contact at this time, however, you can access the information at {www.coloradoalliance.org}.

Colorado Capital Initiatives
Colorado Capital Initiatives helps to build stronger businesses and communities. They do this by offering access to capital, technical assistance, and promoting interaction between small businesses and the community. Their technical training assistance program is called Biz Wiz. It encourages business skills growth and provides a greater opportunity for success through on-on-one educational experience. This program allows small business to get help early in their development so that they can have a better chance for a successful business. Contact CCI at 3003 Arapahoe Street, Suite 205, Denver, CO 80205; 303-308-8121; Fax: 303-308-8120; {www.coloradocapital.org}; {Email: colcap@mho.net}.

Computer Training for Residents of HUD Insured Properties
Neighborhood Networks Center at Island Grove Village Apartments offers job training for low-income families. It enhances self-sufficiency, employability, and economic self-reliance. The services include GED, job training, and computer training. Contact Deanna E. Beaudoin, Resident Initiatives Specialist, Colorado State Office, 633-17th Street, Denver, CO 80202-3607; 303-672-5349; Fax: 303-672-5153; {Email: DeanneE.Beaudoin@hud.gov}.

Connecticut

One-Stop Career Centers
A network of One-Stop Career Centers throughout the state offers a wide range of employment related services including job training. Services vary by location. To find a location near you, please refer to the website {www.ctdol.state.ct.us/ctworks/ctworks.htm}. To learn more about the services they offer, contact your state coordinator.

Deborah M. Nanfito, Programs and Services Coordinator, Connecticut Department of Labor, 200 Folly Brook Blvd, Wethersfield, CT 06109; 860-566-2533; Fax: 860-566-1520

Jean E. Zurbrigen, Deputy Commissioner, Connecticut Department of Labor, 200 Folly Brook Blvd., Wethersfield, CT 06109; 860-566-4388; Fax: 860-566-1520.

Job Service Offices
A system of Employment Service/Job Service offices is located within every state with the goal of assisting millions of job seekers and employers. While services may vary from location to location, many provide job training, skills assessment and related services. With approximately 1,800 Employment Service/Job Service offices nationwide there is bound to be one near you. To learn more about the services offered in your area, contact your state

administrator. James P. Butler, Commissioner, State Labor Department, 200 Folly Brook Boulevard, Wethersfield, CT 06109-1114; 860-566-4384; Fax: 860-566-1520; {www.ctdol.state.ct.us}.

Information Hotline
The Education and Employment Information Center has a hotline to provide you with the information you need to get on your career track. This service is offered by the Department of Higher Education and the Board of Governors for Higher Education. Call 800-842-0229 or, in the Hartford area call 860-947-1810; {www.ctdhe.org/dheweb/EEIC.htm}.

Help For Displaced Homemakers
The State of Connecticut offers a Displaced Homemakers Program that is designed to help you become economically self-sufficient. They offer you information, referral, counseling, assessment of skills, job training for

various occupations, job placement, and support services, such as child care and transportation assistance. Use the list below to locate a service center near you or refer to the website for updated information. {www.ctdol.state.ct.us/progsupt/jobsrvce/discjt.htm}

- Region I: Ansonia/Waterbury, Danbury/Torrington, Bridgeport/Stamford, Norwalk, Greenwich YWCA of Eastern Fairfield County - "Job Readiness Program", Connie Condon, Executive Director, 753 Fairfield Avenue, Bridgeport, CT 06604; 203-334-6154 Fax: 203-579-8882.

- YWCA of Greenwich - "New Horizons", Elizabeth K. Berry, Executive Director, 259 East Putnam Avenue, Greenwich, CT 06830; 203-869-6501, ext. 215.

- YWCA of Darien/Norwalk - "Beginning Again", Rita Shaughnessey, Executive Director, 49 Old Kings Highway North, Darien, CT 06820; 203-858-4910.

- Family Service of Greater Waterbury - "Step by Step", Carol Belfarti, Coordinator, 34 Murray Street, Waterbury, CT 06710; 203-756-8317; Fax: 203-756-8310.

- Region II: New Haven, Meriden, Middletown YWCA of Meriden - "Open DOHR", Shane Rood, Executive Director, 169 Colony Street, Meriden, CT 06450; 203-235-9297; Fax: 203-237-7571.

- Region III: Hartford, New Britain, Bristol Hartford College for Women of the University of Hartford - "Look Forward", Gail Champlin, Director - Counseling Center, 50 Elizabeth Street, Hartford, CT 06105; 860-768-5619; Fax: 860-768-5680.

- YWCA of New Britain - "Look Forward", Tracey Madden Hennessey, Executive Director, 22 Glen Street, New Britain, CT 06051; 860-225-4681, ext. 288; Fax: 860-826-7026

- Region IV: Northeast: Willimantic/Danielson Southeast: Norwich/New London ACCESS Job Source, Kim Bond, Administrative Coordinator, 1315 Main Street, Willimantic, CT 06226; 860-450-7487, ext. 749; Fax: 860-450-7477.

- ACCESS-Multiservices, Lorraine Griffith, Director, 16H Maple Street, Danielson, CT 06239; 860-774-0418; Fax: 860-450-7477.

- ACCESS-Multiservices, Pamela St. John, Program Supervisor, 106 Truman Street, New London, CT 06320; 860-442-4630; Fax: 860-447-1826.

- Multipurpose Service Center: Action for Bridgeport Community Development, Inc., Job Re-entry Program, Donna Austin, 1070 Park Avenue, Bridgeport, CT 06604; 203-366-8241, ext. 275; Fax: 203-394-6175

Learn Construction Skills
The Ansonia Housing Authority formed Curtisey Corporation, a non-profit entity, to provide training and employment activities for its tenants and other low-income individuals enabling them to transition from welfare roles to self-sufficiency. If you are interested in learning construction oriented work skills, they would like to hire you for projects and on-the-job training. The program offers on-the-job employment training and a Family Self-Sufficiency/Innovations Network. For more information, contact Kathy Lester, Curtisey Corporation, 88 Main Street, Ansonia, CT 06401; 203-732-0411; Fax: 203-734-3283; {www.nhc.org/infoproj/jobinfo.htm}.

Educational Center for Women
Caroline House is located in one of the most devastated areas in Bridgeport, CT. For the past four years the School Sisters of Notre Dame, Wilton Province, have ministered and taught in this learning center that is available to needy women who want to learn English as a second

language (ESL), basic computer, and life resource learning skills. Each day about 45 women attend classes together with their preschool children. Within the same facility, children are attending preschool. For further information, contact Maureen Fleming, SSND, Caroline House, 574 Stillman Street, Bridgeport, CT 06608; 203-334-0640; Fax: 203-334-0640.

Help For Women Entrepreneurs

Connecticut women are lucky to have an American Woman's Economic Development Corporation office in their state. Connecticut's programs follow the New York AWED model, offering Start Your Own Business and Managing Your Own Business training seminars and provides individual seminars and workshops. They also may be able to provide you with loan packaging assistance. (See listing under "New York" for more information or contact American Woman's Economic Development Corporation, Fran Pastore, Connecticut Manager, 2001 W. Main Street, Suite 140, Stamford, CT 06902; 203-326-7914; Fax: 203-326-7916.

Re-Employment Training

Career Transition Center offers a variety of services to certified dislocated workers, students and community members in Northeast Connecticut. Some of the resources available are, a job search library, job search and career related videos, internet access and job listings. For those who qualify for funding, there is classroom training, on-the-job training, and apprenticeship training. In addition to this, they also run workshops on resume and cover letter writing, personality testing, communication skills, and much more. Career and Re-Employment Counseling is available, too. For more information on the services that are available, contact Career Transition Center, Quinebaug Valley Community-Technical College, Room 106, Danielson, CT 06239; 860-774-2620; Fax: 860-774-2327; {www.ctdol.state.ct.us/danielsn/transition-ctr.htm}.

Free Workshops

The Department of Labor keeps an up-to-date list of free workshops offered through the state. Some of the current topics are; Networking Skills, Working After 40 & 50 and Then Some, Job Recruitment, Interviewing Skills and Career Planning. For a complete list of workshops and locations, go to {www.ctdol.state.ct.us/ctworks/cldrloc.htm}, or contact 200 Folly Brook Boulevard, Wethersfield, CT 06109; 860-263-6000.

Training for Small Business Owners

The Entrepreneurial Center at the University of Hartford has services to help men and women to start and grow their businesses. Through training, technical assistance and group support, the business owner as well as the business, are developed. There is a workshop entitled " Is Self-Employment For Me?" to let clients decide if they have the qualities to become self-employed. Clients of the Center will also be able to apply for a loan program through People's Bank. For more information, contact the Center in Hartford, 50 Elizabeth Street, Hartford, CT 06105; 860-768-5681; Fax: 860-768-5622. In Bridgeport, the Center is located at 961 Main Street, Bridgeport, CT 06604; 203-382-5582.

Assistance For Small Business Owners

Current and prospective business owners in the Greater New Haven area can take advantage of comprehensive business assistance, resources and consulting services at the Regional Business Resource Center. Some of the services offered are; personalized business consulting, group training seminars, a high-tech computer lab, and a business reference library. Some of the seminars they have are entitled, Success Starting a Business, Development an Annual Financial Plan, and Selling on the Internet. All of this is available at no cost. For more information, call the Regional Business Resource Center, 560 Ella T. Grasso Boulvard, New Haven, CT 06519; 203-624-1493, ext. 224; Fax: 203-562-1106; {www.businessresourcectr.com}.

Delaware

One-Stop Career Centers

A network of One-Stop Career Centers throughout the state offers a wide range of employment related services including job training. Services vary by location. To find a location near you, please refer to the website {www.vcnet.net}. To learn more about the services they offer, contact your state coordinator.

Mr. Michael M. Benefield Jr., Director, DOL/Division of Employment and Training, 4425 N. Market Street, Wilmington, DE 19809-0828; 302-761-8000; Fax: 302-761-6621; {Email: M.Benefield@DET-ADMIN@DOL}

Mr. Robert Clarkin, Employment and Training Administrator, State of Delaware, 4425 N. Market Street, Wilmington, DE 19809-0828; 302-761-8102; Fax: 302-761-6617; {Email: Clarken@DET-MIS@DOL}.

Job Service Offices
A system of Employment Service/Job Service offices is located within every state with the goal of assisting millions of job seekers and employers. While services may vary from location to location, many provide job training, skills assessment and related services. With approximately 1,800 Employment Service/Job Service offices nationwide there is bound to be one near you. To learn more about the services offered in your area, contact your state administrator. Darrell J. Minott, Secretary of Labor, State Department of Labor, 4425 North Market Street, Wilmington, DE 19802; 302-761-8000; Fax: 302-761-6621; {www.delawareworks.com}.

Other State Programs
The state of Delaware has designed a program to get you back to work. Their A Better Chance Welfare Reform Program combines all programs that the state offers to welfare clients including job training. Services are provided to clients through the joint efforts of DSS, Department of Labor, the Economic Development Office and Contractors. For more information, contact Beverly Ennis, Workforce Development, Delaware Economic Development Office, 99 Kings Highway, Dover, DE 19901; 302-739-4271; Fax: 302-739-2027; {www.delawareworkforce.com/welfare.htm}

For more information about the Delaware Department of Health and Social Services Division of State Service Centers, contact Anne M. Farley, Director, Lorraine Mekulski, Deputy Director, 1901 N. Du Pont Highway, Chas Debnam Bldg., New Castle, DE 19720; 302-577-4961; Fax: 302-577-4975; {Email: dhssinfo@state.de.us}.

Christian Programs
Ursuline Companions in Mission is a Christian association of lay women and men who seek to make a difference in the lives of the poor through a variety of programs including job training. They have service delivery sites in Delaware, Illinois, Kentucky, Minnesota, Missouri, New Mexico, and Ohio. Programs vary from location to location. For more information, contact Ursuline Companions In Mission, Sr. Jane Quinlan, College of New Rochelle, College Center, Room 155, New Rochelle, NY 10805; 914-654-5270; Fax: 915-654-5290; {www. theursulines.org}; {Email: ursulinecomp@hotmail.com}.

Search For A Job Online
The Virtual Career Network is a sophisticated online search engine concerned with all things related to employment in Delaware. While no specific programs are offered for women, the Job Seeker Services area allows you to create your resume and place it in a talent bank accessible by employers. You can also search through an electronic job bank for the job of your choice, to research occupations that may be of interest, and to review training opportunities. For example, by entering your chosen field i.e. secretary, the system makes suggestions as to where to obtain training for that occupation. Check out the website at {www.vcnet.net/}.

Clerical Training For Underemployed Residents
Employee Training and Development at Professional Staffing Inc. offers a free 8-week course for underemployed or unemployed adults. It teaches entry level skills for employment in business and banking. Some of the areas covered in class are: intro to computers, Word, general office skills and alphabetic keyboarding, and job search skills. A Certificate of Completion is awarded and there is placement assistance. For more information, contact Professional Staffing, 919 Market Street, Suite 505, Wilmington, DE 19801; 302-652-3519; {Email: pturgon@aol.com}.

Training For Sussex County Residents
The Sussex Tech Adult Division's motto is " We Build Careers". They offer a variety of training programs, many of them for only a small fee. At the center, you can learn new skills or build on existing ones. The areas of training are:

Computer & Internet, Career Development, Certificate Programs, Transportation, Medical Training, Electrical, Apprenticeship, and GED. For information on these programs, contact Sussex Tech Adult Division, Route 9, P.O. Box 351, Georgetown, DE 19947-0351; 302-856-9035; Fax: 302-856-7875; {www.techtraining.net}; {Email: techadmin@techtraining.net}.

District of Columbia

One-Stop Career Centers
A network of One-Stop Career Centers throughout the District offers a wide range of employment related services including job training. Services vary by location. To find a location near you, please refer to the website {http://does.ci.washington.dc.us}. To learn more about the services they offer, contact DC's coordinator, Gregory P. Irish, DC Department of Employment Services, 500 C Street, NW, Suite 600, Washington, DC 20001; 202-724-7185; Fax: 202-724-1357.

Job Service Offices
A system of Employment Service/Job Service offices is located within every state with the goal of assisting millions of job seekers and employers. While services may vary from location to location, many provide job training, skills assessment and related services. With approximately 1,800 Employment Service/Job Service offices nationwide there is bound to be one near you. To learn more about the services offered in your area, contact your state administrator Mr. Gregory P. Irish, Director, DC Department of Employment Services, 500 C Street, NW, Room 600, Washington, DC 20001; 202-724-7100; {http://does.ci.washington.dc.us}.

Opportunities for Women
All Kinds Of Opportunities For Women in DC
You are fortunate to live near the National Women's Business Center. They have many programs for women at all stages of business development including Introduction to Business Ownership; Up and Running; Marketing: Getting Results; Federal Procurement Series; The Advanced Training Institute; The Business Council; The Roundtable; Exploring Entrepreneurship; SPIRIT and Skills For Self-Employment; Online Advantage Series; and The Bottom Line.

Their mission is to be the premier provider of training in the DC areas for women that want to start or expand their own business. They do that through low cost business training, networking, mentoring, and other ways. For more information, contact the National Women's Business Center, 1001 Connecticut Avenue, NW, Suite 312, Washington, DC 20036; 202-785-4WBC; 202-785-4110; {www.womensbusinesscenter.org}; {Email: info@womensbusinesscenter.org}.

Culinary Training For The Unemployed
You can learn all the necessary skills to gain employment as a kitchen worker. The DC Central Kitchen operates out of a fully equipped 10,000 square foot, health code-approved industrial kitchen. The twelve-week training course follows a curriculum prepared in cooperation with Cornell University's School of Hotel Management, and includes all facets of entry-level work in a professional kitchen. Class size varies from 10 to 20 students each cycle. Participants attend classes Monday through Friday, from 8:30 AM to 3:30 PM. Instruction is provided by full-time staff chefs in all areas of kitchen skills. The training program emphasizes not only the technical aspects of kitchen work, but also the importance of punctuality, following directions, and positive work attitudes. Participants' self-sufficiency and esteem increases as a result of enhanced job skills, which is key to the transition out of homelessness. Upon successful completion of the program, graduates work actively with DC Central Kitchen staff to connecting with a network of area food service employers. For more information, contact DC Central Kitchen, 425 Second Street, NW, Washington, DC 20001; 202-234-0707; Fax: 202-986-1051; {www.dccentralkitchen.org/Programs/JobTraining.asp}.

Homeless People Eat While Learning Kitchen Skills

At the Dinner Program for Homeless Women, anyone (and their children) may receive an appetizing and nutritious dinner in a stable and safe environment, and be provided the support and opportunity needed to achieve their full potential. In addition to basic services, the Dinner Program provides a food services training program to eight trainees per cycle. Each cycle lasts two months, depending upon the individual. Trainees learn to prepare and serve meals in a sanitary environment. They also receive weekly case management services to assist with goals related to employment, housing, and special needs such as substance abuse and mental health issues. In addition, women seeking training in other fields are referred to other programs that provide job training and placement assistance. For more information, contact Dinner Program for Homeless Women, 945 G Street, NW, Washington, DC 20001; 202-737-9311; Fax: 202-347-7217; {www.geocities.com/~dphomelesswom}; {Email: dphomelesswom@hotmail.com}.

Training, Training, Training

Another national program that locals can benefit from is Wider Opportunities for Women (WOW) which works nationally and in its home community of Washington, DC to achieve economic independence and equality of opportunity for women and girls. What began as a local Washington effort to help women help themselves has become a multi-faceted women's employment organization, recognized nationally for its skills training models, technical assistance, and advocacy for women workers. WOW can help you learn to earn, with programs emphasizing literacy, technical and non-traditional skills, welfare-to-work transition, and career development as they have for 30 years. Join the more than 10,000 women WOW has trained for well paid work since 1964. Contact the National Office: WOW, 815 15th Street, NW, Suite 916, Washington, DC 20005; 202-638-3143; Fax: 202-638-4885.

Local Training Office: WOW, 204 Riggs Road, NE, Washington, DC 20011; 202-526-7066; Fax: 202-526-4030; {www.w-o-w.org/ default.htm}; {Email: info@w-o-w.org}.

Computer Training For Inner City Residents

Byte Back is a nonprofit organization that provides computer training for low-income youth and adults. They offer these services in order to increase the participant's skills and marketability. They offer three types of training at 8 different locations. The Byte Back Class is a regular computer training class that will prepare the students for jobs that require computer skills, but that are not necessarily in the computer industry. The Internship Program is for selected students that demonstrate a significant interest and ability. It will prepare them for a job within the computer industry. Lastly, there is the Power Up Youth Program, which involves using the computer as a medium of communication and computer skills. This is currently a pilot program offered at the headquarters office after school hours. For more information, contact the Byte Back Headquarters/Power Up, 815 Monroe Street, NE, Washington, DC 20017; 202-529-3395; Fax: 202-529-4684; {http://byteback.org}; {Email: infor@byteback.org}.

Free Workshops

The Department of Employment Services maintains a list of free career workshops at their website. Some of the topics they cover are: Interview Preparation, Introduction to Job Search Planning, Internet Navigation, Self-Identification/Assessment, and many more. To find out where and when the workshops are being held, go to {http://does.ci.washington.dc.us/pw-ws.html}, or contact DOES, 500 C Street, NW, Room 600, Washington, DC 20001; 202-727-7500.

Florida

One-Stop Career Centers

A network of One-Stop Career Centers throughout the state offers a wide range of employment related services including job training. Services vary by location. To find a location near you, please refer to the website {www.floridajobs.org/wps/onestop}. To learn more about the services they offer, contact your state coordinator.

Ms. Kim Doyle, Brevard Local Learning Lab, 1519 Clearlake Road, Suite A-116, Cocoa, FL 32922; 407-504-2060; Fax: 407-504-2065; {www.brevard.cc.fl.us/joblink}; {Email: kdoyle@job-link.net}.

Ms. Kathleen McLeskey, Director Division of Jobs and Benefits, Florida Department of Labor and Employment Security, 1320 Executive Center Drive, Atkins Building, Suite 300, Tallahassee, FL 32399-0667; 850-488-7228; Fax: 850-487-1753.

James Finch, One-Stop Team Leader, Florida Department of Labor and Employment Security, 1320 Executive Center Drive, Atkins Building, Tallahassee, FL 32399-0667; 850-488-7228; Fax: 850-487-1753.

Job Service Offices
A system of Employment Service/Job Service offices is located within every state with the goal of assisting millions of job seekers and employers. While services may vary from location to location, many provide job training, skills assessment and related services. With approximately 1,800 Employment Service/Job Service offices nationwide there is bound to be one near you. To learn more about the services offered in your area, contact your state administrator. Doug Jamerson, Secretary, Department of Labor & Employment Security, 2012 Capital Circle, SE, Suite 303 Hartman Building, Tallahassee, FL 32399-2152; 850-922-7021; Fax: 850-488-8930; {www2.myflorida.com/les}.

Unemployment Compensation /Benefit Eligibility
The Florida Training Investment Program was established as a statewide three year pilot program designed to extend unemployment compensation benefit eligibility to dislocated workers throughout Florida who have lost their jobs, have limited marketable skills, and enroll in vocational training intended to lead to employment in an occupation for which there is a labor market demand. Applications for the training investment program may be obtained at any Florida unemployment compensation claims office, job service office or by writing to: Division of Unemployment Compensation, Tip Unit, Bureau of Claims Administration, 107 East Madison Street, Room 325, Tallahassee, FL 32399-0225; 850-921-3893.

You Can Get A "Man's" Job and Wages
Central Florida Jobs & Education Partnership, Inc. strives to train and find employment for women in non-traditional jobs that allows them to earn typically higher wages. Just last year, 40 women were trained and placed in non-traditional jobs and are now earning up to $40.00 per hour and average $10.05 per hour. You can receive training in: truck driving, computer electronics, drafting, police/corrections officer, auto mechanic, electrician, assemblers/packagers, air conditioning tech, and auto sales. For more information, contact CFJEP, 1801 Lee Road, Suite 307, Winter Park, FL 32789; 407-741-4365; Fax: 407-741-4394; {Email: kacornett@ hotmail.com}.

Grow Your Own Business
The Women's Business Development Center can provide you with quality business education, technical assistance and access to capital. Their focus is on women, minorities and low- and moderate-income individuals who are starting or growing their own businesses. Business education programs incorporate both traditional and non-traditional methods of learning. In classroom settings, business owners and professionals teach participants about entrepreneurship, market research, financial analysis and business planning. Non-traditional programs include one-on-one business counseling, a mentor/protege program, business specialty workshops and networking forums. The Center also assists clients with preparation of loan packages and will present loans to financial institutions. The Center has been designated an intermediary for the SBA Women's Prequalification Loan Program and has a satellite office in downtown Miami at the SBA's Business Resource Center. Social skills training for women on welfare has been initiated and will be offered with dual goals of enhancing employability as well as providing the first step to self-employment. For more information: Women's Business Development Center (WBDC), Christine Kurtz-White, Director, 7600 Red Road, Suite 211-A, Coral Gables, FL 33143; 305-668-6167; Fax: 305-348-2931; {Email: obermann@fiu.edu} (Program Coordinator); {Email: rojasm@fiu.edu} (Financial Consultant).

In Florida, contact Center for Employment Training, 301 Southwest 14th Ave., Delray Beach, FL 33444; 561-265-1405; Fax: 561-243-2596; {Email: mailto:d_gainer@cetmail.cfet.org}.

Find A Mentor For Your Women Owned Business Endeavor

The mission of the Women Business Owners Of North Florida is to create and recognize opportunities to lift up the successes of women in the business world, both individually and collectively. What this means for you is that WBO will support your vision with practical educational opportunities and with mentors who offer encouragement, advice and networking assistance. Contact Women Business Owners Of North Florida, P.O Box 551434, Jacksonville, FL 32255-1434; 904-278-9270; {www.jaxwbo.org/}.

The Old Reliable

The YWCA of Jacksonville has a transitional housing program in which they offer free employment training such as resume development and interview skills. A computer lab is onsite to develop computing skills. Program is only open to women living in the transitional housing program for which they pay 30% of their current income. Contact YWCA, 325 E Duval St., Jacksonville, FL 32202-2794; 904-354-6681.

Community Colleges

Florida is blessed with a large number of community colleges with special programs of interest to women. Several are described below.

- *Okaloosa-Walton Community College* offers their Single Parent/Displaced Homemaker Program. If you are returning to school because of a divorce, separation, or the death of a spouse, they can help you. The program assists students with education and training so they can enter the work force with marketable skills and abilities, a support system, referrals, tuition assistance, information leading to high wage vocational employment and textbook loans for qualified students. For more information, Okaloosa-Walton Community College, 100 College Boulevard, Niceville, FL 32578; 850-729-5291 or 850-678-5111; {www.owcc.cc.fl.us/departs/ workforce/displaced_homemaker.html}.

- If you are in the job market due to a divorce, separation, death or disability of a spouse, supporting parent or family member or friend whose financial resources are now no longer available, *Valenica Community College* has 2 programs for you.

  1. The *Displaced Homemaker Program* at Valencia Community College offers multiple services including: classes; follow-up assistance with job searches; individualized personal, educational and vocational counseling; monthly seminars for personal and professional growth; and individual intake appointments to establish specific needs. The Program serves Orange, Osceola, and Seminole Counties. Available at no charge to county residents, the Program also offers confidence building; career direction and assessment; employability skills; job search assistance; referral to social services, training and education; information and advisement; and life management skills. Displaced homemakers who qualify financially receive a weekly stipend from the Valencia Community College Foundation to help them pay for their transportation and child care costs while they attend the all day two-week "Building for Success" classroom sessions.

  2. To assist program graduates who require additional education to sharpen existing skills or to acquire new skills that will enable them to successfully enter the workplace with a meaningful and rewarding career to support themselves and their family, the *Displaced Homemaker Scholarship* is available to qualified applicants to the extent of available funding. Applicants for the Displaced Homemaker Scholarship must be graduates of the Displaced Homemaker Program, have evidence of financial need, exemplify scholastic ability, and must complete Valencia's financial aid application. Selection of the recipient of the Displaced Homemaker Scholarship is made by a Displaced Homemaker Staff Committee. Inquiries about this scholarship and requests for an application should be made to the Women's Center office, and should be filed as early as possible before the defined dates. Applicants selected as Displaced Homemaker Scholars are expected to write to the Displaced Homemaker Program, in care of the Valencia Foundation, about their

experiences at Valencia and the value of the scholarship. Valencia Community College Foundation, P.O. Box 3028, Orlando, FL 32802-3028; 407-317-7950; Fax: 407-317-7956; {www.valencia.org/442.html}; {Email: Foundation@gwmail.valencia.cc.fl.us}.

- *Edison Community College* offers a program for displaced homemakers called Fresh Start. It focuses on the client's immediate needs to promote social and economic growth. The services offered are vocational and career testing, counseling, development of employability skills, and personal assessment and development. Contact: Annette Massen Spates, Coordinator, Howard Hall 125, Fort Myers, FL 33919-5598; 941-489-9005; {www.edison.edu/student_services/freshstart.htm}.

- *Santa Fe Community College* Displaced Homemaker Program/Focus on the Future offers confidential assistance to homemakers who are 35 years of age or older who lack skills or experience in today's job market and have lost the financial support of a spouse or family member due to death, divorce, separation or disability. The program provides instruction in goal setting, personal growth and development (including financial planning, stress and time management) and job search techniques (including applications, resumes and interviewing). Individual and career counseling is also available to help people make the transition to independence through personal development, further education or employment. Free month-long classes and special workshops are scheduled throughout the year. Call the Displaced Homemaker Program: Focus on the Future at 352-395-5047 for further information. This program is made possible by a grant from the State of Florida, Department of Education. Northwest Campus, 3000 NW 83rd Street, Gainesville FL 32606; 352-395-5047; {http://admn.santafe.cc.fl.us/~DispHome/ index.htm}; {Email: nancy.griffin@santafe.cc.fl.us}. The main campus contact is Santa Fe Community College, 401 NW 6th St., Gainesville, FL 32601; 352-395-5645.

- The *Roseanne Hartwell Women's Center* is part of the Florida Community College in Jacksonville. They have two programs of special interest to women. The Challenge program is designed to meet the specific needs of displaced homemakers. Specially trained staff conduct classes and provide advising with personal skills, as well as job placement. Five week classes are held continuously throughout the year. One and two day workshops are held at various times during the year. There is no fee for Challenge. For more information or to arrange for an interview, call 604-633-8316; or contact 101 West State Street, Room 3100, Jacksonville, FL 32202-3056; {www.fccj.org/OpenCampus/women.html}.

Women Investigating New Goals & Services (WING)

Women Investigating New Goals & Services (WING) is a program for displaced homemakers. The center is for women returning to school, re-entering the job market, or looking for self-employment opportunities. They offer workshops, computer classes, information and support services. The workshops consist of personal development skills, assessment of skills, interests and values, and employability techniques. For more information, contact. WINGS, 1000 Coconut Creek Boulevard, Building 41, Coconut Creek, FL 33066; 954-973-2398; {http://fs.broward.cc.fl.us/comm/ied/wings/about.html}; {Email: cfaber@broward.cc.fl.us}.

Customized Services for Hispanic Businesses

The Hispanic Business Initiative Fund of Greater Orlando provides business assistance for Hispanic Businesses. At the beginning, they do a thorough analysis of the business. Then they work with the entrepreneur to determine the individual's and the business' strengths, weaknesses, and opportunities resulting in a customized service package. Their services include Business Planning, Marketing, Minority Business Certification, and Bilingual Business Seminars, just to name a few. The also run a Business Leadership Program that offers seminars for entrepreneurs. Those provide business owners with practical information on how to operate their business successfully. It covers topics such as Cash Flow and Budget for Small Business, Effective Time Management, and Leadership Skills for Entrepreneurs. Contact HBIF, 3700 34th Street, Suite 100, Orlando, FL 32805; 407-428-5872; Fax: 407-428-5873; {www.hbiforl.org/index.html}.

The Northeast Florida Community Action Agency

The Northeast Florida Community Action Agency provides low-income people with self-sufficiency services at no charge. Those include job training, education, vocation training, mentorship and more. This also includes Supportive

Services such as child care assistance, transportation, books, and more. Contact the Northeast Florida Community Action Agency, 406 West Adams Street, Suite 200, Jacksonville, FL 32202; 904-358-7474; Fax: 904-791-9299; {www.nfcaa.org}; {Email: info@nfcaa.org}.

Georgia

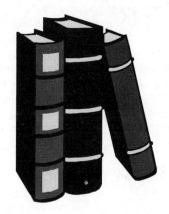

One-Stop Career Centers
A network of One-Stop Career Centers throughout the state offers a wide range of employment related services including job training. Services vary by location. To find a location near you, please refer to the website [www.g1careernet.com]. To learn more about the services they offer, contact your state coordinator.

Helen Parker, One-Stop Lead, Assistant Commissioner, Employment Service, Sussex Place, Suite 400, I-48 International Blvd., NE, Atlanta, GA 30303-1751; 404-656-6380; Fax: 404-657-8285; {Email: Helen.Parker @dol.state.ga.us}

Michael Thurmond, Commissioner, Georgia Department of Labor, Sussex Place, Suite 600, 1-48 International Blvd., NE, Atlanta, GA 30303-1751; 404-656-3011; Fax: 404-656-2683; {Email: Michael.Thurmond@dol.state.ga.us}.

Job Service Offices
A system of Employment Service/Job Service offices is located within every state with the goal of assisting millions of job seekers and employers. While services may vary from location to location, many provide job training, skills assessment and related services. With approximately 1,800 Employment Service/Job Service offices nationwide there is bound to be one near you. To learn more about the services offered in your area, contact your state administrator. David Poythress, Commissioner, GA Department of Labor, 148 International Boulevard, NE, Atlanta, GA 30303; 404-656-3011; Fax: 404-656-2683; {www.dol.state.ga.us}.

Education and Training Services in Northwest Georgia
If you live in northwest Georgia and are looking for job training, you ought to know about the Northwest Georgia Career Depot. They offer a comprehensive system of education and job training programs designed for life-long learning in both formal training and self-directed learning formats. Among their many programs is the Family and Children Services that provides free pre-employment training for individuals who need temporary assistance while they are seeking employment. New Connections is a program for single parents and displaced homemakers with services that include assessment, counseling, job readiness and job search training, and life management skills. New Connections works with other programs to help students find appropriate training to become employed and the program is free. An Adult Literacy Program offers free training for the beginning reader through the General Equivalency Diploma (GED) or High School Diploma. Many counties now offer training in English as a second language.

For information on the Career Depot project, contact Gwen Dellinger, CVRDC, P.O. Box 1793, Rome GA 30162-1793; 706-295-6485; Fax: 706-802-5567; {Email: gwen@jtpa.cvrdc.org }; {www.careerdepot.org/train}.

Training For Female Prisoners and Low-income Women
Prison Ministries with Women offers a range of services that include fee based computer training for low-income women, non-traditional job training (renovation), housing for single women, one-on-one sponsoring, mentoring for women, counseling for ex-offenders, furniture, and household goods. Female prisoners and ex-prisoners are eligible for all services except computer training, low-income women for computer training. For more information, contact Prison Ministries with Women, 465 Boulevard, SE #205, Atlanta, GA 30312; 404-622-4314; Fax: 404-624-0313.

Help Is Just A Phone Call Away
Forced to go into the work world suddenly or do you need help getting your job skills upgraded? Women Work! is for you. They have over 1400 sites across the country to help women from diverse backgrounds achieve economic

self-sufficiency through job readiness, education, training and employment. Women Work! provides these services through a network of programs in every state. Women Work! also takes on the toughest women's employment issues and fights for them in Congress and in state legislatures. For more information on Women Work! or to find a location near you contact Women Work! Regional Representative, Region IV, Department Of Technology and Adult Education, Lydia Webber, Director of Special Services, 1800 Century Place NE, Suite 400, Atlanta, GA 30345; 404-679-1654; Fax: 404-679-1675.

Training For Domestic Violence Victims
Gresham's Arms of Love serves battered women and their children by offering a resource center for job training and placement for clients, transitional housing, 24 hour child care for residents, legal advocacy, teen support groups, and women's support groups in metro Atlanta. For more information, contact Gresham's Arms of Love, Inc., P.O. Box 42188, Atlanta, GA 30311; 404-622-9944; Domestic Violence Resource Center, 215 Lakewood Way, SW, Suite 1070, Atlanta, GA 30315; 404-622-9944.

Start Your Own Business
If you are planning, expanding or strengthening a business, the WEDA program is for you. It is a 21-seminar series for women business owners, lasting two-and-one-half hours each week. This program was condensed in 1995 to a five-hour program. WEDA also provides mentoring and one-on-one counseling. The majority of clients are African-American women; however, it is open to all individuals. Topics covered in the training program include marketing, business planning, accounting and finance, contract negotiation, and domestic and international procurement. Women's Economic Development Agency (WEDA), Joyce Edwards, Chairperson for Board, 675 Ponce de Leon Avenue, Atlanta, GA 30308; 404-853-7680; Fax: 404-853-7677; {Email: dorothy.fletcher@internetmci.com}.

Work First!
Work First! is a program aimed at people that receive public assistance. The number one objective is to find a job for every person that applies for public aid. Applicants first get help to remove any employment barriers, such as lack of child care and transportation. Then, the county offices provide job-specific training. DECS works with businesses to hire and train the applicants. For more information on this program, contact your local Department of Family and Children's Services, 2 Peachtree Street, NW, Suite 19-490, Atlanta, GA 30303; 404-657-7660; {www2.state.ga.us/departments/dhr/dfcs.html}.

Training for Minorities and Youths
The Minority Worker Training Program is available for people 18-25 years from environmentally impacted communities in Atlanta. The Youth Apprenticeship Job Training Program is open to qualified public housing residents, ages 16-30, to train them to enter one of the building trades apprenticeship training programs. Both are similar programs whose focus is to train the participants to work in the construction and environmental remediation industry. The training involves comprehensive basic academic and GED preparation, life skills, job readiness, counseling, mentoring, and an awareness of safety, health and environmental justice issues. Trainees that do not join a union apprenticeship program, will receive on going job placement assistance. To find out more, contact Clark Atlanta University, Environmental Justice Resource Center, 223 James P. Brawley Drive, SW, Atlanta, GA 30314; 404-880-6911; {www.ejrc.cau.edu/traininstitute.htm}; {Email: ejrc@cau.edu}.

Training for Single Parents, Students, Displaced Homemakers, and Others
New Connections to Work is a training and employment program available in Middle Georgia. It provides skills training and job placement for single parents, displaced homemakers, single pregnant women, TANF recipients, students looking for skills training in the non-traditional higher paid employment field, and individuals and businesses looking for customized workforce preparation and training. Some of the services that are part of the program include; achievement assessment, counseling, job-readiness/job retention, life management workshops, and skills training. For more information, contact Middle Georgia Tech, Economic Development Programs, 80 Cohen Walker Drive, Warner Robbins, GA 31088; 478-988-6852; {www.mgti.org/econ_dev/newconnect.htm}.

Vocational Training For North Georgia Residents
Goodwill Industries of North Georgia has customized vocational services available in North Georgia for people that face employment barriers. There is Comprehensive Career Counseling and Planning, Classroom and On-The-Job

Training, and Job Placement. Their job training covers food service, hospitality services, self-employment, pre-employment skills, GED, non-traditional/construction trades for women, and more. To see if you qualify to participate, contact Goodwill Industries of North Georgia, 2201 Glenwood Avenue, SE Atlanta, GA 30316; 404-486-8400; TDD: 404-377-4290; {www.ging.org/JobPost/JobOppFS.html}; {Email: buddy@ging.org}.

Employment Programs for Seniors
The Senior Community Service Employment Program is a work training program for seniors that want to re-enter the job market. Eligible participants are 55 or older, in good health, meet income requirements, and reside in Georgia. Trainees work 20 hours per week at a public or nonprofit agencies such as hospitals, schools, senior centers, and day care centers. Contact Pearlie Love-Yearby, Athens Community Council on Aging, 135 Hoyt Street, Athens, GA 30601; 706-549-4850; Fax: 706-549-7786; {Email:ACCA@negia.net}.

Hawaii

One-Stop Career Centers
A network of One-Stop Career Centers throughout the state offers a wide range of employment related services including job training. Services vary by location. To find a location near you, please refer to the website {http://dlir.state.hi.us/wdd}. To learn more about the services they offer, contact your state coordinator.

Ms. Lorraine H. Akiba, Director, Department of Labor and Industrial Relations, 830 Punchbowl Street, Rm. 321, Honolulu, HI 96813; 808-586-8844; Fax: 808-586-9099

Ms. Elaine Young, Workforce Development Division Administrator, Department of Labor and Industrial Relations, 830 Punchbowl Street, Room 329, Honolulu, HI 96819; 808-586-8820; Fax: 808-586-8822.

Job Service Offices
A system of Employment Service/Job Service offices is located within every state with the goal of assisting millions of job seekers and employers. While services may vary from location to location, many provide job training, skills assessment and related services. With approximately 1,800 Employment Service/Job Service offices nationwide there is bound to be one near you. To learn more about the services offered in your area, contact your state administrator. Lorraine H. Akiba, Director, Department of Labor & Industrial Relations, 830 Punchbowl Street, Room 320, Honolulu, HI 96813; 808-586-8844; Fax: 808-586-9099; {www.dlir.state.hi.us}.

Women Work!
Women Work! is a state affiliate of the national membership organization dedicated to helping women from diverse backgrounds achieve economic self-sufficiency through job readiness, education, training and employment. For more information, contact Hawaii Women Work!, Janet Morse, President, Hawaii Literacy, Inc., 200 N. Vineyard Blvd., Suite 403, Honolulu, HI 96817; 808-537-6706; {Email: hliteracy@aol.com}.

Idaho

One-Stop Career Centers
A network of One-Stop Career Centers throughout the state offers a wide range of employment related services including job training. Services vary by location. To find a location near you, please refer to the website {www.idahoworks.state.id.us}. To learn more about the services they offer, contact your state coordinator.

Ms. Cheryl Brush, Idaho Department of Labor, 317 Main Street, Boise, ID 83735, 208-334-6303; Fax: 208-334-6430; {Email: cbrush@labor. state.id.us}.

Ms. Pat Debban, Idaho Department of Labor, 317 Main Street, Boise, ID 83735; 208-334-6399; Fax: 208-334-6430; {Email: pdebban@ labor.state.id.us}.

Job Service Offices

A system of Employment Service/Job Service offices is located within every state with the goal of assisting millions of job seekers and employers. While services may vary from location to location, many provide job training, skills assessment and related services. With approximately 1,800 Employment Service/Job Service offices nationwide there is bound to be one near you. To learn more about the services offered in your area, contact your state administrator. Roger B. Madsen, Director, Department of Labor, 317 Main Street, Boise, ID 83735; 208-334-6110; Fax: 208-334-6430; {www.labor.state.id.us}.

Service Corps of Retired Executive (SCORE)

Service Corps of Retired Executive (SCORE) is a national nonprofit organization that offers entrepreneur education in the formation, growth, and success of small businesses. You can receive free business counseling and monitoring from working and retired executives and business owners. You can also meet with a counseling person or use Email counseling at their web site. Besides that , they offer low-cost workshops through their local chapters. Topics include, Developing A Business Plan, Financial Management Techniques, Starting Your Home-Based Business, and Taking Your Business Global. The "how to" workshops , wisdom articles, and other featured articles can be accessed at their web site. Contact the SCORE Association at 800-634-0245 to find a location near you. SCORE, 1020 West Main Street, #290, Boise, ID 83702; 208-334-1696; Fax: 208-334-9353; TDD: 208-334-9637; {www.score.org}.

Idaho Migrant Council, Inc.

Idaho Migrant Council, Inc. provides employment and training services for low-income families and low-income migrant and seasonal farmworkers, primarily of Hispanic background. The Council offers ESL training at their centers and/or assists in enrollment in other ESL and GED classes. They have on-the-job training opportunities for their clients and pay for tuition, books, stipends and supportive services for vocational training. For farmworkers, they have employment and training counselors to help teach marketable skills and work experience in non-agricultural work. To find out how to benefit from these services, contact the Idaho Migrant Council, Inc., Twin Falls Community Resource Center, 406 Gardner, Twin Falls, ID 83301; 208-734-3336; {Email: crc26@micron.net}.

Magic Valley Youth and Adult Services, Inc.

Magic Valley Youth and Adult Services, Inc. has been providing services to youths and adults of the Magic Valley region for over 17 years. They offer education and training through individualized service and community resource coordination. They have a variety of client-centered services including individualized assessment; educational and career counseling; workshops; supportive services and long term follow-up. The Adult program is for those over 22 years and involves career counseling, financial assistance, direction to education and training institutions, classroom instruction and workshops. The Youth program is geared towards individuals ages 14 - 21. It helps them to learn new skills, develop work ethics, maintain or improve basic skills, learn application, resume, and interviewing skills, and more. Participants in these programs must meet demographic and income requirements. For more information, contact the Magic Valley Youth and Adult Services, Inc., 1869 Addison Avenue E, Twin Falls, ID 83301; 208-734-4435; FAX: 208-734-4479; {Email: mvyas@micron.net}.

The Workplace, Inc.

The Workplace, Inc. provides employment services to people that are unemployed or underemployed. Services are available for participants of the Department of Health and Welfare Self-Reliance Program as well as those at risk of going on benefit assistance. Also, low income individuals with kids under 18 may be eligible for services, free of charge. Some of the available services are assessment, job search and placement, short term pre-vocational training, work opportunity training, case management, career counseling, and follow up services. For more information, contact The Workplace, Inc., 1139 Falls Avenue East, Twin Falls, ID 83301; 208-733-5728.

Illinois

One-Stop Career Centers
A network of One-Stop Career Centers throughout the state offers a wide range of employment related services including job training. Services vary by location. To find a location near you, please refer to the website {www.ides.state.il.us/program/employer.htm}. To learn more about the services they offer, contact your state coordinator.

Mr. Herbert D. Dennis, Manager, One-Stop Lead, JTPA Programs Division Department of Commerce and Community Affairs, 620 East Adams, 6th Floor, Springfield, IL 62701; 217-785-6006; Fax: 217-785-6454; {Email: herb.dennis@accessil.com}.

Linda Renee Baker, Director, Illinois Department of Employment Security, 401 South State Street, Suite 615 South, Chicago, IL 60650; 312-793-5738; Fax: 312-793-9306.

Job Service Offices
A system of Employment Service/Job Service offices is located within every state with the goal of assisting millions of job seekers and employers. While services may vary from location to location, many provide job training, skills assessment and related services. With approximately 1,800 Employment Service/Job Service offices nationwide there is bound to be one near you. To learn more about the services offered in your area, contact your state administrator. Lynn Doherty, Director, Department of Employment Security, 401 South State Street, Suite 624, Chicago, IL 60605; 312-793-9279; Fax: 312-793-9834; {www.ides.state.il.us}.

Christian Programs
Ursuline Companions in Mission is a Christian association of lay women and men who seek to make a difference in the lives of the poor through a variety of programs including job training. They have service delivery sites in Delaware, Illinois, Kentucky, Minnesota, Missouri, New Mexico, and Ohio. Programs vary from location to location. For more information, contact Ursuline Companions In Mission, Sr. Jane Quinlan, College of New Rochelle, College Center, Room 155, New Rochelle, NY 10805; 914-654-5270; Fax: 915-654-5290; {www.theursulines.org}; {Email: ursulinecomp@hotmail.com}.

Gain Computer Literacy and More
Erie Technology Center is a comprehensive computer laboratory dedicated to the computer and information literacy of community residents. It is a program of Erie Neighborhood House, a settlement house located in Chicago. The Technology Center provides free computer and information literacy training to adult students taking in English, General Equivalency Diploma (GED), basic literacy, math, and career preparation classes at Erie Neighborhood House. As part of their regular classes, students use technology tools to complete their class assignments, write autobiographies, compile statistics, and create graphs. In addition, specific training is also provided in common application software, interfacing with Windows, using network resources, Email, and the Internet.

Currently, the Technology Center offers both daytime and evening classes to meet working students' needs. Their Pathways to Success (PTS) program is a job training program preparing adults to find jobs in the banking industry, which typically offers benefits in addition to living wages. Students, most of whom receive public assistance, learn English, math, personal budgeting, finance, workplace and stress management in the four-month program. The Technology Center serves as a "smart classroom" for PTS students to experience technology tools that they will be using in the workplace. Specific training is provided in touch-keyboarding, 10-key, Microsoft Office Professional, Email, and the Internet. A program titled First Step: Women, Technology, and Literacy provides training to women struggling to enter and remaining in the workforce to comply with federal welfare-to-work legislation. Working with low-literacy students (less than 6th grade reading level), staff teaches a combination of basic literacy and computer skills in a modern workplace environment simulated in the Technology Center. Every seat has a computer and access to software tools. Learning exercises in the areas of reading, writing, and pre-employment workshops are used to teach computer literacy. For more information, contact Erie Neighborhood House, 1347 W Erie St., Chicago, IL 60622-5722; 312-666-3430; { www.luc.edu/depts/curl/prag/pragusr/erie/}; {Email: eriehouse@ luc.edu}.

Find Out Where You Can Receive Job Training
The Workforce Center provides easy access to information about employment opportunities and job training to any Rock Island resident on a call or walk-in basis. Contact Walter Trice or Kristia Tinsley, Workforce Center, Martin Luther King Community Center, 630 9th Street, Rock Island, IL 61201; 309-732-2999; Fax: 309-732-2991.

Help In Evanston Township
Evanston Township General Assistance offers education and job training programs, including clerical training and GED preparation, and assists applicants in procuring employment. Provides substance abuse services and temporary financial assistance to eligible applicants. For more information, contact Evanston Township General Assistance, 1902 Main Street, Evanston, IL 60201; 847-475-4481.

Technical Opportunities
The Joliet Junior College Institute of Economic Technology offers a program called Technical Opportunities Program for Women in Non-Traditional Careers. It consists of a 16-week course offered at no charge to interested

women. The 120-hour hands-on program introduces women to specific career paths requiring acquisition of technical skills. The women are provided the foundation necessary to gain access to education, training and entry-level technical jobs. Program participants receive hands-on training in areas such as building and industrial maintenance, computer aided design/ architectural drafting, automotive service technology, electrical automated systems technology, electronics technology and chemical process operations technology. Three field trips to area manufacturers are included in the program, as well as stress management, workplace survival skills and job search on the Internet. For more information contact Sandy Cyrkiel at Joliet Junior College, 1215 Houbolt Road, Joliet, IL 60432-4077; 815-280-1526; 815-280-1506; {www.jjciet.org/top.htm}.

Help For Women In Transition
Home of the Sparrow is a non-profit transitional shelter for homeless women, women with children and expectant mothers and their infants. They provide transitional shelter, referral services, support, and encouragement daily to those in need. Residents are provided with: in-house counseling; job training; job placement; financial counseling; educational assistance; parenting classes; and assistance securing permanent housing. They are always open. For more information please call or write: Executive Director Rev. Phyllis Mueller, Home of the Sparrow, P.O Box 343, McHenry, IL 60051; 815-344-5171; Fax: 815-363-6001; {http://user.mc.net/~sparrow/}.

Learn Job Skills In a Supportive Environment
The Enterprising Kitchen is an innovative non-profit organization that provides meaningful employment along with job training to impoverished women living in Chicago. Participants are paid to assemble, package and help market products such as handmade soaps and grain-based goods. They offer women without strong work histories the chance to work in a supportive environment as they acquire valuable work habits and job skills. The women they employ participate in a holistic curriculum specially geared to meet their particular needs so that the workday is divided between curriculum time and production. Participants are paid to learn and work in an environment designed to encourage independence and personal development. 100% of all proceeds directly benefits job training and employment for women. For more information, contact The Enterprising Kitchen, 4545 N. Broadway, Chicago, IL 60640; 800-818-6158; Fax: 773-506-3881; {www.theenterprisekitchen.org}; {Email: info@ theenterprisekitchen.org}.

Gain Basic Job Skills

PASS Adult Education offers you the following services aimed at giving you basic skills for employment: adult basic education, secondary education, GED preparation, high school credit courses, introduction to computers, job seeking skills, literacy, family literacy programs, and English as a second language. They serve Warren, Henderson, and Mercer counties in Illinois. There is a $3 fee for the computer class. For more information, contact PASS Adult Education, 620 South Main #103, 620 South Main #15, Monmouth, IL 61462; 309-734-3818; Fax: 309-734-2041; {Email: pearson@misslink.net}.

Employment and Training Program For Women

The Southwest Women Working Together WETP provides education assistance and employment placement to displaced homemakers and single mothers. Job counselors often address the employment needs of women who are public aid recipients or homeless. In addition to financial aid and employment services, the program provides job readiness workshops, resume preparation classes, skills assessments, employment training seminars, and job support groups for women. Furthermore, the program sponsors an annual non-traditional job fair that introduces women to careers in fields that provide higher earning potential than traditional fields. For more information, contact Southwest Women Working Together, 4051 West 63rd Street, Chicago, IL 60629; 773-582-0550; Fax: 773-582-9669; {www.swwt.org/}; {Email: swwt@megsinet.net}.

Training For Low-Income People

The Center for Employment Training (CET) is a private, non-profit, community based organization that provides quality employment training for those who need it most. They offer extensive life skills and workplace know-how instruction through a program that includes job preparedness training, job development and placement. CET keeps students in training until they are placed and conducts follow-up on all placements to ensure stable employment and job growth. CET's primary activity is classroom skill training, which is provided year-round. CET does not screen applicants through testing, but accepts anyone who is willing to do the necessary work. Courses are offered on an open-entry, open-exit basis and students complete training at their own pace. CET training is intensive, with students attending 5 days and 35 to 40 hours per week for an average of seven months. CET training is competency based, highly individualized, and hands-on from day one. The average training course at CET maintains a 20-1 student/teacher ratio. CET's unique mode of training involves an integration of skill training, basic skill instruction and human development conducted in a simulated work setting. At least twenty-five job training options are offered at CET nationwide. These include automated office skills, building maintenance, electronic assembly, medical assistant, truck driving, and shipping/receiving. Skill offerings vary from one center to another. A typical CET center offers 4-5 skills and may serve up to 250 persons annually. For more information, contact their national headquarters: CET Corporate Offices, 701 Vine St., San Jose, CA 95110; 408-287-7924; 800-533-2519; {www.cet2000.org }. In Illinois, contact Center for Employment Training, 1307 South Wabash Ave., 3rd Floor, Chicago, IL 60605; 312-913-0055; Fax: 312-913-0937.

Work At A Trade

The Illinois Department of Employment Security (IDES) in cooperation with educators, business and trade unions, will help you get the training you need for high-paying, skilled jobs through a program called Women Step Up To Opportunity. Contact any of these organizations for more information:

* Illinois Employment Security Department, 401 S State St., Chicago, IL 60605-1225; 312-793-5700; {www.ides.state.il.us/individual/special/women.htm}.

* Illinois Department of Commerce and Community Affairs (DCCA), 620 E Adams St., Springfield, IL 62701-1615; 217-524-7568.

* Women Employed, 22 W Monroe St. # 1400, Chicago, IL 60603-2505; 312-782-3902.

- Midwest Women's Center, 202 South State Street, Suite 900, Chicago, IL 60604; 312-922-8530

- Chicago Women in Trades, 220 South Ashland Avenue, Chicago, IL 60607; 312-942-1444

Non-traditional Work

Women in Trades, in partnership with five organizations in different states, will provide technical assistance to employers, contractors, and labor organizations on mega construction projects in the Midwest. They will work with contractors and apprenticeship programs meeting their goals for hiring women in job sites. These groups refer qualified tradeswomen to jobs, and most provide pre-apprenticeship programs to give women the skills needed in apprenticeship programs. They can give information on career awareness on the range of job options for women too. For further information on programs in your state call: Lauren Sugerman, Executive Director, Chicago Women in Trades, 220 S. Ashland, Chicago, IL 60607; 312-942-1444 (For information specifically on pre-apprenticeship programs, at Chicago Women in Trades, contact Elise Wilson, Employment and Counseling Associate at the above phone number.)

Look At All These Programs For Women

Richland Community College has several programs designed around the career needs of women. All programs focus on employment and provide career guidance and job search assistance and you may be enrolled in more than one at a time.

- The *Options/Opportunities Programs* serve homemakers who are widowed, divorced, or separated and need help finding a job. They help low-income single parents, displaced homemakers, and men and women on public aid with tuition, child care, mileage, and books. Call 217-875-7200, ext. 232, for more information, {www.richland.cc.il.us/sds/optoppor/index.html}.

- The *Opportunities Program at RCC* assists with education, training and employment for TANF recipients. Post secondary, vocational skills, career assessment and non-traditional programs are available. Supportive services include child care and transportation. For referrals, call Barb Mosier at 217-421-6568; {www.richland.cc.il.us/sds/optoppor/index.html}

- The *Displaced Homemaker Program* offers career training workshops, career counseling, educational assistance and job placement assistance to homemakers who are divorced, widowed or separated and need to work to survive. Call Bobbie Henson at 217-875-7211, ext. 572; {www.richland.cc.il.us/sds/optoppor/index.html}.

- The *Single Parent Program* offers career training workshops, career counseling, educational assistance, job placement assistance, tuition, and child care costs for low-income single parents or single pregnant women who enroll in vocational courses. Call Kendall Dolly, Coordinator at 217-875-7211, ext. 480; {www.richland.cc.il.us/saals/perkins/singleparents/index.htm}.

- *Options In Technology* offers career training workshops, career counseling, educational assistance, job placement assistance, tuition, and child care costs for students who enroll in non-traditional courses or who seek non-traditional employment. Call Bobbie Henson at 217-875-7211, ext. 572; {www.richland.cc.il.us/sds/optoppor/index.html}.

- The *RCC Opportunities Center* offers 25-hour GED classes to TANF recipients. The focus is on entering the job market while obtaining a high school equivalency. Call Sandra Montgomery at 217-421-6568. For Job Readiness and Job Search referrals call Sandra Montgomery at 217-875-7211, ext. 574.

The RCC Opportunities Center is located at 1500 East Condit St., 2nd Floor. Call or write Richland Community College, One College Park, Decatur, IL 62521; 217-875-7200; {www.richland.cc.il.us/}.

Management Training

Founded in 1976, Women in Management was developed by a group of women in business to meet the need for training and support seminars for woman managers and women seeking management positions. The Near West Cook County Chapter was founded in 1991. Theirs is a membership organization. For more information, contact Patricia Davis, President, PRO Office Services, Oak Park, IL 60302; 708-386-3717; Fax: 708-848-4099; {www.oprf.com/WIM/index.html}; {Email: griz@megsinet.net}.

Other Chapters in Illinois Include:

For information on other Illinois chapters, go to the Women In Management website at {www.wimonline.org}.

Women Entrepreneurs in Chicago

The Women's Business Development Corporation can provide you with a variety of entrepreneurial training courses and seminars: one-on-one counseling; financial assistance and loan packaging for micro-loans, the SBA Prequalification Loan Program and other SBA and government loan programs including the mentor/protege program. They also offer WBE certification and private and public sector procurement; annual conference and Women's Buyers Mart; and extensive advocacy and policy development for women's economic and business development issues. Founded in 1986, the WBDC serves women business owners in the greater Chicago area, and advocates for women business owners nationwide. Contact Women's Business Development Center (WBDC), Hedy Ratner and Carol Dougal, Co-Directors, 8 South Michigan Avenue, Suite 400, Chicago, IL 60603; 312-853-3477; Fax: 312-853-0145; {www.wbdc.org}; {Email: wbdc@wbdc.org}.

Help For Illinois Displaced Homemakers

Illinois maintains a Network for Displaced Homemakers. There are 12 Displaced Homemaker Centers located throughout Illinois. Each provides services that assist displaced homemakers to achieve economic independence and become financially contributing members of society. A displaced homemaker is an individual who has worked in the home for a substantial number of years providing unpaid household services for family members, is not gainfully employed, had difficulty in securing employment, and was dependent on the income of another family member but is no longer supported by such income or was dependent on federal assistance but is no longer eligible for such assistance. Example of services offered are workshops, career life planning, counseling, and support groups, referrals to local community resources, identification of educational and training programs, job placement and job search assistance. The network itself functions as an information clearinghouse. Call for information and referrals to employment and training programs as well as to displaced homemaker centers in your geographical area. Contact Kathy Malcolm - Coordinator, Black Hawk College, 301 42nd Ave., E. Moline, IL 61244; 309-755-2200, ext. 230; Fax: 309-755-9847; {Email: malcolmk@outr01.bhc.edu}.

Training For Hispanics

The Hispanic Connections program enrolls a minimum of forty people per year in a six-week job training program which addresses basic employability skills and provides an opportunity for on-the-job training with the assistance of local businesses and not-for-profit agencies. For more information, contact Lutheran Social Services of Illinois, Hispanic Connections, 3455 North Chicago, Chicago, IL 60068; 773-292-5180.

Training For Dislocated Workers

Rock Valley College provides a Dislocated Worker Program for residents that have been unemployed by layoff termination or plant closure. The services it provides are; counseling, job skills workshops, job search assistance, job placement, and on-the-job training. It is free of charge to those that qualify. It also includes; books, child care, and transportation. For more information, contact Rock Valley College, Eleventh Street Center, 3134 11th Street, Rockford, IL 61109; 815-395-6600 ext. 319; Fax: 815-395-1899.

Career Planning

The Workforce Preparation Center at Parkland College has a free job skills and career planning program. The program helps individuals to gain skills which will make them more employable. Computer classes are part of the program also. There is also an Adult Education Program that offers free classes in GED preparation, English as a

Second Language, Reading Improvement Skills, and Mathematics. For more information, contact the WPC, 201 North Randolph Street, Champaign, IL 61820; 217-355-4836; Fax: 217-355-5091. For the Adult Education Program, call 217-351-2538; 2400 West Bradley Avenue, Champaign, IL 31821. For both programs: ; {www.parkalnd.cc.il.us/coned}; {Email: sboileau@parkland.cc.il.us}.

Microenterprise Program
University of Illinois Springfield's Community Outreach Partnership Center has partnered with the Lincoln Land Community College in the development of a microenterprise program targeted at HUD residents in Central Illinois. The program includes training and mentoring for individuals that want to develop, expand or sustain a microenterprise. It also provides a loan program to help them in their business. Contact the Community Outreach Partnership Center, PAC 360, University of Illinois, Springfield, Springfield, IL 62794-9243; 217-206-6646; Fax: 217-206-6542; {www.uic.edu/UI-Service/programs/UIS_DRUL-42SSRU.html}.

Indiana

One-Stop Career Centers
A network of One-Stop Career Centers throughout the state offers a wide range of employment related services including job training. Services vary by location. To find a location near you, please refer to the website {www.state.in.us/dwd}. To learn more about the services they offer, contact your state coordinator.

Carol Baker, Director, Program Development, Indiana Department of Workforce Development Indiana Government Center, 10 N. Senate Avenue, Indianapolis, IN 46204-2277; 317-233-3919; Fax: 317-233-4793.

Job Service Offices
A system of Employment Service/Job Service offices is located within every state with the goal of assisting millions of job seekers and employers. While services may vary from location to location, many provide job training, skills assessment and related services. With approximately 1,800 Employment Service/Job Service offices nationwide there is bound to be one near you. To learn more about the services offered in your area, contact your state administrator; {www.state.in.us/dwd}.

Timothy Joyce, Commissioner, Department of Workforce Development, Indiana Government Center South, 10 North Senate Avenue, Room E204, Indianapolis, IN 46204-2277; 317-233-5661; Fax: 317-233-1670

Bruce Kimery, Assistant Commissioner/Comptroller, Department of Workforce Development Indiana Government Center South, 10 North Senate Avenue, Room E204, Indianapolis, IN 46204-2277; 317-232-7675; Fax: 317-233-1670.

Help For Women and Minorities
Are you an Indiana woman or minority who owns a business? The Women and Minorities in Business Group (WMBG) offers counseling for emerging and mature businesses. Client needs are determined, evaluated and advised at no cost. Services include: workshops and seminars, direct counseling, information clearinghouse and referral source, and general information including statistics regarding women- and minority-owned businesses. They also administer the Minority Outreach Resource Executive (MORE) Program in six regions. Apply Through: Indiana Small Business Development Corporation (ISBD Corp.), 1 N. Capitol Ave. # 1275, Indianapolis, IN 46204-2025; 317-264-2820.

Single Parent/Displaced Homemaker Programs
Get assistance with vocational education, job training, career counseling, job placement, and life management training. Also, support groups to single parent, homemaker, displaced homemaker or single pregnant women in Decatur County and most surrounding areas. Contact Single Parent/Homemaker Project Services, 1025 Freeland Rd, Greensburg, IN 47240; 812-663-8597; {www.treecity.com/library/ resource/single.htm}.

Business Training
You can get assistance with tuition, books, uniforms, child care (licensed centers), and gas vouchers (transportation) for business training at the McDowell Adult Education Center. They will help in job seeking, including interviewing, resume preparation, and interest surveys. Contact McDowell Adult Education Center - BCSC Person in Charge: Nancy Rympa, Single Parent/Displaced Homemaker Program, 2700 McKinley Avenue, Columbus, IN 47201; 812-376-4451; {www.bcsc.k12.in.us/mcdowell/index.htm}.

Help For Farm and Migrant Workers
Transition Resources Corporation is a non-profit organization that serves the needs of farm workers, including migrant workers, and their families. They can help with free services that include financial and tutorial assistance for GED, Ivy Tech or other education, assessment and testing, career counseling, training, job placement. They also offer emergency help with food, financial, etc. To be eligible, you must have done farm work for at least 25 days or for $400. For more information, contact Transition Resources Corporation, 220 Clifty Drive, Unit J, Madison, IN 47250; 800-664-6066; 812-273-5451; Fax: 812-273-1881.

Learn To Be a Certified Nursing Assistant
The Certified Nursing Assistant Program at McDowell has a course where you can develop skills which could lead to entry level employment in the health care field. Special emphasis is placed on increasing skills for the job market; learning medical terminology, and understanding the everyday health needs of the patient, as well as one's self, one's family, and the elderly. Students who successfully complete one semester of Nurse Assistant training, may also qualify for long-term health care certification, after practicum training (2 week period) in a health care facility. Fees: $10 + books for high school; higher for non-credit students. Contact the Certified Nursing Assistant Program - McDowell, 2700 McKinley Ave., Columbus, IN 47201; 812-376-4451.

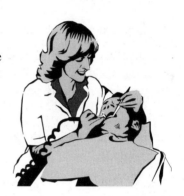

Help in Bartholomew County
The following are career service providers in Bartholomew County compiled from a list at {http://columbus.in.us/iris/search/query.asp}.

- You can take courses in marketing education, basic office services and entrepreneurship with opportunity for on-the-job training and community-based work with pay. There are no fees. Contact the Co-operative Office Education/Basic Office Services, 2650 Home Avenue, Columbus, IN 47201; 812-376-4240.

- Computer Training (Interim) is a company that can offer you free 90-minute classes throughout the week if you are actively seeking employment through Interim Personnel. Contact Computer Training (Interim), 1504 N. Lincoln, Greensburg, IN 47240; 812-379-1070; Fax: 812-663-9096.

- Computer Training (Kelly) provides free computer training courses for people registered with Kelly with all levels of prior computer skills. Schedules vary; call for details. Computer Training (Kelly), 810 Brown Street, Suite B, Columbus, IN 47201; 812-378-3757.

- Computer Training (Manpower) offers free computer training courses to clients who intend to seek employment through their services. Computer courses utilize a computer tutorial with help from a training assistant. Contact Computer Training (Manpower), 1309 North National Road, Columbus, IN 47201; 812-376-4111.

- The Columbus Housing Authority offers a program entitled Project Self-Sufficiency for individuals who are highly motivated for increased independence and currently on Housing Authority list. If you are residing in public housing, they offer you: child care, transportation, education, job development, job training, and counseling. Services are free. Contact Family Self-Sufficiency - Columbus Housing Authority, 801 McClure Road, Columbus, IN 47201; 812-376-2523.

- The Columbus Area Career Connection offers you classes in: Agriscience & Technology, Child Educare, Construction/Building, Trades Cooperative, Office Education, Cosmetology, Culinary Arts, Electronics Engineering, Drawing/CAD, Family & Consumer Science, Health Occupations, Industrial Cooperative Education, Industrial Technology, Machine Trades, Printing, Power Systems/Auto Technology, and Welding. You can receive credit toward your high school diploma while experiencing both classroom and work-based training. You also get workplace skills while laying the foundation for life-long learning. There are no fees. For more information, contact Columbus Area Career Connection, 2650 Home Avenue, Columbus, IN 47201; 812-376-4240; Fax: 812-376-4699.

- Health Careers Training offers choices in dental, veterinarian, physical therapy, radiology or nurse assistant. Students are placed at work sites for on-the-job training. This is a fee-based program. For more information, contact Health Careers Training, 2650 Home Ave., Columbus, IN 47201; 812-376-4240.

- Horizon House - Human Services, Inc. has a transitional shelter for homeless families who are highly motivated to make a permanent change in their lives. They can help you with job training/ coaching, short-term shelter; long-term case management; parenting classes; budget counseling; daily living skills; and nutrition classes. This office is also the intake site for after hours emergency lodging through the Salvation Army. There are no fees. Contact the Horizon House - Human Services, Inc., 724 Chestnut Street, P O Box 588, Columbus, IN 47202; 812-376-9710.

- IMPACT offers you job training and a work readiness program to help you become self-sufficient. Their services include: job training; education assistance; job placement; child care; transportation; medical coverage for up to 12 months; and limited financial assistance with uniforms, tools, etc. To be eligible, you must be a single parent, disabled parent, unemployed/ underemployed parent or teenage parent head of household; income and resource guidelines. There are no fees. Contact IMPACT (Indiana Manpower Placement & Comprehensive Training), 2330 Midway Street, Suite 3, Columbus, IN 47202; 812-376-9361.

- The Restaurant Dining-McDowell Education Center offers training in commercial food service. As a student, you will help operate a restaurant that serves lunch to the public three days a week. Call for information about fees. Contact Restaurant Dining-McDowell Education Center, 2700 McKinley Avenue, Columbus, IN 47201; 812-376-4451.

- You can acquire workplace skills while completing academic subjects needed to graduate and prepare for future education/work. Students receive a "Passport" that details their competency and skill levels for prospective employers and colleges. Services include: classes in physics, chemistry, biology, algebra, communication, composition, business, manufacturing and electronics; team teaching; peer tutoring; guest speakers; field trips; extensive hands-on instruction in tech lab. There are no fees. For more information, contact Technology Preparation Classes, 2650 Home Ave., Columbus, IN 47201; 812-376-4240.

- You can take free courses including topics such as building trades, welding, auto and diesel mechanics, electronics, printing, machine trades and drafting. Projects include: elaborate houses built; structures for Holiday Festival of Lights are hand forged and wired; microprocessor repair; computerized technology. For more information, contact Trade and Industry, 2650 Home Ave., Columbus, IN 47201; 812-376-4240.

- The Bartholomew County Division of Family & Children is a state agency that provides social services to adults, children, and families including job training. Contact Bartholomew County Division of Family & Children, 2330 Midway Street, Suite 3, P.O. Box 587, Columbus, IN 47202; 812-376-9361.

Job Training For Unemployed Single Dads

JobWorks provides job training and placement services to non-custodial dads that are unemployed and behind on their child support payments. After an initial assessment, there is a job search workshop, vocational training, job placement and post-placement support. This allows the father to get hourly employment to meet not only his child support obligations, but also his own living expenses. For information on how to participate with this program, contact Job Works, 201 East Rudisil Boulevard, Suite 206, Fort Wayne, IN 46806-1756; 219-745-2000; 888-750-WORK(9675); Fax: 219-745-0114; {Email: information@jobworksinc.org}.

Help For Disadvantaged Young Adults

JobWorks and the Community Centers of Indianapolis have joined together to administer the Youth Employment Development Network (YEDN). This program is for hard-to-employ youth and young adults in the near Westside neighborhoods of Indianapolis. YEDN has three distinct youth employment and training services; Year-round Youth Employment services, In-School Youth Employment services, and Summer Youth Employment services. There are over 20 youth-serving programs involved in YEDN. Each of the programs involves skills training, employment services, and opportunities to youths year round. For more information, contact JobWorks , 3602, East Michigan Street, Suite E, Indianapolis, IN 46201-3467; 317-532-1200; Fax: 317-532-1207; {www.jobworksinc.org/indianapolis.htm}; {Email: eahlbrand@indy.jobworksinc.org}.

Goodwill Industries of Central Indiana

Goodwill Industries of Central Indiana offers a variety of job training programs to help individuals to become self-sufficient. Each program has eligibility requirements.

- Transitional Employment Program offers employment with Goodwill to people with limited skills or no work history. They may work in a variety of setting. This program helps the employees develop confidence and the competence to find employment outside of Goodwill.

- ABE, Adult Basic Education, involves individualized instruction in reading, math, and writing skills, as well as GED preparation.

- The Business Career Education program prepares people for a career in the clerical field. It teaches basic compute skills, customer service, and problem solving.

- Microsoft Office User Specialist (MOOS) Training is for people that have some computer knowledge in order to pass the Microsoft Office User Specialist exam.

- At the Computer Graphic Training Center students get intensive, individualized instruction on Macintosh equipment. This is a 6 month training session.

- In the Industry-Specific Job Training program people can prepare clients for jobs in health care and advanced manufacturing technology. Additional training programs are in development.

For more information, contact Goodwill Industries, 1635 West Michigan Street, Indianapolis, IN 46222; 317-264-1264; TDD: 317-264-1219; Fax: 317-264-1336; {Email: hstevens@goodwill-indy.org}. For a list of other Goodwill locations and the training programs they offer, go to {www.goodwill.org/job3.html}.

Training for Seniors

Seniors can get work experience and on-the-job training through the Senior Community Service Employment Program. It is for people 55 and older that do not make more than a specified income from social security and pension, the amount changes yearly. For more information, contact the Lake County Economic Opportunities Council, Inc., Senior Community Service Employment Program, 5518 Calumet, Hammond, IN 46320; 219-937-3500; Fax: 219-932-0560.

Iowa

One-Stop Career Centers
A network of One-Stop Career Centers throughout the state offers a wide range of employment related services including job training. Services vary by location. To find a location near you, please refer to the website {www.iowaworkforce.org/index.html}. To learn more about the services they offer, contact your state coordinator.

Cynthia P. Eisenhauer, Director, One-Stop Lead, Iowa Department of Workforce Development, 1000 East Grand Avenue, Des Moines, IA 50319; 515-281-5365; Fax: 515-281-4698; {Email: Cynthia. Eisenhauer@iwd.state.ia.us}.

Job Service Offices
A system of Employment Service/Job Service offices is located within every state with the goal of assisting millions of job seekers and employers. While services may vary from location to location, many provide job training, skills  assessment and related services. With approximately 1,800 Employment Service/Job Service offices nationwide there is bound to be one near you. To learn more about the services offered in your area, contact your state administrator. Cynthia Eisenhauer, Director, Department of Workforce Development, 1000 E. Grand Avenue, Des Moines, IA 50319; 515-281-5365; Fax: 515-281-4698; {www.iowaworkforce.org/index.html}.

Would You Like To Be Self-Employed?
The Institute of Social and Economic Development Focuses on low-income, unemployed and underemployed individuals. They encourage self-sufficiency through the growth of a small business and other self -employment opportunities. They can provide services for any person who wants to start or expand a business employing up to five employees, including the owner. For more information, contact Institute of Social and Economic Development, 1901 Broadway, Suite 313, Iowa City, IA 52240; 319-338-2331; Fax: 319-338-5824; {www.ised.org}.

Training For Older Workers
The Older Worker Employment & Training program provides free training through part-time employment (20 hours/week). As an enrollee, you will be assigned to government agencies, non-profit corporations and schools that provide a "community service". You will be paid minimum wage with federal Older Americans Act funds. While in the program, you will also attend classroom training and gain experience that will lead to unsubsidized employment. This means a job not paid for by the program or other federal funds. Interested persons ages 55 years and over are encouraged to contact the Older Worker Employment & Training, Catherine Pratscher-Woods Coordinator, Great River Bend AAA, 736 Federal Street, Davenport, IA 52803; 319-324-9085; 800-892-9085; Fax: 319-324-9384.

Goodwill Industries of Central Iowa
Goodwill Industries of Central Iowa offer a number of work programs for its residents. The Work Adjustment Program which is a vocational assessment program. The Work Services program helps disabled people achieve their maximum vocational potential either through employment at Goodwill, or within supported employment in the community. Work Experience works with vocationally disadvantaged people that provides work habit/attitude training and assessment. They also offer supported employment, job placement and Adult Basic Education. To find out more about the programs, contact Goodwill Industries of Central Iowa, 4900 NE 22nd Street, Des Moines, IA 50313; 515-265-5323; Fax: 515-265-0645; {www.goodwill.org/states/IA/Des_Moines.htm}. For a list of other Goodwill locations and the training programs they offer, go to {www.goodwill.org/job3.html}.

Promise Jobs
Promise Jobs is a program that focuses on helping people to become self-sufficient. It is available for people of families that are eligible for FIP cash assistance. The main focus of the program is education, work and training services, and job placement. It also provides funds for child care to make the transition easier. To find out if you are eligible to participate in the program, contact the Department of Human Services, Division of Economic Assistance, Hoover State Office Building, 5th Floor, 1305 East Walnut Street, DesMoines, IA 50319; 515-281-3163/3131; Fax: 515-281-7791; {www.dhs.state.ia.us/economicassistance/economicassistance.asp}.

The Educational Equity Program
The Educational Equity Program at Iowa Lakes Community College has a variety of job related services available, most of them at no cost. People that are eligible for these services are, homemakers looking for employment; returning students; divorced, separated, widowed, or disabled spouses; single heads of households; displaced workers; or anyone looking for a new direction. The services available include Displaced Homemaker Services, Dislocated Worker Services, Office Skills Classes, Career and Academic Assessment and Advisement, Gender Equity Services, Workshops and Seminars, Job Search Skills, and more. They can also help to enroll participants in educational programs. For more information, contact Educational Equity Program, Iowa Lakes Community College, 300 South 18th Street, Estherville, IA 51334; 712-362-7926; {Email: lwiegman@ilcc.cc.ia.us}.

Kansas

One-Stop Career Centers
A network of One-Stop Career Centers throughout the state offers a wide range of employment related services including job training. Services vary by location. To find a location near you, please refer to the website {entkdhr.ink.org/cgi-dir/one-stop/doc2.cgi}. To learn more about the services they offer, contact your state coordinator.

Mr. Roger Aeschliman, Acting Secretary, Kansas Department of Human Resource, 401 SW Topeka Blvd., Topeka, KS 66603-3182; 785-296-7474; Fax: 785-368-6294.

Heather Whitley, Director of Employment and Training, Kansas Department of Human Resources, Division of Employment and Training, 401 SW Topeka Blvd., Topeka, KS 66603-3182; 785-296-7874; Fax: 785-296-5112.

Job Service Offices
A system of Employment Service/Job Service offices is located within every state with the goal of assisting millions of job seekers and employers. While services may vary from location to location, many provide job training, skills assessment and related services. With approximately 1,800 Employment Service/Job Service offices nationwide there is bound to be one near you. To learn more about the services offered in your area, contact your state administrator., Linda Weaver, Secretary, Kansas Department of Human Resources, 401 Topeka Boulevard, Topeka, KS 66603; 785-296-2159; Fax: 785-368-6294; {www.hr.state.ks.us}; {Email: ljweaver@hr.state.ks.us}.

Kansas Job Training
Heartland Works, Inc. is a private company that administers job training in Kansas with Job Training Partnership Act. The focus of Heartland Works and JTPA is to assist individuals in becoming productive members of the workforce. Their services include basic skills training designed to help participants overcome deficiencies in reading, writing and math and prepare for the GED test, and career reemployment opportunities through an network of Career Reemployment Centers, where clients can interact with training representatives to conduct career research, attend career development workshops, create customized resumes/cover letters, practice their job search skills and attend computer classes. In addition, each center has a wealth of career development resources in a variety of mediums including access to the Internet. Classroom training opportunities are available through contracts with several vocational schools, technical colleges and community colleges as well as other educational providers for classroom training enrollments. Training is directed toward acquiring specific job skills in high demand occupations and will typically last six months to two years. Based on eligibility and overall need, a client may receive assistance with the cost of tuition, books, tools, uniforms and other necessary materials. To locate a service provider near you, refer to the list below or contact {Email: heartlandjtpa@cjnetworks.com}; {www.heartlandworks.org}.

Heartland Works Field Offices

*   Heartland Works Topeka, 1430 SW Topeka Blvd., Topeka, KS 66614; 785-233-3131; Fax: 785-233-3433; {Email: heartlandwrk1@cjnetworks.com}.

- Heartland Works Lawrence, 2518 Ridge Court, Suite 105, Lawrence, KS 66049; 785-865-5463; Fax: 785-865-5465; {Email: heartlandwrk2@cjnetworks.com}.

- Heartland Works Manhattan, 1019B Poyntz, Manhattan, KS 66502; 785-539-0591; Fax: 785-539-1053.

- Heartland Works Satellite Office Marysville, 1021 Broadway, Marysville, KS 66508; 785-562-2238; Fax: 785-562-3036.

- Heartland Works Satellite Office, 818 Kansas Ave., Atchison, KS 66002; 785-367-0090.

- Heartland Works Satellite Office, Junction City, 136 West 3rd Street, Junction City, KS 66441; 785-762-8870.

Women Work!
Women Work! A state affiliate of the national membership organization dedicated to helping women from diverse backgrounds achieve economic self-sufficiency through job readiness, education, training and employment. Contact Kansas Women Work!, Cynthia Shanley, President, New Directions-KSU, 2323 Anderson Avenue Suite 221, Manhattan, KS 66502; 785-532-6561; {Email: shanley@ ksu.edu}.

Sharpen Skills
The Neosho County Community College Campus offers assistance to local community citizens needing help to overcome obstacles in order to achieve their employment goals at their Center for Academic and Vocational Excellence. It is located in the lower level of the Chapman Library on the Neosho County Community College

Campus in Chanute, Kansas and is locally known as the CAVE. It consists of a computer lab, testing room, two classrooms, study areas, and offices. It is accessible to persons with physical challenges. CAVE computers provide academic tutorials to improve reading, writing, science, and math skills. In addition, word processing programs, software used in business and work settings, and programs geared toward the vocational needs of business and industry are also available. Services offered include: academic tutoring; adult basic education (ABE); computer-sided instruction; computer literacy training; developmental instruction; choices; GED preparation and testing; Internet exploration; job listings/career options; keyboarding program; problem solving skills course; resume design; seminars and workshops; and study groups. For additional information about the Center for Academic and Vocational Excellence please contact: The Panther CAVE, Neosho County Community College, 800 West 14th Street, Chanute, KS 66720; 316-431-2820, ext. 279; {www.neosho.cc.ks.us/students/Current/cave.htm}.

Kentucky

One-Stop Career Centers
A network of One-Stop Career Centers throughout the state offers a wide range of employment related services including job training. Services vary by location. To find a location near you, please refer to the website {www.state.ky.us/agencies/wforce}. To learn more about the services they offer, contact your state coordinator.

Ms. Julia Gustafson, One-Stop Team Leader, Kentucky Cabinet for Workforce Development, 500 Mero Street, 12th Floor CPT, Frankfort, KY 40601; 502-564-9146; Fax: 502-564-9504.

Ms. Pam Anderson, Program Director, Career Connection, 305 West Broadway, Louisville, KY 40202; 502-574-2500; Fax: 502-574-4288.

Ms. Margaret Whittet, Commissioner, Department of Employment Services, Cabinet for Human Resources, 275 E. Main Street, Frankfort, KY 40621; 502-564-5331; Fax: 502-564-7452.

Job Service Offices

A system of Employment Service/Job Service offices is located within every state with the goal of assisting millions of job seekers and employers. While services may vary from location to location, many provide job training, skills assessment and related services. With approximately 1,800 Employment Service/Job Service offices nationwide there is bound to be one near you. To learn more about the services offered in your area, contact your state administrator. Rhonda K. Richardson, Commissioner, Department of Employment Services, 275 East Main Street, Frankfort, KY 40621; 502-564-5331; Fax: 502-564-7452; {www.desky.org/jobservices/jobservice.htm}.

Other State Programs

The Office of Labor Management Relations and Mediation (OLMRM) offers a variety of training programs designed to assist labor and management move toward a more cooperative and productive relationship based on trust. The training programs can be designed, based on time availability, to meet specific needs. For more information, contact Kentucky Labor Cabinet, 1047 U.S. 127S, Suite 4, Frankfort, KY 40601; 502-564 3070; Fax: 502-564-5387; {www.state.ky.us/agencies/labor/labrhome.htm}.

Christian Programs

Ursuline Companions in Mission is a Christian association of lay women and men who seek to make a difference in the lives of the poor through a variety of programs including job training. They have service delivery sites in Delaware, Illinois, Kentucky, Minnesota, Missouri, New Mexico, and Ohio. Programs vary from location to location. For more information, contact Ursuline Companions In Mission, Sr. Jane Quinlan, College of New Rochelle, College Center, Room 155, New Rochelle, NY 10805; 914-654-5270; Fax: 914-654-5290; {www.theursulines.org}; {Email: ursulinecomp@hotmail.com}.

Career Resources

Career Resources, Inc. has specialized services available for those that have been laid off and are either receiving or have used up their unemployment insurance. The services are provided at their Solution Centers and include individualized career counseling, career search assistance, and training programs for those who lack current marketable skills. They also have job banks, access to computers, phone, fax, and copier use for job searching. Corporate Headquarters: 505 South Third Street, Suite 201, Louisville, KY 40202-1884; 502-574-4780; Fax: 502-574-4778; {www.careerresourcesinc.org}; {Email: info@careerresourceinc.org}. Contact one of the locations in your area:

- Bullit County-Shepersville Square, 445 Highway 44, Shepherdsville, KY 40165; 502-955-9131; Fax: 502-543-4861

- Nia Center- 2900 West Broadway, Suite 100, Louisville, KY 40211-1279; 502-574-4100; Fax: 502-574-1197

- Riverport-6900 Riverport Drive, Louisville, KY 40258-2851; 502-933-3045; Fax: 502-933-3047

- Shelby County-409 Washington Street, Shelbyville, KY 40065-1127; 502-647-5422; Fax: 502-647-5421

Small Business Help

Jewish Family and Vocational Service has a couple of programs to help Kentucky businesses. The Center for Microenterprise Development helps clients to gain economic self-sufficiency through self-employment. This program includes business idea research, business plan development, marketing, financial planning, technical assistance and access to capital. It is targeted at refugees, immigrants, and women. They also have the Family Business Center which is pa partnership with UL's College of Business. The program provides business/technical and behavioral science services to family businesses. It also includes networking, family forums, and family business consultation. The services of JFVS are provided on a sliding scale. Contact the JFVS, 3640 Dutchmans Lane, Louisville, KY 40208; 502-452-6341; {www.jfvs.com/jfvscare.htm}; {Email: jfvs@jfvs.com}.

Creative Employment Program

Center for Women and Families, Inc.-Creative Employment Program is open to single parents/displaced homemakers, low-income individuals, and women and men in career transitions. The program has been created to deliver specialized employment programs and counseling so that people can successfully provide for themselves.

Essential skills and information are taught so that people can grow in both their careers and personal lives. Some of the services provided are, job readiness workshops, individual career counseling, and computer training. Contact the Center for Women and Families, Inc., 226 West Breckingridge Street, PO Box 2048, Louisville, KY 40203; 502-581-7200; 502-581-7221; Fax: 502-581-7204; {Email: cwf@ntr.net}.

Help For Seniors to Returning to Work
The Senior Community Service Employment Program helps low-income seniors get back into the workforce. They are placed with a non-profit organization and work 20 hours a week during which they receive pay from AARP. There, they learn valuable skills. The next step is that they receive one on one counseling in order to find a better paying, permanent job. Eligible participants are low-income and 55 years or older from Jefferson, Kentucky Bullitt, Kentucky Shelby, and Kentucky Oldham counties. Contact the Senior Community Service Employment Program, 756 South 1st Street, Burdorf Building, Suite 204, Louisville, KY 40202; 502-584-0309; Fax: 502-584-0307; {Email: schridsdal@aol.com}.

Career Development
The Career Development Center at the Louisville Urban League provides services for African-Americans and individuals of low to moderate income in order to prepare for employment. The services available for job training and development include computer training, life skills, and job readiness training. One-on-one counseling and placement services are also available. Contact Juanita Sands, Louisville Urban League, 1535 West Broadway, Louisville, KY 40203; 502-561-6830; TDD: 502-585-2136; Fax: 502-585-2335; {www.lul.org}; {Email: jsands@lul.org}.

Louisiana

One-Stop Career Centers
A network of One-Stop Career Centers throughout the state offers a wide range of employment related services including job training. Services vary by location. To find a location near you, please refer to the website {www.ldol.staet.la.us}. To learn more about the services they offer, contact your state coordinator.

Ms. Dawn Watson, Project Administrator, Louisiana Department of Labor, 1001 N. 23rd Street (Zip 70804), P.O. Box 94094, Baton Rouge, LA 70804-9094; 504-342-7629; Fax: 504-342-7664.

Job Service Offices
A system of Employment Service/Job Service offices is located within every state with the goal of assisting millions of job seekers and employers. While services may vary from location to location, many provide job training, skills assessment and related services. With approximately 1,800 Employment Service/Job Service offices nationwide there is bound to be one near you. To learn more about the services offered in your area, contact your state administrator.

Ms. Robin Houston, Secretary, Department of Labor, P.O. Box 94094, Baton Rouge, LA 70804-9094; 225-342-3013; Fax: 225-342-3778.

Ms. Gayle Joseph, Assistant Secretary for the Office of Employment Security, Department of Labor, P.O. Box 94094, Baton Rouge, LA 70804-9094; 225-342-3013; Fax: 225-342-5208.

Occupational Information
The Louisiana Occupational Information System is a comprehensive online guide to educational/training providers in the state. You can search by geographic area, occupational training desired, or institutions. Go to {http://lois/ldol.state.la.us/lois/default.asp} and click on "training."

Women's Services

The Governor's Office of Women's Services is the official state agency legislatively charged to advocate on behalf of women. OWS coordinates public (local, state, federal), private, corporate, foundation, non-profit, volunteer, educational, and other funding sources to develop programs to address the needs of women. There are five locations: Lake Charles, Baton Rouge, New Orleans, Shreveport, and Lafayette. Depending on the location, you can receive individualized career counseling and assessment; basic skills enhancement; building and industrial trades preparatory training; clerical/medical training; job placement services; customer service training and referrals to other training opportunities. If you are interested in working at a job traditionally held by men, the Non-Traditional Training Program will be of interest. Women in this program may be economically disadvantaged, unemployed, a dislocated worker, or a Find Work participant. Training varies from 9 to 12 weeks and you can learn skills in basic electricity, industrial wiring, circuitry, AC/DC motors, mechanical devices and systems, blueprint reading and schematics, and applied mathematics including algebra, geometry, and basic computer literacy. For more information, contact Administrative Office, Governor's Office of Women's Services, 1885 Wooddale Blvd., 9th Floor, Baton Rouge, LA 70806; P.O. Box 94095, Baton Rouge, LA 70804-9095; 225-922-0960; Fax: 225-922-0959; {Email: owsbradm@cmq.com}; {www.ows.state.la.us/}.

Local Centers

- Baton Rouge Displaced Homemakers Ctr., 2712A Wooddale Boulevard, Baton Rouge, LA 70805; 225-925-6922; Fax: 225-922-2574.

- Lafayette Displaced Homemakers Ctr., 1304 Bertrand Dr., Suite C-1, Lafayette, LA 70506; 318-262-5191; Fax: 318-262-5192.

- Lake Charles Displaced Homemakers Ctr., 2120 Hodges Street, Lake Charles, LA 70601; 318-491-2656; Fax: 318-491-6844.

- New Orleans Displaced Homemakers Ctr., 980 Navarre Ave., LA Technical College, New Orleans, LA 70124; 504-483-4664; Fax: 504-483-4664.

- Shreveport Displaced Homemakers Ctr., 752 Dalzell, Shreveport, LA 71104; 318-676-7137; Fax: 318-676-5691.

Help For Women Entrepreneurs

Women Entrepreneurs for Economic Development, Inc. (W.E.E.D.) was founded in 1989 by three businesswomen. Since its inception, W.E.E.D. has assisted over 200 women in becoming economically self-sufficient. They assist women in the Orleans Parish area of New Orleans. Contact Women Entrepreneurs for Economic Development Inc. (W.E.E.D.), Paula Pete, Executive Director, Cynthia Beaulieu, Director of Training, 1683 North Claiborne Avenue, New Orleans, LA 70116; 504-949-8885; Fax: 504-949-8885.

Back To High School

Hamilton Terrace Learning Center in Shreveport, LA, which won the Innovations in American Government award given by Harvard University and the Ford Foundation is a "second-chance" high school whose student body includes welfare recipients, working adults, and high school students who have been expelled from other schools. For more information, contact Hamilton Terrace Learning Center, c/o Caddo Parish School Board, 1105 Louisiana Ave., Shreveport, LA 71101; 318-222-4518.

Women Small Business Owners Assistance

The Women's Business Center is a program that was developed by the Southeast Louisiana Black Chamber of Commerce (SLBCC) to assist women in Jefferson Parish, but serves nine other parishes including: Orleans, St. Bernard, St. Tammany, St. James, St. John the Baptist, St. Charles, Tangipahoa, Plaquemines and Washington. The

Center can provide you with training, counseling and mentoring to aid and encourage the growth and development of small businesses, owned and controlled by women. Many of the clients served through the Center have started their own businesses. The Center is located in JEDCO West, an incubator program in Harvey, LA. For more

information, contact Southeast Louisiana Black Chamber of Commerce (SLBCC), Women's Business Center, Laverne Kilgore, Director, 2245 Peters Road, Suite 200, Harvey, LA 70058; 504-365-3866; Fax: 504-365-3890; {www.gnofn.org/~slbcc/wbc}; {Email: wbc200@bellsouth.net}.

Women Business Owners

Women Business Owners Association works to establish women business owners as an integral and influential element of the business community and promotes the success of women-owned businesses. Greater New Orleans area business owners wanting to exchange information and share experiences formed WBOA as an organization consisting of women who own businesses and associates who support women in business. In 1998, WBOA celebrated its nineteenth year. WBOA was created to: foster training, technical assistance and other learning opportunities oriented toward your needs, encourage, support, and represent women-owned businesses, cultivate economic stability of women-owned businesses, and initiate and support legislation benefiting small businesses. For more information contact WBOA, 109 West William David Parkway, Metairie, LA 70011; 504-456-0505; {www.wboa.org/Default.htm}.

Help For Displaced Homemakers

The Center for Displaced Homemakers/Office of Women's Services provides services to women or men who are separated, divorced, widowed or have a handicapped spouse. If this sounds like you, you can benefit from adjustment counseling; job readiness training; weekly support group and assessment and referrals, legal assistance, resume preparation, and personal development workshops. They also act as a processing center for dislocated workers and displaced homemakers eligible for training at Women's Employment and Training Center. There are no fees for qualified clients. For more information, contact Center for Displaced Homemakers, 752 Dalzell, Shreveport LA 71104; 318-676-7137; Fax: 318-676-5691; Site Manager: Doreen McGaffey.

Job Training/Enterprise Program

The Church Army of Western Louisiana is a homeless care network based in Lafayette, LA. Projects include a day shelter, an emergency home for unaccompanied adult women, a transitional home for men, a community/activity center, and a job-training and enterprise program that is currently in development. For more information, contact Church Army of Western Louisiana, P.O. Box 2747, Lafayette, LA 70502; 318-237-7647.

Help With Your Small Business

To get help with your small business, go to the Division for Small and Emerging Business Development. They offer resources to certified small and emerging businesses in order to make them competitive in their area. Some of the on-going activities are, business plan development, marketing plans, financial projection statements, computer accounting training, and more. Their services are provided through Small Business Development Centers, consultants, and trained professional that have developed a partnership wit the Division. Workshops and training that are useful to small businesses are provided. You can download a Certification Application from their web site and a list of approved service providers is coming soon. Small and Emerging Business Development, 339 Florida Boulevard, Suite 212, PO Box 44153, Baton Rouge, LA 70804; 225-342-5373; Fax: 225-342-6820; {www.lded.state.la.us/New/sebd/sebdmain.htm}; {Email: web-sebd@lded.state.la.us}.

Migration and Refugee Services

Migration and Refugee Services are available for newly arrived refugees families and immigrants. The Employment Services involve job development, employment counseling, career counseling, workshops, placement, follow-up, and more. In addition to work assistance, they have English as a Second Language help and Citizenship Testing. For more information, contact Catholic Charities Agency, 1990 South Acadian Thruway, PO Box 1668, Baton Rouge, LA 70821-1668; 225-346-0660; Fax: 225-336-8745.

Maine

One-Stop Career Centers
A network of One-Stop Career Centers throughout the state offers a wide range of employment related services including job training. Services vary by location. To find a location near you, please refer to the website {www.mainecareercenter.com}. To learn more about the services they offer, contact your state coordinator.

Ms. Valerie Landry, Commissioner, Maine Department of Labor, 20 Union St., P.O. Box 309, Augusta, ME 04330; 207-287-3788; Fax: 207-287-5292.

Job Service Offices
A system of Employment Service/Job Service offices is located within every state with the goal of assisting millions of job seekers and employers. While services may vary from location to location, many provide job training, skills assessment and related services. With approximately 1,800 Employment Service/Job Service offices nationwide there is bound to be one near you. To learn more about the services offered in your area, contact your state administrator. Valerie R. Landry, Commissioner of Labor, ME Department of Labor, P.O. Box 309, Augusta, ME 04330; 207-287-3788; Fax: 207-287-5292; {http://janus.state.me.us/labor}.

Help Is Just A Phone Call Away
Forced to go into the work world suddenly or do you need help getting your job skills upgraded? Women Work! is for you. They have over 1400 sites across the country to help women from diverse backgrounds achieve economic self-sufficiency through job readiness, education, training and employment. Women Work! provides these services through a network of programs in every state. Women Work! also takes on the toughest women's employment issues and fights for them in Congress and in state legislatures. For more information on Women Work! or to find a location near you contact Women Work! Regional Representative, Region I, Thia Hamilton, Maine Centers for Women, Work and Community, 200 Madison Ave., Skowhegan, ME 04976; 207-474-0788.

Training In Trade And Technical Occupations For Women
Why should a woman choose a trade or technical occupation? How about for money, satisfaction, and/or control of her life? Women Unlimited offers a program that includes basic trade and technical skills training, physical conditioning, job-based math and literacy, and personal and career development. The program is 14 weeks long, meeting 3 days per week for 8 hours a day at sites throughout Maine. Upon completion of the program, they connect you with contractors and employers hiring for entry-level and skilled positions. For more information, contact Martha Piscuskas, Executive Director, 71 Winthrop St., Augusta, ME 04330; 207-623-7576; 800-281-5259; {www.womenunlimited.org}; {Email: staff@womenunlimited.org}.

Help For Fledgling Women Owned Businesses
Coastal Enterprises, Inc. (CEI) is a private non-profit community development corporation that provides financing and technical assistance to Maine businesses that provide income, ownership or employment opportunities to low-income people. One of their programs is The Women's Business Center that emerged from CEI's experience in assessing women's business owners' needs, and providing women's business owners with training, technical assistance, financing and advocacy. If you have already started your own business anywhere in Maine, they can help you. You can benefit from CEI's counseling, as well as their capacity to provide access to capital through its SBA Microloan Program, the SBA Women's Pre-Qualification Loan Program and other resources. For more information, contact Coastal Enterprises Inc. (CEI), Women's Business Center, Betsy Tipper, Telecommunications Business Counselor, 7 North Chestnut Street, Augusta, ME 04330; 207-621-0245; Fax: 207-622-9739; {www.ceimaine.org}; {Email: jmr@ceimaine.org}.

Plug Into A Statewide Network of Resource Centers For Women

If you are a displaced homemaker, single parent, welfare recipient, or simply a worker in transition, Maine Centers for Women, Work, and Community can set you on the path towards self-sufficiency. This statewide women's economic development organization offers training and assistance in workforce preparation, entrepreneurship, leadership development, comprehensive assessment, referral, training, placement, and other support services through 15 resource centers and outreach sites located throughout the state. Specifically, you can benefit from workshops on employability training, career/life planning, job search skills, self-esteem, assertiveness training, self-employment issues, and personal resource management. All services are free and confidential. Note that services may vary by location. To locate a location near you, refer to the list below or contact the administrative office at Maine Centers for Women, Work, and Community, Stoddard House, University of Maine at Augusta, 46 University Drive, Augusta ME 04330-9410; 207-621-3440; 800-442-2092 (ME only); Fax: 207-621-3429; {http://mcwwc.uma.maine.edu}; {Email: adaigle@maine.edu}.

Maine Centers for Women, Work and Community Office Locations

- MCWWC, University College, 355 Maine Avenue, Bangor, ME 04401-6130; 800-442-2092; 207-581-6132; Fax: 207-581-6130; {Email: searles@maine.edu}.

- MCWWC, Bath-Brunswick Center UMS, 275 Bath Road, Brunswick, ME 04011; 207-721-8636; 800-442-2092; Fax: 207-729-8261; {Email: virginia.powers@maine.edu}.

- MCWWC, Mill Mall, 240 State Street, Ellsworth, ME 04605; 207-667-1834; 800-442-2092; Fax: 207-667-7450.

- MCWWC, 48 Perham Street, Farmington, ME 04938; 207-778-2463; 800-442-2092; Fax: 207-778-2757.

- MCWWC, P.O. Box 382, Located at 106 Main Street, Houlton, ME 04730; 207-532-9313; 800-442-2092 (ME only); Fax: 207-532-3639; {Email: audrey@maine.edu}.

- MCWWC, Lewiston-Auburn College USM/UMA, 51-55 Westminster Street, Lewiston, ME 04240; 207-753-6621; 800-442-2092; Fax: 207-753-6658; {Email: ebrown@maine.edu}.

- MCWWC, 28 Balsam Drive, Millinocket, ME 04462; 207-723-9331; 800-442-2092; Fax: 207-723-9128.

- MCWWC, NMTC 33 Edgemont Drive, Presque Isle, ME 04769; 207-764-0050; 800-442-2092 (ME only); Fax: 207-769-6608; {Email: mewilcox@ainop.com}.

- MCWWC, Saco-Biddeford Center UMS, 110 Maine Street, Suite 1101, Saco, ME 04072; 207-286-1722; Fax: 207-283-9865.

- MCWWC, St. John Valley, NMTC 33 Edgemont Drive, Presque Isle, ME 04769; 207-764-0050; 800-442-2092; (ME only); Fax: 207-769-6608; {Email: mewilcox@ainop.com}.

- MCWWC, 200 Madison Avenue, Skowhegan, ME 04976-1305; 207-474-0788; 207-474-7865; 207-474-0598; 800-442-2092; Fax: 207-474-3684; {Email: womwork@somtel.com}.

- MCWWC, 175 Main Street, South Portland, ME 04106; 207-799-5025; Fax: 207-799-5443; {Email: mcwwc@gwi.net}.

- MCWWC, Thomaston Center UMS, 42 Main Street, Thomaston, ME 04861; 207-354-6312; 800-442-2092; Fax: 207-354-2128; {Email: cogger@maine.edu}.

- MCWWC, Box 13G, 19 Hillside Avenue, Waterville, ME 04901; 207-872-9482; 800-442-2092; Fax: 207-877-8382; {Email: wcwwc@mint.net}.

- Outreach Rumford-Mexico Center UMS, 9 Brown Street, Mexico, ME 04257; 207-364-2945; 207-753-6621; 800-442-2092; Fax: 207-364-8377; {Email: ebrown@maine.edu}.

Maine's "Parents as Scholars" Program

Maine has created a "Parents as Scholars" program in which students at two- and four-year degree-grant programs will receive a package of aid equivalent to the same cash assistance, medical coverage, and other services they would have received had they become TANF (Temporary Assistance for Needy Families) recipients. To the extent that resources permit, a TANF-eligible person must be allowed to participate if she does not have the skills needed to find work that will support a family at 85% of the median state family income; the education will improve the family's ability to be self-supporting, and she has the aptitude to complete it successfully. Contact Mary Henderson

or Chris Hastedt, Maine Equal Justice Project, P.O. Box 5347, Augusta, ME 04332-5347; 207-626-7058; Fax: 207-621-8148; {www.mejp.org/page2.html#anchor758951}; {Email: info@mejp.org}.

Train For A New Job

Are you interested in changing your type of work? If so, and you are in Maine, an organization called the Training and Development Corporation (TDC) may be able to help you. Among other things, TDC assists eligible farm workers in obtaining free training for many types of work. TDC can help pay for a college education or other types of training. For example, learning English, construction, nursing, mechanics, child care work, and many other areas in which you may be interested. Their toll-free number is 800-371-7543. Contact the service provider nearest you.

- Training & Development Corporation, 2 Main St., Corinna, ME 04928; 207-278-5500.

- Training & Development Corporation, 1 Cumberland Pl., Bangor, ME 04401-5085; 207-945-9431.

- Training & Development Corporation, 14 High St., Ellsworth, ME 04605-1706; 207-667-7543.

- Training & Development Corporation, 18 School St., Bucksport, ME 04416; 207-469-6385.

- Training & Development Corporation, Rt. 15, Dover Foxcroft, ME 04426; 207-564-8438.

- Training & Development Corporation, 257 Harlow St. # 201, Bangor, ME 04401-4944; 207-942-9492.

Business Assistance in the Tri-County Area

Before you start your microenterprise, contact the Androscoggin Valley Council of Governments for one-on-one counseling. The counseling involves services such as writing a business plan, budgeting, and marketing and management. They also provide informative training sessions. The topics of previous seminars have included Starting Your Own Business, Market Research, and Financing Your Product. Contact Chris Logan or Jane Mickeriz, SBDC Counselor, AVCOG, 125 Manley Road, Auburn, ME 04210; 207-783-9186; Fax: 207-783-5211; {www.avcog.org}.

Training for Underemployed Residents

The Maine Quality Centers Program has free customized education and training for unemployed and underemployed people, as well as businesses. The free training will help to increase the skills of the participants which will allow them to find profitable employment. Contact James McGowan, Maine Quality Centers, Center for Career Development, SMTC 2, Fort Road, South Portland, ME 04106; 207-767-2542, ext. 107; {www.mtcs.net/quality.htm}; {Email: jmcgowan@ccdme.org}.

Work for Seniors

The Senior Community Service Employment Program is for low-income people, 55 and older. It will find part-time employment in the area of community services. The participants will receive training while earning a wage. The goal is to gain enough experience from the part-time job to find more lucrative full-time employment down the road. Contact the Bureau of Elder and Adult Services, #11 State House Station, Augusta, ME 04333; 207-624-5335; 800-262-2232.

Maryland

One-Stop Career Centers
A network of One-Stop Career Centers throughout the state offers a wide range of employment related services including job training. Services vary by location. To find a location near you, please refer to the website {www.careernet.state.md.us}. To learn more about the services they offer, contact your state coordinator.

Paulette Hall, Executive Director, Office of Employment Services, 1100 Eutaw Street, Room 208, Baltimore, MD 21201; 410-767-2005; Fax: 410-767-2010; {Email: cwalter@careernet.state.md.us}.

John O'Connor, Assistant Secretary, Department of Labor, Licensing and Regulations, 1100 North Eutaw Street, Room 600, Baltimore, MD 21201; 410-767-2400; Fax: 410-767-2986.

Job Service Offices
A system of Employment Service/Job Service offices is located within every state with the goal of assisting millions of job seekers and employers. While services may vary from location to location, many provide job training, skills assessment and related services. With approximately 1,800 Employment Service/Job Service offices nationwide there is bound to be one near you. To learn more about the services offered in your area, contact your state

administrator. John P. O'Connor, Assistant Secretary, Division of Employment & Training Department of Labor, Licensing & Regulation, 1100 North Eutaw Street, Room 600, Baltimore, MD 21201; 410-767-2400; Fax: 410-767-2986; {www.dllr.state.md.us/employment/jobserv.html}.

Information for Women
While the Maryland Commission for Women does not directly provide job training services, they can steer you towards the right program for you. They exist to provide information and referral services to inform women about their legal rights and services available to them and provide for the increased participation of women at all levels of employment as well as voluntary and paid decision-making positions. They also maintain a list of women's organizations and a Speaker's Bureau. For more information, contact Maryland Commission for Women, 45 Calvert Street, Annapolis, MD 21401; 410-260-6047; 877-868-2196; TTY: 800-925-4434; Fax: 410-974-2307; {www.dhr.state.md.us/mew}; {Email: mew@dhr.state.md.us}.

Run Your Own Transportation Business
AdVANtage II is a van service and entrepreneurial training program sponsored by Sojourner-Douglass College and funded by a grant from the Baltimore City Department of Social Services. You can receive the training and follow-up support services needed to establish and maintain your own transportation business. They will also help you become certified as a Minority Business Enterprise. In turn, you will provide van services to up to 500 welfare-to-work customers, enabling them to commute to job assignments not served by existing transportation providers. For more information, contact AdVANtage II, Sojourner-Douglass College, 500 N. Caroline St., Baltimore, MD 21205; 410-276-9741.

Training For Low-Income Entrepreneurs
Women Entrepreneurs of Baltimore, Inc. (WEB), can polish your skills through an entrepreneurial training program designed to help economically disadvantaged women become self-sufficient through business development. The main components of the WEB program are: an intensive three-month business skills training course; mentoring; financing strategy development; community networking; resource sharing; and professional business consultation.

For more information, contact Women Entrepreneurs of Baltimore, Inc. (WEB), Amanda Crook Zinn, Chief Executive Officer, 1118 Light Street, 2nd Floor, Baltimore, MD 21230; 410-727-4929; Fax: 410-727-4989.

Help For Single Parents and Displaced Homemakers

Howard Community College's Career Links program services Howard County low-income single parents, displaced homemakers 30 and older, single pregnant women, and low-income individuals pursuing training and/or other employment in non-traditional career fields. They can assist in your efforts to develop marketable work skills and learn effective job search skills. The staff will offer counseling, career planning, job placement , support services. They also offer mentoring, one-on-one tutoring services, workshops and more. You must actively participate in the program until completion. Interested low-income individuals who are single parents, displaced homemakers or single pregnant women residing in Howard County should contact the Counseling and Career Services Office (Room L140; phone: 410-772-4954; {www.howardcc.edu/career/career_links.htm#CareerLinks}). Howard Community College, 10901 Little Patuxent Parkway, Columbia, MD 21044; 410-772-4800; V/TDD: 410-772-4822; {www.howardcc.edu}.

Help For Homemakers

The Maryland Department of Human Resources/Displaced Homemaker Program provides funds to help individuals who have been the homemaker in a family home, and after being dependent on the income of a family member, lost part or all of that income due to separation, divorce, death or disability of the income providing family member, or loss of public assistance benefits. By participating, you will receive guidance for entering or reentering the job market, along with information and referrals to other services. You also get job-training providing opportunities to improve skills necessary for you to gain employment and support for yourself and your family. For more information about the Displaced Homemakers Program, contact Carolyn Edmonds, Department of Human Resources, 311 West Saratoga Street Baltimore, Maryland 21201; 410-767-7661; {www.dhr.state.md.us/transit/ts-dhp.htm}; {Email: mddhr@ mail.state.md.us}.

Single Parent Program

Community College of Baltimore County has a single parent/displaced homemaker's program that may serve your needs. Through the support of the Maryland State Department of Education, the Department of Human Services, and the Community College of Baltimore County, Dundalk campus, services are provided to support single parents (both male and female), displaced homemakers and single pregnant women in their efforts to reach their academic and career goals. The Changes Program includes both credit and non-credit courses, as well as, career counseling and testing, personal counseling, and special referral services. Services also include financial support for tuition cost, GED assistance, book fees, child care and transportation. The Program provides help with job placement needs, including resume development, employer contacts and strategies for effective job interviewing and assisting individuals to gain training  leading to economic self sufficiency. For more information about these services, call the Displaced Homemaker's Program, Community College of Baltimore County, 7200 Sollers Point Road, Baltimore, MD 21222-4694; 410-285-9808; Fax: 410-285-9903; {www.dundalk.cc.md.us/}.

Help For Those In Career Changes and Life Transitions

If you are experiencing career changes or life transitions, Allegany College of Maryland/Career Transitional Services offers you the support and direction needed to become self-sufficient. Some participants are recent high school graduates preparing for entry into the workplace while others are adults ready to explore new career options as a result of changing family structure or an unstable job market. All have in common the desire for guidance, training and related services offered in an atmosphere that is designed to foster their individual success. For more specific information contact Allegany College of Maryland, Cumberland Campus, 12401 Willowbrook Road, SE, Cumberland, MD 21502-2596; Career Search/Job Placement, Ellen Durr: 301-784-5141, General: 301-784-5005; Fax: 301-724-6892; {www.ac.cc.md.us/ceps2.htm}; {Email: ellen@ac.cc.md.us}.

Many Direct Services For Women
While the Montgomery County Commission for Women works to bring about changes in conditions creating inequities for women, their Counseling and Career Center provides direct services to individual women. You could benefit from personal and career counseling, groups and workshops, information referral and many other services. Contact The Commission for Women, 255 North Washington Street, 4th floor, Bank of America Building, Rockville, MD 20850-1703; 301-279-1800; TTY: 301-279-1034; Fax: 301-279-1318; {www.co.mo.md.us/cfw}; {Email: cfw@co.mo.md.us}.

Programs In The Baltimore Area
Mayor's Office of Employment Development is the city department responsible for effective delivery of employment and training services to the citizens of Baltimore. OED offers services to adult residents which include: career development assessment, job search assistance, employer job banks, occupational skills training, literacy & GED programs, work-experience internships, on-the-job training, and support services. Contact Office of Employment Development, 417 Fayette Street, Suite 468, Baltimore, MD 21202; 410-396-3009; (Information Line); {www.pratt.lib.md.us/slrc/job/govoff.html}.

Branch Offices

- Eastside Career Center, 3001 E. Madison Street, Baltimore, MD 21205; 410-396-9030.

- Northeast Career Center, 100 W. 23rd Street, Baltimore, MD 21218; 410-396-6580.

- Baltimore Urban League Career Center, Mondawmin Mall, Baltimore, MD 21215; 410-523-1060.

- Southwest Career Center, 201 S. Arlington Street, Baltimore, MD 21223; 410-396-3670.

- The Career Connections, 101 W. 24th Street, Baltimore, MD 21218; 410-396-6722.

Senior Training
Senior Aides Program provides part-time subsidized work experience and training for low-income Baltimore City residents 55 years or older. The goal is for individuals in the program to move from subsidized work into jobs in the community. For more information, contact Senior Aides Program, 303 E. Fayette Street, 5th Floor, Baltimore, MD 21201; 410-396-4486 or 4487.

Baltimore County Programs
Baltimore County Office of Employment and Training CareerNet provides occupational skills training and other services such as: career counseling, job search and placement assistance, and ALEX job bank listings. Their training programs include: administrative assistant, microcomputer office assistant, medical office specialist, secretary/word processing, accounting/bookkeeping, computer technology, printing technology, machine tool technology, and general office clerk. Services are free to Baltimore County residents who meet income eligibility guidelines or are dislocated workers. For more information, contact Baltimore County Office of Employment and Training CareerNet, 1 Investment Place, Suite 409, Towson, MD 21204; 410-887-4473; Fax: 410-887-5773.

Office Locations

- Catonsville, 27 Mellor Ave., Baltimore, MD 21228, 410-887-0940.

- Eastpoint, 7930 Eastern Boulevard, Baltimore, MD 21224, 410-282-4004.

- Randallstown, Liberty Family Resource Center, 3525 Resource Drive, Randallstown, MD 21133, 410-887-0630.

- Towson, 1228 E. Joppa Road, Towson, MD 21286, 410-887-4128.

- Baltimore County Reemployment Assistance Center, Dulaney Center II, 901 Dulaney Valley Road, Suite 100, Towson, MD 21204, 410-887-4400.

Assistance for Dislocated Workers

Dislocated Workers can find free help at the Baltimore County Reemployment Assistance Center. Their services include career counseling, workshops and seminars, retraining through local colleges, job search and placement assistance, and more. To be eligible, you must be a resident of Baltimore County or laid off by a Baltimore County employer. For more information, contact the Baltimore County Reemployment Assistance Center, 901 Dulaney Valley Road, Suite 100, Towson, MD 21204; 410-887-4400.

Workforce Development Network

The Workforce Development Network will train eligible persons so they will become employable in today's job market. They offer assistance to dislocated workers, older workers, economically disadvantaged people, and youths. The training is based on the individuals career goals and circumstances. They offer training in a variety of career fields reflecting the current job market. Some of the services available are enhanced job skills, career development advisement, training related supplemental, job placement assistance, paid training/tuition, and much more. Contact one of the following Workforce Development Offices for more information:

- Calvert County, 200 Duke Street, Prince Rederick, MD 20678; 410-535-8819
- Charles County, 175 Post Office Road, Waldorf, MD 20602; 301-645-8720; 301-843-3833
- St. Mary's County, 245 Washington Street, Leonardtown, MD 20650; 301-475-5597

Business Resource Center

Through counseling, training, technical assistance, and other services, the Montgomery County Business Resource Center helps business owners imagine and develop their businesses. They offer counseling on a variety of topics, business plan, start-up, general and financial management, just to name a few. In addition to that, they offer workshops monthly, many of which are free. So, if you are thinking of starting a business, want help with your business plan, or other business concerns, contact the Business Resource Center, Rockville Regional Library, 99 Maryland Avenue, Rockville, MD 20850; 240-777-2041/0140.

Training in Carpentry, Woodwork and Landscaping

The Montgomery County Conservation Corps is a program that has a goal to improve the employment possibilities and responsibility of out-of-school and unemployed youth ages 17 to 25, and to also help preserve Montgomery County's natural and historic resources. The trainees, or corps members, get marketable skills in conservation, carpentry, landscaping, and woodworking. The corps members spend 6-12 months in the advanced training program. Two or 3 mornings each week are devoted to GED preparation and academic development, which includes computer training, and work in the field the rest of the week. They also earn a wage while doing this. To find out if you are eligible for this program, contact Montgomery County Conservation Corps, Wheaton, MD 20902; 301-929-5554; Fax: 301-929-5560; {www.co.mo.md.us/hhs/mccc}; {Email: mccc@co.mo.md.us}.

Massachusetts

One-Stop Career Centers

A network of One-Stop Career Centers throughout the state offers a wide range of employment related services including job training. Services vary by location. To find a location near you, please refer to the website {www.detma.org/jobseeker/centers/careercenters.htm}. To learn more about the services they offer, contact your state coordinator.

Mr. Jonathan Raymond, One-Stop Lead, Department of Labor and Workforce Development, 1 Ashburton Place, Room 1402, Boston, MA 02108; 617-727-6573; ext. 107; Fax: 617-727-1090.

Job Service Offices

A system of Employment Service/Job Service offices is located within every state with the goal of assisting millions of job seekers and employers. While services may vary from location to location, many provide job training, skills assessment and related services. With approximately 1,800 Employment Service/Job Service offices nationwide there is bound to be one near you. To learn more about the services offered in your area, contact your state administrator. Nils Nordberg, Commissioner, Division of Employment & Training, 19 Staniford Street, 3rd Floor, Boston, MA 02114; 617-626-6600; Fax: 617-727-0315; {www.detma.org/programs/empserv.htm}.

Career Seminars

Among their many services, FutureWorks offers the following training opportunities at no cost: career seminar - This 2-day seminar will give you information about the most effective ways to get a job in today's job market including finding job leads, developing a resume, interviewing and negotiating salary. Career specialists are on staff to serve job seekers in seminars, workshops and individual advising. A resource room includes job postings, employer directories, newspapers, information about New England employers, training institutions and community resources. Experienced staff are available to help you with questions about employers and the job market. Workshops are offered each month in one hour sessions devoted to various job search topics. You may attend as often as you wish. For more information, contact FutureWorks, One Federal Street - Bldg 103-3, Springfield, MA 01105-1160; 413-858-2800; Fax: 413-858-2810; TTY/TDD: 413-858-2800; Information & Success Hotline 413-858-2882; {www.futureworks-now.com}.

Consulting and Training

The Center for Business and Technology is part of the Division of Economic and Business Development that was created to generate and support economic growth by supporting industry and businesses in the region. They are a leading provider of training programs and consulting services that consistently meet the changing technology and workplace demands of individuals, business and industry. CBT offers a wide range of consulting and training services, as well as topics of personal interest. Courses are offered as open enrollment seminars or closed contracts with individual organizations. For more information, contact Center for Business and Technology (CBT), Springfield Technical Community College, 1 Armory Sq., Springfield, MA 01105-1204; 413-755-4225; Fax: 413-739-5066; {www.stcc.mass.edu/cbtsite/atopcbt.html}.

Computer Information

MASSCIS, for Windows is a PC based system that provides comprehensive information about the worlds of work and education for career planners of all ages. It is a product/service of the Massachusetts Occupational Information Coordinating Committee (MOICC) within the Massachusetts Division of Employment and Training (DET). You can use MASSCIS to find information about work and education, and about occupations, training programs, and financial aid. MASSCIS is available at all Division of Employment and Training (DET) Service Centers, Massachusetts Career Centers, high schools, community colleges, colleges, and various other sites. To find the address of the nearest D.E.T Employment Service Center or Massachusetts One Stop Career Center visit {www.detma.org/ empserv.htm}. MASSCIS can also be tried free of charge at the Higher Education Information Center at the Boston Public Library, 700 Boylston Street, Boston, MA 02116; 617-536-0200; Information Hotline: 800-442-1171 (MA only).

Training Directory

The Employment and Training directory provides access to Internet resources where you can search for jobs or create an online resume, search for educational/training information and resources, or search a database of day care providers. To access it, visit {www.detma.org/ emp_train.htm}. Remember that Internet access is often available at public libraries. The Employment and Training directory is maintained by the Massachusetts Division of Employment and Training, 19 Staniford Street, Boston, MA 02114; 617-626-5400; {www.detma.org/jobseeker}.

Help For Minority Women

In addition to their work certifying companies as minority or women-owned or controlled, and publishing a directory listing of verified firms, the State Office of Minority and Women Business Assistance (SOMWBA) also offers technical assistance. This means you could benefit from management seminars and workshops for minority and women entrepreneurs on a wide variety of business topics. You can register for the workshops online at their website. For more information, contact Business Development Office, 10 Park Plaza, Room 3740, Boston, MA 02116; 617-973-8692; Fax: 617-973-8637; {www.state.ma.us/somwba}.

Get Help With Starting Your Own Business

The Center for Women & Enterprise, Inc. (CWE) is a non-profit educational organization whose mission is to empower women to become economically self-sufficient and prosperous through entrepreneurship. The first center of its kind in Massachusetts, CWE provides courses, workshops, round tables, one-on-one consulting, and loan packaging assistance to women who seek to start and/or grow their own businesses. While services are open to everyone, scholarships target low-income women. For more information, contact Massachusetts Center for Women & Enterprise Inc., Andrea Silbert, Director, Renaissance Park, 1135 Tremont Street, Boston, MA 02120; 617-536-0700; Fax: 617-536-7373; {http://asilbert@cweboston.org}; {Email: info@cweboston.org}.

Training Fisherman for a New Career

The Fisherman and Families Resource Center helps all types of fisherman, their eligible family members, and fishing related industry workers from Boston and the North Shore to make the transition to a new career. Free employment and training services are available to eligible individuals. Employment and Training Counseling offers career counseling to determine career goals, research training opportunities and search for appropriate employment. The counseling is complimented by workshops on topics such as Motivation/Goal Setting, Skills Assessment, and Job Club. They also offer Introduction to Computer instruction, Basic Education instruction, and English as a Second Language. Contact Angela Sanfilippo, Glouchester Fisherman and Family Assistance Center, 11 Parker, Glouchester, MA 01930; 978-283-2504, ext. 12; {www.commcorp.org/wss/fisherman/default.htm}; {Email: Asanfilippo@commcorp.org}.

Small Business Assistance Center

Lowell Small Business Assistance Center is a one-stop center for people who want to be in business for themselves. There is free professional consulting, counseling, and information available. Here, small business owners can learn how to make up and communicate a business plan; do a feasibility study and market research; and gain knowledge about business management, financing, and technology. They offer courses, workshops and seminars that cover all aspects of starting and operating a business. Their services are directed to the City of Lowell, but they are also available to individuals regardless of where they reside. Contact the Lowell Small Business Assistance Center, 169 Merrimack Street, Lowell, MA 01852; 978-441-1889; Fax: 978-441-6824; {www.lowellsbac.org/lsbac/index.html}.

Michigan

One-Stop Career Centers

A network of One-Stop Career Centers throughout the state offers a wide range of employment related services including job training. Services vary by location. To find a location near you, please refer to the website {www.state.mi.us/career}. To learn more about the services they offer, contact your state coordinator.

Ms. Linda Kinney, Michigan Department of Career Development, 201 N. Washington Square, Victor Office Center, 4th Floor, Lansing, MI 48913; 517-373-9616; Fax: 517-335-5945.

Economic Development Agency, 201 N. Washington Square, Victor Office Center, 4th Floor, Lansing, MI 48913; 517-373-9808; {www.state.mi.us/career}; {Email: career@state.mi.us}.

Job Service Offices

A system of Employment Service/Job Service offices is located within every state with the goal of assisting millions of job seekers and employers. While services may vary from location to location, many provide job training, skills assessment and related services. With approximately 1,800 Employment Service/Job Service offices nationwide there is bound to be one near you. To learn more about the services offered in your area, contact your state administrator. Jack Wheatley, Acting Director, Michigan Unemployment Agency, 7310 Woodward Avenue, Detroit, MI 48202; 313-876-5901; Fax: 313-876-5587; {www.cis.state.mi.us/ua/homepage.htm}.

Resource Agency

The Michigan Jobs Commission/Michigan Works! is the state's workforce development resource agency. Through 25 local offices workforce development services are delivered close to where you live. Learn about job training opportunities and other workforce development services available in your community by contacting The Department of Career Development, 201 N. Washington Square, Victor Office Center, 1st Floor, Lansing, MI 48913; 517-241-4000; 888-253-6855; { www.michworks.org/mtb/user/MTB_EMPL.EntryMainPage}; {Email: htlp@mesc.state.mi.us}.

All Kinds of Services for Women Seeking Self-Employment

The Women's Initiative for Self-Employment (WISE) Program provides low-income women with the tools and resources to begin and expand businesses. The WISE Program can provide you with a comprehensive package of business training, personal development workshops, credit counseling, start-up and expansion financing, business counseling, peer group support, and mentoring. The creation and expansion of businesses is only one goal of this program. The WISE Program was also designed to fight poverty, increase incomes, raise self-esteem, stabilize families, develop skills and spark a process of community renewal. For more information, contact Ann Arbor Community Development Corporation Women's Initiative for Self Employment (WISE), Michelle Richards, Executive Director, 2002 Hogback Road, Suite 12, Ann Arbor, MI 48105; 734-677-1400; Fax: 734-677-1465; {Email: info@mail.miceed.org}.

Learn A Trade

Women in Trades, in partnership with five organizations in different states, provides technical assistance to employers, contractors, and labor organizations on mega construction projects in the Midwest. They will work with contractors and apprenticeship programs meeting their goals for hiring women in job sites. These groups refer

qualified tradeswomen to jobs, and most provide pre-apprenticeship programs to give women the skills needed in apprenticeship programs. They can give you information on career awareness on the range of job options for women too. For further information, contact Sharon Newton, Executive Director, Women's Resource Center, 25 Sheldon SE, Grand Rapids, MI 49503-4209; 616-458-5443; Fax: 616-458-9933; {www.grwrc.org}; {Email: info@grwrc.org}.

Break Through Barriers

Grand Rapids Opportunities for Women (GROW) is a non-profit economic development organization which provides women from diverse backgrounds — many of whom are facing social or economic barriers — with opportunities to develop the skills and acquire the knowledge needed to achieve financial independence. Focusing on small businesses, GROW can provide you with entrepreneurial training needed to start a small business as well as the follow-up services needed to sustain and expand a business. Since starting a business often affects all aspects of a woman's life, GROW is committed to providing group and individual support for both business and personal development. Contact Grand Rapids Opportunities for Women (GROW), 25 Sheldon SE, Suite 210, Grand Rapids, MI 49503; 616-458-3404; Fax: 616-458-6557; {www.growbusiness.org}, {Email: pbrush@growbusiness.org}.

Opportunity at the Community College

Kirtland Community College has funds available for single parents, homemakers, displaced homemakers, single pregnant women, and sex equity students enrolled in approved vocational programs or courses. These funds may cover tuition, fees, books, supplies, uniforms, transportation, and/or child care. They also offer counseling, car pool list, child care exchange list, community agency liaison assistance and more. No minimum credit load is required for eligibility. Funding is also available for students who are in default on their student loans. To apply or to receive more information contact Single Parent/Displaced Homemaker and Sex Equity Programs, Kirtland Community College, 10775 North St. Helen Road, Roscommon, MI 48653; 517-275-5121, ext. 252; Administrative Center, Room 212, {www.kirtland.cc.mi.us/}.

Get Through Those Changes With Help

The Center for Women in Transition has two programs available to assist you. Women's Support Services: CWIT staff is available to help you find alternatives when going through major life changes that result from divorce, death of a spouse, unemployment/ underemployment, family dysfunction and/or conflict, and other stressful transitions. Fees for these services are based on a sliding scale. The Displaced Homemaker Program assists women who must become the family's primary provider but are underemployed or lack recent job experience. Participants must meet Department of Labor guidelines. Program offerings include the following: career coaching; communication techniques; on-the-job success strategies; interviewing techniques; referral services; "Wardrobe for Work" provides, free of charge, quality used clothing appropriate for professional employment. Funding for this program is provided by Michigan Jobs Commission. Contact 800-848-5991 or {Email: cfwit@macatawa.org} for general information, or contact the service providers listed below for more information. You can also visit their website {www.aplaceforwomen.org} for updated information.

- Holland Center for Women in Transition, 304 Garden Avenue, Holland, MI 49424; Crisis Line 616-392-1970; Business Line 616-392-2829; Help Line 616-396-4357.

- Grand Haven Center for Women in Transition, 520 Franklin Street, Grand Haven, MI 49417; Office 616-846-0674; Help Line 616-846-4357.

- Allegan Center for Women in Transition, 231 Trowbridge Street, Suite 15B, Allegan, MI 49010; 616-673-2299.

Help For Victims
Every Woman's Place, Inc. offers services for victims of domestic violence and sexual assault. You can receive employment training, financial and housing assistance, support groups, safe shelter, legal advocacy, and counseling. They also have a displaced homemaker program. All services are free. For more information, contact Sharon Richards or Addie Randall, Every Woman's Place - Almond Center, 1221 W. Laketon, Muskegon, MI 49441; 616-759-7909; Fax: 616-759-8618.

Training For Farm Workers
The Telamon Corporation has employment & training services for the farm worker population. You can receive classroom training (GED, ESL), on-the-job training, work experience, vocational training, case management, job placement, follow-up, and training-related services. For more information, contact Telamon Corporation, Ruben Santellan, Supervisor, 710 Chicago Dr., Suite 310, Holland, MI 49423; 616-396-5160.

Northern Lower Michigan
The Women's Resource Center (WRC) is a non-profit, community based membership organization dedicated to serving the women and families of northern lower Michigan. Established in 1977, the WRC serves Emmet, Charlevoix, Cheboygan, Otsego and Antrim counties. Services include: Displaced Homemaker Program and Workshops/ Special Programs/Support Groups among others. Contact 24 Hour Crisis Line 616-347-0082; 800-275-1995.

- Petoskey Office, 423 Porter Street, Petoskey, MI 49770; 616-347-0067.

- Cheboygan Office, 217 North Bailey, Cheboygan, MI 49721; 616-627-2380.

- Gaylord Office, 116 E. 5th Street, Gaylord, MI 49735; 517-731-0918.

Business Training for Entrepreneurs
Entrepreneurs in Lansing can get help in starting or expanding their micro-enterprise at the Lansing Community Micro-Enterprise Fund. The business training focuses on the business plan, goal setting and time management, marketing and sales, finance, management and operations, taxes and legal issues, and separation of home and business finance. They also offer technical assistance which begins during, and continues on after the training session. Assistance with loans and networking are also part of their program. To be considered for the 10 week training course, contact Lansing Community Micro-Enterprise Fund 520 West Ionia, Lansing, MI 48933; 517-485-4446; Fax: 517-485-4761.

Training and Consulting Services

Northern Initiatives works with people, communities, and businesses in the Upper Peninsula to improve economic conditions. One of the ways in which they accomplish this goal is by training and consulting services for entrepreneurs. "Designing Your Business in Four Steps" is a 3 hour seminar on mission and goal analysis, marketing, management, and cash flow information. They also have a more involved 12 week course called REAL (Rural Entrepreneurialship through Action Learning). This covers all avenues of starting and owning a business. It includes guest speakers on marketing finance, business and personnel management, and customer service. Contact Northern Initiatives, 228 West Washington Street, Marquette, MI 49855; 906-228-5571; 800-254-2156; Fax: 906-228-5572; {www.northerniniatives.com}; {Email: infor@niup.net}.

Enterprise Development Workshops

The Northwest Michigan Council of Governments sponsors a program for micro-entrepreneurs called Project Invest. Its goal is to help individuals in the area develop and establish successful, income producing businesses, and possibly employ other people in the community. One of the three ways they do this is through Enterprise Development Workshops. It consists of 4 months of training that covers business planning, financial independence and personal effectiveness workshops. With the training, business owners will develop a business plan and personal financial plan. The other services they have to reach their goal, are Individual Business Coaching and Micro-Loan Fund. For more information, contact Rose Foley, NW Michigan Council of Governments, 2194 Dendrinos Drive, PO Box 506, Traverse City, MI 49685-0506; 231-929-5000; Fax: 231-929-5012; {www.nwm.cog.mi.us/ projectinvest.html}; {Email: RAFoley@aol.com}.

Training for Mid-Career and Older Job Seekers

Operation ABLE is a program that helps mid-career and older job seekers to get work and remain employable. Their services of this consist of individual counseling; career assessment; extensive computer training; occupational skills training; job placement assistance, and more. Contact one of the following for information:

- Main Office-171117 West 9 Mile Road, Suite 200, Southfield, MI 48075-4500; 248-443-0370; 800-922-HIRE; Fax: 248-443-1960
- Hannan House 4750 Woodward Avenue, Room 201, Detroit, MI 48201; 313-832-4925

Minnesota

One-Stop Career Centers

A network of One-Stop Career Centers throughout the state offers a wide range of employment related services including job training. Services vary by location. To find a location near you, please refer to the website {www.mnworkforcecenter.org/index.htm}. To learn more about the services they offer, contact your state coordinator.

Mr. Howard E. Glad, Director, Minnesota Workforce Center System, 390 North Robert Street, St. Paul, MN 55101; 651-296-7510; Fax: 651-296-0994; TTY: 651-282-5909; {Email: hglad@ngwmail.des. state.mn.us}.

Job Service Offices

A system of Employment Service/Job Service offices is located within every state with the goal of assisting millions of job seekers and employers. While services may vary from location to location, many provide job training, skills assessment and related services. With approximately 1,800 Employment Service/Job Service offices nationwide there is bound to be one near you. To learn more about the services offered in your area, contact your state administrator. Jane Brown, Commissioner, Minnesota Department of Economic Security, 390 North Robert Street, St. Paul, MN 55101; 651-296-3711; Fax: 651-296-0994; {www.MNWorkForceCenter.org}.

Help for Displaced Homemakers

The Displaced Homemaker Program provides the transitional services and vocational preparation needed to assist you in moving to training or employment. Enrollment is limited to one year and is free to those eligible. With 53 locations throughout the state, you can take advantage of workshops, support groups and networking, self-esteem building, one-to-one personal or vocational counseling, job seeking methods, employment support groups, and resume development to help you build confidence, identify skills, and seek training or employment. Other services may include referral for remedial education, child care, legal assistance, and other support services. Transportation, child care, and work or school expenses are covered as funds are available. For more information on the Displaced Homemaker Program or to find the location of your local office, contact: Susan Johnson, Minnesota Department of Economic Security/Workforce Services Branch, 390 North Robert Street, St. Paul, MN 55101; 651-296-6060; {www.mnworkforcecenter.org}; {Email: susan.m.johnson@state.mn.us}.

Here's An Example
The Central Lakes College Meta 5 is an example of a Displaced Homemaker Program mentioned above. META 5 serves Beltrami, Cass, Crow Wing, Mille Lacs, Morrison, Todd and Wadena counties. Located in Brainerd, Minnesota, they are sponsored by Central Lakes College and funded through the Department of Economic Security. Meta 5 services are offered free to those who are eligible. The mission of META 5 is to meet the specific needs of anyone attempting to make the difficult transition from home and financial dependency to the workplace and financial independence. Many people have outdated training and education, no recent work history or experience, and are often victims of age discrimination. The training and services offered provide a supportive environment designed to enhance and build self-esteem and confidence. They offer you career planning and job preparation workshops; pre-employment skills including resume writing; information and referrals to appropriate services; one-to-one guidance in making career choices; group support with others in similar situations; computerized career information programs. For more information contact META 5 at 218-855-8010; 218-855-8000, or contact Central Lakes College, 501 West College Drive, Brainerd, MN 56401; {www.clc.mnscu.edu/supserv/ meta5/index.html}; {Email: lfranz@gwmail.clc.mnscu.edu}.

Christian Programs
Ursuline Companions in Mission is a Christian association of lay women and men who seek to make a difference in the lives of the poor through a variety of programs including job training. They have service delivery sites in Delaware, Illinois, Kentucky, Minnesota, Missouri, New Mexico, and Ohio. Programs vary from location to location. For more information, contact Ursuline Companions In Mission, Sr. Jane Quinlan, College of New Rochelle, College Center, Room 155, New Rochelle, NY 10805; 914-654-5270; Fax: 914-654-5290; {www.theursulines.org}; {Email: ursulinecomp@hotmail.com}.

Comprehensive Career Services
The Life-Work Planning Center serves women in transition, including displaced homemakers, non-displaced homemakers, Hispanic women and youth, teen and young moms, and women transitioning from welfare to work. They provide a supportive environment where you can explore career and job options, build self-esteem, acquire confidence to make decisions, set goals, and become self-sufficient. Their services include workshops and support groups, one-to-one peer counseling, career testing and assessment. They regionally serve individuals in Blue Earth, Brown, Faribault, LeSueur, Martin, Nicollet, Sibley, Waseca and Watonwan Counties. Life-Work Planning Center has four convenient locations in four counties.

- Union Square Business Center, 201 North Broad Street, Suite 100, Mankato, MN 56001; 507-345-1577; 800-369-5166; {www.lwpc.org/}.

- New Ulm WorkForce Center, 1618 South Broadway, New Ulm, MN 56073; 507-354-3138.

- 118 South Main St., Fairmont, MN 56031; 507-238-9361; 800-433-1706.

- Relations Center, 204 Second Street NW, Waseca, MN 56093; 507-345-1577; 800-369-5166.

Learn A Trade
Women in Trades, in partnership with five organizations in different states, will provide technical assistance to employers, contractors, and labor organizations on mega construction projects in the Midwest. They will work with

contractors and apprenticeship programs meeting their goals for hiring women in job sites. These groups refer qualified tradeswomen to jobs, and most provide pre-apprenticeship programs to give women the skills needed in apprenticeship programs. They can give you information on career awareness on the range of job options for women too. For further information on programs in your state, call Pat Wagner, Minnesota Women in the Trades, Minnesota Women's Building, 550 Rice Street, St. Paul, MN 55103; 651-228-9950; Job Hotline number: 651-257-7528.

Employment and Business Services For Women

If you are looking for direction or assistance in developing your career, and you are a low income or Native American woman searching for employment, starting or expanding a business, WomenVenture is the resource for you. They can help you identify your career direction, make a career change, enter/re-enter the workforce or try for that perfect job. They can also help you get started with a new business idea or grow an existing business. Their career development services are on a sliding fee scale and include individual consulting, Myers-Briggs Type Indicator, and Strong Interest Inventory. Classes include Career & Life Planning for Women and How to Ace an Interview. There is also a Career & Employment Transition Group for Women. Specific training programs include a program geared towards challenging the boundaries of men's work through pre-apprenticeship training and placement programs in construction or printing. Another program prepares women for jobs that require minimal training or experience, but offer good pay and benefits, in such fields as banking, administrative support, food service and many other areas. They offer training in resume development; personal empowerment; sexual harassment prevention; interviewing techniques; job search strategies; job placement; job retention support; library and computer access. For more information, contact WomenVenture, 2324 University Avenue, St. Paul, MN 55114; 651-646-3808; 800-793-7535; Fax: 651-641-7223; {www.rrtrade.org/women/WBC/index.htm}; {Email: wbc@tvutd.com}.

Women's Business Training

If your new or existing business could benefit from expert technical assistance, Women in New Development may be right for you. They can assist you in your business goals through one-on-one counseling, classroom training (using a variety of workshop formats), an annual regional Women's Business Conference, and through several networking organizations. Since 1969, WIND has served the small business communities of Beltrami and Cass Counties in rural northwestern Minnesota. In 1995, WIND received funding to establish new sites in Hubbard and East Polk County. Services were also extended into Clearwater County. WIND provides technical assistance to new and existing businesses. In addition, WIND also provides training services to eight additional counties in northwestern Minnesota in collaboration with the Northwest Minnesota Foundation. For more information, contact Women in New Development (WIND), Susan Hoosier, WIND Coordinator, 2715 15th Street NW, P. O. Box 579, Bemidji, MN 56601; 218-751-4631; Fax: 218-751-8452; {Email: bicap@northernnet.com}.

Help For Women Business Owners

This site is located in rural Minnesota on the White Earth Reservation. They provide one-on-one counseling and the following training seminars: Starting a Business; Customer Service; The Business Plan; Organized Record Keeping; Entrepreneurial Peak Performance; Effective Management; The Marketing Plan; Entrepreneurial Confidence; Preparing for Financing. This site networks with the demonstration sites in Fargo, ND and Bemidji, MN to plan conferences and special programs. For more information, contact Women's Business Center, White Earth Reservation Tribal Council, Mary Turner, Director, 202 South Main Street, P.O. Box 478, Mahnomen, MN 56557; 218-935-2827; Fax: 218-935-9178.

Developing Career Skills

Mainstay Inc. Career Planning Services purpose is to provide career planning for women and men in transition and to encourage self-reliance and independence by identifying and developing career skills. At Mainstay, they offer a relaxed, creative and confidential atmosphere where you can explore your alternatives, recognize your skills and examine your career goals. Mainstay's goal is to help people within the nine county area of southwestern Minnesota to build new lives. They achieve this goal through a variety of programs including career assessments and workshops pertaining to life and job search skills. For additional information, contact Mainstay, Inc., 308 North Third Street, P.O. Box 816, Marshall, MN 56258; 507-537-1546; 800-554-2481; {www.swmnmall.com/mainstay/}; {Email: mainstay@bresnanlink. net}.

Job Training Services
The Southeastern Minnesota Private Industry Council is a nonprofit organization that has job training services for low income adults and youth. They have a variety of services for people looking for employment. Available is; Career and Skill Assessment, Life Skills Training, Job Search Classes, On-The-Job Training, Dislocated Worker Training, and much more. SEMPIC serves Olmstead, Rice, Mower, Steele, Goodhue, Wabasha, Freeborn, Fillmore, Houston, and Dodge counties. Contact SEMPIC, Civic Drive Plaza, 300 11th Avenue, NW, Suite 110, Rochester, MN 55901; 507-292-5180; {www.semnpic.org}.

The Job Training Center that is operated by SEMPIC has short-term, hand-on skills training where employment is their goal. It is a combination of technical skills training and interpersonal workplace skills development set at each individuals own pace. Tuition scholarships are available on a sliding fee basis. Participants can also receive support services with transportation and work/training related expenses. They offer courses in Office Skills and Computing, Skilled Trades and Special Programs. For more information, contact the Job Training Center, 300 11th Avenue, NW, Rochester, MN 55901; 507-292-5152; {www.semnpic.org/jtc.html}.

Mississippi

One-Stop Career Centers
A network of One-Stop Career Centers throughout the state offers a wide range of employment related services including job training. Services vary by location. To find a location near you, please refer to the website {www.decd.statee.ms.us/main/jobl_default.htm}. To learn more about the services they offer, contact your state coordinator.

Mr. Thomas E. Lord, Executive Director, Employment Security Commission, P.O. Box 1699, Jackson, MS 39215-1699; 601-961-7400; Fax: 601-961-7405.

Ms. Jean Denson, Director, Mississippi Development Authority, Employment Training Division, 301 West Pearl Street, Jackson, MS 39225-4568; 601-949-2234; Fax: 601-949-7405.

Job Service Offices
A system of Employment Service/Job Service offices is located within every state with the goal of assisting millions of job seekers and employers. While services may vary from location to location, many provide job training, skills assessment and related services. With approximately 1,800 Employment Service/Job Service offices nationwide there is bound to be one near you. To learn more about the services offered in your area, contact your state administrator. Thomas E. Lord, Executive Director, Mississippi Employment Security Commission, P.O. Box 1699, Jackson, MS 39215-1699; 601-961-7400; Fax: 601-961-7405; {www.mesc.state.ms.us}.

Entrepreneur Training For Women of Color
If you live in Mound Bayou or Ruleville in Bolivar County and would like to become more self-sufficient, check out the economic entrepreneurial centers run by the National Council of Negro Women (NCNW) in those areas. For more information, contact Mississippi Women's Economic Entrepreneurial Project (MWEEP), Jo Thompson, Director, 602 North Road Avenue, Mound Bayou, MS 38762; 601-741-3342; Fax: 601-741-2195 or 601-335-3060; {www.ncnw.com}; {Email: jthompson@tecinfo.com}.

Women Work!
Women Work! is a state affiliate of the national membership organization dedicated to helping women from diverse backgrounds achieve economic self-sufficiency through job readiness, education, training and employment. Contact Mississippi Women Work!, Chris Tanner-Watkins, President, SP/DH Program, Hinds Community College, Utica Campus, Utica, MS 39175; 601-885-7042; 601-885-6062.

Help For Displaced Homemakers and Single Parents

Meridian Community College can boost your business skills by providing you with counseling, advocacy support and community referrals and networking with agencies. A refresher class is also offered in which single parents

and/or displaced homemakers can brush up on basic skills before entering college. Seminars, support groups, and workshops are offered to refine your skills in self-confidence, time management, stress management, and money management skills, as well as working toward achieving career goals. If you are a single parent or a homemaker who needs to upgrade your skills to enter the job market, visit or call the program coordinator. The office is located in Meridian Hall on the MCC campus. Contact Meridian Community College Single Parent/Displaced Homemaker Services, 910 Highway 19 North, Meridian, MS 39307; 601-484-8836; {www.mcc.cc.ms.us/ online_catalog/Single%20Parent/displace.htm}.

You Could Get A Job Usually Held By Men

Itawamba Community College has a Non-Traditional Workplace/Job Readiness Training program that provides assistance to individuals, especially women, entering non-traditional training programs. They can provide you with a broad range of services and support ranging from career orientation to mentor matching for participants in the program. The program operates concurrently or sequentially with the college's skills training activities and is free to eligible individuals. For more information, contact Itawamba Community College, 602 West Hill Street, Fulton, MS 38843; 601-862-3101; Fax: 601-862-4608; {www.icc.cc.ms.us/stu_services.htm}.

Help for Minority-Owned Businesses

Minority owned businesses and individuals can get help to start or expand their businesses at the Rural Minority Business Development Center. They teach the clients to become competitive by helping them acquire skills through business exchange, counseling, management training, and technical assistance. Services include: Business Plan Preparation, Construction Related Services, Marketing Development, and Manufacutring/ISO9000 Assistance. Eligible participants must have at least 51% ownership of the business and be affiliated with one of the following groups: African-American, Hispanic, Asian-Pacific American, Native American, Asian Indians, Hasidic Jews, and/or socially and economically disadvantaged individuals. For more information, contact the RMBDC nearest to you; {www.mississippi.org/main/minority/default.htm}.

- Mississippi MRMBDC, Standard Oil Building Annes, 200 North State Street, PO Box 849, Jackson, MS 39205; 601-359-3448; Fax: 601-354-7623
- MRMBDC, The Gulf Coast Business Technology Center, 1636 Popps Ferry Road, Suite 221, Biloxi, MS 39532; 228-396-9185; Fax: 228-392-0940
- MRMBDC, The Coahoma Community College Skill Technology Center, 510 Sun Belt Drive, Clarksdale, MS 38614; 662-627-9119; Fax: 662-627-9171

Missouri

One-Stop Career Centers

A network of One-Stop Career Centers throughout the state offers a wide range of employment related services including job training. Services vary by location. To find a location near you, please refer to the website {www.works.state.mo.us/mw2.htm }. To learn more about the services they offer, contact your state coordinator.

Tom Jones, Director, One-Stop Lead, Division of Workforce Development, P.O. Box 1087, Jefferson, City, MO 65102; 573-751-3349; 888-447-2696; Fax: 573-751-8162; {Email: tjones@wfd.state.mo.us}.

Rick Beasley, One-Stop Coordinator, Missouri Division of Workforce Development, 2023 St. Mary's Boulevard, Jefferson City, MO 65109; 573-751-7796; Fax: 573-526-8204; {Email: rbeasley@mail.state.mo.us}.

Job Service Offices

A system of Employment Service/Job Service offices is located within every state with the goal of assisting millions of job seekers and employers. While services may vary from location to location, many provide job training, skills

assessment and related services. With approximately 1,800 Employment Service/Job Service offices nationwide there is bound to be one near you. To learn more about the services offered in your area, contact your state administrator. Karla McLucas, Director, Department of Labor & Industrial Relations, P.O. Box 504, Jefferson City, MO 65102-0504; 573-526-8115; Fax: 573-751-4135; {www.dolir.state.mo.us/index.htm}.

Information Hotline

The Work Connections/Career Information Hotline (800-392-2949) provides dislocated workers and other individuals throughout the state of Missouri with information on occupations, education and training, financial aid, and job hunting information. The Career Information Hotline hours of operation are 9:00 a.m. to 9:00 p.m., Monday through Thursday and 9:00 a.m. to 5:00 p.m. on Friday. Individuals placing calls to the Hotline after hours will receive a voice message asking them to leave a message as their call will be returned. A career counselor is available by appointment to answer any career related questions. The Hotline is cosponsored by University Outreach and Extension and the Missouri Division of Job Development and Training. For further information contact the Missouri Workforce Development Division, P.O. Box 1087, Jefferson City, MO 65102-1087; 888-447-2695; {http://outreach.missouri.edu/career_options/index.html}.

Help For Low-Income Seniors

The Experienced Worker Program addresses the special needs of economically disadvantaged Missourians over the age of 55 who are seeking employment in growth industries by offering a variety of training services tailored to their needs. For further information contact the Missouri Workforce Development Division, P.O. Box 1087, Jefferson City, MO 65102-1087; 573-751-3999; {www.dolir.state.mo.us/es/d4c14.htm}.

Job Training Placement

On-The-Job Training: Employment Service, through the Trade Adjustment Assistance Act and various Job Training Partnership Act contracts, assists in identifying, referring and placing eligible applicants in training positions provided by private sector employers. The employer agrees to provide the supervision and training necessary to help the trainee to become a skilled employee. During the training period, the trainee is paid relative to the occupation and the employer is reimbursed for training expenses accrued as agreed in the contract. For more information, contact Department of Labor and Industrial Relations, P.O. Box 504, 3315 West Truman Boulevard Room 213, Jefferson City, MO 65102-0504; 573-751-9691; Fax: 573-751-4135; {www.dolir.state.mo.us/es/ d4c17.htm}.

Training for Women

The mission of the Missouri Women's Council is to help Missouri Women achieve economic self-sufficiency by supporting education, training, and leadership opportunities. Each year the Missouri Women's Council reviews pilot program proposals across the state and selects projects to fund which promote training, employment, and support Missouri women in the workplace. As a funding source, they are aware of the newest job training programs and may be able to provide you with referrals. For more information, contact Missouri Women's Council, P.O. Box 1684, 421 East Dunklin Street, Jefferson City, MO 65102; 573-751-0810, 877-426-9284; Fax: 573-751-8835; {www.womenscouncil.org/}; {Email: wcouncil@mail.state.mo.us}.

Workforce Preparation for Women

This program is currently served in two Missouri locations; Mineral Area College in Park Hills and Jefferson College in Hillsboro. These programs focus on self-esteem, foundation skills and competencies as identified by an assessment process, and a workforce preparation plan developed by each student. Experts from education, business, and industry serve as speakers and consultants for the training sessions. Furthermore, the program matches each student with a mentor. For more information on this program, please contact Dr. Nancy Wegge, Consortium Director, Jefferson College, Hillsboro, MO 63050; 573-431-1951; Fax: 573-431-9397.

Assess Your Skills

The St. Louis Agency on Training and Employment (SLATE) can help you assess your skills and training needs. If their assessment suggests that training is necessary, they may be able to provide tuition assistance. This training, provided at several approved public or private technical schools, colleges or universities, must be in a growth area and lead to full-time employment. They also offer the laid-off worker an opportunity for on-the-job training, if eligible. During your training period, you are employed full-time and receive normal company benefits. For providing this training, your employer is reimbursed a portion of your wage. The employer agrees to retain you full-time after training is completed. For more information, contact St. Louis Agency on Training and Employment, 317 North 11th Street, Suite 400, St. Louis, MO 63101; 314-589-8000; Fax: 314-231-7923; {www.works.state.mo.us/slate/index.html}.

Christian Programs

Ursuline Companions in Mission is a Christian association of lay women and men who seek to make a difference in the lives of the poor through a variety of programs including job training. They have service delivery sites in Delaware, Illinois, Kentucky, Minnesota, Missouri, New Mexico, and Ohio. Programs vary from location to location. For more information, contact Ursuline Companions In Mission, Sr. Jane Quinlan, College of New Rochelle, College Center, Room 155, New Rochelle, NY 10805; 914-654-5270; Fax: 914-654-5290; {www.theursulines.org}; {Email: ursulinecomp@hotmail.com}.

Job Training For Mothers To Be

Worldwide Love For Children has a three-fold purpose: to minister to the mother-to-be, the prospective parents, and to the child. Among their many services for expecting mothers is help with life goals, such as education and job training. These are provided by Esther's Maternity Haven, a licensed maternity home, run by Worldwide Love For Children. For more information, contact Worldwide Love For Children, P.O. Box 6206, Springfield, MO 65801-6206; 417-869-3151.

Support For Women Business Owners

If you are thinking of starting a business or already own one, the St. Louis chapter of the National Association of Women Business Owners (NAWBO) can help. You can benefit from one-on-one counseling, mentoring, monthly educational and networking meetings, and referrals to women-owned businesses. More importantly, they have an educational program called Success Savvy that consists of a series of classes to help women start and grow a successful business. Course topics include Do I Really Want To Be In Business, Writing a Business Plan, Basic Accounting for Your Business, Writing a Marketing Plan, and When and How to Use Professionals. The program also includes a Smart Business conference with seminars designed to educate women in the various stages of business ownership. For more information, contact NAWBO - St. Louis (National Association of Women's Business Owners - St. Louis), Irina Bronstein Executive Director, 706 North Jefferson, St.Louis, MO 63103; 314-436-2223, toll-free: 888-560-9813, Fax: 314-436-1176; {www2.stlmo.com/nawbo/}; {Email: nawbostl@ ibm.net}.

Connect With Your Career

St. Charles County Community College has two programs of interest to women in transitional times. Free Adult Re-entry Workshops are held each semester to help the student who has been out of school for a number of years ease back into the classroom situation. Topics covered are goal setting and decision-making, career exploration, assertiveness training, time and stress management, college services, and study skills improvement. A Single Parent/Displaced Homemaker Program can assist you in acquiring new skills or update current skills in order to enter or re-enter the job market. All services, including seminars and individual career consultations, are provided at no charge. Persons who might benefit include single parents and/or displaced homemakers who wish to better define their career interests and/or make a career change, as well as those returning to the workforce after a brief or prolonged absence. For more information, contact the Career Connection office in 1206 ACAD or call 314-922-8248. St. Charles County Community College, 3601 Mid Rivers Mall Dr., St. Peters, MO 63376-0975; {www.stchas.edu/students/carcon.htm}.

Training For Food Stamp Recipients

The Missouri Jobs, Employment and Training program prepares food stamp recipients for employment to help avoid long term dependence by achieving self-sufficiency. An educational and vocational assessment is completed with a case manager to develop employment goals and also to identify any barriers. Afterwards, the participant is referred to an activity in line with the employment goals and monitored until completion. Other services may include transportation allowances and work related expense payments. Eligible participants are food stamp recipients that are not receiving Temporary Assistance benefits and reside in one of the following counties: Cape Girardeau, Dunklin, Lincoln, Mississippi, New Madrid, Pemiscot, Pike, St. Charles, St. Louis, Scott, Stoddard, Warren, and the city of St. Louis. For more information, contact the Division of Family Services, P.O. Box 88, Jefferson City, MO 65103; 573-751-3221, 800-735-2466; {www.dss.state.mo.us/dfs/fjobs.htm}; (Email: askdss@mail.state.mo.us}.

Rural Missouri Inc. (RMI)
Rural Missouri Inc. (RMI) has programs that assist low-income, seasonally employed farm workers that want to obtain full-time, permanent employment or want to go to school. Some of the training programs available are Classroom Training which offers tuition assistance, Apprenticeship Program that provides skilled training, and On-The-Job Training where participants are placed in permanent positions. These programs are available to low-income, seasonally employed farm workers and/or their dependents. Contact RMI 1014 Northeast Drive, Jefferson City, MO 65109; 573-635-0136; 800-234-4971; (www.rmiinc.org}; {Email: rmiinc.org}.

Skills Training for Adults
The Workforce Development Division has a program for adults 18 and older that have limited income, are unemployed, and who are not self-sufficient to prepare for work. They offer skills training; assessment of skills, needs, and employment goals; job search assistance; job development and placement; on-the-job training, and more. Contact the Division of Workforce Development, 421 East Dunklin, P.O. Box 1087, Jefferson City, MO 65102-1087; 800-877-8698; {www.ecodev.state.mo.us/wfd/jobseekers/servicesforadults.htm}.

Help for Youths To Find Employment
This program is for in-school and out-of-school youths in Missouri, ages 14 to 21, that meet income guidelines. The goal is to improve their long-term job opportunities. It encourages graduation from school or enrollment in a GED program. It also aids them in obtaining employment through work experience and to improve their academic skills so they can successfully go from school to work. Some of the services offered are individual assessment to determine vocational, educational, occupational, literacy, and life skills; classroom training; work experience at a non-profit workplace; on-the-job training, and more. For more information, contact the Division of Workforce Development, 421 East Dunklin, P.O. Box 1087, Jefferson City, MO 65102-1087; 800-877-8698; {www.ecodev.state.mo.us/wfd/jobseekers/servicesforyouth.htm}.

Training for Youths Through Community Service
In this program, eligible Missouri youths, ages 14 to 21, obtain job skills through community service. The services offered are job placement through work experience at state and community parks and conservation sites, GED classes for high-school dropouts; employability skills training at the work site and through group activities; and career exploration activities. For more information, contact the Division of Workforce Development, 421 East Dunklin, P.O. Box 1087, Jefferson City, MO 65102-1087; 800-877-8698; {www.ecodev.state.mo.us/wfd/jobseekers/conservationcorps.htm}.

Training for Laid Off Workers
The purpose of the Dislocated Worker Program is to help permanently laid-off Missouri workers to reenter the workforce. It provides education, experience, and skills assessment, help with basic education, or obtaining a GED, skill training, on-the-job training, job development placement and counseling to overcome the trauma of job loss and the associated problems. For more information, contact the Division of Workforce Development, 421 East Dunklin, P.O. Box 1087, Jefferson City, MO 65102-1087; 800-877-8698; {www.ecodev.state.mo.us/wfd/jobseekers/dislocated.htm}.

Training for Long-Term Welfare Recipients
Participants in this program are long-term welfare recipients, non-custodial parents, and others that meet certain requirements. Its purpose is to move them to economic self-sufficiency by offering the following services; work readiness information and education; work experience/community service; on-the-job training; job placement; post employment, and job retention services; job creation through public and private wage subsidies; and supportive services such as childcare and transportation following employment. For more information, contact the Division of

Workforce Development, 421 East Dunklin, P.O. Box 1087, Jefferson City, MO 65102-1087; 573-751-3999; {www.ecodev.state.mo.us/wfd/jobseekers/welfaretowork.htm}l

Services for Veterans
Together, the Disabled Veteran's Outreach Program and the Local Veteran's Employment Representative Program offer prioritized employment and training services for eligible veterans. Also, the Disabled Veteran's Outreach Program specialists provide case management and direct development and training opportunities for veterans, with special emphasis placed on veterans with service-connected disabilities. The services provided with this program are counseling; testing; identification of employment and training opportunities; monitoring job listings from federal contractors to ensure eligible veterans get priority referrals to those jobs, and more. For more information, contact the Division of Workforce Development, 421 East Dunklin, P.O. Box 1087, Jefferson City, MO 65102-1087; 573-751-3999.

Assistance for Migrant and Seasonal Farm Workers
The purpose of the program is to help with job and training opportunities tailored to the preferences, needs, and skills of the migrant and seasonal farm worker. Outreach services are available to eligible individuals. Certain requirements need to be met and exclusions apply. For more information, contact the Division of Workforce Development, 421 East Dunklin, P.O. Box 1087, Jefferson City, MO 65102-1087; 573-751-3999.

Montana

One-Stop Career Centers
A network of One-Stop Career Centers throughout the state offers a wide range of employment related services including job training. Services vary by location. To find a location near you, please refer to the website {http://jsd.dli.state.mt.us}. To learn more about the services they offer, contact your state coordinator.

Mr. Bob Simoneau, Director, Workforce Development Bureau, Montana Department of Labor and Industry, P.O. Box 1728, Helena, MT 59624; 406-444-2607; Fax: 406-444-3037.

Job Service Offices
A system of Employment Service/Job Service offices is located within every state with the goal of assisting millions of job seekers and employers. While services may vary from location to location, many provide job training, skills assessment and related services. With approximately 1,800 Employment Service/Job Service offices nationwide

there is bound to be one near you. To learn more about the services offered in your area, contact your state administrator. Patricia Haffey, Commissioner, Department of Labor & Industry, State Capitol, Helena, MT 59624; 406-444-3555; Fax: 406-444-1394; {http://jsd.dli.state.mt.us}.

Women's Career Development
The Career Training Institute (CTI) has many services concerned with women's career development. CTI is Montana's central Women's Business Center and the area leader in delivery of services to women for job training, welfare-to-work, displaced homemakers, non-traditional careers, and other special target demonstration projects for women in transition to the workplace. CTI's OWBO grant targets new and expanding businesses for women in four rural counties where they maintain close contact with area employers who benefit by access to a trained workforce, and to unions, other businesses and contractors. With this many services, you know there is something there for you. CTI is located in Helena's Family Investment Center, a local one-stop education and training agency. Career Training Institute and Women's Business Center (CTI), Maureen Garrity, Director, 347 North Last Chance Gulch, Helena, MT 59601; 406-443-0800, 800-254-6607; Fax: 406-442-2745; {www.ctibrc.org }; {Email: mgarrity@ctibrc.org}.

Get On Your Path
Whatever your career goals, Career Transitions, Inc., can help you achieve them. They want to assist you in becoming self-sufficient and strengthen your community through workforce development, education, training and

employment. Find your future through their assessment tools that explore skills and interests and match to job goals, training and career paths. These include: math and English evaluation; reading evaluation (free literacy tutoring available); interest; values, and aptitude inventories; and the Meyers-Briggs personality profile. They can also help you with programs focusing on job search, communication, and self-esteem. Then, get your business skills together through classes on interviewing, applications, resume and cover letter, computer and office skills training, computer literacy, advanced software training, computerized accounting, Internet basics, non-traditional occupations/entrepreneurship CAD, computer maintenance and repair, commercial driver's license, small business development, and much more. For more information or to sign up for their weekly orientation, contact the address and phone below, Career Transitions Inc., 91 Southview Quaw School, Belgrade, MT 59714; 406-388-6701; {www.careertransitions. com/}; {Email: info@careertransitions.com}.

Assistance for Low-Income Entrepreneurs
The Human Resource Development Council of Bozeman (HRDC) offers microbusiness training, technical assistance, and loan funds for low-income entrepreneurs. A community action agency serving Gallatin County in southwestern Montana has developed a partnership to improve an existing microbusiness incubator program by providing crucial, but previously lacking, loan funds to low-income people seeking to pursue microbusiness enterprises. For more information, contact Jeffrey K. Rupp, Executive Director, Charles Hill, Project Director, Human Resource Development Council, 321 East Main St., Suite 300, Bozeman, MT 59715; 406-587-4486; Fax: 406-585-3538; {Email: hrdcjr@aol.com}.

Help for Farm and Ranch Workers
Rural Employment Opportunities, Inc. offers free services to farm and ranch workers and their dependents if the worker has worked in a seasonal agricultural job within the past 2 years. They must also be low-income and in compliance with selected service regulations and legally authorized to work in the US. Their goal is to train clients with new skills that will lead them to permanent year-round employment. They assist in the development of an employment goal, teach techniques to gain employment, and can also help with the cost of tuition, tools and work clothes, and other family needs. REO works with businesses to develop training position as and permanents jobs for the participants of the program. The types of training programs they offer are; classroom, on-the-job, work experience, training assistance, life skills, and REO Techmobile. For more information, contact REO, P.O. Box 831, Helena, MT 59624-0831; 406-442-7850; Fax: 406-442-7855; {www.mt.net/~reo/index.htm}; {Email: reo@mt.net}.

Montana Community Development Corporation
It is the purpose of the Montana Community Development Corporation to sustain communities and to create income opportunities for low and moderate income residents. They work with new and expanding businesses ranging from a single owner to large corporations. They offer entrepreneurs counseling, training, and loans. Other services deal with writing a business plan, marketing assistance with packaging promotion and market analysis, financial assistance with analysis, planning, loan packaging and more. They work in the following counties: Missoula, Ravalli, Sanders, Mineral, and South Lake. For more information, contact Montana Community Development Corporation, 103 East Main, Missoula, MT 59802; 406-728-9234; Fax: 406-542-6671; {www.mtcdc.org}; {Email: mcdc@mtcdc.org}.

Help for Disabled to Find Work
Vocational Rehabilitation Program aims to help residents with disabilities to achieve independence through work. There are a variety of services designed to assist, find, or maintain employment for the clients. The services vary by the client's needs. They may include evaluation services, career counseling and guidance services, training, job development and placement services, and more. Eligible persons are those that have a physical or mental disability, the disability keeps them from getting or keeping a job, and they need VR services to help them get or keep a job. For more information, contact Vocational Rehabilitation,111 Sanders, Suite 307, P.O. Box 4210, Helena, MT 59604-4210; 877-296-1197; 406-444-2590 (voice & TDD); Fax: 406-444-3632; {www.dphhs.state.mt.us/dsd/govt_programs/vrp/vrs/index.htm}.

Micro-Business Training

The Human Resource Development Council of Bozeman has a micro-business training program for low-income entrepreneurs in Gallatin County. These services include training, technical assistance, and support services, as well as a revolving loan fund to help business owners pursue their ideas. For more information, contact Jerry K. Rupp, Executive Director, Human Resource Development Council, District IX, 321 East Main Street, Suite 300, Bozeman, MT 59715; 406-587-4486; Fax: 406-585-3538.

Nebraska

One-Stop Career Centers

A network of One-Stop Career Centers throughout the state offers a wide range of employment related services including job training. Services vary by location. To find a location near you, please refer to the website {www.dol.state.ne.us/workforce.htm}. To learn more about the services they offer, contact your state coordinator.

Mr. Michael J. Holland, Director, Job Service Division, Nebraska Department of Labor, P.O. Box 94600, 550 South 16th Street, Lincoln, NE 68509-4600; 402-471-3405; Fax: 402-471-2318.

Ms. Kathy Plager, One-Stop/Workforce Development Coordinator, Nebraska Department of Labor, P.O. Box 94600, 550 South 16th Street, Room 309, Lincoln, NE 68509-4600; 402-471-9928; Fax: 402-471-2318.

Mr. Fernando Lecuona, III, Commissioner of Labor, Nebraska Department of Labor, P.O. Box 94600, 550 South 16th Street, Lincoln, NE 68509-4600; 402-471-3405; Fax: 402-471-2318.

Job Service Offices

A system of Employment Service/Job Service offices is located within every state with the goal of assisting millions of job seekers and employers. While services may vary from location to location, many provide job training, skills assessment and related services. With approximately 1,800 Employment Service/Job Service offices nationwide  there is bound to be one near you. To learn more about the services offered in your area, contact your state administrator. Michael J. Holland, Director of Job Service Division, Department of Labor, 550 S. 16th Street, Lincoln, NE 68509-4600; 402-471-3405; Fax: 402-471-2318; {www.dol.state.ne.uw/jobserv.htm}.

Other State Programs

Nebraska Vocational Equity Programs, located in educational sites and community based organizations, are staffed by professionals who are responsible for administering locally designed programs. Their goal is to assure access to quality vocational education programs. Programs are federally funded and are administered by the Nebraska Department of Education (NDE) with financial support from participating institutions. Below is a list of service providers. Get in touch with one near you for information about specific programs. Contact them online at {http://nde4.nde.state.ne.us/EEO/VocEQ/Equity.Html}

- Burke High School, Zoo and Non-traditional Career Academies, 12200 Burke Blvd., Omaha, NE 68154; 402-557-3264.

- Central Community College, Platte Campus, 4500 63rd St., P.O. Box 1027, Columbus, NE 68602-1027; 402-461-2480; 800-642-1083.

- Central Community College, Non-traditional Careers/Single Parent, Displaced Homemaker, Hastings Campus, 1024 Hastings, P.O. Box 1024, Hastings, NE 68602-1024; 402-461-2480; 800-742-7872.

- Crete PS Special Programs Office, Single Parent/Displaced Homemaker, Crete Public Schools, 920 Linden Ave., Crete, NE 68333; 402-826-5228.

- Grand Island YWCA, Single Parent/Displaced Homemaker, Incarcerated Women, Grand Island YWCA, 234 E. 3rd, Grand Island, NE 68801-5912; 308-384-8170.

- Lincoln Public Schools, Teen Parents, 5901 'O' Street, Lincoln, NE 68510: 402-436-1817.

- Lincoln YWCA, Safety Professionals, Teen Parents, 1432 'N' St., Lincoln, NE 68508: 402-434-3494.

- McCook Community College, Single Parent/ Displaced Homemaker, 1205 East Third St. McCook, NE 69001-2631; 308-345-6303; 800-658-4348.

- Metropolitan Community College, Single Parent/ Displaced Homemaker, P.O. Box 3777 Omaha, NE 68103-0777; 402-457-2319; 800-228-9553.

- Mid Plains Community College, Single Parent/Displaced Homemaker, 1101 Halligan Drive, North Platte, NE 69101; 308-532-8740.

- Norfolk Public Schools, Non-traditional Careers/Teen Parent, Norfolk Public Schools, 512 Philip Ave., P.O. Box 139, Norfolk, NE 68702; 402-644-2516; 402-644-2500.

- Northeast Community College, Non-traditional Career Camp, Single Parent/Displaced Homemaker, 801 East Benjamin Ave., P.O. Box 469, Norfolk, NE 68702-0469; 402-644-0435; 402-644-0471; 800-348-9033; Direct line to Displaced Homemaker/Single Parent Program: 402-644-0471;Contact Deb Milligan; {www.wjag.com/nccstory.htm}.

- Omaha YWCA, 222 S. 29th, Omaha, NE 68131-3577; 402-345-6555.

- Southeast Community College, RR 2, Box 35-A, Beatrice, NE 68310-9683; 402-345-6555; 800-233-5027.

- Southeast Community College, Non-traditional Careers/Single Parent, Southeast Community College, 8800 'O' St., Lincoln, NE 68520-1299; 402-437-2629; 800-642-4075.

- Southeast Community College, Technology Careers for Women, 600 State St., Milford, NE 68405-9397; 402-761-8202.

- University of Nebraska-Lincoln, Nebraska Career Information System, Single Parent/Displaced Homemaker NH 421, Lincoln, NE 68588-0552; 402-472-2570

- Western NE Community College, Single Parent/Displaced Homemaker, 1601 East 27th St., Scottsbluff, NE 69162, 308-635-6121; 800-348-4435.

- Western NE Community College, Non-traditional Careers, 371 College Drive, Sidney, NE 69162; 308-254-7414; 800-222-9682.

Assistance Finding and Keeping a Job for People With Disabilities

Nebraska's Vocational Rehabilitation Department provides services for people with a mental or physical disability that keeps them from getting or keeping a job. They help their clients make career plans, learn job skills, coordinate services for independent living, and getting and keeping a job. While their services are administered for each individual client, the major ones are, vocational counseling, job matching, custom training, assistive technology, independent living, and job placement. For more information, contact Vocational Rehabilitation, P.O. Box 94987, 301 Centennial Mall, South, Lincoln, NE 68509; 402-471-3644; 877-637-3422; {www.vocrehab.state.ne.us}.

Training for Disadvantaged & Special Needs Youths

Economically disadvantaged and special needs youths, ages 14 to 21, can receive training from Job Training of Greater Omaha. They offer remedial and basic education, GED, skill training, on-the-job training, job search assistance and more. They also have a summer youth program and an 8 week career exploration and work experience program. The mentoring program uses professionals as role modes for career development programs. For more information, contact Job Training of Greater Omaha, 24221 North 21st Street, Omaha, NE 68110; 402-444-4700; Fax: 402-444-3755.

Training for People Getting Assistance
Project Resolve aims to change the opportunities of those with disadvantaged social circumstances through education, training and employment. The services it offers are job search preparation and assistance, and job development. For more information, contact Tammy Jensen, Project Resolve-Goodwill Industries, 1111 South 41st Street, Omaha, NE 68105; 402-341-4609; {www.goodwillomaha.com}.

Computer Office Training
For those that meet income guidelines and are displaced workers, there is a 12 to 20 week computer office skills program. Job search assistance is included in the program. For more information, contact SER Jobs for Progress, Inc., 4911 South 25th Street, Omaha, NE 68107; 402-734-1321.

Job Services for Young Adults
Success Prep is a program open to people ages 16 to 25 years old, in the metropolitan area. They will receive training in job survival skills and transition-to-work services. For more information, contact Success Prep, c/o Boys & Girls Club of Omaha, 2606 Hamilton Street, Omaha, NE 68131; 402-342-5135; Fax: 402-345-3154.

Painter and Dry Wall Apprenticeship
The Painters & Allied Trades Local Union 109 has a Drywall Finisher Apprentice training for 2 years and a Painter Apprentice training for 4 years. An Apprentice Program is a combination of on-the-job and classroom training. The trainee receives pay while he/she learns from a trades person. After training is completed, the apprentice will be qualified to work anywhere in the nation in that trade. For more information, contact Painters & Allied Trades Local Union 109, 4523 Military Avenue, Omaha, NE 68106; 405-556-9373.

Nevada

One-Stop Career Centers
A network of One-Stop Career Centers throughout the state offers a wide range of employment related services including job training. Services vary by location. To find a location near you, please refer to the website

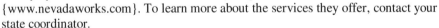

{www.nevadaworks.com}. To learn more about the services they offer, contact your state coordinator.

Ms. Carol A. Jackson, Director, Employment Security Division Department of Employment, Training and Rehabilitation, 500 East Third Street, Carson City, NV 89713; 702-687-4440; Fax: 702-687-3903.

Mr. George Govlick, ES Administrator, Employment Security Division Department of Employment, Training and Rehabilitation, 500 East Third Street, Carson City, NV 89713; 702-687-4630; Fax: 702-687-3903.

Job Service Offices
A system of Employment Service/Job Service offices is located within every state with the goal of assisting millions of job seekers and employers. While services may vary from location to location, many provide job training, skills assessment and related services. With approximately 1,800 Employment Service/Job Service offices nationwide there is bound to be one near you. To learn more about the services offered in your area, contact your state administrator.

Mylar Florence, Director, Department of Employment, Training & Rehabilitation, 1830 East Sahara, Las Vegas, NV 89104; 702-486-7923; Fax: 702-486-7924; {http://detr.state.nv.us/es_jobseeker.htm}.

Stanley P. Jones, Administrator, Nevada Employment Security Division, 500 East Third Street, Carson City, NV 89713; 702-687-4635; Fax: 702-687-3903.

Economic Self-sufficiency

Nevada MicroEnterprise Initiative is a similar program whose mission is to enhance the economic self-sufficiency and quality of life of low- to moderate-income individuals through entrepreneurial training, business technical assistance and loans for new and expanding businesses throughout the State of Nevada. These programs are designed to give you economic power by providing the most comprehensive entrepreneurial services. NMI's programs provide women and men with business skills as well as life skills. Contact Nevada MicroEnterprise Initiative (NMI), 1600 E. Desert Inn Road, Suite 209E, Las Vegas, NV 89109; 702-734-3555; Fax: 702-734-3530; {www.nmimicro.org };{Email: asiefert@nmimicroorg}.

Nevada MicroEnterprise Initiative (NMI), 116 East 7th Street, Suite 3, Carson City, NV 89701; 702-841-1420; Fax: 702-841-2221; {Email: reno@nmimicro.org}.

Training For Low-Income People

The Center for Employment Training (CET) is a private, non-profit, community based organization that provides quality employment training for those who need it most. They offer you extensive life skills and workplace know-how instruction through a program that includes job preparedness training, job development and placement. CET keeps students in training until they are placed and conducts follow-up on all placements to ensure stable employment and job growth. CET's primary activity is classroom skill training, which is provided year-round. CET does not screen applicants through testing, but accepts anyone who is willing to do the necessary work. Courses are offered on an open-entry, open-exit basis and students complete training at their own pace. CET training is intensive, with students attending 5 days and 35 to 40 hours per week for an average of seven months. CET training is competency based, highly individualized, and hands-on from day one. The average training course at CET maintains a 20-1 student/teacher ratio. CET's unique mode of training involves an integration of skill training, basic skills instruction and human development conducted in a simulated work setting. At least twenty-five job training options are offered at CET nationwide. These include automated office skills, building maintenance, electronic assembly, medical assistant, truck driving, and shipping/receiving. Skill offerings vary from one center to another. A typical CET center offers 4-5 skills and may serve up to 250 persons annually. For more information, contact their national headquarters: CET Corporate Offices, 701 Vine St., San Jose, CA 95110; 408-287-7924; 800-533-2519; {Email: cfet@best.com}; {www.best.com/~cfet/main.htm}; or Center for Employment Training, 520 Evans Avenue, Reno, NV 89512; 775-348-8668 Fax: 775-348-2034; {www.cet2000.org }; {Email: m_smith@cetmail.cfet.org}.

Help For Displaced Homemakers

HELP of Southern Nevada offers you hands on assistance in your search for unsubsidized employment. If you have lost your sole source of income through death of a spouse, divorce, separation or disability, please call to see if you are eligible to begin the HELP of Southern Nevada week-long job seeking skills workshop for displaced homemakers and begin on the road to self-sufficiency. HELP offers you educational opportunities through the Culinary Training School, computer classes, receptionist training, medical assistant training in the dialysis field, literacy training and re-entry schooling at the community college. To see if you qualify, please contact the Displaced Homemaker Program at HELP of Southern Nevada, 953-35B East Sahara Ave., Suite 208, Las Vegas NV 89104; 702-369-4357; {www.lvrj.com/communitylink/helpofsn/dh.html}.

Help For Veterans and Other Job Seekers

This program is available to unemployed Nevadans so they can gain the skills needed for today's labor market and to find a permanent job. Career Enhancement Program (CEP) participants receive on-the-job training, basic academic and/or vocational classroom training specifically geared towards their needs. This is done through individualized re-employment plans, job search workshops and coaching, aptitude and skills proficiency testing, vocational guidance and counseling, basic education improvement, and more. Employers receive financial assistance to train new workers on the job. Contact the Department of Employment, Training, and Rehabilitation, Employment Security

Division, 500 East Third Street, Carson, NV 89713-0021;775-684-3909; TDD: 775-687-5353; Fax: 775-684-3910 {http://detr.state.nv.us/es/es_cep.htm}.

Help For Economically Disadvantaged and More

The Great Basin College Re-entry Center has a program for Career and Life Planning. It is designed to identify and meet the needs of economically disadvantaged people, single parents, pregnant/parenting teens, displaced homemakers, disabled people, and high school dropouts. It provides job placement services, pre-employment training, career counseling, and career guidance. It links employers, education, and human service agencies to help these people gain employment. For more information, contact Great Basin College, Re-entry Center, 1500 College Parkway, Elko, NV 89801; 702-738-2184; {www.gbcnv.edu}.

Help for Low-Income Single Parents

The Truckee Meadows Community College Re-Entry Center assists low-income single parents, and displaced homemakers. Besides assistance with schooling costs and job search skills, they offer personal job search workshops, job placement, and much more. There is also a resource area where students have access to the Internet, can learn software and practice keyboard skills. For more information, contact Truckee Meadows Community College Re-Entry Center, 4001 South Virginia, Room E4, Reno, NV 895023; 775-826-9041; Fax: 775-824-8623; {www.tmcc.edu}.

Job Assistance for Everyone

JOIN, Inc., Job Opportunities in Nevada, serves northern Nevada as a workforce service provider. Clients are offered job readiness skills, assistance to re-enter the workforce by upgrading skills, entrance into a GED program, and funding for classes or specialized training. They also have a specialized division that works with unemployed professional, ProNet, and one that works with workers 55 years and older, Golden Opportunity. Their clients include professionals, laid-off workers, welfare recipients, and young people just starting out. For more information about their services, contact JOIN, Inc., 560 Mill, Reno, NV 89502; 775-785-JOIN(5646); 775-785-6106; {www.join.org}; {Email: info@join.org.}.

Vocational Counseling

All people looking for new employment can seek the guidance of a vocational counselor for help in making good career decisions. There, they can assess their goals and interest, develop an effective job search plans, make useful contacts, and receive valuable suggestions. Contact your local Employment Security Division Job Link Office or the Department of Employment, Training, and Rehabilitation, Employment Security Division, 500 East Third Street, Carson City, NV 89713-0021; {www.detr.state.nv.us/es/es_voc.htm}; {Email: detrinfo@govmail.state.nv.us}.

New Hampshire

One-Stop Career Centers

A network of One-Stop Career Centers throughout the state offers a wide range of employment related services including job training. Services vary by location. To find a location near you, please refer to the website {www.nhworks.org }. To learn more about the services they offer, contact your state coordinator.

Mr. John Ratoff, Commissioner, Department of Employment Security, 32 South Main Street, Rm. 204, Concord, NH 03301; 603-224-3311; Fax: 603-228-4145.

Ms. Doris LaChance, Chief of Operations, New Hampshire Employment Service, 32 South Main St., Concord, NH 03301; 603-228-4051; Fax: 603-229-4321.

Job Service Offices

A system of Employment Service/Job Service offices is located within every state with the goal of assisting millions of job seekers and employers. While services may vary from location to location, many provide job training, skills

assessment and related services. With approximately 1,800 Employment Service/Job Service offices nationwide there is bound to be one near you. To learn more about the services offered in your area, contact your state administrator.

John J. Ratoff, Commissioner, Department of Employment Security, 32 South Main Street, Concord, NH 03301-4857; 603-228-4000; Fax: 603-228-4145; {www.nhes.state.nh.us}.

Joseph Weisenburger, Deputy Commissioner, Department of Employment Security, 32 South Main Street, Concord, NH 03301; 603-228-4064; Fax: 603-228-4145.

Women Entrepreneurs Take Note

The Women's Business Center, Inc. is a collaborative organization designed to encourage and support women in all phases of enterprise development. They provide you with access to educational programs, financing alternatives, technical assistance, advocacy, and a network of mentors, peer advisors and business and professional consultants. They can address your women-owned business needs through several targeted programs: Seminars for Women Entrepreneurs; WBC Newsletter; Monthly Peer Advisory Meetings; Internet for Small Business Workshops; and The Entrepreneur's Network. For more information, contact Women's Business Center, Inc., Rachael Stuart, Executive Director, 150 Greenleaf Avenue, Unit 8, Portsmouth, NH 03801; 603-430-2892; Fax: 603-430-3706; {www.womenbiz.org}; {Email: beth@womenbiz.org }.

Find Job Training At An Office Near You

The New Hampshire Job Training Council is a private, non-profit organization committed to helping people learn new skills so they can begin new careers. Since 1983, they have assisted more than 25,000 state residents of all ages and backgrounds to get the training they have needed to get back to work. Their training services are available statewide and they have offices in most cities in New Hampshire. To find a location near you, contact New Hampshire Job Training Council, 64 B Old Suncook Road, Concord, NH 03301; 603-228-9500; 800-772-7001 (NH only); Fax: 603-228-8557; TDD: 800-622-9180; {www.partnersforcommunity.org/new_england_farm_workers. htm}; {Email: nhjtc@orgtheenterprise}.

Re-Training For Farm Workers

If you are a farm worker considering a different kind of work, you can get information about job training services. Workers can also visit the New England Farm Workers' Council, 370 Union Street, Manchester, NH 03103; 603-622-8199; 800-562-3848; Fax: 603-622-8230.

Help For Disabled Persons

New Hampshire Vocational Rehabilitation helps people with disabilities not only get and keep a job, but also to develop a life time career. Those with physical, mental, emotional, and learning disabilities which create a substantial problem getting or keeping a job, are eligible for assistance. A counselor assists in developing an employment plan that will mo0ver the client towards employment. Some of the services available are diagnostic testing, vocational evaluation, and vocational counseling which can lead to training and job placement. For more information, contact the New Hampshire Vocational Rehabilitation, 78 Regional Drive, Concord, NH 03301; 603-271-3471; 800-299-1647.

Apprenticeship Program

Apprenticeship is a combination of on the job training and related classroom instruction. The trainee obtains a lifelong increased earning capacity, making them more competitive and able to get and keep a good paying job anywhere in the country. The apprentice is sponsored to learn one of more than 800 trades in the apprenticeship program, such as; roofer, plumber, machinist, drafter, millwright, auto mechanic and office equipment repair. The term of the program varies from 1-6 years, depending on the occupation to be learned. The apprentice will have full-time employment, supervised training, increasing scale of wages, improved job security, and more. To learn more, contact the Director of Apprenticeship, NH Department of Labor, State Office Park, South 95 Pleasant Street, Concord, NH 03301; 603-271-6850.

Help For Small Business Owners
The goal of the New Hampshire Small Business Development Center is to contribute to the economic vitality of New Hampshire by providing businesses and communities with the tools they need to reach their goals. They have Business Consulting Services, Training Sessions, and Materials and Business Information Referrals. There is free one-on-one confidential business counseling, low cost training programs, and access to information and referrals. Their workshops cover topics such as, How To Start Your Own Business, Internet Marketing Basics, and Customer Services Tips for the Hospitality Industry. To learn more, contact the New Hampshire Small Business Development Center, State Director's Office and Administrative Offices, University of New Hampshire, The Whittemore School of Business, 108 McConnell Hall, Durham, NH 03824; 603-862-2200; Fax: 603-862-4876; {www.nhsbdc.org}; {Email: mec@christa.unh.edu}.

New Jersey

One-Stop Career Centers
A network of One-Stop Career Centers throughout the state offers a wide range of employment related services including job training. Services vary by location. To find a location near you, please refer to the website {www.wnjpin.net/OneStopCareerCenter/welcome/onestops_new/onestops_main.htm}. To learn more about the services they offer, contact your state coordinator.

Ms. Connie O. Hughes, One-Stop Lead Director, Workforce New Jersey, New Jersey Department of Labor, John Fitch Plaza, CN 055, Trenton, NJ 08625; 609-292-6236; Fax: 609-777-0483; {Email: chughes@dol.state.nj.us}.

Mr. Melvin Gelade, Commissioner, New Jersey Department of Labor, John Fitch Plaza, CN 110, Trenton, NJ 08625-0110; 609-292-2323; Fax: 609-633-9271; {Email: mgelade@dol.state.nj.us}.

Job Service Offices
A system of Employment Service/Job Service offices is located within every state with the goal of assisting millions of job seekers and employers. While services may vary from location to location, many provide job training, skills assessment and related services. With approximately 1,800 Employment Service/Job Service offices nationwide there is bound to be one near you. To learn more about the services offered in your area, contact your state administrator.

Mel Gelade, Commissioner, New Jersey Department of Labor, CN 110, Trenton, NJ 08625-0110; 609-292-2323; Fax: 609-633-9271; {www.wnjpin.net}.

Frederick C. Kniesler, Deputy Commissioner, New Jersey Department of Labor, CN 110, Trenton, NJ 08625-0110; 609-292-7275; Fax: 609-777-3197.

Training For Women Business Owners
The New Jersey National Association of Women Business Owners manages the EXCEL training and counseling program. Their training programs are divided into three stages: Stage I: Thinking About Starting a Business - Are You an Entrepreneur; Stage II: Creating or Assessing Your Business Plan - Start Right, Build Right; Stage III: Looking to Grow Your Business - Grow Smart. They offer training seminars throughout the state. For more information, contact New Jersey NAWBO Excel, Harriet Scooler, Project Director, 225 Hamilton Street, Bound Brook, NJ 08805-2042; 732-560-9607; Fax: 732-560-9687; {www.njawbo.org}; {Email: njawbo@njawbo.org}.

Learn Basic Skills
Catholic Community Services offers training classes in basic skills as well as ABS, ESL, and GED in Elizabeth, Jersey City, Orange, Newark, and Union City. Counseling & job placement are also available with experienced

instructors. For more information, contact Catholic Community Services, 425 Paramus Road, Paramus, NJ 07652l; 201-689-6200; Fax: 201-444-3172; {Email: ccsbergen@hotmail.com}.

Help For Displaced Homemakers
New Jersey has a network of service providers for displaced homemakers whose goals include: advocating for the needs of displaced homemakers, expanding existing services, founding centers at new sites, fundraising, and providing training to its members. To find a location near you, contact Mickie McSwieney, Displaced Homemakers Network of NJ, Inc., Circle Branch P.O. Box 5545, Trenton, NJ 08638-5545; 732-774-3363. You may also benefit from information provided by their funding source: The Women's Fund of NJ, 355 Chestnut Street, Union, NJ 07083; 908-851-7774; Fax: 908-851-7775; {www.wfnj.org/Displaced%20Homemakers.htm}.

Career Counseling and Job Placement
Take advantage of programs at the Women's Center of County College of Morris that offer individual career counseling, resume preparation, job placement, education and training referrals, career workshops, interest and aptitude testing, resources for financial assistance, child care information, support groups, computer workshops, and computer lab. Offices are located in Randolph, Morristown, Butler, and Pompton Lakes. Randolph location has free support group for working women every Thursday, 7 to 9 PM. Group emphasizes coping skills in workplace and juggling home/work environments. For more information, contact Elaine Muller, SCC/133, County College of Morris, Randolph, NJ 07869; 973-328-5025; Fax: 973-328-5146; {www.ccm.edu/womenscenter}; {Email: womenscenter@ccm.edu}.

Sheltered Employment
The Occupational Training Center can provide people with disabilities full or part time employment in a supportive setting giving them additional time to prepare for competitive employment or whose long term goal is permanent sheltered employment. Support services may include vocational and personal adjustment counseling, employability skills training, and placement assistance. For more information, contact Mark Stephenson, Assistance Executive Director, Occupational Training Center, 10 Ridgedale Avenue, Cedar Knolls, NJ 07927; 973-292-1884.

Training and Temporary Employment For Older Workers
If you are 55 years of age and older and meet income guidelines, Green Thumb, Inc. can provide you with temporary employment and training. They offer classroom and on-the-job training in community service positions, in private sector both part-time and full-time. In particular, they target non-English speaking, handicapped, and homeless individuals. A minimum wage is provided while participant is in training or assigned to community service. Contact Sydelle Norris, Director, P.O. Box 8303, Trenton, NJ 08650; 609-890-2121; Fax: 609-890-2124; {www.greenthumb.org}; {Email: snydor@earthlink.net}.

For Career Changing And Job Seeking Women
The Women's Rights Information Center offers you seminars, job bank, workshops, resume writing, interview practice, including videotaping. Classes cover WordPerfect 5.1, Windows/Word for Windows, Lotus 123, and Intro to Computer Basics. One-on-one career and resume counseling is available for a small donation. They are open 5 days and some evenings. Call to receive their quarterly calendar. ESL classes are offered several times each week. They also offer occupational training for single parents and displaced homemakers and an annual Women's Career Expo. For more information, contact Women's Rights Information Center, 108 W. Palisade Ave., Englewood, NJ 07631; 201-568-1166; Fax: 201-568-0762; {www.womensrights.org}; {Email: wmnsrts1@bellatlantic.net}.

Training, Counseling, Referrals
The Urban League for Bergen County offers you employment counseling, job referrals, employment training, mortgage counseling, and more. For more information, contact Vicky Washington, Urban League For Bergen County, 106 W Palisade Ave., Englewood, NJ 07631-2619; 201-568-4988; {www.njcommunity.com/servlet/ sites_ProcServ/DBPAGE=cge&GID=0000100001087651457950467677}; {Email wiblb@bergen.org}.

Learn Food Service or Property Maintenance
Bergen County Community Action Program, Inc. offers Adult Basic Education and ESL classes, as well as, vocational training programs for entry level jobs in the food service and property maintenance fields. In addition

BCCAP oversees Bergen County Head Start which provides child care for poor and low-income working families. For further information Community Action Programs, 227 E. Hanover St., Trenton, NJ 08608-1803; 201-968-0200, ext. 7026.

Learn How To Find A Job

The Bergen Employment Action Project of the United Labor Agency, AFL-CIO offers a continual series of full day job search classes for any job seeker. Topics include attitudes, stress management, support systems, resume-polishing, locating job openings, and interviewing skills. Graduates may come in for consultations and to review job leads online and hard copy, Tuesday and Thursday from 2:00-4:00. All services are free. Contact Bergen Employment Action Project (BEAP), AFL-CIO Community Services, 214 State Street, Hackensack, NJ 07601; 201-489-7476; Fax: 201-342-0608; {www.njcommunity.com/servlet/sites_ProcServ/DBPAGE=cge&GID= 00001000010876420409693504}; {Email wib8@bergen.org}.

All Kind Of Services For Job Seekers

The Bergen WorkForce Center unites many of the county's employment readiness programs and services needed to build the skilled labor force that will meet the rapidly changing business demands. This "One Stop" career center assists those who are eligible and most in need of employment and training services. They offer individual and group career counseling designed to assist women who are divorced, separated, widowed and/or raising children on their own to obtain high wage/high skill employment. Job search/placement assistance, resume preparation, vocational and academic assessment, academic skills refresher courses, GED preparations, ESL courses, technical and computer job skills training are also provided. Financial assistance is available for transportation, tuition and child care. Their Training for Trades Program is a free short term job training program for unemployed women and men who are interested in working in construction. The Bergen County Technical Schools, Career Life Counseling Program and the Catholic Community Services Hispanic Women's Resource Center, both well known for their services to women and minorities have formed a partnership to provide this innovative, hands-on-training, job readiness and job placement assistance to those who enroll in the program. For more information contact Jeff Sprague. They also have a program for displaced homemakers and single parents called New Beginnings. For more information contact Weptanomah Carter. Bergen Workforce Center, 540 Hudson Street, Hackensack, NJ 07601; 201-329-9600, ext. 5615; {www.njcommunity.com/servlet/sites_ProcServ/DBPAGE=cge&GID= 00001000010879793732686049}; {Email lawbre@bergen.org}.

Learn Job Search Skills

The Professional Services Group enhances job search skills in a professional environment with fax, copy and

computer facilities. Meetings are held Mondays and Thursdays from 9:00-4:00 and Fridays from 9:00-12:00. They offer seminars in job search skills including resume writing, networking and interviewing, and career counseling. Members must volunteer 3 hours per week. For more information, contact Professional Services Group, 506 Jersey Avenue, New Brunswick, NJ 08901; 732-418-3304; Fax: 732-937-4504.

Employment Seminar

WISE Women's Center runs an employment seminar every Monday from 10:00-12:00 am. You can benefit from specific employment skill training and a course on how to start your own business, etc. For more information on different categories, contact WISE Women's Center, Patricia Palmer, Director, Essex County College, 303 University Ave.; Newark, NJ 07105; 973-877-3395; {www.essex.edu/services/org/Wise}.

Learn To Work In A Kitchen

Let's Celebrate's Job Training Program (JobPower) offers a free comprehensive 16-week program of culinary instruction and training. Your only requirements are a desire and willingness to learn, a positive attitude, and commitment to completing the program. For information contact Mrs. Haney, 201 Cornelison Ave., Jersey City, NJ 07304; 201-433-5438; 201-451-4049; Fax: 201-332-1728.

Help For The Worker In Transition

Passaic County Workforce Development Center offers many different re-employment services. Participants may be of many different employment and business backgrounds. They have a Career Resource Room and computer

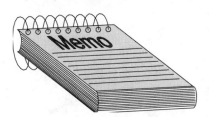

training for your benefit. For information contact Dr. Wayne Dyer, 388 Lakeview Ave., Clifton, NJ 07011; 973-340-9800; {www.pccareercenter. org}.

Help For Displaced Homemakers

Women In Transition is a state-funded program for displaced homemakers in Passaic County. This program offers you supportive counseling, job search skills and computer training. It is open to women who need to return to work or who are underemployed because of loss of support due to death, disability of spouse, separation, divorce or abusive behavior by their spouse. They also offer individual and group counseling, typing and computer training, and an eight week job readiness class designed to enhance women's self-esteem and confidence in making career and job choices, as well as practical help in facing the job search process. No fee for qualified applicants. For more information contact Kate McAteer, Coordinator, Women in Transition, Wayne Counseling and Family Services, 1022 Hamburg Turnpike, Wayne, NJ 07470; 973-694-9215.

Sussex County Community College

Sussex County Community College offers One-Stop Career Service Center providing skill assessment, training, and job placement for unemployed residents. Contact Director of Counseling, Sussex County Community College, 1 College Hill Rd, Newton, NJ 07860-1146; 973-300-2207; 973-579-5400; {www.sussex.cc.nj.us/misc}.

Many Job Services

The Kean Office of Continuing Education offers career counseling, vocational interest testing (Strong, Myers-Briggs), resume consultation, workshops on starting your own business, and job enhancement. Fees range from $25-75. For more information contact Kean Office of Continuing Education, 1000 Morris Ave., Union, NJ 07083; 908-527-2211.

Vocational Training

Abilities of Northwest Jersey, Inc. is a vocational training agency that assists people with disabilities in Warren, Northern Hunterdon, and Western Morns Counties. Their mission is to improve the employability and quality of life for their clients through individualized services. They have six different programs, each with a variety of services. Employment Pathways places persons with disabilities into integrated work settings. Some of the services that go along with that program are, job development and placement, job coaching, job sampling and more. The Community Rehabilitation program develops vocational goals by providing work experience in a structured environment. There, they develop work habits, behaviors, interpersonal skills, stamina, work performances, and adjustment to work routine. For more information on these and other programs available, contact Abilities of NW Jersey, Inc., 264 Route 31 North, Washington, NJ 07882; 908-689-1118; Fax: 908-689-6363; {www.abilities-nw.com}; {Email: michele@abilities-nw.com}.

Train For Work In Retail

The Retail Skills Center provides skills assessment, training, and job placement in the area of retail sales associate. It also services as a clearinghouse for potential employers. The offer a free 3 week certified training course taught by instructors from union County College. It also includes placement and counseling services. Applicants must go to the Center for assessment and orientation. For more information, visit the Retail Skills Center located at Jersey Gardens on the north side of the lower level, behind the Management Office. Jersey Gardens, 651 Kapkowski Road, Elizabeth, NH 07201; 908-355-4444; {www.jerseygardetns.com/gi/rsc.html}; {Email: retailskills@earthlink.net}.

Learn Landscaping and Horticulture

The greater Newark Conservancy runs a Horticulture and Landscaping Job Training Program that teaches youth and community residents to learn marketable skills through landscaping and horticulture. At the same time, they improve upon the environment of Newark and its surrounding communities. The program has supervised training for students, the unemployed, employees of local business, and inmates on work release. For more information contact the Greater Newark Conservancy, 303-9 Washington Street, 5th Floor, Newark, NH 07102; 973-642-4646; Fax: 973-642-2218; {www.citybloom.org}; {Email: info@citybloom.org}.

New Mexico

One-Stop Career Centers
A network of One-Stop Career Centers throughout the state offers a wide range of employment related services including job training. Services vary by location. To find a location near you, please refer to the website {www.dol.state.nm.us/nmworks/front.asp}. To learn more about the services they offer, contact your state coordinator.

Ms. Claire Lissance, One-Stop Coordinator, New Mexico Department of Labor, Tiwa Building (Zip 87102), 401 Broadway, NE, P.O. Box 1928, Albuquerque, NM 87103; 505-841-8513; {Email: clissance@ state.nm.us}.

Job Service Offices
A system of Employment Service/Job Service offices is located within every state with the goal of assisting millions of job seekers and employers. While services may vary from location to location, many provide job training, skills assessment and related services. With approximately 1,800 Employment Service/Job Service offices nationwide there is bound to be one near you. To learn more about the services offered in your area, contact your state administrator.

Clinton D. Harden, Jr., Secretary, New Mexico Department of Labor, P.O. Box 1928, Albuquerque, NM 87103; 505-841-8409; Fax: 505-841-8491.

Janet M. Thompson, Deputy Secretary, New Mexico Department of Labor, P.O. Box 1928, Albuquerque, NM 87103; 505-841-9042; Fax: 505-841-8491.

Other State Programs
The Job Training Division has several programs of interest. For more information on any of the following programs, contact Job Training Division, 1596 Pacheco St., Santa Fe, NM 87502; 505-827-6827; Fax: 505-827-6812; {www.dol.state.nm.us}.

- Are you looking for a job? Do you need additional training to get a job? Do you need a little help? The New Mexico Department of Labor has Employment Service Counselors (career counselors) to help you in the following areas: to make appropriate and practical career decisions; to provide you with up-to-date labor market information; to provide you with information about educational and vocational training facilities and financial aid for education; to help you develop practical action plans to achieve your career goals; to provide you with testing services to determine your career interests, aptitudes, etc. These services are available at no cost if you are looking for a job or are considering a career change. You do not have to be receiving unemployment benefits to utilize these services.

- Do you want a job but need some basic job skills? Do you want to change jobs but need some formal training to be hired? You can take advantage of a classroom training program that provides up to 104 weeks for qualifying individuals. Courses can be taken at any community college or university in New Mexico. Costs that are covered include tuition, books, fees, supplies, and may include transportation and day care. You may be eligible if you are new to the workforce or have been out of the workforce for a period of time.

- Do you have the basic skills but feel you might not be hired because you need time to learn the job duties? If so, you may be eligible for their On-The-Job Training Program. If you are eligible, the employer who hires you can be reimbursed up to 50% of your wages for up to six months. This job training service is provided for economically disadvantaged adults and youth, dislocated workers and others who face significant employment barriers.

- Have lots of skills and education but no experience? Would you like to gain work experience and basic job skills by working in a non-profit organization (public or private)? If so, here's a program for you. To be eligible you must be new to the workforce, or have been out of the workforce for a period of time and must meet certain income eligibility.

Christian Programs

Ursuline Companions in Mission is a Christian association of lay women and men who seek to make a difference in the lives of the poor through a variety of programs including job training. They have service delivery sites in Delaware, Illinois, Kentucky, Minnesota, Missouri, New Mexico, and Ohio. Programs vary from location to location. For more information, contact Ursuline Companions In Mission, Sr. Jane Quinlan, College of New Rochelle, College Center, Room 155, New Rochelle, NY 10805; 914-654-5270; Fax: 914-654-5290; {www.theursulines.org}; {Email: ursulinecomp@hotmail.com}.

Learn To Be Self-Sufficient

The Women's Economic Self-Sufficiency Team (WESST Corp.) assists low-income and minority women throughout New Mexico. They can offer counseling and mentoring through professional volunteers including attorneys, accountants, insurance agents and benefits counselors. If you decide to start a new business, they can assist you in obtaining capital funds as WESST Corp. is a micro-lender under SBA's micro-loan program. Their focus encompasses the area of Las Cruces and Farmington, New Mexico, with program services provided to women in Dona, Ana, Luna, Otero and Sierra counties, with limited outreach to El Paso, Texas. Contact their main office or locate the office nearest to you listed below: New Mexico Women's Economic Self-Sufficiency Team (WESST Corp.), Agnes Noonan, Executive Director, 414 Silver Southwest, Albuquerque, NM 87102; 505-241-4753; 800-GO-WESST; Fax: 505-241-4766; {www.wesst.org}; {Email: wesst@swcp.com}.

Other Locations

- WESST Corp. - Santa Fe, NM, Marisa Del Rio, Regional Manager, 3900 Paseo del Sol, Santa Fe, NM 87505; 505-988-5030, Fax: 505-988-4177; {Email: JCBBrad@aol.com}.

- WESST Corp. - Taos, NM, Regional Manager, 1128-A Paseo del Pueblo Sur, Taos, NM 87571; 505-758-3099; Fax: 505-751-1575; {Email: zurawski@laplaza.org}.

- WESST Corp. - Roswell, NM, Roberta Ahlness, Regional Manager, 200 West First, Suite 202, Roswell, NM 88201; 505-624-9850; Fax: 505-624-9845; {Email: wesst@dfn.com }.

- WESST Corp. - Las Cruces, NM, Jennifer Craig, Regional Manager, 301 N. Solano, Suite 2, Las Cruces, NM 88004; 505-541-1583, Fax: 505-647-5524; {www.zianet.com/wesstlc}; {Email: jencraig@zianet.com}.

- WESST Corp. - Farmington, NM, Joretta Clement, Regional Manager, 1909 East 20th, Suite 9, Farmington, NM 87401; 505-325-0678; Fax: 505-325-0695; {Email: 4business@acrnet.com}.

Training for Veterans

Veterans have priority over non-veteran in job placement, counseling, testing, referral to supportive services, job development and job training. Veteran employment representatives and disabled veteran outreach program representative provide these services to veteran. Contact the Department of Labor, P.O. Box 1928, Albuquerque, NM 87103; 87103; 505-841-8440.

Job Assistance for Rural Residents

Home Education Livelihood Program (HELP) is a multi-purpose organization that provides services to rural low-income residents, migrant farm workers and children. Their program include: human services; employment and training; community and economic development; housing and child development. The job training program services include: adult basic education, English as a second language; GEP preparation classes, labor market orientation, work experience, or on-the-job training. For more information, contact their state office at HELP, 5101 Copper NE, Albuquerque, NM 87108; 505-265-3717; Fax: 505-265-5412.

New York

One-Stop Career Centers
A network of One-Stop Career Centers throughout the state offers a wide range of employment related services including job training. Services vary by location. To find a location near you, please refer to the website {www.wdsny.org/osos2.htm }. To learn more about the services they offer, contact your state coordinator.

Ms. Fredda Peritz, Community Service Division Director, New York State Dept. of Labor, State Office Building Campus, Room 576, Albany, NY 12240-0002; 518-457-3584.

James T. Dillon, Acting Commissioner, New York State Department, Building 12, State Office Building Campus, Albany, NY 12240; 518-457-9000; Fax: 518-457-6908.

Job Service Offices
A system of Employment Service/Job Service offices is located within every state with the goal of assisting millions of job seekers and employers. While services may vary from location to location, many provide job training, skills assessment and related services. With approximately 1,800 Employment Service/Job Service offices nationwide there is bound to be one near you. To learn more about the services offered in your area, contact your state administrator.

James T. Dillon, Acting Commissioner, New York State Department, Building 12, State Office Building Campus, Albany, NY 12240; 518-457-9000; Fax: 518-457-6908; {www.labor.state.ny.us}.

Help In Harlem
East Harlem Partnership for Change (EHPC) is a grass roots community based membership organization. With East Harlem Employment Service/STRIVE as its managing agent, they have embarked upon a two-year employer driven

community focused job training and placement initiative. The goal of this initiative is to place 400 young men and women in entry-level unsubsidized jobs. For more information, contact Robert Carmona, President & Chief Executive Officer, 1820 Lexington Avenue, New York, NY 10029; 212-828-4070; 212-360-1100; Fax: 212-360-5634, or 212-360-6225.

Help Is Just A Phone Call Away
The Displaced Homemaker program provides counseling, training advocacy, job development and supportive services to those that have been displaced from their primary career as unpaid homemakers. A displaced homemaker is someone who has lost their support due to divorce, death, disability, permanent loss of employment of a spouse or mate, or loss of public assistance for dependent children. In the end, the homemaker will develop self-confidence and the skills needed to compete in the work force. For more information, contact Queens Women's Network Displaced Homemaker Program, 161-10 Jamaica Avenue, Suite 416, Jamaica, NY 11432; 718-657-6200; Fax: 718-739-6974.

Networking For Hi-Tech Women
Webgrrls International provides a forum for women in or interested in new media and technology to network, exchange job and business leads, form strategic alliances, mentor and teach, intern and learn skills needed to succeed in an increasingly technical workplace and world. They offer ongoing workshops focusing on enhancing business and communication such as refining negotiating skills. The original chapter was founded in New York City

and many new branches continue to be added around the country. For more information, contact New York City Webgrrls, 50 Broad Street, Suite 1614, New York, NY 10004; {www.acteva.com/go/nycgrrls}; {Email: nyc@webgrrls.com}.

Training For Low-Income People

The Center for Employment Training (CET) is a private, non-profit, community based organization that provides quality employment training for those who need it most. They offer you extensive life skills and workplace know-how instruction through a program that includes job preparedness training, job development and placement. CET keeps students in training until they are placed and conducts follow-up on all placement to ensure stable employment and job growth. CET's primary activity is classroom skill training, which is provided year-round. CET does not screen applicants through testing, but accepts anyone who is willing to do the necessary work. Courses are offered on an open-entry, open-exit basis and students complete training at their own pace. CET training is intensive, with students attending 5 days and 35 to 40 hours per week for an average of seven months. CET training is competency based, highly individualized, and hands-on from day one. The average training course at CET maintains a 20-1 student/teacher ratio. CET's unique mode of training involves an integration of skill training, basic skills instruction and human development conducted in a simulated work setting. At least twenty-five job training options are offered at CET nationwide. These include automated office skills, building maintenance, electronic assembly, medical assistant, truck driving, and shipping/receiving. Skill offerings vary from one center to another. A typical CET center offers 4-5 skills and may serve up to 250 persons annually. For more information, contact their national headquarters or one of the addresses below.

CET Corporate Offices, 701 Vine St., San Jose, CA 95110; 408-287-7924; 800-533-2519; {www.cet2000.org}; {Email: cfet@best.com}.

Center for Employment Training, East Tremont Ave., Bronx, NY 10460; 718-893-4582; Fax: 718-893-4680; {Email: s_coaxum@ cetmail.cfet.org}

Get The Help You Need To Start Your Own Business

Founded in 1976, the American Woman's Economic Development Corporation is the premier national not-for-profit organization committed to helping entrepreneurial women start and grow their own businesses. Based in New York City, AWED also have offices in southern California, Connecticut and Washington, D. C. Join over 100,000 women who have benefitted from formal course instructions, one-to-one business counseling, seminars, special events

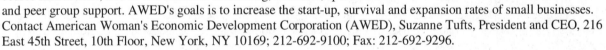

and peer group support. AWED's goals is to increase the start-up, survival and expansion rates of small businesses. Contact American Woman's Economic Development Corporation (AWED), Suzanne Tufts, President and CEO, 216 East 45th Street, 10th Floor, New York, NY 10169; 212-692-9100; Fax: 212-692-9296.

Train To Start Your Own Business

The Entrepreneurial Assistance Program can provide you with classroom instruction and individual counseling, business plan development for minorities, women, dislocated workers, public assistance recipients, public housing recipients. They serve those seeking to start a new business or who have owned a business for five years or less. For more information, contact Empire State Development Office, Entrepreneurial Assistance Program, 633 3rd Avenue, New York, NY 10017; 212-803-2410; 800-STATE-NY; {www.empire.state.ny.us}; {Email: esd@empire.state.ny.us}.

Training and Loans For New Women Business Owners

The Women's Venture Fund, Inc. is based on a radically simple idea: empowering women, particularly low-income women to create new businesses by making micro-loans available to them, and then ensuring their success through their mentoring and training component. The Fund makes micro-loans to entrepreneurial women who cannot get funding through conventional sources. If you have great ideas, but desperately need small loans, business planning, and the moral support it takes to develop a business into reality, contact Women's Venture Fund, Inc., Maria Semidei-Otero, President, 155 East 42nd Street, Suite 316, New York, NY 10017; 212-972-1146; Fax: 212-972-1167.

Career and Life Planning For Women In Transition

Everywoman Opportunity Center, Inc. is a not-for-profit corporation that has served Western New York since 1977. Everywoman administers numerous programs, the largest of which is the Displaced Homemaker Program. Their mission is to help women move toward personal and economic self-sufficiency, which they accomplish by using a holistic approach to career/life planning. Women in transition often lack confidence and direction. Everywoman's individualized services are designed to bolster your self-confidence while developing the best plan for you as a participant. Participants can attend seminars and career planning classes, and/or receive one-to-one career counseling, depending on their needs. They can help you enter, re-enter or move forward in the world of paid employment by teaching job search skills, assisting with career decisions and helping to remove other barriers to career success. This often involves links with other agencies providing further education or skills training, or assistance with child care, housing, legal issues, counseling, etc. To this end, Everywoman has developed a network of referrals to meet participants' other needs. For more information, contact their main office or any of their numerous outreach locations below. State Department of Labor, Everywoman Headquarters, 237 Main St. Suite 330, Buffalo, NY 14203; 716-847-1120; Fax: 716-847-1550; {www.everywoman.org}; {Email: ewocbuf@ everywoman.org}.

Outreach Locations

- Sandra Velasco, Everywoman Opportunity Center, Greenacres Blvd. 2440 Sheridan Drive, Tonawanda, NY 14150; 716-837-2260; Fax: 716-837-0124; {www.everywoman.org}; {Email: ewocton@everywoman.org}.

- Susan Reilly, Everywoman Opportunity Center, 10825 Bennett Road, Dunkirk, NY 14048; 716-366-7020; Fax: 716-366-1925; {Email: ewocdf@everywoman.org}.

- Linda Randolph, Everywoman Opportunity Center, 800 Main Street Third Floor, Niagara Falls, NY 14301: 716-282-8472: Fax: 716-282-4868; {Email: ewocnf@everywoman.org}.

- Mary Snodgrass, Everywoman Opportunity Center, 132 North Union, Suite 107, Olean, NY 14760; 716-373-4013; Fax: 716-373-7668; {Email: ewocol@everywoman.org}.

- Everywoman Opportunity Center, 583 Niagara Street, Buffalo, NY 14201; 716-886-2050; Fax: 716-886-0245; {Email: ewocws@everywoman.org}.

Beef Up Your Math, English, and Computer Skills

Here's a program that focuses on self development training with workshops and remedial classes math, English and computer training. They also offer course work in areas such as domestic violence and others. For more information, contact Iris Arroyo, Bensonhurst Displaced Homemaker Program, 1708 West 10th Street, Brooklyn, NY 11223; 718-946-8570; Fax: 718-946-8572; {Email: bicdhp@erols. com}.

Career Services Galore

Bronx Community College has a program that offers you career, educational, and vocational counseling and referral services; employment counseling and placement; vocational skills training in computers, customer service and office skills; job readiness cycles every month. Contact Olga Martinez, Bronx Community College DHC, 181 St. Street & University Ave., Gould Residence Hall, Room 309, Bronx, NY 10453; 718-289-5824; Fax: 718-289-6341.

Career Preparation Just For Women

The Women's Center was established in 1970 to meet the employment and training needs of women who held a marginal place in the paid labor force. Committed to the career and economic self-sufficiency of African American and other women, the Center works to provide women with the information and skills they need to obtain jobs that enable them to support themselves and their families. Specifically, they can provide you with services including a job readiness program for displaced homemakers and other women; entrepreneurial training; resume and interview assistance; job ready assessment and job development. Other individual and group support services are also provided. For more information, contact Merble Reagon, Executive Director or Carolyn Johnson, Smart DHP

Director, Women's Center for Education & Career, Advancement, 45 John Street, Suite 605, New York, NY 10038; 212-964-8934; Fax: 212-964-0222.

Get Ready For Work With Computer Training Plus

F.E.G.S. Employment Readiness Center offers a 10-week computer training and upgrading program, a job readiness program providing life skills information, from budgeting to health issues. Additionally, the Center can offers you employment service when you are job ready. For more information, contact Faye Sutherland, 16-18 Old Doc Road, Yaphank, NY 11980; 631-205-0183.

Many Services For Women

This center provides training and assistance for many different needs that women like you may have. You can receive training in assertiveness, communication skills and stress management to help develop self-esteem and self-confidence. If you like, legal and financial issues can be addressed and referrals to appropriate county and community agencies are made. To assist your efforts toward self-sufficiency, job market information, job referrals, resume prep and interview strategies are stressed. An introduction to Windows and Word for Windows is provided if you need to beef up your computer skills. For more information, contact Martha Baron Kaufman, S.C. Dept. of Labor, Veterans Memorial Highway, BLDG 17, North County Complex, Hauppage, NY 11788; 631-853-6620; 631-853-6510; {www.co.suffolk.ny.us/labor}.

A Dozen Programs For Displaced Homemakers

If you find yourself on your own without your accustomed financial support and are seeking to enter the job market, these programs are here to assist you. Find the one listed below that is nearest to you.

- *Women in SelfHelp (WISH)* has over 20 years of experience assisting displaced homemakers to enter or re-enter the job market. WISH graduates pursue careers and training in diverse fields including business, education, technical/non-traditional, health care, and human services. WISH can provide you with a 6 week course in job readiness and career exploration. Topics include: writing an effective resume; successful interview techniques; job search strategies; goals clarification; introduction to computer skills; assertiveness training; and a brush up on basic academic skills. After the program is completed, you can enter a weekly Job Club where job search strategies are put into action. For more information, contact Carol Marsh or Ingrid Niles, Women In Self Help, 503 Fifth Ave., 4th Floor, Brooklyn, NY 11215; 718-768-9700; Fax: 718-369-3192; {Email: CMarsh503@aol.com}.

- This program offers an eight week *Computer Based Job Readiness Program.* This program offers 80 hours of computer skills training along with business math, business English, job readiness skills and self-esteem workshops. They also offer job placement is provided along with other supportive services. Contact Displaced Homemakers Multiservice Center, E. Nadine Holsey, Economic Opportunity Commissions, DHMC, 134 Jackson Street, Hempstead, NY 11550; 516-486-2800; Fax: 516-292-3176

- A center for *Displaced Homemakers at Westchester Community College* assists women who are divorced, separated, widowed or whose spouse is unemployed or disabled to successfully re-enter the workforce. Their program offers extensive information, referral, career decisions counseling, work readiness, and employment training programs. Contact Marilyn Wald, Westchester Community College, Project Transition, 75 Grasslands Road, Valhalla, NY 10595; 914-785-6825; Fax: 914-785-6508; {Email: mbw@wcc.co.westchester.ny.us}

- This program offers a range of free services including: Human Potential Seminar; five session support group for active job hunters; career mentor program; self-development workshops; career information library; and employment matching service for mature workers. To participate, you must come to an informational session at 12:30 on any Wednesday or at 7:00 pm on the first Monday of the month. Contact Displaced Homemakers Women-in-Transition, Dr. Rita Lieberman, Rockland Co. Guidance Center, Displaced Homemaker Program, 83 Main Street, Nyack, NY 10960; 845-358-9390; Fax: 845-358-4980.

- This program runs 6-four week re-entry cycles a year. They are 40 hours of computer literacy and 40 hours of job search. Three times a year, during the cycles, they offer 1 credit college course in public speaking. For more information, contact Albany Displaced Homemaker Center, Lois Johnson, Albany DHC, 227 S. Pearl Street, Albany, NY 12202; 518-434-3103; Fax: 518-434-3211; {Email: adhc@albany.net}.

- Here's another *Displaced Homemakers Center* that serves individuals, primarily women, who are "displaced" in their lives due to loss of a job, disability, separation or divorce, death or disability of a partner, financial losses, or other changes in their economic or personal situations. DHC provides information support, and practical assistance with problem solving and decision making. Contact Displaced Homemakers Center Of Tompkins County, Dammi Herath or Sandra Hill, Tompkins County DHC, 315 N. Tioga Street, Ithaca, NY 14850; 607-272-1520; Fax: 607-272-2251; {Email: dhc@clarityconnect.com}.

- Providing a variety of services for the displaced homemaker of any age, this is designed to assist the person towards self-sufficiency. Offered are crisis, individual, and group counseling, information about community resources, classes in self-development and return-to-work skills, professional resumes, employment resource center and job referrals. They also present specialized workshops for public and community groups. Lifespan's Displaced Homemaker Center, Linda Lewis-Watkins, Lifespan's DH Program, 79 N. Clinton Avenue, Rochester, NY 14604; 716-244-8400; Fax: 716-454-3882; {www.wdsny.org/monroe/lifespan.htm}; {Email: les1job@aol.com}.

- This work re-entry program offers a workshop that provides a unique intensive group experience that will enable you to clarify your goals and implement specific action plans leading to improved career opportunities.

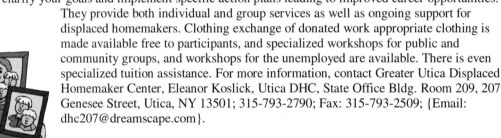 They provide both individual and group services as well as ongoing support for displaced homemakers. Clothing exchange of donated work appropriate clothing is made available free to participants, and specialized workshops for public and community groups, and workshops for the unemployed are available. There is even specialized tuition assistance. For more information, contact Greater Utica Displaced Homemaker Center, Eleanor Koslick, Utica DHC, State Office Bldg. Room 209, 207 Genesee Street, Utica, NY 13501; 315-793-2790; Fax: 315-793-2509; {Email: dhc207@dreamscape.com}.

  - *Displaced Homemakers* have become displaced from their careers as homemakers with the loss of financial support often because of separation, divorce or death. They need job readiness training to become self-supporting. Services provided are job exploration, job market exploration, job readiness training workshops, education, and basic computer skills training. This is a grant funded program and there are no fees involved. Referral information is always available. Contact Syracuse Displaced Homemaker Program, Peggy Hanousek or Sandy Gordon, Regional Learning Service DHC, 3049 East Genesee St., Syracuse, NY 13224-1644; 315-446-0550; Fax: 315-446-5869.

- This job readiness program offers 4-six week cycles at *Schenectady County Community College* and one in *Saratoga County* annually. Workshops include key-boarding, introduction to computers skills/self assessment career exploration, applications, resume writing, interviewing skills, "Meet the Employer", job values, goal setting, job retention, and techniques for dealing with stress. The services of a job placement counselor are offered to job readiness participants. DHP - Schenectady Community Action Program, Keith Houghton, Schenectady/ Fulmont DHC, C/O SCAP, 433 State Street, Schenectady, NY 12305; 518-374-9181, Fax: 518-374-9190.

  The courses are also available at Project Lift, Fulton-Montgomery Community College, 2805 State Highway 67, Johnstown, NY 12095; 518-762-4651, ext. 346; Fax: 518-762-4334; {Email: dpiurek@fmcc.suny.edu}.

- The Displaced Homemaker Program offered through the *Schoharie County Community Action Program* offers women who are re-entering or entering the workforce a series of classes designed to broaden their skills. Classes are free, and are open to all women regardless of age or income. Specific job skills such as Windows 95 training are offered along with skills assessment, resume writing and interview strategies. Contact Schoharie

Displaced Homemaker Program, Center Info: Barbara Rivenburgh, Cindy Massick, Diane Garufi, or Theresa Moore, 150 E. Main Street, Cobleskill, NY 12043; 518-234-2568; Fax: 518-234-3507; {Email: sccapinc@midtel.net}.

- *YWCA* provides free employment training for Displaced Homemakers, (widowed, divorced, separated, single parent) seeking to re-enter the workforce. Their program runs Monday - Friday, 9:00am - 4:00pm, and includes instruction in typing, business math, business correspondence, resume writing, interviewing skills, speech, ethics and morality in the workplace, and computer software. Employment seminars and group and individual counseling are also integrated part of the program. You can also participate in a mentorship program with a local corporation one day a week. As a graduate, you can receive assistance with your job search and job placement by their placement manager. The program has a 96% rating in successful placement. Contact Debra Palmieri or Susan McCarty, Senior Social Worker, YWCA - NYC DHC, 610 Lexington Ave., New York, NY 10022; 212-735-9729; Fax: 212-759-3158.

Women's Programs in NYC
The following is a list of agencies providing job, career and education information for women in NYC. Contact them directly for more information about the services they offer.

- *Access for Women*, New York City Technical College, 250 Jay Street, Brooklyn, NY 11201; 718-260-5730; Fax: 718-260-5415; {www.foresitenet.com/accesshome.htm}; Technical program for dislocated workers, divorced or separated women, and homemakers.

- *Center for Women's Development*, 1650 Bedford Avenue, Brooklyn, NY 11225; 718-270-5155; Personal counseling, advocacy, workshops for women. No daycare. (Free).

- *National Association for Female Executives*, 30 Irving Place, 5th floor, New York, NY 10003; 212-477-2200; {www.nafe.com}; {Email: nafe@nafe.com}; Networking groups. (Small fee).

- *Brooklyn College Women's Center*, 227 New Ingersoll Hall, Brooklyn, NY 11210; 718-951-5777; workshops, speakers and legal referrals. No daycare. (Free).

- *Neighborhood Women Of Williamsburg-Greenpoint*, Maria Fava, 249 Manhattan Avenue, Brooklyn, NY 11211; 718-388-6666; offers free job training and placement, and career counseling to women. It is part of a network of service providers in the area that assist victims of domestic violence.

- *Brooklyn Public Library*, Education, Job & Computer Center, Grand Army Plaza, Brooklyn, NY 11238; 718-230-2177; {www.brooklynpubliclibrary.org/central/ejic.htm}; various computer programs, books and other materials on careers and job hunting. No daycare. (Free).

- *New Images for the Widowed, Inc.*, 263 West End Avenue, Suite 7B, New York, NY 10023; 212-972-2084; support groups, counseling. No daycare. (Small fee).

- *Brooklyn Job Service Center*, 250 Schermerhorn Street, Brooklyn, NY 11201; 718-780-9316; group and individual counseling, support groups. (Free).

- *Careers for Women*, 80 Fifth Avenue, Suite 1104, New York, NY 10011; 212-807-7633; placement in sales, public relations, advertising & marketing. Seminars. No daycare. (Free or small fee).

- *NYS Minority & Women's Business Division Empire State Development*, 633 3rd Ave., New York, NY 10017; 212-803-2200; 212-803-2411; business assistance, financing & procurement. No daycare. (Free)

- *Carroll Gardens Neighborhood Women*, 294 Smith Street, Brooklyn, NY 11231; 718-624-3475; Non-traditional college program (Fee) ESL, GED, adult ed. (Free). No daycare.

- *NYU School of Continuing Education*, Center for Career/Life Planning, 50 West 4th Street, Shimkin Hall, Room 330, New York, NY 10012-1165; 212-998-7060; {www.scps.nyu.edu/dyncon/ccel/cour_.html}; career counseling. No daycare. (Fee) Family daycare training. (Free).

- *Crystal Quilt*, 532 LaGuardia Place, New York, NY 10012; 212-941-4994; {www.crystalquilt.org}; cultural and educational programs. (Small Fee).

- *Non-traditional Employment for Women (NEW)*, 243 W. 20th Street, New York, NY 10011; 212-627-6252; Fax: 212-255-8021; {www.new-nyc.org}; {Email: new@nyc.org}; training & apprenticeships for non-traditional blue collar jobs. No daycare. Women 18+ (Free)

- *Community Sponsors for Young Mothers*, 15 Claver Place, 4th Floor, Brooklyn, NY 11238; 718-857-3323; alternative high school for pregnant teens, ages 14-19. No daycare. (Free).

- *Union Center for Women*, 401 95th Street, Brooklyn, NY 11209; 718-748-7708; {www.unioncenterforwomen.org}; support groups, classes, workshops for women of all ages. No daycare. (Small Fee).

- *Fresh Start Training Program*, 1756 Ocean Avenue, Brooklyn, NY 11230; 718-338-9200; displaced homemakers counseling, and career education workshops. No daycare. (Free).

-

- *Women in Community Service*, Department of Labor, Job Corps, 201 Varick St., New York, NY 10014; 212-683-9723; vocational training, and referrals. Low-income teens. Ages 16-24 (Free).

- *Women in Need*, 115 West 31 St., Suite 7, New York, NY 10001; 212-695-4758; {www.women-in-need.org}; homeless women with children, and substance abusers. Provides housing, education & job assistance. Daycare.

- *La Guardia Community College*, 31-10 Thompson Avenue, L.I.C., NY 11101; 718-482-5340/5397; medical billing, medical terminology, and fiberoptics training to dislocated workers at no cost. No daycare. (Free).

- *Women in Self-Help (WISH)*, NYS Displaced Homemaker Center, 421 Fifth Ave., 2nd Floor, Brooklyn, NY 11215; 718-768-9700; re-entry program for displaced homemakers, career counseling. No daycare. (Free).

- *GED classes* for summer (July-August), Kingsborough Community College, Small Business Development Center, 2001 Oriental Blvd., Building T-4204, Brooklyn, NY 11235; 718-368-4619; Small business counseling. No daycare. (Free).

- *Women's Center for Education and Career Advancement*, 45 John Street Suite 605, New York, NY 10038; 212-964-8934; SMART Program for displaced homemakers. (Free). New Directions entrepreneur program for women who live in public housing. Career counseling, education and personal development courses. Resume workshops. No daycare. (Free).

Fresh Beginnings

If you are a displaced homemaker; have lost your source of support or must enter the job market, the Agudath Israel Fresh Start Training Program can provide you with individual counseling, career counseling, job counseling, job development, job placement and skills training to prepare you for work. They offer a unique job-readiness group that focuses on building self-esteem and setting future goals. The peer group interaction together with workshops in such areas as interview skills, resume writing, health, legal, and financial issues will help you adjust to your new situation in life. They also have on site computer training in Microsoft Word 97, to help you meet the challenges of today's job market. Contact Rachel Perl, Agudath Israel/ Fresh Start DHC, 1756 Ocean Avenue, Brooklyn, NY 11230; 718-338-9200; Fax: 718-377-3151.

Training and Job Placement Services, Agudath Israel of America Project Corp., 84 Williams Street, 16th Floor, New York, NY 10038; 212-809-5935.

Job Training For Homeless People

The Coalition For The Homeless offers a First Step Readiness Program designed to (re)integrate homeless, formerly homeless, and unemployed women into the workforce. The program provides the technical skills and emotional support they need to negotiate the arduous transition to economic independence. Often, the circumstances of homelessness result in emotional insecurity, instability, and isolation. Many of the participants are fleeing domestic violence. An eight-week class, post-graduate counseling and follow-up services and support, a mentor program, and work internships enable First Step students to overcome the barriers that prevent them from succeeding in the working world. The students also learn the concrete skills needed to set and obtain their goals. Graduates go on to employment, further education, or vocational training. For more information, contact Coalition For The Homeless, 89 Chambers Street, New York, NY 10007; 212- 964-5900, ext. 113; Fax: 212-964-1303; {www.coalitionforhomeless.org}; {Email: cfthomeless@aol.com }.

Apprenticeship Training

Currently there are over 800 trades approved for apprenticeship training. These areas include, construction, manufacturing, communication, public utilities, wholesale and retail finance, insurance and public administration. The Apprenticeship Program includes on-the-job training and classroom teaching so that the apprentice can learn the theoretical and practical aspects of the job. New apprentices earn 50% of the journey wages and at the end of their training, will generally earn 90-95% of the journey worker wage. For more information, contact the Department of Labor, State Office Building 12, Room 440, Albany, NY 12240; 518-457-1996; Fax: 518-457-1996; {www.labor.state.ny.us/html/apprentc/app6.htm}.

Help For Business Owners

At any of the New York Small Business Development Centers you will be able to access free customized business advisement and seminars. They also have specialty program such as: the Veterans Business Outreach Program for veterans; The Manufacturing and Defense Development Center for businesses hurt by defense spending costs; and The Self-Employment Assistance Program that encourages people that receive unemployment benefits to start their own business; and the International Business Program that helps small businesses to expand into the world market. To find a center near you, contact the state office at SBDC, State University Plaza, 41 State Street, Albany, NY 12246; 518-443-5398; Fax: 518-465-4992.

Veterans Services

Veteran scan get a competitive edge in the labor market through the services of the Department of Labor's veteran staff. They have job placement services, employment counseling testing, job search information and training programs. For more information, contact the Department of Labor, State Office Building 12, Albany, NY; {www.labor.state.ny.us/html/vets.htm}; Vet-Employment Hotline: 888-VETS-NYS (888-838-7697).

Nurse's Aide Training

Through the New Horizons Adult Educational Program, high school graduates, 21 and over can benefit from their job training services. They offer career counseling and word processing (must type 35 wpm). Their Nurse's Aide training consists of classroom training and practical experience in a hospital. Must have a high school diploma and complete a placement exam. Contact New Horizons Adult Educational Program, St. John The Baptist Church, 75 Lewis Ave., Brooklyn, NY 11206; 718-455-1166.

Training In a Variety of Things

The Brooklyn Adult Learning Center has job training with stipend. They offer services in the areas of electronics, clerical, computer, nurse's assistant, LPN, and offer job placement. Contact Brooklyn Adult Learning Center, 475 Nostrand Ave., Brooklyn, NY 11216; 718-638-2635.

The SUNY/Educational Opportunity Center offers a variety of job training and placement for low income people. SUNY/Educational Opportunity Center, 470 Vanderbilt Avenue, Brooklyn, NY 11238; 718-636-7924. Training in technical and business programs.

SUNY/Educational Opportunity Center, 163 West 125th Street, Room 1524, New York, NY 10027; 212-961-4408. Computer training, junior accounting, general office clerk, keyboard specialists, and security officer. High school diploma or GED required. Must be 18 or older.

North Carolina

One-Stop Career Centers
A network of One-Stop Career Centers throughout the state offers a wide range of employment related services including job training. Services vary by location. To find a location near you, please refer to the website { www.commerce.state.nc.us/categories/employment.htm }. To learn more about the services they offer, contact your state coordinator.

Mr. Michael Aheron, One-Stop Lead, Governor's Commission on Workforce Preparedness JobLink, 301 North Wilmington Street, Raleigh NC 27601; 919-715-3300; Fax: 919-715-3974; {www.joblink. state.nc.us}; {Email: maheron@work.commerce.state.nc.us }.

Job Service Offices
A System of Employment Service/Job Service offices is located within every state with the goal of assisting millions of job seekers and employers. While services may vary from location to location, many provide job training, skills assessment and related services. With approximately 1,800 Employment Service/Job Service offices nationwide there is bound to be one near you. To learn more about the services offered in your area, contact your state administrator. Raymond W. Goodman, Chairman, Employment Security Commission of North Carolina, 700 Wade Avenue, Raleigh, NC 27605; 919-733-7546; Fax: 919-733-1129; {www.esc.state.nc.us}.

Bridges
Bridges is a program that offers help to women so that they can become economically sufficient. The program has job placement and job readiness services. Contact Bridges, Lois Cook Steele, President, YWCA of Wilmington NC, Inc., 245 South 17 Street, Wilmington, NC 28401; 910-762-7886.

Job Training in Raleigh
The Raleigh Rescue Mission seeks to meet the physical, mental and spiritual needs of men, women and children who are in crisis and homeless. In pursuit of its purpose, the Mission provides food, clothing, shelter, education, job training, rehabilitation and hope for a new life. The Mission believes that education and job training are essential if an individual is to re-enter society successfully. The Mission supports an active Learning Center that includes a variety of opportunities, including General Education Degree (GED), computer literacy training and certification, life-skill development and job training. They maintain a complete computer laboratory housing several computers all with Window-based applications and peripherals. Their Adult Basic Education includes reading, writing and public speaking, money management and budgeting, math, and employment preparation. Contact Raleigh Rescue Mission, 314 East Hargett Street, Raleigh, NC 27601; 919-828-9014; Fax: 919-833-6162; {www.raleigh-rescue.org/index.html}.

Training In Customer Service and Computer Applications
The Women's Center is a non-profit organization dedicated to the emotional, physical and financial empowerment of all women to lead self-directed lives. While the Women's Center of Wake County provides services to all women, the emphasis of their service delivery is for low-income and homeless women. The Women's Center provides job

training in customer service relations and basic computer applications offering women the opportunity to join a rapidly increasing job market. They strive to offer unemployed and under-employed women the opportunity to develop skills that can begin a career with staying power and upward mobility. The Center uses an approach to job training that considers not just hard skills but soft skills such as conflict resolution at work, work ethic issues, dress codes, self-esteem, and emotional well-being. Customer Service Training includes 90 hours of classroom and hands-on computer lab training. The Center uses Customer Service software, developed by industry training professional, which offers the trainees a realistic environment in which to learn the necessary skills. For more information, contact Women's Center of Wake County, 128 E. Hargett St., Suite 10, Raleigh, NC 27601; 919-829-3711; {www.wcwc.org/}.

Training For Low-Income People

The Center for Employment Training (CET) is a private, non-profit, community based organization that provides quality employment training for those who need it most. They offer you extensive life skills and workplace know-how instruction through a program that includes job preparedness training, job development and placement. CET keeps students in training until they are placed and conducts follow-up on all placement to ensure stable employment and job growth. CET's primary activity is classroom skill training, which is provided year-round. CET does not screen applicants through testing, but accepts anyone who is willing to do the necessary work. Courses are offered on an open-entry, open-exit basis and students complete training at their own pace. CET training is intensive, with students attending 5 days and 35 to 40 hours per week for an average of seven months. CET training is competency based, highly individualized, and hands-on from day one. The average training course at CET maintains a 20-1 student/teacher ratio. CET's unique mode of training involves an integration of skill training, basic skills instruction and human development conducted in a simulated work setting. At least twenty-five job training options are offered at CET nationwide. These include automated office skills, building maintenance, electronic assembly, medical assistant, truck driving, and shipping/receiving. Skill offerings vary from one center to another. A typical CET center offers 4-5 skills and may serve up to 250 persons annually. For more information, contact their national headquarters: CET Corporate Offices, 701 Vine St., San Jose, CA 95110; 408-287-7924; 800-533-2519; {www.best. com/~cfet/main.htm}; {Email: cfet@best.com}.

Center for Employment Training, 1731 Freeway Drive, Reidsville, NC 27320; 910-349-6620; {www.cet2000.org }.

Help For Displaced Homemakers

If you are a woman who has lost your husband's financial support through disability, divorce or death, the North Carolina Council for Women has a special program for you. With centers throughout the state, you won't even have to travel far to take advantage of it. Each center is required to provide job counseling programs, job training and placement services, health education and counseling services, financial management services, educational services including information about secondary and post-secondary education programs beneficial to displaced homemakers seeking employment, and information about employment in the public or private sectors, education, health, public assistance, and unemployment assistance programs. For more information, contact the main office or the regional offices listed below.

North Carolina Council for Women, Merrimon-Wynne House, 526 N. Wilmington St., 1320 Mail Service Center, Raleigh, NC 27699-1320; 919-733-2455; Fax: 919-733-2464.; {www.doa.state.nc.us/doa/cfw/cfw.htm}; {Email: april.reese@ncmail.net}.

- Southwestern Region, James K. Polk Bldg., 500 W. Trade St., Box 360, Charlotte, NC 28202; 704-342-6367

- Northwestern Region, 1400 Battleground Ave., Suite 202, Greensboro, NC 27408; 336-334-5094

- Western Region, 46 Haywood St., Suite 349, Asheville, NC 28801; 828-251-6169

- Southeastern Region, P.O. Box 595, New Bern, NC 28560; 252-514-4868

- Northeastern Region, 404 St. Andrews Dr., Greenville, NC 27834; 252-830-6595.

Displaced Homemaker Programs, Funded by the North Carolina Council for Women (Listed by County)

Alamance
Heidi Norwick, Women's Resource Center in Alamance County, 236 N. Mebane Street, Suite 128, Burlington, NC 27215; 336 -227-6900; Fax: 336-227-6336.

Catawba
Wanda Horvath, Catawba Valley Community College, 2550 Highway 70 SE, Hickory, NC 28602-9699; 828-327-7000, ext. 222; Fax: 828-327-7276.

Cherokee
Robin Mauney, Cherokee County Reach, P.O. Box 977, Murphy, NC 29806; 828-837-8064; Fax: 828-837-2097.

Cleveland
Mildred T. Hershenson, Cleveland County Abuse Prevention, P.O. Box 2895, Shelby, NC 28151-2895; 704-487-9325; Fax: 704-487-9314.

Columbus
Theresa Triplett, Southeastern Community College, P.O. Box 151, Whiteville, NC 28472; 910-642-7141; Fax: 910-642-5658.

Cumberland
Sylvia Ray, Women's Center, P.O. Box 2384, Fayetteville, NC 28302; 910-323-3377; 800-849-8519; Fax: 910-323-8828.

Forsyth
Marian Ackerman, Winston-Forsyth County Council for Women, 660 West 5th Street, Winston-Salem, NC 27101; 336 -727-8409; Fax: 336-275-7069.

Gates
Reba Green-Holley, NC Cooperative Extension Service, P.O. Box 46, Gatesville, NC 27938; 252-357-1400; Fax: 252-357-1167.

Guilford
Marian O'Connor-Franklin, Women's Resource Center, 623 Summit Avenue, Greensboro, NC 27405; 336-275-6090; Fax: 336-275-7069.

Halifax
Regina Walden, Cooperative Extension Service, P.O. Box 37, Halifax, NC 27839; 252-583-5161; Fax: 252-583-1683.

Hertford
Connie Piland, Roanoke-Chowan SAFE, P.O. Box 98, Ahoskie, NC 27910; 252-332-4047; Fax: 252-332-7903.

Jackson
Jean Bockstahler, REACH of Jackson County, P.O. Box 1828, Sylva, NC 28779; 828-631-0818; Fax: 828-631-0818.

Johnson County
Keri Christensen, Harbor, Inc, P.O. Box 1903 Smithfield, NC 27577; 919-934-0233; Fax: 919-934-1240

Lee
Susan Swanking, HAVEN in Lee County, Inc., P.O. Box 3191, Sanford, NC 27330; 919-774-8923; Fax: 919-774-4192

Mecklenburg
Pat Grigg, Mecklenburg County Women's Commission, 700 N. Tryon Street, Charlotte, NC 28202; 704-336-3784; Fax: 704-336-4198.

Nash/Edgecombe
Millie Walker YWCA of Rocky Mount, 1000 Hunter Hill, Rocky Mount, NC 27804; 919-937-7300, Fax: 919-937-4685

New Hanover
Lois Cook Steele, YWCA, 22 S. 17th Street, Wilmington, NC 28401; 910-762-7886; Fax: 910-762-7885.

Orange
Julia Mack, Orange County Women's Center, 210 Henderson Street, P.O. Box 1057, Chapel Hill, NC 27514; 919-968-4610, Fax: 919-932-3125.

Pamlico
John T. Jones, Pamlico Community College, P.O. Box 185, Grantsboro, NC 28529; 252-249-1851; Fax: 252-249-2377.

Pitt
Diana Lucas, Pitt County Violence Program Inc., P.O. Box 8429, Greenville, NC 27835; 252-758-4400; Fax: 252-752-4197.

Rutherford
Kim Morgan, Family Resources Center, P.O. Box 845, Spindale, NC 28160; 828-286-3411; Fax: 828-286-3417.

Surry
Helen Worrell, Tri-County Women's Resource Center, P.O. Box 1265, Mount Airy, NC 27030; 336-789-3500; Fax: 336-789-8545.

Swain
Darlene Bradley, Swain/Qualla SAFE Inc., P.O. Box 1416, Bryson City, NC 28713; 828-488-9038; Fax: 828-488-9038.

Wake
Jean Williams, The Women's Center, 128 E. Hargett Street, Raleigh, NC 27601; 919-829-3714; Fax: 919-829-9960.

The Dislocated Worker Program is for workers that have lost their job due to plant closings and layoffs where it is unlikely that they will return to their former line of work. The program can be designed specifically for the needs of the individual needs of the worker. The retraining activities include on-the-job training and institutional training. The basic readjustment services include; outreach, intake, employability planning, counseling, testing, job clubs, and more. For more information, contact Mary Brown, Workforce Development Unit, 700 Wade Avenue, Raleigh, NC 27605; 919-733-6745; Fax: 919-733-8130; {Email: Brown.Mary.A@esc.state.nc.us}.

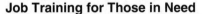

Job Training for Those in Need
The Division of Employment and Training offers job training activities and services through a network of 25 local Workforce Development Boards. To find one near you, contact the Division of Employment and Training, 4316 Mail Service Center, 313 Chapanoke Road, Suite 120, Raleigh, NC 27699-4316; 919-661-6010; Fax: 919-662-4770; {www.ncdet.com/individual/jobtraining.asp}.

North Dakota

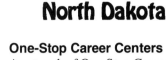

One-Stop Career Centers

A network of One-Stop Career Centers throughout the state offers a wide range of employment related services including job training. Services vary by location. To find a location near you, please refer to the website {www.state.nd.us/jsnd}. To learn more about the services they offer, contact your state coordinator.

Ms. Jennifer Gladden , Executive Director, Job Training Division, Job Service North Dakota, 1000 E. Divide Ave., P.O. Box 5507, Bismarck, ND 58506-5507; 701-328-2868; Fax: 701-328-4193; {Email: jgladden@pioneer.state.nd.us}.

Job Service Offices

A system of Employment Service/Job Service offices is located within every state with the goal of assisting millions of job seekers and employers. While services may vary from location to location, many provide job training, skills assessment and related services. With approximately 1,800 Employment Service/Job Service offices nationwide there is bound to be one near you. To learn more about the services offered in your area, contact your state administrator. Jennifer Gladden, Executive Director, Job Service North Dakota, P.O. Box 5507, Bismarck, ND 58506-5507; 701-328-2868, 800-732-9787; Fax: 701-328-4193; {www.state.nd.us/jsnd}.

Help For Women Entrepreneurs

Have you always wanted to start a business or are you interested in expanding your existing woman-owned business? The Women's Business Institute serves North Dakota entrepreneurs statewide. Information and counseling services are available through a toll-free Entrepreneur's Hotline. Training seminars can help you refine skills in management, marketing, financing, government contracting and entrepreneurial self-confidence. For example, past topics have included: Meet the Lenders; Communication Styles; Women & Investing - Taking Charge of Your Financial Future; How to Get Published; Retail Display; Power Networking; Analyzing Company Information Using Spreadsheets; and many others. Group mentoring is available through Business Success Teams. They offer a statewide business conference and a regionwide Women's Showcase which includes a trade show, seminars, main stage of activity and celebrity entertainment. They are also in the beginning stages of developing a kitchen incubator. For more information, contact Women's Business Institute (WBI), Penny Retzer, Director, 320 North Fifth Street, Suite 203, P. O. Box 2043, Fargo, ND 58107-2043; 701-235-6488; Fax: 701-235-8284; {www.rrtrade.org/women/wbi}; {Email: wbinstitute@ corpcomm.net}.

Assistance For Women Business Owners

The Women's Business Program offers a wide variety of services. They can assist you by providing counseling and technical assistance for women entrepreneurs in the following areas: maintaining a database of women-owned businesses; administering the women's incentive grant program; certifying women-owned businesses for federal and state contracting; supporting the Women's Business Leadership Council; providing information and support through trade shows and conferences; and serving as an information clearinghouse on economic development service providers. For more information about WBDP, contact Tara Holt, ND Women's Business Program, 418 East Broadway, Suite 25, Bismarck ND 58501; 701-258-2251; Fax: 701-222-8071; {Email: holt@btigate.com}.

Training for Dislocated Farmers/Ranchers and Farm Workers

Survival Program offers employment and training assistance for dislocated farmer/ranchers and farm workers. It provides assistance in preparing for reemployment in the form of job counseling, testing, assessment and job market information; assistance with the cost of moving for a new job; help with the cost of traveling for a job interview in North Dakota; retraining services such as GED, self-employment training, vocational classroom training, on-the-job training, and more. Services that are received will be based on an assessment of individual needs. For more information, contact the State Office, Job Service North Dakota, P.O. Box 5507, Bismarck, ND 58506-5507; 701-328-2868; Fax: 701-328-4193; 800-732-9787; {www.state.nd.us/jsnd}.

On-The-Job Training

Training with this program is done at the work place, and teaches the trainee a bona fide skill and/or qualifies them for a particular occupation through demonstration and practice. The employer signs a contract to hire the trainee(s) as a regular employee and trains them as agreed upon in the contract. This training is at the entry level. Its goal is the retention of the trainee as a permanent employee. Contact your local job service office. Job Service North Dakota, P.O. Box 5507, Bismarck, ND 58506-5507; 701-328-2868; Fax: 701-328-4193; 800-732-9787; {www.state.nd.us/jsnd}; {Email: dberg@state.nd.us}.

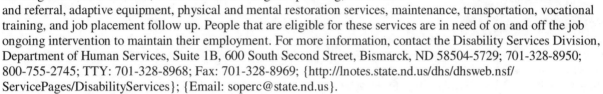

Training and More for Disabled People

Vocational Rehabilitation Employment Services provides training and employment services to people with disabilities. Some of the services provided are diagnosis and evaluation, vocational counseling and planning, information and referral, adaptive equipment, physical and mental restoration services, maintenance, transportation, vocational training, and job placement follow up. People that are eligible for these services are in need of on and off the job ongoing intervention to maintain their employment. For more information, contact the Disability Services Division, Department of Human Services, Suite 1B, 600 South Second Street, Bismarck, ND 58504-5729; 701-328-8950; 800-755-2745; TTY: 701-328-8968; Fax: 701-328-8969; {http://lnotes.state.nd.us/dhs/dhsweb.nsf/ServicePages/DisabilityServices}; {Email: soperc@state.nd.us}.

Assistance for Native American Business Owners

The North Dakota/South Dakota Native American Business Development Center offers free assistance to enrolled Native American that reside in or whose business is, or will, reside within the ND/SD service area. It is their goal to ensure the survival of new and existing Native American entrepreneurs. They have general business counseling and information, assistance in developing business plans, help to identify financial assistance, business seminars, assistance in marketing minority business products and much more. For more information, contact ND/SD Native American Business Development Center, 3315 University Drive, Bismarck, ND 58504; 701-530-0608; Fax: 701-530-0607; {www.united-tribes.tec.nd.us/business_DVCTR}; {Email: ndsdnabdc@hotmail.com}.

Help For Small Business Owners

The mission of the North Dakota Small Business Development Center is to increase the effectiveness and profitability of existing and soon-to-be businesses. One of the ways they accomplish this goal is by providing business education and training programs to individuals, businesses, and public groups. They also offer free management counseling and technical assistance. To locate a center near you, contact the State Lead Center SBDC, 118 Gamble Hall, UND, Grand Forks, ND 58202; 701-777-3700, 800-445-7232; Fax: 701-777-3225; {http://bpa.und.nodak.edu/sbdc/content.html}; {Email: ndsbc@sage.und.nodak.edu}.

Free Truck Driver Training

EW Wylie offers a free 10 week truck driver training program that will earn you a certificate at the end. This course requires that you must give EW Wylie 50,000 miles after the successful completion of the training. If you leave before the contract requirements, you must pay them a fee for the training. Contact, Chuck Johnson at EW Wylie, 222 40th Street, SW, Fargo, ND 58103; 701-282-5550.

Ohio

One-Stop Career Centers

A network of One-Stop Career Centers throughout the state offers a wide range of employment related services including job training. Services vary by location. To find a location near you, please refer to the website {www.ohioworks.com/prod}. To learn more about the services they offer, contact your state coordinator.

Ms. Jean Sickles, One-Stop Project Manager, Ohio Bureau of Employment Services, 145 South Front Street, P.O. Box 1618, Columbus, OH 43216-1618; 614-728-8107; Fax: 614-728-9094; {www.obes.org/}; {Email: Jlsickles@obes01.a1.ohio.gov}.

Job Service Offices

A system of Employment Service/Job Service offices is located within every state with the goal of assisting millions of job seekers and employers. While services may vary from location to location, many provide job training, skills assessment and related services. With approximately 1,800 Employment Service/Job Service offices nationwide there is bound to be one near you. To learn more about the services offered in your area, contact your state  administrator. Ohio Department of Jobs & Family Services, 30 East Broad Street, 32nd floor, Columbus, OH 43266-0423; 614-466-6282; Fax: 614-466-2815; {www.state.oh.us/odjfs}.

Western Reserve Business Assistance

If you are a woman business owner, the Western Reserve Business Center for Women can assist you by providing information and support to help you flourish including home-based business assistance, referrals, networking and mentoring, sources of financing, Western Business Enterprise (WBE) Certification Assistance, and government contract assistance and alternatives to assisted living. Also offered are dynamic training programs such as: Basic Business Skills; Personal Selling Skills; Promoting Self-Confidence; Time Management; Goal Setting; Developing Focus and Strategy; Evaluating Your Business Idea; Researching Your Market; Building Sales and New Businesses; Products/Services; Financial Statements; Taxes and Record-keeping; Employee/Contractor Issues; and Improving Internal Operations. The Western Reserve Business Center for Women serves Medina, Portage, Stark, Summit and Wayne Counties. Contact Western Reserve Business Center for Women, Karen Franks, Director, University of Akron, Community and Technical College, Division of Business Technology, Polsky M185-W, Room 185, Akron, OH 44325-6002; 330-972-5592; Fax: 330-972-5573; {www.commtech.edu/current/programs/WRBCW}; {Email: kdf@ uakron.edu}.

Business Planning Help

The Micro-Business Assistance program offers business plan development and one-on-one counseling for new and existing small businesses. Resources include technical and marketing assistance, micro loans, computer and Internet training. For more information, contact Micro-Business Assistance (MBA) Pyramid Career Services, Mary Ellen Hess, Executive Director, Elaine Sherer, MBA Program Manager, 2400 Cleveland Avenue North, Canton, OH 44709; 330-453-3767; Fax: 330-453-6079; {Email: pyramid@ezo.net}.

Networking For Women

Women Entrepreneurs Inc. (WEI) is a networking and membership organization for women business owners. They primarily provide specific seminars for growing and expanding businesses. They are also an SBA micro-loan technical assistance recipient. WEI provides loan packaging services and works with a variety of local lending institutions. For more information, contact Women Entrepreneurs Inc., Lyn Marsteller, Director, Sandy Evers, Program Director, Bartlett Building, 36 East 4th Street, Suite 925, Cincinnati, OH 45202; 513-684-0700; Fax: 513-665-2452; {Email: wei@eos.net}.

Help For Low-Income Businesswomen

Glenville Development Corporation provides long-term training to low-through moderate-income women to assist them in personal and business development. This is part of a community development corporation that provides a number of services to low-income individuals. For more information, contact Glenville Development Corporation Micro-Enterprise Program, Rosalind Brewster, Micro-Enterprise Development Officer, 10640 St. Clair Ave., Cleveland, OH 44108; 216-851-8724; Fax: 216-851-8941; {Email: glenville@interax. com}.

Procurement And International Trade

The Women's Business Initiative offers training for start-ups and existing women business owners. They specialize in procurement and international trade issues. They also offer the Women's Network for Entrepreneurial Training (WNET) mentoring program. For more information, contact Greater Columbus Women's Business Development Center, Linda Steward, Program Director, Dee Walker, Project Coordinator, 37 North High Street, Columbus, OH 43215-3065; 614-225-6081; 614-225-6082; Fax: 614-469-8250; {www. columbus.org/busi/sbdc/index.html}; {Email: linda_Steward@ columbus.org}.

Business Network

The Ohio Women's Business Resource Network (OWBRN) is a statewide effort to assist women business owners. Their mission is to promote successful women's entrepreneurship. This umbrella network promotes information sharing, technical assistance and education among participating member organizations. OWBRN seeks to provide consistent baseline services to women across the state. For more information, contact Ohio Women's Business Resource Network (OWBRN), Mary Ann McClure, Director, 77 South High Street, 28th Floor, P.O. Box 1001, Columbus, OH 43266-0101; 614-466-2682; 800-848-1300; Fax: 614-466-0829; {Email: msacct@eurekanet.com}; {Email: lsaikas@odod. ohio.gov}.

Low-Income Women Assistance

The Women's Development Center provides a long-term training program. This program focuses first on personal development and then on entrepreneurship. They target primarily low-income women. The Center assists women with packaging their loans. For more information, contact Women's Development Center, Evelyn France, Executive Director, 42101 Griswold Road, Elyria, OH 44035; 216-324-3688; Fax: 216-324-3689.

Business Center

The Enterprise Center sponsored by Ohio State University Extension offers programs geared towards women and men. In the statewide network, this Center is one of the international trade assistance centers. For more information, contact Enterprise Center, Dr. Don McFeeters, Executive Director, Kendra Conley, Coordinator, Women's Business Center, Ohio State University, 1864 Shyville Road, Piketon, OH 45661; 740-289-2071; Fax: 740-289-4591; {www.ag.ohio-state.edu/~prec/}; {Email: enterprise@agvax2.ag.osu.edu}.

Empower Women

EMPOWER primarily works with start-up women business owners on one-on-one counseling and business plan development. They have developed a mentoring program, using SBA's WNET Program as a model. They also assist women-owned businesses with loan packaging. For more information, contact EMPOWER Pyramid Career Services, Mary Ellen Hess, Director, P.O. Box 9365, Canton, OH 44711; 330-453-3767; Fax: 330-453-6079.

Christian Programs

Ursuline Companions in Mission is a Christian association of lay women and men who seek to make a difference in the lives of the poor through a variety of programs including job training. They have service delivery sites in Delaware, Illinois, Kentucky, Minnesota, Missouri, New Mexico, and Ohio. Programs vary from location to location. For more information, contact Ursuline Companions In Mission, Sr. Jane Quinlan, College of New Rochelle, College Center, Room 155, New Rochelle, NY 10805; 914-654-5270; Fax: 914-654-5290; {www.theursulines.org}; {Email: ursulinecomp@hotmail.com}.

Learn A Trade

Women in Trades, in partnership with five organizations in different states, can provide technical assistance to employers, contractors, and labor organizations on mega construction projects in the Midwest. They help contractors and apprenticeship programs meet their goals for hiring women in job sites. These groups refer qualified tradeswomen to jobs, and most provide pre-apprenticeship programs to give women the skills needed in apprenticeship programs. They can give you information on career awareness on the range of job options for women too. For further information on programs in your state call Kathy Augustine, Executive Director, Hard Hatted Women, 4207 Lorain, Cleveland, OH 44113; 216-961-4449; Fax: 216-961-0927; {www.hardhattedwomen.org}; {Email: hhw@raex.com}.

Help For Displaced Homemakers

This program enables individuals who have been dependent on a spouse for financial support to become financially self sufficient. Once you have attended an orientation and have been accepted to Project Succeed, you will sign up for their support group titled Personal Enrichment and Career Development. You must pre-register for these groups. Call The Center for Women at 419-530-8570 to sign up. They also have a program called Project Succeed which offers you support groups; workshops on stress management, assertiveness, and self-esteem; career development workshops; job seeking skills assistance; assistance in returning to college as an adult student; scholarships for credit and non-credit courses at the University of Toledo. For more information, contact The University of Toledo, Catharine S. Eberly Center for Women, Tucker Hall 0168, Toledo, OH 43606-3390; 419-530-8570; Fax: 419-530-8575; {www.student-services.utoledo.edu/eberly-ctr/index.html}; {Email: ecwomen@utnet.utoledo.edu}.

Business Training for Disabled

Enterprise Works is a self-employment program for people with disabilities in Ohio. While working with a Rehabilitation Services Commission vocational rehabilitation counselor, the client can decide if owning a business is right for them, and if so, how to make it successful. The program provides participants with the skills and knowledge needed to run a small business. They have two types of classes; The Small business Management Overview, which is a self-assessment seminar, and the Business Plan Development, where they test the possibility of their ideas. For more information, contact Bob Larkin, Enterprise Works, 88 East Broad Street, Suite 1770, Columbus, OH 43215; 800-867-2997; TTY: 800-750-0750; Fax: 614-459-9071; {www.state.oh.us/rsc/VR_Services/BSVI/enterpriseworks.html}.

Training in Manufacturing Field

Tech Solve has a Manufacturing Pre-Employment Training program. It is an employer-sponsored night school program that, according to the company, helps good workers get good jobs in good companies. Applicants must pass academic testing (which includes 9th grade math and English), drug testing, and police checks. A high school diploma or GED is required, but previous manufacturing experience is not needed. This program gives unemployed and underemployed workers the chance to turn their skills into tuition free training and a foot in the door at many of Cincinnati's best manufacturing companies. Participants will earn a Certificate in Manufacturing Production. Applicants must pay a fee for drug screening and academic testing, however, assistance is available for that fee. For more information, contact Sue Leitner, Institute of Advanced Sciences (TechSolve), 1111 Edison Drive, Cincinnati, OH 45216-2265; 513-948-2000; 800-345-4482; Fax: 513-948-2109; {www.iams.org}.

Training for Low-Income Urban Residents

Low income urban community residents can take advantage of a free 3 week pre-employment counseling and training support program. It helps them to get, keep, and upgrade employment opportunities. The goal of the program, is to simply get jobs for these clients. For more information, contact Jobs Plus Employment Network, 1625 Vine Street, Cincinnati, OH 45210; 513-241-1800.

Help for Franklin County Residents

The Private Industry Council of Columbus and Franklin County offers a variety of services for eligible residents of Franklin County. The 2 groups of people they work with are individuals on a limited income and dislocated workers. Due to the availability of funds, they do an assessment to determine who will receive their help. The services include a complete assessment, training, support services and job placement assistance. The job training provides either vocational or occupational training that will lead to a certificate, enabling the client to enter a higher skilled level of employment. There are also Basic Skills Instruction and GED Preparation classes available. To help strengthen the workforce, they offer a variety of training programs for individuals so they can become more productive and successful. There is classroom training, on-the-job training, customized job training, and entrepreneurial training. They also have a Youth Institute for at-risk and out-of-school young people. Besides that, they have a Non-Traditional Careers for Women program, a Printing Industry Training Program for Bindery Press Operator Assistant program, and TechLINK, which will develop entry-level service technicians for automotive careers. For more information on the many services they offer, contact PIC of Columbus and Franklin County, 400 East Town Street, Columbus, OH 43215; 614-228-3907; Fax: 614-225-6341; TechLINK:614-253-5627

Ohio Works First

If you are a participant of Ohio Works First, you can train in a food service program with classes in Culinary Skills and Table Service. Emphasis is put on the culinary skills. Hospitality Plus trains people to cook for upscale restaurants, hospitals, nursing home, bakeries, and more. You must have a high school diploma or a GED to participate. They also offer job placement assistance. For more information, contact Hospitality Plus, 47 East State Street, Akron, OH 44308; 330-869-6968.

Oklahoma

One-Stop Career Centers
A network of One-Stop Career Centers throughout the state offers a wide range of employment related services including job training. Services vary by location. To find a location near you, please refer to the website {www.workforceok.org}. To learn more about the services they offer, contact your state coordinator.

Mr. Glen E. Robards, Jr., Director of JTPA, Employment Security Commission, 2401 North Lincoln, Will Rogers Bldg., Rm. 408, Oklahoma City, OK 73152; 405-557-5329; Fax: 405-557-7256.

Job Service Offices
A system of Employment Service/Job Service offices is located within every state with the goal of assisting millions of job seekers and employers. While services may vary from location to location, many provide job training, skills assessment and related services. With approximately 1,800 Employment Service/Job Service offices nationwide there is bound to be one near you. To learn more about the services offered in your area, contact your state administrator. Jon Brock, Executive Director, Employment Security Commission, 2401 North Lincoln, 215 Will Rogers Memorial Office Building, Oklahoma City, OK 73105; 405-557-7201; Fax: 405-557-7256; {www.oesc.state.ok.us/ES./default.htm}.

Help Is Just A Phone Call Away
Forced to go into the work world suddenly or do you need help getting your job skills upgraded? Women Work! is for you. They have over 1400 sites across the country to help women from diverse backgrounds achieve economic self-sufficiency through job readiness, education, training and employment. Women Work! provides these services through a network of programs in every state. Women Work! also takes on the toughest women's employment issues and fights for them in Congress and in state legislatures. For more information on Women Work! or to find a location near you contact Women Work! Regional Representative, Region VI, Patty McGuire, Displaced Homemaker Program, High Plains AVTS, 3921 34th Street, Woodward, OK 73801-0009; 405-571-6149; Fax: 405-571-6190.

Vocational Technology
Mid-America Vo-Tech Displaced Homemaker/Single Parent/Single Pregnant Woman Program is available to qualified students to assist them in reaching their professional and career goals. Mid-America Vo-Tech is located approximately 20 miles south of Norman, Oklahoma at Wayne America. For additional information Chickasha Center, Marge Albin-Walker, 1401 N. Michigan Avenue, Chickasha, OK 73018; 405-224-7220; or Mid-America Vo-Tech, Counseling Office, Box H, Wayne, OK 73095; 405-449-3391; Fax: 405-449-3395; {http://cust.iamerica.net/mavotech/service.html}.

Displaced Homemaker/ Women in Non-traditional Jobs
These programs offer assistance to women that have been displaced as their primary job as a homemaker due to divorce, death or disability of a spouse, or are single parents. Below is a list of organizations that offer job training assistance.

Caddo Kiowa Technology Center, Sue Pond, P.O. Box 190, F. Cobb, OK 73038-0190; 405-643-5511; Fax: 405-643-3017; {http://bct.ck.tec.ok.us/first/aboutck.htm}; {Email: spond@ck.tec.ok.us}. Displaced Homemaker and Nontraditional Jobs for Women programs.

Tulsa Technology Center, Jill Gaylor, 3420 South Memorial, Tulsa, OK 74145-1390; 918-828-5217; Fax: 918-828-5219; {Email: www.tulsatech.org; jgaylor@tulsatech.org Displaced Homemaker and Nontraditional Jobs for Women program.

Francis Tuttle Institute, Jennifer Haile-Egbert, 12777 North Rockwell Avenue, Oklahoma City, OK 73142-2789; 405-717-4252; Fax: 405-717-4790; {www.Francistuttle.com}; {Email: Jhaile-Egbert@Francistuttle.com}. Displaced Homemaker and Nontraditional Jobs For Women programs.

Kiamichi Technology Center, P. Gail Huddleston, 301 Kiamichi Drive, McAlester, OK 74501; 918-426-0940, ext. 232; 888-567-6630; Fax: 918-426-1626; {www.kavts.tec.ok.us}; {Email: ghuddleston@kavts.tec.ok.us}. Displaced Homemaker program.

Kiamichi Technology Center-Poteau, Chad Hull, P.O. Box 825, Poteau, OK 74953-0825; 918-647-4525, ext. 214; 888-567-6632; Fax: 918-647-4527; {www.kavts.tec.ok.us}; {Email: chull@davts.tec.ok.us}. Displaced Homemaker Program.

Meridian Technology Center, Janet Fenken, 1312 South Sangre Road, Stillwater, OK 74074-1899; 405-377-3333; Fax: 405-377-9604; {www.meridian-technology.com}; {Email: janetf@meridian-technology.com}. Displaced Homemaker program.

Moore Norman Technology Center, Cara Ditto, 4701 12th Avenue, NW, Norman, OK 73069-8399; 405-364-5763 ext. 7267; Fax: 405-360-9989; {www.mntechnology.com}; {Email: cditto@mntechnology.com}. Displaced Homemaker program.

Northeast Technology Centers, Sandra McElroy, P.O. Box 825, Pryor, OK 74362-0825; 918-825-5555, ext. 50; Fax: 918-825-5513; {www.nevtsouth.tec.ok.us}. Displaced Homemaker program.

Training for Native Americans
A variety of tribes have received grants so that they can offer employment and training programs. Below is a list of those tribes and the services that are available with each.

Four Tribes Consortium, Jeff Foster, 115 1/2 SW Second Street, Anadarko, OK 73005; 405-247-2021; Fax: 405-247-2582; job placement, job development, on-the-job training, computers for public use, counseling, and youth services.

Cherokee Nation-Falling Leaves Job Corps, Chad Smith, P.O. Box 948, Tahlequah, OK 74465; 918-456-0671; Fax: 918-458-7633; {www.cherokee.org; job placemtn}, welfare to work, job development, on-the-job training, computers for public use, internet service, school to work, youth programs, veteran services, senior citizen center.

Chicasaw Nation, Bill Anoatubby, P.O. Box 1548, Ada, OK 74820; 580-426-2603; Fax: 580-436-2109; {www.chickasaw.net}; job placement, welfare to work, job development, on-the-job training, computers for public use, counseling, youth programs, senior citizen center.

Citizen Potawatomi Nation, John A. Barrett, Jr., 1601 South Gordon Cooper Drive, Shawnee, OK 74801; 405-275-5269; Fax: 405-878-4668; {www.potawatomi.org}; job placement services, welfare to work, job development, on-the-job training, transportation, school to work, counseling, youth programs, veteran services.

Inter-Tribal Council, Inc., Floyd Leonard, P.O. Box 1308, Miami, OK 74355; 918-542-4486; Fax: 918-540-2500; job placement, welfare to work, job development, on-the-job training, transportation, counseling, youth programs.

Otoe-Missouria Tribe, Jim Grant, 8151 Highway 177, Red Rock, OK 74651; 580-723-4466; Fax: 580-723-4595; job placement, welfare to work, job development, on-the-job training, transportation, counseling, youth programs, veterans services.

Pawnee Nation of Oklahoma, Robert Chapman, P.O. Box 470, Pawnee, OK 74058, 918-762-3621; Fax: 918-762-6446; job placement, on-the-job training, counseling, and youth programs.

Training for Older Workers in Tulsa, Creek, and Osage Counties

Tulsa Senior Services has a Job Training and Placement program for people 55 years and older that reside in Tulsa, Creek, or Osage counties. For those 55 to 59 years, the services are available only if they meet income guidelines. For residents 60 and older, the services are available regardless of income. The services offered are; job recruitment, job testing, employment counseling, job readiness and skills training, job placement, and more. For more information, contact Tulsa Senior Services, 5950 East 31st Street, Tulsa, OK 74135-5106; Senior Line: 918-664-9000; Fax: 918-664-9922; {http://165.121.201.66/Default.htm}.

Vocational Training

Oklahoma Goodwill Industries strives to better the quality of life for vocationally disadvantaged people by expanding their opportunities through vocational and supportive programs. There are a variety of training programs available. The Business Office and Communications Training program prepares clients for entry-level positions in the clerical field. For class information, contact June Mahob at 405-236-4451 ext. 56 or Email: june@goodwill.org. Through the Work Adjustment Training/Sheltered Program, the training and skills experience may include janitorial skills, industrial contacts, and readiness skills. The Developmental Disabilities Services Division has a goal to place every client into secure employment, whether within the Goodwill system or integrated into employment in the community. The Waiver Program involves in-house training and employment to increase job skills for community employment. For more information, contact Oklahoma Goodwill Industry, 410 Southwest Third, Oklahoma City, OK 73109; 405-236-4451; Fax: 405-235-7215; {www.okgoodwill.org}; {Email: mailbox@okgoodwill.org}.

Oregon

One-Stop Career Centers

A network of One-Stop Career Centers throughout the state offers a wide range of employment related services including job training. Services vary by location. To find a location near you, please refer to the website {www.workforce.state.or.us/ocn/onestops/map.html}. To learn more about the services they offer, contact your state coordinator.

Marc Overbeck, Governor's Office of Education and Workforce Policy State One-Stop Office, 255 Capitol Street NE, Suite 126, Salem, OR 97310; 503-378-3921, ext. 33; Fax: 503-378-4789; {Email: marc.overbeck@state.or.us}.

Job Service Offices

A system of Employment Service/Job Service offices is located within every state with the goal of assisting millions of job seekers and employers. While services may vary from location to location, many provide job training, skills assessment and related services. With approximately 1,800 Employment Service/Job Service offices nationwide, there is bound to be one near you. To learn more about the services offered in your area, contact your state administrator. Virlena Crosley, Director, Employment Department, 875 Union Street, NE, Salem, OR 97311; 503-947-1470; 800-237-3710; Fax: 503-947-1472; {www.emp.state.or.us}.

Self-Sufficiency Programs

The Department of Human Resources works to help Oregonians achieve a maximum level of independence through their employment and self-sufficiency programs. This means reducing or eliminating barriers to employment, achieving and maintaining employment and increasing income levels. They can offer you a broad range of career opportunities, as well as training to gain and improve skills. Some of their occupational oriented training programs include: alcohol and drug training; child protective services; emergency medical technicians training, including the mobile training unit; long-term care; adult foster care training; training for nursing facility staff and elder abuse. For more information, contact Oregon Department of Human Resources, 500 Summer Street, NE, E25, Salem, OR 97301-1098; 503-945-5944; Fax: 503-378-2897; TTY: 503-945-5928; {www.hr.state.or.us/}; {dhr.info@state.or.us}.

Help Is Just A Phone Call Away

Forced to go into the work world suddenly or do you need help getting your job skills upgraded? Women Work! is for you. They have over 1400 sites across the country to help women from diverse backgrounds achieve economic self-sufficiency through job readiness, education, training and employment. Women Work! provides these services through a network of programs in every state. Women Work! also takes on the toughest women's employment issues and fights for them in Congress and in state legislatures. For more information on Women Work! or to find a location near you contact Oregon Women Work!, Charleen Maclean, President, Transitions to Success, Lane Community College, 4000 East 30th Avenue, Eugene, OR 97405; 541-747-4501, ext. 2840; Fax: 541-744-4173; {www.lanecc.edu/stuser/womprog/trans1.htm}; {Email: macleanc@lanecc.edu}.

Break Through Barriers

SOWAC provides business training, mentoring and financing services for women and men with barriers including low-income Hispanic entrepreneurs and very rural entrepreneurs. Join more than 288 students who have participated in their training program or 65 businesses which they have helped start-up or expand in Jackson, Josephine and Klamath counties. As a training graduate, you may apply to SOWAC's Mentor Program to receive assistance from an experienced person who volunteers expertise over a six month period, and/or for a SOWAC business loan of up to $25,000. SOWAC is funded by the SBA Office of Women Business Ownership, private foundations, client fees, interest income and local contributions. For more information, contact Southern Oregon Women's Access to Credit (SOWAC), Mary O'Kief, Director, 33 North Central, Suite 209, Medford, OR 97501; 541-779-3992; Fax: 541-779-5195; {www.sowac.org}; {Email: sowac@sowac.org}.

Business Assistance for Native Americans By Native Americans

Organization of Native American Business & Entrepreneurial Network (ONABEN) is a non-profit public benefit corporation created by Northwest Indian Tribes to increase the number and profitability of private enterprises owned by Native Americans. ONABEN offers training, individual counseling, assisted access to markets and facilitated access to capital for its clients. The 4 tribes hosting an ONABEN Service Center pays annual dues of $2,500 and serves 5 of the 9 federally recognized tribes in Oklahoma. The sites, located on reservations in Oregon, Washington and California, deliver services to all citizens regardless of tribal affiliation. Some have up to 40% of users coming from the surrounding non-Native community. For more information, contact ONABEN - A Native American Business Network, Tom Hampson, Director, 520 Southwest 6th Avenue, Suite 930, Portland, OR 97204; 503-243-5015; Fax: 503-243-5028; {www.onaben.org}; {Email: chinookl@onaben.org}.

Help For Displaced Homemakers and Single Parents

Whether a single parent or displaced homemaker, if your interest is preparing immediately for the job market or exploring the possibility of returning to school, the Newmark Center has the staff and support to assist you. They offer an innovative approach to student and client services because they share a building and a philosophy of seamless service with community agencies like Adult and Family Services, Consumer Credit Counseling, and the Small Business Development Center. As a student, you can choose from a menu of classes including life skills, academic skill enhancement, career and job development, and introduction to computers and word processing. Students eligible for the Single Parent/Displaced Homemaker program benefit from a free clothing closet, transportation vouchers, and use of the lending library, as well as access to all adult basic education classes available at Southwestern Oregon Community College. Services are free of charge. Contact Newmark Center: Adult Learning Skills Program, Southwestern Oregon Community College, 1988 Newmark, Coos Bay, OR 97420; 541-888-7116; Fax: 541-888-7120; {http://www.southwestern.cc.or.us/academics/adult_lrn.html}.

Apprenticeship Training

Apprenticeship Training is a combination of on-the-job training with a journey worker and classroom education which prepares an apprentice for an occupation in a skilled trade and craft. Some of the registered occupations with Apprenticeship and Training are, bricklayer, carpenter, operating engineer, pipefitter, plumber and die maker. The variety of available occupations depends on the local industry needs. Classes on such things as safety, blueprint reading, and mathematics, generally meet from 3-6 hours a week. After completion of the program, workers can expect to maintain good employment with good pay. Contact the Apprenticeship Training Bureau of Labor and Industries, Apprenticeship and Training Division, 800 NE Oregon Street, #32, Portland, OR 97232; 503-731-4072.

Programs for Veterans

Veterans' Employment and Training Services (VETS) provide maximum level of employment and training opportunities for veterans. Vocational guidance, job search workshops, job development, training, on-the-job training, and more services are offered. Contact your nearest Employment Department Office for more information. Employment Department, 875 Union Street, NE, Salem, OR 97311; 503-947-1470; Fax: 503-947-1472; 800-237-3710; {www.emp.state.or.us}.

Job Training For Displaced Workers

This program will help those that have been displaced by corporate downsizing or other forms of work displacement. Their service area is in Coos and Curry Counties. They offer different programs to satisfy the needs of these workers. The Jobs Plus program is for a targeted workforce only. The On-The-Job Training reimburses the trainees up to 50% while they are training on the job. The clients get work experience with a public or private non-profit organization in the Work Experience program. The Services for Job Seekers involves basic training, computer training, interviewing, and more. For more information, contact South Coast Business Employment Corporation, 1160 Newport, Coos Bay, OR 97420; 541-269-2013; 800-858-5777; Fax: 541-267-0194; {www.scbec.org}.

Start Your Own Business

This program is designed to help business owners achieve their personal and business goals through improved management, organization, and operation of their business. The services available to attain that goal may include; confidential one-on-one counseling to learn the basic of how to start a business, instructions on how to prepare a business plan, instruction on preparing a marketing plan, and an objective point-of-view on business decisions. For more information, call the Roseburg Area Chamber of Commerce, 410 SE Spruce Street, P.O. Box 1026, Roseburg, OR 97470; 541-672-2648; Fax: 541-673-7868; {www.roseburgareachamber.org}.

Help For People Making a Major Life Change

The Adult Learning Skills Program is a free program that provides access to information, skills and resources for individuals in the process of a major life change. They offer a variety of classes and services to prepare the participants for success in their family and the workforce. Some of the many classes available are; basic skills, GED, computers, keyboarding/typing, Microsoft Work, life skills, workplace skills, and clerical skills building. The is also a Career Resource Center with information on job searching, writing resumes, cover letters and preparing for job interviews. For more information, contact Southwestern Adult Basic Skills Program, 2110 Newmark Avenue, Coos Bay, OR 97420; 541-888-7116; 800-962-2838; Fax: 541-888-7120; {http://wolf.southwestern.cc.or.us/alsp/index.html}.

Pennsylvania

One-Stop Career Centers

A network of One-Stop Career Centers throughout the state offers a wide range of employment related services including job training. Services vary by location. To find a location near you, please refer to the website {www.pacareerlink.state.pa.us}. To learn more about the services they offer, contact your state coordinator.

Linda Trimpey, Chief Operating Officer, Career Development Marketplace System, 1723 Labor and Industry Building, Seventh and Forster Streets, Harrisburg, PA 17120; 717-787-7184; Fax: 717-772-1461.

Mr. Michael J. Acker, Deputy Secretary for Workforce Development and Safety, Department of Labor and Industry, 1720 Labor and Industry Building, Seventh and Forster Streets, Harrisburg, PA 17120; 717-787-8665; Fax: 717-772-1461.

Job Service Offices

A system of Employment Service/Job Service offices is located within every state with the goal of assisting millions of job seekers and employers. While services may vary from location to location, many provide job training, skills assessment and related services. With approximately 1,800 Employment Service/Job Service offices nationwide there is bound to be one near you. To learn more about the services offered in your area, contact your state administrator.

Johnny J. Butler, Secretary, Department of Labor & Industry, 1700 Labor and Industry Building, Harrisburg, PA 17121; 717-787-3756; Fax: 717-783-5225; {www.li.state.pa.us/index.html}.

Alan Williamson, Deputy Secretary, Employment Security & Job Training Department of Labor & Employment Security, 1700 Labor and Industry Building, Harrisburg, PA 17121; 717-787-3907; Fax: 717-787-8826; {www.li.state.pa.us/index.html}.

Job Training Assistance
The Delaware County Office of Employment & Training is interested in supporting you in your quest to achieve your career goals. They can help you assess your skill level and determine occupational needs. Then they can provide any of the following: basic education skills, including ABE/GED/ESL training; occupational skills training; referrals to supportive services; employer interview referrals. In addition, the office participates in regional cooperative efforts with private industry councils, community colleges, job centers, assistance offices, chambers of commerce, and commerce departments implementing regional strategies for developing the workforce as a tool for economic development in southeastern Pennsylvania. The staff also works with local school districts and employers to develop concrete school-to-work strategies, again with the focus on workforce development. For more information, contact Delaware County Office of Employment & Training, 20 S. 69th Street, Upper Darby, PA 19082-2521; 610-713-2200; Fax: 610-713-2224; {www.co.delaware.pa.us/depts/oet.html}.

Women Work!
Women Work! is a state affiliate of the national membership organization dedicated to helping women from diverse backgrounds achieve economic self-sufficiency through job readiness, education, training and employment. Contact Mary Ann Eisenreich, Regional Manager, Regional Enterprise Tower, 425 Sixth Avenue, Suite 1680, Pittsburgh, PA 15219; 866-PAWOMEN (toll-free) 412-201-7424; {www.pawomenwork.com}; {Email: pawomenwork@aol.com}.

Job Training For Adults And Teens
Aliquippa Alliance for Unity and Development, Inc. is a private non-profit corporation providing service in business development, commercial development, education and social services. AAUD service area is Aliquippa, Center and Hopewell. Education services include summer programs for teens through 21 years old, computer classes in computer basics, WordPerfect and Lotus, low or no cost desktop publishing services, GED preparation program for AFDC parents and a variety of job training and career development services for adults and teens. For more information, contact Aliquippa Alliance for Unity and Development, Inc. (AAUD), Pauline Cooper, Executive Director, 300 Main Avenue, Aliquippa, PA 15001; 724-378-7422; Fax: 724-378-9809.

Learn Professional Horticultural Skills
Awbury Arboretum is a unique cultural and historic landscape that offers horticultural job training for adults as well as educational programs to school children, families and others. For more information, contact Awbury Arboretum Association, The Francis Cope House, 1 Awbury Rd., Philadelphia, PA 19138; 215-849-2855; Fax 215-849-0213; {http://awbury.org/}. To find out if you qualify for the program, contact the Office of Emergency Shelter and Services, 1315 Cherry Street, Philadelphia, PA 19138; 215-686-6738

Puerto Rican Human Services
Congreso de Latinos Unidos is a multicultural, human services agency based in the Puerto Rican and Latino community of North Philadelphia. Congreso has a range of health, education, employment, and social services. In addition to a job training program, they also offer emergency housing assistance, a community Learning Center that offers continuing adult education and job training, HIV/AIDS program, drug and alcohol treatment, maternal and child health education, Latina domestic violence program, youth programs, prevention of child abuse and neglect, and a Women's Center. Contact Congreso, 719 W. Girard Avenue, Philadelphia, PA 19123; 215-763-8870; {www.libertynet. org/cdlu/}.

Training Programs For Women and Minorities
The Workforce 2000 Advisory Council designs and implements training programs to prepare minorities and women for the workplace of the future. Their programs include computer and Internet training, and a year-round education and training program to prepare youth for careers in the health industry among others. For more information, contact The Workforce 2000 Advisory Council, 1207 Chestnut Street, 3rd Fl., Philadelphia, PA 19107; 215-851-1848; Fax: 215-665-9886; {www.wf2000online.org}; {Email infor@wf2000online.org}.

Youths Learn To Manage Parks
Organized in 1991, the Cobbs Creek Community Environmental Education Center (CCCEEC) is designed to institutionalize the practice of Urban Environmental Education. Their Park Management Program is a career path for area high school youths to learn and become trained in preserving and protecting neighborhoods. For more information, contact Cobbs Creek Community Environmental Center, Carole Chew-Williams, c/o Penn State Cooperative Extension, 4601 Market Street, 2nd floor, Philadelphia, PA 19139; 215-471-2223; Fax: 215-471-2231;

{Email: Rednet44@aol.com}; (When sending Email, please use "Cobbs Creek" in the title of your message); {www.cobbscreek.org}.

Training For Home Health Care
HomeCare Associates provides 6 to 12 weeks of job readiness and skills training for entry level home health-care jobs. Training is followed by a paid 90-day placement in a private company, during which time HomeCare Associates provides job coaching, peer mentoring, and counseling support. The private company agrees to hire the trainee in a permanent job if she proves satisfactory. For more information, contact HomeCare Associates, 1314 Chestnut Street, Philadelphia, PA 19107; 215-735-0677.

Get Paid To Take Notes
The Court Reporting Institute offers courses in court reporting, scoping (court reporting editing), medical transcription, administrative assisting, and office technology. Financial aid and placement assistance are available for qualified students Contact Court Reporting Institute (CRI), 1845 Walnut Street, 7th Floor, Philadelphia, PA 19103; 215-854-1854; Fax: 215-854-1880; {www.papsa.org/crit.html}.

Jewish Career Assistance
The Jewish Employment and Vocational Service (JEVS) provides Philadelphia-area residents with employment assistance, educational programs, and health-related services. They offer a range of services and programs for career changers, the unemployed, those seeking to improve their careers, high school and college students, and senior citizens. For more information, contact Jewish Employment & Vocational Service, 1845 Walnut St., Philadelphia, PA 19103-4708; 215-854-1800; Fax: 215-854-1880.

Empowering Women Entrepreneurs
The Women's Business Development Center (WBDC) is dedicated to the economic empowerment of women. The Center enables women to launch new businesses and to more successfully run their existing businesses. If you are a start-up, emerging or established woman entrepreneur, they offer you a unique continuum of supportive services including: Premier FastTrac I & II, comprehensive course work culminating in the development of a viable business plan for each entrepreneur; individualized business consulting in management, marketing, and financial matters; loan packaging; procurement and certification assistance. By offering a full range of services and utilizing the expertise of successful women business owners to deliver its programs, the Women's Business Development Center will be the Greater Philadelphia Region's focal point for women's economic empowerment opportunities. For more information, contact Women's Business Development Center (WBDC), Geri Swift, President, 1315 Walnut Street, Suite 1116, Philadelphia, PA 19107-4711; 215-790-9232; Fax: 215-790-9231; {Email: wbdc@erols.com}.

Job Assistance For Low-income Women
Community Women's Education Project provides secondary and post-secondary education, educational support systems, and connections to the workplace for low-income women and their families in their community. You can join more than 13,000 adults and children who have benefited from CWEP's programs, developing the educational skills they need to move into economic self-sufficiency. Contact Community Women's Education Project, 2801

Frankford Avenue, Philadelphia, PA 19134; 215-426-2200; Fax: 215-426-3284; {http://users.nni.com/cwep};
{Email: CWEP@nni.com}.

Find Satisfying Work

OPTIONS is dedicated to empowering individuals to achieve satisfaction throughout each stage of their working
lives and to expand options within the workplace for diverse individuals. They can offer you assistance with your
job search, career change, or career management. Their services are offered with reduced fees available for low-
income clients. Other organizational training and consulting includes career management, diversity and sexual
harassment prevention. For more information, contact OPTIONS, 225 S. 15th Street, Suite 1635, Philadelphia, PA
19102-3916; 215-735-2202; Fax: 215-735-8097; {www.optionscareers.org}; {Email: Info@ optionscareers.com}.

Work At A Job Traditionally Held By Men

Tradeswomen of Purpose/Women in Non-Traditional Work facilitates a nationally recognized job training program
that prepares low-income women for non-traditional occupations. As a graduate of the program, you can expect to
begin a new job at an average hourly wage of $12 per hour. TOP/WIN can also provide technical assistance to

employers, labor unions and other job training providers on issues such as recruitment
and retention of women in non-traditional work and on managing a diverse workforce.
For more information, contact TOP/WIN, 2300 Alter Street, Philadelphia, PA 19146,
215-545-3700 (PA); 609-728-5931 (NJ); Fax: 215-545-8713;
{www.workplacesolutions.org/about/topwin.cfm}; {Email: topwin1@aol.com}.

Training for Seniors and Disadvantaged Workers

Green Thumb provides training and employment opportunities for mature and
disadvantaged workers, dislocated workers, and welfare participants. They currently
have five programs to meet the needs of the clients. The Senior Community Service Employment Program helps
low-income seniors to find work in the community. Experience Works! works with employers to fill job vacancies
with mature workers regardless of their income. Got/IT Information Technology Training is a computer training
program for older and disadvantaged workers. Geezer.com is place where older workers can market their crafts,
products, goods, and start their own business. For more information, or for an office near you, contact Green Thumb
State Office, 817 South Market Street, Mechanicsburg, PA 17055-4700; 800-854-1578; Fax: 717-790-0119;
{www.greenthumbpa.org}; {Email: jobready@ greenthumbpa.org}.

Breachmenders

Breachmenders has an employment training program that offers job readiness classes for unemployed and
underemployed residents. Along with that, job search assistance is also available. Their School-to-Career program is
a work experience/mentorship program open to at-risk African American youths from the Oakland/Hill District
community. For more information, call Breachmenders, 200 Robinson Street, Pittsburgh, PA 15213; 412-621-2530.

Greenhouse/Nursery Training

To learn Greenhouse/Nursery procedures, this program offers hands-on experience 4 days a week at Brookside Farm
Market, and job readiness skills on day a week at CCAC North Campus. The outcome is that the students will be
able to perform basic and advanced greenhouse procedures independently, gain job development skills, and find
successful job placement. For more information, contact Workforce Training, Byers Hall, Room 205, 808 Ridge
Avenue, Pittsburg, PA 15212; 412-237-2724; {www.ccac.edu/wf_train/comserv.html}; {Email:
training@ccac.edu}.

Training for a New Career

The Jobs and Career Education Center provides services and materials to unemployed and underemployed
people, displaced homemakers, teenage and adult students, people that want to change careers, and potential small
business owners. Information on job search, resume and letter writing, interviewing, career choices, employment test
preparation, summer jobs, and more are covered. Some of their free classes are Career Exploration Workshop, Job
Hunting on the World Wide Web, and Financial Aid Resources. For more information contact Job and Career
Education Center, 4400 Forbes Avenue, First Floor, Pittsburgh, PA 15213-4080; 412-622-3133; Fax: 412-622-3136;
{www.clpgh.org/clp/JCED}.

Free Machining Training for High School Graduates

During training, students will learn the basics and get hands-on experience with lathes, milling machines, surface grinders, the radical armdrill press, the band saw, and calipeers, micrometers, and indicators. There are also four workshops that introduce the students to the different computer programs used in machine shops. Machine text books are also supplied at no cost. Career placement staff work with the students from beginning to end so they can place them with an area manufacturer. For more information, contact Manufacturing 2000, Admissions Office, P.O. Box 112534, Pittsburgh, PA 15241-2534; 800-822-9337; {www.duq.edu/iet/maching.html}.

Training in Construction and For Unemployed

Hill Community Development Corporation currently offers two different job training programs. H.E.L.P. (Hill Employment Linkage Program) has training and information concerning the construction industry. For more information on HELP, contact Greg Jones at the number listed below. The goal of the Job*Links program is to provide attitudinal training and placement assistance for unemployed and underemployed residents in Oakland and the surrounding neighborhoods. It accomplishes this by offering job readiness training, placement assistance, and establishing strong relationships with employers. It also provides one-on-one counseling for resume writing, interview skills, and cold calls. For more information, contact Hill Community Development Corporation, 2015-17 Center Avenue, Pittsburgh, PA 15219; 412-765-1320; Fax: 412-765-1329; {www.pitt-edu./~hilldc}.

Training in Food Service

Rainbow Kitchen Community Services helps low income families through a number of programs, one of which, is job training. Their New Leaf Food Service Training Program teaches individuals culinary and job readiness skills to prepare them for employment in the food service industry. People that are eligible for their services are; single parents working part-time and unable to make ends meet, seniors on a low fixed-income, ill or disabled people in chronic need. For more information, contact Rainbow Kitchen, 135 East Ninth Avenue, Homestead, PA 15120-1601; 412-464-1892; Fax: 412-464-1069; {http://trfn.clpgh.org/rainbow/C.kitchen}

Puerto Rico

One-Stop Career Centers

A network of One-Stop Career Centers throughout the state offers a wide range of employment related services including job training. Services vary by location. To find a location near you and to learn about the services they offer, contact your state coordinator.

Carmen McCullogh, Assistant Secretary for Human Resources, Puerto Rico Department of Labor and Human Resource, 505 Munoz Rivera Avenue, Hato Rey, PR 00918; 809-754-2130; Fax: 809-756-1070.

Aura Gonzalez-Rios, Esq., Secretary of Labor, Puerto Rico Department of Labor and Human Resource, 505 Munoz Rivera Avenue, Hato Rey, PR 00918; 809-721-2119; Fax: 809-763-2227.

Help For Women Entrepreneurs

The Women's Business Institute (WBI) at University of the Sacred Heart, Center for Women's Entrepreneurial Development (CWED) offers technical assistance to women interested in establishing a business. If you are a woman business owner, they provide a place to expose and share ideas, objectives and experiences. The WBI will contribute to the social and economic development of women through training on empowerment and business ownership as an alternative in attaining economic independence. For more information, contact Women's Business Institute (WBI), Universidad Del Sagrado Corazon, (The University of the Sacred Heart), Joy Vilardi de Camacho, Director, Center for Women's Entrepreneurial Development, P.O. Box 12383, San Juan, PR 00914-0383; 787-728-1515; 787-727-6545; Fax: 787-727-5519; {Email: hylsa@juno.com}.

Job Service Offices

A system of Employment Service/Job Service offices is located within every state with the goal of assisting millions of job seekers and employers. While services may vary from location to location, many provide job training, skills

assessment and related services. With approximately 1,800 Employment Service/Job Service offices nationwide there is bound to be one near you. To learn more about the services offered in your area, contact your state administrator. Carmen McCulloch, Assistant Secretary, Human Resources, 505 Munoz Rivera Avenue, Hato Rey, PR 00918; 787-754-2132; Fax: 787-756-1070.

Rhode Island

One-Stop Career Centers
A network of One-Stop Career Centers throughout the state offers a wide range of employment related services including job training. Services vary by location. To find a location near you, please refer to the website {www.networkri.org/Layer1/about.htm}. To learn more about the services they offer, contact your state coordinator.

Dr. Lee Arnold, Director, Howard Center, 1511 Pontiac Avenue, Cranston, RI 02920-4407; 401-462-8100; Fax: 401-462-8105; {Email: larnold@dlt.state.ri.us}.

Mr. Robert Palumbo, Associate Director of Program Operations, Howard Center, 1511 Pontiac Avenue, Cranston, RI 02920-4407; 401-462-8100; Fax: 401-462-8105.

Ms. Wendi Miller, One-Stop Project Manager, Howard Center, 1511 Pontiac Avenue, Cranston, RI 02920-4407; 401-462-8000; Fax: 401-462-8105; {Email: wmiller@dlt.state.ri.us }.

Job Service Offices
A system of Employment Service/Job Service offices is located within every state with the goal of assisting millions of job seekers and employers. While services may vary from location to location, many provide job training, skills assessment and related services. With approximately 1,800 Employment Service/Job Service offices nationwide there is bound to be one near you. To learn more about the services offered in your area, contact your state administrator. Dr. Lee Arnold, Director, Howard Center, 1511 Pontiac Avenue, Cranston, RI 02920-4407; 401-222-3600; Fax: 401-222-2731; {www.dlt.state.ri.us}; {Email: larnold@dlt.state.ri.us}.

Free Nursing Assistant Training
The New England Gerontology Academy offers free job training for eligible persons interested in working as Certified Nursing Assistants. Eligible trainees live in Rhode Island; are low-income or unemployed; at least 18 years old; have a clean criminal record; are able to work nights, weekends, holidays, or evening hours; are reliable dependable, and have good interpersonal skills. Candidates that are selected for this program may be eligible for support services which include a 100% childcare subsidy and a transportation allowance. Screening is on Wednesdays. For more information, contact the New England Gerontology Academy, 669 Elmwood Avenue, Providence, RI 02907; 401-467-1970.

Training for DHS Participants
The Department of Human Services/ Family Independence Program Training provides participants of DHS with educational, vocational, and other job skill preparedness services in order to qualify them for work. Training can include, technical skills training for skilled manufacturing, and/or service sector jobs, child care training and certification programs for employment in the child care industry, and resume writing, interviewing, and networking workshops. For more information, contact Christine C. Ferguson, Director, Department of Human Services, 600 New London Avenue, Cranston, RI 02920; 401-462-2121; Fax: 401-462-3677.

South Carolina

One-Stop Career Centers
A network of One-Stop Career Centers throughout the state offers a wide range of employment related services including job training. Services vary by location. To find a location near you, please refer to the website {www.sces.org/1stop/1stopmain.htm}. To learn more about the services they offer, contact your state coordinator.

Mr. Joel T. Cassidy, Executive Director, Employment Security Commission, 1550 Gadsden Street, P.O. Box 995, Columbia, SC 29202; 803-737-2617; Fax: 803-737-2642.

Job Service Offices

A system of Employment Service/Job Service offices is located within every state with the goal of assisting millions of job seekers and employers. While services may vary from location to location, many provide job training, skills assessment and related services. With approximately 1,800 Employment Service/Job Service offices nationwide there is bound to be one near you. To learn more about the services offered in your area, contact your state administrator. Joel Cassidy, Executive Director, SC Employment Security Commission, P.O. Box 995, Columbia, SC 29202; 803-737-2400; Fax: 803-737-2642; {www.sces.org/es/index.htm}.

Women Work!

Women Work! is a state affiliate of the national membership organization dedicated to helping women from diverse backgrounds achieve economic self-sufficiency through job readiness, education, training and employment. Contact: South Carolina Women Work!, Gilda Kennedy, President, South Carolina Department Of Social Services, 3150 Harden Street, Columbia, SC 29204; 803-898-9375; Fax: 803-898-9177; {Email: gkennedy@dss.state.sc.us}.

Help For Women Entrepreneurs

The mission of the Center for Women Entrepreneurs at Columbia College of South Carolina is to expand economic opportunities for women by advancing entrepreneurship and providing resources to assist in successful business start-ups, maintenance of growth, and exploration of new business opportunities. You could benefit from services that include individual consultations, management and technical assistance, annual women's conference, round table luncheon series, resource guides, seminars and workshops, and internships. The focus on communications through the Online Women's Business Center enables the project to serve not only mature women ready to start businesses or women already in business, but young female entrepreneurs in high schools. As local support for this project can attest, the Center for Women Entrepreneurs is an active advocate of collaborative ventures among resources that support women entrepreneurs. For more information, contact Center for Women Entrepreneurs, Columbia College of South Carolina, 4901 Colonial Drive, Columbia, SC 29203; 803-786-3375; Fax: 803-786-3804; {www.colacoll.edu}; {Email: susdavis@colacoll.edu or smckee@colacoll.edu}.

Help For People with Disabilities

Goodwill Industries strives to help people with disabilities and special needs to become independent through education, training, and employment. They help those with vocational disadvantages like welfare dependency, illiteracy, homelessness, and language barriers. The staff works with local employers to place the clients in meaningful jobs which frees them from welfare an other types of public support. Some of the services they offer to meet their goals are; work adjustment, on-the-job training, adult basic education, community based employment, food service programs, and more. For more information, contact Goodwill Industries of Upper South Carolina, Inc., 100 Industrial Drive, Greenville, SC 29607; 864-467-3200; Fax: 864-467-3206; {www.goodwill-uppersc.org}; {Email: goodwill@goodwill-uppersc.org}.

Training for Farmworkers

The Migrant and Seasonal Farmworkers program has counseling, testing, training, and job referral services. Their goal is to move the seasonal workforce from areas of supply to areas of demand. Those that have worked for a farm for the past 24 months, are eligible for services. Some restrictions do apply. Contact the Employment Security Department, 1550 Gadsden Street, Columbia, SC 29202; 803-737-9935; Fax: 803-737-0202; {www.sces.org}; {Email: jobs@sces.org}.

Services for Veterans

There are many types of services available to veterans. The Veterans Apprenticeship and On-The-Job Training program, education programs, Disabled Veterans Outreach Program with intensive training and employment, Private Sector Jobs program, and more. All of these are designed to help our veterans find successful employment and maintain that employment. For more information, contact State Veteran's Representative, SC Employment Security Commission, Columbia, SC; 803-737-9936; Fax: 803-737-2642.

South Dakota

One-Stop Career Centers

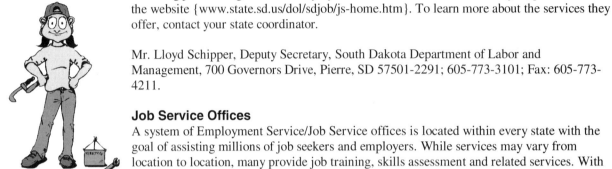

A network of One-Stop Career Centers throughout the state offers a wide range of employment related services including job training. Services vary by location. To find a location near you, please refer to the website {www.state.sd.us/dol/sdjob/js-home.htm}. To learn more about the services they offer, contact your state coordinator.

Mr. Lloyd Schipper, Deputy Secretary, South Dakota Department of Labor and Management, 700 Governors Drive, Pierre, SD 57501-2291; 605-773-3101; Fax: 605-773-4211.

Job Service Offices

A system of Employment Service/Job Service offices is located within every state with the goal of assisting millions of job seekers and employers. While services may vary from location to location, many provide job training, skills assessment and related services. With approximately 1,800 Employment Service/Job Service offices nationwide there is bound to be one near you. To learn more about the services offered in your area, contact your state administrator. Craig Johnson, Secretary, South Dakota Department of Labor and Management, 700 Governors Drive, Pierre, SD 57501-2277; 605-773-3101; Fax: 605-773-4211; {www.state.sd.us/dol/dol.htm}.

Help For The Homeless

The Good Shepherd Center offers job, lifestyle and computer training, laundry and shower facilities, children's center and free counseling for homeless individuals. For more information, contact Good Shepherd Center - Family Center, Jim Walden, Director, 300 N. Main Avenue, Sioux Falls, SD 57104; 605-332-3176.

Help For People In Transition

The Watertown Area Career Learning Center has a program called the WIA dislocated worker program which has assisted dislocated workers and economically disadvantaged persons since the late 1980s. The Career Learning Center offers job search workshops, counseling, resume development and more. For more information, contact Sandy Albertsen, Director, Watertown Area Career Learning Center or The Entrepreneur Network for Women (ENW), Kay Solberg, Director or Becky Doerr, Business Specialist, 100 South Maple, P.O. Box 1505, Watertown, SD 57201-0081; 605-882-5080; Fax: 605-882-5069; {www.network4women. com}; {Email: network4women@basec.net}.

Women Work!

Women Work! is a state affiliate of the national membership organization dedicated to helping women from diverse backgrounds achieve economic self-sufficiency through job readiness, education, training and employment. Contact South Dakota Women Work!, Diana Melvin, Growing Up Together, 809 East Dakota, Pierre, SD 57501, 605-224-3189; Fax: 605-224-8339.

Vocational Services in Sioux Falls

Proteus, Inc. offers eligible applicants, depending upon availability of funds, assistance with financial aid for vocational schools and colleges, subsidized on-site training programs, employment counseling, job placement, testing and evaluation, financial assistance in relocating for education training and job placement, and emergency financial services such as, but not limited to, emergency food, shelter, and transportation costs. Proteus serves Sioux Falls and surrounding communities in Minnehaha County. This program is for those that have 50% of their work from farm working, not as owners, but working on or with the farm. For more information, contact Proteus, Inc., Kathy Knudson Career Development Coordinator, 301 S. Garfield Avenue Suite 6D, Sioux Falls, SD 57104-3140; 605-338-4352; Fax: 605-338-4396.

Training for Dislocated Workers and Eligible Adults

The Workforce Investment Act Customized Training Program offers training for eligible adults and dislocated workers that meet the special requirements of an employer or group of employers. The employer(s) in turn, make a commitment to employ the participants of the program. The outcome is the development of a well-trained and skilled workforce that are needed for specific occupations. Training may be a combination of classroom and on-the-job training. For more information, contact Workforce Investment Act, Department of Labor, Kneip Building, 700 Governors Drive, Pierre, SD 57501-2277; 605-773-5017; {www.state.sd.us/dol/WIA/training.html}.

Assistance for Native American Business Owners

The North Dakota/South Dakota Native American Business Development Center offers free assistance to enrolled Native Americans who reside in or whose business is, or will, reside within the ND/SD service area. It is their goal to ensure the survival of new and existing Native American entrepreneurs. They have general business counseling and information, assistance in developing business plans, help to identify financial assistance, business seminars, assistance in marketing minority business products, and much more. For more information, contact ND/SD Native American Business Development Center, 3315 University Drive, Bismarck, ND 58504; 701-530-0608; Fax: 701-530-0607; {www.united-tribes.tec.nd.us/business_DVCTR}; {Email: ndsdnabdc@hotmail.com}.

Tennessee

One-Stop Career Centers

A network of One-Stop Career Centers throughout the state offers a wide range of employment related services including job training. Services vary by location. To find a location near you, please refer to the website {www.state.tn.us/labor-wfd/cchome.html}. To learn more about the services they offer, contact your state coordinator.

Mr. Michael E. Magill, Special Assistant to the Governor, Workforce Development Office, 400 Deaderick Street, Citizens Plaza Building, Ste. 200, Nashville, TN 37243; 615-253-1324; Fax: 615-253-1329.

Ms. Jocelyn E. Frazier, Director, Tennessee One-Stop Career Development Centers, 400 Deaderick Street, Citizens Plaza Building, Suite 200, Nashville, TN 37243; 615-253-1324; Fax: 615-253-1329.

Job Service Offices

A system of Employment Service/Job Service offices is located within every state with the goal of assisting millions of job seekers and employers. While services may vary from location to location, many provide job training, skills assessment and related services. With approximately 1,800 Employment Service/Job Service offices nationwide there is bound to be one near you. To learn more about the services offered in your area, contact your state administrator. Hazel Albert, Acting Commissioner, TN Department of Employment Security, 12th Floor - Volunteer Plaza, 500 James Robertson Parkway, Nashville, TN 37245-0001; 615-741-2131; Fax: 615-741-3203; {www.state.tn.us/labor-wfd/jobserv.htm}.

Empowering Women Business Owners Statewide

The National Association of Women Business Owners (NAWBO) is a membership-based organization that informs, empowers and promotes women business owners and invites its members to impact the social, political and economic communities. In Tennessee, they have established chapters in Chattanooga, Memphis and Tri-Cities, thus creating a statewide partnership of women business owners. The Nashville NAWBO has established the first, SBA-funded women's business center in Tennessee known as the Women's Resource Center. They offer you on-site business counseling services, training programs and technical assistance if you are a woman business owner in Middle Tennessee, which includes 21 counties. Through the consortium of Sister NAWBO Chapters and a corporate partnership with Bell South and the Tennessee Economic Development Center, the Women's Resource Center can also provide training programs statewide through satellite, two-way interactive videoconferences and the Internet. Contact The National Assn. for Women Business Owners - Nashville Chapter (NAWBO), Janice S., Thomas,

Executive Director, P.O. Box 292283, Nashville, TN 37229-2283; 615-952-2444; Fax: 615-952-3511; {Email: tnwrc@bellsouth.net}.

Training For Low-Income People
The YWCA of Greater Memphis/Women in Trades Project trains women in apprenticeship and nontraditional occupations. For further information on the workshops and other activities, call YWCA of Greater Memphis, 1044 Mississippi Blvd., Memphis, TN 38126; 901-948-8899; Fax: 901-942-9383; {www.workplacesolutions.org/about/ywca.cfm}.

Women Work!
Women Work! is a state affiliate of the national membership organization dedicated to helping women from diverse backgrounds achieve economic self-sufficiency through job readiness, education, training and employment. Contact Tennessee Women Work!, LaSherrie McKinnie, President, West Tennessee Area Health Education Center, 295 S. Belle View, Memphis, TN 38104; 901-274-9009.

Help For Single Parents and Others
Shelby State Community College has a New Horizons Program that can help in a number of ways. They conduct workshops on job training, interviewing techniques, stress management, and coping with single parenting. They offer career planning as well as information and referral to job training. They can assist you in preparing for college entrance tests and/or in applying for and obtaining Pell Grants for full-time student enrollment. They even provide a stipend for child care or transportation for those who qualify. For more information, contact Shelby State Community College New Horizons Program, Brenda Smith, Director, Building F, Room 309, 737 Beale St., P.O. Box 40568, Memphis, TN 38174-0568; 901-544-5063; Fax: 901-544-5480; {www.jericho.org/_sscc_nh.html}.

Business Training for Low Income People
The Jubilee Project provides small business training with emphasis on low-income clients. A mentoring program and business development is part of the training. They also market local handcrafts and other businesses, promote youth development, community service education, and more. For more information on how they can help you, contact Jubilee Project, P.O. Box 657, Sneedville, TN 37869; 423-733-4195.

Help for Disadvantaged Workers
This program is open to economically disadvantaged adults and youth and workers that have been laid-off. They can receive employment and training services to ensure productive employment. Supportive services such as transportation and child are provided during training. For more information, contact Middle Tennessee Career Center, 621 Mainstreet Drive, Suite 20, Nashville, TN 37228; 615-862-8890; Fax: 615-862-8910.

Training for Inner City People
Bethlehem Centers of Nashville has several programs available for inner-city residents. They include job training and adult literacy programs. They want to improve the skills of the clients so they will be able to find permanent employment. For more information, contact Bethlehem Center of Nashville, 1417 Charlotte Avenue, Nashville, TN 37203; 615-329-3386; Fax: 615-329-0261.

Preparing Minority Youths for Business
INROADS develops and places young minority people in business and industry to prepare them for corporate and community leadership. They do this through training and development, including professional exposure. The organization works closely with corporate sponsors in order to place seniors after graduation from the program. For more information, contact INROADS of Nashville, Inc., First American Center, 12th Floor, 315 Deadrick Street, Box 97, Nashville, TN 37238; 615-255-7397; Fax: 615-255-1838.

Help To Become Sufficient
The goal of the Food Stamps-Employment and Training program is to provide a bridge from dependency to self-sufficiency. Life skills training and career preparation assistance is provided to accomplish this goal. There are a number of opportunities for the participants to prepare for employment. Assessment and Employment Plan is an

analysis of the clients skills, education, and interests. The Program Component Opportunities is made up of things such as job placement/supervised, Job Success Clinic, vocational/technical education, workforce training, and more. For more information, contact the Division of Employment and Workforce Development, Department of Labor and Workforce Development, Andrew Johnson Tower, 8th Floor, 710 James Robertson Parkway, Nashville, TN 37243-0655; 615-741-6642; Fax: 615-741-5078; {www.state.tn.us/labor-wfd/empwfd.html}; {Email: lkelley@mail.state.tn.us}.

Texas

One-Stop Career Centers
A network of One-Stop Career Centers throughout the state offers a wide range of employment related services including job training. Services vary by location. To find a location near you, please refer to the website {www.twc.state.tx.us}. To learn more about the services they offer, contact your state coordinator.

Ms. Ruth Burrell, One-Stop Project Director, Texas Workforce Commission, 101 E. 15th Street, Room 526T, Austin, TX 78201; 512-463-6438; Fax: 512-463-8547; {Email: ruth.burrell@twc.state.tx.us}.

Job Service Offices
A system of Employment Service/Job Service offices is located within every state with the goal of assisting millions of job seekers and employers. While services may vary from location to location, many provide job training, skills assessment and related services. With approximately 1,800 Employment Service/Job Service offices nationwide there is bound to be one near you. To learn more about the services offered in your area, contact your state administrator. Mike Sheridan, Acting Executive Director, Texas Workforce Commission, 101 E. 15th St., Austin, TX 78778; 512-475-2216; Fax: 512-475-1133; {www.twc.state.tx.us}.

Assistance For Women Business Owners
The Texas Center for Women's Business Enterprise is a public/private initiative dedicated to the entrepreneurial success of Texas women. If you are thinking about starting a business or already own one and would like to expand it, TxCWBE can help you. As a member of this new generation of entrepreneurial women, they will prepare you for business success by dealing with topics including: certification information; Internet training for small businesses; business plans; loan assistance referral program; women's construction network; and consortium and contributing partners. Conveniently located in the capital city, TxCWBE has served Texas women for over 11 years. In 1996, Texas ranked 2nd out of the 50 states with 552,000 women-owned businesses, employing over 1 million people and generating $129.6 billion in sales. In addition to providing current training for today's businesses, the TxCWBE has also assisted in capitalizing women-owned businesses with $13 million in bank loans. For more information, contact Texas Center for Women's Business Enterprise (TXCWBE), Susan Spencer, Executive Director and Contract Administrator, Michele Pettes, Senior Advisor/Trainer, Joy Williamson, Training Assistant, 300 Cheyenne, Killeen, TX 76543; 254-200-2003; Fax: 254-200-2002 or 4100 Ed Blustien Drive, Austin, TX 78721; 512-472-8522; Fax: 512-472-8513; {www.txcwbe.org}; {Email: info@txcwbe.org}.

Christian Job Training
Mission Waco offers the Wings Job Training Program. In their words, "Mission Waco has long acknowledged the importance of helping the poor secure jobs as part of its ministry toward Christian discipleship. Dealing with the root causes of poverty requires serious involvement in the marketplace. Due to years of welfare entrapment and a lost work ethic, many of the poor became dependent on a system which stole their personal pride and responsibility. Now, through various changes, those who can work are returning to the community to find work. But for many, basic job getting and keeping skills are difficult. With "Wings", there is the freedom to "fly" from the nest of that cycle." For more information, contact Mark Pearson & Matt Sciba, Mission Waco, 628 N.15th Street, Waco, TX 76707; 254-753-4900; {www.missionwaco.org/}.

Training For Low-Income People

The Center for Employment Training (CET) is a private, non-profit, community based organization that provides quality employment training for those who need it most. They offer you extensive life skills and workplace know-how instruction through a program that includes job preparedness training, job development and placement. CET keeps students in training until they are placed and conducts follow-up on all placement to ensure stable employment and job growth. CET's primary activity is classroom skill training, which is provided year-round. CET does not screen applicants through testing, but accepts anyone who is willing to do the necessary work. Courses are offered on an open-entry, open-exit basis and students complete training at their own pace. CET training is intensive, with students attending 5 days and 35 to 40 hours per week for an average of seven months. CET training is competency based, highly individualized, and hands-on from day one. The average training course at CET maintains a 20-1 student/teacher ratio. CET's unique mode of training involves an integration of skill training, basic skills instruction and human development conducted in a simulated work setting. At least twenty-five job training options are offered at CET nationwide. These include automated office skills, building maintenance, electronic assembly, medical assistant, truck driving, and shipping/receiving. Skill offerings vary from one center to another. A typical CET center offers 4-5 skills and may serve up to 250 persons annually. For more information, contact their national headquarters: CET Corporate Offices, 701 Vine St., San Jose, CA 95110; 408-287-7924; 800-533-2519; {www.cet2000.org}; {Email: s_avila@cetmail.cfet.org }.

Center for Employment Training, 10102 North Loop Dr., Socorro, TX 79927; 915-859-1070; Fax: 915-860-9089; {Email: s_avila@cetmail. cfet.org}.

Learn About Procurement and More

The North Texas Women's Business Development Center, Inc. (NTWBDC) is a collective effort of the National Association of Women Business Owners (NAWBO), the Greater Dallas Chamber of Commerce Women's Business Issues Division, the North Texas Women's Business Council, and the Bill Priest Institute for Economic Development. One area of focus is women's government contracting opportunities in addition to long-term training, counseling and mentoring. North Texas Women's Business Development Center Inc. For more information, contact North Texas Women's Business Development Center Inc., Branda Williams, Technical Counseling and Programs, Bill J. Priest Institute for Economic Development, 1402 Corinth Street, Suite 1536, Dallas, TX 75215-2111; 214-428-1177; Fax: 214-428-4633; {Email: women@onramp.net}.

Women Work!

Women Work! is a state affiliate of the national membership organization dedicated to helping women from diverse backgrounds achieve economic self-sufficiency through job readiness, education, training and employment. Contact Texas Women Work!, Judy Jackson, President, Counseling and Career Services, NE Texas Community College, P.O. Box 1307, Mt. Pleasant, TX 75456; 903-572-1911, ext. 205; Fax: 903-572-6712; {Email: jjackson@ntcc.cc.tx.us}.

Help For Displaced Homemakers and Single Parents

The Richland College Working Wonders Program is designed to prepare and support single parents/displaced homemakers in preparing for new careers. You too can have an exciting new career! Are you a single parent or displaced homemaker in transition looking for change? You'd like a new career with opportunities, but, you say, "I haven't worked in years," "I have no skills," "I can't afford to go back to school," and "What about the kids?" The Working Wonders Program is here to help you meet the challenges of entering or re-entering the workforce by providing you with the support and encouragement you need to get started and succeed. Services provided include: enrollment/registration assistance; academic advising; financial aid assistance; crisis intervention; personal counseling; community referrals; career exploration; textbook loans; child care referrals; and more. For more information, please contact Carol Castillo, Coordinator at 972-238-6972, room C157. Mailing address: Richland College, Adult Resource Center, Dallas County Community College District, 12800 Abrams Road, Dallas, TX 75243-2199; 972-238-6106; {www.rlc.dcccd.edu/ce/ARC/WorkWon.html}.

Community College Program

Single Parent / Displaced Homemaker Services at McLennan Community College can provide you with special services to help you achieve your goals at MCC. Services include counseling, mentoring, funds to assist with child care or transportation, and community referral service. For more information, contact McLennan Community College, Career Development Office, 1400 College Drive, Waco, TX 76708; 254-299-8614; 254-299-8414; {http://mccweb.mcc.cc.tx.us/students/career/single.html}.

Apprenticeship Training

Apprenticeship Training is a combination of on-the-job training with a journey worker and classroom education which prepares an apprentice for an occupation in a skilled trade and craft. Some of the occupations registered with the Texas Bureau of Apprenticeship and Training are, bricklayer, carpenter, operating engineer, pipefitter, plumber and die maker. The variety of available occupations depends on the local industry needs. Classes on such things as safety, blueprint reading, and mathematics, generally meet from 3-6 hours a week. After completion of the program, workers can expect to maintain good employment with good pay. Contact the Bureau of Apprenticeship and Training, Texas Workforce Commission, 101 East 15th Street, Austin, TX 78778; 512-463-9767; {www.twc.state.tx.us/svcs/apprentice.html}.

Help For Members of the Community in Need

Charitable Choice, Faith Based and Community Based Services was established to coordinate workforce development services between local workforce development boards, faith based, and community based organizations to benefit needy people in communities. Organizations submit their information by geographic area so they individual can find training or other services suited to their needs. The services available may include, job-skills training, GED, counseling services, job-readiness and job search. The organizations contact information and details on their programs are listed. To search the board, go to www.twc.state.tx.us/svcs/charchoice/chchoice.html. Texas Workforce Commission, Workforce Development Division, Charitable Choice, 101 East 15th Street, Austin, TX 78778; 512-463-2222.

Training for the Disabled

This program helps work-injured citizens in returning to work. It offers training to learn job skills in trade school, college, university, on the job, or at home. Training to learn appropriate work behaviors and other skills to find and keep jobs to satisfy employer expectations is also taught. They will offer job placement assistance compatible with the clients physical and/or mental ability. Eligible disabilities are; mental illness, hearing impairment, impaired function of arms or legs, back injury, alcoholism or drug addiction, mental retardation, learning disability, traumatic brain injury, and other physical or mental disabilities. To locate an office nearest to you, call 800-628-5115. Texas Rehabilitation Commission, 4900 North Lamar Boulevard, Austin, TX 78751; 512-424-4000 (general info); {www.rehab.state.tx.us/services.html}.

Help for Veterans

There are two programs available that offer training assistance to veterans in Texas. The On-The-Job Training Program, and the Apprenticeship Program for Veterans. For a list of organizations that have been approved to train veteran students, check out these web sites; Apprenticeship: {www.twc.state.tx.us/svcs/vetsvcs/tsaa/vaap.html} and On-The-Job: {www.twc.state.tx.us/svcs/vetsvcs/tsaa/vaoj.html}. Texas Workforce Commission, 101 East 15th Street, Austin, TX 78778; 512-463-2814.

Utah

One-Stop Career Centers

A network of One-Stop Career Centers throughout the state offers a wide range of employment related services including job training. Services vary by location. To find a location near you, please refer to the website {www.dws.state.ut.us}. To learn more about the services they offer, contact your state coordinator.

Mr. James Whitaker, One-Stop Coordinator, Utah Department of Workforce Services, P.O. Box 45249, Salt Lake City, UT 84145; 801-526-WORK (9675); Fax: 801-536-7420; {Email: wscfam.jwhitak@state. ut.us}.

Job Service Offices
A system of Employment Service/Job Service offices is located within every state with the goal of assisting millions of job seekers and employers. While services may vary from location to location, many provide job training, skills assessment and related services. With approximately 1,800 Employment Service/Job Service offices nationwide there is bound to be one near you. To learn more about the services offered in your area, contact your state administrator.

Robert C. Gross, Executive Director, Department of Workforce Services, 140 East 300 South P.O. Box 45249, Salt Lake City, UT 84145; 801-526-WORK (9675); Fax: 801-536-7420; {www.dws.state.ut.us}.

Curtis Johnson, Administrator, Department of Employment Security, 140 East 300 South, P.O. Box 45249, Salt Lake City, UT 84145-0249; 801-536-7401; Fax: 801-536-7420.

Training for Women Business Owners
You can receive training to help you establish or expand your business in a program established by the Utah Technology Finance Corporation (UTFC) dubbed the Utah Office of Women's Business Ownership. Training is available both in Salt Lake City and in outlying areas of the state. In addition, they maintain a database of women business owners in the state of Utah. UTFC administers the SBA microloan program for Utah. For more information or to locate a service provider near you, contact Utah Technology Finance Corporation, Kathy Thompson, 177 East 100 South, Salt Lake City, UT 84111; 801-364-1521, ext. 3; Fax: 801-364-4361.

High Tech Business Center
The Women's Business Center at the Chamber supports the success of women and men business owners throughout Utah with counseling, training and loan packaging assistance. With more than 30 committees and task forces, the Chamber provides you with unique networking opportunities as well as a full service export assistance program. Their onsite high-tech center offers access to the Internet and all types of business software. Women business owners can access help with marketing, management, finance and procurement. There is a modest fee for some services, but scholarships and specialized training are available for socially or economically disadvantaged women. Contact the Women's Business Center at the Chamber, Salt Lake Area Chamber of Commerce, Ramona Rudert, Director, 175 East 400 South, Suite 600, Salt Lake City, UT 84111; 801-328-5051; Fax: 801-328-5098; {www.saltlakechamber.org/chamber_info/womans_business/index.htm}; {Email: ramona@slachamber.com}.

Short-Term Intensive Training
In today's job market, technical skills are critical to both new and experienced workers. Mountainland Applied Technology Center short-term, non-credit, competency based training is important to adults preparing for competitive jobs in the Mountainland region communities. This program offers you training in a wide variety of employable skills including: accounting, basic office skills, boiler operation & maintenance, building construction, certified nurse aide, commercial drivers license, computer programming, computer repair, computer training, critical work skills, customer service, data entry, dispatch academy, electrical repair/maintenance, electronic assembly, emission failure diagnosis & repair, entrepreneurship, first aide and CPR, flagging, forklift safety, home health aide, home health aide for certified nurse aides, Internet, major appliance repair, medical terminology, coding and insurance billing, network management, pilot/escort certification, small business tax education, speedbuilding, statistical process control and quality management, typing/keyboarding, and vehicle safety inspection. For more information, contact Information, Utah Valley State College, 9875 South Geneva Road, Office MT-203, Orem, UT 84058; 801-764-7528; {www.uvsc.edu/matc}; {Email: info@uvsc.edu}.

Help for Laid Off Workers
The Dislocated Worker Program offers employment and training for workers that have lost their jobs because of economic conditions. That includes workers from plants that have been closed or had mass layoffs, long-term unemployed workers, and some formerly self-employed people, including ranchers and displaced homemakers. For

more information, contact your nearest Employment Center or the Department of Workforce Services, P.O. Box 45249, Salt Lake City, UT 84145; 801-526-9675; {www.dws.state.ut.us/JS/Special Programs/dislocat.htm}; {Email: www@dwsa.state.ut.us}.

Training for Older Workers
The Older Worker Program or the Green Thumb Program have part time employment and training opportunities for people 55 years or older that meet income requirement. For more information, contact your nearest Employment Center or the Department of Workforce Services, P.O. Box 45249, Salt Lake City, UT 84145; 801-526-9675; {www.dws.state.ut.us/JS/SpecialPrograms/oworker.htm}; {Email: www@dwsa.state.ut.us}.

Youth Employment and Training Programs
Youth Employment and Training Programs are designed to help students earn money and stay in school through part-time and summer employment. There are age and income requirements that vary sponsor to sponsor. For more information, contact your nearest Employment Center or the Department of Workforce Services, P.O. Box 45249, Salt Lake City, UT 84145; 801-526-9675; {www.dws.state.ut.us/JS/SpecialPrograms/youth.htm}; {Email: www@dwsa.state.ut.us}.

Trade Adjustment Assistance
The Trade Adjustment Assistance is an employment and training program that helps workers that have lost their jobs because of America's foreign trade policy. For more information, contact your nearest Employment Center or the Department of Workforce Services, P.O. Box 45249, Salt Lake City, UT 84145; 801-526-9675; {www.dws.state.ut.us/JS/SpecialPrograms/trade.htm}; {Email: www@dwsa.state.ut.us}.

Vermont

One-Stop Career Centers
A network of One-Stop Career Centers throughout the state offers a wide range of employment related services including job training. Services vary by location. To find a location near you, please refer to the website {www.det.state.vt.us/miscfile/distofc.htm}. To learn more about the services they offer, contact your state coordinator.

Mr. Robert Ware, Director of Jobs & Training, Department of Employment & Training, 5 Green Mountain Drive, P.O. Box 488, Montpelier, VT 05602; 802-828-4151; Fax: 802-828-4374; {www.det.state.vt.us}; {Email: bware@pop.det.state.vt.us}.

Job Service Offices
A system of Employment Service/Job Service offices is located within every state with the goal of assisting millions of job seekers and employers. While services may vary from location to location, many provide job training, skills assessment and related services. With approximately 1,800 Employment Service/Job Service offices nationwide there is bound to be one near you. To learn more about the services offered in your area, contact your state administrator. Susan D. Auld, Commissioner, Department of Employment & Training, P.O. Box 88, Montpelier, VT 05601-0488; 802-828-4300; Fax: 802-828-4022.

Training For New And Existing Women Business Owners
The Women's Small Business Program offers a continuum of services to women seeking to identify, start, stabilize and expand a small business. You could benefit from services that include: Getting Serious, a workshop to determine a business idea and whether business meets personal goals; Start-Up, a 15 week intensive course to develop a business plan and business management skills; Working Solution, topic specific workshops for micro-business owner; and a graduate association to foster ongoing networking and access to information. They also offer comprehensive skills training and the opportunity to connect with other women entrepreneurs. Grants and scholarships for training are available to income eligible women. For more information, contact Women's Small Business Program, Trinity College, 208 Colchester Avenue, Burlington, VT 05401; 802-846-7160; TDD: 802-860-

1428, or the Women's Agricultural Network, 590 Main Street, UVM, Burlington, VT 05405-0059; 802-656-3276 ; 800-435-5634 (VT); {www.thinkvermont.com/business/workforce/smb.shtml}.

Entrepreneurial Training
Northeast Employment and Training Program was incorporated in 1978 as a non-profit agency for the purpose of delivering educational and charitable programs to low-income Vermonters. One of their offerings is the Vermont Entrepreneurial Training Program, a classroom-training program providing an in-depth look at starting and operating a business. It is taught over Vermont Interactive Television and in individual classrooms. The program is regularly scheduled in September, January and April, but can and will be taught on demand. The program is divided into modules of which students may take all or any one. The cost of individual modules range from $25 to $200. The course information is project based along the creation of a business plan. Students are not graded on work performance but do a self analysis of learning. For more information, contact Northeast Employment and Training Program, P.O. Box 186, Johnsbury, VT 05819-0186; 802-748-8935; Fax: 802-748-8936; {www.vt-neto.org/index.html}.

Training Assistance for Welfare Recipients
Reach Up is a program in Vermont's welfare-to-work program. It offers access to education, vocational training, and job placement for welfare recipients. It also administers the Community Service Employment Program which provides participants temporary subsidized work placements to public and non-profit organizations. For more information, contact Reach Up, Department of Social Welfare, 103 South Main Street, Waterbury, VT 05676; 802-241-2800; Fax: 802-241-2830; {www.thinkvermont.com/business/workforce/reach_up.shtml}.

Assistance for Micro-Business Owners
The Micro Business Development Program has a goal to promote self-employment and business expansion opportunities for low-income residents. They achieve this through free, one-to-one technical assistance and business development workshops. Their specialists work in the regional Community Action Program agencies and in conjunction with each of the five regional Job Start Regional Loan Review Boards. For more information, contact one of the CAP agencies in your area.

- Central Vermont Community Action Council, Inc., P.O. Box 747, Barre, VT 05641; 800-639-1053
- Champlain Valley Office of Economic Opportunity, Inc., P.O. Box 1603, Burlington, VT 05402; 800-287-7971
- Bennington-Rutland Opportunity Council, Inc., 60 Center Street, Rutland, VT 05701; 800-717-2762
- Northeast Kingdom Community Action Council, Inc., P.O. Box 346, Newport, VT 05855; 800-639-4065
- Southeastern Vermont Community Action Council, Inc., 18 Bridge Street, P.O. Box 369, Bellow Falls, VT 05101; 800-464-9951

Training for Apprenticeship
Currently there are over 800 trades approved for apprenticeship training. These areas include, construction, manufacturing, communication, public utilities, wholesale and retail finance, insurance and public administration. The Apprenticeship Program includes on-the-job training and classroom teaching so that the apprentice can learn the theoretical and practical aspects of the job. New apprentices earn 50% of the journey wages and at the end of their training, will generally earn 90-95% of the journey worker wage. For more information, contact the Department of Employment and Training, Jobs Training Division, 5 Green Mountain Drive, P.O. Box 488, Montpelier, VT 05601-0488; 802-828-5082; {www.thinkvermont.com/busines/workforce/apprentice.shtml}; {Email: Apprentice@mail.det.state.vt.us}.

Apprenticeship Training for Students
The Student Apprenticeship program is for student s16 years and older that combines on-the-job training with classroom instruction. The student spends most of their educational time on a job-site working under his/her mentor. The school provides the courses that supplement the curriculum and the student gets paid. There are currently 31 approved curriculum in the following areas; video production, precision machine technology, diesel technician, automotive customer service trainee, building maintenance, marine/recreational vehicle technology, printing computer graphics, and much more. To learn more, contact the Department of Education, 120 State Street, Montpelier, VT 05620-2501; 802-828-3131; {www.thinkvermont.com/business/workforce/literacy.shtml}.

Virginia

One-Stop Career Centers

A network of One-Stop Career Centers throughout the state offers a wide range of employment related services including job training. Services vary by location. To find a location near you, please refer to the website {www.careerconnect.state.va.us/oscenters.htm}. To learn more about the services they offer, contact your state coordinator.

Dr. William L. Carlson, Governor's Employment and Training Department, Seventh and Franklin Building, 701 East Franklin Street, 10th Floor, Richmond, VA 23219; 804-786-2270; Fax: 804-786-2340; {Email: wlc@richmond.infi.net}.

Job Service Offices

A system of Employment Service/Job Service offices is located within every state with the goal of assisting millions of job seekers and employers. While services may vary from location to location, many provide job training, skills assessment and related services. With approximately 1,800 Employment Service/Job Service offices nationwide there is bound to be one near you. To learn more about the services offered in your area, contact your state administrator. Dr. Thomas J. Towberman, Commissioner, VA Employment Commission, 703 East Main Street, Richmond, VA 23219; 804-786-3001; Fax: 804-225-3923; {www.vec.state.va.us}.

Financial Assistance For Job Training

If you need more job skills to become self-sufficient or to make it in this job market, then the Piedmont Works Education for Independence Program may be able to help you. They can provide you with financial assistance for tuition and books as well as child care and transportation reimbursements while you attend school or job training. Eligible persons are 22 years or older, single parents, displaced homemakers, or single pregnant women. Participants typically attend PVCC, CATEC or local adult education programs with the goal of obtaining a GED, Career Studies Certificate, or an Associate of Applied Science degree. Making decisions about your career that will affect your family and your future can be confusing and overwhelming. They can help you set goals and make a plan of action through a variety of services including the following listings.

- Career Exploration for Women - This is a special one credit Student Development course at PVCC designed especially for your needs. Examine your interests, abilities, circumstances, and needs in the context of the job market, available training programs, and non-traditional career opportunities. Personal and Career Counseling; Gender Equity Education; Tuition Assistance; Textbooks and Class Materials; GED Preparation.

- Training on the Job - Provides information to help you find internships, cooperative education placements and work-study jobs, volunteer and work experience opportunities in the community to learn skills outside the classroom; Professional Development; Job Search Assistance; Child care - The Education for Independence Program can assist with child care expenses while you attend school; Transportation - Education for Independence can assist with transportation expenses so that you can attend school; Tutoring and Study Skills; Information and Referral; Career Development.

They have two locations to serve you:

PVCC, 501 College Drive, Room 206, Charlottesville, VA 22902; 804-961-5228; Fax: 804-961-5224.

FOCUS, 1508 Grady Avenue, Charlottesville, VA 22903; 804-977-5627; 804-977-2662; Fax: 804-977-3495; {piedmontworks.org/independ.htm}; {Email: bgibson@pvcc.cc.va.us}.

Training for Those Under 22

Teensight offers a variety of services for men and women under the age of 22. All assistance and services are provided free of charge. The Teensight program is part of Focus: A Women's Resource Center, a non-profit organization. Teensight is composed of several programs. Each of these programs works to overlap with the others. The mission of Teensight is to offer a holistic, complete and comprehensive service for the young adults in their area. For more information, find the location nearest you from the list below or contact Teensight, 1508 Grady Avenue, Charlottesville, VA 22903; 804-295-8336; Fax: 804-295-8336; {http://monticello.avenue.gen.va.us/Community/ Agencies/Teensight/home.html}.

The following Teensight regions offer job training

- Region IX - For men and women (teens or older) who reside in the counties of Orange, Culpeper, Madison, Fauquier or Rappanhannock, Teensight provides employment assistance free of charge to those that qualify. Employment assistance includes Pre-Employment and Work Maturity training, employment skills training, job development, and employment placement assistance. Teensight can provide financial assistance for tuition, child care, transportation, and other items on a needs-based basis. For more information, please call Teensight Plus, 634 Schoolhouse Rd., Madison, VA 22727; 540-948-3562.

- Region X - Teensight can provide employment assistance for men and women under the age of 22 who reside in the City of Charlottesville, or in the counties of Albemarle, Greene, Fluvanna, Louisa or Nelson, as long as they qualify under federal guidelines. Employment assistance includes Pre-Employment and Work Maturity training, employment skills training, job development, and employment placement assistance. Teensight can provide financial assistance for tuition, child care, transportation, and other items on a needs-based basis. For more information, please call Teensight, 1508 Grady Avenue, Charlottesville, VA 22903; 804-295-8336; Fax: 804-295-8336.

Training For Low-Income Adult Women

The Center for Employment Training (CET) is a private, non-profit, community based organization that provides  quality employment training for low-income adult women who need it most. They offer you extensive life skills and workplace know-how instruction through a program that includes job preparedness training, job development and placement. CET keeps students in training until they are placed and conducts follow-up on all placements to ensure stable employment and job growth. CET's primary activity is classroom skill training, which is provided year-round. CET does not screen applicants through testing, but accepts anyone who is willing to do the necessary work. Courses are offered on an open-entry, open-exit basis and students complete training at their own pace. CET training is intensive, with students attending 5 days and 35 to 40 hours per week for an average of seven months. CET training is competency based, highly individualized, and hands-on from day one. The average training course at CET maintains a 20-1 student/teacher ratio. CET's unique mode of training involves an integration of skill training, basic skill instruction and human development conducted in a simulated work setting. At least twenty-five job training options are offered at CET nationwide. These include automated office skills, building maintenance, electronic assembly, medical assistant, truck driving, and shipping/receiving. Skill offerings vary from one center to another. A typical CET center offers 4-5 skills and may serve up to 250 persons annually. For more information, contact their national headquarters: CET Corporate Offices, 701 Vine St., San Jose, CA 95110; 408-287-7924; 800-533-2519; {www.best.com/~cfet/main.htm}; {Email: cfet@best.com}.

Center for Employment Training, 2762 Duke St., Alexandria, VA 22314; 703-461-9767 Fax: 703-461-9761 {Email: d_jroosa@cetmail. cfet.org}.

Work In Politics

If you are a young Republican woman who is interested in the political process, this program could provide you with some valuable experience when you enter the workforce. The Dorothy Andrews Kabis Memorial Internship is a program offered to four undergraduate women each year. The interns have a one-month experience at NFRW headquarters in Alexandria, VA, and they are housed at Georgetown University. No monetary allowance is given, but round trip airfare is provided. Applicants must be 21 years of age or older, and should have a general knowledge of government, a keen interest in Republican politics, campaign experience, as well as some clerical office skills.

For more information, contact National Federation Of Republican Women, 124 North Alfred Street, Alexandria, VA 22314; 703-548-9688; Fax: 703-548-9836; {www.nfrw.org/programs/internships.htm}; {Email: mail@NFRW.org}.

Job Training For The Economically Disadvantaged
The Job Training Agency provides help with job training and employment. Eligible job seekers must be economically disadvantaged. For more information, contact Job Training Agency, 102 Heritage Way, NE, Suite 202, Leesburg, VA 22075; 703-777-0540.

Training Help for Workers over 55
The Senior Community Service Employment Program provides training and placement to low-income individuals that are 55 years or older and that are unemployed, or have poor employment prospects. The services they offer are job search assistance, supportive services, skill training, literacy training or other training that is needed to prepare the worker for a job. The participants generally work a 20 hour work week for a private or public non-profit organization which is a stepping stone to private employment. For more information, contact Pat Cummins, The Governor's Employment and Training Department, Seventh and Franklin Building, 701 East Franklin Street, 10th Floor, Richmond, VA 23219;804-786-2295; {www.cns.state.va.us/getd}; {Email: pwcummings.getd@state.va.us}.

Assistance for Young Adults
The Opportunity Knocks program is aimed at adults aged 18-25 that are economically disadvantaged, unemployed, low achieving, or school dropouts. They become members of a crew which teaches them to interact with others in a positive and constructive way. The key elements of this program are supportive services, work experience, morning calisthenics, assessments, vocational skills and academic training, life-skills training, volunteer activities, post program job placement with benefits and follow-up services. Some of the work experience and volunteer activities are made up of: repairing playgrounds, low income and elderly housing, providing staff assistance to homeless and battered women shelters, nursing homes and other places in need; maintenance services of water treatment plants, parks, and other places; and volunteer services for meals on wheels, fire departments, and other projects. For more information, contact Faye Palmer, The Governor's Employment and Training Department, Seventh and Franklin Building, 701 East Franklin Street, 10th Floor, Richmond, VA 23219; 804-786-2299; {Email: afpalmer.getd@state.va.us}.

Aid for Economically Disadvantaged People
The Economic and Employment Improvement Program for Disadvantaged Persons is made up of different projects that aim to improve employability and provide assistance to disadvantaged people by education and skills training. Contact Faye Palmer, The Governor's Employment and Training Department, Seventh and Franklin Building, 701 East Franklin Street, 10th Floor, Richmond, VA 23219; 804-786-2299; {Email: afpalmer.getd@state.va.us}.

Bainbridge Blackwell Community Development Corporation. The program provides services to disadvantaged, chronically unemployed, underemployed, and transitioning residents of Richmond. Special emphasis is placed on the African-American male population. It offers an attitudinal/motivational workshop, job development/placement, one-stop center, speakers bureau, and business round table.

Danville Community College offers a program that recruits 15 African-American males, ages 25-29, that are unemployed and in need of training. Individual vocational plans are developed for each person.. Basic and GED training and general maintenance tech training are also provided. They offer job placement services with follow-up visits.

Greater Peninsula Private Industry Council provides on-the-job training for African-American men, ages 18-35, that have recently been released from jail. The program teaches the participants in-demand skills which will improve their employability.

New Visions, New Ventures, Inc. provides micro-enterprise training, counseling and instruction on credit worthiness and bankability, and mentoring to female prison inmates during the year before their release. This process may begin with entry into a job that is similar to the self-employment goal, or an employment arrangement that can lead to a purchase agreement in the future.

Training for Youths

The Summer Youth Employment and Training Institute is a week long event on education continuation, and/or starting a career. It is for youths ages 14-18 that come from economically disadvantaged families or are in foster care. During the week, students will attend seminars, education and business fairs, workshops and plan development sessions so they will be able to write their own plan of action. The best plan of each group receives a $50 prize and can go on to compete for a scholarship. Participants also engage in social activities, a talent show, and a tour of the area. All of these things will provide them with experiences that will benefit them when they pursue their employment goal. For more information, contact Abria M. Singleton at 804-786-2409; {Email: Amsingleton.getd@state.va.us} or Raymond C. Cousins at 804-786-2409; {Email: rccousins.getd@state.va.us}; The Governor's Employment and Training Department, Seventh and Franklin Building, 701 East Franklin Street, 10th Floor, Richmond, VA 23219.

Job Training Programs For Low Income People

The Northern Virginia Family Service has two job training programs for low income people. They enable the participants to move from low wages or unstable employment, to stable professional work that gives them benefits and opportunities for advancement.

Training Futures is a 21-week clerical training program that is based in a simulated office environment. It is the program's goal to meet the needs of Northern Virginia employers looking for qualified clerical workers, and to help unemployed or underemployed people obtain quality jobs. This is accomplished by teaching computer skills, business math, business English, keyboarding, 10 key calculator, filing, customer service and job search skills. Participants also intern at local businesses.

CTOP-Construction Training Opportunities Program is a 10 week training course in one skill that is currently needed by the construction industry. Some examples of skills that are taught are sprinkler repair, electrical wiring or masonry. The first week of training is classroom instruction, after that construction companies pay the trainees to work Monday through Thursday. On Fridays and Saturdays training is taken into the classroom. During the 10 weeks, comprehensive support is given to ensure completion of training and job retention. An additional 10 weeks of case management is given after graduation. For more information, contact the main office at 100 North Washington Street, #400, Falls Church, VA 22046; 703-533-9727.

Training for TANF Recipients

Greater Richmond Employment Assistance Team has a 3 week, 80 hour job readiness course for recipients of TANF that are referred by their counselor. The focus is on self-esteem , workplace behavior, and everyday life skills. The Job Placement Center matches candidates with employers. For more information speak to your TANF counselor or contact the Job Placement Center, 4501 Williamsburg Road, Richmond, VA 23231; 804-222-0400.

Washington

One-Stop Career Centers

A network of One-Stop Career Centers throughout the state offers a wide range of employment related services including job training. Services vary by location. To find a location near you, please refer to the website {www.wa.gov/esd/1stop}. To learn more about the services they offer, contact your state coordinator.

Paul Trause, Deputy Assistant Commissioner, Washington State Employment Security Department, 605 Woodland Square Loop, P.O. Box 9046 MS/6000, Olympia, WA 98507-9046; 360-438-4123, Fax: 360-438-3173; {Email: ptrause@esd.wa.gov}.

Peggy Zimmerman, WorkSource Implementation Executive Director, Washington State Employment Security Department, 605 Woodland Square Loop, P.O. Box 9046 MS/600, Olympia, WA 98507-9046; 360-438-3258; Fax 360-438-4041; {Email: pzimmerman@esd.wa.gov}.

Job Service Offices

A system of Employment Service/Job Service offices is located within every state with the goal of assisting millions of job seekers and employers. While services may vary from location to location, many provide job-training, skills assessment and related services. With approximately 1,800 Employment Service/Job Service offices nationwide there is bound to be one near you. To learn more about the services offered in your area, contact your state administrator. Carver C. Gayton, Commissioner, Employment Security Department, P.O. Box 9046, Olympia, WA 98507-9046; 360-902-9301; Fax: 360-902-9383; {www.wa.gov/esd/AgencyInfo/directoies/jsclist.htm}.

Training Assistance For Women and Minority Business Owners

You can access resources and technical assistance to start or expand your business through the Minority & Women Business Development program. MWBD can provide you with entrepreneurial training, contract opportunities, bonding assistance, export assistance, and access to capital for start-ups or expanding businesses in the minority and women's business community. For more information, contact Minority & Women's Business, 406 Water St. SW, Olympia, WA 98501-1047; 360-753-9693 or Community Trade & Economic Development, 906 Columbia St. SW, Olympia, WA 98501-1216; 360-753-4900; {http://edd-dev.cted.wa.gov/bac/mwbd}.

Business Assistance For Native Americans and Others

ONABEN - A Native American Business Network, is a non-profit public benefit corporation created by Northwest Indian Tribes to increase the number and profitability of private enterprises owned by Native Americans. ONABEN offers training, individual counseling, assisted access to markets and facilitated access to capital for its clients. The 4 tribes hosting an ONABEN Service Center pays annual dues of $2,500 and serves 5 of the 9 federally recognized tribes in Oklahoma. The sites, located on reservations in Oregon, Washington and California, deliver services to all citizens regardless of tribal affiliation. Some have up to 40% of users coming from the surrounding non-Native community. For more information, contact ONABEN - A Native American Business Network, Tom Hampson, OWBO Coordinator, 3201 Broadway, Suite C, Everett, WA 98201; 425-339-6226; Fax: 425-339-9171; {www.onaben.org}; {Email: chinookl@onaben.org}.

Help For Displaced Homemakers

If you have lost your source of support through divorce or the loss of a spouse, you can take advantage of several programs throughout the state designed to help you gain self-sufficiency. These programs are coordinated by the Higher Education Coordinating Board of Washington State/Displaced Homemaker Program whose aim is to provide "real solutions to those who face barriers to education, training, and employment." You can access overall information about these programs at {www.hecb.wa.gov/college/homemaker/#definition} or refer to the list below to locate a service center near you. Specific information is provided wherever it was available.

Displaced Homemaker Program Locations by County

Asotin/Columbia/Garfield

Impact!, Walla Walla Community College/Clarkston Center, 1470 Bridge Street, Clarkston, WA 99403; 509-758-1725, 888-922-1716; Fax: 509-758-9512; {Email: petrova.ruark@po.ww.cc.wa.us}.

Benton/Franklin

Columbia Basin College, 2600 North 20th Avenue, Pasco, WA 99301; 509-547-0511, ext. 2325; Fax: 509-546-0401; {www.cbc2.org/}; {Email: bcasey@cbc2.org}.

Chelan/Douglas

Lifestyles Displaced Homemaker Program, YWCA of Wenatchee Valley, 212 First Street, Wenatchee, WA 98801; 509-662-3531; Fax: 509-665-9394; {Email: ywcawen@televar.com}.

Clark/Wahkiakum

The Southwest Washington Regional Displaced Homemaker Center can give you the tools to get back on your feet and provide for yourself and your family. They have centers open in Clark and Cowlitz counties and offer free services to displaced homemakers who live in the four county region covering Clark, Cowlitz, Skamania and Wahkiakum counties. Information and referrals are provided to local and regional organizations and agencies that can help you during the transition between unemployment and employment. They offer Job Readiness Classes, four-week/60 hour sessions, that address: discovering hidden job skills; dealing with stress, anger, and health issues; how to stretch your current income; legal assistance; learning about the jobs that are available in the area; how to fill out job applications and write resumes; personal and group counseling; support groups; educational advising. One-day outreach workshops are held throughout the four county region to provide information on employment and educational opportunities, building self-esteem, and networking with others in the same situation. For more information, please contact Becky Merritt, Southwest Washington Regional Displaced Homemaker Center, Clark College, 1800 East McLoughlin Blvd., Vancouver, WA 98663; 360-992-2321; 360-992-2366; Fax: 360-992-2849; {www.clark.edu/ StudentServices/StudentSupportServices/Displaced/}; {Email: bmerritt@clark.edu}.

YWCA of Clark County

YWCA of Clark County, 3609 Main St., Vancouver WA 98663-2225; 360-696-0167; Fax: 360-693-1864.

Cowlitz

Lower Columbia College, 1600 Maple Street, P.O .Box 3010, Longview, WA 98632-0310; 360-577-3429; Fax: 360-578-5470; {http://lcc.ctc.edu/programs/wit-dh}; {Email: jarmstro@lcc.ctc.edu}.

Kitsap/Mason

Kitsap/Mason, Displaced Homemaker Program, Olympic College, 1660 Chester Avenue, Bremerton, WA 98310-1699; 360-475-7557; Fax: 360-475-7477; {http://oc.ctc.edu/services/womenprg.shtml}; {Email: jjohnson@oc.ctc.edu}.

Kittitas/Yakima

Yakima Valley Community College, P.O. Box 22520 (16th and Nob Hill), Yakima, WA 98907; 509-574-4993; Fax: 509-574-4731; {www.yvcc.cc.wa.us/}.

Pierce

The Women's Center offers a large range of services to Pierce College students, employees, and community members. Some of those services include: information resources; workshops special events; women's library; women's lounge; support groups; individual counseling; student leadership; scholarship information. The Displaced Homemaker Program is also located in the Women's Center. This program is free and offers 160 hours of classroom instruction, 6 hours of support groups, and 2 hours of individual counseling for eligible displaced homemakers. Workshop exercises and topics include: computer training; aptitude testing; interests testing; career exploration; dependable strengths articulation process; developing a vocational plan; job search skills, resume writing and interviews; putting plans into action. For more information, contact Pierce College Women's Center, Fort Steilacoom Campus, Room 300J, 9401 Farwest Drive SW, Lakewood, WA 98498-1999; 253-964-6298; {www.pierce.ctc.edu/ Users/Depts/Womenctr/main.htm}

Skagit

Northwest Displaced Homemaker Center, Skagit Valley College, 2405 East College Way, Mount Vernon, WA 98273; 360-416-7762; Fax: 360-416-7890.

Snohomish/King

The cornerstone of the Pathways for Women YWCA employment program is their Displaced Homemaker Program, which provides comprehensive instruction and assistance with job placement for women entering or re-entering the workforce. They work creatively with women who are displaced homemakers to ease the transition they must make as they become wholly self-supported. Participants then take part in a comprehensive instruction workshop that allows 58 hours of self-assessment, job readiness training, assistance with career decisions and job placement. During the intensive workshops, women learn how to identify their marketable skills, how to network, and how to access the hidden job market. The women participating in the program also enjoy supportive services through the counseling staff who teach women skills in coping with stress, with anger, and with going through transitions. Also, women can participate in assertiveness training and self-esteem building programs. Contact Pathways for Women YWCA, 6027-208th St. SW, Lynnwood, WA 98036; 425-774-9843, ext. 223; Fax: 425-670-8510; {www. ywcaworks.org/snohomish.html}; {Email: amilling@ywcaworks.org}.

Edmonds Community College Women's Programs offer workshops, support groups, women's studies and agency sponsored groups. Contact Edmonds Community College, 20000 68th Ave. West, Lynnwood, WA 98036-5999; 425-640-1309; Fax: 425-771-3366; {www.edcc.edu/WomensPrograms.htm}.

Swinomish Indian Tribal Community, P.O. Box 388, LaConner, WA 98257; 360-466-1732.

Stevens/Spokane/Whitman
This is a free program that assists displaced homemakers in finding resources, support, and help so they can make informed decisions about their future. Personal counseling, one-day workshops and a pre-employment training program are offered. Programs that build self-esteem, teach coping skills, develop life and career plans, and basic computer training are spotlighted. ChangePoint, Community Colleges of Spokane, 3305 W. Ft. George Wright Drive, Spokane, WA 99224-5228; 509-533-3755/3752; Fax: 509-533-3226; {http://ielhp.spokane.cc.wa.us}, {Email: dhitchens@lodge.spokane.cc.wa.us}.

Whatcom
The Northwest Washington Displaced Homemaker Center has a program called Turning Point that can help you start on the road to discovery. In friendly, supportive surroundings you can explore your personal strengths and interests, and you can learn ways to present your skills to prospective employers. Turning Point is a program of the Northwest Displaced Homemaker Center. It offers free workshops on building self-esteem and assertive communication skills for individuals needing to earn a livable wage. It also offers free classes that help with: career and life planning; personal skills; assessments; job search skills (resume writing and interview techniques); job market trends; and exploring career, training, and employment opportunities. Classes are small and confidential, with numerous opportunities for self-growth. Graduates report long-lasting increases in their self-esteem. The majority of individuals who attend are either working or enrolled in a training program within 60 days of class completion. They represent a wide variety of interests, programs and careers. Contact Turning Point at Whatcom Community College, 237 West Kellogg Road, Bellingham, WA 98226; 360-676-2170, ext. 3416; Fax: 360-676-2171; {www.whatcom.ctc.edu/servs/turning.htm}; {Email: rbailey@ whatcom.ctc.edu}.

Meeting Basic Needs in Seattle
Seattle is blessed with many programs that address job training and career development. Contact any of the service providers listed below for more information. Updated contact information can be found at {www.metrokc.gov/dad/guide/jobs.htm}

- *Asian Counseling and Referral Services*: Vocational and employment training, and job placement. 1032 South Jackson, Suite 200, Seattle, WA 98104; 206-720-5374.

- *Central Area Motivation Program*: Must be clean and sober; offer ex-offender program. 722 18th Ave., Seattle, WA 98122; 206-329-4114, ext. 305.

- *Downtown Human Services Council*: Job readiness, placement; bilingual Spanish. 115 Prefontaine Pl. South, Seattle, WA 98104; 206-461-3865.

- *DSHS*, Dept. of Vocational Rehabilitation: Help for people with disabilities (including alcohol/drug dependence or mental illness) to re-enter employment. Call for appointment. 1700 East Cherry St., Seattle, WA 98122; 206-720-3200.

- *El Centro de la Raza*: Training and placements; call for appointment; bilingual. 2524 16th Ave. South, Seattle, WA 98144; 206-329-7960.

- *Interaction Transition*: Employment assistance, referrals; work with recent releases from jails. 16th Ave., Seattle, WA 98122; 206-324-3932.

Job Service Centers

- Belltown: 2106 2nd Ave., Seattle, WA 98121; 206-464-6449.

- North Seattle: 12550 Aurora N., Seattle, WA 98133; 206-440-2500.

- Rainier: 2531 Rainier South, Seattle, WA 98122; 206-721-6000.

- Urban League of Metropolitan Seattle: Job bank; limited support. 105 14th Ave., Seattle, WA 98116; 206-461-3792.

- United Indians of All Tribes Foundation: Employment referral and placement. 1945 Yale Pl. SE, Seattle, WA 98102; 206-325-0070.

- Women & Family Center, Millionaire Club: Day jobs available, must be sober; job referral and employment training. 113 1st Ave. North, Seattle, WA 98109; 206-301-0833.

- YWCA, Employment Service: Job preparation, referral and placement. 118 5th Ave., Seattle, WA 98101; 206-461-4448 (voice mail).

- YWCA, West Seattle Center: Job preparation, referral and placement. 4800 40th SW, Seattle, WA 98116; 206-461-4485.

- YWCA, East Cherry, Employment Services: Job boards, readiness, placement help for low-income women. 2820 East Cherry, Seattle, WA 98112; 206-461-4882.

- ANEW, Apprenticeship and Non-Traditional Employment for Women: Employment training in trades and industry; income eligibility applies. P.O. Box 2490, 3000 NE 4th Street, Renton, WA 98056; 206-235-2212.

- Center for Career Alternatives (CCA): Various training courses; help with job search and placement. Must call for appointment. 901 Rainier Ave. South, Seattle, WA 98144; 206-322-9080.

- Pacific Associates: Training, job search and placement. 6 months sobriety. 2200 6th Ave., Suite 260, Seattle, WA 98121; 206-728-8826.

- Pioneer Human Services, Pioneer Industries: Paid training, then placement. Call by Wednesday for intake appointment Friday. Need clean UA at intake. 7000 Highland Parkway SW, Seattle, WA 98106; 206-762-7737.

- Seattle Indian Center: Employment training and referrals. 611 12th Ave. South, Suite 300, Seattle, WA 98144; 206-329-8700.

- Washington Works: Job training; job search support; most clients on AFDC. 616 1st Ave., Fifth Floor, Seattle, WA 98104; 206-343-9731.

Train to Become A Tradesperson
The Apprenticeship Program is a combination of classroom studies and on-the-job training under the supervision of a journey level craft person or trade professional. After completion of the program, the apprentice will have journey

level status which will allow for nationwide mobility at journey level scales. Some of the trades to be learned include, automotive mechanics, cement mason, electrical workers, iron workers, and roofers. This program also offers Pre-Apprentice Training through a variety of programs. For more information on the program, contact Gerri Woolf, Apprenticeship Program Coordinator, Washington State Employment Security Department, Employment and Training Division; 360-438-4037; {Email: gwoolf@esd.wa.gov}. The following is a list of pre-apprentice training contacts.

ANEW (Apprentice and Nontraditional Employment for Women) is a five month comprehensive trades training to low-income women that live in King County. Courses include carpentry, electrical, blueprint reading, forklift training, job/life skills training, and nontraditional career exploration. For more information, contact ANEW, P.O. Box 2490, Renton, WA 98056; 425-235-2212; Fax: 425-235-7864; {Email: anew99@hotmail.com}.

Apprenticeship Opportunities Project offers assistance for residents of King County to prepare and apply to apprenticeship programs in construction work. Some of the services offered are community outreach, individual skills assessment and counseling, support services, and mentoring. Contact Apprenticeship Opportunities Project, 1155 Harrison, Seattle, WA 98109; 206-381-1384; Fax: 206-381-1389; {Email: lisaaop@aol.com}.

Direct Placement Apprenticeship Programs
The following are direct placement programs that recruit qualified persons to become apprentices and/or trainees in highway construction jobs. Recruitment of women and minorities is emphasized. Assistance is in the area of meeting EEO/OJT goals, referral and screening, attendance at Pre-Construction conferences, and recruitment assistance. For more information, contact one of the following:

Spokane OIC's; The Lindman Nonprofit Center, 315 West Mission Avenue, Suite 10, Spokane, WA 99202; 509-325-9493; 800-481-8774; Fax: 509-325-4883. Serves eastern Washington.

Puget Sound OIC; P.O. Box 22329, Seattle, WA 98122-0329; 801 SW 16th Street, Seattle, WA 98055; 206-721-5980; 800-963-3277; Fax: 206-721-4537.

Life Skills/Women's Programs Institute for Extended Learning
Life Skills/Women's Programs Institute for Extended Learning have a variety of programs that introduce women to the trades as well as basic math and English skills. Women in Non-traditional settings focuses on math, English, computer basics, life skills, and an overview of non-traditional opportunities. The course lasts for 10 weeks. Paths to Trades and Technology are short courses that are conducted off-site in the area. For more information, contact LifeSkills/Women's Programs Institute for Extended Learning, Community Colleges of Spokane, W-3305 Fort George Wright Drive, Spokane, WA 99204; 509-533-3131; Fax: 509-533-3226; {www.ielhp.spokane.cc.wa.us}; {Email: sbettinger@lodge.spokane.cc.wa.us}.

Nontraditional Employment for Women
Columbia Industries NEW (Nontraditional Employment for Women) runs a 10 week program that is free for individuals that meet federal guidelines. It includes GED preparation, basic math and reading skills, remediation, blueprint reading, safety classes, job/life skills training, physical fitness, tours, and guest speakers from apprenticeship programs in the community. To see if you qualify, contact Columbia Industries NEW, 900 South Dayton, P.O. Box 7346, Kennewick, WA 99336, 509-582-4142.

Multiple Trades Program
Seattle Vocational Institute has a Multiple Trades Program that prepares students to enter into any of the construction trade apprenticeships. It strongly emphasizes basic job skills such as punctuality, perseverance, positive attitude, and work ethics. Students will also be trained in safety, tool and material identification and proper use, blueprint reading and trades math. Certificates are provided in First Aid/CPR, traffic control, and fork lift operation. The open entry/ open exit allows the student to join the class every month. Remedial education is also available. For

more information, contact SVI, 2120 South Jackson Street, Seattle, WA 98144; 206-587-4940; Fax: 206-587-4949; {Email: bmarkholt@sccd.ctc.edu}.

Transition to Trades

The Transition to Trades program will prepare student to compete for entry level positions as apprentices in skilled trades occupations. Course modules include training in basic carpentry, plumbing, electrical, applied mathematics, blueprint reading, flagging, industrial safety, aerobic conditioning and weight training, and non-traditional career exploration. Selected modules may be taken on a part-time basis with approval from the instructor. For more information, contact Transition to Trades, Clover Park Technical College, 4500 Steilacoom Boulevard SW, Tacoma, WA 98499; 253-589-5824.

Youth Building Program

The Youth Building program has a goal to help residents of Tacoma, ages 18-24, to obtain employment and/or training related to building and construction trades, and emerging technology career fields. Some of the services offered are, educational assistance, work experience projects, career counseling and exploration, on-the-job training

opportunities, support services, job search assistance, and assistance in connecting with a n apprenticeship program. For more information, contact Youth Building Tacoma, 733 Market Street, Room 21, Tacoma, WA 98402; 253-591-5450/ 253-594-7951.

Help for Permanently Laid Off Workers

The state offers employment and training services to dislocated workers because they are generally highly-productive people that lost their job through no fault of their own. You are a dislocated worker if you lost your job under one or more of the following circumstances; you have been terminated , laid off, or received a notice of termination; you lost your job and are unlikely to return because of plant closure, mass layoffs, foreign competition, or lack of demand for your skills; you are self-employed but the economy or a natural disaster has put you out of work; you are a displaced homemaker who is either unemployed or working a job that does not support your household. Resources vary depending on the type of job you had or where you live. Some of the services available for qualified people are, workshops that teach you how to look for a job, help assessing how your skills apply to today's job market, job development, and relocation assistance. Assistance can be obtained at Worker Retraining Units, Counseling Centers, Career/Employment Centers through local community and technical college, WorkSource Centers of Job Service Centers. To get more information on available services, or to find a Worker Retraining Coordinator, contact; Washington State Employment Security Department, Employment Services, P.O. Box 9046, Olympia, WA 98507-9046; 360-438-3275; {www.wa.gov/esd/dw}.

Help For People at Risk

Pioneer Human Services helps people at risk which includes, but is not limited to, alcoholics and other chemically dependent persons, convicts, work release participants, and those under jurisdiction of the courts. They strive to create opportuniit6es for them to achieve personal, economic, and social development through training, employment, housing, and rehabilitation services. The Pioneer Enterprise group operates self-supporting businesses that provide a majority of the PHS program clients with the employment and job training aspects of the PHS mission. For more information, contact Pioneer Human Services, 7440 West Marginal Way, South, Seattle, WA 98108; 206-768-1990; Fax: 206-768-8910; {www.pioneerhumanserv.com/index.html}.

Job Readiness Training Program For the Needy

Washington Works offers job training and job search assistance to their clients, that are mostly on AFDC. They have 12 job readiness training programs which includes topics like professional behavior, computer skills, administrative and basic skills. They cultivated employers so they can generate jobs for their graduates. They say that 75% of the students graduate and of those 74% have a job within 6 months. For more information, contact Washington Works, 616 1st Avenue, 5th Floor, Seattle, WA 98104; 206-343-9731.

West Virginia

One-Stop Career Centers

A network of One-Stop Career Centers throughout the state offers a wide range of employment related services including job training. Services vary by location. To find a location near you, please refer to the website {www.state.wv.us/bep}. To learn more about the services they offer, contact your state coordinator.

Ms. Quetta Muzzle , Director, Employment Service and JTPA Division Bureau of Employment Programs, 112 California Ave., Rm. 616, Charleston, WV 25305; 304-558-1138; Fax: 304-558-1136.

Ms. Lisa Wells, One-Stop Project Manager, WV Bureau of Employment Programs, 112 California Avenue - 5204, Charleston, WV 25305; 304-558-3461; 304-558-3470; {Email: st1597@stmail. wvnet.edu}.

Job Service Offices

A System of Employment Service/Job Service offices is located within every state with the goal of assisting millions of job seekers and employers. While services may vary from location to location, many provide job training, skills assessment and related services. With approximately 1,800 Employment Service/Job Service offices nationwide there is bound to be one near you. To learn more about the services offered in your area, contact your state administrator. Quetta Muzzle, Director, WV Bureau of Employment Programs, 112 California Avenue, Charleston, WV 25305-0112; 304-558-1138; Fax: 304-558-1136; {www.stae.wv.us/bep/jobs}.

Other State Programs

- The Northern Panhandle Private Industry Council can provide you with a list of job search and training service providers by contacting 2003 Warwood Avenue Wheeling, WV 26003-7103; 304-277-2011; Fax: 304-277-2013; {www.state.wv.us/bep/jobs/JTP/default.htm}.

- The Private Industry Council of Kanawha County can both provide and refer you to a list of job search and training service providers by contacting 405 Capitol Street, Suite 506, Charleston WV 25301; 304-344-5760; Fax: 304-344-5762; {www.state.wv.us/bep/jobs/JTP/pickan.htm}.

The following is a list of the Governor's Program Subcontractors compiled from the website {www.state.wv.us/bep/jobs/JTP/ govpsubs.htm}. These service providers offer a variety of programs that are briefly described below.

- Huntington Housing offers on-the-job training, classroom training in various occupations. First phase provides six months of classroom training in occupations such as carpentry, painting, electrical work, landscaping and lead-based paint abatement. After completion of classroom training, second phase involves on-the-job training. 30 Northcott Court, P.O. Box 2183, Huntington, WV 25722; 304-526-4400; Fax 304-526-4427.

- Mid-Ohio Valley Regional Council offers an older worker program that includes classroom training for a certified nursing assistant. Contact P.O. Box 247, 531 Market Street, Parkersburg, WV 26101; 304-422-4993; Fax 304-422-4998.

- North Central OIC provides classroom training for business education, nurse's aide and child care provider. Contact 120 Jackson Street, Fairmont, WV 26554; 304-366-8142; Fax 304-366-8143.

- NAACP Jobs Program offers on-the-job training and life skills. Contact Suite 206, 910 4th Avenue, P.O. Box 1611, Huntington, WV 25717; 304-523-7819; Fax 304-523-1266.

- Wyoming County Opportunity Council, Inc. offers on-the-job training, basic skills and life skills. Contact Box 1509, Oceana, WV 24870; 304-682-8271; Fax 304-682-8274.

- Division Of Technical & Adult Education Services provides classroom training in various occupations such as pre-employment skills training/working maturing skills; skills cluster; work experience; limited use of advanced learning technology for education, job preparation and skills training; remedial education and basic skills training; internship training; and vocational training-institutional skills training. Contact Building 6, Room B-044, Capitol Complex, Charleston, WV 25305; 304-558-2681; Fax 304-558-1055.

- Construction Trades, Training & Advancement Program (CTTAP) provides occupational skills training serving participants in various construction trades and advancement programs. Contact 2301 Seventh Avenue, Charleston, WV 25312; 304-346-3863; Fax: 304-346-3862.

- Mercer County EOC offers on-the-job training; life skills; and basic skills. Contact 212 Federal Street, Bluefield, WV 24701; 304-324-0450; Fax: 304-324-8822.

- Potomac Highlands Support Services offers training in culinary arts. Contact P.O. Box 869, Airport Road, Petersburg, WV 26847; 304-257-1221; Fax: 304-257-4958.

- Potomac Highlands Support Services provides training for home health aide/certified nursing assistant. Contact P.O. Box 869, Airport Road, Petersburg WV 26847; 304-257-1221; Fax: 304-257-4958

- Career Works Associates Ltd. offers career transition and outplacement services. Contact 1207 Quarrier Street, Suite 304, Charleston, WV 25301; 304-344-2273; 800-718-5941; Fax: 304-343-0328.

- Charleston OIC provides feeder programs, nursing assistant and clerical/word processing. Contact 737 Virginia Street West, Charleston, WV 25302; 304-344-9681; Fax: 304-344-5965.

- Potomac Highlands Support Services offers on-the-job training (OJT) with life management skills/workforce development or basic education skills. Contact P.O. Box 869, Airport Road, Petersburg, WV 26847; 304-257-1221: Fax: 304-257-4958.

- MULTI-CAP, INC. provides work experience, on-the-job training, and occupational skills. Contact P.O. Box 3228, Charleston, WV 2 5332; 304-342-1300; Fax: 304-344-1098.

- The J.O.B.S. Company provides classroom training in retail and consumer sales. Remediation and basic skills training are also available. Contact 411 Capital Street, P.O. Box 3763, Charleston, WV 25337; 304-344-0048; Fax: 304-345-3295.

You Can Work At Home

If you live in rural West Virginia and would like to learn about alternative approaches to economic development such as networks of home-based business entrepreneurs, the Center for Economic Options can help. This is a non-profit, statewide, community-based organization that promotes opportunities to develop the economic capacity of West Virginia's rural citizens, particularly women, and communities. The Center creates unusual approaches to economic development including home-based business support and works with communities to help build support for small and micro-businesses. For more information, contact Center for Economic Options, Inc., Pam Curry, Executive Director, 214 Capitol Street, Suite 200, P.O. Box 191, Charleston, WV 25321-0191; 304-345-1298; Fax: 304-342-0641; {www. centerforeconoptions.org/}; {Email: econoptns@citynet.net}.

Training In Technology

The Multi-County Community Action Against Poverty, Inc. brings together human, financial and material resources of the public and private sectors of Kanawha, Putnam, Boone, Clay, and Fayette counties to remove the causes of poverty, and to assist the poor in lifting themselves from poverty. Among a large variety of programs and services designed to help disadvantaged people, their job training services include Women in Non-Traditional Jobs, Welfare-To-Work, Single Parent/Displaced Homemaker programs, and Training in Technology Center. For more information, contact Multi-County Community Action Against Poverty, Inc., 1007 Bigley Ave., Charleston, WV 25302; 304-342-1300 Fax: 304-344-1166; {www.multi-cap.org/}.

Help For Single Parents and Displaced Homemakers

The primary goal of the Bluefield State College Single Parent/Displaced Homemaker Program is to assist single parents, single pregnant women and displaced homemakers in acquiring marketable educational and occupational skills that will enable them to support themselves and their families. They can provide you with: scholarship information; a mentor (through INSPIRE); support and encouragement; special workshops and seminars; information about daycare and daycare financial support; assist with admissions and financial aid paperwork; make referrals to community agencies, as appropriate; and more. You can obtain more information by contacting: Robin Dishner, Educational Outreach Counselor, Bluefield State College - Conley Hall Room 307, 219 Rock Street, Bluefield, WV 24701; 304-327-4500; {www.bluefield.wvnet.edu/}; {Email: rdishner@bscvax.wvnet.edu }.

Wisconsin

One-Stop Career Centers

A network of One-Stop Career Centers throughout the state offers a wide range of employment related services including job training. Services vary by location. To find a location near you, please refer to the website {www.dwd.state.wi.us/dwe/Directory.htm}. Mr. Ron Hunt, Director, One-Stop Lead, Job Center Bureau Department of Workforce Development, P.O. Box 7972, 201 E. Washington Avenue, Room 211, Madison, WI 53702; 608-266-2687; 888-258-9966; Fax: 608-267-2392.

Job Service Offices

A System of Employment Service/Job Service offices is located within every state with the goal of assisting millions of job seekers and employers. While services may vary from location to location, many provide job training, skills assessment and related services. With approximately 1,800 Employment Service/Job Service offices nationwide there is bound to be one near you. To learn more about the services offered in your area, contact your state administrator. Linda Stewart, Secretary, Department of Workforce Development, GEF-I, 201 E. Washington Avenue, P.O. Box 7946, Madison, WI 53707-7946; 608-267-7276; Fax: 608-266-1784; {www.dwd.state.wi.us}.

Women Work!

Women Work! is a state affiliate of the national membership organization dedicated to helping women from diverse backgrounds achieve economic self-sufficiency through job readiness, education, training and employment. Contact Wisconsin Women Work!, Bonnie Withrow, President, Western Wisconsin Technical College, 1310 Townline Road, Tomah, WI 54660; 608-785-9574; {Email: withrowb@western.tec.wi.us}.

Learn A Trade

Women in Trades, in partnership with five organizations in different states, will provide technical assistance to employers, contractors, and labor organizations on mega construction projects in the Midwest. They will work with contractors and apprenticeship programs meeting their goals for hiring women in job sites. These groups refer qualified tradeswomen to jobs, and most provide pre-apprenticeship programs to give women the skills needed in apprenticeship programs. They can give you information on career awareness on the range of job options for women too. For further information on programs in your state call:

Nancy Nakkoul, Projects Coordinator, Employment Options, Inc., 2095 Winnebago Street, Madison, WI 53704; 608-244-5181.

Nancy Hoffman, Director, Non-traditional Employment Training Program, YWCA of Greater Milwaukee, 101 E. Pleasant, Milwaukee, WI 53212; 414-224-9080.

Access Business Education Programs and/or Business Lending Programs

The Wisconsin Women's Business Initiative Corporation is an economic development corporation providing quality business education, technical assistance and access to capital. They consult, educate and mentor small and micro-businesses throughout Wisconsin. You could benefit from approximately 200 business courses and workshops offered in Milwaukee, Madison, Racine/Kenosha, Green Bay/Fox Valley, Beloit/Janesville annually. Topics include business planning, entrepreneurship, management, marketing, finances, and the Internet. In addition, if you are a woman, person of color, or low-income individual who owns or can demonstrate the ability to operate a small business, they can provide access to loans of $100-$25,000 to help you along.

Wisconsin Women's Business Initiative Corporation, 2745 Dr. Martin Luther King Jr. Drive, Milwaukee, WI 53212; 414-263-5450; Fax: 414-263-5456.

WWBIC - Madison Office, 217 S. Hamilton Street, Suite 201, P.O. Box 1082, Madison, WI 53701; 608-257-7409; Fax: 608-257-7429; {www. wwbic.com}; {Email: info@wwbic.com}.

Help For Displaced Homemakers and Single Parents

Mid-State Technical College Displaced Homemaker and Single Parent Programs provides services to help you regain a sense of balance in your life. Their goal is to assist you in gaining confidence so you may evaluate your abilities, establish goals, and choose appropriate training or employment to eventually become emotionally and economically self-sufficient. Guidance is given through both individual and group advising in areas such as self-concept, career exploration, job seeking strategies and self-management skills. Support group activities are offered to all participants. For further information, refer to {www.midstate.tec.wi.us/} or contact the Mid-State Technical College campus closest to you from the list below and request the Students Services Department. Contact 888-575-6782.

- Mid-State Technical College, 500 32nd St., NE, Wisconsin Rapids, WI 54494; 715-442-5300.

- Mid-State Technical College, 2600 W. 5th St., Marshfield, WI 54449; 715-387-2538.

- Mid-State Technical College, 933 Michigan Ave., Stevens Point, WI 54481; 715-344-3063.

- Mid-State Technical College, 401 N. Main St., Adams, WI 53910; 608-339-3379.

Help For Minority Business Owners

The Minority Business Development program is available to minority entrepreneurs to encourage and generate the growth of their businesses. They are provided with financial consultation and technical assistance, marketing and certification assistance, and also technical assistance and grant information for owners that are disabled. The business owners will also be certified to participate in the state's minority business purchasing and contracting program. In addition to these services, they maintain a directory of certified firms, in a computer database, that allows buyers to access the information by product or service area, county or commodity code. For further information, contact the Wisconsin Department of Commerce, Bureau of Minority Business Development, P.O. Box 7970, Madison, WI 53707; 608-267-9550; 414-220-5360; {www.commerce.state.wi.us/ED/ED-MBD-Index.html}.

Wyoming

One-Stop Career Centers

A network of One-Stop Career Centers throughout the state offers a wide range of employment related services including job training. Services vary by location. To find a location near you, please refer to the website {http://onestop.state.wy.us/appview/wjn_home.asp}. To learn more about the services they offer, contact your state coordinator.

Pam Miller, Administrator, Employment Resources Division, P.O. Box 2760, 100 West Midwest, Casper, WY 82602-2760; 307-235-3200; Fax: 307-235-3278.

Job Service Offices

A System of Employment Service/Job Service offices is located within every state with the goal of assisting millions of job seekers and employers. While services may vary from location to location, many provide job training, skills assessment and related services. With approximately 1,800 Employment Service/Job Service offices nationwide there is bound to be one near you. To learn more about the services offered in your area, contact your state administrator.

Frank S. Galeotos, Director, Department of Employment, 122 West 25th Street, Herschler Building, 2nd Floor East, Cheyenne, WY 82002; 307-777-6402; Fax: 307-777-5805; {http://wydoe.state.wy.us}.

Beth Nelson, Administrator, Department of Employment, Division of Employment Resources, 122 West 25th Street, Cheyenne, WY 82002; 307-777-7672; Fax: 307-777-5805.

A Good Resource

The Wyoming Commission for Women can assist you with a number of employment issues as well as offer you referrals. Their mission is to work to improve the quality and equality of life for Wyoming's women. The Commission For Women focuses its actions on the needs and concerns of Wyoming women in the following areas: educational opportunities, employment, family and community, public policy, legal rights and responsibilities. For more information, contact Wyoming Women's Center, 1000 West Griffith, P.O. Box 20, Lusk, WI 82225; 307-334-3693; Fax: 307-334-2254; {http://{wydoe.state.wy.us/wcwi/}.

GRANTS FOR COMMUNITIES

Communities and nonprofits across America are taking advantage of some incredible grant programs to improve their town and surrounding countryside. You can plant trees, rehab houses, and even preserve the arts or history of your town. There is money to help support new businesses in small towns. You can even get money to bring the world to your city through the internet or start a public radio station. The closing of a military base does not mean the downturn of your town's economy. There are programs established to help generate new uses for the land and buildings. You just need to take advantage of these programs to make your town a lively and growing community. Here are a few success stories:

★ $8,000 for the Aurora Sculpture Garden that also included a job training program for youth.

★ $20,000 to support folk arts programs in Colorado including collecting oral histories, creating a sculpture, and hosting cowboy poetry festivals.

★ $10,000 to develop a play on the early days of the railroad in Tennessee.

★ $225,000 to create a trail linking various art and community sites in Arizona.

★ Money to support a living history group in a ghost town in Colorado.

★ $25,000 for wrought iron fencing in rehabilitation of houses in New Orleans.

Now don't forget to read the first part of this book, "Types of Assistance and Grants Sources," as well as "More Help In Finding a Grant." These sections provide some great starting places for your money hunt. Many community organizations can benefit from checking out the federal governments NonProfit Gateway at {www.nonprofit.gov}. This site provides wonderful links to departments and agencies that have programs of interest to communities. You can also usually find out what types of programs have been funded before to give you an idea of how your project matches with the program.

Many communities are designated by their state or the federal government as Empowerment Zones or Enterprise Communities. What does this mean for you? It means, no waiting in line! You get to be first up to the money pot to help improve your town. You also become entitled to special benefits, such as tax deductions, matching grants, or loan guarantees. Information on these programs are listed later in this chapter. You can also check out the website {www.ezec.gov} that provides information for Rural Empowerment Zones and Enterprise Communities, but also has a link to Urban information as well.

The Rural Information Center provides information and referral services to anyone interested in working to maintain the vitality of America's rural areas. They have a wide variety of general and funding information; they can cerate customized information packages; and they can direct you to other resources and services that may assist you with your project. You can check out the center at Rural Information Center, National Agricultural Library, Room 304, 10301 Baltimore Ave., Beltsville, MD 20705; 800-633-7701; {www.nal.usda.gov/ric/}.

When you think of community grants, keep in mind your state, county, and city governments. In addition, there are also community development organizations and chamber of commerce associations. They have a great deal to offer in they way of resources, services, and funding possibilities. These can be located in the blue pages of your phone book, by contacting your city hall or county seat, as well as through the Governor's office. Remember that the key is to ask, ask, and ask. Some good starting places include your state operator (listed in the Appendix of this book), who can direct you to resources. You can check out your state webpage at {www.state.xx.us - NOTE: replace xx with your state postal abbreviation}. Other places to consider include:

★ National Community Development Association, 522 21st St., NW, #120, Washington, DC 20006; 202-293-7587; {www.ncdaonline.org};

★ National Association of Counties, 440 First St., NW, Suite 800, Washington, DC 20001; 202-393-6226; {www.naco.org}.

Don't forget that you vote for your Senator and your Representative. They want you to vote for them again, so they will do whatever they can to assist you in your cause. You can contact their local office, again by looking in the blue pages of your phone book, or Your Senator, The Senate, Washington, DC 20510; 202-224-3121; {www.senate.gov}; or your Representative, The United States House of Representatives, Washington, DC 20515; 202-224-3121; {www.house.gov}. The federal government has even created a special website called U.S. State and Local Gateway at {www.statelocal.gov} that provides links to information by type, topic, current issues, hotlinks, and more. This is a great resource for gathering contacts.

Happy hunting!

Bring Trees To Your Town

Cooperative Forestry
P.O. Box 96090
Washington, DC 20090
202-205-1389
www.fs.fed.us/spf/coop/ucf_general.htm

The U.S. Department of Agriculture operates the Urban and Community Forestry Program that provides competitive project grants to support people in urban areas and community settings to sustain shade trees, forest lands, and open spaces. These are offered through the regional divisions. This program assisted 10,235 communities to improve green spaces. Grants may also be distributed through the State Urban and Community forestry Offices. In addition, a listing of local non-profit tree planting organizations is included that may be a further resource.

Regional Offices

1. Northern Region
Northern Idaho, Montana, North Dakota
USDA Forest Service
Federal Building
P.O. Box 7669
200 E. Broadway
Missoula, MT 59807
406-329-3521

2. Rocky Mountain Region
Colorado, Kansas, Nebraska, South Dakota,
Parts of Wyoming
USDA Forest Service
P.O. Box 25127
Lakewood, CO 80225
740 Simms St.

Golden, CO 80401
303-275-5742

3. Southwestern Region
Arizona, New Mexico
Tonto National Forest
2324 E. McDowell Rd.
Phoenix, AZ 85006
602-225-5271

4. Intermountain Region
Southern Idaho, Nevada, Utah, parts of
Wyoming
USDA Forest Service
Federal Building
324 25th St.

Ogden, UT 84401
801-625-5189

5. Pacific Southwest Region
   California, Hawaii
   1323 Club Dr.
   Vallejo, CA 94592
   707-562-9025

6. Pacific Northwest Region
   Oregon, Washington
   USDA Forest Service
   P.O. Box 3623
   333 SW 1st Ave.
   Portland, OR 97208
   503-808-2351

7. Southern Region
   Alabama, Arkansas, Florida, Georgia, Kentucky,
   Louisiana, Mississippi, North Carolina,
   Oklahoma, South Carolina, Tennessee, Texas,
   Virginia

USDA Forest Service
1720 Peachtree Rd., NW
Suite 850S
Atlanta, GA 30367
404-347-1647

8. Alaska Region
   USDA Forest Service
   3301 C St., Suite 522
   Anchorage, AK 99503
   907-271-2550

9. Northeastern Area
   Connecticut, Delaware, Illinois, Indiana, Iowa,
   Maine, Maryland, Massachusetts, Michigan,
   Minnesota, Missouri, New Hampshire, New
   Jersey, New York, Ohio, Pennsylvania, Rhode
   Island, Vermont, West Virginia, Wisconsin, and
   District of Columbia
   USDA Forest Service
   Northeastern Area State and Private Forestry
   11 Campus Blvd, Suite 200
   Newtown Square, PA 19073
   610-557-4133

State Urban and Community Forestry Coordinators

Alabama
Alabama Forestry Commission
513 Madison Ave.
P.O. Box 302550
Montgomery, AL 36130
334-240-9360

Alaska
Alaska Department of Natural Resources
3601 C St., Suite 1034
Anchorage, AK 99503
907-269-8466

Arizona
Arizona Department of State Lands
1616 W. Adams St.
Phoenix, AZ 85007
602-542-2518

Arkansas
Arkansas Forestry Commission
3821 W. Roosevelt Rd.
Little Rock, AR 72204
501-296-1863

California
California Department of Forestry
2524 Mulberry St.
Riverside, CA 92501
909-782-4140

Colorado
Colorado State Forest Service
Colorado State University
203 Forestry Building
Fort Collins, CO 80523
970-491-6303

Connecticut
Connecticut Division of Forestry
79 Elm St.
Hartford, CT 06106
860-424-3630

Delaware
Delaware Department of Agriculture
2320 S. DuPont Highway
Dover, DE 19901
302-739-4811

District of Columbia
DC Department of Public Works
1105 O St., SE
Washington, DC 20032
202-727-5559

Florida
Florida Division of Forestry
3125 Conner Blvd.
Tallahassee, FL 32399
850-414-9912

Georgia
Georgia Forestry Commission
6835 James B. Rivers/Memorial Dr.
Stone Mountain, GA 30083
404-298-3935

Hawaii
Hawaii Division of Forestry and Wildlife
1151 Punchbowl St., Room 325
Honolulu, HI 96813
808-672-3383

Idaho
Idaho Department of State Lands
P.O. Box 670
Coeur D'Alena, ID 46260
208-664-2171

Illinois
Illinois Department of Natural Resources
Division of Forest Resources
524 S. 2nd St.
Springfield, IL 62701
217-782-2361

Indiana
Indiana Department of Natural Resources
9245 N. Meridian, Suite 118
Indianapolis, IN 46260
317-915-9390

Iowa
Iowa Department of Natural Resources
Wallace State Office Building
Des Moines, IA 50319
515-242-5966

Kansas
Kansas Forest Service
2610 Claflin Rd.
Manhattan, KS 66502
785-532-3308

Kentucky
Kentucky Division of Forestry
627 Camanche Trail
Frankfort, KY 40601
502-564-4496

Louisiana
Louisiana Department of Agriculture and Forestry
P.O. Box 1628
Baton Rouge, LA 70821
504-952-8018

Maine
Maine Forest Service
22 State House Station
Augusta, ME 04333
207-287-4988

Maryland
Maryland Forest Service
580 Taylor Ave.
Annapolis, MD 21401
410-260-8507

Massachusetts
Massachusetts Department of Environment
Management
100 Cambridge St., 19th Floor
Boston, MA 02202
617-727-3180

Michigan
Michigan Department of Natural Resources
Box 30452
Lansing, MI 48909
517-335-3354

Minnesota
Minnesota DNR Forestry
1200 Warner Rd.
St. Paul, MN 55106
651-772-7565

Missouri
Missouri Department of Conservation
P.O. Box 180
Jefferson City, MO 65102
573-751-4115

Montana
Montana DNRC, Forestry Division
2705 Spurgin Rd.
Missoula, MT 59804
406-542-4284

Nebraska
Nebraska Forest Service
8015 W. Center Rd.
Omaha, NE 68124
402-444-7804

Nevada
Nevada Division of Forestry
1201 Johnson St., Suite D
Carson City, NV 89706
775-684-2506

New Hampshire
New Hampshire Division of Forests and Lands
P.O. Box 1856
Concord, NH 03301
603-271-3457

New Jersey
New Jersey Forest Service
501 E. State St.
P.O. Box 404
Trenton, NJ 08625
609-292-2532

New Mexico
New Mexico State Forestry
P.O. Box 1948
Santa Fe, NM 87504
505-827-8093

New York
New York State Department of Environmental
Conservation
50 Wolf Rd., Room 424
Albany, NY 12233
518-457-7370

North Carolina
North Carolina Division of Forest Resources
P.O. Box 29581
Raleigh, NC 27626
919-733-2162

North Dakota
North Dakota Forest Service
1511 E. Interstate Ave.

Bismarck, ND 58501
701-328-9944

Ohio
Ohio DNR Division of Forestry
1855 Fountain Square Court, H-1
Columbus, OH 43224
614-265-6707

Oklahoma
Oklahoma Forestry Services
Department of Agriculture
2800 N. Lincoln Blvd.
Oklahoma City, OK 73105
405-521-3864

Oregon
Oregon Department of Forestry
2600 State St.
Salem, OR 97310
503-945-7391

Pennsylvania
Pennsylvania DCNR
Forest Advisory Services
P.O. Box 8552
Harrisburg, PA 17105
717-783-0385

Rhode Island
Rhode Island Division of Forest Environment
1037 Hartford Pike
North Scituate, RI 02857
401-647-3367

South Carolina
South Carolina Commission of Forestry
5500 Broad River Rd.
Columbia, SC 29210
803-896-8864

South Dakota
South Dakota State Forestry
523 E. Capitol

Foss Building
Pierre, SD 57510
605-773-3594

Tennessee
Tennessee Division of Forestry
Box 40627 Melrose Station
Nashville, TN 37204
615-837-5520

Texas
Texas Forest Service
301 Tarrow Dr.
College Station, TX 77804
409-845-2641

Utah
Utah Division of Forestry,
Fire & State Land
P.O. Box 145703
Salt Lake City, UT 84114
801-538-5505

Vermont
Vermont Department of Forests, Parks & Recreation
103 S. Main St., Building 10 South
Waterbury, VT 05671
802-241-3673

Virginia
Virginia Department of Forestry
P.O. Box 3758
Charlottesville, VA 22903
804-977-6555

Washington
Washington Department of Natural Resources
P.O. Box 47037
Olympia, WA 98504
206-902-1703

West Virginia
West Virginia Division of Forestry
Rt. 2, Box 1100
Fairmount, WV 26554
304-367-2793

Wisconsin
Wisconsin Department of Natural Resources
P.O. Box 7921
Madison, WI 53707
608-267-0843

Wyoming
Wyoming State Forestry
1100 W. 22nd St.
Cheyenne, WY 82002
307-777-7586

Local Non-Profit Tree Planting Organizations

Arizona
Trees for Tucson
P.O. Box 27210
Tucson, AZ 85726
602-791-3109

California
Friends of the Urban Forest
Presidio of San Francisco
Building 1007
San Francisco, CA 94129
415-561-6890

People for Trees
P.O. Box 120505
San Diego, CA 92112
619-234-8733

Tree Foundation of Kern
1412 17th St., Suite 222

Bakersfield, CA 93001
805-325-6650

California Releaf
Trust for Public Lands
116 New Montgomery St.
Third Floor
San Francisco, CA 94105
415-495-5660

North East Trees
4701 Olson St.
Los Angeles, CA 90041
213-255-4863

Sacramento Tree Foundation, Inc.
201 Lathrop Way
Suite F
Sacramento, CA 95815
916-924-8733

Tree Musketeers
136 Main St.
El Segundo, CA 90245
310-322-0263

Tree People
12601 Mulholland Dr.
Beverly Hills, CA 90210
818-623-4848

Colorado
Denver Digs Trees
715 S. Franklin St.
Denver, CO 80209
303-722-6262

Florida
Greenscape of Jacksonville
3100 University Blvd., S., Suite 112
Jacksonville, FL 32216
904-724-5518

Releaf Sarasota County, Inc.
2620 Grafton St.
Sarasota, FL 34231
941-922-3693

Mayor's Beautification Program, Inc.
P.O. Box 2104
Tampa, FL 33601
813-221-8733

Georgia
Savanna Tree Foundation, Inc.
3025 Bull St.
Savannah, GA 31405
912-233-8733

Trees Atlanta
96 Poplar St., NW
Atlanta, GA 30303
404-522-4097

Illinois
Openlands Project
220 S. State St., Suite 1880
Chicago, IL 60604
312-427-4256

Iowa
Trees Forever
770 7th Ave.
Marion, IA 52302
319-373-0650

Louisiana
Baton Rouge Green
448 N. 11th St.
Baton Rouge, LA 70801
225-381-0037

Shreveport Green
610 Marshal St., Suite 210
Shreveport, LA 7101
318-222-6455

Michigan
Greening of Detroit
415 Burns Dr.
Whittier Tower
Detroit, MI 48214
313-821-8733

Minnesota
Tree Trust
6300 Walker St., Suite 227
St. Louis Park, MN 55416
612-920-9326

Missouri
Fourest Releaf of Missouri
4207 Lindell Blvd., Suite 120
St. Louis, MO 63108
314-533-5323

New Jersey
Trees New Jersey
P.O. Box 583
Bordentown, NJ 08505
609-298-2999

New Mexico
Tree New Mexico, Inc.
P.O. Box 81827
Albuquerque, NM 87198
505-265-4554

New York
Bronx Green-up
New York Botanic Garden
200 St. and Kazimiroff Blvd.
Bronx, NY 10458
718-817-8995

Trees New York
51 Chambers St., Suite 1412
New York, NY 10007
212-227-1887

Oregon
Friends of Trees
2831 Martin Luther Blvd.
Portland, OR 97212
503-282-8846

Texas
Dallas Trees and Parks Foundation
2121 San Jacinto, Suite 810
Dallas, TX 75201
214-953-1184

SPARK School Park Program
P.O. Box 1562
Houston, TX 77251
713-247-2909

Trees for Houston
P.O. Box 13096
Houston, TX 77212
713-840-8733

Tree Folks, Inc.
P.O. Box 704
Austin, TX 78767
512-443-5323

Utah
TreeUtah
364 E. Broadway
Salt lake City, UT 84111
801-364-2122

Virginia
Fairfax Releaf
P.O. Box 6141
McLean, VA 22106
703-324-1409

Washington
Treemendous Seattle
1602 Dexter Ave., N
Seattle, WA 98108
206-281-8415

Money For Small Businesses In Small Towns

Rural Business-Cooperative Service
1400 Independence Ave., SW
Room 5050 South Building
Washington, DC 20250
202-720-1400
www.rurdev.usda.gov/rbs/busp/rbeg.htm
Do you have a small or new business with less than 50 new employees and earn less
than $1 million in gross revenues? The Rural Business Enterprise Grant program is
administered by the Rural Business-Cooperative Service, and provides grant funds to
a local or regional intermediary which in turn, lends funds in a flexible manner to local businesses. Funds are
designed to facilitate the development of small and emerging private business, industry, and related employment.
Money can be used for the acquisition and development of land, and the construction of buildings, plants,
equipment, access streets and roads, parking areas, utility and service extensions, refinancing, fees, technical
assistance, startup operating cost, working capital, providing financial assistance to a third party, production of
television programs to provide information to rural residents; and to create, expand, and operate rural distance
learning networks. Forms are available from and may be filed in any USDA Rural Development State Office.

Money For Your Own Forest

Cooperative Forestry
P.O. Box 96090
Washington, DC 20090
202-205-1389
www.fs.fed.us/spf/coop/programs.htm
Landowner Assistance Programs help private landowners protect, improve, restore, and sustain forests. The Forest

Legacy Program protects private forest lands from being converted to nonforest uses. The Forest Stewardship Program helps private forest landowners develop plans for the sustainable management of their forests. The Stewardship Incentives Program provides financial assistance to private landowners to carry out their stewardship plans. Technical and financial assistance is provided, and is usually delivered through the State Foresters.

Money For Your Small Town

Cooperative Forestry
P.O. Box 96090
Washington, DC 20090
202-205-1389
www.fs.fed.us/spf/coop/rca.htm
Rural Community Assistance Programs help rural communities build skills, networks, and strategies to address social, environmental, and economic changes. The Forest Products Conservation and Recycling program helps communities and businesses find new and expanded business opportunities based on forest resources. The Market Development and Expansion program helps develop new markets for forest-based goods and services. For more information, you may also contact the Rural Community Assistance Regional Coordinators.

Region1
USDA Forest Service
Federal Building
200 E. Broadway
P.O. Box 7669
Missoula, MT 59807
406-329-3230
(Idaho, Montana, North Dakota, Utah, parts of Wyoming)

Region 2
USDA Forest Service
P.O. Box 25127
Lakewood, CO 80225
740 Simms St.
Golden, CO 80401
303-275-5741
(Colorado, Kansas, Nebraska, South Dakota, parts of Wyoming)

Region 3
USDA Forest Service
Federal Building, 517 Gold Ave., SW
Albuquerque, NM 87102
505-842-3421
(Arizona, New Mexico)

Region 5
USDA Forest Service
State and Private Forestry
1323 Club Dr.
Vallejo, CA 94592

707-562-8910
(California, Hawaii)

Region 6
USDA Forest Service
P.O. Box 3623
333 SW 1st Ave.
Portland, OR 97208
503-808-2346
(Oregon, Washington)

Region 8
USDA Forest Service
1720 Peachtree Rd., NW, Suite 846 N
Atlanta, GA 30367
404-347-7486
(Alabama, Arkansas, Florida, Georgia, Kentucky, Louisiana, Mississippi, North Carolina, Oklahoma, South Carolina, Tennessee, Texas, Virginia)

Region 10
USDA Forest Service
3301 C St., Suite 522
Anchorage, AK 99503
907-271-2519
(Alaska)

Region Northern Area
USDA Forest Service
180 Canfield St.
Morgantown, WY 26505
304-285-1538

(Connecticut, Delaware, Illinois, Indiana, Iowa, Maine, Maryland, Massachusetts, Michigan, Minnesota, Missouri, New Hampshire, New Jersey, New York, Ohio, Pennsylvania, Rhode Island, Vermont, West Virginia, Wisconsin)

MONEY FOR TELECOMMUNICATIONS

Technology Opportunities Program
Office of Telecommunications and Information Applications
National Telecommunication and Information Administration
U.S. Department of Commerce
1401 Constitution Ave., NW, Room 4092
Washington, DC 20230
202-501-5136
www.ntia.doc.gov/otiahome/top/index.html
The Technology Opportunities Program (TOP) promotes the widespread availability and use of advanced telecommunications technologies in the public and non-profit sectors. The TOP gives grants for model projects demonstrating innovative uses of network technology. TOP has made matching grants to state, local, and tribal governments, health care providers, schools, libraries, police departments, and community-based non-profit organizations. TOP projects demonstrate how networks support lifelong learning for all Americans, help public safety officials, protect the public, assist in the delivery of health care and public health services, and foster communication, resource-sharing, and economic development within rural and urban communities.

Money For Public Television and Radio In Your Town

Public Telecommunications Facilities Program
Office of Telecommunications and Information Applications
National Telecommunications and Information Administration
U.S. Department of Commerce
1401 Constitution Ave., NW, Room 4625
Washington, DC 20230
202-482-5802
www.ntia.doc.gov/otiahome/ptfp/index.html
The Public Telecommunications Facilities program assists through matching grants in the planning and construction of public telecommunications facilities. It supports public radio and television stations and public telecommunication services and facilities available
to, operated by, and controlled by minorities and women. The program also funds radio reading services and descriptive video services for the disabled, and numerous distance learning facilities that provide instructional programming for students and professionals.

MONEY TO IMPROVE YOUR TOWN

Economic Development Administration
U.S. Department of Commerce
14th and Constitution Ave., NW, Room 7800B
Washington, DC 20230
202-482-5081
www.doc.gov/eda/html/pwprog.htm

The Public Works Development Facilities Program provides grants to help distressed communities attract new industry, encourage business expansion, diversify local economies, and generate long-term private sector jobs. Among the types of projects funded are water and wastewater facilities, primarily serving industry and commerce; access roads to industrial parks or sites; port improvements; business incubator facilities; technology projects; sustainable development activities; export programs; brownfields redevelopment and other infrastructure projects. The program is primarily intended to benefit low and moderate-income populations, unemployed and underemployed residents and to help stop out-migration as well as to assist areas experiencing long-term economic distress due to industrial restructuring and business relocation. Eligible applicants should contact the Economic Development Representative in the area.

Economic Development Representative

Atlanta Region
Economic Development Administration
401 West Peachtree Street, NW, Suite 1820
Atlanta, GA 30308
404-730-3002
Serves Alabama, Florida, Georgia, Kentucky, Mississippi, North Carolina, South Caroline, Tennessee

Austin Region
Economic Development Administration
327 Congress Ave.
Suite 200
Austin, TX 78701
512-381-8144
Serves Arkansas, Louisiana, New Mexico, Oklahoma, Texas

Chicago Region
Economic Development Administration
111 North Canal St, Suite 855
Chicago, IL 60606
312-353-7706

Serves Illinois, Indiana, Michigan, Minnesota, Ohio, Wisconsin

Denver Region
Economic Development Administration
1244 Speer Boulevard, Room 670
Denver, CO 80204
303-844-4715
Serves Colorado, Iowa, Kansas, Missouri, Montana, Nebraska, North Dakota, South Dakota, Utah, Wyoming

Philadelphia Region
Economic Development Administration
Curtis Center
Suite 140 South
Independence Square West
Philadelphia, PA 19106
215-597-4603
Serves Connecticut, Delaware, District of Columbia, Maine, Maryland, Massachusetts, New Hampshire, New Jersey, New York, Pennsylvania, Rhode Island, Vermont, Virginia, West Virginia

Help For Your Distressed Town

Economic Development Administration
U.S. Department of Commerce
14th and Constitution Ave., NW, Room 7800B
Washington, DC 20230
202-482-5081
www.doc.gov/eda/html/econadj.htm
The Economic Adjustment Program helps states and local areas design/implement strategies for facilitating adjustment to changes in their economic situation that are causing or threaten to cause serious structural damage to the underlying economic base. Such changes may occur suddenly or over time, and result from industrial or corporate restructuring, new Federal laws/requirements, reduction in defense expenditures, depletion of natural resources or natural disasters. An applicant may be a state, a city, an Indian Tribe, a designated Redevelopment Area, a community development corporation, or a nonprofit organization.

The area to be assisted must either have experienced or anticipate a change in the economic situation of the area, or have high unemployment and low per capita income. Activities can include creation or expansion of targeted business development and financing programs including grants for revolving loan funds, infrastructure improvements, organizational development, and market or industry research and analysis. Eligible applicants should contact the Economic Development Representative in the area. See previous item above for a listing or Economic Development Representative.

MONEY IF A MILITARY BASE CLOSES

Office of Economic Adjustment
400 Army Navy Dr., Suite 200
Arlington, VA 22202
703-604-2420
http://emissary.acq.osd.mil/oea/home.nsf
When a military base closes, opportunities are created for local communities to consider the reuse of large parcels of land and surplus personal property and buildings in ways not previously envisioned. The office of Economic Adjustment can provide state and local government directly impacted by a base closure with technical and financial assistance in the form of economic adjustment grants to aid in the planning and the orderly, economical reuse of closing bases. In addition, the Office of Economic Conversion Information (OEIC) at {www.oeci.doc.gov} is a clearinghouse of information needed to anticipate, plan for, and respond to, defense downsizing. The OEIC is designed to serve the basic information needs of three major groups of customers- communities, industries, and workers. In addition, the Clearinghouse is a valuable resource for policy makers and public service providers at the federal, state, and local level.

IS YOUR TOWN NEAR AN HISTORIC BATTLEFIELD?

National Center for Cultural Resources Stewardship and Partnership Programs
National Park Service
1849 C St., NW, NC 330
Washington, DC 20240
202-343-9583
www.cr.nps.gov/helpyou.htm
Once a year as part of its grants program the American Battlefield Protection Program (ABPP) invites proposals for battlefield preservation projects. The ABPP and its partners have helped protect and enhance more than 100 battlefields. Most partners contribute matching funds or in-kind services to these projects. The ABPP supports historical research, cultural and archaeological surveys, battlefield assessment, public education, and more.

Local Historic Preservation

Certified Local Government Program
Heritage Preservation Services
National Park Service
1849 C St., NW, NC330
Washington, DC 20240
202-343-6005

www.cr.nps.gov/helpyou.htm
Local governments strengthen their local historic preservation efforts by achieving Certified Local Government status from the National Park Service. The National Park Service and State governments, through their State historic preservation offices, provide valuable technical assistance and small matching grants to hundreds of diverse communities whose local governments are endeavoring to keep for future generations what is significant from their community's past.

PRESERVE YOUR NEIGHBORHOOD

Challenge Cost-Share Program
Heritage Preservation Services
National Park Service
1849 C St., NW, NC200
Washington, DC 20240
202-343-9575
www.cr.nps.gov/helpyou.htm
The Challenge Cost-Share Program was established so
that the National Park Service could increase participation
by neighboring communities, volunteer groups,
universities, and others to preserve natural, recreational,
and cultural resources for which the Service is responsible. Through "small dollar" projects (maximum $30,000
Federal share with a required match of non-Federal cash or in-kind services), mutually beneficial projects related to
the Service's mission are carried out. A broad range of projects have been funded, including National Trails projects,
historic structure rehabilitation, videos, general cleanups, and much more.

State Historic Preservation Offices
Since 1968, over $800 million in grant funds has been awarded to 59 States, territories, Indian Tribes, local
governments, and the National Trust for Historic Preservation. Projects eligible for funding and the criteria used to
select them are developed annually by the State Historic Preservation Offices. Among the kinds of activities funded
are the following: architectural, historical, archaeological surveys, publications, exhibits, videos, and more. For
more specific information contact your State Historic Preservation Office.

Alabama
Alabama Historical Commission
468 South Perry St.
Montgomery, AL 36130
334-242-3184
www.preserveala.org

Alaska
Alaska Department of Natural Resources
Office of History and Archeology
550 West 7th Ave.
Suite 1310
Anchorage, AK 99501
907-269-8721
www.dnr.state.ak.us/parks/oha_web

Arizona
Arizona State Parks
1300 West Washington
Phoenix, AZ 85007

602-542-4174
www.pr.state.az.us

Arkansas
Arkansas Historic Preservation Program
323 Center St., Suite 1500
Little Rock, AR 72201
501-324-9880

California
Office of Historic Preservation
Department of Parks and Recreation
P.O. Box 942896
Sacramento, CA 94296
916-653-6624
http://cal-parks.ca.gov

Colorado
Colorado Historical Society
1300 Broadway

Denver, CO 80203
303-866-3395
www.coloradohistory-oahp.org

Connecticut
Connecticut Historical Commission
59 S. Prospect St.
Hartford, CT 06106
860-566-3005

Delaware
Division of Historical and Cultural Affairs
P.O. Box 1401
Dover, DE 19903
302-739-5313

District of Columbia
Historic Preservation Division, Suite 305
941 N. Capitol St., NW, Room 2500
Washington, DC 20002
202-442-4570
www.dcra.org

Florida
Division of Historical Resources
Department of State
500 S. Bronough St.
Tallahassee, FL 32399
850-488-1480
www.dos.state.fl.us/dhr/contents.html

Georgia
Historic Preservation Division
57 Forsyth St., NW, Suite 500
Atlanta, GA 30303
404-656-2940
www.dnr.state.ga.us/dnr.histpres/

Hawaii
Department of Land and Natural Resources
P.O. Box 621
Honolulu, HI 96809
808-587-0401
www.hawaii.gov/dlnr

Idaho
Idaho State Historical Society
1109 Main St., Suite 250
Boise, ID 83702
208-334-2682

Illinois
Illinois Historic Preservation Agency
1 Old State Capitol Plaza

Springfield, IL 62701
217-785-1153

Indiana
Department of Natural Resources
402 West Washington St.
Indiana Government Center South, Room W256
Indianapolis, IN 46204
317-232-1646

Iowa
State Historical Society of Iowa
Capitol Complex
East 6th and Locust St.
Des Moines, IA 50319
515-281-8824

Kansas
Kansas State Historical Society
6425 Southwest 6th Ave.
Topeka, KS 66615
785-272-8681

Kentucky
Kentucky Heritage Council
300 Washington St.
Frankfort, KY 40601
502-564-7005

Louisiana
Department of Culture, Recreation and Tourism
P.O. Box 44247
Baton Rouge, LA 70804
225-343-8200
www.crt.state.la.us

Maine
Maine Historic Preservation Commission
55 Capitol St., Station 65
Augusta, ME 04333
207-287-2132
http://janus.state.me.us/mhpc/

Maryland
Maryland Historical Trust
100 Community Place, Third Floor
Crownsville, MD 21032
410-514-7600
www.ari.net/mdshpo

Massachusetts
Massachusetts Historical Commission
220 Morrissey Boulevard
Boston, MA 02125

617-727-8470
www.state.ma.us/sec/mhc

Michigan
State Historic Preservation Office
Michigan Historical Center
717 West Allegan St.
Lansing, MI 48919
517-373-1630
www.sos.state.mi.us/history/preserve/preserve.html

Minnesota
Minnesota Historical Society
345 Kellogg Boulevard West
St. Paul, MN 55102
651-296-2747
www.mnhs.org

Mississippi
Mississippi Department of Archives and History
P.O. Box 571
Jackson, MS 39205
601-359-6850

Missouri
State Department of Natural Resources
205 Jefferson
P.O. Box 176
Jefferson City, MO 65102
573-751-4422
www.mostateparks.com

Montana
State Historic Preservation Office
1410 8th Ave.
P.O. Box 201202
Helena, MT 59620
406-444-7717
www.hist.state.mt.us

Nebraska
Nebraska State Historical Society
P.O. Box 82554
1500 R St.
Lincoln, NE 68501
403-471-4745

Nevada
Historic Preservation Office
100 N. Stewart St.
Capitol Complex
Carson City, NV 89701
775-684-3440

New Hampshire
NH Division of Historical Resources
P.O. Box 2043
Concord, NH 03302
603-271-6435
www.state.nh.us/nhdhr

New Jersey
Department of Environmental Protection
401 East State St.
P.O. Box 402
Trenton, NJ 08625
609-292-2885

New Mexico
Historic Preservation Division
Office of Cultural Affairs
228 East Palace Ave.
Santa Fe, NM 87503
505-827-6320
www.museums.state.nm.us/hpd

New York
Parks, Recreation and Historic Preservation
Agency Building #1
Empire State Plaza
Albany, NY 12238
518-474-0443
www.nysparks.com

North Carolina
Division of Archives and History
4610 Mail Service Center
Raleigh, NC 27699
919-733-7305
www.hpo.dcr.state.nc.us

North Dakota
State Historical Society of North Dakota
612 E. Boulevard Ave.
Bismarck, ND 58505
701-328-2666
www.state.nd.us/hist

Ohio
Ohio Historic Preservation Office
567 E. Hudson St.
Columbus, OH 43211
614-297-2600
www.ohiohistory.org/resource/histpres

Oklahoma
Oklahoma Historical Society
2100 N. Lincoln Blvd.

Oklahoma City, OK 73105
405-521-2491
www.ok-history.mus.ok.us

Oregon
State Parks and Recreation Department
1115 Commercial St., NE
Salem, OR 97301
503-378-5019
www.prd.state.or.us/about_shpo.html

Pennsylvania
Pennsylvania Historical and Museum Commission
P.O. Box 1026
Harrisburg, PA 17108
717-787-2891
www.phmc.state.pa.us

Rhode Island
Rhode Island Historic Preservation and Heritage
Commission
Old State House
150 Benefit St.
Providence, RI 02903
401-222-2678

South Carolina
Department of Archives and History
8301 Parkland Rd.
Columbia, SC 29223
803-896-6100
www.state.sc.us/scdah

South Dakota
State Historic Preservation Office
Cultural Heritage Center
900 Governors Dr.
Pierre, SD 57501
605-773-3458
www.sdhistory.org

Tennessee
Department of Environment and Conservation
401 Church St.
L & C Tower 21st Floor
Nashville, TN 37243
615-532-0109
www.state.tn.us/environment/hist/

Texas
Texas Historical Commission
P.O. Box 12276

Austin, TX 78711
512-463-6100
www.thc.state.tx.us

Utah
Utah State Historical Society
300 Rio Grande
Salt Lake City, UT 84101
801-533-3500
http://history.utah.org

Vermont
Vermont Division for Historic Preservation
National Life Building, Drawer 20
Montpelier, VT 05620
802-828-3211
www.state.vt.us/dca/historic

Virginia
Department of Historic Resources
2801 Kensington Ave.
Richmond, VA 23221
804-367-2323

Washington
Office of Archeology and Historic Preservation
P.O. Box 48343
420 Golf Club Rd., SW
Suite 201, Lacey
Olympia, WA 98504
360-407-0753

West Virginia
West Virginia Division of Culture and History
Historic Preservation office
1900 Kanawha Boulevard East
Charleston, WV 25305
304-558-0220

Wisconsin
State Historical Society of Wisconsin
816 State St.
Madison, WI 53706
608-264-6500
www.shsw.wisc.edu/ahi/index.html

Wyoming
Wyoming State Historic Preservation Office
2301 Central Ave., 4th Floor
Cheyenne, WY 82002
307-777-7013
http://commerce.state.wy.us/cr/shpo

MONEY FOR NATIVE AMERICANS

Tribal Preservation Program
Heritage Preservation Services
National Park Service
1849 C St., NW, NC 200
Washington, DC 20240
202-343-4280
www.cr.nps.gov/helpyou.htm
Grant information is available to tribal organizations and Native American groups for carrying out cultural projects and programs as directed under the National Preservation Act.

MORE HELP FOR NATIVE AMERICANS

Native American Graves Protection and Repatriation Act
National Park Service
Archeology and Ethnography Program
1849 C St., NW, NC340
Washington, DC 20240
202-343-8161
www.cr.nps.gov/helpyou.htm
The Native American Graves Protection and Repatriation Act addresses the rights of lineal descendants, Indian tribes, Alaska Native villages and corporations, and Native Hawaiian organizations to certain Native American human remains and cultural items with which they are affiliated. Grants are available to museums and to Indian tribes for the purposes of assisting in the inventory, documentation, and repatriation of Native American human remains and cultural items.

Grants For Sea

National Maritime Initiative
National Park Service
NRHE-2280
1849 C St., NW, Room NC400
Washington, DC 20240
www.cr.nps.gov/helpyou.htm
The National Maritime Heritage Grants Program is a Federal assistance program established to help State and local governments and private nonprofit organizations carry out their maritime heritage activities. It provides funds for Maritime Heritage Education Projects and Maritime Heritage Preservation Projects designed to reach a broad audience and enhance public awareness and appreciation. Education programs can include hands-on participation, waterborne-experience programs in historic vessels and field schools.

Preservation Grants

National Center for Preservation Technology and Training
NSU Box 5682
Natchitoches, LA 71497

318-357-6464
www.ncptt.nps.gov
The Preservation Technology and Training Grants Program is among the few preservation and conservation grants programs devoted to training, technology and basic research. It has developed partnerships for innovative work in preservation and conservation.

Help Strengthen Your Town

Office of Juvenile Justice and Delinquency Prevention
Juvenile Justice Resource Center
2277 Research Blvd.
Mail Stop 2K
Rockville, MD 20850
301-519-5535
800-638-8736
www.ojjdp.ncjrs.org/programs/drugfree.html
The Drug-Free Communities Support Program is designed to strengthen community-based coalition efforts to reduce youth substance abuse. The coalitions are made up of young people, parents, media, law enforcement, school officials, religious organizations, and other community representatives. The program enables these coalitions to enhance collaboration and coordination in an effort to target illegal drugs, alcohol, and tobacco. The coalitions will also encourage citizen participation in substance abuse reduction efforts and disseminate information about effective programs.

Grants for Appalachia

Appalachian Regional Commission
1666 Connecticut Ave., NW, Suite 700
Washington, DC 20009
202-884-7799
www.arc.gov
The Appalachian Regional Commission (ARC) awards program grants for projects that further the goals identified by the Commission. Program grants are awarded to state or local agencies and governmental entities, local governing boards, and nonprofit organizations. Because states originate all ARC program grants, a potential applicant must apply to the program manager in his or her state. ARC awards grants each year for research on topics that directly impact economic development in the Appalachian Region. They also support an Entrepreneurship Initiative that gives entrepreneurs greater access to capital, educates and trains entrepreneurs; encourages strategies to maximize the economic strengths of local communities; and provides support for business incubators.

FEDERAL EMPOWERMENT ZONES OFFER JOBS, JOB TRAINING AND SMALL BUSINESS HELP

Each year, the Federal government awards billions of dollars in grant money and low interest loans to communities and nonprofit groups that want to rebuild their neighborhoods. And what makes it even better, if your community falls within a federally designated Empowerment Zone (EZ), your community will actually receive a special preference when you apply for any grant money.

What exactly is an Empowerment or Enterprise Zone? They are specific geographic areas that typically have high unemployment, low incomes, and show a great need for financial and technical help in tackling chronic economic problems. In the case of Empowerment Zones, the Federal government has designated over 100 such areas that require large amounts of money to get things moving in a positive direction.

Entrepreneurs Can Use Empowerment/Enterprise Zones

If you want to start a business, look at starting one in these zones. Just by committing a business to one of these zones, you can get special breaks from the Federal government such as:

- $3,000 tax credit for hiring or training Empowerment Zone employees
- $20,000 additional write offs for tangible property expenses
- low rate tax exempt bond financing

Check out the website {www.ezec.gov} that provides a wealth of information on Rural EZ/EC, as well as providing a link to Urban EZ/EC programs.

Job Seekers Can Take Advantage of Empowerment/Enterprise Zones

If a business is going to get $3,000 in tax breaks just to train you, job seekers should look at businesses in these zones for ready and available employment. If you don't have the skills employers want to hire you, you can show them where they can get money to train you for free.

There are also a number of employment training programs that will give special consideration if the job seeker lives in one of these zones. The programs that fit this category and are described in detail in this chapter include:

- Money to Provide Poor Kids with Special Job Training
- Money to Train Poor Adults for New Jobs
- Money for Summer Jobs for Poor Kids
- Money to Train Poor Kids in New Job Skills
- Money to Set Up Job Information Centers
- Money to Train High School Dropouts

Fix Up Your Neighborhood

In addition to helping yourself and your business, you can also help your neighborhood. Remember, that's the main reason for the programs. Be sure that your elected officials and local organizations know how to take full advantage of these programs. You might even be able to educate a politician about money he didn't even know existed!

Once an area has been designated by the Federal government as an Empowerment Zone, it becomes eligible to receive special preferences when applying for federal money to help rebuild the area. The federal funding programs outlined in this section provide communities with money to achieve hundreds of different goals, including:

- ★ job training
- ★ summer jobs for kids
- ★ making schools safer
- ★ child care for the poor
- ★ rebuilding public utilities
- ★ drug reduction programs
- ★ environmental cleanup
- ★ low income housing loans
- ★ lead poisoning reduction
- ★ community bank investment
- ★ getting rid of noisy airplanes
- ★ keeping kids out of gangs
- ★ building a local health information database
- ★ helping the homeless

List of Empowerment/Enterprise Zones

Empowerment Zones

Urban Empowerment Zones
Atlanta, GA
Baltimore, MD
Chicago, IL
Detroit, MI
New York, NY
Philadelphia, PA
Camden, NJ

Urban Supplemental Zones
Los Angeles, CA
Cleveland, OH

Rural Empowerment Zones
Kentucky Highlands (Clinton, Jackson, Wayne Counties, KY)
Mid-Delta Mississippi (Bolivar, Holmes, Humphreys, Leflore Counties, MS)
Rio Grande Valley Texas (Cameron, Hidalgo, Starr, Willacy Counties, TX)

Urban Enhanced Enterprise Communities
Boston, MA
Houston, TX
Kansas City, KS - Kansas City, MO
Oakland, CA

Urban and Rural Enterprise Communities

Alabama
Rural: Chambers County, Greene and Sumter Counties
Urban: Birmingham

Arizona
Rural: Arizona Border Region (Cochise, Santa Cruz, and Yuma Counties)
Urban: Phoenix

Arkansas
Rural: Mississippi County, Eastern Arkansas (Cross, Lee, Monrow, and St. Francis County)
Urban: Pulaski County

California
Rural: Imperial County, City of Watsonville (Santa Cruz County)
Urban: Los Angeles (South Central/Huntington Park), San Diego, San Francisco (Hunters Point)

Colorado
Urban: Denver

Connecticut
Urban: Bridgeport

Delaware
Urban: Wilmington

District of Columbia
Urban: Washington

Florida
Rural: Jackson County
Urban: Dade County/Miami, Tampa

Georgia
Rural: Crisp and Dooly Counties, Central Savannah River Area (Burke, Hancock, Jefferson, McDuffie, Taliaferro, and Warren Counties)
Urban: Albany

Illinois
Urban: East St. Louis, Springfield

Indiana
Urban: Indianapolis

Iowa
Urban: Des Moines

Kentucky
Rural: McCreary County
Urban: Louisville

Louisiana
Rural: Northeast Louisiana Delta (Madison County), Macon Ridge (Catahoula, Concordia, Franklin, Morehouse, and Tensas County)
Urban: Ouachita Parish

Massachusetts
Urban: Lowell, Springfield

Michigan
Rural: Lake County
Urban: Flint, Muskegon

Minnesota
Urban: Minneapolis, St. Paul

Mississippi
Rural: North Delta (Panola, Quitman, and Tallahatchie Counties)
Urban: Jackson

Missouri
Rural: City of East Prairie (Mississippi County)
Urban: St. Louis

Nebraska
Urban: Omaha

Nevada
Urban: Clark County/Las Vegas

New Hampshire
Urban: Manchester

New Jersey
Urban: Neward

New Mexico
Rural: Mora, Taos, and Rio Ariba Counties
Urban: Albuquerque

New York
Urban: Albany, Buffalo, Newburgh-Kingston, Rochester

North Carolina
Rural: Halifax, Edgecombe, and Wilson Counties
Urban: Charlotte

Ohio
Rural: Greater Portsmouth (Scioto County)
Urban: Akron

Oklahoma
Rural: Southeast Oklahoma (Choctaw and McCurtain Counties)
Urban: Oklahoma City

Oregon
Rural: Josephine County
Urban: Portland

Pennsylvania
Rural: City of Lock Haven (Clinton County)
Urban: Harrisburg

Rhode Island
Urban: Providence

South Carolina
Rural: Williamsburg County and Lake City (Florence and Williamsburg Counties)
Urban: Charleston

South Dakota
Rural: Beadle and Spink Counties

Tennessee
Rural: Fayette and Haywood Counties, Scott County
Urban: Memphis Nashville

Texas
Urban: Dallas, El Paso, San Antonio, Waco

Utah
Urban: Ogden

Vermont
Urban: Burlington

Virginia
Rural: Accomack and Northampton Counties
Urban: Norfolk

Washington
Rural: Lower Yakima County
Urban: Seattle, Tacoma

West Virginia
Central Appalachia (Braxton, Clay, Fayette, Nicholas, and Roane Counties)
Urban: Huntington

Wisconsin
Urban: Milwaukee

Who To Contact For Further Information

Community Connections
P.O. Box 7189
Gaithersburg, MD 20898-7189
800-998-9999

Dennis Kane
EZ/EC Initiative
U.S. Department of Housing and Urban Development
451 7th St., SW, Room 7130
Washington, DC 20410
202-708-6339

Empowerment/Enterprise Zone Programs

For each program, you'll find the following information:

- *Program title*: this is the official title of the grant program used by officials in Washington, D.C.
- *Contact person*: this is the person designated by a particular agency to handle questions about a specific program.
- *Telephone number*: use this number to get more information on how to apply for these money programs.
- *Program description*: offers a brief explanation of what the money is used for.
- *Type of Preference*: describes what kind of special consideration Empowerment Zone communities receive when applying for programs.
- *Program Amount*: gives amount federal government has to spend each year on a program.

Individual states have their own Enterprise Zone programs, and among all 50 states, there are over 1,000 areas that have been targeted to receive special financial awards to help in their redevelopment efforts. Following this section of the federal redevelopment programs for Empowerment Zones, you will find a state-by-state listing of programs designed to help communities redevelop. But first, see what's available from the Federal government:

General Development Grants
(Community Development Block Grant Program)
HUD Building
Block Grant Assistance, CPD
U.S. Department of Housing and Urban Development
451 7th St., SW, Room 7282
Washington, DC 20410
202-708-1577
or
Zita Blankenship, rural areas
HUD Building
Block Grant Assistance, CPD
U.S. Department of Housing and Urban Development
451 7th St., SW, Room 7184
Washington, DC 20410
202-708-1322
Annual formula grants to entitled metropolitan cities and urban counties and to states for distribution to non-entitled communities. The program allows these entities to carry out a wide range of community development activities directed toward neighborhood revitalization, economic development, and improved community facilities and services.
Type of Preference: States may give priority for Empowerment Zone/Enterprise Community small cities. Entitlement communities may also target funds received to designated areas.
Program Amount: $4.6 billion.

Money for Drug and Violence Prevention Programs in Schools
(Safe and Drug-Free Schools and Communities)
Bill Modzeleski
U.S. Department of Education
4000 Portals Building
600 Independence Ave., SW
Washington, DC 20202-6123
202-260-3954
The current Drug Free Schools and Communities Program is the Federal government's major effort in the area of drug and violence and education and prevention. The program targets resources where they are most needed. States will receive 50 percent of their funds based on the Title I formula; the other 50 percent will be based on their school age population and states will determine criteria for selecting high need local educational agencies (LEAs) and target funds to these districts. States and local communities continue to have the primary role in developing and implementing drug and violence prevention and education programming. The Department of Education will provide national leadership in the areas of drug and violence prevention through information, technical assistance evaluation efforts, and direct loans.

In addition, the Safe and Drug Free Schools Communities Act authorizes state grants for Drug and

Violence Prevention Programs which provide funding to state and local educational agencies as well as governors. The new program authorizes a broader range of prevention activities. Newly authorized activities include mentoring, comprehensive health education, community service and character education, acquisition of metal detectors, and hiring of security personnel. States and local educational agencies will still be required to assess needs and measure program outcomes and use this information to formulate policies and program initiatives. A new national evaluation system will be established to assess the impact of the program.
Type of Preference: none
Program Amount: Estimated to be $565 million for the entire program.

Money for Urban Colleges to Help in Redevelopment

(Urban Community Service Program)
Sarah Babson
Center for International Education
U.S. Department of Education
600 Independence Ave., SW
Washington, DC 20202-5247
202-260-3472
The Urban Community Service Program provides grants to urban institutions of higher education (IHEs) to assist projects designed to encourage the use of urban IHEs as sources of skills, talents, and knowledge that can serve the urban areas in which they are located. Grants are made for planning activities, applied research, training, resource exchanges or technology transfers, delivery of services, and activities to design and implement programs to assist urban communities to meet and address their pressing and most severe problems. In awarding the grants, priority is given to applications proposing joint projects with existing local, state and federal programs.
Type of Preference: Priority to Empowerment Zones/Enterprise Communities.
Program Amount: $1.5 million.

Money to Lend to Others

(Community Development Financial Institutions)
Mark Bender
HUD Building
U.S. Department of Housing and Urban Development
451 7th St., SW, Room 7136
Washington, DC 20410
202-622-0201
Proposed legislation would provide funding for Community Development Banks and other community development financial institutions to provide money for development in financially underserved areas.
Type of Preference: Language in legislative proposal would give priority to CDBs serving Empowerment Zones/Enterprise Communities.
Program Amount: $382 million proposed over 4 years.

Money to Develop New Housing and Businesses

(John Heinz Neighborhood Development Program)
Stella Hall
American Communities
P.O. Box 7189
Gaithersburg, MD 20898-7189
202-708-2186
800-998-9999
Under this program, U.S. Department of Housing and Urban Development funds community based organizations to increase their capacity to carry out housing and community development activities and to achieve long term financial support for these activities. The activities must benefit low and moderate income persons within the neighborhood. Eligible activities are those which will:
- create permanent jobs in the neighborhood;
- establish or expand businesses within the neighborhood, such as a business incubator program;
- develop new housing;
- rehabilitate existing housing;
- manage housing stock within the neighborhood;
- deliver essential services with lasting benefit to neighborhoods;
- plan or finance voluntary neighborhood improvement efforts.
Type of Preference: Competitive preference for Empowerment Zones/ Enterprise Communities.
Program Amount: $5 million.

Help in Planning Health Care Services

(Rural Health Technical Assistance)
Jerry Coopey
Office of Rural Health
5600 Fishers Lane, Room 9-05

Rockville, MD 20857
301-443-0835
Support to empower designated rural Empowerment Zones/Enterprise Communities through leadership training, strategic planning, and health systems development.
Type of Preference: Preference for rural Empowerment Zone/Enterprise Community designees.
Program Amount: Technical Assistance.

Money to Help Create New Jobs
(Urban and Rural Community Economic Development Priority Area)
Joseph Carroll
Administration for Children and Families
Office of Community Services
370 L'Enfant Promenade, SW
Washington, DC 20447
202-401-9346
Grants to private locally initiated nonprofit community development corporations to support business development activities which create employment opportunities for low income people. Funds are used by grantees to develop job creation projects through business, physical or commercial development. More generally, they are used to improve the quality of the economic and social environment of low income residents including displaced workers, at-risk teenagers, public housing residents, and homeless individuals.
Type of Preference: Weighted consideration for serving Empowerment Zones/Enterprise Communities and Empowerment Zone/Enterprise Community eligible areas.
Program Amount: $21.834 million.

Money for Drug Abuse Prevention Programs
(Substance Abuse Prevention Demonstrations)
Kent Auguston
Center for Substance Abuse Prevention
5600 Fishers Lane
Rockwall Building 2, Room 9D10
Rockville, MD 20857
301-443-0365
Grants to states, local governments, and nonprofit and for-profit entities for substance abuse prevention demonstration projects. Grants will support development and assessment of innovative models for addressing high risk youth and community-wide approaches to substance abuse prevention, including community partnerships in managed care settings, and linkages with primary care programs and programs such as HEAD Start.

Type of Preference: Weighted consideration for serving Empowerment Zones/Enterprise Communities and Empowerment Zone/Enterprise Community eligible areas.
Program Amount: $42.0 million.

Money to Help Improve Your School
(Community Schools Program)
Terry Lewis
Family and Youth Services
U.S. Department of Health and Human Services
300 C St., SW
Washington, DC 20201
202-205-8102
Funds consortia of community-based organizations, schools, and others to develop neighborhood strategies to curb violence and promote positive academic and social achievement. Grants will be awarded in every state.
Type of Preference: Weighted consideration for serving Empowerment Zones/Enterprise Communities and Empowerment Zone/Enterprise Community eligible areas.
Program Amount: $25.9 million.

Money for Food Programs
(Community Food and Nutrition Program)
Joseph Carroll
Administration for Children and Families
Office of Community Services
370 L'Enfant Promenade, SW
Washington, DC 20447
202-401-9346
Grants to states, public agencies, and private nonprofit organizations to coordinate existing food assistance resources, assist in identifying sponsors of child nutrition programs and to develop innovative approaches for meeting the nutrition needs of low-income people. Health prevention is an important element of this program.
Type of Preference: Weighted consideration for serving Empowerment Zones/Enterprise Communities and Empowerment Zone/Enterprise Community eligible areas.
Program Amount: $4 million.

Early Childhood Development Programs

Money for Child Care Programs for Parents in Public Housing

(Early Child Care Program)
Maggie Taylor
U.S. Department of Housing and Urban Development
Room 7262, 451 7th St., SW
Washington, DC 20410
202-708-4300
Child care program for parents of children living in or near public housing, including parents who are homeless or are at risk of being homeless. Funds for a section of this program are administered through a joint memorandum of understanding between U.S. Department of Housing and Urban Development and U.S. Department of Health and Human Services. A portion of the U.S. Department of Housing and Urban Development-administered funds are targeted toward homeless families.
Type of Preference: Preference for Empowerment Zones/Enterprise Communities.
Program Amount: Funded at $15 million; set aside of $9 million for "homeless" child care.

Money for Early Childhood Education Programs

(Early Childhood Education)
Ray Miner
U.S. Department of Education
Room 4627, 600 Independence Ave., SW
Washington, DC 20202-6123
202-205-9805
The purpose of the Early Childhood Education program is to improve special education and early intervention services for infants, toddlers, and children with special needs from birth through eight years of age. This group includes infants and toddlers birth through age 2 with developmental delays or conditions that are likely to cause developmental delays, and those at risk of substantial developmental delays if they do not receive early intervention services. Children ages 3 through 8 are also included if they need special education because of a disability. The Early Childhood Education program supports research, development, outreach, technical assistance, and training activities that together constitute a systematic approach for improving services for young children with disabilities. Grants, contracts, and cooperative agreements are authorized to public agencies and private nonprofit and, in some cases, profit organizations.
Type of Preference: Competitive preference for Empowerment Zones/ Enterprise Communities.
Program Amount: $2 million.

Money for Lead Poisoning Prevention Programs

(Childhood Lead Poisoning Prevention Projects - State and Community-Based)
David L. Forney
Lead Poisoning Prevention Branch
Centers for Disease Control
4770 Buford Hwy, NE
Mail Stop F-42
Atlanta, GA 30341
404-488-7330
Grants to state governments and local governments serving areas with more than 500,000 people for developing, improving, and expanding their capacity to address the problem of childhood lead poisoning in high-risk populations. Grantees undertake various activities, including lead poisoning screening; medical management to ensure that children exposed to lead receive proper treatment and follow-up services; environmental investigation; program evaluations; and other related activities.
Type of Preference: Weighted consideration for serving Empowerment Zones/Enterprise Communities and Empowerment Zone/Enterprise Community eligible areas.
Program Amount: $7.5 million.

Learn and Serve (K-12)

(Learn and Serve - K-12)
Hugh Bailey
The Corporation for National and Community Service
1201 New York Ave., NW
Washington, DC 20525
The major purpose of Learn and Serve is to fund school and community based service-lending programs for school age youth via State Education Agencies (SEAs), local school districts, Indian tribes, U.S. Territories, grant making entities, and State Commissions. These programs engage youth in service to their communities to enrich academic learning, promote personal growth, and help youth develop skills needed for productive citizenship.
Type of Preference: Not applicable.
Program Amount: $37.5 million.

Economic Development/Job Creation Programs

Money for General Housing and Business Development

(Section 108 Loan Guarantee)
Paul Webster
U.S. Department of Housing and Urban Development
Financial Management Division
451 7th St., SW, Room 7180
Washington, DC 20410
202-708-1871
Under this program, U.S. Department of Housing and Urban Development guarantees notes issued by units of general local government. Section 108 funds may be used to finance a wide array of economic revitalization and development activities that include housing and rehabilitation of privately owned buildings for residential purposes; expansion of for-profit businesses including equipment and physical plant; financing and rehabilitation of low income and public housing; acquisition, construction, or rehabilitation of neighborhood and community facilities; site improvement on community owned land which could be leased to a developer to carry out a commercial or industrial development project; site development including structural removal and land clearing; purchase of land or buildings for any authorized economic development use; and infrastructure development which can include street reconstruction and/or sewer system repairs.
Type of Preference: Set aside of $500 million in loan guarantees for Empowerment Zones/Enterprise Communities.
Program Amount: $2.054 billion in loan guarantee authority.

Money to Supplement General Development Grant Programs

(Section 108 Economic Revitalization Grants)
Paul Webster
U.S. Department of Housing and Urban Development
Section 108 Loan Guarantee
451 7th St., SW, Room 7180
Washington, DC 20410
202-708-1871
The program provides grants to be used in tandem with Section 108 guaranteed loans for economic revitalization projects located in Empowerment Zones/Enterprise Communities. These grants will enhance the viability of such projects (through interest rate subsidies, debt service/operating reserves, etc.) and increase the likelihood that the Section 108 loans

can be repaid from project revenue.
Type of Preference: Set aside of up to $300 million in grants for Empowerment Zones.
Program Amount: $300 million.

Money and Help for General Community Development Projects

(Community Development Block Grant (CDBG) Program)
U.S. Department of Housing and Urban Development
Block Grant Assistance, CPD
451 7th St., SW, Room 7282
Washington, DC 20410
202-708-1577
or
Zita Blankenship, rural areas
U.S. Department of Housing and Urban Development
Block Grant Assistance, CPD
451 7th St., SW, Room 7282
Washington, DC 20410
202-708-1322
Also see the description of CDBG under "Community Building." CDBG funds may be used to provide direct assistance and technical assistance to for-profit businesses (including microenterprises) and to public and private organizations to facilitate economic development by owners of microenterprises and persons developing microenterprises by providing credit, technical assistance and general support such as peer support programs and counseling. CDBG funds may also be used for business incubators and public infrastructure serving businesses. Special consideration in meeting the program's targeting requirements for low-and moderate-income benefit will be given to employees who reside in, or businesses that are located in, census tracts that meet the Federal Empowerment Zone/Enterprise Community criteria.
Type of Preference: States may give priority for Empowerment Zone/Enterprise Community small cities. Entitlement communities may also target funds received to designated areas.
Program Amount: $4.6 billion.

Money and Help for Small Business Owners

(One Stop Capital Shop)
Karen Hontz
Small Business Administration
409 3rd St., SW, Suite 7125
Washington, DC 20416
202-205-6573
Deliver financial, business and technical assistance to small, minority and women-owned businesses through the following components:
- Small Business Lending Companies
- Micro-Enterprise Lenders
- Regular/Specialized Small Business Investment Companies
- Certified Development Companies
- Business Information Centers
- Service Corps of Retired Executives (SCORE)
- Small Business Development Centers

Additional assistance will be provided on federal contracting, surety bonds and SBIR. Also, technical assistance will be provided to minority firms through Small Business Administration's (7)(j) grant programs and to women-owned firms through Small Business Administration's women's demonstration projects.
Type of Preference: Located in Empowerment Zones or Enterprise Communities.
Program Amount: $3.2 billion over 5 years.

Money for General Small Business Development

(Development Grants (RBEG))
Bonnie S. Justice
U.S. Department of Agriculture
Rural Business and Cooperative Development Service
14th and Independence Ave.
Washington, DC 20250
202-720-1490
The Rural Development Administration assists public bodies and nonprofit corporations to finance and facilitate development of small and emerging private business enterprises located in areas outside the boundary of a city of 50,000 or more and its immediately adjacent urbanized area.
Type of Preference: Set aside for Empowerment Zones/Enterprise Communities.
Program Amount: $9.5 million set aside.

Money to Help Refinance Community Development Projects

(Intermediary Relending Program)
Pandor H. Hadjy
U.S. Department of Agriculture
Rural Business and Cooperative Development Service
14th and Independence Ave., SW

Washington, DC 20250-3200
202-690-4106
The Rural Development Administration finances business facilities and community development projects not within the outer boundary of any city having a population of 25,000 or more. This is achieved through loans made by the Rural Development Administration to intermediaries that provide loans to ultimate recipients for business facilities and community development projects in a rural area.
Type of Preference: Set aside for Empowerment Zones/Enterprise Communities.
Program Amount: $10 million set aside.

Money to Improve Roads, Water Projects, Sewers

(Economic Development Administration Public Works Program)
David McIllwain
U.S. Department of Commerce
Economic Development Administration
14th and Constitution Ave., NW, Room 7326
Washington, DC 20230
202-482-5265
Grants are provided to units of government, and public or private nonprofit organizations to help distressed communities attract new industry, encourage business expansion, diversify their economies, and generate long-term, private sector jobs. Among the types of projects funded are water and sewer facilities primarily serving industry and commerce; access roads to industrial sites or parks; port improvements; and business incubator buildings. Proposed project must be located within an Economic Development Administration-designated Redevelopment Area or directly benefit an RA, and must be consistent with an approved Overall Economic Development Program.
Type of Preference: Points added to Empowerment Zones/Enterprise Communities.
Program Amount: $195 million.

Money to Create Redevelopment Plans

(Title IX Economic Adjustment)
David Witschi
Director of Economic Adjustment Division
Economic Development Administration
U.S. Department of Commerce
14th and Constitution Ave., NW
Washington, DC 20230
202-482-2659
Grants to units of government, and public or private nonprofit organizations to develop and implement

local economic adjustment strategies designed to address a serious contraction of their economic base which may have occurred suddenly or over time. The impact on jobs and income must be severe, and actually, or potentially, long term. The economic contraction may be the consequence of increasing global competition, technological innovation, changing consumption patterns, federal actions, such as elimination of trade restrictions and cutbacks in defense spending and natural disasters. Economic Development Administration may provide communities with virtually any of the tools that may be needed, singularly or in combination, to design and/or implement economic adjustment strategies appropriate to the particular circumstances. This flexibility may be used to promote and support the use of innovative approaches to addressing different types of economic adjustment problems. Such tools include construction of public facilities, technical/management assistance, and business development assistance including Revolving Loan Funds.

Type of Preference: Targeted to communities including Empowerment Zone/Enterprise Community eligible communities which meet the dislocation criteria.

Program Amount: $45 million.

Money To Plan and Implement Economic Development

(Planning Programs for States and Urban Areas)
Luis Bueso
Director of Planning Division
HCHB, Room 7319
Economic Development Administration
U.S. Department of Commerce
14th and Constitution Ave., NW
Washington, DC 20230
202-482-2873
Grants to help economically distressed states, cities, and urban counties undertake significant new economic development planning, policy-making, and implementation efforts. The grants finance the administrative expenses to support significant

economic development planning and implementation activities, such as economic analysis, definition of project goals, determination of project opportunities, and formulation and implementation of a development program.

Type of Preference: Points added to Empowerment Zones/Enterprise Communities.

Program Amount: $4.87 million.

Money to Help Organize Development and Solve Problems

(Local Technical Assistance Program)
Dick Hage
Acting Director of Technical Assistance and Research
HCHB, Room 7315
Economic Development Administration
U.S. Department of Commerce
14th and Constitution Ave., NW
Washington, DC 20230
202-482-4085
Grants designed to assist in solving specific economic development problems, respond to developmental opportunities, and build and expand local organizational capacity in distressed areas.

Type of Preference: Points added to Empowerment Zones/Enterprise Communities.

Program Amount: $1.5 million.

Money to Guarantee Private Development Loans

(Business and Industry)
Pandor H. Hadjy
U.S. Department of Agriculture
Rural Business and Cooperative Development Service
14th and Independence Ave., SW
Washington, DC 20250-3200
202-690-4106
The Rural Development Administration improves, develops or finances business, industry, and employment and improves the economic and environmental climate in rural communities, including pollution abatement and control. This purpose is achieved through bolstering the existing private credit structure through guarantee of quality loans that will provide lasting community benefits. It is not intended that the guarantee authority will be used for marginal or substandard loans or to "bail out" lenders having such loans. This type of assistance is available only to businesses located outside the boundary of a city with a population of 50,000 or more and its immediately adjacent urbanized area.

Type of Preference: Set aside for Empowerment Zones/Enterprise Communities.

Program Amount: $11 million.

Money to Develop Technology Outreach Programs

(Manufacturing Extension Partnership (MEP))
Kevin Carr
National Institute of Standards and Technology
Building 301, Room C121
Gaithersburg, MD 20899
301-975-4676
The Manufacturing Extension Partnership (MEP) provides matching grants (50% declining to 33% over 6 years) to nonprofit organizations, states, local governments, universities and community colleges to establish manufacturing technology and outreach centers. Centers provide assistance to small- and medium-sized manufacturing firms in adopting advanced manufacturing methods and technologies. Additionally, MEP provides one-time planning grants to states to develop and/or coordinate state-wide technology infrastructure which provides service to such industries. The ultimate mission of the MEP is to improve U.S. manufacturing competitiveness by providing small businesses access to a national network of technical, business and training resources necessary to become world-class.
Type of Preference: None
Program Amount: $80.1 million.

Money to Improve Your Community

Richard Saul
Office of Community Services
370 L'Enfant Promenade, SW, Fifth Floor
Washington, DC 20447
202-401-9341
Grants to Community Action Agencies for developing and implementing innovative approaches to address the critical needs of the poor common to a number of communities. Grantees, in partnership with other public and private organizations, develop an array of innovative programs, including homelessness, microenterprise/self-employment, minority youth life skills, case management, teenage pregnancy, and comprehensive integrated services.

Type of Preference: Weighted consideration for service Empowerment Zones/Enterprise Communities and Empowerment Zone/Enterprise Community eligible areas.
Program Amount: $7.977 million.

Money for You to Open Your Business

(Job Opportunities for Low-Income Individuals)
Nolan Lewis
Office of Community Services
370 L'Enfant Promenade, SW, Fifth Floor
Washington, DC 20447
202-401-5282
Grants to nonprofit organizations (including community development corporations) to demonstrate and evaluate ways to create new employment and business opportunities for AFDC recipients and other low-income individuals. Grantees must develop programs that create new jobs through self-employment/microenterprise, expansion of existing businesses, and/or development of business ventures.
Type of Preference: Weighted consideration for service Empowerment Zones/Enterprise Communities and Empowerment Zone/Enterprise Community eligible areas.
Program Amount: $5.5 million.

Education and Job Linkages

Money for Training Programs for Students Not Going to College

(School to Work Opportunities)
J.D. Hoye (U.S. Department of Education)
School to Work Program
400 Virginia Ave., SW, Room 210
Washington, DC 20024
202-401-6209
It will assist students in making the transition from school to a good first job in a high skill, high wage career track. Each school-to-work program must include work-based learning activities, school-based learning activities and connecting activities. Communities, through collaboration of secondary and post secondary educators, employers, labor, parents and other key parties, will be responsible for giving youth access to skills and employment opportunities that will launch them on paths leading to high skills, high wage careers.
Type of Preference: Competitive grant programs.
Program Amount: $100 million ($50m U.S. Department of Labor; $50m U.S. Department of Education).

Money for Training Programs in Poor Urban Areas

(School-to-Work Urban/ Rural Opportunities Grants)
Karen Clark (U.S. Department of Education)
School to Work Program
400 Virginia Ave., SW, Room 210
Washington, DC 20024
202-219-6214
School-to-work Urban/ Rural Opportunities Grants
will be awarded on a competitive basis to
demonstration projects providing school-to-work
opportunities programs aimed at youth residing in
high-poverty areas in urban and rural communities.
Type of Preference: Limited to high poverty areas.
Coordination between the Empowerment Zone or
Enterprise Community activities and the School-to-
Work High Poverty grants is encouraged.
Program Amount: $25 million.

Money to Help Start School To Work Programs

(Federal School-To-Work Implementation Grants to
Local Partnership Grants)
Marian Banfield (U.S. Department of Education)
School to Work Program
400 Virginia Ave., SW, Room 210
Washington, DC 20024
202-401-6222
or
Janet Moore (U.S. Department of Labor)
School to Work Program
400 Virginia Ave., SW, Room 210
Washington, DC 20024
202-401-3822
Federal School-to-Work Implementation Grants to
Local Partnerships will be competitively awarded to
communities that are prepared to undertake a school-
to-work program. This program is designed to provide
support and funds to communities that have built a
sound planning and development base for School-to-
Work Opportunities programs and that are ready to
begin implementing a local School-to-Work
Opportunities program. Local grants are to involve
local partners directly and accelerate actual operation

of programs nationwide by enrolling significant
numbers of school-to-work participants.
Type of Preference: Coordination between the
Empowerment Zone or Enterprise Community
activities and the Federal School-to-Work
Implementation grants is encouraged.
Program Amount: $10-12 million.

Education and Training Programs

Money for Low-Income Education Programs

(Title I of the Improving America's Schools Act)
Mary Jean LeTendre
U.S. Department of Education
600 Independence Ave., SW
Room 4400 Portals
Washington, DC 20202-6132
202-260-0826
Chapter 1 of the Elementary and Secondary Education
Act provides extra instruction to help low-achieving
students in low-income areas reach high academic
standards. Chapter 1 funds, which are distributed to
local educational agencies on a formula basis, can be
used for a variety of purposes including coordination
of services, mentoring and tutoring programs, and
after-school and summer educational activities.
Empowerment Zones and Enterprise Communities are
encouraged to incorporate these pre-existing Chapter
1 resources in their strategic plans. In addition,
pending legislation would create a new authority
under this program to carry out demonstration projects
that show the most promise of enabling children
served under the program to meet challenging state
standards. Among the projects that could be funded
would be those that demonstrate promising strategies
of integration of education services with each other
and with health, family and other social services,
particularly in Empowerment Zones and Enterprise
Communities. State and local educational agencies,
other public agencies, nonprofit agencies and
consortia of those bodies would be eligible for
discretionary grants.
Type of Preference: Pending
Program Amount: $7.2 billion for entire Chapter 1
program.

Money for Gifted and Talented Student Programs

(Jacob K. Javits Gifted and Talented Students
Education Program)
Caroline Warren, OERI
U.S. Department of Education

555 New Jersey Ave., NW
Washington, DC 20202
202-219-2206
Under pending legislation, this program would demonstrate that programs and strategies for gifted and talented students can be used to help all students in a school to achieve their potential and to meet challenging state performance standards. The program would target discretionary grants to schoolwide efforts to provide challenging curricula and enriching instruction (often offered in gifted and talented programs) to all students. At least half of the awards will be given to high poverty schools.
Type of Preference: Competitive preference to Empowerment Zones/Enterprise Communities.
Program Amount: Estimated to be $3 million.

Access To Training and Education Programs
(Family Investment Centers (FIC))
Marcia Martin
U.S. Department of Housing and Urban Development
Office of Community Relations and Involvement
Room 4112
451 7th St., SW
Washington, DC 20410
202-708-4214
Under FIC, families living in Public and Indian Housing will be provided better access to training and educational opportunities.
Type of Preference: Competitive preference for Empowerment Zones/Enterprise Communities.

Money to Set Up Literacy Programs at Work
(National Workplace Literacy Program)
Dr. Carol Towey
U.S. Department of Education
Division of Adult Education and Literacy
600 Independence Ave., SW
Washington, DC 20202-7240
202-205-9872
The National Workplace Literacy Program provides assistance for demonstration projects that teach literacy skills needed in the workplace through exemplary education partnerships between (1) business, industry, or labor organizations, and (2) state educational agencies, local educational agencies, institutions of higher education or schools (including area vocational schools, employment and training agencies, or community-based organizations). This program must give priority to applications from partnerships that include small businesses.
Type of Preference: Competitive preference to Empowerment Zones/Enterprise Communities.
Program Amount: No new funding.

Money to Develop New Programs for the Disabled
(Rehabilitation Act Special Demonstration Projects)
Pamela Martin
Rehabilitation Services Administration
U.S. Department of Education
Washington, DC 20202-2531
202-205-8494
The Special Demonstration projects are designed to establish programs for providing rehabilitation services to expand and improve rehabilitation services to individuals with disabilities. Emphasis is given to providing services to those who are unserved or underserved, and those who are blind or deaf who can benefit from comprehensive services. In addition, projects to increase client choice and other activities are authorized.
Type of Preference: Competitive preference for Empowerment Zones/Enterprise Communities.
Program Amount: $2 million.

Money for Programs That Create Jobs for the Disabled
(Rehabilitation Act Projects with Industry Program)
Fred Ibister
Rehabilitation Services Administration
U.S. Department of Education
Washington, DC 20202-2531
202-205-9297
The Projects with Industries Program initiates programs to create and expand job and career opportunities for individuals with disabilities in the competitive labor market. Services generally include intake, evaluation, pre-vocational training, job development and placement. Services to employers may include job-site and equipment modification, application of rehabilitation technology, and employee recruitment. Each grantee must develop a Business Advisory Council with representation from private industry, organized labor and individuals with disabilities and their representatives.
Type of Preference: Competitive preference for Empowerment Zones/Enterprise Communities.
Program Amount: $1.7 million.

Money to Create Public Charter Schools

(Charter Schools)
John Fiegle
U.S. Department of Education
1250 Maryland Ave., SW
Room 4000 Portals Building
Washington, DC 20024
202-260-2671
Pending legislation would create a new authority to
fund the planning and start up of public charter
schools in states that have passed legislation
approving charter school experiments. In these states,
most regulatory requirements have been removed,
leaving schools free to sharpen their focus, mission
and identity. Charter schools are operated by key
stakeholders such as teachers and parents. Under the
proposal, state educational agencies or local
educational agencies would be able to apply for a
single grant of up to three years, in partnership with
the teachers, parents, or others developing the public
charter school. An application could cover any
combination of one or more schools.
Type of Preference: Competitive preference
Program Amount: Estimated to be $6 million.

Learn and Serve America: Higher Education

(Learn and Serve America: Higher Education)
Hugh Bailey
The Corporation for National and Community Service
1201 New York Ave., NW
Washington, DC 20525
This program engages diversity of communities,
students, and institutions in service-learning efforts
that meet critical needs while enhancing education for
citizenship. Higher Education programs address
community needs in four key areas: education, public
safety, human needs, and environment.
Type of Preference: None
Program Amount: $12.5 million.

Money for Bilingual Education Programs

(Bilingual Education)
Terry Sullivan
Office of Bilingual Education and Minority Language
  Affairs
Room 5619 MES
600 Independence Ave., SW
Washington, DC 20202
202-205-9752
Title VII of the Elementary and Secondary Education
Act, also known as the Bilingual Education Act,
authorizes three grant competitions to fund discrete
programs tailored to the needs of the various client
school districts.

Enhancement Grants - Local educational agencies
can apply for a grant of two years in order to develop
new programs, to enhance existing programs, or to
meet the short-term needs of districts that currently
have no bilingual programs.
Type of Preference: Competitive
Program Amount: $22.4 million.
System-Wide Grants - These grants are for district-
wide programs for applicants with significant
concentrations of language minority students. These
five-year grants are likely to serve all eligible students
in a district.
Type of Preference: Competitive
Program Amount: $17.4 million.
Comprehensive Grants - These grants provide
assistance to all eligible students within a single
school or small group of schools. Such a grant might
be appropriate in districts having concentrations of
language minority students in a number of selected
schools within a district.
Type of Preference: Competitive
Program Amount: $74.1 million.

Money to Train Kids in the Construction Industry

(Youthbuild)
Ronald J. Herbert
Office of Community Planning and Development
U.S. Department of Housing and Urban Development
451 7th St., SW, Room 7134
Washington, DC 20410
202-708-2035
The Youthbuild program consists of two parts:
planning and implementation grants. The purpose of
the program is to expand the supply of permanent
affordable housing for homeless and low- and very
low-income persons and to provide economically
disadvantaged young adults with opportunities to
obtain an education, employment skills and
meaningful on-site work experiences as a service to
their communities.
Type of Preference: Preference points to
Empowerment Zones.
Program Amount: $74.1 million.

Employment Programs

Money to Provide Poor Kids With Special Job Training

(Youth Fair Chance)
Beverly M. Bachemin
U.S. Department of Labor
Room N5637, 200 Constitution Ave., NW
Washington, DC 20210

202-219-7674
This program is designed to provide comprehensive employment and training services to youth (14-21 years) and young adults (22-30 years) in high poverty areas of urban and rural communities. The program concentrates resources in small geographic areas to provide an integrated array of services and thereby increases the chances that high-risk youth will find jobs, develop careers and lead productive lives.
Type of Preference: Targeted to high-crime, high-poverty urban and rural areas. Additional points given to applications from Empowerment Zones and Enterprise Communities.
Program Amount: $25 million.

Money to Train Poor Adults for New Jobs
(Job Training Partnership Act (JTPA) Title II-A, Adult Training Program)
Dolores Battle
U.S. Department of Labor
Room N4459, 200 Constitution Ave., NW
Washington, DC 20210
202-219-6236
This job training program is designed to increase the employability of poor adults. When they are job ready, the program helps them find and keep employment. Funds are provided to states and local areas based on unemployment and poverty levels. A wide range of employment and training services are eligible activities, including: a required skills and services assessment and development of an employment plan, vocational counseling, literacy and basic skills training, occupations skills training (either in classrooms or on the job), job search assistance, job placement and support services.
Type of Preference: Formula to states and localities. (States and localities may provide preference for assistance to Empowerment Zones/Enterprise Communities.)
Program Amount: $1,054.8 billion.

Money for Summer Jobs for Poor Kids
(Job Training Partnership Act (JTPA) Title II-B, Summer Youth Employment Program)
Donald Kulick
U.S. Department of Labor

Room N4463, 200 Constitution Ave., NW
Washington, DC 20210
202-219-6236
This program provides grants to states and local areas for summer youth employment programs. Funds are provided to states and local areas based on unemployment and poverty levels. Eligible activities include a wide range of activities that are available during the summer vacation months that enhance basic skills, encourage school completion, provide exposure to the world of work and enhance citizenship skills. These activities include assessment, vocational counseling, basic and remedial education, job skills training (either in classrooms or on-the-job), work experience and limited supportive services.
Type of Preference: Formula to states and localities. (States and localities may provide preference for assistance to Empowerment Zones/Enterprise Communities.)
Program Amount: $867 million.

Money to Train Poor Kids Job Skills
(Job Training Partnership Act (JTPA), Title II-C, Youth Training Program)
Josephine Nieves
U.S. Department of Labor
Room N4459, 200 Constitution Ave., NW
Washington, DC 20210
202-219-6236
This program provides grants to states and local areas for job training programs for economically disadvantaged youth. Funds are provided to states and local areas based on unemployment and poverty levels. Eligible activities include: a required skills and services assessment and development of an employment plan, vocational counseling, literacy and basic skills training, occupational skills training (either in classrooms or on-the-job), job search assistance, job placement, and support services. The program requires that youth be provided with pre-employment and work maturity skills training and work experience combined with skills training.
Type of Preference: Formula to states and localities. (States and localities may provide preference for assistance to Empowerment Zones/Enterprise Communities.)
Program Amount: $598.7 million.

Money to Set Up Job Information Centers
(One-Stop Career Centers)
Grace Kilbane
U.S. Department of Labor
Room N4470, 200 Constitution Ave., NW
Washington, DC 20210

202-219-5257
This is a system of career centers to provide any job seeker, student, or employer with streamlined access to a comprehensive menu of state of the art, user friendly, employment, education and training information and services. These centers will enable workers, students, and employers to access a wide range of high quality information about jobs and careers, labor markets, skill standards, education and training programs, and financing options.
Type of Preference: Special consideration given to proposals for locating centers in Empowerment Zones/Enterprise Communities.
Program Amount: $120 million.

Money to Train High School Dropouts

(Job Corps, Job Training Partnership Act (JTPA) Title IV)
Peter Rell
U.S. Department of Labor
Room N4510, 200 Constitution Ave., NW
Washington, DC 20210
202-219-8550
This is a highly intensive, primarily residential training program for severely disadvantaged youth ages 16 through 21. It is designed to make these youth more responsible citizens, prepared to obtain and hold productive jobs or enroll in vocational and technical schools, junior colleges or other institutions for further education or training. Job Corps is a federally administered program through a network of 108 Job Corps centers (including 2 new centers) located in 44 states, Puerto Rico, and the District of Columbia.
Type of Preference: Targeted to most economically disadvantaged youth. New Job Corps sites will be selected competitively. Additional points will be awarded for sites located in Empowerment Zones and Enterprise Communities.
Program Amount: $1.1 billion.

Environmental Protection Programs

Money to Develop Recreation Areas and Parks

(Urban Park and Recreation Recovery Program)
Chris Ashley
National Park Service
Recreation Grants Division
800 N. Capitol St., NW, Suite 400
Washington, DC 20020
202-343-3700
Under this program, federal grants are provided to local governments for the rehabilitation of recreation areas and facilities, demonstration of innovative approaches to improve park system management and recreation opportunities, and development of improved recreation planning. Eligible activities include resource and needs assessments, coordination, citizen involvement and planning, and program development activities to encourage public definition of goals.
Recovery Action Program grants have a 50 percent local match requirement to local governments for the development of local park and recreation system recovery plans. They assist local efforts to develop priorities and strategies for overall recreation recovery. State, local and private funds may be used as the nonfederal share of project costs. U.S. Department of Housing and Urban Development CDBG funds are the type of federal funds used for local match. All properties assisted through this program must be open to the public.
Rehabilitation grants are matching capital grants (70% federal and 30% local) to local governments for purpose of rebuilding, remodeling, or expanding existing facilities.
Innovative grants are matching (70% federal and 30% local) to local governments to cover costs of personnel, facilities, equipment, supplies or services designed to demonstrate innovative and cost effective ways to enhance park and recreation opportunities at the neighborhood level. Innovative grant funds may be used to address common problems related to facility operations and the delivery of recreation services.
Type of Preference: Priority to applicants located in Empowerment Zones and Enterprise Communities.
Program Amount: $7.5 million.

Money to Study Clean Up of Contaminated Land Sites

(Brownfields Economic Redevelopment Initiative)
Superfund
Environmental Protection Agency
401 M St., SW
Washington, DC 20460
800-424-9346

Funding to examine ways to convert contaminated sites to clean, productive uses.
Program Amount: $200,000.

Money to Show Industries How To Prevent Pollution

(Eco-Industrial Parks and Environmental Technology Initiatives)
EPA's ETI Information Line
Environmental Protection Agency
401 M St., SW, Mail Code 2111
Washington, DC 20460
202-260-2686
Funding to demonstrate how industrial parks can prevent pollution, minimize waste generation, and maximize energy and water efficiency.
Program Amount: $5 million.

Money to Help Businesses Prevent Pollution

(Pollution Prevention Grants Program)
Lena Hann
Environmental Protection Agency
401 M St., SW
Washington, DC 20460
202-260-2237
This program helps to promote the use of source reduction techniques by businesses. Includes funding for experts to provide on-site technical advice and to assist in the development of source reduction plans, targeting assistance to businesses that lack information, and provide training in source reduction techniques.
Type of Preference: Program favors candidates pursuing multi-media source reduction.
Program Amount: $6 million.

Money to Study How Pollution Affects Minorities and the Poor

(Environmental Justice Grants Program)
Dr. Clarice Gaylord and Daniel Gogal
Office of Environmental Justice
Environmental Protection Agency
Room 2710, Mail Code 3103
Washington, DC 20460
800-962-6215
Grants to examine the impacts of environmental problems on minority and economically disadvantaged communities.
Program Amount: $3 million.

General Help With Environmental Problems

(Technical Assistance in Understanding Environmental Problems, Regulations and Permits; Training Environmental Management)
Harriet Tregonning

Environmental Protection Agency
401 M St., SW
Washington, DC 20460
202-260-2778
U.S. Environmental Protection Agency Headquarters and regional office contacts are being provided to applicants and designees who wish to address the environmental protection, health and safety aspects of their Empowerment Zone or Enterprise Community strategic plan. These contacts can provide information on the grants, technical assistance and training opportunities that are available.
Program Amount: variable

Equal Opportunity Programs

Money to Help Fight Housing Discrimination

(Fair Housing Initiatives Program (FHIP))
Maxine Cunningham
HUD Building
U.S. Department of Housing and Urban Development
451 7th St., SW, Room 5234
Washington, DC 20410
202-708-0800
A competitive funding program that funds public and private nonprofit organizations, state and local government agencies and other public and private groups formulating or carrying out programs to prevent or eliminate discriminatory housing practices.
Type of Preference: Competitive preference for areas unserved or underserved by fair housing enforcement organizations.
Program Amount: $17 million.

Money to Study Gender Discrimination in Education

(Women's Educational Equity)
Carolyn Andrews
U.S. Department of Education
Women's Educational Equity
600 Independence Ave., SW
Portals Room 4500
Washington, DC 20202-6140
202-260-2670
This program promotes educational equity for girls and women, including those who suffer multiple discrimination based on gender and race, ethnicity, national origin, disability or age. It supports the development of model curricula and teacher training programs designed to help women and girls become active participants in academic fields and careers in which they have been historically under represented. The program supports demonstration and local implementation projects to prevent sexual harassment,

increase opportunities for women and girls in nontraditional fields through leadership training and school-to-work transition programs, and help pregnant and parenting teens remain in school, graduate, and prepare their children for preschool. Discretionary grants would be available to public agencies, private nonprofit agencies, organizations and institutions.
Type of Preference: competitive preference for Empowerment Zones/Enterprise Communities.
Program Amount: $3.1 million.

Family Support Programs

Money to Train Parents of Disabled Parents
(Training Personnel for the Education of Individuals with Disabilities — Parent Training and Information Center Program [Individuals With Disabilities Education Act, Part D, Section 631(c)])
Jack Tringo
Office of Special Education Programs
U.S. Department of Education
600 Independence Ave., SW
MES Room 3517
Washington, DC 20202
202-205-9032
The purpose of the Parent Training program is to provide training and information centers for parents of children with disabilities and persons who work with parents to enable them to participate more effectively with professionals in meeting the educational and early intervention needs of children with disabilities. Awards are made to private, nonprofit organizations that have governing boards or committees that have a majority of members who are parents of children with disabilities and that include professionals in the fields of special education and early intervention.
Type of Preference: Competitive preference for Empowerment Zones/Enterprise Communities.
Program Amount: $2.7 million.

Money to Train Parents How to Be Better Parents
(Even Start)
Donna Campbell
Compensatory Education Programs
U.S. Department of Education
600 Independence Ave., SW
Room 4400 Portals Building
Washington, DC 20202-6132
202-260-0996
Even Start is a family focused program providing participating families with an integrated program of early childhood education, adult literacy and basic

skills instruction, and parenting education. All projects have some home-based instruction and provide for the joint participation of parents and children. The program is administered by states. Legislation requires collaboration between schools and communities in the application and implementation process and gives priority to projects serving families in eligible Title I schoolwide attendance areas.
Type of Preference: Legislation requires states to give preference to Empowerment Zones/Enterprise Communities.
Program Amount: $102 million.

Money for Family Violence Prevention
(Family Violence Prevention and Services Discretionary Funds Program)
William Riley
Administration for Children and Families
U.S. Department of Health and Human Services
901 D St., SW
Fifth Floor West Wing
Washington, DC 20447
202-401-5529
Grants to state and local agencies, and Native American Tribes and Tribal organizations who are, or have been recipients of Family Violence Prevention and Services Act grants; state and local private nonprofit agencies experienced in the field of family violence prevention; and public and private nonprofit educational institutions, community organizations and community-based coalitions, and other entities that have designed and implemented family violence prevention information activities or community awareness strategies.
Type of Preference: Weighted consideration for Empowerment Zones/Enterprise Communities and Empowerment Zone/Enterprise Community eligible areas.
Program Amount: $500,000.

Money for Family Support Centers
(Family Support Center Demonstration Program)
Sheldon Shalit
Office of Community Services
U.S. Department of Health and Human Services
370 L'Enfant Promenade, SW, Fifth Floor

Washington, DC 20447
202-401-4807
The Family Support Center Demonstration Program provides grants to support the design, development and operation of Family Support Centers to prevent family homelessness. Family Support Centers provide comprehensive and intensive support services that enhance the physical, social and educational development of low and very low income individuals and families who were previously homeless and currently residing in government subsidized housing or at risk of becoming homeless.
Type of Preference: Weighted consideration for service Empowerment Zones/Enterprise Communities and Empowerment Zone/Enterprise Community eligible areas.
Program Amount: $7.4 million.

Money to Address the Critical Needs of the Poor

(Demonstration Partnership Program)
Richard Saul
Office of Community Services
U.S. Department of Health and Human Services
370 L'Enfant Promenade, SW, Fifth Floor
Washington, DC 20447
202-401-9341
Grants are provided to Community Action Agencies for developing and implementing innovative approaches to address critical needs of the poor common to a number of communities. Grantees, in partnership with other public and private organizations, develop an array of innovative programs including homelessness, micro enterprise/self-employment, minority youth life skills, case management, teenage pregnancy, and comprehensive integrated services.
Type of Preference: Weighted consideration for service Empowerment Zones/Enterprise Communities and Empowerment Zone/Enterprise Community eligible areas.
Program Amount: $7.977 million.

Homelessness Programs

Money to Address General Needs of the Homeless

(U.S. Department of Housing and Urban Development's Homeless Programs)
Jacquie Lawing
Division of Housing and Urban Development
Office of Community Planning and Development
Deputy Assistant Secretary for Economic

Development
451 7th St., SW, Suite 7204
Washington, DC 20410
202-708-0270
U.S. Department of Housing and Urban Development administers each of the homeless assistance programs listed below. However, the Department is working to restructure the delivery of homeless assistance to foster better coordination of homeless assistance within communities, improve the ability of communities to assess and meet the individual needs of homeless persons, and increase the placement of homeless individuals and families into permanent housing. The goal is to replace the currently fragmented approach with a "continuum of care" system. This will be reflected in the competition structure for these programs.

Money to Develop Transitional Housing for the Homeless

(Supportive Housing Program (SHP))
Jean Whaley
HUD Building
U.S. Department of Housing and Urban Development
451 7th St., SW, Room 7254
Washington, DC 20410
202-708-4300
The program promotes the development of supportive housing and supportive services, including innovative approaches to assist homeless persons in the transition from homelessness and to enable them to live as independently as possible. Funds can be used to provide: transitional housing; permanent housing provided in conjunction with supportive services; innovative supportive housing projects; supportive services; and facilities in which supportive services are provided.
Type of Preference: Competitive preference points to Empowerment Zones/Enterprise Communities.
Program Amount: $600 million.

Money to Build Emergency Shelters and Services for the Homeless

(Emergency Shelter Grants Programs (ESG))
Mark Johnston
HUD Building
U.S. Department of Housing and Urban Development
451 7th St., SW, Room 7262
Washington, DC 20410
202-708-1226, ext. 4487
Provides grants to states, metropolitan cities, urban counties, and territories according to the formula used for Community Development Block Grants (CDBG). Eligible activities include renovation, major

rehabilitation, or conversion of buildings for use as emergency shelters for the homeless. With certain limitations, grantees may also spend funds on essential services for the homeless, and homeless prevention efforts. In addition, grantees may spend funds on shelter operating costs such as maintenance, insurance, utilities, rent and furnishings. To receive a grant each grantee must have an approved Comprehensive Housing Affordability Strategy (CHAS).
Type of Preference: Funds are distributed by formula (localities can target to Empowerment Zones/Enterprise Communities.)
Program Amount: $156.8 million.

Money for Rental Assistance Programs for the Homeless

(Shelter Plus Care (S+C))
David Pollock
HUD Building
U.S. Department of Housing and Urban Development
451 7th St., SW, Room 7266
Washington, DC 20410
202-708-1234, ext. 4494
Provides grants for rental assistance through four component programs:
Tenant-based Rental Assistance - Participants reside in housing of their choice;
Sponsor-based Rental Assistance - Provides grants to provide rental assistance through contracts with sponsor organizations;
Project Based Rental Assistance - grants to provide rental assistance through contracts between the grant recipient and owners of existing structures.
Single Room Occupancy for Homeless Individuals - provides grants for rental assistance in connection with the moderate rehabilitation of single room occupancy housing units.
Type of Preference: Competitive preference for Empowerment Zones/Enterprise Communities.
Program Amount: $150 million.

Money to Create Single Room Occupancy for the Homeless

(Single Room Occupancy (SRO) Dwellings for Homeless Individuals)
David Pollock
HUD Building
U.S. Department of Housing and Urban Development
451 7th St., SW, Room 7262
Washington, DC 20410
202-708-1234, ext. 4494
The purpose of the Section 8 Moderate Rehabilitation Program for Single Room Occupancy Dwellings for

Homeless Individuals is to provide rental assistance on behalf of homeless individuals in connection with the moderate rehabilitation of SRO dwellings. Resources to fund the cost of rehabilitating the dwellings must be from other sources. However, the rental assistance covers operating expenses of the SRO housing, including debt service for rehabilitation financing, provided the monthly rental assistance per unit does not exceed the moderate rehabilitation fair market rent for an SRO unit, as established by U.S. Department of Housing and Urban Development.
Type of Preference: Competitive preference for Empowerment Zones/Enterprise Communities.
Program Amount: $150 million.

Free Unused Federal Properties for the Homeless

(Title V - Surplus Federal Property for Use to Assist the Homeless)
Mark Johnston
HUD Building
U.S. Department of Housing and Urban Development
451 7th St., SW, Room 7262
Washington, DC 20410
202-708-1226, ext. 4487
This program allows suitable federal properties that are categorized as unutilized, under utilized, excess, or surplus to be made available to states, units of local government and nonprofit organizations for use to assist the homeless. Properties can be used to provide shelter, services storage, or other uses of benefit to the homeless. The program provides no funding and properties are made available on an "as is" basis. Properties are leased without charge, although the homeless organization must pay for operating and repair costs. Depending on the availability of the property, and other factors, leases may also be from one-to twenty years. Surplus properties may also be deeded to the organization.
Type of Preference: Applies to any surplus federal property in an Empowerment Zone/Enterprise Community eligible area.

Money to Support the Family

(Family Support Center Demonstration Program)
Elise Morgan
Administration for Children and Families
U.S. Department of Housing and Urban Development
370 L'Enfant Plaza Promenade, SW
Sixth Floor Aerospace Building
Washington, DC 20447
202-401-4621
Grants to a variety of public and private community based organizations to support the design, development, and operation of Family Support Centers to prevent family homelessness. Family Support Centers provide comprehensive and intensive supportive services that enhance the physical, social, and educational development of low and very low-income individuals and families, who were previously homeless, currently residing in government subsidized housing or at risk of becoming homeless.
Type of Preference: Weighted consideration for Empowerment Zones/ Enterprise Communities and Empowerment Zone/Enterprise Community eligible areas.
Program Amount: $7.4 million.

Housing Programs

Money to Help Make Housing More Affordable to Low Incomes

(Home Investment Partnerships (HOME))
Mimi Kolesar
HUD Building
U.S. Department of Housing and Urban Development
451 7th St., SW, Room 7162
Washington, DC 20410
202-708-2470
Grants to states and units of general local government to implement local housing strategies designed to increase homeownership and affordable housing opportunities for low- and very-low-income persons. Eligible uses of funds include tenant-based assistance, housing rehabilitation, assistance to first-time homebuyers, and new construction, under certain circumstances. Under the HOME program, U.S. Department of Housing and Urban Development is developing and testing model housing programs, in conjunction with the private sector and participating jurisdictions.
Type of Preference: Funds are distributed by formula to states and units of general local government.
Program Amount: $1.4 billion.

Money to Help Low Income Families Pay Their Rent

(Rental Assistance Certificates)
John H. Greer
Deputy Assistant Secretary for Multi-Family Housing
  Programs
U.S. Department of Housing and Urban Development
451 7th St., SW, Room 6106
Washington, DC 20410
202-708-2495
Project-Based Rental Assistance Certificates. A project-based certificate program encourages owners to construct or rehabilitate rental housing for very low income families at rents within the U.S. Department of Housing and Urban Development-established fair market rents for the area. Assistance is tied to specific units under an assistance contract with the owner for specified term.
Type of Preference: Up to $500 million set aside to designated Empowerment Zones/Enterprise Communities.
Program Amount: Up to $500 million proposed for project-based certificates in designated Empowerment Zones/Enterprise Communities.

Money to Insure Multifamily Housing Projects Mortgages

(Multifamily Insurance Processing)
John H. Greer
Deputy Assistant Secretary for Multi-Family Housing
  Programs
U.S. Department of Housing and Urban Development
451 7th St., SW, Room 6106
Washington, DC 20410
202-708-2495
FHA would direct all field offices to give priority to processing any application for multifamily mortgage insurance for a project located in an Empowerment Zone.
Type of Preference: Priority processing in Empowerment Zones only.

Money for Social Service Directors for Elderly Housing Projects

(Service Coordinator Program)
John H. Greer
Deputy Assistant Secretary for Multi-Family Housing
  Programs

U.S. Department of Housing and Urban Development
451 7th St., SW, Room 6106
Washington, DC 20410
202-708-2495
This program makes funds available to Section 8 elderly project owners to employ an on-site social service coordinator and, in some cases, aides. U.S. Department of Housing and Urban Development will award additional points to applications for projects within Empowerment Zones.
Type of Preference: Points in Empowerment Zones only.
Program Amount: $9 million.

Money to Counsel Homeowners on Money Matters

(SF Housing Counseling Grants)
Joan Morgan
U.S. Department of Housing and Urban Development
451 7th St., SW, Room 9282
Washington, DC 20410
202-708-0614
Grants to public or nonprofit entities to serve as U.S. Department of Housing and Urban Development-approved housing counseling agencies providing counseling to homebuyers, homeowners, and tenants under U.S. Department of Housing and Urban Development programs and for homeowners with conventional mortgages or mortgages insured or guaranteed by other governmental agencies.
Type of Preference: Points in Empowerment Zones only.
Program Amount: $12 million.

Money to Spread the Word About FHA Mortgage Insurance

(SF Program Outreach)
Emelda Johnson
Deputy Assistant Secretary for Single Family Housing
U.S. Department of Housing and Urban Development
451 7th St., SW, Room 9282
Washington, DC 20410
202-708-3175
800-CALL-FHA
U.S. Department of Housing and Urban Development outreach effort to commercial lenders to encourage their use of FHA single family mortgage insurance programs for home purchase and home improvement loans in Empowerment Zone/Enterprise Communities. U.S. Department of Housing and Urban Development offices would also make special efforts to market the U.S. Department of Housing and Urban Development-owned single family inventory to nonprofits, local governments, and other low-income

housing providers.
Type of Preference: Available in all Empowerment Zone/Enterprise Communities as appropriate.
Program Amount: No funds required.

Money to Improve U.S. Department of Housing and Urban Development Owned or Insured Properties

(Flexible Subsidy Program)
John H. Greer
Deputy Assistant Secretary for Multi-Family Housing Programs
U.S. Department of Housing and Urban Development
451 7th St., SW, Room 6106
Washington, DC 20410
202-708-2495
This program makes operating assistance and capital improvement loans to owners of certain subsidized projects where U.S. Department of Housing and Urban Development holds the note or insures the loan.
Type of Preference: Points in Empowerment Zones only.
Program Amount: $116.4 million.

Money to Insure Mortgages on Multifamily Housing Projects

(Multifamily Housing)
David Villano
Farmers Home Administration (FMHA)
Multi-Family Housing Division
Room 5337 South Building
14th and Independence Ave., SW
Washington, DC 20250
202-720-1608
Under this program, Farmers Home Administration provides insured loans to construct new facilities or to purchase/rehabilitate existing facilities to provide modernized rental or cooperative housing for persons with very-low, low and moderate incomes, for those age 62 and older, and for handicapped persons in communities of not more than 10,000 and 20,000 population if the community is not within an MSA. The loans are repayable in not more than 50 years. Provisions are made for interest reductions so that

low-income tenants may pay a rent within their means. Rent paid by low-income tenants also can be supplemented through a rental assistance program administered by the Farmers Home Administration.
Type of Preference: Set aside for Empowerment Zones/Enterprise Communities.
Program Amount: $152 million.

Money to Fix Up Your House
(Rural Community Housing Development)
Joseph Carroll
Office of Community Services
U.S. Department of Housing and Urban Development
370 L'Enfant Promenade, SW
Washington, DC 20447
202-401-9346
Grants to states, public agencies, and private nonprofit organizations to help low-income homeowners improve their housing through self-help rehabilitation.
Type of Preference: Weighted consideration for serving Empowerment Zones/Enterprise Communities and Empowerment Zone/Enterprise Community eligible areas.
Program Amount: $3 million.

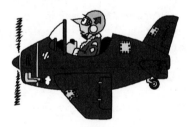

Infrastructure Improvement Programs

Money to Develop Sewers and Sanitation Services
(Water and Waste Loans)
Laurence G. Bowman
AG Box 1548
U.S. Department of Agriculture
Rural Development Administration
Water and Waste Disposal Division
14th and Independence Ave., SW
Washington, DC 20250
202-720-9589
The Rural Development Administration Water and Waste Disposal Loan funds are used to develop water and waste disposal (including solid waste disposal and storm drainage systems in rural areas and towns with a population not in excess of 10,000. The funds are available to public entities such as municipalities, counties, special purpose districts, Indian tribes, and

corporations not operated for profit. The Rural Development Administration also guarantees water and waste disposal loans made by banks and other eligible lenders.
Type of Preference: Set aside for Empowerment Zones/Enterprise Communities.
Program Amount: $1.5 million set aside.

Money to Reduce Cost of Water and Waste Disposal
(Water and Waste Grants)
Laurence G. Bowman
AG Box 1548
U.S. Department of Agriculture
Rural Development Administration
Water and Waste Disposal Division
14th and Independence Ave., SW
Washington, DC 20250
202-720-9589
The Rural Development Administration Water and Waste Disposal Grant funds are used to reduce water and waste disposal costs to a reasonable level for rural users. Grants may be made up to 75 percent of eligible project costs in some cases. Eligible applicants are the same types that are eligible for loans.
Type of Preference: Set aside for Empowerment Zones/Enterprise Communities.
Program Amount: $19 million set aside.

Money for Airport Planning and Development
(Airport Improvement Program)
James Borsori
Airport Financial Support Division
U.S. Department of Transportation
400 7th St., SW
Washington, DC 20590
202-267-8822
The Airport Improvement Program provides grants to states, units of local government, airport authorities, Indian Tribes and some private owners for airport planning and development.
Type of Preference: Discretionary funding prioritized according to specific statutory set-asides and priorities.
Program Amount: $1.45 million.

Money for Bridges
(Bridge Replacement and Rehabilitation Program)
Charles Chambers
Office of Engineering Bridge Division
U.S. Department of Transportation
400 7th St., SW
Washington, DC 20590
202-366-4617

The Bridge Replacement and Rehabilitation Program provides for the construction, reconstruction, rehabilitation, resurfacing, restoration, and operational improvements for bridges (including bridges on public roads of all functional classifications). Up to 40% of these funds may be transferred to its NHS or STP Programs.
Type of Preference: Funds are distributed by formula to the states.
Program Amount: $2.55 billion.

Money for Roadways

(National Highway System (NHS) (23 U.S.C. Section 104(b) (1)))
Tom Weeks
U.S. Department of Transportation
400 7th St., SW
Washington, DC 20590
202-366-5002
The National Highway System provides funds for the construction, reconstruction, rehabilitation, resurfacing, restoration, and operational improvements for roadways designated on the National Highway System. Up to 50% of a state's NHS apportionment may be transferred to its STP Program. Transit projects may be eligible for non-transferred NHS funds under certain conditions.
Type of Preference: Funds are distributed by formula to the states.
Program Amount: $3.331 billion.

Money for Rural Areas to Develop Essential Utilities

(Community Facility)
John R. Bowles
South Agricultural Building
U.S. Department of Agriculture
Rural Development Administration
Room 6312, 14th and Independence Ave., SW
Washington, DC 20250
202-720-1496
The Rural Development Administration provides funds to construct, enlarge, extend, or otherwise improve community facilities providing essential services in rural areas and towns with a population of 20,000 or less. The funds are available to public entities such as municipalities, counties, special-purpose districts, Indian tribes, and corporations not operated for profit. The Rural Development Administration also guarantees community facility loans made by banks or other eligible lenders.
Type of Preference: Set aside for Empowerment Zones/Enterprise Communities.
Program Amount: $6.1 million set aside.

Money to Develop the Information Superhighway

(National Information Infrastructure Grants)
Larry Parks
U.S. Department of Commerce
14th and Constitution Ave., NW, Room 5415
Washington, DC 20230
202-482-6050
50% matching grants to state and local governments, nonprofit educational entities, health-care providers, libraries and community information providers for planning and demonstration projects of information networks that will permit interconnection and inter-operability among and between user communities and national "backbone" networks. The purpose of the program is to facilitate the development of the national telecommunications and information infrastructure by promoting the widespread availability of advanced telecommunications technologies especially to: enhance the delivery of social services, traditionally provided by the Government, such as education and health care; and support the formation of a nationwide, multimedia, high-speed interactive infrastructure of varied information technologies.
Type of Preference: Priority for Empowerment Zone/Enterprise Community eligible areas.
Program Amount: $26 million.

Money to Develop Community Transportation Projects

(Section 26 Planning and Research Funds)
Lynn Sahaj
Office of Budget and Policy
U.S. Department of Transportation
400 7th St., SW, Room 9310
Washington, DC 20590
202-366-2053
Provides funds for research planning, training, and design of local transportation facilities and projects, including such activities in Empowerment Zones/Enterprise Communities.
Type of Preference: Additional consideration for Empowerment Zone/Enterprise Community status.
Program Amount: $92 million.

Money for Bus and Railroad Stations

(Section (3) Capital Program)
Lynn Sahaj
Office of Budget and Policy
U.S. Department of Transportation
400 7th St., SW, Room 9310
Washington, DC 20590
202-366-2053

Provides federal discretionary funds for the construction and rehabilitation of transit bus and rail facilities, station improvements, the purchase and lease of vehicles, and supportive design elements such as walkways, transit malls, and open space in local areas, including Empowerment Zone/Enterprise Community areas.
Type of Preference: Additional consideration for Empowerment Zone/Enterprise Community status.
Program Amount: $1.724 billion.

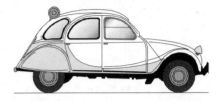

Money for Local Transit Services
(Urbanized Area Formula Program (as amended))
Lynn Sahaj
Office of Budget and Policy
U.S. Department of Transportation
400 7th St., SW, Room 9310
Washington, DC 20590
202-366-2053
Provides formula-based operating and capital assistance for local transit services, including services in Empowerment Zone/Enterprise Community areas.
Type of Preference: Expedited administrative processing for Empowerment Zone/Enterprise Community status.
Program Amount: $2.299 billion.

Money for Transportation Services in Rural Areas
(Non-urbanized Area)
Lynn Sahaj
Office of Budget and Policy
U.S. Department of Transportation
400 7th St., SW, Room 9310
Washington, DC 20590
202-366-2053
Provides capital and operating assistance for transportation programs in rural areas and urban areas smaller than 50,000 population, including Empowerment Zone/Enterprise Community areas.
Type of Preference: Administrative preference for Empowerment Zone/Enterprise Community status.
Program Amount: $132.9 million.

Money to Coordinate Transportation Plans
(Transportation Planning/Community Participation Training)
Lynn Sahaj
Office of Budget and Policy
U.S. Department of Transportation

400 7th St., SW, Room 9310
Washington, DC 20590
202-366-2053
Technical assistance to communities to work with regional and state planning organizations on transportation plans (necessary to ensure Empowerment Zone/Enterprise Community projects are in the state's pipeline for federal funding).
Type of Preference: Targeted to Empowerment Zones/Enterprise Communities.

Money to Reduce Air Pollution Caused by Traffic
Surface Transportation Program (STP) Congestion Mitigation and Air Quality Improvement (CMAQ))
Lynn Sahaj
Office of Budget and Policy
U.S. Department of Transportation
400 7th St., SW, Room 9310
Washington, DC 20590
202-366-2053
These funds support projects that reduce vehicle emissions in Clean Air non-attainment areas. Eligible activities might include the transit and transit-related portions of pedestrian-oriented and mixed use development projects and other transportation projects that reduce automobile emissions.
Type of Preference: Expedited administrative processing consideration for Empowerment Zone/Enterprise Community status.
Program Amount: $1.028 billion.

Public Safety Programs

Money To Stop Drug Crime in Public Housing
(Public Housing Drug Elimination Program)
Sonja Burgess
U.S. Department of Housing and Urban Development
451 7th St., SW, Room 4102
Washington, DC 20410
202-619-8201
Grants to eligible Public and Indian Housing Authorities (HAs) to eliminate drug-related crime in and around the premises of public and Indian housing developments. HAs are encouraged to develop a plan to sustain drug elimination activities over a period of years. Eligible activities include employment of security personnel, HA police, and investigators, implementation of physical improvements to enhance security, development of voluntary tenant patrols, and drug prevention, intervention and treatment programs to reduce the use of drugs.

Type of Preference: none
Program Amount: $251.75 million total funding.

Money to Develop Community Policing Programs

(Community Policing)
Joe Brann
Discretionary Grant Programs Division
U.S. Department of Justice
633 Indiana Ave., NW, Room 602
Washington, DC 20531
202-514-2058
Grantees will demonstrate a comprehensive model of community policing, which will result in a department-wide change in philosophy and mode of providing law enforcement services to the community. Training and technical assistance will be provided to the demonstration programs and other interested jurisdictions.
Type of Preference: Priority consideration to Empowerment Zones/Enterprise Communities.

Money to Help Kids Stay Out of Gangs

(Youth and Gangs)
Thomas Albrecht
Bureau of Justice Assistance
U.S. Department of Justice
633 Indiana Ave., NW, Room 1042
Washington, DC 20531
202-514-5948
Grants to develop prevention and intervention strategies to assist youth in avoiding pressures to use drugs and/or become involved in criminal activities or gangs will be continued. New programs will assist criminal justice agencies in providing effective services to children and their families, and train teenage students to manage anger and resolve conflict without violence.
Type of Preference: Targeted technical assistance to Empowerment Zones/Enterprise Communities.

Money for Jails, Boot Camps, and Correctional Programs

(Demonstration Programs)
Thomas Albrecht
Bureau of Justice Assistance
U.S. Department of Justice
633 Indiana Ave., NW, Room 1042
Washington, DC 20531
202-514-5943
Grants for the development and implementation of correctional options that include community-based incarceration, weekend incarceration, correctional boot camps, transitional programs, aftercare services,

drug courts, day reporting, structured fines, etc.
Type of Preference: Targeted technical assistance to Empowerment Zones/Enterprise Communities.
Program Amount: $12 million.

Free Help to Develop Alternatives to Jail

(Technical Assistance)
Thomas Albrecht
Bureau of Justice Assistance
U.S. Department of Justice
633 Indiana Ave., NW, Room 1042
Washington, DC 20531
202-514-5943
Technical assistance and support to public agencies to help them plan, develop, implement, improve or expand alternatives to traditional modes of incarceration.
Type of Preference: Targeted technical assistance to Empowerment Zones/Enterprise Communities.
Program Amount: see above.

Money and Help to Develop Boot Camp Jail Programs

(Boot Camp Prisons)
Thomas Albrecht
Bureau of Justice Assistance
U.S. Department of Justice
633 Indiana Ave., NW, Room 1042
Washington, DC 20531
202-514-5948
Grants to implement boot camp programs.
Type of Preference: Targeted technical assistance to Empowerment Zones/Enterprise Communities.
Program Amount: see above.

Money to Reduce and Prevent Crime

(Byrne Discretionary Grant Program)
Dick Ward
U.S. Department of Justice
633 Indiana Ave., NW
Washington, DC 20531
202-514-5943
The Bureau of Justice Assistance (BJA) assists states and local jurisdictions in making communities safe through the Edward Byrne Memorial State and Local Law Enforcement Assistance Discretionary Grant Program. Discretionary grant funds are used for

demonstration programs, training, technical assistance, and national scope programs to reduce and prevent crime and violence and for criminal justice system improvement at the state and local levels.
Type of Preference: Priority consideration is given to Empowerment Zones/Enterprise Communities.
Program Amount: $50 million.

Juvenile Justice and Delinquency Prevention

Money for Youth/Adult Mentoring Programs
(Mentoring (U.S. Department of Justice))
Cora Roy
U.S. Department of Justice
633 Indiana Ave., NW
Washington, DC 20531
202-616-3659
This new program authorizes the Administrator to award three-year grants to local education agencies for mentoring program designed to link at-risk youth with responsible adults to provide guidance, promote personal and social responsibility, increase educational participation, discourage use of illegal drugs, violence, weapon use, and other criminal activity, discourage gang involvement, and encourage participation in community service and activities.
Type of Preference: Funding priority is to be given to high crime areas with a high percentage of Elementary and Secondary Education Act fund eligible youth and high dropout rates.
Program Amount: $4 million.

Money to Reduce Crime and Revitalize Communities
(Weed and Seed)
Steve Rickman
U.S. Department of Justice
633 Indiana Ave., NW
Washington, DC 20531
202-616-1152

Grants to develop comprehensive, multi-agency approaches to combating violent crime, drug use, and gang activity, and to coordinate efforts to revitalize distressed neighborhoods. Grants will also be available for Safe Haven programs that provide an integrated array of social services and activities for youth and their families in a safe setting. Thirty-six communities received funding.
Type of Preference: Special consideration for Empowerment Zones/Enterprise Communities.
Program Amount: $28.5 million ($225,000 for new sites).

Money to Help Retrain Juvenile Delinquents
(Prevention)
Donna Bowres
U.S. Department of Justice
633 Indiana Ave., NW
Washington, DC 20531
202-616-9618
This program supports Title V of the JJDP Act, which authorizes the Administrator to make grants, through state advisory groups, to units of local government for a broad range of delinquency prevention programs and activities to benefit youth who have had contact with or are likely to have contact with the juvenile justice system. Services to children, youth and families include recreation, tutoring and remedial education, work skills, health and mental health, alcohol and substance abuse prevention, leadership development and accountability. Eligible units must be in compliance with OJJDP's Formulate Grants Program, submit a three-year plan to the state and to the Administrator, appoint a local policy board empowered to administer the local program, plan for coordination of services, and provide a 50% cash or in-kind match.
Type of Preference: Priority in awards is given to applicants that coordinate and collaborate in the provision of services, involve the private nonprofit and business sectors and develop or enhance a statewide subsidy program to local governments that are dedicated to early intervention and delinquency prevention.

State Enterprise Zones Offer Jobs and Small Business Help

Like the Federal Empowerment Zone programs, each state has its own benefit programs for designated areas in need of economic rebuilding. As designated Enterprise Zones, thousands of economically depressed communities all across the country have been earmarked to receive billions of dollars in economic stimulation packages.

Entrepreneurs Can Use Empowerment/Enterprise Zones

If you want to start a business, look at starting it in one in these zones. By simply locating a business in one of these zones, you can receive all kinds of benefits. For example:

- California will pay up to 50% of a new employee's wages in the form of a tax credit.
- In Kansas, if your small town retail store creates two new jobs, you won't have to pay sales tax to the state.
- New Jersey businesses receive a $1,500 tax credit for hiring an employee who lives in the enterprise zone where the business operates.
- New York offers businesses lower utility rates in enterprise zones.
- Texas offers special tax reductions for franchises in enterprise zones.
- Arizona offers women business owners an 80 percent reduction on property taxes.
- Florida offers a $50,000 corporate income tax credit.

By using these generous tax credits, states hope to lure businesses into these economically depressed Enterprise Zones and bring jobs to the area. These efforts to stimulate economic growth in depressed areas will ultimately prove beneficial for hundreds of thousands of citizens.

Job Seekers Can Take Advantage of Empowerment/Enterprise Zones

If you're out of work, try to locate businesses that you'd like to work for in a state-designated Enterprise Zone. Let the business know that they'll receive a big tax break if they hire you. For example:

- Alabama will give an employer $2500 of tax credit for every new employee (they get $2500 for hiring you).
- California will give half the cost of an employee's salary in tax credits (they can hire you at $50,000, but it only costs them $25,000).
- Colorado gives employers $200 toward health insurance for an employee.
- Connecticut gives $500 grants for every job created.
- Indiana gives $7,500 of tax credit per employee (they can pay you $25,000, but it really only costs them $17,500).
- Louisiana gives $5000 if a business hires an ex-aerospace employee.

How to Find Your State Empowerment/Enterprise Zones

If you are not sure where the enterprise zones are located in your state, contact the office listed in the state-by-state listing below.

State by State Listing of Programs

Below you will find a state-by-state listing of Enterprise Zone Programs. The following states have programs in place: Alabama, Arizona, Arkansas, California, Colorado, Connecticut, Delaware, Florida, Hawaii, Illinois, Indiana, Kansas, Kentucky, Louisiana, Maryland, Michigan, Minnesota, Missouri, Nebraska, New Jersey, New York, Ohio, Oklahoma, Oregon, Pennsylvania, Rhode Island, South Carolina, Tennessee, Texas, Utah, Virginia, West Virginia, and Wisconsin.

For each state entry, you will find the number of zones in the state, the incentives available to businesses in those zones, eligibility requirements, and a contact for more information. The state contact is usually located in the Department of Commerce of the Department of Economic Development for the state, and can provide you with a listing of credits, incentives, and zones for the state.

Alabama

Number of Zones: 27

Zone and Tax Incentives:
- An employer's maximum tax credit for operating in the zone can't exceed $2,500 per new permanent employee hired
- Income tax credit for hiring 30% of new employees who were formerly unemployed, of 80% during the first year, 60% in the second, 40% in the third year and 20% in the fourth and fifth year
- Tax credit for new investment of 10% of the first $10,000 invested, 5% on the next $90,000 invested and 2% on the remaining
- $1,000 tax credit for training each new employee
- Sales and use tax refund for building materials, machinery and equipment
- Certain income and corporate franchise tax exemptions for a five year period

Eligibility Criteria:
Must be located in or locating within the boundaries on an enterprise zone
- Must generally fall into Standard Industrial Classification (SIC) codes 20-42, 44-49 or consist of major warehousing, distribution center, regional or corporate headquarters of companies in the referenced SIC codes
- Must expand its labor force, make new capital investment or prevent loss of employment
- May not have closed or reduced employment elsewhere in Alabama in order to expand into the enterprise zone
- Must obtain an endorsement resolution approved by the appropriate local governing authority prior to participation in the program

For additional benefits, a business must meet the criteria outlined above and:
- Businesses must certify that at least 35% of their new qualified employees are residents of the zone
- Must give preference and priority to Alabama manufacturers, suppliers, contractors and labor, except when not reasonably possible

To apply, contact:
Bill Babington
Enterprise Zone Program Coordinator
401 Adams Ave.
P.O. Box 5690
Montgomery, AL 36103-5690
334-242-0492

Alaska

The state does not have an authorized enterprise zone program.

Arizona

Number of Zones: 22

Zone and Tax Incentives:
Businesses must certify that at least 35% of their new qualified employees are residents of the zone.

- One fourth of the taxable wages paid to each qualified employee, not to exceed $500 in the first year
- One third of the taxable wages paid to each previously qualified employee, not to exceed $1,000 in the second year of continuous employment
- One-half the taxable wages paid to each previously qualified employee, not to exceed $1,500, in the third year of continuous employment
- Qualified "new employee" considered economically disadvantaged for purposes of the Job Training Partnership Act
- Small minority or women-owned manufacturing businesses are eligible for an assessment ratio of 5% on all personal and real property in the zone for 5 years

Eligibility Criteria:
- Must be at least one-quarter square mile
- Must have a population of at least 1,000 persons
- Must have one of the following two:
    - Unemployment rate of 150% of the statewide rate for the preceding two years, or
    - Poverty rate of 150% of the statewide rate

To apply, contact:
Patty Duff
Enterprise Zone Program Administrator
Arizona Department of Commerce
3800 N. Central Ave., Suite 1650
Phoenix, AZ 85012-1908
602-280-1340
Email: Pattyd@azcommerce.com

Arkansas

Number of Zones: Legislation in July, 1996 established the entire state as one enterprise zone, referred to as Advantage Arkansas.

Zone and Tax Incentives:
- Sales and use tax refund for building materials, machinery and equipment
- $3,000 employer tax credit per net new employee, if at least 35% of the employees live in the same or adjacent county and receive some form of public assistance or have been considered hard to employ, or lacking in basic skills

Eligibility Criteria:
- Manufacturers with Standard Industrial Classification codes (SIC) 20 to 39 adding at least one new employee
- Warehouse operations (no retail sales) and 25 or more new employees
- Computer firms defined as SIC 7375 (Information Retrieval Services) and 7376 (Computer Facilities Management Services) adding at least one new employee
- Office sector business or control center with no retail sales and 100 or more new employees
- Corporate headquarter with no retail sales and 25 or more new employees
- Trucking sector business defined as SIC 4231 with no retail sales and 25 or more new employees
- To be eligible to apply for tax benefits, a company or business must have an expansion (or new plant) project which will result in a new increase in employment

Application Process:
To apply, the company must fill out an application form and project plan with the local governing body of municipality or county in whose jurisdiction the facility is located. If the local governing body approves, they must pass a resolution endorsing the project. The application form, project plan and the resolution must be forwarded to the Arkansas Industrial Development Commission.

To apply, contact:
Gregory Dale
Enterprise Zone Program Coordinator
Arkansas Department of Economic Development
One State Capitol Mall
Little Rock, AR 72201
501-682-7310

California

Number of Zones: 39 enterprise zones. Trade or business must be conducted within the zone.

Zone and Tax Incentives:
- Sales and Use Tax Credits: 100% for the purchase of qualifying machinery and parts. Limits: Individuals--$1 million; Corporations--$20 million
- Hiring Tax Credit: Up to 50% (declines by 10%

each year) of wages paid to each qualified employee
- Business Expense Deduction: Tangible personal property may be deducted as a business expense in the first year it is place in service. Limit: $10,000.
- Interest Expense Deduction: Deduction from income is allowed on the amount of "net interest" earned on loans made to a trade or business in an enterprise zone.
- Net Operating Loss Carryover: Net operating losses of individuals or corporations doing business in an enterprise zone may be carried over to future years to reduce the amount of taxable enterprise zone income for those years.
- Local enterprise zone incentives include the expeditious processing of plans and permits.
- Reduced utility rates
- Low-interest revolving loans
- Expeditious processing of plans and permits

Eligibility Requirements:
Qualified businesses must:
- Employ at least 50% of its program area employees who are residents of high density unemployment areas; or
- Employ at least 30% of its program area employees who are residents of high density unemployment areas, and contributes to an approved community service program; or
- Have at least 30% of its owners who are residents of high density unemployment areas

To apply, contact:
Keith Coppage
Enterprise Zone Program Manager
Department of Commerce
801 K St., Suite 1700
Sacramento, CA 95814
916-324-8211
www.commerce.ca.gov

Colorado

Number of Zones: 18

Zone and Tax Incentives:
- Three Percent Investment Tax Credit. Businesses making investments in equipment used exclusively in an enterprize zone may claim a credit against their Colorado income taxes equal to 3% of the amount of the

investment, subject to limitations.
- $500 Job Tax Credit. Businesses hiring new employees in connection with a "new business facility" located in an enterprise zone may claim a tax credit against state income taxes of $500 for each new employee, subject to limitations.
- Double Job Tax Credit for Agricultural Processing. An additional credit of $500 per new business facility employee may be claimed by businesses which add value to agricultural commodities through manufacturing or processing.
- $200 Job Tax Credit for Employer Health Insurance. A taxpayer with a qualifying new business facility is allowed a two-year $200 tax credit for each new facility employee who is insured under a qualifying employer-sponsored health insurance program.
- R&D Tax Credit. Taxpayers who make private expenditures on research and experimental activities (as defined by federal tax law) conducted in an enterprise zone qualify for an income tax credit of 3 percent, subject to limitations.
- Credit to Rehabilitate Vacant Buildings. Owners or tenants of commercial buildings in an enterprise zone which are at least 20 years old and which have been vacant for at least two years may claim a credit of 25% of the cost of rehabilitating each building. The credit is limited to $50,000.
- Credit for Contribution to Zones. There is a 25% credit, up to $100,000 for private contributions to local administrators for enterprise zone development projects and for promoting child care in zones.
- Exemption from state sales and use tax for manufacturing, mining, and aircraft equipment. Purchases of manufacturing machinery, machine tools, and parts are exempt form the 3% sales and use tax statewide.
- Local Government Tax Incentives. Any city or county within an enterprise zone is authorized to

negotiate with individual taxpayers who have qualifying new business facilities: (a) an incentive payment equal to not more than the amount of the increase in property tax liability over pre-enterprise zone levels; and (b) a refund of local sales taxes on purchases of equipment, machinery, machine tools, or supplies used in the taxpayer's business in the enterprise zone.

Eligibility Criteria:
- Unemployment rate at least 25% above the state 12-month average
- Population growth rate less than 25% of the state average rate for the most recent 5-year period for which data are available; or
- Per capita income less than 75% of the state average
- Total zone population may not exceed 50,000

To apply, contact:
Evan Metcalf
Colorado Department of Local Affairs
1625 Broadway, Room 1700
Denver, CO 80202
303-892-3840

Connecticut

Number of Zones: 17

Zone and Tax Incentives:
- Five-year, 80% abatement of local property taxes on real estate improvements and personal property acquisitions
- Ten-year, 50% credit on corporate business taxes, and a $1,500 grant ($75,000 maximum) for each new job (minimum of three) created within a 24-month period for qualifying manufacturing firms, if at least 30% of all new hires are from urban enterprise zones or form the community's disadvantaged population
- Certain service companies may be eligible for a $500 grant per job created
- Low-cost loans and free technical assistance
- Job training and job placement assistance
- Exemptions from state real estate conveyance taxes, and sales taxes on machinery replacement parts
- A minimum 7-year graduated tax deferral on increased assessments for improvements to property

Eligibility Criteria:
- 25% or more of the population below poverty level
- 25% or more of the population dependent on welfare
- An unemployment rate twice that of the state average

To apply, contact:
Anne Karas
Department of Economic and Community Development
Infrastructure and Real Estate Division
505 Hudson St.
Hartford, CT 06106
860-270-8143

Delaware

Number of Zones: 30 targeted low income census tracts plus additional public and non-profit economic development areas in the City of Wilmington, plus New Castle, Kent and Sussex counties.

Zone and Tax Incentives:
- Delaware exporters who qualify as an Export Trading Company can receive exemption from Delaware income and mercantile taxes
- Corporate income tax credits and gross receipts tax reductions are available to: manufacturers, wholesalers, laboratories or similar facilities used for scientific, agricultural or industrial research, development or testing; computer processors, engineering firms, consumer credit reporting services or any combination of these activities, the administration and management support required for any of these activities who invest a minimum of $200,000 in a new or expanded facility and hires a minimum of five new employees
- The program provides credits of $450 for each new qualified employee and $450 for each $100,000 investment. During the 10-year life of the credits, credits can't exceed 50% of the company's pre-credit tax liability in any one year. Unused credits may be carried forward for ten years.
- Firms which qualify for targeted industry credits and locate in one of the targeted areas, qualify for corporate income tax credits of $650 for each new employee and $650 for each new $100,000 investment. (Blue Collar Jobs Act)

- Qualifying firms are not subject to gross receipts taxes for the first five years and will then have these gross receipts taxes reduced on a declining scale for a period of ten years
- Selected commercial and retail businesses which locate in one of the 30 targeted census tracts and meet the minimum investment and employment criteria, qualify for corporate income tax credits of $450 per new qualified employee and $450 for each $100,000 investment. These businesses also qualify for the ten-year reduction in gross receipts taxes.

Eligibility Criteria:

"Targeted Areas" for targeted industries are:
- Any real property located within the state or any political subdivision, or instrumentality thereof.
- Any real property located within the state and owned by an IRS section 501(c)(3) organization which is organized and operated solely for the purpose of fostering economic development within the state
- Any Foreign Trade Zone located within the state
- 30 specifically identified targeted Census tracts

"Targeted Areas" for commercial and retail businesses are:
- Thirty specifically identified low-income census tracts

Highlights:

Green Industries Initiative: Tax credits through "Blue Collar Jobs Act" to promote reduction of wastes - recycling. Greatest success coming from the development of industrial parks.

To apply, contact:
Donna A. Murray
Senior Business Development Specialist
820 N. French St.
Wilmington, DE 19801
302-577-8472

District of Columbia

The District of Columbia does not have an authorized enterprise zone program.

Florida

Number of Projected Zones: 34

Zone and Tax Incentives:
- Enterprise Zone Jobs Tax Credit (Corporate Income Tax)
- Enterprise Zone Jobs Tax Credit (Sales and Use Tax)
- Enterprise Zone Property Tax Credit
- Sales tax refund for building materials used in rehabilitation of real property
- Sales tax refund for business machinery and equipment
- Sales tax exemption for electrical energy
- Community Contribution Tax Credit Program

In addition to these state incentives, local governments may offer additional incentives. For additional information, please call the contact person in the enterprise zone in which you are interested.

Area Eligibility Criteria:
- Housing conditions
- Per capita income
- Percent of elderly and youth residents
- Unemployment
- Per capita local taxes
- Percent of vacant commercial space
- Crime rate
- Increase in property values

To apply, contact:
Burt Von Hoff
Office of Tourism, Trade and Economic Development
2001 The Capitol
Tallahassee FL 32399-0001
850-487-2568

Georgia

The state does not have an authorized enterprise zone program.

Hawaii

Number of Zones: 17

Zone and Tax Incentives

State Incentives:
- Seven-year exemption from general excise taxes on the gross proceeds from all business within the zone
- 80% income tax abatement the first year, decreasing 10% each year over the next six years
- Income tax credit equal to 80% of the unemployment insurance premium paid during the first year declining 10% each year for the next six years

County Incentives:
May include, but are not limited to the following:
- Property tax abatement or freeze, or tax increment financing
- "Fast track" or priority permit processing
- Zoning or building permit waivers or variances
- Priority consideration for Community Development Block Grant or other federal programs
- 3 year exemption from any increase in property tax resulting from new construction

Eligibility Criteria:
A nominated area must consist of contiguous U.S. census tracts based on the 1980 U.S. Census and meet one of the following two requirements:
- At least 25% of the population must have incomes below 80% of the median income of the county or
- An unemployment rate 1.5 times the state average

Eligibility Criteria:
In order to be eligible to participate in the program, a business located in an enterprise zone must be engaged in manufacturing, wholesaling, or the repair and/or maintenance of tangible property and must also derive at least 50% of its annual gross receipts from eligible transactions conducted within the zone. Eligible businesses must satisfy low income hiring or employment requirements.

New Business:
Businesses that startup in or move to an EZ (Enterprise Zone) must increase their average annual number of full-time employees by at least 10% in the first year. The average annual number of full-time employees in the years 2 to 7 can fluctuate, but cannot be less than the average number of employees required in the first year. (Note: New businesses will be considered "new" throughout their seven years of eligibility.)

Existing Businesses:
Businesses already in an EZ must increase their average annual number of full-time employees by at least 10% in the first year. The average annual number of full-time employees must also increase by at least 10% annually in years 2 to 7.

To apply, contact:
> Tom Brandt
> Enterprise Zone Coordinator
> Business Services Division
> Department of Business, Economic
> Development and Tourism
> #1 Capital District Bldg.
> 250 S. Hotel St.
> Honolulu, HI 96813
> 808-586-2593
> Fax: 808-586-2589

Mailing address:
> P.O. Box 2359
> Honolulu, HI 96804

Idaho

The state does not have an authorized enterprise zone program.

Illinois

Number of Zones: 93

Zone and Tax Incentives:
- Sales Tax Exemption: A state sales tax exemption is permitted on building materials used in an enterprise zone. The materials must be purchased from a place of business which is located in the municipality or county which has established the enterprise zone.
- Enterprise Zone Machinery and Equipment/Pollution Control Facilities Sales Tax Exemption; A state sales tax exemption is available on purchases of specified building

materials that will be used or consumed in the manufacturing or assembly process or in the operation of a pollution control facility within an enterprise zone. Businesses must make a $5 million investment which causes the creation of 200 full-time equivalent jobs or an investment of $40 million for the retention of 2,000 full-time jobs.

- Enterprise Zone Utility Tax Exemption: State utility tax exemption on gas, electricity and the Illinois Commerce Commission's administrative charge. Businesses must make a $5 million investment which causes the creation of 200 full-time jobs or an investment of $20 million for the retention of 1,000 full-time jobs.
- Enterprise Zone Investment Tax Credit: State investment tax credit of .5% is allowed a taxpayer who invests in qualified property in a zone.
- Jobs Tax Credit: A taxpayer conducting a trade or business in an Enterprise Zone may receive a $500 tax credit per eligible employee hired to work in a zone during the taxable year, if the taxpayer hires 5 or more eligible employees.
- Dividend Income Deduction: Individuals, corporations, trusts, and estates are not taxed on dividend income from corporations doing substantially of their business in a zone.
- Interest Deduction: Financial institutions are not taxed on the interest received on loans for development within an enterprise zone.
- Contribution Deduction: Businesses may deduct, from taxable income, double the value of a cash or in-kind contribution to an approved project on a designated zone organization.

Local Incentives:
- Abatement of property taxes on new improvements
- Homesteading and shopsteading programs
- Waiver of business licensing and permit fees
- Special local financing programs and other resources

To apply contact:
   Thomas R. Henderson
   Dept. of Commerce and Community Affairs
   Enterprise Zone Program
   620 East Adams, 3rd Floor
   Springfield, IL 62701
   217-785-6145

Indiana

Number of Zones: 23

Zone and Tax Incentives:
- Gross Income Tax Exemption: All enterprise zone income exceeding the income earned in the enterprise zone prior to its designation is exempt from the state gross income tax
- Employment Expense Credit: Employer income tax for 10% of resident employee wages up to $1,500 per employee
- Inventory Tax Credit: A taxpayer will receive a credit against the personal property tax liability equal to the personal property tax on all inventory located in the zone
- Equity Investment Credit: Individual investors receive up to a 30% income tax credit for the purchase of equity in start-up or expanding enterprise zone firms
- Loan Interest Credit: A tax credit of 5% of interest earned on loans to enterprise zone businesses or on loans for improvements to real property, including residential property
- Employee Tax Deduction: A tax deduction equal to one-half of adjusted gross income up to $7,500 for employees who live and work in the zone
- Neighborhood Assistance Program: Priority will be given to the enterprise zone program for state Neighborhood Assistance Program tax credits

Eligibility Criteria:
- 25% of resident households are below the poverty level established by the U.S. Census; or average rate of unemployment for the most recent 18 month period at least 150 percent of the statewide rate for the same period
- An area greater than .75 square miles, but less than 3 square miles with a continuous boundary
- Property suitable for a mix of development - commercial, industrial, residential
- The designation of an Urban Enterprise Association meeting requirements of the Act
- General distress of area
- A statement by the applicant indicating its willingness to provide specified economic development incentives

To apply, contact:
   Urban Enterprise Zone Program Director
   Department of Commerce

One North Capitol, Suite 700
Indianapolis, IN 46204
317-232-8911

Iowa

The state does not have an authorized enterprise zone program.

Kansas

Number of Zones: 78

Method of Designation
-   The minimum will be a county and several counties may join into a region. Each city over 2,000 in population must agree to participate in the program

Zone and Tax Incentives:
-   Sales tax exemption for manufacturing, if two or more net new jobs are created
-   Sales tax exemption for all other non-retail business if five or more net new jobs are created
-   Sales tax exemption for retail in cities under 2,500 if two or more net new jobs are created
-   Investment tax credit of $1,000/$100,000 for non-retail businesses, with same criteria noted above
-   Job creation tax credit of $1,500 for non-manufacturing and if five or more net new jobs are created
-   $2,500 per employee in a non-metropolitan region, same conditions

In all areas of the state:
-   Sales tax exemption for specific qualified business facilities if two or more new jobs are created
-   Investment tax credit for specific business facilities of $1,000/$100,000
-   Job creation tax credit of $1,500 per new job created for specific qualified business facilities

To apply contact:
Dave Ross
Business Finance Specialist
Kansas Department of Commerce and Housing
700 Southwest Harrison St., Suite 1300
Topeka, KS 66603-3712
785-296-5298

Kentucky

Number of Zones: 10

Zone and Tax Incentives:
-   Building materials used in remodeling, rehabilitation, or new construction within the zone area, and new and used equipment and machinery purchased by a qualified business for use in the zone are exempt from sales and use taxes.
-   Commercial vehicles purchased and used for a qualified business solely for business purposes shall be exempt from motor vehicle usage taxes.
-   Vehicles purchased and used by a qualified business solely for business purposes are exempt from motor vehicle usage taxes, limited to the first $20,000 of the retail price of the vehicle
-   A qualified business is allowed a credit against the tax levied equal to 10% of wages paid to each employee who has been unemployed for at least 90 days or who has received public assistance benefits, based on need and intended to alleviate poverty, for at least 90 days prior to employment with the qualified business, up to $1,500 per employee. Any unused credit may be carried forward for up to five years
-   A local government has the option to levy an ad valorem tax rate on qualified property within a zone of one-tenth of one cent upon each $100 of value

Eligibility Criteria:
-   A continuous boundary
-   An average rate of unemployment at least 1.5 times the national average for the past 18 months
-   70% of its residents with incomes below 80% of the locality's median income, or
-   Experienced a population decline of 15% or more between 1970 and 1980

Rural as well as urban areas are eligible.

Business Eligibility:
To qualify for zone incentives, businesses must meet requirements related to location of work, resident employees, unemployment and welfare.

Tax Exemptions

To apply, contact:
> Business Information Clearinghouse
> Division of Business and Entrepreneurship
> Development
> Department of Community Development
> Cabinet for Economic Development
> Capital Plaza Tower, 22nd Floor
> Frankfort, KY 40601
> 502-564-4252, ext. 4317
> 1-800-626-2250 (in Kentucky)

Louisiana

Number of Zones: 1,670

Zone and Tax Incentives:
- Qualified businesses receive $2,500 tax credit per new employee if they hire a minimum of five new employees in the first 5 years of the project
- Qualified businesses receive a $5,000 credit for an aerospace or aviation employee, or AFDC recipient
- Business identified under standard industrial classification code may qualify for $5000 tax credit for each certified new employee

Area Eligibility Criteria:
- Urban and rural parishes are eligible
- Considerations are given for:
  - unemployment and youth unemployment
  - per capita income
  - migration
  - residents receiving public assistance

Local government must agree to:
- apply to the U.S. Department of Commerce to have the enterprise zone declared to be a free trade zone
- devise and implement a program to improve police protection within the zone
- assist the State Department of Economic Development (DED) in certifying employers to be eligible for the zone benefits
- authorize the DED to supersede certain specified local regulations and ordinances which may serve to discourage economic development within the zone
- assist the DED in evaluating progress made in any enterprise zone within its jurisdiction

To apply, contact:
> Ed Baker or Marylyn Friedkin

Louisiana Department of Economic Development
Business Incentive Division
P.O. Box 94185
Baton Rouge, LA 70804-9185
225-342-9228
225-342-5402

Maine

Program authorization expired June, 1992. No reauthorization has been issued.

Maryland

Number of Zones: 29. Zone designation is for ten year periods.

Zone and Tax Incentives:
- Local real property tax credit for new investment for 10 years
- Income tax credit for each new full-time job created of 500; for disadvantaged workers the credit is $3,000 ($1,500 the first year, $1,000 the second year, $500 the third year). Reimbursement for on the job training--OJT (20-50%).
- Larger loans for qualified businesses form Maryland's existing loan programs
- Amount of the credit is 80% of the taxes due on any expansion, renovation or capital improvement in the property over the first 5 years, for the next 5 years the credit decreases 10% annually

Eligibility Criteria:
Must meet one of the following requirements:
- Unemployment rate of 150% of the U.S. or the Maryland unemployment rate, whichever is higher, for the preceding eighteen months
- Poverty rate, as measured by the U.S. Census, of 125% of the national average
- 70% of the residents with incomes less than 80% of the median family income in the city or county
- Population decline or loss

Highlights:

Background:
No more than six zones may be designated in any 12 month period. No more than one zone may be designated within any county during a calendar year.

To apply, contact:
> Jerry Wade
> Enterprise Zone Program Administrator
> Department of Employment and Economic
> Development
> 217 East Redwood St.
> Baltimore, MD 21202
> 410-767-6438
> Fax: 410-333-8309

Massachusetts

The state does not have an authorized enterprise zone program.

Michigan

Number of Zones: The state's Renaissance Zones programs works by granting virtually tax-free status to any business or resident presently in a zone or moving into a zone. The zones are designed to provide selected communities with the most powerful market-based incentive, virtually no state or local taxes, to spur new jobs and investment.

To apply, contact:
> John Czarnecki or Karla Campbell
> Michigan Economic Development
> Corporation
> 201 N. Washington Square
> Victor Office Center
> Lansing, MI 48913
> 517-373-9148

Minnesota

Number of Zones: 6 border city zones

Zone and Tax Incentives:
- $1,500 income tax credit per existing employed worker in the zone
- State paid property tax credit for a portion of property taxes paid by existing or new commercial or industrial facilities located in the zone

Eligibility Criteria:
- A city with a contiguous border with a city in another state or with a contiguous border with a city in Minnesota which has a contiguous border with a city in another state
- Qualifying local contributions

- Determined to be economically or fiscally distressed

To apply, contact:
> Meredith Udoibok
> Department of Trade and Economic
> Development
> 500 Metro Square
> 121 7th Place East
> St. Paul, MN 55101
> 651-297-4132

Mississippi

The state does not have an authorized enterprise zone program.

Missouri

Number of Zones: 61

Zone and Tax Incentives:
- Up to $400 in training credits other than JTPA or state training program
- Refund of unused tax credits earned by new facilities at a rate of 50% or up to $50,000 for the first year, and 25% or up to $25,000 for the second year
- State income tax exemption of 50% for 10 years to be earned by a zone business if 30% if the firm's employee's are zone residents or have exhausted their unemployment compensation benefits
- Tax credits if 30% of new employees are zone residents or are considered "difficult to employ", available for 10% of the first $10,000 in investment, 5% of the next $90,000 and 2% of excess over $100,000
- New Jobs Credit: Up to $400 in tax credits for each new job
- Improved Real Property Tax Abatement (local incentive):
  - For improvements; 50-100% for 10-25 years

Eligibility Criteria:
The following minimum job and investment qualification requirements must be maintained as an annual average in offer to receive tax credits each tax year of the 10-year period.
- New Facility: Two new jobs and $100,000 new investment credit
- Expanding Facility: Two new jobs and $100,000 new investment credit or if less, 25% more than the previous investment at the old facility
- Replacement of old facility with new facility: two new jobs and business facility credit of $1,000,000

To apply, contact:
>Mike Heimericks
>Coordinator, Enterprise Zone Program
>Tax Benefits Programs
>Missouri Department of Economic
>Development
>P.O. Box 118
>Jefferson City, MO 65102
>573-751-9051

Montana

The state does not have an authorized enterprise zone program.

Nebraska

Number of enterprise zones: Five enterprise zones are established

Zone and Tax Incentives:
Qualified businesses can receive tax credits up to $75,000;
- $4,500 for each new employee and $3,000 per $75,000 of investment provided at least 50% of the new employees are zone residents
- $4,500 for each new employee who is a zone resident, $1,500 for non-zone residents, and $1,000 per $75,000 of investments; or
- the normal provisions for tax credits provided by the Employment Expansion and Investment Incentive Act
    - $1,500 per employee and $1,000 per $75,000 of investment

Eligibility Criteria:
Local Government Eligibility Criteria:
Any city, village, tribal government area, or county may apply for designation of an area within the city village, tribal government area, or county as an enterprise zone.
- Must encompass an area which is at least one but no more than sixteen square miles of one or more discrete areas
- If it is composed of more than one discrete area, each separate area must meet eligibility criteria
- Must have a combined total population of not less than 250 persons

Community Eligibility Criteria:
Communities must meet statutory thresholds of economic distress and areas must meet two of the following three criteria:
- An unemployment rate at least 200% above the state's average unemployment rate, as determined by the 1990 Census
- The average poverty rate exceeds 20% in the census tracts or block groups within the area for metropolitan or primary class cities; or, the average poverty rate exceeds 20% for the area as determined by the 1990 Census
- Documentation of population loss in the area has decreased by at least 10% between decennial censuses

Application Process:
The enterprise zone application must include:
- Geographic description of the proposed target area
- Adoption of a Resolution of Intent to establish a zone
- Conducting a Public Hearing on the question of establishing a local enterprise zone
- A vote of approval by the local governing body
- Appointment of an Enterprise Zone Association Board
- Preparation of an economic redevelopment plan and redevelopment strategies
- Documentation of commitments by local governments of general revenue and other resources to encourage community economic development
- Preparation of a formal application
- Approval of application by the enterprise zone board
- Submission of an enterprise zone application to the Nebraska Department of Economic Development for Review

Qualified zone business activities include:
- The assembly, fabrication, manufacture or

procession of tangible personal property
-   Farming, ranching or the feeding or raising of livestock
-   The performance of data processing, telecommunications, or insurance services
-   The performance of financial services
-   The administrative headquarters for any business may qualify for enterprise zone tax incentives, even if the activities of the business are excluded because of its retail sales

To apply, contact:

> Ron Troutman
> Nebraska Dept. of Revenue
> 301 Centennial Mall South
> P.O. Box 94818
> Lincoln, NE 68509-4818
> 402-471-5880
> Fax: 402-471-5608

Nevada

The state does not have an authorized enterprise zone program.

New Hampshire

(Labor Surplus Areas). The state does not have an authorized enterprise zone program.

New Jersey

Number of Zones: 20

Zone and Tax Incentives:
-   A one-time tax credit of $1,500 for the full-time hiring of residents of a city where a zone is located who have been unemployed or dependent upon public assistance for at least 90 days, or
-   Credit of $500 for hiring certain full-time employees
-   If an eligible firm does not qualify for employee tax, it may receive an incentive tax credit of eight percent of investment in the zone by an approved "in lieu" agreement
-   Sales tax exemptions for materials and for tangible personal property
-   Possible state regulatory relief by zone request
-   Priority for financial assistance from New Jersey Local Development Financing Fund (LDFF) and Job Training Program

Eligibility Criteria:
-   Businesses must be certified as a qualified business within a designated zone by the Urban Enterprise Zone Authority
-   A business must either be located in the zone when it becomes effective, or meet certain employment tests if the business is started or moves into the zone after the zone is effective
-   An area is defined by a continuous border
-   Must have one of the following
    -   have an unemployment rate 50% above the national average
    -   Income of 25% of the populations is below the poverty level
    -   20% of the residents depend on public assistance

To apply, businesses must make an application to the local municipal zone coordinator on an Authority application form. The local coordinator verifies that the business is within the zone and forwards the application to the Authority for review and approval. For information, contact:

> Kelly A. Woods
> NJ Urban Enterprise Zone Program
> New Jersey Dept. of Commerce and Economic Development
> 20 W. State St., CN-829
> Trenton, NJ 08625-0829
> 609-292-1912

New Mexico

Number of Zones: 2

Zone and Tax Incentives:
-   Fast tracking of infrastructure projects (based on the community's and county's ICIP)
-   Tax credits to property owner for rehab-qualified business facilities
-   Special set aside and preferences from the state Housing Department
-   Tax increment method of financing a locally controlled enterprise zone fund
-   Local property tax abatement for 10 years on qualified property
-   Special CDBG funds for infrastructure grants and low-interest economic development loans
-   Special technical assistance for all development issues
-   The federal Empowerment Zone/Enterprise Community program with over $7 billion in

resources
- The coordinated federal and state Technology Transfer initiative
- NAFTA and the growing trade corridors
- HUD's Colonias program with over $200 million targeted at the border states.

To apply contact:
Karen Wentworth
State Enterprise Zone Program Officer
NM Economic Development Dept.
1100 St. Francis Dr.
Santa Fe, NM 87503
505-827-0300

New York

Number of Zones: 52. Upon passage of the 2000-2001 state budget, the Zones Program is now called Empire Zones. The Empire Zones are virtually tax-free zones designed to attract new businesses to New York, as well as encourage the growth of existing businesses.

Zone and Tax Incentives:
- A 100% exemption from increases in assessment based on improvements for up to 7 years.
- A 50% refundable wage tax credit for up to 5 years for hiring full time employees in newly created jobs
- Increased investment tax credit at 8-10% for new investments in the zone
- Capital corporation investment tax credit equal to 25% of the stock of the corporations
- State sales tax exemption on building materials used in construction or rehabilitation of commercial or industrial real property
- Local real property tax abatements at the local level
- Special reduction on utility rates
- Priority for programs and services available through other state agencies

Eligibility Criteria:

Size of Zones:
- Up to 2 square miles within a town with a population of less than 25,000

Eligible Census Tracts:
- Poverty rate of at least 20%
- Unemployment rate of at least 25% above the state unemployment rate
- Zone population of at least 2,000

Counties which do not contain an eligible census tract may apply based on the following criteria:
- Poverty rate of at least 13%
- Unemployment rate of at least 25% above the state unemployment rate
- Zone population of at least 2,000
- Of the total land, 25% must be vacant, abandoned, or otherwise available for industrial or commercial development

Application Process:
A city, town, village or county may apply to have an area designated as a zone. However, in New York City, an individual borough may not apply on its own; only the New York City government may apply for a zone within New York City. Each application must include:
- A map of the proposed zone showing existing streets, highways, etc.
- A statement from the local private industry council governing board of the service delivery area established under the Job Training Partnership Act describing the resources and assistance to be provided to the proposed zone by that program
- Evidence that the views of the residents of the proposed zone and the state and local elected officials and private organizations representing those residents have been considered in the preparation of the application
- A development plan for the proposed zone

To apply, contact:
Fred DiMaggio
Director, Empire Zones Program
30 S. Pearl St.
Albany, NY 12245
518-292-5240

North Carolina

The state does not have an authorized enterprise zone program.

North Dakota

The state does not have an authorized enterprise zone program.

Ohio

Number of Zones: 330

Method of Designation:

Distress-based: A distress-based (full authority) zone may be created if the local authority petitions with certification documents that specific distress levels exist within the designated zone. The six distress criteria are:
- 125% of the state average unemployment during the most recent 12 months.
- at least 10% population loss between 1970-1990.
- prevalence (minimum of 5%) of vacant or demolished commercial or industrial facilities.
- specific vacant industrial facilities.
- income weighted tax capacity of the school district is below 70% of the state average.
- 51% of the population is below 80% of the area's median income

Non Distress-Based: Non Distress-Based zones are not required to document distress. Under this limited zone authority, communities may not consider projects involving intra-state relocations unless a waiver is obtained.

Zone and Tax Incentives:
- Exemption of real and/or personal property assessed values of up to 75% for up to 10 years or an average of 60% over the term of the agreement on new investments in buildings, machinery/equipment and inventory and improvements to existing land and buildings for a specific project. These statutory limits can reach 100% with school board approval.

For information about Ohio's Enterprise Zone Program contact:
Ohio Department of Development

Economic Development Division
Office of Tax Exemption Incentives
77 S. High St., 28th Floor
Columbus, OH 43266
614-466-2480

Oklahoma

Number of Zones: Over 200 areas, including counties, communities, and census tracts.

Zone and Tax Incentives: (limited to manufacturing firms)
- Double the regular state investment new job tax credits available elsewhere in the state.
- Low interest loans by Enterprise Zone districts.

Eligibility Criteria:
An area must be economically distressed, as determined by the Oklahoma Department of Commerce.

To apply, contact:
Jeff Wallace
Director of Programs
Oklahoma Department of Commerce
Box 26980
Oklahoma City, OK 73126-0980
405-815-6552

Oregon

Number of Zones: 48

Zone and Tax Incentives:
- Property tax exemption of 100% for three years to eligible business firms making an investment in qualified property. Qualified property includes new construction and machinery and equipment not already on the county tax rolls for the following kinds of investments:
  - New building or structure with a cost of a $25,000 or more.
  - Addition to or modification of an existing building or structure with a cost of $25,000 or more (only the increase in value is eligible).
  - Site preparation that was necessary for and undertaken within six months before qualifying new construction (only the increase in value is eligible).

- Machinery and equipment that was newly purchased, leased or transferred from outside the country.

Eligibility Criteria:

To qualify, a pre-certification form must be filed by an eligible business with the local enterprise zone manager before the firm makes an investment and before it hires new employees.

- Firms must receive at least 75% of their annual gross receipts by providing goods, products, or services to other businesses through activities such as manufacturing, assembly, fabrication, processing, shipping or storage.
- The firm must invest in qualified property which may be owned or leased by the firm.
- New business firms must hire at least one employee after pre-certification and must increase employment by at least 110% over the firm's employment at recertification.
- Contiguous area no larger than 12 square miles, excluding navigable waters
- Urban businesses (contiguous urbanized portion) must meet one of the following three criteria:
    - Per capita income less than 80% of the state or MSA (Metropolitan Statistical Average) in which the zone is located:
    - Incidence of poverty at least twice as great as the state or MSA average; or
    - Unemployment rate at least twice the state or MSA rate
- Non-urban businesses must be entirely within the economically lagging area as certified by the Governor.

Application Process:

Upon completion of the investment and after the employees have been hired, the pre-certified business firm files its "Oregon Enterprise Zone Property Tax Exemption Application" form with the county assessor between July 1 and August 31. A late application may be filed with the count assessor between Sept. 1 and Sept. 15 with a late filing fee. Approval of an application is based on the provisions of the Oregon Enterprise Zone Act and Oregon Department of Revenue administrative rules.

To apply, contact:
    Oregon Economic and Community
    Development Department
    775 Summer St., NE, Suite 200
    Salem, OR 97301-1280

1-800-233-3306 TTY and Toll-Free (in Oregon)
503-945-8318

Economic Development

Pennsylvania

Number of Zones: The state is divided into 6 regions.

Zone and Tax Incentives:

- Assistance in preparing and revising business plans to ensure that commercial loan applications are given appropriate consideration.
- Low-interest gap loans to reduce bank risk exposure and secure ban approval of commercial loan applications.
- Export market development
- Federal procurement bid assistance
- New product market assessment
- Customized job training
- A 20% tax credit on state Corporate Net Income Tax for the value of investments to rehabilitate or improve buildings or land which are located within boundaries of designated enterprise zones.

Eligibility Requirements:

Financially disadvantaged areas are eligible based upon information compiled by the Department of Community and Economic Development.

Application Process:

An eligible municipality can apply directly to the Department for planning funding or through a redevelopment authority. The application must be accompanied by a copy of a resolution by the local governing body authorizing submittal of the application directly to the Department or on behalf of the local governing body by the county redevelopment authority.

To apply, contact:
    David S. Messner
    Coordinator, Enterprise Zone Program
    Strategic Planning and Operations Office
    Department of Community and Economic
    Development

551 Forum Bldg., Room 318
Harrisburg, PA 17120
717-787-7400

Rhode Island

Number of Zones: 11

Zone and Tax Incentives:
- Priority use of job training community development funds.
- Resident business owner tax deduction -- $50,000 per year from net worth of income during first three years, $25,000 per year during 4th and 5th years.
- Donation tax credit -- A taxpayer is eligible for a credit of 20% for any cash donation against the state tax imposed for donations to public supported improvement projects in the zone.
- Payroll tax credit -- maximum of $10,000 credit per employee during the first five years of zone operation.
- Tax benefits for business -- A qualified business must have a minimum of 25% Enterprise Workers to receive credits. The credit is 50% of wages and salaries paid to qualified enterprise zone workers in excess of the wages and salaries paid to employees in the prior year.
- Interest Income Credit -- a maximum $10,000 tax credit on interest earned on loans to qualified businesses.
- Enterprise Worker Tax Exemption -- enterprise workers receiving more than 90% of gross income from a qualified business in the zone may deduct from state gross income either $5,000 or the amount earned per year for a period of two taxable years (or whichever is less).

Eligibility Criteria:
- Businesses must complete an application and submit it to their local zone point of contact
- Poverty within the zone
- A locally developed course of action
- Businesses must add new employees to their company and are also encouraged to hire unemployed, underemployed and disadvantaged individuals
- The zone can't consist of more than five contiguous census tracts or portions, thereof

To apply, contact:
Victor Barrows

Urban Development Manager
Economic Development Corporation
Division of Planning
One West Exchange St.
Providence, RI 02903
401-222-2601

South Carolina

Number of Zones: Entire state is considered an enterprise zone.

Job Tax Credits: For firms engaged in manufacturing, processing, warehousing, wholesaling, research and development and service related industries there is a credit against corporate income tax of:
- $4,500 per job in less developed counties;
- $2,500 per job in moderately developed counties
- $1,500 per job in developed counties and
- $3,500 per job in underdeveloped counties
The four classifications have a 10 job minimum to qualify.

Business enterprises locating in a business or industrial park jointly established and developed by two or more counties:
- may qualify for the dollar credit of the participating county which has the greatest dollar credit, regardless the participating county in which the business is located
- are permitted additional job tax credits, for each new full-time job created, of $500 annually for five years, beginning with year two through six after the creation of the job

Expansions which occur within the five-year certification period are also eligible to receive job tax credits. Credits may be applied against corporate income taxes.
- The number of jobs must meet the minimum criteria of 10
- Credits are $300, $600, or $1,000, depending upon the county of location
- Credits are for a five year period for each full-time job created

Multi-County Industrial Park Incentives:
- Special income tax credit
- Businesses are entitled to the greater jobs tax credit allowed for the most disadvantaged county within the multi-county compact at the

least job creation threshold; and, the dollar amount of the credit is increased by $500 per year for each employee during the five year tax credit window

Eligibility Criteria:
- The Tax Commission classifies each county as "less developed," "moderately developed," "developed," or "underdeveloped" and may offer tax incentives to qualified businesses throughout the county according to designation
- Classification is determined annually by the county's relative ranking in the state for levels of average unemployment and average per capital income

To apply, contact:
> South Carolina Department of Commerce
> P.O. Box 927
> Columbia, SC 29202
> 800-868-7232 or 803-734-9818

South Dakota

The state does not have an authorized enterprise zone program.

Tennessee

Number of Zones: 2. One zone designated in Memphis and one in Nashville.

Zone and Tax Incentives:
- Job creation payments of up to $1,000 per net new employee. Businesses must not make retail sales and employ at least 25 persons within the zone
- Reimbursement of sale and use taxes (local and state) for building materials bought by qualified businesses with the zone
- Reimbursement of 1.3% of the purchase price of industrial machinery for use within the zone
- Reimbursement of 20% (up to $100,000) of the qualified business' contribution to a public school within an enterprise zone
- Exemption from business tax imposed by state and local government on the privilege of selling goods or services
- All income from interest earned on loans to qualified businesses for improvements, operations, or real property is exempt from state income tax
- Funds for state educational assistance grants and

guaranteed student loans are set aside for zone residents

Eligibility Criteria:
- Eligibility for the designation is based on poverty, unemployment and general distress
- Businesses must meet new hire requirements
  - 30% of new hires must be residents of zone and/or be economically disadvantaged individuals
  - Must meet new hire requirements through increase in employment
  - Businesses with multiple locations can use only the employee population working in the zone to meet certification requirements

To apply, contact:
> Don Waller
> Director, Local Planning
> Department of Economic and Community
> Development
> William R. Snodgrass Tennessee Tower
> 10th Floor, 312 Eighth Ave. North
> Nashville, TN 37243-0405
> 615-741-2211

Texas

Number of Zones: 182

Zone and Tax Incentives:
- Refund of up to $1.25 million in state sales or use tax paid or taxes paid for building materials and machinery and equipment for use in the enterprise zone by a state-designated enterprise project at the rate of no more than $250,000 per year. The project is allowed up to a $2,000 refund for each of 110% of the new or retained permanent jobs for a 5-year designation period for up to 625 jobs.
- Franchise tax reductions for state-designated enterprise projects to be based on 50% reduction of increased apportioned taxable capital or 5% apportioned earned surplus income as calculated on each franchise tax report during the 5-year designation period.
- One-time state sales tax refund of up to $5,000 paid for machinery and equipment. The refund is based upon $500 for each job retained.
- One-time franchise tax refund of up to $5,000 based upon $500 for each new job created by a

qualified business in a state-designated enterprise zone when at least 20 new jobs have been created.
- Five percent reduction n electric utility rates
- Priority and preference for all economic development programs of the Texas Department of Commerce and potential priority or preference for other programs administered by the state.

Eligibility Criteria:
- Must have a continuous boundary that encompasses at least one square mile but no more than 20 square miles, excluding waterways and transportation arteries.
- Must have an unemployment rate of at least 1.5 times the national, state or local average for the preceding 12 months or has experienced at least a 9% population loss during the most recent six-year period, or has experienced a population loss of at least 3% for the most recent three-year period.
- Must meet one of seven criteria based on income levels, structural conditions, tax arrearages, loss of jobs or business, declaration as a state or federal disaster area.
- Businesses must be located in or committed to located in a state designated enterprise zone. The business must also commit to hire at least 25% of its new employees from residents of the enterprise zone or to hire economically disadvantaged persons as defined by state law.

Highlights:
More than 35,000 jobs have been committed to be created since 1987. Over 210 Enterprise Zone Projects have been approved to date, stimulating investment of more than $5 billion into Texas communities.

To apply, contact:
Craig Pinkley
Texas Department of Economic Development
Texas Enterprise Zone Office
P.O. Box 12728

Austin, TX 78711-2728
512-936-0269

Utah

Number of Zones: 10. Zones are designated on a county basis.

Zone and Tax Incentives:
- 10% of the first $100,000
- 5% of the next $250,000
- Job Tax Credit Consisting of:
  - $750 per job for manufacturing businesses
  - $1,250 per job if the business is in one of the three targeted groups designated by the county

Eligibility Criteria:

County must meet two of the following criteria:
- Unemployment of 150% of the state average
- Net out migration during the past three years
- Poverty rate of 120% of the state average

An Enterprise Zone plan indicating the local contributions must be submitted. In addition, the county must also complete an economic development plan.

To apply, contact:
John Wilkinson
Enterprise Zone Coordinator
Division of Business and Economic Development
324 South State, Suite 50
Salt Lake City, UT 84111
801-538-8782

Vermont

Program authorization expired December, 1992. No reauthorization has been issued.

Virginia

Number of Zones: 52

Zone and Tax Incentives:

Businesses that qualify for state incentives are provided:

- A general tax credit against state business income, franchise or license tax
- State business income tax credit, decreasing from 80% in the first year to credit 60% for the second through tenth year
- A Sales Tax Exemption (in the form of a refund) for purchases of any qualified business for up to five years
- Refundable Real Property Improvement Tax Credit: A credit of 30% not to exceed $125,000 over a 5 year period is available for rehabilitation projects that cost at least $50,000
- In addition to the state incentives, each designated locality offers its own package of incentives including local tax rebates, business loans, job training, public improvements, fast track permitting and development fee waivers.

Eligibility Criteria:
- A business is required to incur at least 50% of its adjusted gross expenses for a taxable year as a result of business activity within the zone.
- A new business must hire a work force in which 40% or more of those employed have incomes below 80% of the median income of the locality prior to employment.
- An existing business must increase its full-time work force by 10% or more over the average of the base taxable year with at least 40% of the increase meeting the same employee income criteria.

Zone Designation Criteria:
- At least 25% of the population has an income level below 80% of the median income for the jurisdiction, or
- The unemployment rate is at least 50% above the state average, or
- Demonstrate a floor area vacancy rate of industrial and/or commercial properties of 25% or more

To apply, contact:
> Nicole Thompson
> Enterprise Zone Program Manager
> Department of Housing and Community Development
> 501 N. 2nd St.
> Richmond, VA 23219-1321
> 804-371-7030

Washington

The state does not have an authorized enterprise zone program.

West Virginia

The state does not have an authorized enterprise zone program.

Wisconsin

Legislation was enacted in 1988. Program was expanded in 1993. Legislation authorizes the designation of up to 14 zones. Designation period is seven years. Up to three one-year extensions may be authorized.

Number of Zones: 12

Zone and Tax Incentives:

State tax credits of $21 million are available with 10% held in a reserve fund. The remaining credits are allocated to each zone based on population within the zone with minimums established depending on the size of community. Businesses must be certified by the state before they can incur eligible expenses or claim tax credits. The development zone tax credits include:
- Non-refundable sales tax credit for the amount of sales tax paid on building materials and equipment used in a trade or business.
- A non-refundable 2.5% location credit for the costs of acquiring, constructing, rehabilitating, remodeling, or repairing real property that is used in a trade or business.
- A non-refundable jobs credit for hiring certain target groups equal to 20% of the first $13,000 in qualified wages for the first and second years of employment.
- A non-refundable 2.5 percent investment credit

on depreciable tangible personal property used in a trade or business.
- A non-refundable 5% additional research credit on increased expenditures.
- Non-refundable resident credit for employees who are residents of the zone of 10% of the first 2 years wages up to $6,000; a maximum of $600 per employee.
- Non-refundable dependent care credit up to $1,200 per child, per year for the first 2 years of employment.

Eligibility Criteria

Cities, towns, villages, Indian reservations, and, in some cases, counties may apply to designate areas within their jurisdictions as development zones. In order to be considered, the area must meet at least two of the following six criteria:
- The unemployment rate is at least 150% of the state average over the last 18 months
- At least 40% of those residing in the area are members of households that have household income levels at or below 80% of the statewide median household income
- The area is Urban Development Action Grant program eligible
- The property value of the last assessment is lower than the assessment two years earlier
- The percentage of households receiving Aid for Families with Dependent Children (AFDC) in the area is at least 150% of the percentage of households receiving AFDC in the state
- At least 5% of the work force of the locality submitting the application was permanently laid off within the last 18 months

Areas must also meet the following criteria:
- Continuous border following natural or man-made boundaries
- Contiguous blocks, census tracts, or similar units
- If located within an MSA (Metropolitan Statistical Area), the zone must:
  - Contain less than 5% of the valuation of the property of the city, village, or town

- If located within an MSA, the zone must:
  - Contain less than 5% of the valuation of the property of the city, village, or town
- If located in a city or the first class, the population of the area is not less than 4,000 nor greater than 5% of the city's population
- If located in a village, town, or city other than a first class city, the population cannot be less than 4,000
- If not part of a MSA, the population must be at least 1,000 but not more than 5,000
- If located within the boundaries of an Indian reservation, the population must be 5,000 or less

Designation is competitive and based on:
- The degree of distress
- Economic development strategy
- Expansion of employment opportunities for the target population
- Coordination of employment and training programs
- Organizational capacity
- Other impacts

Highlights:
Through July 1996, the Wisconsin Department of Development has certified 261 businesses. It also created a Development Opportunity Zone in 1994 that generates projects specifically geared to particular company expansions. One was created in West Alice, WI with an allocation of $3 million in tax credits.

To apply, contact:
Bill Wheeler
P.O. Box 7970
Madison, WI 53707
608-267-2045

Wyoming

The state does not have an authorized enterprise zone program.

HOW DO I GET FREE RESEARCH HELP?

It's a jungle out there, and you often don't have a map. In order to learn your way around, it is good to have some people you can call on for directions. The federal government supports hundreds of clearinghouses on topics ranging from agriculture to zoos, so there is something for everyone. When you begin your grant search, these clearinghouses can direct you to organizations, foundations, and even government offices that deal with issues or concerns similar to your request. Once you have found the grant sources, you often need statistics or information to back up your request for funds. Many of these clearinghouses maintain facts and figures on their specialties. You can find out statistics on fisheries, health topics, demographics, safety records, export data, labor issues, and much more.

Want to start a daycare center? You can find out the number of licensed day care facilities in your area, the number of preschool children, and even the average income of your town's residents. Want to export a product? You can find out what countries are increasing or decreasing imports of a particular product; how you can assess the export potential; and even background data on potential foreign partners. Want to start a business? You can find out what programs or forms of assistance are available to women entrepreneurs; where you can receive free management consulting; and help in entering the federal or state procurement market.

These services and resources are just waiting for you. Many of them will help you get the information you need to make your grant request stand out in the crowd. With so many people asking for money, you need to make sure that your request is complete and thorough as possible.

The clearinghouses that follow are divided into topic areas, but make sure you scan through each section, as some may overlap. Many have websites where you have easy access to the information. Often these clearinghouses will provide you with bibliographies or basic searches for their area of expertise. This is where you will find your jungle roadmap. Now all you need to do is follow it.

Animals and Agriculture

Agriculture Exports Clearinghouse

Foreign Agricultural Service
U.S. Department of Agriculture
Room 5074
Washington, DC 20050
202-720-7115
Fax: 202-720-1727
www.fas.usda.gov
Email: fasinfo@fas.usda.gov
The Foreign Agricultural Service compiles and disseminates agricultural trade and commodity production information to agribusinesses and the general public. They offer private companies and cooperatives assistance in marketing their products overseas by collecting and publicizing information on foreign buyers and advertising U.S. export availability. They have a monthly magazine, commodity and trade reports, publications, and fact sheets (many of which are free). They can answer such questions as:
1) What are the market prospects for U.S. food and farm products in Japan?
2) What are some overseas markets and buying trends for a particular product?
3) What are some overseas promotional activities?

4) How do I begin an export business?
5) How do I advertise my product directly to buyers overseas?

Economic Research Service (Agriculture)

U.S. Department of Agriculture
1800 M St., NW
ERS, Room 3100
Washington, DC 20036-5831
202-694-5110
Fax: 202-694-5641
Fax on Demand: 202-694-5700
www.ers.usda.gov
Email: service@econ.ag.gov

The Economic Research Service conducts research on the economic and socio-demographic issues of rural America; the marketing, trade, and consumption of farm commodities; U.S. and foreign economic policies and their effects on trade; and more. They produce monographs and journal articles ranging from very technical research reports to easy-to-read leaflets. They offer situation and outlook reports providing a mixture of outlook and in-depth analysis of current commodity, trade, resource, and policy issues. Most of the information is available free of charge. They can answer such questions as:

1) What are the links between development and world trade?
2) What information exists on the U.S. and world markets for agricultural products?
3) How can farmers better conserve water resources?
4) What are the benefits of organic farming?
5) How can farmers adjust their techniques to keep pace with global market trends?

National Agricultural Statistics Service

NASS-USDA
Room 5805, South
Washington, DC 20250
800-727-9540
202-720-3896
Fax: 202-690-1311
www.usda.gov/nass/
Email: nass@nass.usda.gov

The National Agricultural Statistics Service collects data on crops, livestock, poultry, dairy, chemical use, prices, and labor, and publishes the official USDA State and national estimates through its Agricultural Statistics Board. There are nearly 400 reports annually covering domestic agriculture, such as estimates of production, stocks, inventories, prices, disposition, utilization, farm numbers and land, and other factors. They provide national profiles from regular surveys of thousands of farmers, ranchers, and agribusinesses that voluntarily provide data on a confidential basis. Publications are available and range from free to $12. They can answer such questions as:

1) How has the use of a specific chemical for crop growth changed over the past five years?
2) Has the size of farms increased or decreased over the past ten years?
3) What statistics exist on wildlife damage to crops?
4) How has the weekly crop weather effected crop growth?
5) What data is there on livestock slaughter?

Alternative Farming Systems Information Center

U.S. Department of Agriculture
National Agricultural Library
10301 Baltimore Blvd., Room 304
Beltsville, MD 20705-2351
301-504-6559

Fax: 301-504-6409

www.nal.usda.gov/afsic

Email: afsic@nal.usda.gov

The Alternative Farming Systems Information Center encourages research, education, and information delivery about farming systems that preserve the natural resource base while maintaining economic viability. The Center is the focal point for information on all types of alternative farming practices. They can refer you to organizations or experts, identify current research, furnish you with bibliographies, and more. Brief data base searches are free, while exhaustive searches are conducted on a cost recovery basis. They can answer such questions as:

1) How do you establish and maintain an organic garden?
2) What is involved in building a compost pile?
3) What are the effects of herbicide and fertilizer run off?
4) How can I avoid ground water contamination?
5) What are some solar energy alternatives for agriculture?

Animal Welfare Information Center

National Agricultural Library

U.S. Department of Agriculture

10301 Baltimore Blvd., 5th Floor

Beltsville, MD 20705-2351

301-504-6212

Fax: 301-504-7125

www.nal.usda.gov/awic

Email: awic@nal.usda.gov

The Animal Welfare Information Center is the focal point for all aspects of animal welfare. They have information on the care, handling, and management of animals used in research; training guides and manuals for animal care personnel; ethical issues; animal behavior; and pain control. They have a publications list of free fact sheets, bibliographies, and other resources. They can answer such questions as:

1) What information is there on the ethical and moral issues relating to animals and the philosophy of animal rights?
2) What alternatives are there to the use of live animals in research?
3) What videos exist on the care of animals?
4) What are some of the legislation regarding animal welfare?
5) What are some of the resources available regarding the raising of poultry?

Aquaculture Information Center

National Agricultural Library

U.S. Department of Agriculture

10301 Baltimore Blvd.

Beltsville, MD 20705-2351

301-504-5724

Fax: 301-504-6409

www.nal.usda.gov/asfic/afsaqua.htm

Email: afsaqua@nal.usda.gov

The Aquaculture Information Center collects information on the culture of aquatic plants and animals in freshwater, brackish, and marine environments. Examples include: catfish farming, oyster culture, salmon ranching, and trout farming. They have a publications list of free fact sheets, bibliographies, and other resources. They can answer such questions as:

1) How do you start a catfish farm?
2) What are the effects of sodium, cadmium, and lead on aquatic plants?
3) What types of algae are edible?
4) What is involved in raising snails?
5) What can be done to stop the pollution of freshwater environments?

Food and Nutrition Information Center

Agriculture Research Services
National Agricultural Library, Room 304
10301 Baltimore Blvd.
Beltsville, MD 20705-2351
301-504-5719
Fax: 301-504-6409
TTY: 301-504-6856
www.nal.usda.gov/fnic
Email: fnic@nal.usda.gov

The Food and Nutrition Information Center serves many types of users including educators, students, researchers, and consumers. Reference services are provided. Subjects covered include human nutrition research and education, diet and diet-related diseases, food habits, food composition, nutrition education, and more. The Center offers a variety of services which include answers to specific questions, lending books and audiovisuals, and providing computerized literature searches. A publications list is available, many of which are free. They can answer such questions as:

1) What studies exist on the effects of the school breakfast program?
2) What information can you provide to parents concerned about their overweight children?
3) Do you have information on anorexia nervosa?
4) Is it dangerous to consume caffeine while pregnant?
5) Are canned peaches as nutritious as fresh?

Alternative Farming Systems Information Center (Horticulture)

AFSIC
U.S. Department of Agriculture
10301 Baltimore Blvd., Room 304
Beltsville, MD 20705-2351
301-504-6559
Fax: 301-504-6409
www.nal.usda.gov/afsic

The Alternative Farming Systems Information Center covers technical horticultural or botanical questions, economic botany, wild plants of possible use, herbs, bonsai, and floriculture. They can answer such questions as:

1) How can you grow lavender commercially as a source of essential oils?
2) How do you grow and dry herbs?
3) How much would landscaping improve the value of a home?
4) Which plants can be used for medicinal purposes?
5) How can I control garden insects without using chemical sprays?

Meat and Poultry Hotline

Food Safety and Inspection Service
U.S. Department of Agriculture
Washington, DC 20250-3700
800-535-4555
Fax: 202-690-2859
www.fsis.usda.gov

The Meat and Poultry Hotline takes calls from consumers regarding cases of meat or poultry food poisoning or complaints about meat or poultry spoilage due to improper packaging or processing. They can also provide you with health-oriented information on safe handling and storage of meats and poultry. They can answer such questions as:

1) What should be done during a power outage?
2) What is salmonella and how can people be protected?

3) What are the different type of foodborne illnesses?
4) How long should you cook poultry?
5) What information should be included on meat and poultry labels and what does it mean?

Organic Gardening

Public Information Center, 3404
U.S. Environmental Protection Agency
401 M St., SW
Washington, DC 20460-0003
202-260-7751
Fax: 202-260-6257
www.epa.gov
Email: public-access@epamail.epa.gov
The Public Information Center has free information sheets on organic gardening, composting, and recycling. They can answer such questions as:
1) What plants should be planted near each other to deter pests?
2) What are the dangers of pesticides?
3) Who can I talk to regarding composting and recycling?
4) What are the advantages of organic fertilizers?
5) What is required to maintain a lawn?

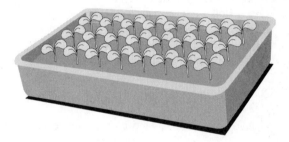

Plant Information Service

U.S. Botanic Garden
245 1st St., SW
Washington, DC 20024
202-225-8333
Fax: 202-225-1561
www.aoc.gov/pages/usbgpage.htm
The U.S. Botanic Garden serves as a center for plant information offering a telephone information service as well as responding to written inquiries, Monday through Friday from 9:00 to 11:30 a.m. They can answer such questions as:
1) What are the benefits of organic gardening?
2) How can I use insects to control garden pests?
3) Which house plants are poisonous?
4) What are the dangers of chemical fertilizers?
5) Which herbs grow best indoors?

Rural Information Center

National Agricultural Library
U.S. Department of Agriculture (USDA)
10301 Baltimore Blvd., Room 304
Beltsville, MD 20705-2351
301-504-5547
800-633-7701
Fax: 301-504-5181
TTY: 301-504-5755
www.nal.usda.gov/ric
Email: ric@nal.usda.gov
The Rural Information Center is designed to provide information and referral services to local government officials, businesses, community organizations, and rural citizens working to maintain the vitality of America's rural areas. The Center provides: customized information products to specific inquiries; refers users to organizations or experts in the field;

performs database searches; furnishes bibliographies; identifies current USDA research and Cooperative Extension System programs; and assists users in accessing the National Agricultural Libraries' extensive collection. There is a cost recovery fee for photocopying articles and searches. They can answer such questions as:

1) Which organizations focus on rural health issues?
2) What resources for the historic preservation of farmland are available in rural areas?
3) How can tourism be promoted in small towns?
4) What are examples of the more innovative economic development projects in rural communities?
5) What rural organizations focus specifically on research and development?

Seafood Hotline

Office of Seafood
Food and Drug Administration
200 C St., SW
Washington, DC 20204
800-SAFEFOOD
Fax: 202-401-3532
http://vm.cfsan.fda.gov/seafood1.html
Email: oco@fdacf.sw.dhhs.gov

The Seafood Hotline can provide consumers with information on how to buy and use seafood products, including storing and handling of seafood, and questions on seafood labeling and nutrition. The Hotline has many free publications on a variety of seafood issues. They can answer such questions as:

1) Can fish be kept frozen for a year?
2) How do you know if a seafood vendor is reputable?
3) What are the dangers of eating raw shellfish?
4) What information is available on canned tuna?
5) What are some seafood safety concerns for people with particular medical conditions?

Business and Industry

Advertising Practices

Federal Trade Commission (FTC)
6th and Pennsylvania Ave., NW
Washington, DC 20580
202-326-2222
Fax: 202-326-3259
www.ftc.gov/bcp/menu-ads.htm
Email: consumerline@ftc.gov
This division of the Federal Trade Commission (FTC) promotes the distribution of truthful information to the public through law enforcement and oversight activities in the following areas: general advertising for deceptive claims; advertising claims for food and over-the-counter drugs, particularly claims relating to safety or effectiveness; tobacco advertising; and performance and energy-savings claims for solar products, furnaces, window coverings, wood burning products, and more. They can answer such questions as:
1) How do you file a complaint with the FTC?
2) When and where is the advertising of tobacco products legal, and what are the reasons behind this?
3) How long are over-the-counter drugs tested before they are released on the market?
4) What penalties are levied against a company that has been charged with deceptive advertising?
5) How effective are over-the-counter diet pills?

Federal Aviation Administration

Office of Public Affairs
800 Independence Ave., SW
Washington, DC 20591
202-267-3883
www.faa.gov
Email: gramick@postmaster2.dot.gov
The Federal Aviation Administration (FAA) is the starting place for
any information on airlines, airports, and aircraft. The FAA regulates
air commerce, develops civil aeronautics, installs and operates airports,
conducts aeronautic research and provides guidance and policy on
accident prevention in general aviation. They keep statistics on air travel, accidents, and more. There are free publications on airline careers, aviation, and airplanes, as well as videos and curriculum guides. They can answer such questions as:
1) Which airlines had penalties of $50,000 or more for safety and security issues?
2) What videos are available on aviation?
3) What historical information is available on women in aviation?
4) What are the current statistics on air traffic accidents?
5) What methods are used to reduce the noise level of new aircraft?

Board of Governors of the Federal Reserve System (Banking)

Publications Services, MS-127
20th and C Sts., NW
Washington, DC 20551
202-452-3244
Fax: 202-728-5886
www.federalreserve.gov
The Federal Reserve System, the central bank of the United States, is charged with administering and making policy for the Nation's credit and monetary affairs. The Federal Reserve helps to maintain the banking industry in sound condition, capable of responding to the Nation's domestic and international financial needs and objectives. It has publications and

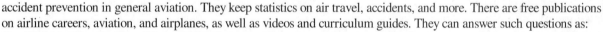

audiovisual materials prepared which are designed to increase public understanding of the functions and operations of the Federal Reserve System, monetary policy, financial markets and institutions, consumer finance, and the economy. They can answer such questions as:

1) How did the Federal Reserve begin and how does it function today?
2) What is the history of the U.S. monetary policy and how is it formulated?
3) Is there a brief overview available on banking regulation?
4) What is the evolution of money?
5) How are checks used, processed, and collected?

Business Assistance Service

Office of Business Liaison
U.S. Department of Commerce
Room 5062
Washington, DC 20230
202-482-1360
Fax: 202-482-4054
www.doc.gov/obl

The Office of Business Liaison is responsible for keeping the Department of Energy Secretary informed of issues affecting the business community. The Office provides information and guidance on programs throughout the federal government. Although it cannot provide legal advice or intervene on an inquirer's behalf with a federal agency, it can alleviate the necessity of making numerous attempts to locate or obtain federal information, programs, and services. Most requests are for information having to do with government procurement, exporting, marketing, statistical sources, and regulatory matters. They can answer such questions as:

1) Where can someone get information on what the government is buying and what steps are required to sell to the government?
2) Who can advise a business on unfair trade practices?
3) Where are the statistics on a specific type of business?
4) Where is there information on federal databases?
5) Is there U.S. tariff information available?

Central and Eastern Europe Business Information Center

U.S. Department of Commerce
International Trade Administration
14th and Constitution Ave., NW, Room 7414
Washington, DC 20230
202-482-2645
Fax: 202-482-4473
www.ita.doc.gov

The Central and Eastern Europe Business Information Center serves as a clearinghouse for information on business conditions in Eastern European countries, and on emerging trade and investment opportunities in those countries. It also serves as a source of information on U.S. government programs supporting private enterprise, trade, and investment in Eastern Europe. The Center also serves as a referral point for voluntary assistance programs. A variety of printed materials are available directly from the Center, as are bibliographies on data available from other sources. Most of the services are free of charge. They can answer such questions as:

1) What are the export procedures for a particular product to Poland?
2) What are the population, economic, commercial, and trade statistics on Romania?
3) Is there a list of contacts for export information in Bulgaria?
4) What political and economic issues should be considered when investing in businesses in Eastern Europe?
5) How can I advertise directly in Eastern European countries?

Commodity Futures Trading Commission

Office of Public Affairs
Commodity Futures Trading Commission
3 Lafayette Center
1155 21st St., NW
Washington, DC 20581
202-418-5080
Fax: 202-418-5525
www.cftc.gov

The Commodity Futures Trading Commission (CFTC) promotes economic growth, protects the rights of customers, and ensures fairness of the marketplace through regulation of futures trading. CFTC regulates the activities of numerous commodity exchange members, public brokerage houses, commodity trading advisers, and others, as well as approves the rules under which an exchange operates. They have free publications and can refer you to other offices within CFTC for specific information. They can answer such questions as:

1) What is the purpose of futures trading?
2) How do you read a commodity futures price table?
3) Do brokers have to be registered, and if so, how does one check on a broker?
4) What are some of the important issues that people should be aware of before entering the futures market?
5) What do I do if I suspect my broker of dishonest or unethical behavior?

Federal Communications Commission

Public Service Commission
445 12th St., SW
Washington, DC 20554
888-225-5322
202-418-0190
Fax: 202-418-0232
TTY: 202-418-2555
www.fcc.gov
Email: psd@fcc.gov

The Federal Communications Commission regulates interstate and
foreign communications by radio, television, wire, satellite, and cable. It is responsible for the development and operation of broadcast services and the provision of rapid, efficient nationwide and worldwide telephone and telegraph services at reasonable rates. They take complaints and have free information on all areas falling within their responsibility. They can answer questions such as:

1) What can be done if someone is having trouble with their cable company?
2) Where do you complain if you find the local D.J.'s show to be offensive?
3) What are the rules regarding pay per call services?
4) Where can you learn more about cellular radio regulations?
5) What happens when radio signals are picked up by consumer electronic products?

Export Country Experts

U.S. Foreign and Commercial Services
Export Promotion Services
U.S. Department of Commerce
Room 2810
Washington, DC 20230
202-482-3809
Fax: 202-482-5819
www.doc.gov

The Country Desk Officers at the U.S. Department of Commerce can provide businesses with information on a market, company, or most any other aspect of commercial life in a particular country. These specialists can look at the needs of an

individual U.S. firm wishing to sell in a particular country in the full context of that country's overall economy, trade policies, and political situation, and also in light of U.S. policies toward that country. Desk officers keep up to date on the economic and commercial conditions in their assigned countries. Each desk officer collects information on the country's regulations, tariffs, business practices, economic and political developments, trade data and trends, market size, and growth. They have free reports and other information available or they can refer callers to other country specialists. They can answer such questions as:

1) How can I expand my business through a foreign franchise?
2) How can I reduce my company's distribution and transportation costs overseas?
3) What type of export opportunities exist for computer manufacturing companies who want to expand to Germany?
4) What are some recent foreign labor trends in Japan?
5) Which markets are growing the fastest overseas?

Economic Research Service

U.S. Department of Agriculture
1800 M St., NW
Washington, DC 20036-5831
202-694-5050
AutoFax: 202-694-5700
www.ers.usda.gov
Email: service@econ.ag.gov

The Economic Research Service conducts research on the economic and socio-demographic issues of rural America; the marketing, trade, and consumption of farm commodities; U.S. and foreign economic policies and their effects on trade; and more. They produce monographs and journal articles ranging from very technical research reports to easy-to-read leaflets. Situation and outlook reports providing a mixture of outlook and in-depth analysis of current commodity, trade, resource, and policy issues are also available. Most of the information is free of charge. They can answer such questions as:

1) What are the links between development and world trade?
2) What information exists on the U.S. and world markets for agricultural products?
3) How can farmers better conserve water resources?
4) What are the benefits of organic farming?
5) How can farmers adjust their techniques to keep pace with global market trends?

Economics: National, Regional, and International

Bureau of Economic Analysis
U.S. Department of Commerce
1441 L St., NW
Washington, DC 20230
202-606-9900
Fax: 202-606-5310
www.bea.doc.gov

The Bureau of Economic Analysis (BEA) provides information on national and regional economics. BEA collects basic information on such key issues as economic growth, inflation, regional development, and the Nation's role in the world economy. It distributes a number of publications that measure, analyze and forecast economic trends, and are available on recorded messages, online through the Economic Bulletin Board, and in BEA reports. They can answer such questions as:

1) What is the average per capita income in the United States?
2) Will the rate of inflation increase or decrease over the next five years, and by what percent?
3) What percentage of the Gross National Product (GNP) does the government spend on health care?
4) How does the United States' national unemployment rate compare to other industrialized countries?
5) What was the unemployment rate in Pennsylvania from 1989-1993?

Exporter's Hotline

Trade Information Center
U.S. Department of Commerce
Washington, DC 20230
800-USA-TRADE
Fax: 202-482-4473
TDD: 800-TDD-TRADE
www.ita.doc.gov/

The Trade Information Center is a comprehensive one-stop shop for information on U.S. Government programs and activities that support exporting efforts. This hotline is staffed by trade specialists who can provide information on seminars and conferences, overseas buyers and representatives, overseas events, export financing, technical assistance, and export counseling. They also have access to the National Trade Data Bank, which provides basic export information, country-specific information, and industry-specific information. They can provide a great deal of free assistance, but there is a fee charged for data bank searches and other technical assistance. They can answer such questions as:

1)   What countries are increasing or decreasing imports of a particular product, and at what rates?
2)   What 10 countries are the top importers of a specific product?
3)   How can a businessman meet prescreened prospects who are interested in a product or service?
4)   How can a business assess their export potential?
5)   How can a businessman obtain background data on potential foreign partners?

Fishery Statistics and Economics Division

Office of Research and Environmental Information
National Marine Fisheries Service
National Oceanic and Atmospheric Administration
U.S. Department of Commerce
1315 East-West Highway, SSMC3
Silver Spring, MD 20910
301-713-2328
Fax: 301-713-4137
www.noaa.gov/fisheries.html

The Fisheries Statistics and Economics Division publishes statistical bulletins on marine recreational fishing and commercial fishing, and on the manufacture and commerce of fishery products. This Division has several annual and biannual reports available. They can answer such questions as:

1)   How many fish were imported in a year, and what kind?
2)   What is the most popular fish to export?
3)   What kinds of fish are frozen?
4)   What statistics exist on processed fish?
5)   How many fish were caught by weekend fishermen?

Office of Industries

United States International Trade Commission
500 E St., SW
Washington, DC 20436
202-205-3296
Fax: 202-205-3161
www.usitc.gov
Email: cunningham@usitc.gov

The Office of Industries at the U.S. International Trade Commission has experts assigned to every com imported into the U.S. These experts are responsible for investigation of the customs laws of the United States and foreign countries; the volume of imports in comparison with domestic production; the effects relating to competition of foreign industries; and

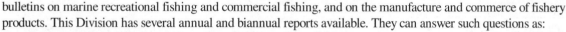

all other factors affecting competition between articles of the U.S. and imported articles. They are knowledgeable about the domestic and foreign industry, and have statistical and factual information. They also have information regarding the tariff schedules. There is no charge for this information. They can answer such questions as:

1) What is the rate of duty for a product from a particular country?
2) What is the rate of import-export, the size of the market and the major producers of women's sweaters?
3) How much of a product is exported and what is the size of the potential market?
4) What happens if someone suspects an imported article is being subsidized or sold at less then fair value?
5) What can a company do if they feel they are being unfairly effected by import trade?

Technical Data Center (Job Safety)

Technical Data Center
Occupational Safety and Health Administration
U.S. Department of Labor
200 Constitution Ave., NW
Room N2625
Washington, DC 20210
202-693-2350
Fax: 202-219-5046
www.osha.gov

The Technical Data Center compiles technical information on all industries covered by the Occupational Safety and Health Administration (OSHA). The Center maintains a library of 6,000 volumes and 200 journals, as well as an extensive microfilm collection of industry standards and OSHA rule-making records. The Center is also the docket office and holds the hearing records on standards, the comments, and final rules. Literature searches are conducted free of charge. They can answer such questions as:

1) What are some hazard training programs that can be implemented in the workplace to teach employees to work safely in a variety of situations?
2) When was a particular company inspected and what violations were found?
3) What are the health hazards of a particular chemical?
4) What are some dangers of working around chemicals while pregnant?
5) Have there been similar reports of spinal cord injuries in a particular job?

Federal Mediation and Conciliation Service (Labor-Management)

Federal Mediation and Conciliation Service (FMCS)
2100 K St., NW
Washington, DC 20427
202-606-8100
Fax: 202-606-4216
www.fmcs.gov
Email: publicinformation@fmcs.gov

The Federal Mediation and Conciliation Service represents the public interest by promoting the development of sound and stable labor-management relationships; preventing or minimizing work stoppages by assisting labor and management in settling their disputes through mediation; advocating collective bargaining, and much more. They can answer such questions as:

1) What is "alternative dispute resolution", and how can it be used?
2) How can companies work to develop effective labor-management committees?
3) What statistics exist on dispute mediation, preventive medication, work stoppages, and contract mediation?
4) What are some steps that companies can take to improve communication between labor and management?
5) What happens when a Federal agency and employee representative reach a negotiation impasse?

Federal Labor Relations Authority

Federal Labor Relations Authority
607 14th St., NW
Washington, DC 20424-0001
202-482-6550
Fax: 202-482-6636
Bulletin Board: 202-512-1387
www.flra.gov

The Federal Labor Relations Authority oversees the Federal service labor-management relations program. It administers the law that protects the right of employees of the Federal Government to organize, bargain collectively, and participate through labor organizations of their own choosing. They can answer such questions as:
1) What laws protect Federal employees?
2) What steps can be taken when labor and management have reached an impasse?
3) How does an employee file a union grievance procedure?
4) How do I get a copy of my local union's collective bargaining agreement?
5) Is an agency permitted to negotiate a particular bargaining proposal?

Labor Statistics Clearinghouse

Division of Information Services
Bureau of Labor Statistics
U.S. Department of Labor
2 Massachusetts Ave., NE
Room 2860
Washington, DC 20212
202-606-5886
Fax: 202-606-7890
TDD: 202-606-5897
Fax on Demand: 202-606-6235
http://stats.bls.gov/opbinfo.htm
Email:blsdatastaff@bls.gov

The Bureau of Labor Statistics (BLS) is the principal data-gathering agency of the Federal Government in the field of labor economics. The Bureau collects, processes, analyzes, and disseminates data relating to employment, unemployment, and other characteristics of the labor force; prices and consumer expenditures; wages, other worker compensation, and industrial relations; productivity; economic growth and employment projections; and occupational safety and health. This office can also provide you with a release schedule for BLS major economic indicators and the recorded message number. BLS can refer you to experts within the Bureau who can answer your specific question, provide you with historical information, and refer you to tables and charts for data. The BLS has publications, periodicals, magnetic tapes, diskettes, and more for sale. They can answer questions such as:
1) What are the employment statistics and the outlook for a particular occupation?
2) What is the unemployment rate for a particular state?
3) What is the current wage for a word processor in Seattle, and what are the usual benefits associated with that position?
4) What is the employment projection for a specific job?
5) What is the consumer/producer price index and how has it changed over time?

Mine Safety Clearinghouse

Office of Information and Public Affairs
Mine Safety and Health Administration
U.S. Department of Labor
4015 Wilson Blvd.

Arlington, VA 22203
703-235-1452
Fax: 703-235-4323
www.msha.gov
Email: ksnyder@msha.gov
The Mine Safety and Health Administration develops mandatory safety and health standards, ensures compliance with such standards, assesses civil penalties for violations, and investigates accidents. It cooperates with and provides assistance to states in the development of effective state mine safety and health programs and improves and expands training programs. The Clearinghouse can provide general information regarding the Mine Safety and Health Administration, as well as free brochures, manuals, and other publications regarding mine safety and health. They can answer such questions as:

1)   How can mine operators train miners effectively to prevent accidents and to avoid unsafe conditions?
2)   What are the inspection procedures for a mine?
3)   What is the latest information on the treatment and prevention of black lung and other respiratory diseases that are common to miners?
4)   What is the latest research on robotics and automation in the mining industry?
5)   What mines have been ordered to close because of safety concerns?

Mineral Commodity Information

Minerals Information
U.S. Geological Survey
983 National Center
Reston, VA 20192
888-ASK-USGS
703-648-6100
Fax: 703-648-6057
http://minerals.usgs.gov
Email: minerals@usgs.gov
The U.S. Geological Survey (USGS) Minerals Resources Program is staffed by mineral experts who distribute a wide variety of mineral-related information and publications to meet and support the needs of the public, as well as government agencies and the scientific and industrial sectors. The staff provides information on the most current as well as past published reports pertaining to minerals, mining, processing, and research. They have statistics on import sources, uses, government stockpile, reserves, world resources, and substitutes. Dozens of commodity specialists are also available to assist you. They can answer such questions as:

1)   What will the price of silver be over the next five years?
2)   What is the role of gold in the international monetary system?
3)   How can industries improve the quality of domestic steel?
4)   How many tons of coal did U.S. industries produce last year?
5)   What methods are used to recycle scrap metal?

Minority Energy Information Clearinghouse

Office of Minority Economic Impact
U.S. Department of Energy
Forrestal Building, Room 5B-110
1000 Independence Ave., SW
Washington, DC 20585
202-586-5876
Fax: 202-586-3075

www.hr.doe.gov/ed/index.html
Email: ann.young@hq.doe.gov
The Minority Energy Information Clearinghouse develops and disseminates information related to energy programs that have an impact upon minorities, minority business enterprises, minority educational institutions, and other minority organizations. They can direct callers to government programs that will assist minority businesses in entering the energy field, as well as giving information about educational programs for minority students who are energy majors. They can answer such questions as:

1) What type of fellowships are available to minority college students attending Historically Black Colleges and Universities who want to pursue energy-related careers?
2) What types of energy-related loans are available to minority businesses?
3) Can I receive a listing of minority energy conferences or workshops?
4) How does the Clearinghouse's electronic bulletin board work?
5) How has recent energy legislation had an impact upon minority businesses?

Overseas Private Investment Corporation

Investor Information Service
1100 New York Ave., NW, MS 7412
Washington, DC 20527
202-336-8663
Fax: 202-408-5155
www.opic.gov
Investor Information Service assists U.S. firms in gathering information on foreign countries and their business environments, as well as facilitating the flow of information about developing countries to potential U.S. investors. OPIC created the Investor Information Service (IIS). Country-specific information is available in kit form on more than 100 countries, as well as on 16 regions. Kits include materials covering the economies, trade laws, business regulations, political conditions and investment incentives of developing countries and regions. Kit costs range from $10-$420. They can answer such questions as:

1) What information exists for someone who wants to set up a fast food business in Greece?
2) What is the latest information on the foreign economic trends and their implications for the U.S. in Hungary?
3) What issues should be considered in purchasing an overseas venture?
4) Is it possible to meet with local business representatives, and experienced U.S. investors, and to attend briefings by the U.S. Ambassador in a foreign country?
5) What is the current investment climate in France? Is it favorable to new U.S. businesses?

Pension Benefit Guaranty Corporation

Communication and Public Affairs Department
1200 K St., NW, Suite 240
Washington, DC 20005-4026
202-326-4040
Fax: 202-326-4042
www.pbgc.gov
The Pension Benefit Guaranty Corporation works to ensure the
solvency and viability of company-sponsored pension plans. They can provide you with information and publications on pension plans, as well as information pertaining to laws and regulations on pensions. They can answer questions such as:

1) What is the Federal pension law?
2) What are pensions plans and how do they operate?
3) What information on plans is a company required to give to members?
4) What are the rights and options of participants?
5) What is the employer's responsibilities regarding pension plans?

Pension and Welfare Benefits Administration

U.S. Department of Labor
200 Constitution Ave., NW
N5619
Washington, DC 20210
202-219-8776
Fax: 202-219-5362
www.dol.gov/dol/pwba/welcome.html

The Pension and Welfare Benefits Administration (PWBA) helps to protect the economic future and retirement security of working Americans. It requires administrators of private pension and welfare plans to provide plan participants with easily understandable summaries; to file those summaries with the agency; and to report annually on the financial operation of the plans. PWBA has publications and other information available. They can answer questions such as:

1) What is the effect of job mobility on pension plans?
2) What is the Employee Retirement Income Security Act (ERISA)?
3) What studies have been done on the investment performance of ERISA plans?
4) What information are pension plans required to provide to participants?
5) What employee benefit documents are available from the Department of Labor?

Federal Procurement Data Center

General Services Administration
7th and D St., SW, Room 5652
Washington, DC 20407
202-401-1529
Fax: 202-401-1546
www.fpds.gsa.gov
Email: linda.hornsby@gsa.gov

The Federal Procurement Data Center stores information about Federal procurement actions, from 1978 to present, that totaled $25,000 or more. The systems contains information on purchasing or contracting office; date of award; dollars obligated; principal product or service; name and address of contractor; and more. Searches and printouts are available on a cost recovery basis. They can answer such questions as:

1) How many contracts did a particular company receive in a given year?
2) Who in the government is buying winter parkas?
3) What types of contracts are being awarded in Franklin county?
4) What has the National Park Service purchased in the last month?
5) Who do I need to talk to in order to sell my particular product?

Science, Technology and Business Division

Library of Congress
101 Independence Ave., SE
Washington, DC 20540
202-707-5639
www.loc.gov

The Science, Technology and Business Division's collection numbers 3.5 million books, nearly 60,000 journals, and 4.4 million technical reports. The collections include such treasures as first editions of Copernicus and Newton and the personal papers of the Wright Brothers and Alexander Graham Bell. The Division has primary responsibility for providing reference and bibliographic services and for recommending acquisitions in the broad areas of science and technology. Reference services are provided to users in person, by telephone, and by correspondence. Indirect reference service is provided through bibliographic guides (Tracer Bullets) and research reports prepared by Division subject specialists and reference librarians. Copies of reference guides are available at no charge. They can answer such questions as:

1) Where can someone begin looking for information on lasers and their applications?
2) What are good sources of information on volcanoes?
3) What resources exist on extraterrestrial life?
4) Where could someone find sources for information on medicinal plants?
5) How would someone go about creating a hologram?

U.S. Securities and Exchange Commission

Office of Public Affairs
450 5th St., NW
Washington, DC 20549
202-942-0020
Fax: 202-942-9654
TTY: 202-628-9039
www.sec.gov

The Securities and Exchange Commission (SEC) administers federal securities laws that seek to provide protection for investors; to ensure that securities markets are fair and honest; and to provide the means to enforce securities laws through sanctions. They have free publications, a public reference room, disclosure reports, and information on how individuals can protect themselves. They can answer such questions as:

1) What are pyramid schemes and how do they work?
2) Where can someone find out if there have been complaints about a particular broker or adviser?
3) How does someone choose investments safely?
4) Who needs to register with the SEC and what is required?
5) What is the SEC and how does it operate?

U.S. Small Business Administration

Answer Desk
409 3rd St., SW
Washington, DC 20416
800-827-5722
202-205-6400
Fax: 202-205-7064
www.sbaonline.sba.gov/helpdesk

The Small Business Administration (SBA) aids, counsels, assists, and protects the interests of small business, and ensures that small business concerns receive a fair portion of government purchases, contracts, and subcontracts. SBA also makes loans and licenses, and regulates small business investment companies. The Small Business Answer Desk helps callers with questions on how to start and manage a business, where to get financing, and other information needed to operate and expand a business. They have a publications catalogue, with most items available for under $5.00. They can answer such questions as:

1) What programs or forms of assistance are available to women entrepreneurs?
2) What help exists for a business interested in developing an export market?
3) Is there a way a business can receive free management consulting?
4) Are there programs designed specifically for businesses in small towns?
5) How does a company enter the federal procurement market?

National Center for Standards and Certification

National Institute of Standards and Technology
Building 820, Room 164
Gaithersburg, MD 20899
301-975-4040
Fax: 301-926-1559
http://ts.nist.gov/ts/htdocs/210/217/bro.htm
Email: ncsci@nist.gov

The National Center for Standards and Certification Information provides a free service which will identify standards for selling any product to any country in the world. This federal agency will tell you what the standard is for a given product or suggest where you can obtain an official copy of the standard. They can answer such questions as:
1) What U.S. industries standards pertain to certain products?
2) What foreign standards apply to a product?
3) What is the latest GATT information on proposed foreign regulations?
4) Where can I locate the organizations that have standards information?
5) How are military standards different for U.S. standards?

Transportation Research Information Services

Transportation Research Board
2101 Constitution Ave., NW
Washington, DC 20418
202-334-2934
Fax: 202-334-2003
www.nas.edu/trb

The Transportation Research Information Services (TRIS) is the prime source of transportation research information in the United States. TRIS is an information clearinghouse designed to identify worldwide sources of transportation research information. TRIS contains more than 250,000 abstracts of completed research and summaries of research projects in progress. TRIS is regularly used by transportation administrators, operators, academics, planners, designers, engineers, and managers. TRIS contains information on various modes and aspects of transportation including planning, design, finance, construction, maintenance, traffic operations, management, marketing, and other topics. Publications are available for a fee. They can answer such questions as:
1) What is the latest research on airport capacity?
2) What information exists on the privatization of toll roads?
3) What data should be considered when building a bypass?
4) What studies have been conducted on land traffic getting to and from airports?
5) What technology exists to weigh trucks in motion rather than at weigh stations?

Women's Bureau Clearinghouse

U.S. Department of Labor
200 Constitution Ave., NW, Room S3306
Washington, DC 20210
800-827-5335
202-219-4486
Fax: 202-219-5529
www.dol.gov/dol/wb/welcome.html
Email: wb-wwc@dol.gov

The Women's Bureau Clearinghouse was designed and established to assist employers in identifying the most appropriate policies for responding to the dependent care needs of employees seeking to balance their dual responsibilities. They can also provide information on women's issues, as well as work force issues that affect women. They offer information and guidance in areas such as women-owned businesses, women workers, alternative work schedules, dependent care issues, and much more. They also have publications and other information available, much of which is free. They can answer such questions as:
1) What are some elder care program options?
2) What is the earning difference between men and women?
3) How does flex time work in companies similar to mine?
4) What are some examples of alternate work schedules and how do they work?
5) What literature and other resources are available on employer-supported child care?

Consumer and Housing

Animal Welfare Information Center

National Agricultural Library
U.S. Department of Agriculture
10301 Baltimore Blvd., 5th Floor
Beltsville, MD 20705-2351
301-504-6212
Fax: 301-504-7125
www.nal.usda.gov/awic
Email: awic@nal.usda.gov

The Animal Welfare Information Center is the focal point for all aspects of animal welfare. They have information on the care, handling, and management of animals used in research; training guides and manuals for animal care personnel; ethical issues; animal behavior; and pain control. They have a publications list of free fact sheets, bibliographies, and other resources. They can answer such questions as:

1) What information is there on the ethical and moral issues relating to animals and the philosophy of animal rights?
2) What alternatives are there to the use of live animals in research?
3) What videos exist on the care of animals?
4) What are some of the legislation regarding animal welfare?
5) Are there resources available regarding the raising of poultry?

Auto Safety Hotline

Office of Defects Investigation (NEF-10)
National Highway Traffic Safety Administration
U.S. Department of Transportation
400 7th St., SW
Washington, DC 20590
800-424-9393
Fax: 202-366-7882
www.nhtsa.dot.gov
Email: hotline@nhtsa.dot.gov

The Auto Safety Hotline can provide information on recalls, defects, investigations, child safety seats, tires, drunk driving, crash test results, seat belts, air bags, odometer tampering, and other related topics. They also accept reports of automobile safety problems. The Hotline publishes the New Car Assessment Program, which provides comparable data on the frontal crashworthiness of selected new vehicles. They have free fact sheets and publications on these topics and more. They can answer such questions as:

1) What is the safest new car?
2) Which child car seats have been recalled?
3) What should you do if you suspect an odometer has been tampered with?
4) How many states have seat belt laws, and what are the statistics regarding their use and benefits?
5) What are the statistics for drunk driving, and what information exists for alcohol's involvement in fatalities?
6) What is the fuel efficiency of a particular car?

Federal Communications Commission

445 12th St., SW
Washington, DC 20554
202-418-0190
Fax: 202-418-0232

www.fcc.gov

Email: fccinfo@fcc.gov

The Federal Communications Commission regulates interstate and foreign communications by radio, television, wire, satellite, and cable. It is responsible for the development and operation of broadcast services and the provision of rapid, efficient nationwide and worldwide telephone and telegraph services at reasonable rates. They take complaints and have free information on all areas falling within their responsibility. They can answer questions such as:

1) What can be done if someone is having trouble with their cable company or does not understand their cable bill?
2) Where do you complain if you find the local D.J.'s show to be offensive?
3) What are the rules regarding pay per call services?
4) Where can you learn more about cellular radio regulations?
5) What happens when radio signals are picked up by consumer electronic products?

Consumer Product Safety Commission

Office of Information and Public Affairs

U.S. Consumer Product Safety Commission

Washington, DC 20207

800-638-2772

Fax: 301-504-0862

www.cpsc.gov

Email: info@cpsc.gov

The Consumer Product Safety Commission (CPSC) protects the public against unreasonable risks of injury from consumer products; assists consumers in evaluating the consumer products and minimizes conflicting state and local regulations; and promotes research and investigation into the causes and prevention of product-related deaths, illnesses, and injuries. The CPSC Hotline can provide you with information on product recalls and will take reports of hazardous products or product-related injuries. You can write to the CPSC for a complete list of publications which describe some of the common hazards associated with the use of consumer products, recommending ways to avoid these hazards. They can answer such questions as:

1) What toys are currently being recalled?
2) What types of consumer products are the most dangerous?
3) What safety information exists for the school playground?
4) Are there special precautions you should take for the elderly?
5) What is some current information regarding poisons?

Credit Information

Office of Consumer Affairs

Federal Deposit Insurance Corporation

550 17th St., NW, Room F-130

Washington, DC 20429

202-942-3100

800-934-3342

www.fdic.gov

Email: consumer@fdic.gov

The Federal Deposit Insurance Corporation (FDIC) was established to promote and preserve public confidence in banks, protecting the money supply through provision of insurance coverage for bank deposits and periodic examinations of insured state-chartered banks that are not members of the Federal Reserve System. The FDIC can provide you with information and an overview of the FDIC, and the major consumer and civil rights laws and regulations that protect bank customers. They can answer questions on such topics as:

1) Equal Credit Opportunity and Age
2) Equal Credit Opportunity and Women

3)   Fair Credit Billing
4)   Fair Credit Reporting Act
5)   Truth in Lending

National Credit Union Administration

Public Information
1775 Duke St.
Alexandria, VA 22314-3428
703-518-6330
Fax: 703-518-6429
www.ncua.gov
Email: pacamail@ncua.gov
The National Credit Union Administration is responsible for chartering, insuring, supervising, and examining federal credit unions and administering the National Credit Union Share Insurance Fund. They have free publications and can refer you to the correct office for more information on credit unions. They can answer such questions as:
1)   How are credit unions chartered?
2)   What are the rules and regulations regarding the organization of credit unions?
3)   Is there a master list of all federally insured credit unions?
4)   How are credit unions liquidated?
5)   How are credit unions insured?

Food and Nutrition Information Center

National Agricultural Library
U.S. Department of Agriculture
10301 Baltimore Blvd., Room 304
Beltsville, MD 20705
301-504-5719
Fax: 301-504-6409
TTY: 301-504-6856
www.nal.usda.gov/fnic
Email: fnic@nal.usda.gov
The Food and Nutrition Information Center serves many types of users
including educators, students, researchers, and consumers. Reference services
are provided. Subjects covered include human nutrition research and education, diet and diet-related diseases, food habits, food composition, nutrition education, and more. The Center offers a variety of services which includes answers to specific questions, lending books and audiovisuals, and providing computerized literature searches. A publications list is available, many of which are free. They can answer such questions as:
1)   What studies exist on the effects of the school breakfast program?
2)   What information can you provide to parents concerned about their overweight children?
3)   Do you have information on anorexia nervosa?
4)   Is it dangerous to consume caffeine while pregnant?
5)   Are canned peaches as nutritious as fresh?

Federal Trade Commission (Fraud)

Public Reference Branch, Room 130
Pennsylvania Ave. at 6th St., NW
Washington, DC 20580
877-FTC-HELP
202-326-2222
Fax: 202-326-2050
TTY: 202-326-2502

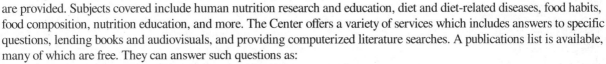

www.ftc.gov

The Federal Trade Commission (FTC) protects consumers against unfair, deceptive, or fraudulent practices. The FTC enforces a variety of consumer protection laws enacted by Congress, as well as trade regulation rules issued by the Commission. Its actions include individual company and industry-wide investigations, administrative and federal court litigation, rulemaking proceedings, and consumer and business education. The FTC has a wealth of information and free publications on a variety of topics. They can answer such questions as:

1) What are the laws regarding shopping by mail or phone?
2) What are some things people should know before looking for a job with a head hunter?
3) What information exists for people checking out mortgages or refinancing?
4) What should someone do if their lifetime membership in a health club expires?
5) What can be done to protect against credit card fraud?

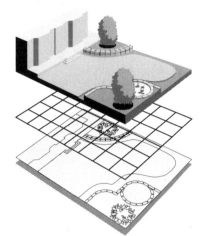

Horticulture Clearinghouse

U.S. Department of Agriculture
10301 Baltimore Blvd.
Beltsville, MD 20705
301-504-5204
Fax: 301-504-6927
www.nal.usda.gov

The Horticulture Clearinghouse covers technical horticultural or botanical questions, economic botany, wild plants of possible use, herbs, bonsai, and floriculture. They can answer such questions as:

1) How can you grow lavender commercially as a source of essential oils?
2) How do you grow and dry herbs?
3) How much might landscaping improve the worth of a home?
4) Which plants can be used for medicinal purposes?
5) How can I control garden insects without using chemical sprays?

HUD USER (Housing)

P.O. Box 6091
Rockville, MD 20849
800-245-2691
Fax: 301-519-5767
TDD: 800-483-2209
www.huduser.org
Email: huduser@aspensys.com

HUD USER, a service of the U.S. Department of Housing and Urban Development, is an information source for housing and community development researchers and policymakers that collects, creates, and distributes a wide variety of materials. You can find information on low-income housing, community development strategies, environmental hazards, land development regulations, population shifts, and housing for elderly and disabled people. A free monthly newsletter and a publications catalogue is available. They can answer such questions as:

1) What information is there on housing for people with special needs?
2) How does one remove lead-based paint from their home?
3) What are "enterprise zones" and what are their goals?
4) What are some federal programs and other sources of assistance for homelessness?
5) What video programs are there on housing issues?

Housing Discrimination

Fair Housing Enforcement Division
Office of Fair Housing and Equal Opportunity
U.S. Department of Housing and Urban Development (HUD)
Washington, DC 20410-2000
800-669-9777
www.hud.gov/fhe

The U.S. Department of Housing and Urban Development administers the law that prohibits discrimination in housing on the basis of race, color, religion, sex, and national origin; investigates complaints of housing discrimination; and attempts to resolve them through conciliation. Two common forms of discrimination are redlining and steering. Redlining is the illegal practice of refusing to originate mortgage loans in certain neighborhoods on the basis of race or ethnic origin. Steering is the illegal act of limiting the housing shown by a real estate agent to a certain ethnic group. HUD refers complaints to state and local fair housing agencies. They can answer such questions as:

1) How do I file a discrimination complaint?
2) What are the regulations regarding housing discrimination?
3) Is sexual harassment a violation of the Fair Housing Act?
4) Can someone be denied housing because of a mental disability?
5) Do landlords have to pay for physical changes to your apartment if you need them, such as grab bars in the bathroom or wider doors?

Public Housing Drug Strategy Clearinghouse

Drug Information and Strategy Clearinghouse
U.S. Department of Housing and Urban Development (HUD)
P.O. Box 6424
Rockville, MD 20850
800-578-3472
Fax: 301-251-5767

Sponsored by the Department of Housing and Urban Development, the Drug Information and Strategy Clearinghouse provides housing officials, residents, and community leaders with information and assistance on drug abuse prevention and drug trafficking control techniques. They have created a database containing information on improving resident screening procedures, strengthening eviction policies, increasing cooperation with local law enforcement, implementing drug tip hotlines, forming resident patrols, starting child care centers, and organizing drug education/prevention activities. The clearinghouse also provides information packages, resource lists, HUD regulations, referrals, and a newsletter. There is no charge for most information. They can answer such questions as:

1) How can housing authorities apply for government grants?
2) What are some anti-drug strategies that have been successfully carried out in public housing units?
3) What are the latest drug abuse prevention theories and have there been demonstration projects based on these models?
4) What resident patrols and related programs have been successful in building drug-free neighborhoods?
5) How can there be an increase in cooperation with local law enforcement and other agencies?

National Injury Information Clearinghouse

U.S. Consumer Product Safety Commission
4330 East-West Highway
Washington, DC 20207
301-504-0424
Fax: 301-504-0025
www.cpsc.gov/about/clrnghse.html

Email: info@cpsc.gov

The National Injury Information Clearinghouse maintains thousands of detailed investigative reports of injuries associated with consumer products. It has access to automated databases with several million incidents of injuries that have been reported by a nationwide network of hospital emergency departments. You can find the victim's background, including age, race, injury diagnosis, consumer product involved, and more. The Clearinghouse distributes documents and will fulfill search requests, usually at no charge. They can answer such questions as:

1) How many children under the age of five are injured each year while playing with toys?
2) Are all-terrain vehicles considered dangerous?
3) How many injuries/deaths have been reported within the last five years for all-terrain vehicles?
4) How many fires are caused each year by electric range/ovens?
5) Which children's clothing manufacturers produce flame retardant materials and how effective are they?

U.S. Postal Service (Mailing)

Office of Consumer Affairs
475 L'Enfant Plaza, SW
Room 5821
Washington, DC 20260-2200
202-268-2281
Fax: 202-268-2304
www.usps.gov

The Postal Service provides mail processing and delivery services to individuals and businesses and protects the mail from loss or theft. They can answer all your postal service questions and provide you with publications and referrals to other postal service departments. They can answer such questions as:

1) How can a business protect itself against mail fraud?
2) What services does the Postal Service offer?
3) How does a business set up a mail room?
4) What international mail services are offered?
5) How can a person stop undesirable material from being delivered to their home?

Meat and Poultry Hotline

Food Safety and Inspection Service
U.S. Department of Agriculture
Washington, DC 20250-3700
800-535-4555
Fax: 202-690-2859
TDD/TTY: 800-256-7072
www.fsis.usda.gov
Email: fsis.webmaster@usda.gov

The Meat and Poultry Hotline takes calls from consumers on cases of meat or poultry food poisoning or complaints about meat or poultry spoilage due to improper packaging or processing. They can also provide you with health-oriented information on safe handling and storage of meats and poultry. They can answer such questions as:

1) What should be done during a power outage?
2) What is salmonella and how can people be protected?
3) What are the different type of foodborne illnesses?
4) How long should you cook poultry?
5) What information should be included on meat and poultry labels and what does it mean?

Mortgage Information Center

Program Evaluation Division
Assistant Secretary for Housing
U.S. Department of Housing and Urban Development (HUD)
451 7th St., SW, Attn: B133
Washington, DC 20410
202-755-7470 ext. 145
Fax: 202-755-7455
Bulletin Board: 202-708-3563

Monthly reports are compiled by the Program Evaluation Division of HUD in areas relating to the mortgage market, securities, taxation, market trends, interest rates, among others. You can receive a free survey of mortgage lending activity and a survey of FHA and conventional mortgage rates. They can answer such questions as:

1) What are the average mortgage rates for different parts of the country?
2) What is the difference in mortgage rates over the past 10 years?
3) What is the average interest rate on new home loans versus existing home loans?
4) What is the number of unsold new houses in a given month?
5) What is the current FHA rate?

Organic Gardening

Public Information Center, 3404
U.S. Environmental Protection Agency
401 M St., SW
Washington, DC 20460
202-260-7751
Fax: 202-260-6257
www.epa.gov
Email: access@epamail.epa.gov

The Public Information Center has free information sheets on organic gardening, composting, and recycling. They can answer such questions as:

1) What plants should be planted near each other to deter pests?
2) What are the dangers of pesticides?
3) Who can I talk to regarding composting and recycling?
4) What are the advantages of organic fertilizers?
5) What is required to maintain a lawn?

Pension Benefit Guaranty Corporation

Public Affairs
1200 K St., NW
Washington, DC 20005-4026
202-326-4040
Fax: 202-326-4042
www.pbgc.gov

The Pension Benefit Guaranty Corporation works to ensure the solvency and viability of company-sponsored pension plans. They can provide you with information and publications on pension plans, as well as laws and regulations on pensions. They can answer questions such as:

1) What is the federal pension law?
2) What are pensions plans and how do they operate?
3) What information on plans is a company required to give to members?
4) What are the rights and options of participants?
5) What is the employer's responsibilities regarding pension plans?

Pension and Welfare Benefits Administration

U.S. Department of Labor
200 Constitution Ave., NW, N5656
Washington, DC 20210
202-219-8921
Fax: 202-219-5362
www.dol.gov/dol/pwba

The Pension and Welfare Benefits Administration (PWBA) helps to protect the economic future and retirement security of working Americans. It requires administrators of private pension and welfare plans to provide plan participants with easily understandable summaries; to file those summaries with the agency; and to report annually on the financial operation of the plans. PWBA has publications and other information available. They can answer questions such as:

1) What is the effect of job mobility on pension plans?
2) What is the Employee Retirement Income Security Act (ERISA)?
3) What studies have been done on the investment performance of ERISA plans?
4) What information are pension plans required to provide to participants?
5) What employee benefit documents are available from the Department of Labor?

Plant Information Service

U.S. Botanic Garden
245 1st St., SW
Washington, DC 20024
202-225-8333
Fax: 202-225-1561
www.aoc.gov/

The U.S. Botanic Garden serves as a center for plant information offering a telephone information service, as well as responding to written inquiries from Monday through Friday, from 9:00 to 11:30 a.m. They can answer such questions as:

1) What are the benefits of organic gardening?
2) How can I use insects to control garden pests?
3) Which house plants are poisonous?
4) What are the dangers of chemical fertilizers?
5) Which herbs grow best indoors?

Seafood Hotline

Office of Seafood
Food and Drug Administration
200 C St., SW
Washington, DC 20201
800-SAFEFOOD
Fax: 202-401-3532
http://vm.cfsan.fda.gov/seafood1.html
Email: oco@fdacf.sw.dhhs.gov

The Seafood Hotline can provide consumers with information on how to buy and use seafood products, including storing and handling of seafood, and questions on seafood labeling and nutrition. The Hotline has many free publications on a variety of seafood issues. They can answer such questions as:

1) Can fish be kept frozen for a year?
2) How do you know if a seafood vendor is reputable?

3) What are the dangers of eating raw shellfish?
4) What information is available on canned tuna?
5) What are some seafood safety concerns for people with particular medical conditions?

Social Security Administration

Social Security Administration
Office of Public Inquiries
6401 Security Blvd.
Room 4-C-5 Annex
Baltimore, MD 21235-6401
800-772-1213
410-965-7700
TTY: 800-325-0778
www.ssa.gov
The Social Security Administration administers the Social Security and Medicare programs. They can assist certain
beneficiaries in claiming reimbursement and developing and adjudicating claims. They can answer such questions as:
1) If you were to retire today, how much would you receive in benefits?
2) What should be done once you turn 65?
3) What is supplemental security income and how do you apply for it?
4) What disability insurance benefits do you qualify for?
5) What survivor benefits are available to children?

Internal Revenue Service (Taxes)

U.S. Department of Treasury
1111 Constitution Ave., NW
Washington, DC 20224
800-829-1040
Fax on Demand: 703-487-4160
www.irs.ustreas.gov
The Internal Revenue Service is responsible for administering and enforcing the
internal revenue laws and related statutes. Its mission is to collect the proper amount of
tax revenue at the least cost to the public. They can answer such questions as:

1) How do you get copies of your back tax forms?
2) What is required when you deduct your home office?
3) What are the rules about writing off a vacation/work trip?
4) What happens if you can't pay your taxes?
5) Can you deduct your mother as a dependent if she lives with you?

Women's Bureau Clearinghouse

U.S. Department of Labor
200 Constitution Ave., NW, Room S3306
Washington, DC 20210
800-827-5335
202-219-4486
Fax: 202-219-5529
www.dol.gov/dol/wb/welcome.html
Email: wb-wwc@dol.gov
The Women's Bureau Clearinghouse was established to assist employers in identifying the most appropriate policies for
responding to the dependent care needs of employees seeking to balance their dual responsibilities. They can also provide
information on women's issues, as well as work force issues that affect women. They can offer information and guidance

in areas such as women-owned businesses, women workers, alternative work schedules, dependent care issues, and much more. They also have many free publications and other information available. They can answer such questions as:
1) What are some elder care program options?
2) What is the earning difference between men and women?
3) How does flex time work in companies similar to mine?
4) What are some examples of alternate work schedules and how do they work?
5) What literature and other resources are available on employer-supported child care?

Criminal Justice

Bureau of Alcohol, Tobacco, and Firearms

Distribution Center
U.S. Department of Treasury
P.O. Box 5950
Springfield, VA 22150-5950
703-455-7801
www.atf.treas.gov

The Bureau of Alcohol, Tobacco, and Firearms (ATF) is responsible for enforcing and administering firearms and explosives laws, as well as those laws covering the production, use, and distribution of alcohol and tobacco products. ATF can provide you with a wealth of information, statistics, and publications. They can answer such questions as:

1) What explosive incidents and stolen explosives occurred in a year by state and by type of explosives?
2) What are the different types of firearms available?
3) What are the license requirements for a given state to carry a weapon?
4) How do law enforcement officials trace firearms?

National Criminal Justice Reference Service

National Institute of Justice/NCJRS
Box 6000
Rockville, MD 20849
800-851-3420
301-519-5500
Fax: 301-251-5212
www.ncjrs.org/
Email: askncjrs@ncjrs.org

The National Criminal Justice Reference Service brings the latest criminal justice research findings to criminal justice policymakers, practitioners, and researchers from around the world. Their database features summaries of books, reports, articles, and audiovisual materials. They have a free bi-monthly catalogue which lists new publications (many of which are free), upcoming conferences, and more. They can answer such questions as:

1) What videotapes are there on criminal justice topics?
2) What information exists on community safety issues?
3) How effective is parole and probation?
4) What drug abuse programs are in place for offenders?
5) What is date rape?

Drug and Crime Data Center and Clearinghouse

1600 Research Boulevard
Rockville, MD 20850
800-666-3332
http://virlib.ncjrs.org/DrugsAndCrime.asp
Email: ondc@ncjrs.org

The Data Center and Clearinghouse serves the drugs-and-crime information needs of federal, state, and local policy makers, criminal justice and public health practitioners, researchers and universities, private corporations, the media, and the general public. The most current data is available on illegal drugs, drug law violations, drug-related crime, drug-using offenders in the criminal justice system, and the impact of drugs on criminal justice administration. The Clearinghouse maintains a database of some 1,500 annotated bibliographies of statistical and research reports, books, and journal articles on drugs and crime. All documents are free. They can answer such questions as:

1) What are the economic costs of drug-related crime?
2) What data exists on the quantity and flow of illicit drugs from cultivation to consequences?
3) What percentage of high school seniors used cocaine last year?
4) What tactics have been used to build integrity and reduce drug corruption in police departments?
5) What percentage of rapists report that their victims were well known to them?

National Clearinghouse on Election Administration

Federal Election Commission
999 E St., NW
Washington, DC 20463
202-694-1100
800-424-9530
Fax: 202-219-8500
www.fec.gov

The National Clearinghouse on Election Administration is an agency of the
Federal Election Commission. Its overall objective is to enhance the
honesty, integrity, and efficiency of the federal election process by providing information and assistance to state and local election officials, to state legislatures and legislative reference bureaus, and to other interested organizations regarding the conduct of Federal elections. They can answer such questions as:

1) What research reports are available on state campaign finance laws?
2) Where can I obtain advice and assistance in making polling places more accessible to the elderly and handicapped?
3) What statistics exist that could summarize state and national voting age populations, the number of registered voters, turnout, and results in presidential elections for 1960 through 1988?
4) What landmark judicial decisions have been made involving elections over the past twenty years?
5) What are the registration techniques and procedures in a particular state?

Equal Employment Opportunity Commission (EEOC)

Publications and Information Center
P.O. Box 12549
Cincinnati, OH 45212-0549
800-669-EEOC
Fax: 513-489-8695
www.eeoc.gov

The purpose of the Equal Employment Opportunity Commission is to eliminate discrimination based on race, color, religion, sex, national origin, or age in hiring, promoting, firing, setting wages, testing, training, and all other terms and conditions of employment. The Commission conducts investigations of alleged discrimination, and provides voluntary assistance programs for employers, unions, and others. They have free publications and information available. They can answer such questions as:

1) What questions cannot be asked in an employment interview?
2) What constitutes sexual harassment?
3) What federal law prohibits employers from discriminating between men and women in the payment of wages, and to whom does the law apply?
4) What can be done if you feel you have been unfairly discriminated against?
5) What information exists to train personnel officers on the prevailing laws and regulations?

Bureau of Justice Assistance Clearinghouse

P.O. Box 6000
U.S. Department of Justice
Rockville, MD 20849

800-688-4252
Fax: 301-251-5212
www.ncjrs.org
Email: askncjrs@ncjrs.org
The Bureau of Justice Assistance Clearinghouse (BJA) informs state and local criminal justice practitioners about BJA products and programs. They provide federal funding and technical assistance to state and local units of government to improve the criminal justice system. They can answer such questions as:
1) What information is available regarding a variety of anti-drug programs?
2) What programs are in place to improve the efficiency of the criminal justice system?
3) What are the estimated costs of drug testing for a pretrial service program?
4) What training programs exist for narcotics enforcement?
5) What are the treatment alternatives to street crimes?

Justice Statistics Clearinghouse

Bureau of Justice Statistics
U.S. Department of Justice
Box 6000
Rockville, MD 20849
800-732-3277
301-519-5500
http://virlib.ncjrs.org/Statistics.asp
Email: askncjrs@ncjrs.org

The Bureau of Justice Statistics (BJS) supports this clearinghouse for those seeking crime and criminal justice data. In addition to distributing BJS publications, the Clearinghouse responds to statistics requests by offering document database searches, statistics information packages, referrals, and other related products and services. They can answer such questions as:
1) What is the annual national estimate of the amount of crime against persons and households?
2) What are some of the characteristics of victims?
3) How differently are juveniles handled from adults?
4) How prevalent is organized crime?
5) What is the recidivism rate, and when criminals are rearrested, with what crimes are they normally charged?

Juvenile Justice Clearinghouse

National Criminal Justice Reference Service
U.S. Department of Justice
Box 6000
Rockville, MD 20849
800-638-8736
http://virlib.ncjrs.org/JuvenileJustice.asp
Email: askncjrs@ncjrs.org
The Juvenile Justice Clearinghouse disseminates publications, research findings, and program evaluations supported by the Office of Juvenile Justice and Delinquency Prevention. In addition, the staff can prepare customized responses to information requests. They can answer such questions as:
1) How do juvenile courts vary in handling drug and alcohol cases?
2) What can a community do in response to youth gangs?
3) What methods have been successful in dealing with juvenile reinstitution?
4) How many juveniles were arrested last year for possession of illegal drugs?
5) What methods are effective in reducing violence in the schools?

National Clearinghouse For Poverty Law (Legal Services)

205 W. Monroe, 2nd Floor
Chicago, IL 60606
312-263-3830
Fax: 312-263-3846

The National Clearinghouse for Poverty Law is the most comprehensive source for information concerning civil poverty law. Also, the Clearinghouse has many publications dealing with issues of vital interest to the non poverty lawyer. Problems with health care, housing, and social security strike people in all economic situations. These are just some of the 20 major areas of law that Clearinghouse publications cover, providing practical information useful to people in all economic and social strata. The Clearinghouse, as a resource center and a legal research system, offers the most complete source of civil poverty law publications that can be found. They have a free publications list. They can answer such questions as:

1)   What information exists on the eligibility requirements for Medicare home health care?
2)   What models exist on establishing pro bono programs?
3)   What are the various issues concerning the tax burden on the poor?
4)   What are the litigation issues concerning homeless persons and emergency shelter?
5)   Where can information be obtained on child custody cases?

National Center for Missing and Exploited Children

699 Prince St.
Alexandria, VA 22314
800-843-5678
703-274-3900
Fax: 703-274-2220
www.missingkids.org

The National Center for Missing and Exploited Children serves as a clearinghouse of information on missing and exploited children; provides technical assistance to citizens and law-enforcement agencies; offers training programs to law-enforcement and social service professionals; distributes photos and descriptions of missing children nationwide; coordinates child protection efforts with the private sector; networks with nonprofit service providers and state clearinghouses on missing persons; and provides information on effective state legislation to ensure the protection of children. They can answer such questions as:

1)   How can a parent work through the civil and criminal justice systems in order to regain custody of the child her ex-husband stole from her?
2)   How can a parent protect children against day care abuse?
3)   What are some of the warning signs of child sexual exploitation?
4)   What is the profile of a runaway and the patterns of runaway behavior?
5)   What information is available to help a child testify in court?

Office for Victims of Crime Resource Center

U.S. Department of Justice
Box 6000
Rockville, MD 20849
800-627-6872
Fax: 301-251-5212
http://virlib.ncjrs.org/VictimsOfCrime.asp
Email: askncjrs@ncjrs.org

The Office for Victims of Crime Resource Center is sponsored by the Office of Victims of Crime. It can provide access to resources, such as more than 7,000 victim-related books and articles, national victimization statistics, federally sponsored victim-related research studies, and information on state victim compensation programs. From the Clearinghouse, you can get free publications, borrow hard-to-find publications, and buy selected videotapes. Information specialists can also conduct database searches. They can answer such questions as:

1) What is the relationship between child abuse and delinquency?
2) What information is there for police when confronting a domestic violence incident?
3) What are some of the programs which compensate victims of crime?
4) What is the criminal justice response to victim harm?
5) How can one improve the use and effectiveness of the Neighborhood Watch program?

Education And The Arts

ERIC Clearinghouse on Adult, Career, and Vocational Learning

Ohio State University Center on Education and Training for Employment
1900 Kenny Rd.
Columbus, OH 43210
800-848-4815
614-292-7069
Fax: 614-292-1260
http://ericacve.org
Email: ericacve@magnus.acs.ohio_state.edu

The Clearinghouse on Adult, Career, and Vocational Learning provides
materials covering all levels of adult and continuing education from:
basic literacy training through professional skill upgrading; vocational
and technical education covering all service areas for secondary,
postsecondary, and adult populations; and career education and career
development programs for all ages and populations. A publications list
and price sheet are available. They can answer questions such as:
1) What research exists on the effectiveness of flex time and job share programs?
2) What is the job placement rate of graduates from vocational schools?
3) What are the statistics on job satisfaction and wage earnings?
4) What are the benefits of vocational education?
5) What information exists on how people can find a job and make effective career choices?

ERIC Clearinghouse on Educational Assessment and Evaluation

College of Library and Information Services
1129 Shriver Laboratory
University of Maryland
College Park, MD 20742
800-464-3742
301-405-7449
Fax: 202-319-6692
http://ericae.net
Email: feedback@ericae.net

The Clearinghouse on Assessment and Evaluation provides information on the assessment and evaluation of education
projects or programs, tests and other measurement devices, methodology of measurement and evaluation, and more. A
publications list and price sheet are available. They can answer such questions as:
1) Do statistics show that tests discriminate against certain minority groups?
2) What tests are given to handicapped children and what is the research behind these tests?
3) Is the Scholastic Aptitude Test (SAT) an effective tool of measurement?
4) What is computer-assisted testing?
5) How often are SAT tests updated and who designs the questions?

Bilingual Education Clearinghouse

National Clearinghouse for Bilingual Education
George Washington University
Center for the Study of Language and Education
2011 Eye St., NW, Suite 2001
Washington, DC 20006

202-467-0867
Fax: 202-467-0867
www.ncbe.gwu.edu
Email: askncbe@ncbe.gwu.edu

The Bilingual Education Clearinghouse provides information to practitioners in the field on curriculum materials, program models, methodologies, and research findings on the education of limited English proficient (LEP) individuals. They also offer an electronic information system, free to users, where access is available to a database of curriculum materials and literature related to the education of LEP persons. An electronic bulletin board is also available which contains news from federal, state, and local education agencies, conference announcements, and other current information. Their newsletter and other publications are available, many of which are free of charge. They can answer such questions as:

1) How do you mainstream language minority students?
2) What computer programs exist to assist in teaching limited English proficient students?
3) What are some of the issues and practices involved in meeting the needs of gifted and talented minority language students?
4) How can parents become involved in the education of limited English students?
5) How can teachers integrate multi-cultural materials in instructional programs?

ERIC Clearinghouse on Counseling and Student Services

School of Education
101 Park Building
University of North Carolina at Greensboro
Greensboro, NC 27412-5001
800-414-9769
910-334-4114
Fax: 910-334-4116
http://ericcass.uncg.edu
Email: ericcass@iris.uncg.edu

The Clearinghouse on Counseling and Student Services provides documents relating to all levels of counseling and personnel services including preparation, practice, and supervision of counselors at all education levels and in all settings; personnel procedures such as testing and interviewing; group work and case work; career planning; and more. They have free publications, and will conduct searches for a fee. They can answer such questions as:

1) How can counselors enhance a student's self-esteem through counseling?
2) What are the emerging priorities for the counseling field?
3) What dropout prevention programs have been effective?
4) What is the current high school dropout rate?
5) What tests are available to students who are undecided on a choice of career?

ERIC Clearinghouse on Disabilities and Gifted Education

The Council for Exceptional Children
1920 Association Dr.
Reston, VA 22091
800-328-0272
http://ericec.org
Email: ericec@cec.sped.org

The Clearinghouse on Disabilities and Gifted Education provides information on all aspects of education and development of handicapped persons, including prevention of handicaps, identification and assessment of handicaps, and intervention and enrichment programs. All aspects of the education and development of gifted persons are covered as well. A publications list and price sheet are available. They can answer such questions as:

1) What are the issues concerning the mainstreaming of a handicapped student?
2) How do you "home school" a gifted child?
3) What is the research concerning the post-school status of learning disabled students?
4) What preschool services are available for children with handicaps?
5) Under what criteria is a child considered gifted?

ERIC Clearinghouse on Educational Management

College of Education
5207 University of Oregon
Eugene, OR 97403-5207
541-346-5043
800-438-8841
Fax: 541-346-2334
http://eric.uoregon.edu
Email: eric@eric.oregon.edu

The Clearinghouse on Educational Management distributes information on the following subjects: the leadership, management, and structure of public and private educational organizations; practice and theory of administration; preservice and inservice preparation of administrators; and tasks and processes of administration. The Clearinghouse also provides information on sites, buildings, and equipment for education, and planning, financing, construction, renovating, and evaluating educational facilities. They can answer such questions as:

1) What are "mentor teachers" and how do you prepare them to assist new teachers?
2) How do you best confront racism in schools?
3) How do you recruit, select, and retain good teachers?
4) What research has been done on the various methods of school discipline?
5) What elements must be considered in the design of a new school?

Educational Research

Office of Educational Research and Improvement's Information Service
U.S. Department of Education
Education Information Branch
Capitol Plaza Building, Suite 300
555 New Jersey Ave., NW
Washington, DC 20208-5641
800-424-1616
www.ed.gov/offices/OERI

The Education Information Branch staff specialists can provide information on topics such as early childhood education, elementary and secondary education, higher education, adult and vocational education, education finance, longitudinal statistical studies, and special education. They have publications and reports, many of which are free. They can answer such questions as:

1) What statistics are there on the number of students who receive loans, grants, and work-study assistance from state sources?
2) What are the statistics on private postsecondary education, such as enrollment, earned degrees conferred, full and part-time faculty members and their salaries, and more?
3) What information is available on how to choose a school for a child and what makes a school good?
4) How can parents help their children become better readers?
5) What are the enrollment outcomes for recent master's and bachelor's degree recipients?

Educational Resources Information Center

ACCESS ERIC
Aspen Systems Corporation
2277 Research Blvd.

Rockville, MD 20850
800-LET-ERIC
Fax: 301-309-2084
www.accesseric.org
Email: accesseric@access.eric.org

Educational Resources Information Center (ERIC) is a nationwide information service set up to collect materials about current developments in education and make them available to the public. The system includes 16 clearinghouses, each of which is responsible for acquiring, processing, and disseminating information about a particular aspect of education. The ERIC database contains bibliographic information, including key descriptors and abstracts, on over 950,000 research documents, journal articles, curricular materials, and resource guides. The Clearinghouses offer a wide variety of services and products, and can answer questions about: subject fields, run computer searches, develop short bibliographies, newsletters, and other free or inexpensive materials; publish monographs; publish handbooks; and develop materials to help you use ERIC.

ACCESS ERIC is the main center for the ERIC clearinghouses. It answers all questions on how to use ERIC and helps anyone stay up-to-date on the latest developments in the education field. They can answer such questions as:

1) How can I use ERIC to answer my education question?
2) What is required to have a database search run on a topic?
3) How can I have something that I have written entered into the ERIC system?
4) Where can I find the latest statistics on an education topic?
5) How can school administrators develop new management tools and practices?

ERIC Clearinghouse on Elementary and Early Childhood Education

University of Illinois at Urbana-Champaign
Children's Resource Center
51 Gerty Dr.
Champaign, IL 61820
800-583-4135
217-333-1386
Fax: 217-333-3767
http://ericeece.org
Email: ericeece@uiuc.edu

The Clearinghouse on Elementary and Early Childhood Education provides information covering all aspects of the cognitive, emotional, social and physical development, and education of children from birth through early adolescence, excluding specific elementary school curriculum areas. Among the topics covered are: prenatal and infant development and care; child care programs and community services for children at local, state, and federal levels; parent, child, and family relationships; home and school relationships; foster care and adoption; and more. A publications list and price sheet are available. They can answer such questions as:

1) How do you start a day care center?
2) How do you choose a day care center and how do you assess a preschooler's development?
3) How can parents become involved in the education of their children?
4) How do you meet the needs of homeless children?
5) How do you help children with their social development?

ERIC Clearinghouse on Higher Education

George Washington University
One Dupont Circle, Suite 630
Washington, DC 20036-1183
800-773-ERIC
202-296-2597

Fax: 202-452-1844

www.eriche.org

Email: mkozi@eric-he.edu

The Clearinghouse on Higher Education provides information covering education beyond the secondary level that leads to a four-year, masters, doctoral or professional degree and that includes courses and programs designed to enhance or update skills obtained in these degree programs. Areas include: academic advising, faculty, continuing education, legal issues, curriculum development, and more. They can answer such questions as:

1) What research and assessments are available on the trends and issues in higher education today?
2) What percentage of staff of higher education facilities are minorities and women?
3) What information is available on the issue of student stress?
4) How do we raise academic standards as a country?
5) What techniques are useful in improving a student's organizational skills?

ERIC Clearinghouse on Information and Technology

Syracuse University School of Education

621 Skytop Rd., Suite 160

Syracuse, NY 13244-5290

800-464-9107

315-443-3640

Fax: 315-443-5448

http://ericir.syr.edu/ithome

Email: eric@ericir.syr.edu

The Clearinghouse on Information and Technology provides information covering educational technology and library and information science at all levels. Instructional design, development, and evaluation with emphasis on educational technology; computers, audio and video recordings, and more. They can answer such questions as:

1) What is the latest research on the value of using computers and applying video technology to enhance learning?
2) What are the various studies comparing the different types of computer based media?
3) Is there an overview of instructional television and its effectiveness for teaching children?
4) At what grade level are computers introduced in the classroom, on average?
5) Are audio recordings an effective tool for teaching foreign languages?

ERIC Clearinghouse on Community Colleges

University of California at Los Angeles

3051 Moore Hall

Box 951521

Los Angeles, CA 90095

800-832-8256

310-825-3931

Fax: 310-206-8095

www.gseis.ucla.edu/ERIC/eric.html

The Clearinghouse on Community Colleges provides information covering the development, administration, and evaluation of two-year public and private community and junior colleges, technical institutes, and two-year branch university campuses. They have free publications and will conduct database searches for a fee. They can answer such questions as:

1) What are the main problems involved with transfer students?
2) How many students working on A.A. degrees in nursing are mothers and other women returning to further their education?
3) How do you implement a cultural exchange or study abroad program?
4) How do you recruit and retain minorities and women at junior colleges?
5) What percentage of students attending two-year programs receive financial assistance?

ERIC Clearinghouse on Languages and Linguistics

Center for Applied Linguistics
4646 40th St., NW
Washington, DC 20016-1859
800-276-9834
202-362-0700
Fax: 202-362-3740
www.cal.org/ericcll
Email: eric@cal.org

The Clearinghouse on Languages and Linguistics provides information on languages and language sciences; all areas of foreign language, second language, and linguistics instruction; cultural and intercultural context of languages; international exchanges; teacher training; and more. Mini-bibliographies and fact sheets are available free of charge. Ready-made search printouts are available for a fee, and prices vary for specific searches. They can answer such questions as:

1) How do you institute teaching English as a second language in the workplace?
2) How do you develop a curriculum and training program for volunteer tutors for limited-English proficient adults?
3) What are the pros and cons of language immersion programs in schools?
4) What are the issues regarding the foreign language requirement?
5) What are some available opportunities abroad for teaching English as a foreign language?

National Clearinghouse on Literacy Education

Center for Applied Linguistics
4646 40th St., NW
Washington, DC 20016-1859
202-362-0700
Fax: 202-362-3740
www.cal.org/ncle
Email: ncle@cal.org

The National Clearinghouse on Literacy Education produces and disseminates materials summarizing current research and information available on selected topics; develops a directory of effective adult literacy programs and projects; and supports a user services program to respond to information requests. They have a publications list available, and many of the items are free. They can answer such questions as:

1) What organizations offer programs for senior citizens interested in learning to read and write?
2) How can workplaces promote English as a second language?
3) What free resources are available to adult literacy instructors?
4) What percentage of U.S. immigrants are illiterate? What programs exist to help them?
5) What type of educational materials and programs are available to teach English to out-of-school youth?

Museum Reference Center

Smithsonian Institution
Office of Museum Programs
900 Jefferson Dr., SW
Washington, DC 20560
202-786-2271
Fax: 202-357-2311
http://museumstudies.si.edu
Email: libmail@sil.si.edu

The Museum Reference Center serves as a clearinghouse for museum programs providing professional development training, advisory assistance, and research services to the national and international museum community and the

Smithsonian staff. The Center participates through the sponsorship of workshops, internships, and professional visitor programs, an audiovisual production loan program, publications, and more. They can answer such questions as:
1)   Where can information be obtained regarding internship programs for museum careers?
2)   What is the latest research on climate control and security for museums?
3)   What information exists on how to train docents and volunteers?
4)   Where can examples of exhibit designs be found?
5)   Where can information be found on collection sharing?

Performing Arts Library

John F. Kennedy Center for the Performing Arts
2700 F St., NW
Washington, DC 20566
202-416-8780
The Performing Arts Library is a joint project of the Library of Congress
and the Kennedy Center, and offers information and reference assistance
on dance, theater, opera, music, film, and broadcasting. The Performing Arts Library serves the research and information needs of the public, artists, and staff of the Center. The Library also identifies and locates the creative and resource materials necessary to develop new works and productions in the performing arts. Reference service is available by phone, in person, or by mail. They can answer such questions as:
1)   How can an orchestral program of Irish composers be tailored for a young audience?
2)   What information exists on different dance companies based in New York?
3)   Is there information on what is required to start a record company?
4)   Are their recordings of interviews or videotapes of famous actresses discussing their works?
5)   Where can recordings be located on poetry readings?

ERIC Clearinghouse on Reading, English and Communication Skills

Indiana University
Smith Research Center
2805 East Tenth St., Suite 150
Bloomington, IN 47408-2698
800-855-5847
812-855-5847
Fax: 812-855-4220
www.indiana.edu/~eric_rec
Email: ericcs@indiana.edu
The Clearinghouse on Reading, English and Communication Skills provides information on reading, English, communication skills, identification, diagnosis and remediation of reading problems, and more. A catalogue of publications including prices is available. The Clearinghouse will also conduct custom database searches for a fee. They can answer such questions as:
1)   How do you teach elementary students listening skills?
2)   How can parents help their child to read?
3)   How do you help a quiet student communicate in the classroom?
4)   Where can teachers obtain written activities for junior high social studies classes?
5)   Is there information on sex stereotypes in children's literature?

ERIC Clearinghouse for
Science, Mathematics, and Environmental Education

Ohio State University
1929 Kenny Rd.
Columbus, OH 43210

800-276-0462
614-292-6717
Fax: 614-292-0263
www.ericse.org
Email: ericse@osu.edu
The Clearinghouse for Science, Mathematics, and Environmental Education acquires educational literature on the following topics: development of curriculum and instructional materials; teachers and teacher education; learning theory; educational programs; and computer applications. They can answer such questions as:
1) Is there information on how to teach a lesson on environmental education?
2) What can be done to boost students' enthusiasm for math?
3) What are some of the common safety hazards in science classrooms?
4) Where can teachers obtain free science instructional materials?
5) Are there financial aid programs available to teachers interested in continuing education?

ERIC Clearinghouse for Social Studies/Social Science Education

Social Studies Development Center
Indiana University
2805 East Tenth St., Suite 120
Bloomington, IN 47408
800-266-3815
812-855-3838
Fax: 812-855-0455
www.indiana.edu/%7Essdc/eric_chess.htm
Email: ericso@indiana.edu
The Clearinghouse for Social Studies/Social Science Education acquires journal articles and documents at all levels of social studies and social science education, including anthropology, economics, geography, sociology, social psychology, civics, and political science, as well as on history and social topics. A publications catalogue is available, including prices. They can answer such questions as:

1) What are some interesting learning activities designed to teach social studies?
2) What resources exist to supplement teachers' lessons on Africa and African Culture?
3) How do you teach geography at home?
4) How can you teach the law incorporating Supreme Court cases?
5) How can teachers stimulate children's interest in anthropology?

ERIC Clearinghouse on Teaching and Teacher Education

American Association of Colleges for Teacher Education
1307 New York Ave., NW, Suite 300
Washington, DC 20005
800-822-9229
202-293-2450
Fax: 202-457-8095
www.ericsp.org
Email: query@aacte.org
The ERIC Clearinghouse on Teaching and Teacher Education acquires, publishes, and disseminates documents conveying research, theory, and practice in teacher education and in all aspects of health education, physical education, recreation education, nutrition education, and more. They can answer such questions as:
1) What are the teacher certification requirements?

2) How effective are student teachers in the classroom?
3) What computer games are there to help kids learn math?
4) What techniques can a teacher use to improve classroom productivity?
5) What are "at risk" students and how can they best be served?

ERIC Clearinghouse on Urban Education

Teachers College
Columbia University Institute for Urban and Minority Education
Main Hall, Room 303, Box 40
New York, NY 10027
800-601-4868
212-678-3433
Fax: 212-678-4012
http://eric_web.tc.columbia.edu
Email: eric-cue@columbia.edu
The Clearinghouse on Urban Education provides information on the programs and practices in schools in urban areas. In addition, the education of racial/ethnic minority children and youth in various settings is studied: on the local, national, and international level; theory and practice of education equity; and urban and minority experiences. A publications list and price sheet are available. They can answer such questions as:

1) What is the current research on effective programs for reducing the dropout rates among inner city high school students?
2) What research is available on the number of pregnant, minority teenagers who obtain their high school diplomas in inner city schools?
3) What information is there on mentoring programs?
4) What issues are involved in linking schools with human service agencies?
5) Are urban schools financed equitably?

Energy and Environment

EPA Control Technology Center Hotline (Air Pollution)

U.S. Environmental Protection Agency (EPA)
AEERL
Research Triangle Park, NC 27711
919-541-0800
The EPA Control Technology Center Hotline provides technical support to state and local agencies and to EPA regional offices in implementing air pollution control programs. They can answer such questions as:
1) What type of computer software can my company use to assess pollution control problems and evaluate potential solutions?
2) What impacts have control technologies had on air pollution?
3) What type of air pollution permits does my company need to operate in my state?
4) How can my company reduce its air pollution control costs?
5) What are the best cost-effective methods to maintain my company's air pollution control equipment?

BACT/LAER Clearinghouse (Air Pollution)

U.S. Environmental Protection Agency (EPA)
Clean Air Technology Center
Research Triangle Park, NC 27711
919-541-0800
Fax: 919-541-5742
www.epa.gov/ttn/cact

The BACT/LAER Clearinghouse assists state and local air pollution control agencies in selecting the best available control technology (BACT) and the lowest achievable emission rate (LAER). It controls new or modified sources in a nationally consistent manner. They can answer such questions as:
1) How can my agency get assistance in compiling inventories of air toxic emissions?
2) How does the EPA estimate air toxic emissions?
3) Where can I get a listing of national emissions estimates and factors for air that is made toxic from motor vehicles?
4) Where can I find out about the toxic emissions for a particular consumer product?
5) How can my company achieve the lowest achievable emission rate for our product?

Asbestos and Small Business Ombudsman Clearinghouse

U.S. Environmental Protection Agency (EPA)
401 M St., SW
Washington, DC 20460
800-368-5888
703-305-5938
Fax: 703-305-6462
www.epa.gov
The assigned mission of the Asbestos Ombudsman Clearinghouse is to provide to the public sector, including individual citizens and community services, information on the handling and abatement of asbestos in schools, the workplace, and the home. In addition, interpretation of the asbestos-in-school requirements and publications are provided to explain recent legislation. The EPA Asbestos Ombudsman receives complaints and requests for information and provides assistance with regard to them. They can answer such questions as:
1) What is asbestos, and in what era was it used?
2) How do I know if I have asbestos in my home or at work and how do I find help to contain or eliminate it?

3) What do I do if I have been exposed to asbestos?
4) How can I safe-proof my house from asbestos?
5) Are the schools in my particular neighborhood safe from asbestos?

Boating Safety Hotline

Office of Boat Safety
U.S. Coast Guard
U.S. Department of Transportation
2100 2nd St., SW
Washington, DC 20593
800-368-5647
202-267-1077
Fax: 202-267-4285
www.uscgboating.org
Email: BoatWeb@mail.rmit.com

The Boating Safety Hotline can provide you with information on such topics of interest to boaters as safety recalls, publications, Coast Guard department contacts and addresses, public education courses, and free Coast Guard Services. They have a wealth of free information and publications to share. They can answer such questions as:

1) What statistics exist on boating accidents?
2) How can parents teach children about water safety?
3) What things do people need to consider in evaluating floatation devices?
4) What licenses or regulations should boaters be aware of before they hit the water?
5) Where can people receive information on water charts and other navigational aids?

National Climatic Data Center

National Oceanic and Atmospheric Administration
U.S. Department of Commerce
Federal Building
151 Patton Ave., Room 120
Asheville, NC 28801
704-271-4800
Fax: 704-271-4876
www.ncdc.noaa.gov
Email: orders@ncdc.noaa.gov

The National Climatic Data Center (NCDC) provides an important historical perspective on climate. Through the use of over a hundred years of weather observations, reference databases are generated. NCDC's data and information are available to everyone including the general public, the legal profession, engineering, industry, agriculture, and government policy makers. They can answer such questions as:

1) What were the weather conditions like in a particular part of a state on a specific day, and can this information be used for a court case?
2) In what parts of the country is the climate moderate allowing energy bills to be held to a minimum?
3) What information is available on severe storms, such as the occurrences of storms, data on the paths of individual storms, deaths, injuries, and estimated property damage?
4) Are droughts becoming more widespread?
5) Is the greenhouse theory becoming a reality?

Energy Efficiency and Renewable Energy Clearinghouse

P.O. Box 3048
Merrifield, VA 22116
800-363-3732
Fax: 703-893-0400

Bulletin Board: 800-273-2955

www.eren.doe.gov

The Energy Efficiency and Renewable Energy Inquiry and Referral Clearinghouse can provide information on how to save energy, as well as information on solar, wind, or any other aspect of renewable energy. They have the latest research on renewable energy technologies and energy conservation, and can refer you to other valuable resources. A list of free publications is available. They can answer questions such as:

1) How can you convert a home to solar heat?
2) How do heat pumps work and are they efficient?
3) What should you look for in a wood-burning appliance?
4) What can be done to improve the energy efficiency of a home?
5) Is the wind a practical source of energy?

Safe Drinking Water Hotline

U.S. Environmental Protection Agency (EPA)

401 M St., SW

Washington, DC 20460

800-426-4791

Fax: 202-260-8072

www.epa.gov/safewater

Email: hotline_sdwa@epamail.epa.gov

The Safe Drinking Water Hotline responds to questions concerning the Safe Drinking Water Act, water standards, regulations, and the Underground Injection Program. It will also provide selected free publications. They can answer such questions as:

1) How do I find out if there is lead in my drinking water?
2) What is the Underground Injection Program?
3) What are some of the newer techniques for removing and disposing of water pollutants?
4) What research is being done to develop safer drinking water?
5) What can I do if there is too much fluoride in my drinking water?

EROS Data Center (Earth Resources)

U.S. Geological Survey

Mundt Federal Bldg.

Sioux Falls, SD 57198

605-594-6511

Fax: 605-594-6589

http://edcwww.cr.usgs.gov

The Earth Resources Observation Systems (EROS) Data Center is a national archive, production, and research facility for remotely sensed data and other forms of geographic information. It receives, processes, and distributes data from the U.S.' Landsat satellite sensors and from airborne mapping cameras. The Center houses over 2,000,000 worldwide scenes of Earth acquired by Landsat satellites and nearly 6,000,000 aerial photographs of U.S. sites. Maps and photographs range from $6 to $65 and can be obtained from the Center's customer service department. The staff can answer such questions as:

1) How can I receive a listing of aerial photographs of a particular hurricane that I am studying?
2) How do the Landsat satellite sensors work?
3) How can EROS help my company's geologic exploration projects?
4) How can EROS help my company form a geochemical assessment of a potential land site that we are interested in developing?
5) Can the Center furnish me with a printout of land ownership lists in my particular county?

Earth Science Information Centers

U.S. Geological Survey
508 National Center
Reston, VA 20192
703-648-6892
888-ASK-USGS
Fax: 703-648-4888
http://mapping.usgs.gov/
Email: esicmail@usgs.gov

Earth Science Information Centers (ESIC) offer nationwide information and sales service for U.S. Geological Survey map products and earth science publications. This network of ESICs provides information about: geologic, hydrologic, and land use maps, books, and reports; aerial, satellite, and radar images and related products; earth science and map data in digital format and related applications software; and geodetic data. ESICs can fill orders for custom products and provide information about earth science materials from many public and private producers. They can answer such questions as:

1) Where can maps of Indian lands be located?
2) What earth-science teaching aids are available?
3) Where can accurate topographic maps be found which show the location and measurable elevation of natural and man made features?
4) Where can out-of-print maps be located?
5) Where can wetlands be found in the state of Ohio?

National Earthquake Information Center

U.S. Geological Survey
Box 25046, DFS, MS967
Denver, CO 80225
303-273-8500
Fax: 303-273-8450
wwwneic.cr.usgs.gov
Email: sedas@gldfs.cr.usgs.gov

National Earthquake Information Center compiles, computes, and distributes digital and analog data on earthquakes that have occurred around the world. They have information on seismograms, earthquake magnitudes, intensities, and epicenter locations. They can answer such questions as:

1) What information exists on the most recent earthquake in California?
2) How many fault lines are known in California and where are they located?
3) What should people do in the event of an earthquake?
4) Where has there been seismic activity around the world in a given month?
5) What is the largest earthquake on record?

Emergency Planning and
Community-Right-To-Know Information Hotline

Booz, Allen & Hamilton, Inc.
401 M St., SW
Washington, DC 20466
800-535-0202
Fax: 703-412-3333
www.epa.gov/swercepp/crtk.html

The Emergency Planning and Community-Right-To-Know Information Hotline (EPCRA) provides information on what types of waste may be hazardous to the public's health. All information is open to local agencies, citizens, attorneys, consultants, and communities. EPCRA helps answer questions on the best ways to remove and store hazardous and solid waste. They can answer such questions as:

1) What constitutes a hazardous chemical release?
2) Which releases are especially dangerous?
3) What type of emergency planning is available for those working around or in contact with hazardous waste?
4) How are companies and communities regulated?
5) What documents are available to the average citizen concerned about waste?

Emissions Clearinghouse

Emission Factor Clearinghouse, MD-14
U.S. Environmental Protection Agency (EPA)
Research Triangle Park, NC 27711
919-541-5285
www.epa.gov/ttn/chief/index.html
The Emissions Clearinghouse is a means of exchanging information on air pollution control matters. It addresses the criteria pollutants and toxic substances from stationary and area sources, as well as mobile sources. The *Emission Factor Clearinghouse Newsletter* is issued quarterly, and contains information on recent publications, inquiries about EPA emission inventory policy, newly developed emission factors, and requests for assistance in dealing with general or specific air pollution emissions. The Clearinghouse does have a database for which there is a user fee. They can answer such questions as:

1) How can I get a FAX Chief system?
2) What information exists on the underground storage of fuel tanks?
3) How can I find an engineer to assist me with my emissions questions?
4) What are atmospheric tanks and how are they used?

National Energy Information Center

U.S. Department of Energy
1F048 Forrestal Building
1000 Independence Ave., SW
Washington, DC 20585
202-586-8800
Fax: 202-586-0727
www.eia.doe.gov
Email: infoctr@eia.doe.gov
The National Energy Information Center provides general reference services on U.S. Department of Energy data. It can provide statistical and analytical data, information, and referral assistance on a wide variety of energy-related issues. A publications directory, including many free publications, is available. They can answer such questions as:

1) What energy-related educational materials exist for elementary and secondary students?
2) What are some of the issues surrounding the Clean Air Act Amendments?
3) What is the short-term energy outlook?
4) What companies have purchased uranium and how much?
5) What is the petroleum supply statistics for a particular month?

National Environmental Data Referral Service

NEDRES Office
National Oceanic and Atmospheric Administration
U.S. Department of Commerce
Environmental Information Services
1305 East-West Highway
Silver Spring, MD 20910

301-713-0575
Fax: 301-713-1249
www.esdim.noaa.gov/
Email: barton@esdim.noaa.gov
The National Environmental Data Referral Service (NEDRES) is designed
to provide convenient, economical, and efficient access to widely scattered
environmental data. NEDRES is a publicly available service which
identifies the existence, location, characteristics, and availability
conditions of environmental data sets. NEDRES database contains only
descriptions, and not the actual data. Major subject categories include
climatology and meteorology, oceanography, geophysics and geology,
geography, hydrology and limnology, terrestrial resources, toxic and regulated substances, and satellite remotely sensed
data. For more information on the NEDRES database, contact the office listed above. They can provide the information
and pointers to data on such questions as:
1) What data exists on the air quality in the U.S.?
2) Where can information be found on the Chesapeake Bay?
3) Where can data be located on the estuarine water of California?
4) How has acid rain affected the environment?
5) How has pollution affected the ocean environment?

Environmental Financing Information Network

Labat-Anderson, Inc.
401 M St., SW, 2731R
Washington, DC 20460
202-564-4994
www.epa.gov/efinpage
Email: efin@epa.gov
The Environmental Financing Information Network is an online database service. They help state and local officials find
different ways to finance and improve the environment in which we live. They assist towns in locating funds to update
wastewater treatment plants and other environmental projects all the way down to the sewage system. Information on
State Revolving Funds and Public-Private Partnerships is included. They can answer such questions as:
1) How can we get financial funding for a nonprofit organization?
2) What are the pros and cons of forming a public or private partnership?
3) What other cities have revamped their waste management system?
4) How can towns or cities find technical assistance to help with new waste technology?
5) What ways can a state economically enhance their waste treatment systems?

U.S. Environmental Protection Agency (EPA)

Public Information Center
401 M St., SW
Washington, DC 20460
202-260-2080
Fax: 202-260-6257
www.epa.gov
Email: public_access@epamail.epa.gov
The Public Information Center of the Environmental Protection Agency should be the first point of contact for all
environmental issues. They have free publications on a variety of environmental topics, and can refer you to other experts
within the EPA for more specific responses to your inquiries. They can answer such questions as:
1) What cars have the best gas mileage?
2) What are the current pesticide regulations?

3) What environmental education materials exist for teachers?
4) What can be done to reduce pollution?
5) What is radon, and how can it be removed from a home?

Center for Environmental Research Information

Technology Transfer
U.S. Environmental Protection Agency (EPA)
26 W. Martin Luther King Dr.
Cincinnati, OH 45268
513-569-7369
513-569-7562 (to order publications)
Fax: 513-569-7566
www.epa.gov/docs/ord/
Email: mailto:ord.ceri@epamail.epa.gov
The Office of Research and Development (ORD) has centralized most of its information distribution and technology transfer activities in the Center for Environmental Research Information (CERI). CERI also serves as a central point of distribution for ORD research results and reports. They have statistics, regulations, and publications available at no charge. They can answer such questions as:
1) How can I protect my home from pesticides and pollution?
2) What types of pollution can cause harm to my family?
3) What safety guidelines must a company or lab follow?
4) How can a business get grant money to do research?
5) What certifications must companies meet in regulating their pollution?

National Marine Fisheries Service

Public Affairs
National Oceanic and Atmospheric Administration
U.S. Department of Commerce
1315 East-West Highway, Room 9272
Silver Spring, MD 20910
301-713-2370
Fax: 202-501-2953 (constituent services)
www.nmfs.noaa.gov
The National Marine Fisheries Service (NMFS) manages the country's stocks
of saltwater fish and shellfish for both commercial and recreational interests. NMFS enforces the Magnuson Fishery Conservation and Management Act to assure that fishing stays within sound biological limits. Scientists conduct research relating to these management responsibilities in science and research centers and have special knowledge of the fish in their geographical area. They can answer such questions as:
1) What is currently being done to protect whales and what statistics exist regarding these mammals?
2) What are some issues currently under discussion regarding fishing on an international level?
3) What is the Habitat Conservation Program and where can someone find out more information about it?
4) What information exists on seafood inspection?
5) What is currently being done to restore the marine habitat in the Chesapeake Bay?

Forest Service

U.S. Department of Agriculture
Public Affairs
201 14th and Independence Ave., SW
Washington, DC 20250
202-205-1760

Fax: 202-205-0885
www.fs.fed.us
Email: mailroom@fs.fed.us
This country's national forests offer more than 114,300 miles of trails, a
Scenic Byway System consisting of nearly 5,000 miles of highways in 32
states, 70 wild and scenic rivers covering nearly 3,500 miles and much
more. *A Guide to Your National Forest* lists regional offices, several private
and one Forest Service Interpretative Association, and a list of State Boards
of Tourism where camping information may be obtained. They can answer
such questions as:

1) What state forests in Maryland offer good sailing opportunities?
2) How far in advance must I reserve a campsite?
3) What is the best time of year to plan a camping trip in Tennessee?
4) Which rivers in North Carolina are recommended for canoeing or rafting?
5) How do I receive a listing of national scenic and historic trails?

Geologic Inquiries Group

U.S. Geological Survey (USGS)
907 National Center
Reston, VA 22092
703-648-4383
Fax: 703-648-4888
http://geology.usgs.gov
The Geologic Inquiries Group is the primary information group of the Geologic Division of the USGS. The Group can
provide information and answers to questions concerning all aspects of geology, such as the geology of specific areas,
energy and mineral resources, earthquakes, volcanoes, geochemistry, geophysics, and other geoscience disciplines, and
geologic map coverage. They have publications available, some of which are free. They can answer such questions as:

1) Where can information be obtained on a particular volcano?
2) Where can geologic maps for a specific area of a state be located?
3) What educational materials exist for teachers who want to teach their students about geology?
4) What geologic information is available on earthquakes?
5) What help is available for someone doing a science project on volcanoes?

National Geophysical Data Center

National Oceanic and Atmospheric Administration
Mail Code E/GC
325 Broadway, Dept. NGB
Boulder, CO 80303
303-497-6826
Fax: 303-497-6513
www.noaa.gov
Email: info@ngdc.noaa.gov
The National Geophysical Data Center (NGDC) combines in a single center all data activities in the fields of solid earth
geophysics, marine geology and geophysics, and solar-terrestrial physics. NGDC fills thousands of requests each year for
data services and publications. Typical specialized data services may include digitization of analog charts, derivation of
geomagnetic indexes, and customized computer graphics. They can answer such questions as:

1) Where can historical earthquake data be obtained?
2) Where can data on solar flare activity be located?
3) What causes avalanches, and what methods are used to ensure the safety of skiers in areas where avalanches typically
    occur?

4) Where are thermal springs and thermal wells located in Nevada?

5) Where can information on earthquake damage to transportation systems be obtained so that new systems can better withstand the effects of an earthquake?

National Response Center (Hazardous Chemicals)

U.S. Coast Guard Headquarters
2100 2nd St., SW, Room 2611
Washington, DC 20593
800-424-8802

The National Response Center receives notification and calls reporting oil spills, hazardous chemical releases, biological and radiological releases that have spilled into the environment. They pass the accidents on to a Federal On-Scene Coordinator, who coordinates and begins the clean-up efforts. The Hotline is open to the general public and to companies to call with sightings. Most of the information available from the Center is free. They can answer such questions as:

1) Has there ever been a report of hazardous waste spilled in a specific neighborhood or location?

2) How can I get a report released about a company regarding hazardous waste?

3) What is hazardous waste?

4) How does the Environmental Protection Agency enforce hazardous waste storage?

RCRA Hotline (Hazardous Waste)

U.S. Environmental Protection Agency (EPA)
401 M St., SW
Washington, DC 20460
800-424-9346
703-412-9810
Fax on Demand: 202-651-2060
www.epa.gov/oswer

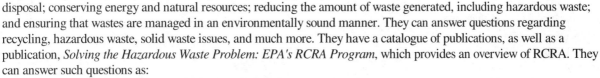

RCRA stands for the Resource Conservation and Recovery Act which has the goals of: protecting human health and the environment from the potential hazards of waste disposal; conserving energy and natural resources; reducing the amount of waste generated, including hazardous waste; and ensuring that wastes are managed in an environmentally sound manner. They can answer questions regarding recycling, hazardous waste, solid waste issues, and much more. They have a catalogue of publications, as well as a publication, *Solving the Hazardous Waste Problem: EPA's RCRA Program*, which provides an overview of RCRA. They can answer such questions as:

1) What are the hazardous waste disposal regulations in my state?

2) Which plant pesticides are considered safe?

3) What are the laws and regulations concerning hazardous waste transportation?

4) How can I begin a recycling program in my community?

5) What are some of the most recent technologies and management strategies for hazardous waste control?

National Water Information Center

U.S. Geological Survey
501 National Center
Reston, VA 20192
800-ASK-USGS
http://water.usgs.gov/
Email: h2Oinfo@usgs.gov

The National Water Information Center answers general questions on hydrology, water as a resource, and hydrologic mapping, as well as providing information on the products, projects, and services of the Water Services Division. The Center also provides information and materials for specific needs and is a reference office for Water-Resources Investigation reports released before 1982. The Information Center has maps showing a wide range of water-resources information. The staff can answer such questions as:

1) How can my company improve its waste disposal practices?
2) Where can I receive information on water resource conditions in my state?
3) What can people do to help reduce the problem of acid rain?
4) How can my company prevent ground water contamination?
5) Where can I receive introductory information on ground water hydraulics?

Indoor Air Quality Information Clearinghouse

P.O. Box 37133
Washington, DC 20013
800-438-4318
Fax: 202-484-1510
Email: iaquinfo@aol.com

The Indoor Air Quality Information Clearinghouse of the
Environmental Protection Agency can provide information and
assistance on indoor air quality problems. It brings together
information on more than 17 issues (from asbestos to wood
preservatives), for the range of agencies involved in addressing those
issues, from health agencies to energy departments. This office also
has information on home humidifiers, residential air cleaners, Sick Building Syndrome, indoor air quality, new carpet,
and more. They can answer such questions as:
1) What is Sick Building Syndrome, and what agency do I contact if I suspect my building is unsafe?
2) How do I identify and eliminate radon gas from my home?
3) How do I determine if the paint in my home is lead based?
4) What is the most recent legislation concerning asbestos-in-school requirements?
5) What is the Toxic Substance Control Act?

Bureau of Land Management

Office of Public Affairs
U.S. Department of the Interior
1849 C St., NW, Room 406-CS
Washington, DC 20240
202-452-5125
Fax: 202-452-5124
www.blm.gov/nhp/index.htm

There are close to 270 million acres of public lands located primarily, but not exclusively, in the West and in Alaska
comprising one-eighth of our nation's land area. It is the charge of the Bureau of Land Management (BLM) to administer
and care for these lands. To accomplish this task, the BLM has a variety of programs and activities, from the very new
Heritage Education program aimed at involving and educating young people about America's cultural heritage to finding
out about the availability of public lands for sale. They have free publications and can direct you to other resources within
the BLM. They can answer such questions as:
1) Where are campgrounds located on BLM lands and what facilities or recreational areas do they have?
2) What videos are available concerning rivers?
3) How can I find out which public lands are for sale in my state?
4) How do I stake a mining claim on federal lands?
5) How can I receive a listing of wildlife habitats on public lands?

U.S. Nuclear Regulatory Commission

Public Document Room
Washington, DC 20555
202-634-3273

Fax: 202-634-3343

www.nrc.gov

The Nuclear Regulatory Commission (NRC) licenses and regulates civilian use of nuclear energy to protect public health and safety and the environment. The NRC licenses persons and companies to build and operate nuclear reactors and other facilities, and to own and use nuclear materials. The Commission makes rules, sets standards, and carefully inspects companies to ensure that they do not violate existing safety rules. They can answer such questions as:

1) What information exists on abnormal occurrences in nuclear facilities?
2) What is the construction permit process for nuclear facilities?
3) What specific operational information must nuclear facilities submit to the NRC?
4) What statistics are available related to nuclear power?
5) How are radioactive materials packaged for transport?

National Oceanic and Atmospheric Administration

14th St. and Constitution Ave.

Washington, DC 20230

202-482-6090

Fax: 202-482-3154

www.noaa.gov

The National Oceanic and Atmospheric Administration gathers data, conducts research, and makes predictions about the state of the environment in which we live. NOAA charts the seas and skies, and enriches our understanding of the oceans, atmosphere, space, and sun. They can refer you to other offices and experts for specific questions, and they also offer a variety of publications and films. They can answer such questions as:

1) What research is being conducted on tropical weather and how can we better predict hurricanes?
2) How has the greenhouse effect changed the environment?
3) What are the physical and chemical processes that occur within the Earth's atmosphere?
4) What is being done to protect marine mammals?
5) What research exists on the solar activity in the upper atmosphere?

Oceanographic Information

National Oceanographic Data Center (NODC)

National Environmental Satellite, Data, and Information Service

National Oceanic and Atmospheric Administration

U.S. Department of Commerce

1315 East West Highway

Silver Spring, MD 20910

301-713-3277

Fax: 301-713-3302

www.nodc.noaa.gov

Email: services@nodc.noaa.gov

The National Oceanographic Data Center (NODC) provides global coverage of oceanographic data and services. NODC's databases cover physical and chemical properties of the world's oceans, seas, and estuaries, plus information on selected continental shelf and coastal waters. Simple questions usually can be answered without charge by telephone or mail, but more complicated ones requiring research or computer processing normally carry a fee. They can answer such questions as:

1) How does the Pacific Ocean temperature vary over a year?
2) How has the Atlantic Ocean been effected by pollution and what data exists on this topic?
3) What are the responsibilities of the NODC and what directories of information do they maintain?
4) Is there any bottom current data on the South China Sea?
5) Is the water warmer in Miami Beach or Myrtle Beach?

National Park Service

Office of Public Inquiries
1849 C St., NW
Washington, DC 20240
202-208-6843
www.nps.gov

Along with other responsibilities, the Park Service administers 350 maintained areas in the National Park System, collects the National Register of Historic Places and a registry of natural sites, and manages the Urban Park and Recreation Recovery Program. It provides technical assistance in planning, acquisition and development of recreation resources, conducts surveys of historic buildings and engineering works, has available programs and resources for teachers, and administers a program in interagency archeological services. Information, including brochures, maps, and a publications catalogue can be ordered from the Government Printing Office. The Office of Public Inquiries can refer you to other Park Service offices and can answer such questions as:

1) What archeological digs are currently in progress and where are they located?
2) What statistics are available on Park Service use, such as total visits, visits by region and state, and overnight stays?
3) Where can I locate videos on historic people or national landmarks?
4) How do I find out whether or not my home is eligible for listing on the National Historic Register?
5) How can I receive a listing of the lesser known National Parks?

National Pesticide Telecommunication Network

Oregon State University
NPTN Ag Chem Extension
333 Weniger
Corvallis, OR 97331-6502
800-858-PEST (7378)
Fax: 541-737-0761

The National Pesticide Telecommunication Network (NPTN) is a toll-free telephone service that provides a wide variety of health information on pesticides. Phones are staffed by pesticide specialists with agricultural, environmental, and public health backgrounds. Inquiries are also answered by graduate students in such fields as biology, anatomy, biochemistry, and entomology. They can answer such questions as:

1) Where can I get information on pesticides that might be found in drinking water wells?
2) What are some guidelines for the safe use of pesticides by farmers?
3) What plants have a natural ability to repel insects?
4) How do I make the transition from pesticide lawn control to natural pest control?
5) What is the toxicity and proper use of the pesticide R-11? How can I dispose of it safely?

Pollution Prevention Information Clearinghouse

Labat-Anderson, Inc.
401 M St., SW
Washington, DC 20460
202-260-1023
Fax: 202-260-0178
Email: ppic@epamail.epa.gov

The Pollution Prevention Information Clearinghouse is designed to help national and international industries reduce pollutants that are released into our environment. They specialize in using education and public awareness to prevent excessive pollution. The Clearinghouse has four information exchange directories that can be ordered. There is no charge for any service. They can answer such questions as:

1) How can pollution prevention benefit businesses?
2) How do you implement a pollution prevention program?

3) Are there training opportunities for pollution control/waste management?
4) How do you get technical assistance for pollution control?
5) What are the differences between large and small waste generators?

EPA Radon Information Hotline

U.S. Environment Protection Agency (EPA), OAR
401 M St., SW (MS6604J)
Washington, DC 20460
800-767-7236
www.epa.gov/iaq/radon

The EPA Radon Information Hotline can answer all your questions concerning radon. The staff can answer such questions as:
1) What is radon? How does it affect people?
2) How do I determine whether or not my home has a radon problem?
3) How can I obtain a radon detector for my home? How does it work?
4) What are some effective radon prevention methods?
5) What are some control methods for eliminating radon in well water?

National Sea Grant Depository

Pell Library Building
The University of Rhode Island
Bay Campus
Narragansett, RI 02882
401-874-6114
Fax: 401-874-6160
http://nsgd.gso.uri.edu
Email: nsgd@gso.uri.edu

The National Sea Grant Depository provides a wide variety of information on America's oceans, Great Lakes, and coastal zones. It maintains the only complete collection of publications generated by the National Sea Grant College Program. Publications include information on: oceanography, marine education, fisheries, coastal zone management, aquaculture, marine recreation and law. The collection includes journal reprints, technical and advisory reports, handbooks, charts, maps, manuals, directories, books, audiovisual materials, computer programs, annual reports, conference proceedings, and newsletters produced by Sea Grant funded researchers. The staff can answer such questions as:
1) What are some of the most common fish found in Alaska?
2) How do I begin a fish culture enterprise?
3) What is the impact of pollution on the marine environment?
4) What can people do to prevent the pollution of coastal waters?
5) What are some of the potential risks to coastal investment?

Small Business Ombudsman Clearinghouse

U.S. Environmental Protection Agency (EPA)
Small Business Ombudsman, 1230C
401 M St., SW
Washington, DC 20460
800-368-5888
703-305-5938
Fax: 703-305-6462
www.epa.gov

The Small Business Ombudsman Clearinghouse helps your business comply with all environmental regulations. They provide information on current policies, safety precautions, and general information on keeping the air you breathe healthy. They are available to assist private citizens, small communities, enterprises, trade associations, technical consultants, and laboratories. Listings on all aspects of current EPA regulatory developments are available at no charge. Over 200 EPA publications are maintained for distribution. They can answer such questions as:

1) Am I covered under the new Clear Air Act requirements?
2) How do I get an I.D. number for hazardous waste disposal?
3) What are the requirements for any underground storage waste?
4) How do I know if my community is following proper safety guidelines?
5) What type of waste material could be hazardous to my community?

National Snow and Ice Data Center

World Data Center-A For Glaciology
CIRES, Box 449
University of Colorado
Boulder, CO 80309
303-492-5171
Fax: 303-492-2468
http://nsidc.org/index.html
Email: nsidc@kyros.colorado.edu

The National Snow and Ice Data Center provides a national and international focus for snow and ice data information services. The Center provides: broad user access to snow and ice data through specialized data reports and inventories in Glaciological Data; through special data sets maintained in the Center; through tailored bibliographies; and through access to the Snow and Ice Library. There is a small fee for some services. They can answer such questions as:

1) How does exhaust from jet aircraft affect cloud cover?
2) Where can data be accessed on glacier fluctuations?
3) How has snow cover varied over time in North America?
4) What current research is being undertaken regarding avalanches?
5) What is the difference between fresh water ice and sea ice?

Solid Waste Information Clearinghouse

P.O. Box 7219
1100 Wayne Ave., Suite 700
Silver Spring, MD 20910
800-67-SWICH
301-585-2898
Fax: 301-589-7068
www.swana.org
Email: info@swana.org

The Solid Waste Information Clearinghouse (SWICH) is concerned with how state and local offices and industries get rid of solid waste. The general public is also welcome to request information. SWICH can show how to economically and ecologically get rid of waste by source reduction, recycling, composting, planning, education, public training, public participation, legislation and regulation, waste combustion, and collection. They can answer such questions as:

1) How can I implement a recycling program in my community?
2) What is the most economical way to dispose of a waste product?
3) How have other communities started and benefited from recycling?
4) What types of disposal is available to my community or business?

National Space Science Data Center

National Aeronautics and Space Administration
Goddard Space Flight Center
Greenbelt, MD 20771
301-286-7354

Data Request: 301-286-6695
Fax: 301-286-1771
http://nssdc.gsfc.nasa.gov/
Email: request@nssdca.gsfca.nasa.gov

The National Space Science Data Center (NSSDC) is an organization that provides a variety of valuable services for scientists throughout the world. The Center furthers the use of data obtained from space and earth science investigations, maintains an active data repository, and supports scientific research. The data are contained on more than 120,000 magnetic tapes, tens of thousands of film products, and optical, video, and magnetic disks. NSSDC works with individual users to address their specific requirements. There is a charge for most data, but it is only on a cost recovery basis. They can answer such questions as:

1) What satellites are currently operating in space and which ones are planned for future launch?
2) What data from space can provide estimates of marine phytoplankton in the ocean?
3) Where can photographs taken from APOLLO be located?
4) What data is available to researchers studying the ozone?
5) What information exists on a particular rocket launch?

Technology Transfer Competitiveness

Administrator
Federal Laboratory Consortium
P.O. Box 545
Sequim, WA 98382
360-683-1005
Fax: 360-683-6654
www.federallabs.org/

The mission of the Federal Laboratory Consortium is to facilitate technology transfer among government, business, and academic entities in order to promote American economic and technological competitiveness. It sponsors conferences and seminars and publishes a free monthly newsletter. For very specific questions from researchers who find themselves at an impasse, the Consortium will conduct a database search to refer the inquirer to an appropriate lab. Write or call for a free general information packet explaining the organization, how to access its services, facilities available for testing, and examples of technology transfers. They can answer such questions as:

1) How can the heat pipes used to cool satellites be converted for use in a business?
2) How can toothpaste used by astronauts benefit those that are used on Earth?
3) What research is being conducted on electric cars?
4) Where can a business locate information on humidity control for a warehouse?

Technology Transfer Program

NASA Scientific and Technical Information Facility
Technology Transfer Office
NASA-CASI
800 Elkridge Landing Rd.
Linthicum Heights, MD 21090-2934
410-859-5300, ext. 242
Fax: 301-621-0134
www.sti.nasa.gov

Technology Transfer is an ideal way to apply the National Aeronautics and Space Administration's (NASA) experience and discoveries to your research or business. The transfer of aerospace technology which embraces virtually every scientific and technical discipline is paying off in a broad spectrum of practical applications in industry. The Technology Transfer System is a network of specialized organizations dedicated to helping industry access, apply, and utilize NASA's pool of innovations and technical resources. This allows you to access a wide range of information, products, services and technical expertise. A staff of experts assists you in pinpointing problems, identifying needs, and exchanging ideas. They can answer such questions as:

1) How can ultra-sensitive measuring devices used to measure space dust be put to use measuring environmental pollutants?
2) How can standard doorknobs be replaced with electronic openers?
3) Is it possible to convert spacesuits for use by firefighters or workers in industrial situations?
4) What lunar tool technology can be used in designing cordless power tools?

Toxic Substance Control Act

U.S. Environmental Protection Agency (EPA)
Environmental Assistance Division
401 M St., SW
Washington, DC 20460
202-554-1404
Fax: 202-554-5603
Email: tsca_hotline@epamail.epa.gov

The Toxic Substance Control Act (TSCA) regulates the storage and removal of toxic substances and spills. They are concerned with safely containing toxic substances that may be harmful to our environment. TSCA is open to the general public as well as to industries and environmental groups. They can answer such questions as:

1) What chemicals can a manufacturer produce, and are they on the toxic inventory list?
2) What can I do if a toxic substance was spilled or contained on my property?
3) What are the latest regulations regarding production and handling of toxic substances?
4) How can I get a listing of places where toxic waste is stored?

Undersea Research

National Undersea Research Program
National Oceanic and Atmospheric Administration (NOAA)
U.S. Department of Commerce
R/OR2, Room 11853
Building SSMC-3
1315 East-West Highway
Silver Spring, MD 20910
301-713-2427
Fax: 301-713-1967
www.nurp.noaa.gov

The National Undersea Research Program (NURP) develops programs and provides support to scientists and engineers to accomplish research underwater for the study of biological, chemical, geological, and physical processes in the world's oceans and lakes. NURP provides investigators with modern undersea facilities including submersibles, habitats, air and mixed gas SCUBA, and remotely operated vehicles. They can answer such questions as:

1) How do I get a grant from NURP?
2) What is the appropriate undersea center for me to contact in my region?
3) How deep in the sea does NURP support scientists work?
4) What kind of research expenses will be covered under a NURP grant?
5) Does NURP support coral reef research?

EPA National Small Flows Clearinghouse (Wastewater)

West Virginia University
P.O. Box 6064
Morgantown, WV 26506

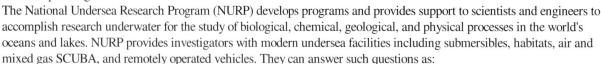

800-624-8301

Fax: 304-293-3161

The National Small Flows Clearinghouse is the center for small systems wastewater technology transfer. The Clearinghouse provides training resources and expertise in management and maintenance of small wastewater systems. It assists small communities in meeting environmental goals and water quality requirements. The Clearinghouse offers products and services to aid consultants, local officials, and developers in designing, constructing, operating, and managing small wastewater systems. Its products and services include databases, publications, video programs, workshops, and seminars. The staff can answer such questions as:

1) How can I find out more about the use of constructed wetlands that are used to treat domestic wastewater?
2) How can I find out more about sequencing batch reactors? How do they compare with conventional continuous waste treatment systems?
3) What should I look for when hiring qualified wastewater personnel?
4) How can our community get the most out of our existing wastewater resources and facilities?
5) What are some current technologies for cleansing polluted water?

Watershed Resource Information System

Terrene Institute

U.S. Environmental Protection Agency (EPA)

4 Herbert St.

Alexandria, VA 22305

800-726-LAKE (5253)

www.epa.gov

The Watershed Resource Information System is an information resource on lake restoration, protection, and management. Its Watershed Information Resource Database contains abstracts and citations of technical materials and information and bibliographies. A specialist will conduct a database search for you for a fee of $25, plus $.10 per page per reference. You may purchase the system for $250 or a demo disk for $20. The staff can answer such questions as:

1) What information exists on different methods for restoring polluted lakes?
2) How can I find out about a particular lake's water quality?
3) What are some effective watershed management techniques?
4) What techniques can be used to reduce the incidence of acidification in lakes?
5) What are some effective methods of reducing toxic substances in lakes?

National Weather Service

National Oceanic and Atmospheric Administration

1325 East-West Highway

Silver Spring, MD 20910

301-713-0622

www.nws.noaa.gov

The National Weather Service, through a network of field offices, predicts the nation's weather and issues storm and flood warnings. They also publish a weekly series of daily weather maps which include the highest and lowest temperatures chart and the precipitation areas. They can send anyone interested a sample copy or subscription information on this material. They also have publications on a variety of weather conditions, as well as films, videos, and slides. They can answer such questions as:

1) What should be done in the event of a hurricane?
2) What is a tornado?
3) How are severe storms forecast and where can more information be obtained about them?
4) Is there information available on monthly and seasonal predictions of temperature and precipitation?
5) What is a flash flood?

Wetlands Protection Hotline

Labat-Anderson, Inc.
401 M St.
MC4502F
Washington, DC 20460
800-832-7828
Fax: 703-525-0201
www.epa.gov/owoc/wetlands/
The Wetlands Protection Hotline is a toll-free telephone service that responds to questions about the value and function of wetlands in our world. The staff is interested in protecting our wetlands and showing how wetlands play an important role in our changing environment. They have free publications and fact sheets available. They can answer such questions as:
1) Where can I get the *1987 Corps of Engineers Wetlands Delineation Manual*?
2) Is there any information available on constructed wetlands?
3) Is it legal to dig out a wetlands area?
4) What is the White House's policy on the protection of wetlands?
5) What regulations must farmers comply with when they have wetlands on their property?

Health

National Institute on Aging

Public Information Office
Building 31, Room 5C27
31 Center Dr., MSC 2292
Bethesda, MD 20892-2292
800-222-2225
Fax: 301-496-1752
www.nih.gov/nia

The National Institute on Aging conducts research related to the aging process and looks at diseases and other special problems related to the needs of the aged. They have a publications list of free items dealing with a variety of consumer issues. They can answer such questions as:

1) What is a good exercise program for an elderly person?
2) What information exists on menopause and how can symptoms be treated?
3) How can the elderly improve their diet?
4) What is osteoporosis and what can be done to minimize its effects?
5) What factors should people be aware of when taking certain medications?

National AIDS Information Clearinghouse

P.O. Box 6003
Rockville, MD 20849
800-458-5231
Fax: 301-251-5343
www.cdc.gov/hiv/dhap.htm
Email: hivmail@cdc.gov

The National AIDS Hotline offers 24-hour service seven days a week to respond to any question about HIV infection and AIDS. Information specialists can refer you to groups in your area, and can direct you to local counseling and testing centers. The Clearinghouse can also connect people with the Clinical Trials Information Center, where they can learn what trials are currently taking place and what the requirements are for participants. They have free resources and publications on AIDS and HIV infection. They can answer such questions as:

1) What videos are available on AIDS that are appropriate for kids?
2) What are the signs and symptoms of infection?
3) How can parents most effectively discuss AIDS with their children?
4) What information exists on AIDS clinical trials?
5) Where can someone get information on caring for an AIDS patient at home?

National Clearinghouse for Alcohol and Drug Information

P.O. Box 2345
11426 Rockville Pike, Suite 200
Rockville, MD 20852
800-729-6686
Fax: 301-468-6433
TDD: 800-487-4889
www.health.org

The National Clearinghouse for Alcohol and Drug Information (NCADI) gathers and disseminates current information on alcohol and drug-related subjects, and can make referrals to other alcohol, tobacco, and drug resource experts. The Clearinghouse is the national resource center for information on the latest research results, popular press and scholarly journal articles, videos, prevention curricula, print materials, and program descriptions. Services include subject searches on an in-house database and response to inquiries for statistics and other information. NCADI can make referrals to self-help organizations, and can provide information on drug and alcohol abuse treatment. They have a publications catalogue listing, booklets, videos, and posters which range in price from free to $25. They can answer such questions as:

1) How do you implement a drug-free workplace program, and what are the laws regarding drug testing at the workplace?
2) How do you teach kids about the dangers of drugs and alcohol, and what are the warning signs parents should know?
3) What are the effects of Fetal Alcohol Syndrome and where can people turn for more information about it?
4) What are some statistics on drug abuse among college students and what prevention programs exist?
5) What research is being done on children of alcoholics and are there support groups in place for them?

National Institute of Allergy and Infectious Diseases

NIAID Office of Communications and Public Liaison
Building 31, Room 7A50
31 Center Dr., MSC 2520
Bethesda, MD 20892-2520
301-496-5717
Fax: 301-402-0120
www.niaid.nih.gov/
The National Institute of Allergy and Infectious Diseases (NIAID) conducts and supports research to study the causes of allergic, immunologic, and infectious diseases, and to develop better means of preventing, diagnosing, and treating these illnesses. Some studies look at the role of the immune system in chronic diseases, such as arthritis, and at disorders of the immune system, as in asthma.
NIAID has become the lead component at the National Institutes of Health for coordinating and conducting AIDS research. They have publications, journal articles, and more. They can answer such questions as:

1) What research is currently being done on allergies to pollen?
2) What is the current research being undertaken on AIDS?
3) How can I help my child handle asthma?
4) What is Chronic Fatigue Syndrome and what are the options for treating it?
5) What research exists on problems associated with the immune system?

Alzheimer's Disease Education And Referral Center

P.O. Box 8250
Silver Spring, MD 20907-8250
800-438-4380
Fax: 301-495-3334
www.alzheimers.org/adear
Email: adear@alzheimers.org
The Alzheimer's Disease Education and Referral Center distributes information about Alzheimer's disease to health professionals, patients and their families, and the general public. The Center provides information about the diagnosis and treatment of Alzheimer's disease, research, and services available to patients and family members. The bibliographic references of the Center are included in a computerized index that includes references to patient and professional education materials, including information about health promotion programs. A list is available of free publications, in addition to a free newsletter. They can answer such questions as:

1) What are the symptoms of Alzheimer's disease and what are the causes?
2) What research has been done to evaluate special long-term care units for Alzheimer patients?
3) Where are research centers located which deal with Alzheimer's?
4) What are some statistics on Alzheimer's?
5) What help is available for families caring for an Alzheimer's patient at home?

National Arthritis and
Musculoskeletal and Skin Diseases Information Clearinghouse

National Institute of Health
1 AMS Circle
Bethesda, MD 20892-3675
301-495-4484
Fax: 301-718-6366
TTY: 301-565-2966
www.nih.gov/niams
Email: NIAMSWEB-L@mail.nih.gov

The National Institute of Arthritis and Musculoskeletal and Skin Diseases handles inquiries on arthritis, bone diseases, and skin diseases. They conduct and support basic and clinical research concerning the causes, prevention, diagnosis, and treatment of these diseases. They serve as an information exchange for individuals and organizations involved in public, professional, and patient education. The Clearinghouse has free publications on a variety of topics and can search their database for other information that might be needed. They can answer questions such as:

1)   What can be done to prevent osteoporosis and who is most at risk for acquiring this disease?
2)   Does chocolate cause acne and how can acne be treated?
3)   What information exists on joint replacement for people who suffer from severe arthritis?
4)   What are some different types of birth marks, and how can they be removed?
5)   What educational materials are there for a continuing education forum on arthritis?

Asthma Clearinghouse

National Asthma Education Program
P.O. Box 30105
Bethesda, MD 20824-0105
301-592-8573
Fax: 301-592-8563
www.nhlbisupport.com/asthma/index.html

The Asthma Clearinghouse is a new clearinghouse providing publications, reports, resources, and referrals to experts in the field of asthma. One report, *The Executive Summary: Guidelines for the Diagnosis and Management of Asthma*, explains the diagnosis, therapy, and other important considerations for those that suffer from asthma. They can answer such questions as:

1)   What materials are available for kids that explain the causes and treatment of asthma?
2)   What conditions trigger an asthma attack?
3)   Are there different types of asthma?
4)   What are some forms of treatment for asthma sufferers?
5)   What are the guidelines for treatment of asthma?

Blood Resources

National Blood Resource Education Program
P.O. Box 30105
Bethesda, MD 20824-0105
301-592-8573
Fax: 301-592-8563
www.nhlbi.nih.gov/

The National Blood Resource Education Program was established to ensure an adequate supply of safe blood and blood components to meet our country's needs, ensuring that blood and blood components are transfused only when therapeutically appropriate. The Program helps health professionals understand the risks and benefits of blood transfusions, and ensures that patients receive appropriate information regarding transfusions. They also work to increase public awareness that donating blood is a safe process. They can answer such questions as:

1) What should people should be aware of when donating blood?
2) Is it still possible to get AIDS from blood transfusions?
3) Can you donate your own blood before you undergo surgery in the event you might require a transfusion?
4) How long can blood be kept before it is no longer usable?
5) What are some of the problems that people encounter when they have unusual blood types?

The Cancer Information Service

National Cancer Institute
Building 31, Room 10A03
31 Center Dr.
Bethesda, MD 20892-2580
800-4-CANCER
800-435-3848
Fax: 301-402-0894
TTY: 800-332-8615
www.nci.nih.gov/

The toll-free Cancer Information Service can provide accurate, up-to-date information about cancer and cancer-related resources in local areas. A wide variety of free publications on specific types of cancer, treatment methods, coping methods, and other cancer-related subjects are distributed. A database is available, that can access information on clinical trials and treatment options. The Cancer Information Service can help you locate materials and research on a specific type of cancer. They can answer such questions as:

1) Is the new prostate cancer test accurate, and to what degree?
2) How often should you get a mammogram and at what age should you begin?
3) What are the side effects of a particular anti-cancer drug?
4) What are the different stages of breast cancer?
5) What are clinical trials and where can I participate in them?

National Clearinghouse on Child Abuse and Neglect Information

330 C St., SW
P.O. Box 1182
Washington, DC 20447
800-FYI-3366
703-385-7565
Fax: 703-385-3206
www.calib.com/nccanch
Email: nccanch@calib.com

The Clearinghouse on Child Abuse and Neglect Information was established to help professionals and concerned citizens locate information on child abuse and neglect. They collect and disseminate a wide variety of information including publications, audiovisuals, public awareness materials, and more, and can refer you to other resources. Stock publications and many other services are provided at no cost to the user. User fees are required however, for services such as custom database searches and bibliographies. They can answer such questions as:

1) What statistics exist on the incidence of child abuse and neglect?
2) What laws exist that protect children against child abuse?
3) What is the role of the courts in child protection?
4) What funding sources are there for child abuse and neglect programs?
5) What role do teachers play in the prevention and treatment of child abuse?

National Institute of Child Health and Human Development

P.O. Box 3006
Rockville, MD 20847
301-496-5133
Fax: 301-496-7101
www.nichd.nih.gov

The National Institute of Child Health and Human Development conducts and supports research in maternal and child health and the population sciences. They will respond to individual inquiries on related topics such as studies on reproductive biology and contraception, fertility, mental retardation, and developmental issues. They have free publications and can refer you elsewhere for additional information. They can answer such questions as:

1) Is reversing letters a sign of a reading disability?
2) What are the possible causes of Down Syndrome?
3) What are some important issues to think about when considering a vasectomy?
4) Where is there research being conducted on mental retardation?
5) What are the newest forms of birth control being used?

National Information Center for Children and Youth with Disabilities

P.O. Box 1492
Washington, DC 20013-1492
800-695-0285
202-884-8200
Fax: 202-884-8441
www.nichcy.org
Email: nichcy@aed.org

The National Information Center for Children and Youth with Disabilities operates a national clearinghouse providing free information to assist parents, educators, caregivers, advocates, and others in helping children and youth with disabilities to become active members of the community. The staff provides personal responses to specific questions, as well as information on local, state, or national disability groups for parents, prepared information packets, publications on current issues, and technical assistance to parent and professional groups. They can answer such questions as:

1) How can I help my hyperactive child?
2) At what age do public schools begin mainstreaming students?
3) Can the Center provide a listing of national Down Syndrome support groups?
4) Where can I obtain captioned films for the deaf?
5) How do I make my home more wheelchair accessible? Are there any financial assistance programs available to help me accomplish this?

Cholesterol Information

National Cholesterol Education Program Information Center
National Heart, Lung, and Blood Institute
P.O. Box 30105
Bethesda, MD 20824-0105
301-592-8573
Fax: 301-592-8563
www.nhlbi.nih.gov/

Do you know your cholesterol number or has your doctor advised you to change your diet? The National Cholesterol Education Program (NCEP) is for you. NCEP aims to raise awareness and understanding about high blood cholesterol as a risk factor for coronary heart disease and the benefits of lowering cholesterol levels as a means of preventing coronary heart disease. They have specialists on staff to answer questions and they provide printed information on cholesterol, diet, and high blood pressure to the public and health professionals. They can answer such questions as:

1) Is it possible to eat bacon on a low cholesterol diet?
2) Are medications required when trying to lower cholesterol levels?
3) How does exercise affect cholesterol levels?
4) What are the different types of home cholesterol test kits available?
5) What do the cholesterol numbers mean and what is meant by good and bad cholesterol?

National Institute on
Deafness and Other Communication Disorders Clearinghouse

31 Center Dr., MSC 2320
Bethesda, MD 20892-3456
301-496-7243
Fax: 301-402-0018
TTY: 301-402-0252
Email: nidcd@aeric.com

The National Institute on Deafness and Other Communication Disorders disseminates information on normal and disordered processes of human communication. They have information about hearing, balance, smell, taste, voice, speech, and language for health professionals, patients, and the general public. They have fact sheets, bibliographies, information packets, and directories. They can answer such questions as:

1) What are the treatment options for someone who has aphasia?
2) What can be done for children with frequent ear infections?
3) Are all hearing aids created equal?
4) What can be done to help someone who stutters?
5) What are the current statistics on deafness and hearing disorders?

National Institute of Dental and Craniofacial Research

Information Office
Building 31, Room 2C35
31 Center Dr., MSC-2290
Bethesda, MD 20892
301-496-4261
Fax: 301-496-9988
www.nidr.nih.gov
Email: nidrinso@od31.nidr.nih.gov

The National Institute of Dental and Craniofacial Research conducts research on the causes, prevention, diagnosis, and treatment of diseases and conditions of the mouth and teeth. They have free publications and posters on a variety of topics, and can refer people to experts for further information. They can answer such questions as:

1) What are the oral problems related to AIDS?
2) What information exists on fever blisters and canker sores?
3) What are the causes of periodontal disease and what are some effective treatment options?
4) Are fluoride treatments safe and when should they be started?
5) What are dental sealants and how effective are they in preventing cavities?

National Diabetes Information Clearinghouse

1 Information Way
Bethesda, MD 20892
301-654-3327
Fax: 301-907-8906
www.niddk.nih.gov/
Email: ndic@info.niddk.nih.gov

The National Diabetes Information Clearinghouse was established to increase the knowledge and understanding of diabetes among patients, health professionals, and the general public. The Clearinghouse has a publications list available, with items ranging in price from free to $25, and a free quarterly newsletter featuring news about diabetes. They can also search their database for information on a specific topic. They can answer such questions as:

1)   What is the latest research on the ways to manage diabetes, along with nutrition and diet information?
2)   What are the issues and reports regarding diabetes and athletics?
3)   What is gestational diabetes and the special risks and dangers it presents?
4)   What are the types of insulins currently available, along with the time action of the insulin preparations?
5)   What are some common foot care problems frequently experienced by diabetics?

National Digestive Diseases Information Clearinghouse

2 Information Way
Bethesda, MD 20892-3570
301-496-3583
Fax: 301-496-7422
www.niddk.nih.gov/
Email: nddic@info.niddk.nih.gov

The Digestive Diseases Information Clearinghouse provides information about digestive diseases to educate the public, patients and their families, as well as physicians and other health care providers. The Clearinghouse provides information products and services such as factsheets, as well as an inquiry and referral service, information about research developments, and organizational and governmental activities related to digestive diseases. The Clearinghouse also maintains a database containing references to literature, products, programs, and services. A list of free publications is available. They can answer such questions as:

1)   What are the surgical procedures involved in having a gall bladder removed and are there options to surgery?
2)   What are the symptoms, causes, and treatments of ulcers?
3)   How do you prevent heartburn?
4)   What is a hiatal hernia and does it always require surgery?
5)   What is pancreatitis?

Disabilities Information Clearinghouse

Clearinghouse on Disability Information Programs
U.S. Department of Education
330 C St., SW, Room 3132
Mary Switzer Building
Washington, DC 20202
202-205-8241
Fax: 202-401-2608
www.ed.gov/offices/

The Clearinghouse on Disability Information responds to inquiries on a wide range of topics. Information is especially strong in the areas of Federal funding for programs serving individuals with disabilities, Federal legislation affecting the disability community, and Federal programs benefiting people with disabilities. A publications list is available, many of which are free. The Clearinghouse also maintains a database of sources for equipment to assist disabled people. They can answer such questions as:

1)   What information exists about housing disabled people?
2)   What handicapped assistance loans are available?
3)   What is the law regarding Equal Employment Opportunities for handicapped persons?
4)   What are the requirements for public education of students with handicaps?
5)   How can businesses best accommodate workers with disabilities?

Disease Information

Centers for Disease Control
Information Resources Management Office
Mail Stop C-15
1600 Clifton Rd., NE
Atlanta, GA 30333
404-332-4555
Fax on Demand: 404-332-4565

The Centers for Disease Control (CDC) has developed a Voice Information System that allows anyone using a touch tone telephone to obtain prerecorded information on particular health issues. The materials include information about certain diseases or health areas, symptoms and prevention methods, immunization requirements, current statistics, recent disease outbreaks, and other available printed materials. Currently information is available on AIDS, Chronic Fatigue Syndrome, encephalitis, hepatitis, Lyme disease, malaria, and more. They can answer such questions as:

1) What are the current statistics on AIDS?
2) Have there been recent disease outbreaks and where have they occurred?
3) Are vaccines required for travel to Africa?
4) When should children be immunized?
5) What is Chronic Fatigue Syndrome and where can I learn more about this condition?

Drug Evaluation Clearinghouse

Center for Drug Evaluation and Research
Food and Drug Administration (FDA)
5600 Fishers Lane
Rockville, MD 20857
301-594-1012
www.fda.gov/cder

The Center for Drug Evaluation and Research responds to inquiries covering a wide spectrum of drug issues. They develop policy with regard to the safety, effectiveness, and labeling of all drug products, as well as evaluate new drug applications. The Center conducts research and develops scientific standards on the composition, quality, safety, and effectiveness of drugs. A list of guidelines is available to help manufacturers comply with the requirements of the regulations. The staff will respond to requests for information regarding the laws, regulations, policies, and functions of the FDA as it pertains to drugs. Materials are available on pharmaceuticals, drug labeling, and consumer education. They can answer such questions as:

1) What are the pros and cons of estrogen?
2) What information exists on the different forms of The Pill?
3) Do over-the-counter hair growth products really work?
4) What research has been done on Norplant?
5) What information is required on drug package labels?

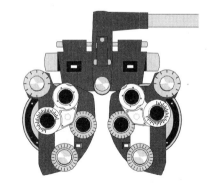

National Eye Institute

Office of Health, Education and Communication
Building 31, Room 6A32
31 Center Dr.
Bethesda, MD 20892-2510
301-496-5248
Fax: 301-402-1065
www.nei.nih.gov/
Email: 2020@b31.nei.nih.gov

The National Eye Institute (NEI) conducts and supports research related to the cause, natural history, prevention, diagnosis, and treatment of disorders of the eye and visual system. NEI distributes information on eye disorders, and can refer people to other organizations. They have free publications on a variety of topics. They can answer such questions as:

1) What is the latest information about cataracts and how can they safely be removed?
2) Are disposable contact lenses safe?
3) What are the causes of blindness?
4) How can glaucoma be detected early and are there treatment options to be considered?
5) What is Age-Related Macular Degeneration?

Food and Drug Information

Office of Consumer Affairs, HFE-88
Food and Drug Administration
5600 Fishers Lane, Room 16-85
Rockville, MD 20857
301-827-4422
Fax: 301-443-9767
www.fda.gov/oca/oca.htm

The Food and Drug Administration (FDA) is charged with ensuring that food is safe and wholesome; that drugs, biological products, medical devices are safe and effective; that cosmetics are safe; that the use of radiological products does not result in unnecessary exposure to radiation; and that all of these products are honestly and informatively labeled. The Office of Consumer Affairs of the FDA handles consumer inquiries on issues under the FDA's responsibility, and serves as a clearinghouse for FDA publications (most of which are free). They can also refer callers to the appropriate office for more information. Topics covered include foods, nutrition, federal regulations, cosmetics, drug labeling, medical devices, pharmaceuticals, and more. They can answer such questions as:

1) What nutritional information is available for pregnant women?
2) Are extended wear lenses safe?
3) What information is required on food labels, and what does it mean?
4) What are the different forms of birth control and how effective are they?
5) What is the status of breast implants and where can someone turn for more information on the subject?

National Health Information Center

Referral Specialist
Office of Disease Prevention and Health Promotion
P.O. Box 1133
Washington, DC 20013
301-565-4167
800-336-4797
Fax: 301-984-4256
www.health.gov/nhic
Email: nhicinfo@health.org

The National Health Information Center is a health information referral organization that puts people with health questions in touch with those organizations that are best able to answer them. The Center's main objectives are to identify health information resources, channel requests for information to these resources, and develop publications on health-related topics of interest to health professionals, the health media, and the general public. The Center meets these objectives by using a variety of information resource materials, a database of health-related organizations, and an information referral system. There is a publications catalogue available, with prices ranging from free to $5, and the Center covers topics such as community health, school health, worksite health, nutrition, and more. They can answer such questions as:

1) What health education program materials exist for employers and how can they be implemented at the worksite?
2) What organizations and support groups exist for people suffering from cerebral palsy?
3) What toll-free numbers are available for various health information?
4) What is the latest information about a specific rare disease and where can people turn for support?
5) How physically fit are America's six-year-olds and what statistics exist on this topic?

Health Care Delivery

Bureau of Primary Health Care
Health Resources and Services Administration
5600 Fishers Lane, Room 7-05
Rockville, MD 29857
301-594-4110

The Bureau of Primary Health Care helps assure that health care services are provided to medically underserved populations and to persons with special health care needs. The Bureau serves as a national focus for the development of primary health care delivery capacity, and for placement of health care professionals in Health Professional Shortage Areas to promote sustained sources of health services. Support for primary health care is provided primarily through Community Health Centers, Migrant Health Centers, Services for Special Populations, Services for Residents of Public Housing, and the National Health Service Corps. They can answer such questions as:

1)   How can nurses or doctors get their college loans repaid through service?
2)   What programs exist for migrant health care?
3)   What programs deal with the special health care needs of the homeless?
4)   What research is being undertaken on meeting the health care needs of the elderly in this country?
5)   What areas of the country are currently designated as health professional shortage areas?

Health Care Policy Clearinghouse

Agency for Health Care Policy and Research
P.O. Box 8547
Silver Spring, MD 20907-8547
800-358-9295
TDD: 888-586-6340
Fax on Demand: 301-594-2800
www.ahcpr.gov
Email: info@ahcpr.gov

The Agency for Health Care Policy and Research (AHCPR) is the primary source of Federal support for research on problems related to the quality and delivery of health services. AHCPR programs evaluate health services, assess technologies, and improve access to new scientific and technical information for research users. Research findings are disseminated through publications, conferences, and workshops. Materials are available on medical treatment effectiveness, health care costs and utilizations, health care expenditures, health information systems, health technology assessment, and funding opportunities for grants and contracts. They can answer such questions as:

1)   What are clinical practice guidelines for the treatment of cataracts?
2)   What statistics exist on medical expenditures?
3)   How effective is a specific treatment strategy for ulcers?
4)   What type of person uses a nursing home and what is their average medical condition upon entering such a facility?
5)   What are some treatment options for depression and how effective are they?

Clearinghouse on Health Indexes

National Center for Health Statistics
U.S. Department of Health and Human Services
Public Health Service
6525 Belcrest Rd.
Hyattsville, MD 20782
301-436-8500
www.cdc.gov/nchs/

The National Center for Health Statistics provides information assistance in the development of health measures to health researchers, administrators, and planners. The Clearinghouse's definition of a health index is a measure that summarizes data from two or more components and purports to reflect the health status of an individual or defined group. Services provided to users include annotated bibliographies and a reference and referral service. A publications catalogue is available, with items ranging in price from free to $20. They can answer such questions as:

1) What are the typical characteristics of persons with and without health care coverage?
2) What type of health care is provided to adolescents?
3) What method of contraception is used most frequently in the U.S.?
4) What data exists on the current living arrangements of women of childbearing ages in the U.S.?
5) What survey data exists on the firearm mortality among children?

National Heart, Lung, and Blood Institute Information Center

P.O. Box 30105
Bethesda, MD 20824-0105
301-592-8573
Fax: 301-592-8563
www.nhlbi.nih.gov/
Email: NHLBIinfo@rover.nhlbi.nih.gov
The National Heart, Lung, and Blood Institute is responsible for the scientific investigation of heart, blood vessel, lung, and blood diseases. The Information Center can provide the most current

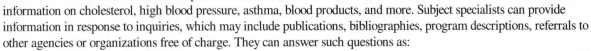

information on cholesterol, high blood pressure, asthma, blood products, and more. Subject specialists can provide information in response to inquiries, which may include publications, bibliographies, program descriptions, referrals to other agencies or organizations free of charge. They can answer such questions as:

1) What are the treatment options for someone suffering from emphysema?
2) What should the level of cholesterol be in blood, and how can it be lowered?
3) What information exists on high blood pressure and is medication the only real option to lowering blood pressure?
4) What is the current research on angioplasty?
5) What help is there for children who have asthma?

High Blood Pressure Information

National High Blood Pressure Education Program
P.O. Box 30105
Bethesda, MD 20824-0105
301-592-8573
Fax: 301-592-8563
www.nhlbi.nih.gov/
The National High Blood Pressure Education Program Information Center is a source of information on educational materials for consumers, providers, and planners of high blood pressure control services. The goal of the Center is to reduce death and disability related to high blood pressure through programs of professional, patient, and public education. Print and audiovisual materials, as well as research reports are available. A free newsletter, *InfoMemo*, covers topics of interest concerning blood pressure. They can answer such questions as:

1) Is there a way to lower your high blood pressure through diet and exercise?
2) What is the effect of alcohol on blood pressure?
3) What research exists on alternative therapies such as biofeedback in reducing blood pressure?
4) How can a blood pressure education program be instituted in the workplace?
5) What resources exist for health educators who work with patients with high blood pressure?

Homelessness

National Resource Center on Homelessness and Mental Illness
Policy Research Associates, Inc.
262 Delaware Ave.

Delmar, NY 12054
800-444-7415
Fax: 518-439-7612
www.prainc.com/nrc
Email: nrc@pranic.com

Under contract with the National Institute of Mental Illness, Policy Research Associates develops and disseminates new knowledge about the coordination of housing and services for homeless mentally ill persons. The Center publishes a newsletter, and has free information packets and can conduct database searches. They can refer you to organizations concerned with homelessness and mental illness, as well as Federal programs in the field. They can answer such questions as:

1) What are some of the health issues particularly related to homeless people?
2) What are grant programs currently available to homeless organizations to improve services?
3) What self-help programs exist for homeless people?
4) What are some of the issues organizations need to consider when dealing with homeless children?
5) What housing demonstration programs have succeeded with the homeless population?

Public Housing Drug Strategy Clearinghouse

Drug Information and Strategy Clearinghouse
U.S. Department of Housing and Urban Development (HUD)
P.O. Box 8577
Silver Spring, MD 20907
800-955-2232
Fax: 301-251-5767

Sponsored by the Department of Housing and Urban Development, the Drug Information and Strategy Clearinghouse provides housing officials, residents, and community leaders with information and assistance on drug abuse prevention and drug trafficking control techniques. They have created a database containing information on improving resident screening procedures, strengthening eviction policies, increasing cooperation with local law enforcement, implementing drug tip hotlines, forming resident patrols, starting child care centers, and organizing drug education/prevention activities. The Clearinghouse also provides information packages, resource lists, HUD regulations, referrals, and a newsletter. There is no charge for most of this information. They can answer such questions as:

1) How can housing authorities apply for government grants?
2) What are some anti-drug strategies that have been successfully carried out in public housing units?
3) What are the latest drug abuse prevention theories and have there been demonstration projects conducted that are based on these models?
4) What resident patrols and related programs have been particularly successful in building drug-free neighborhoods?
5) How can there be an increase in cooperation with local law enforcement and other agencies in preventing drug abuse?

Indian Health Clearinghouse

Indian Health Service
5600 Fishers Lane, Room 635
Rockville, MD 20857
301-443-3593
Fax: 301-443-0507
www.ihs.gov

The Indian Health Services provides comprehensive health services through IHS facilities, tribally contracted hospitals, health centers, school health centers, and health stations. Reports, directories, brochures, and pamphlets are available. They can answer such questions as:

1) How can doctors get their student loans repaid by working for the Indian Health Service?
2) Where are there health professional shortages within the Indian Health Service?
3) Where are health service facilities currently located?
4) What are some of the health care needs specific to Native Americans?
5) What research is being conducted on substance abuse programs for Native Americans?

National Kidney and Urologic Diseases Information Clearinghouse

3 Information Way
Bethesda, MD 20892
301-654-4415
Fax: 301-907-8906
www.niddk.nih.gov/
Email: nkudic@aerie.com

The National Kidney and Urologic Disease Information Clearinghouse (NKUDIC) is an information resource and referral organization seeking to increase the knowledge and understanding of kidney and urologic diseases. They can provide education and information on kidney and urologic diseases to patients, professionals, and the public, as well as make referrals to other appropriate organizations. The Clearinghouse provides products and services such as publications, a computerized database of educational materials, and annotated bibliographies and topical literature searches on selected topics. A publications sheet is available, with most items being free. They can answer such questions as:

1) What are the symptoms, diagnosis, and treatment of kidney stones?
2) What are the different types of urinary incontinence that some elderly people experience?
3) What information exists about the success rate of kidney transplant operations?
4) What professionals deal with kidney and urologic diseases in my area and what services do they provide?
5) What help is there for men who suffer from impotence?

National Maternal and Child Health Clearinghouse

8201 Greensboro Dr., Suite 600
McLean, VA 22102
703-821-8955
800-434-4MCH
www.nmchc.org

The National Maternal and Child Health Clearinghouse provides education and information services in maternal and child health. The Clearinghouse provides current information through the collection and dissemination of publications on maternal and child health topics, and provides technical assistance in educational resource development, program planning, and topical research. They can also refer individuals to other organizations for further information. A publications catalogue is available, with most items free. They can answer such questions as:

1) What are the dangers of lead poisoning, and how can I protect my children?
2) What are the special nutrition needs of pregnant adolescents?
3) What are some of the concerns and issues pregnant women need to know about to ensure a healthy pregnancy?
4) How can parents be sure they are feeding their children nutritious foods?
5) Where can one go for more information on breastfeeding?

Medical Devices Clearinghouse

Center for Devices and Radiological Health
Food and Drug Administration
Consumer Staff
1350 Piccard Dr.
Rockville, MD 20850

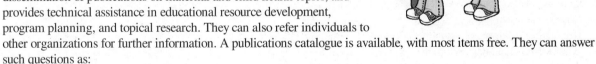

888-463-6332
301-827-3990
Fax: 301-443-9535
www.fda.gov/cdrh/index.html
Email: dsma@cdrh.fda.gov

The Center for Devices and Radiological Health is responsible for analyzing factors affecting the safe and effective use of medical devices and radiation-emitting products by lay users and on patients. They answer consumer inquiries by telephone or mail on general issues relating to medical devices or radiation-emitting products. Inquiries can be answered on such products as thermometers, hearing aids, contact lenses, condoms, magnetic resonance imaging devices, hemodialysis equipment, tampons, medical x-rays, pacemakers, and artificial hearts. Publications cover topics such as pregnancy test kits, IUDs, eyeglass lenses, ultraviolet radiation, including general information on medical devices and radiological health products. They can answer such questions as:

1) How effective are condoms and what standards are they required to meet?
2) Are breast implants still considered unsafe?
3) Is it safe to make your own sterile fluids to wash your contacts?
4) What should people be aware of before they undergo an x-ray?
5) Are ultrasounds safe?

National Library of Medicine

8600 Rockville Pike
Bethesda, MD 20894
888-346-3656
301-496-6095
800-338-7657 (regional library)
Fax: 301-496-2809
www.nlm.nih.gov/

The National Library of Medicine (NLM) is the world's largest research library in a single scientific and professional field. The collection today stands at four million books, journals, technical reports, manuscripts, microfilms, and pictorial materials. The Library's computer-based Medical Literature Analysis and Retrieval System (MEDLARS) has bibliographic access to NLM's vast store of biomedical information. All of the MEDLARS databases are available through NLM's online network of more than 20,000 institutions and individuals. NLM charges a user fee for access to the system. They can answer such questions as:

1) What videos are available on a specific health topic?
2) How can a researcher access NLM's database from home?
3) How can a search be conducted for a specific health topic?
4) What reference guides exist to help researchers locate materials?
5) Where can information on ethics in health care be found?

Mental Health Clearinghouse

National Institute of Mental Health
6001 Executive Blvd.
Room 8184, MSC 9663
Bethesda, MD 20892
301-443-4513
Fax: 301-443-4279
Fax on Demand: 301-443-5158
www.nimh.nih.gov/
Email: nimhinfo@nih.gov

The National Institute of Mental Health conducts and supports research to learn more about the causes, prevention, and treatment of mental and emotional illnesses. The Institute collects and distributes scientific and technical information related to mental illness, as well as educational materials for the general public. A publications list is available, with items ranging from free to $25. They can answer such questions as:

1) What are the latest statistics and information on bipolar disorder?
2) What are the various treatment options for someone suffering from depression?
3) What current research is available on the causes and treatment of schizophrenia?
4) What information should you be aware of when looking for a mental health professional?
5) What help exists for people who experience panic attacks?

Minority Health Clearinghouse

Office of Minority Health Resource Center
P.O. Box 37337
Washington, DC 20013
800-444-6472
Fax: 301-589-0884
TT: 301-589-0951
www.omhrc.gov

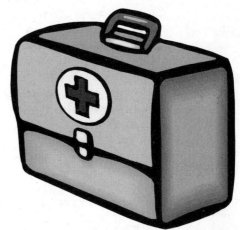

The Office of Minority Health Resource Center's mission is to improve the health status of Asians, Pacific Islanders, Blacks, Hispanics, and Native Americans. Major activities include: the dissemination of accurate and timely information regarding health care issues and status through conferences and workshops; the awarding of grants for innovative community health strategies developed by minority coalitions; and research on risk factors affecting minority health. The Resource Center has information on minority health-related data and information resources available at the federal, state, and local levels and provides assistance and information to people interested in minority health and minority health programs. They have a database of minority health-related publications, as well as organizations and programs that concentrate on minority health. They can answer such questions as:

1) How can minority health goals be achieved?
2) What research is being conducted regarding African Americans and their particular risk for high blood pressure?
3) What are health issues particular to Alaskan Natives?
4) What programs are effective in encouraging pregnant Mexican Americans to seek prenatal care?
5) Are there programs specific to Native Americans with substance abuse problems?

National Institute of Neurological Disorders and Stroke

Office of Communications and Public Liaison
P.O. Box 5801
Bethesda, MD 20824
800-352-9424
Fax: 301-402-2186
www.ninds.nih.gov

The National Institute of Neurological Disorders and Stroke conducts and supports research on the causes, prevention, diagnosis, and treatment of neurological disorders and stroke. They have free publications on a wide variety of consumer materials and can refer people to other organizations for further information. They can answer such questions as:

1) What is Bell's Palsy and what are the ways in which it is treated?
2) What are the different forms of multiple sclerosis?
3) What current research is being conducted on strokes?
4) What can be done to minimize or reverse the effects of Parkinson's?
5) Is there relief available for chronic pain sufferers?

Center for Nutrition Policy and Promotion

Center for Nutrition Policy and Promotion
U.S. Department of Agriculture
1120 20th St., NW, Suite 200 North
Washington, DC 20036
202-418-2312
Fax: 202-208-2321
www.usda.gov/cnpp

The Center for Nutrition Policy and Promotion conducts applied research in food consumption, nutrition knowledge and attitudes, dietary survey methodology, food composition, and dietary guidance and nutrition education techniques. The Center uses the research data to monitor the food and nutrient content of diets of the American population, assess dietary status and trends in food consumption, further understand the factors that influence consumer food choices, maintain the National Nutrient Data Bank of the nutrient content of foods, provide dietary guidance in food selection and preparation and in food money management. The Center reports results of research in both technical and popular publications, and a publications list is available. They can answer such questions as:

1) What are the dietary guidelines for Americans?
2) What is the composition of specific foods?
3) What data exists on what people eat?
4) What factors influence consumer food choices?
5) How aware are people of the relationship between diet and health?

National Institute for Occupational Safety and Health

Division of Standard Development and Technology Transfer
Technology Information Branch
4676 Columbia Parkway
Mail Stop C-13
Cincinnati, OH 45226-1998
800-35-NIOSH
Fax: 513-533-8573
www.cdc.gov/niosh
Email: pubstaff@cdc.gov

The National Institute for Occupational Safety and Health provides technical information on programs and issues dealing with occupational safety and heath. The Clearinghouse maintains a database through which they can search for journal articles and other materials on a specific topic. They have publications, reports, and bibliographies, many of which are free. They can answer such questions as:

1) Are video display terminals dangerous to the average individual?
2) What is Carpal Tunnel Syndrome and what can be done to treat it?
3) What are some of the dangers of working in a dry cleaning store?
4) How many deaths occurred on a particular job site?
5) What do I do if I suspect a health problem in my workplace?

National Clearinghouse For Primary Care Information

8201 Greensboro Dr., Suite 600
McLean, VA 22102
703-821-8955

The National Clearinghouse For Primary Care provides information services to support the planning, development, and delivery of ambulatory health care to urban and rural areas that have shortages of medical personnel and services. They distribute publications focusing on ambulatory care, financial management, primary health care, and health services administration. The Clearinghouse provides information on federal guidances and policies affecting primary care delivery.

A list is available of free publications on community health centers, migrant health centers, childhood injury prevention efforts, clinical care, and many other health concerns. They can answer such questions as:

1) What information should be considered when establishing a rural medical practice?
2) What are some of the ways older adults can improve their nutrition and is there information that can be distributed to these clients?
3) What are particular health problems of the migrant population and how can these be addressed?
4) What are some of the characteristics of successful dental programs in community and migrant health centers?
5) What is the status of medical personnel shortages in inner city hospitals and what is being done to alleviate this crisis?

National Rehabilitation Information Center

8455 Colesville Rd., Suite 935
Silver Spring, MD 20910
800-34-NARIC
800-346-2742
Fax: 301-587-1967
www.naric.com/naric
Email: naric@capaccess.org

The National Rehabilitation Information Center (NARIC) is a library and information center on disability and rehabilitation. The Center is funded by the National Institute for Disability and Rehabilitation Research to collect and disseminate the results of federally-funded research projects. In addition, the Center includes commercially-published books and journal articles in its collection. They also maintain a database of disability and rehabilitation materials which they will search for a small fee. NARIC provides quick reference and referral services, database searches, and photocopies of documents in the collection. They publish a newsletter and other directories and provide information specialists to field the many questions on various topics of concern to people. A list of publications is available, with items ranging in price from free to $25. They can answer such questions as:

1) What resources, support, and information are available for people suffering from traumatic brain injury?
2) Where can you buy a computer keyboard which responds correctly to your patterns of movement if you have cerebral palsy?
3) How effective have supported employment programs been in improving employment opportunities for people with severe disabilities?
4) What are the different education methods available to educate a deaf child, and what are some of the factors to consider when making this choice?
5) What information exists on helping someone who has suffered a spinal cord injury?

Office on Smoking and Health

Centers for Disease Control
4770 Buford Highway, NE
Mail Stop K-50
Atlanta, GA 30341
770-488-5705
800-CDC-1311
Fax: 301-986-5001
www.cdc.gov/tobacco

The Smoking Hotline can answer all your questions regarding cigarettes and stop smoking methods. They can provide fact sheets, pamphlets, posters and other publications, as well as information in response to inquiries. The Center can access information on the Combined Health Information Database, and their library and reading room are open to the

public. The Infomemo newsletter contains information on disease prevention, education, and control. They can answer such questions as:
1)   What are the pros and cons of various stop smoking methods?
2)   What is the current status report on smoking?
3)   How does smoking affect a person's health?
4)   What are the ways in which a person over 50 might stop smoking?
5)   What are the rules or regulations regarding smoking in an office or other public place?

National Clearinghouse for Professions In Special Education

The Council for Exceptional Children
1920 Association Dr.
Reston, VA 22091
800-641-7824
703-264-9476
Fax: 703-264-1637
www.cec.sped.org/cl/ncpseabo.htm
The National Clearinghouse for Professions in Special Education provides information that will help people in making a career choice. They have information about the demand for special educators in the U.S., about college and university programs that prepare people for these careers, about financial assistance available, and more. They can answer such questions as:

1)   What fellowships are available to work with the deaf?
2)   How is music therapy used to work with individuals with disabilities?
3)   What different sorts of careers are possible in special education?
4)   What type of training is required to work with autistic children?
5)   How has mainstreaming affected the special education job market?

Sudden Infant Death Hotline

National Sudden Infant Death Syndrome Resource Center
2070 Chainbridge Rd., Suite 450
Vienna, VA 22182
703-821-8955
Fax: 703-821-2098
www.circsol.com/SIDS/
Email: sids@cirsol.com
The Sudden Infant Death Clearinghouse was established to provide information and educational materials on Sudden Infant Death Syndrome (SIDS), apnea, and other related issues. The staff responds to information requests from professionals, families with SIDS-related deaths, and the general public by sending written materials and making referrals. The Clearinghouse maintains a library of reference materials and mailing lists of state programs, groups, and individuals concerned with SIDS. Their publications include bibliographies on SIDS and self-help support groups, a publications catalogue, and a newsletter. They can answer such questions as:
1)   What is crib death?
2)   What are the current views on home monitoring to prevent SIDS?
3)   How can parents help the grieving process in children after the death of a sibling?
4)   How many children died of SIDS in a given state last year?
5)   How can SIDS be distinguished from child abuse and neglect?

Family Violence and Sexual Assault Institute

1310 Clinic Dr.
Tyler, TX 75701
903-595-6600

Fax: 903-595-6799
The goal of the Family Violence and Sexual Assault Institute is to provide information services to practitioners and researchers who are working to prevent family violence and provide assistance for victims. A publications list and price sheet are available. They can answer such questions as:

1) What journal articles and bibliographies are there on elder abuse, as well as what statistics, copies of legislation, and organizations concerned with elder abuse issues exist?
2) What are some of the signs of sexual abuse?
3) What are some centers and organizations concerned with child maltreatment?
4) What bibliographies are there on the characteristics of abusive and neglecting parents?
5) What agency should a person contact first if abuse is suspected?

National and World Affairs

Agriculture Exports Clearinghouse

Foreign Agricultural Service
U.S. Department of Agriculture, Room 5074
Washington, DC 20250
202-720-7115
Fax: 202-720-1727
www.fas.usda.gov
Email: fasinfo@fas.usda.gov
The Foreign Agricultural Service disseminates agricultural trade and commodity production information to agribusinesses and the general public. They offer private companies and cooperatives assistance in marketing their products overseas by collecting and publicizing information on foreign buyers and advertising U.S. export availability. They have a monthly magazine, commodity and trade reports, publications, and fact sheets (many of which are free). They can answer such questions as:
1) What are the market prospects for U.S. food and farm products in Japan?
2) What are some overseas markets and buying trends for a particular product?
3) What are some overseas promotional activities?
4) How do I begin an export business?
5) How do I advertise my product directly to buyers overseas?

Arms Control and Disarmament Agency

Office of Public Information
2201 C St., NW
Washington, DC 20451
800-581-ACDA
202-647-6575
Electronic Bulletin Board: 202-736-4436
www.state.gov/www/global/arms/bureauac.html

The Arms Control and Disarmament Agency (ACDA) coordinates the ongoing negotiations between the United States and other nuclear powers to reduce their arsenals. This federal agency also takes the lead in other efforts to reduce the risk of war by, for example, verifying other countries' compliance with the Nuclear Non-Proliferation Treaty and other international agreements. Weapons sales to foreign governments, technology transfer, and treaties are also important elements of arms control. The Agency can answer such questions as:
1) What details exist on certain weapons systems and what analyses have been done on the impact that such systems have on arms control agreements, treaties, and negotiations?
2) What are some of the economic issues related to defense strategies?
3) What is the INF Treaty?
4) What is the current status of arms control and disarmament goals?
5) What is the current arms control policy of the U.S.?

Central Intelligence Agency

Public Affairs
Washington, DC 20505
703-482-0623
Fax: 703-482-1739
www.cia.gov
The Central Intelligence Agency (CIA) is strictly a foreign intelligence organization and has no domestic or law enforcement duties. The CIA occasionally issues unclassified publications which provide additional research aids to the

academic and business communities. The majority of these reports contain foreign or international economic and political information or are directories of foreign officials. They are available for sale. They can answer such questions as:
1) What is the history of the CIA?
2) What are the steps involved in the intelligence cycle?
3) What agencies or departments are involved with the intelligence community?
4) What involvement does the White House have in intelligence activities?
5) Who oversees the CIA?

Export Country Experts

U.S. Foreign and Commercial Services
Export Promotion Services
U.S. Department of Commerce, Room 2810
Washington, DC 20230
202-482-6220
800-872-8723
Fax: 202-482-4473
www.ita.doc.gov

The Country Desk Officers at the U.S. Department of Commerce can provide businesses with information on a market, company, and any other aspect of commercial life in a particular country. These specialists can look at the needs of an individual U.S. firm wishing to sell in a particular country in the full context of that country's overall economy, trade policies, and political situation, bearing in mind current U.S. policies toward that country. Desk officers keep up-to-date on the economic and commercial conditions in their assigned countries. Each officer collects information on the country's regulations, tariffs, business practices, economic and political developments, trade data and trends, market size, and growth. They have free reports and other information at their fingertips or they can refer callers to other country specialists. They can answer such questions as:
1) How can I expand my business through a foreign franchise?
2) How can I reduce my company's distribution and transportation costs overseas?
3) What type of export opportunities exist for computer manufacturing companies who want to expand to Germany?
4) What are some recent foreign labor trends in Japan?
5) Which markets are growing the fastest overseas?

Country Officers

U.S. Department of State
2201 C St., NW
Washington, DC 20520
202-647-4000
www.state.gov

Hundreds of country experts at the U.S. Department of State are responsible for following all activities in their assigned countries, from a political, economic, and social perspective. These officers are in constant contact with embassies, deliver and receive documents from those embassies, and write reports on the current activities in the country. They have several publications they can send, plus up-to-date information on each country's population, culture, geography, political condition, and more. Call to ask for the number of a specific country officer. They can answer such questions as:
1) What is the current political situation of a particular country?
2) What is the current population, as well as the health situation of a country?
3) Are there any travel advisories for a particular country?
4) Is there a brief overview of a specific country available?
5) What is the status of human rights in a particular country?

U.S. Customs Service

Public Information Office
U.S. Department of the Treasury
P.O. Box 7407
Washington, DC 20044
202-927-6724
www.customs.ustreas.gov

The U.S. Customs Service collects the revenue from imports and enforces customs and related laws. It assists in the administration and enforcement of over 400 provisions of law on behalf of more than 40 government agencies. They have many free publications and information on customs rules and travel tips. They can answer such questions as:

1) What are the rules regarding the bringing of pets into the U.S.?
2) Is there a limit to the amount of a particular item one can bring into the country?
3) What are duty-free exemptions, and restricted or prohibited articles?
4) What is required when a traveler declares articles?
5) What is the current duty rate for a particular item?

Defense Technical Information Center

8725 John J. Kingman Rd., Suite 0944
Ft. Belvoir, VA 22060-6218
800-225-3842
703-767-8274
www.dtic.mil
Email: help@dtic.mil

The Defense Technical Information Center (DTIC) is the clearinghouse within the Department of Defense (DOD) for acquiring, storing, retrieving, and disseminating scientific and technical information to support the management and conduct of DOD research, development, engineering, and studies programs. DTIC services are available to DOD and its contractors and to other U.S. Government organizations and their contractors. Organizations may also become eligible for service under certain programs. DTIC also responds indirectly to the general public's information requests. Most products and services are free, but, there are some fees for technical reports and online access. *A DTIC Handbook for Users* is available. They can answer such questions as:

1) What technical reports exist concerning aeronautics?
2) Is there a listing of defense contractors and/or potential contractors?
3) How does a company obtain defense contract work?
4) What type of security clearance procedures are used for defense contractors?

Defense Clearinghouse

Directorate for Public Communication
U.S. Department of Defense
1400 Defense Pentagon, Room 1E757
Washington, DC 20301-1400
703-697-5737
www.defenselink.mil

The Department of Defense is responsible for providing the military forces needed to deter war and protect the security of our country. The Directorate for Public Communication is a good starting point for Defense Department information. They have publications available, some of which are free, and they can direct you to other sources within the Department. They can answer such questions as:

1) What is the current Department of Defense budget, and how has it changed since the previous year?
2) What is the status of our troops overseas?
3) What is the federal government's security strategies?

4) What Department of Defense bases have closed within the last year?
5) How can I sell my company's products or services to the Army?

Federal Emergency Management Agency

500 C St., SW
Washington, DC 20472
800-480-2520
202-646-4600
Fax: 202-646-4086
www.fema.gov

The Federal Emergency Management Agency (FEMA) is the part of our government which deals with planning for and/or coordinating relief in various national emergencies. FEMA plans for nuclear attacks, security emergencies, disaster recovery aid, and helps to coordinate food, shelter, and financial aid in the event of any natural or man made disasters. FEMA has a publications catalogue which lists free publications on subjects such as civil defense, earthquakes, floods, hurricanes, tornadoes, and more. They can answer such questions as:
1) How can people best prepare for an earthquake?
2) What information exists on emergency medical services needed during a time of crisis?
3) How can homeowners repair their home after a flood?
4) Are there plans available on how to build an effective fallout shelter?
5) What are some safety tips for winter storms?

American Foreign Policy Information Clearinghouse

Bureau of Public Affairs
U.S. Department of State
2201 C St., NW, Room 6808
Washington, DC 20520-6810
202-647-6575
Fax: 202-647-7120
www.state.gov
Email: publicaffairs@panet.us-state.gov

The Department of State receives thousands of reports daily, and produces hundreds of publications, speeches, and conferences on foreign policy issues. The Bureau of Public Affairs informs the American people on foreign policy and advises the Secretary of State on public opinion. If unable to answer an inquiry directly, the staff will direct you to the appropriate source. This bureau issues various publications covering U.S. foreign relations, some of which are free. They can answer such questions as:
1) Where can someone get a copy of the PLO-Israel Peace Treaty and what information does it contain?
2) Are there resource materials available that would allow a business to learn more about the relationship between the U.S. and a foreign country before they invest in that country?
3) What information exists on global terrorism?
4) Where could one find out more information on human rights practices in a particular country?
5) How can one access the U.S.'s or a foreign country's diplomatic records?

Immigration and Naturalization Service

Central Office
425 Eye St., NW
Washington, DC 20536
202-514-4316
www.usdoj.gov/ins

The Immigration and Naturalization Service (INS) facilitates the entry of persons legally admissible as visitors or as immigrants to the United States, provides assistance to those seeking permanent resident status, and apprehends those

who attempt illegal entry into this country. They have established a telephone service system that provides pre-recorded information on immigration and citizenship-related topics. They can answer such questions as:
1) Where is the local INS office located for a particular community?
2) What are the rules regarding the marriage of a foreign citizen to a U.S. citizen?
3) What are the citizenship requirements for children born outside the U.S.?
4) What constitutes political asylum?
5) What are some visa requirements for travel overseas?

Agency for International Development (AID)

Document Information Services Clearinghouse
1500 Wilson Blvd., Suite 1010
Arlington, VA 22209
703-351-4006
Fax: 703-351-4039
www.usaid.gov

AID's Center for Development Information and Evaluation (CDIE) produces an evaluation publications series which includes a broad range of subjects of interest to those working in international development. The series comprises project impact evaluations, program evaluations, special studies, program design and evaluation methodology reports, and discussion papers. The CDIE Evaluation Publications List is arranged by general subject category and by type of report within each category. Each document is available for $3. They can answer such questions as:
1) What research has been conducted on family planning issues?
2) How do private volunteer organizations assist in the development of a country?
3) How has the emergency food program operated in a particular country?
4) How have health programs been successfully initiated in developing countries and how can they be sustained?
5) What types of agriculture programs have been attempted and what are the results of those programs?

National Clearinghouse for U.S.-Japan Studies

Indiana University
2805 East Tenth St., Suite 120
Bloomington, IN 47408
800-266-3815
812-855-3838
Fax: 812-855-0455
www.indiana.edu/~japan
Email: japan@indiana.edu

The National Clearinghouse for U.S.- Japan Studies is a database system providing timely and comprehensive information about educational resources available to teach about Japan. The Clearinghouse collects, analyzes, abstracts, and creates a database of materials and resources that can assist school systems and individual teachers in developing and implementing curricula and lessons on broad areas of Japanese culture and society, and on U.S.-Japan relationships. The Clearinghouse also includes items such as videos, films, some simulations, artifact kits, and the like, and teacher-developed materials. They can answer such questions as:
1) What information exists on the Japanese educational system?
2) Where can I obtain copies of Japanese War relocation records?
3) What information is available on the Japanese stock market?
4) What are current U.S. trade policies toward Japan?
5) How can I locate programs that offer study abroad opportunities in Japan?

Other

Boating Safety Hotline

Office of Boating Safety
U.S. Coast Guard
U.S. Department of Transportation
2100 2nd St., SW
Washington, DC 20593
800-368-5647
202-267-1077
Fax: 202-267-4285
www.uscgboating.org
Email: BoatWeb@mail.rmit.com

The Boating Safety Hotline can provide you with information on such topics of interest to boaters as safety recalls, publications, Coast Guard department contacts and addresses, public education courses, and free Coast Guard Services. They have a wealth of free information and publications to share. They can answer such questions as:
1) What statistics exist on boating accidents?
2) How can parents teach children about water safety?
3) What things do people need to consider regarding floatation devices?
4) What licenses or regulations should boaters be aware of?
5) Where can people receive information on water charts and other navigational aids?

Children's Literature Center

Library of Congress
Washington, DC 20540
202-707-5535
Fax: 202-707-4632
www.loc.gov/rr/child

The Children's Center prepares lists and scholarly bibliographies and provides other reference services for individuals and organizations who study, produce, collect, interpret, and disseminate children's books, films, television programs, or other forms of materials destined for children's information and recreational use, usually outside of the classroom. The Library holds approximately 200,000 children's books and related items, such as boxed and board games, sound recordings, maps, and illustrations. The Center also provides many publisher's catalogues that list titles to be published in the upcoming year, a wide range of periodicals about children's literature, and lists from rare and used book sellers. They can answer such questions as:
1) How can literature be used in the classroom to teach history to 7th graders?
2) What information sources exist for Japanese children's books published after World War II?
3) How can children learn about people with disabilities through literature?
4) Are there books specific to helping children deal with the issues of death and dying?
5) Where could a writer locate materials to help with a book on teaching children to be aware of strangers?

Congressional Research Service

Library of Congress
Washington, DC 20540
202-707-5700
Fax: 202-707-6745
www.loc.gov/rr

The Congressional Research Service (CRS) at the Library of Congress prepares hundreds of non-partisan background reports each year on current issues large and small, domestic and foreign, social and political. CRS also publishes hundreds of major Issue Briefs each year designed to keep members of Congress informed on timely issues. Written in simple and direct language, these briefs provide background information and are updated daily. These studies generated by CRS cover almost any topic imaginable and are a fantastic resource for students, researchers, and anyone else who needs statistics or an analysis of a subject. You must request free copies of these reports through your U.S. Representative or Senator (202-224-3121 Congress Switchboard). The CRS Reports can answer such questions as:

1) What is the history of abortion rights in the U.S. and what legislation is currently before Congress regarding abortion?
2) What information exists on the protection of endangered sea turtles?
3) What is the current status of nuclear missile proliferation in the world?
4) What reports have been done on obscenity on television and radio?
5) What programs are there for working in a foreign country?

Federal Assistance Programs Retrieval System

Federal Domestic Assistance Catalog Staff
General Services Administration
300 7th St., SW, Suite 101
Washington, DC 20407
202-708-5126
800-669-8331
www.cfda.gov

The Federal Assistance Programs Retrieval System (FAPRS) is your online link to the Catalog of Federal Domestic Assistance. It contains federal domestic assistance programs, including federal grants, loans, loan guarantees, and technical assistance. Their database contains more than 1,000 assistance programs administered by 51 federal agencies, with summaries of agency functions, descriptions of assistance programs, eligibility criteria, and contact information. Users include state and local governments, small businesses, researchers, and libraries. Fees are on a cost-recovery basis, with no initiation or monthly fees. Contact FAPRS for telephone and data processing charges. They can answer such questions as:

1) What assistance programs would help a rural hospital obtain needed medical equipment?
2) How can a student obtain a doctorate in housing policy at no cost?
3) How can schools obtain science equipment from the government?
4) How can a choreographer receive funds to create a dance?
5) Where can a business turn for assistance in the field of energy?

American Folklife Center

Library of Congress
Washington, DC 20540
202-707-5510
Fax: 202-707-2076
www.loc.gov/folklife

The American Folklife Center at the Library of Congress has been a national advocate for the preservation and presentation of American folklife. The Center serves a varied constituency (state and local organizations, scholars, researchers, students, and the general public), maintains relations and coordinates programs with other federal agencies, and offers a wide range of programs and services. The Folklife Center has conducted or assisted with surveys or major field projects in many states. It conducts research projects based on the documentary collections of the Library of Congress. It sponsors a variety of conferences, workshops, concerts, and other events at the Library and elsewhere. The Archive houses more that 35,000 hours of audio recordings, controls more than 100,000 pages of manuscript materials, and maintains over 4,000 books, directories, and periodicals dealing with folk music and folklore. They can answer such questions as:

1) What information or recordings exist regarding early jazz?
2) Where can someone locate information on Native American architecture?
3) Where are recordings on Australian folk songs?

4) What data is there on the native crafts of Hawaii?
5) Are there videos available to educate students about various cultures?

Forest Service

U.S. Department of Agriculture
Public Affairs Office
Mailing:
   P.O. Box 96090
   Washington, DC 20090
201 14th and Independence Ave., SW
Washington, DC 20250
202-205-1760
Fax: 202-205-0885
www.fs.fed.us
Email: mailroom@fs.fed.gov
The nation's National Forests offer more than 114,300 miles of trails, a Scenic Byway System consisting of nearly 5,000 miles of highways in 32 states, 70 wild and scenic rivers covering nearly 3,500 miles and much more. *A Guide to Your National Forest* lists regional offices, several private and one Forest Service Interpretative Association, and a list of State Boards of Tourism where camping information may be obtained. They can answer such questions as:
1) What state forests in Maryland offer good sailing opportunities?
2) How far in advance must I reserve a campsite?
3) What is the best time of year to plan a camping trip in Tennessee?
4) Which rivers in North Carolina are recommended for canoeing or rafting?
5) How do I receive a listing of national scenic and historic trails?

Genealogy Research

Reference Services Branch
700 Pennsylvania Ave., NW
Washington, DC 20408
202-501-5400
Fax: 202-501-7154
www.nara.gov/research
Email: inquire@nara.gov
The National Archives maintains the historically valuable records of the U.S. Government dating from the Revolutionary War era to the recent past. They preserve records and prepare finding aids to facilitate their use and makes records available for use in research rooms. They can provide assistance and training aids to help you with your research. They can answer such questions as:
1) Where can information be located regarding ship passenger arrival records?
2) What ship plans are available on World War II navy vessels?
3) How can military service and pension records be accessed?
4) How can people most easily trace their family history?
5) Where are prisoner-of-war records of the Civil War maintained?

Geographic Names Information

Branch of Geographic Names
U.S. Geological Survey (USGS)
523 National Center
Reston, VA 20192
888-ASK-USGS
703-648-4544
Fax: 703-648-5644

http://mapping.usgs.gov

The USGS Branch of Geographic Names maintains a national research, coordinating, and information center to which all problems and inquiries concerning domestic geographic names can be directed. This office compiles name information, manages a names data repository, maintains information files, and publishes materials on domestic geographic names. The Branch works on standardizing names within the Federal government by keeping track of all the names put on maps that the various government agencies publish. They also assist the Board of Geographic Names in resolving name problems, such as if a name is derogatory or the usage is conflicting. The USGS, in cooperation with the Board of Geographic Names, maintains the National Geographic Names Data Base and compiles The National Gazetteer of the United States of American on a state-by-state basis. They can answer such questions as:

1) Where are islands located referred to as "No Man's Island"?
2) Where can a researcher find the location of a town that no longer exists?
3) What background information exists on the name of a town?
4) What is a variant name for the town of Rocky Gap, Colorado?
5) What are the geographic coordinates for a particular location?

Geography and Map Division

Library of Congress
Washington, DC 20540
202-707-6277
Fax: 202-707-8531
www.loc.gov/rr/geogmap
Email: maps@loc.gov

The Geography and Map Division of the Library of Congress provides cartographic and geographic information for all parts of the world to the Congress, federal and local governments, the scholarly community, and to the general public. It is the largest and most comprehensive cartographic collection in the world, numbering 4.5 million maps, 60,000 atlases, and 6,000 reference works. The Division also has custody of over 350 globes, 2,000 three-dimensional plastic relief models, and a large number of cartographic materials in other formats. They can answer such questions as:

1) What maps are available for genealogists tracing a family history in Virginia?
2) What maps exist on colonial America?
3) Where can aerial photos be located in order to assess erosion and flood damage in a particular area?
4) Are there maps of old railroad lines available?
5) Where can information be located on Revolutionary War battlefields?

Bureau of Indian Affairs

Office of Public Affairs
U.S. Department of the Interior
1849 C St., NW
Washington, DC 20240
202-208-3711
Fax: 202-501-1516
www.doi.gov/bureau-indian-affairs.html

The Bureau of Indian Affairs principal objectives are to encourage and assist Indian and Alaska Native people to manage their own affairs under the trust relationship with the federal government; to facilitate the full development of their human and natural resource potential; and to mobilize all aids for their advancement. The Bureau can provide you with a wide variety of information on Native Americans, the history of the Bureau and more. They have publications and fact sheets, and can refer you to other resources for more information. They can answer such questions as:

1) What tribes are currently recognized by the U.S.?
2) What are the demographics of American Indians?
3) Which state has the largest percentage of American Indians?
4) What are the labor force estimates by states for Native Americans?
5) How do Indian Tribes govern themselves?

Library of Congress

101 Independence Ave., SE
Washington, DC 20540
202-707-5000
www.loc.gov
Email: lcweb@loc.gov
The Library of Congress is the national library of the United States, offering diverse materials for research including the world's most extensive collections in many areas such as American history, music, and law. They not only have books and periodicals, but also prints, photographs, films, music, and more. This office can direct you to the correct division within the Library. If your question requires extensive research and you cannot come to the Library, they have lists of freelance researchers to assist you for a fee. Many Divisions have their own databases to search citations or bibliographies or literature guides to help readers locate published materials on a particular subject. There may be a charge involved for some services, although many are free. To begin a search, researchers should first contact their local library, and then, proceed to the Library of Congress if they are unable to find adequate information. The Library can answer such questions as:
1) Where can one find information about medicinal plants?
2) What are some good reference sources for children's literature?
3) Where can information be found on medieval law?
4) How can books in Braille be accessed?
5) Where can literature guides on a variety of science topics be found?

Manuscript Division

Library of Congress
Washington, DC 20540
202-287-5387
Fax: 202-707-6336
www.loc.gov/rr/mss
The Manuscript Division holds nearly 50 million items, including some of the greatest manuscript treasures of American history and culture. Among these are Jefferson's rough draft of the Declaration of Independence, James Madison's notes on the Federal Convention, George Washington's first inaugural address, the paper tape of the first telegraphic message, Abraham Lincoln's Gettysburg Address and second inaugural address, Alexander Graham Bell's first drawing of the telephone, and many more. The holdings encompass approximately 11,000 separate collections. The Reading Room is open only to qualified researchers. Only under exceptional circumstances are undergraduates permitted to consult manuscripts. The staff at the Division can answer such questions as:
1) Where can copies of George Washington's speeches be located for a biography of Washington?
2) Are records kept of nongovernmental organizations which have significantly affected American life, such as the NAACP?
3) Where is information held on the first Supreme Court justices?
4) How did the Declaration of Independence change from the rough draft version to the final copy?
5) What resources exist for a researcher studying the generals active in World War II?

Motion Picture Broadcasting and Recorded Sound Division

Library of Congress
Washington, DC 20540
202-707-8572
Fax: 202-707-2371
www.loc.gov/rr/mopic
The Motion Picture Broadcasting and Recorded Sound Division has responsibility for the acquisition, cataloging, preservation, and service of the motion picture and television collections, including items on film, videotape, and videodisc. The Division has similar responsibilities for the Library's collections of sound recordings and radio programs. Viewing facilities are provided for those doing research of a specific nature, and must be scheduled well in advance. The reference staff answers written and telephone inquiries about its holdings. They can answer such questions as:

1) What World War II newsreels were produced in Germany?
2) What collections exist for films produced prior to 1915?
3) Where can a researcher look for information on silent films and their music?
4) Where can Afro-American folk music be found?
5) Are their recordings of authors, poets, and other artists reading their own works, such as Robert Frost?

National Park Service

Office of Public Affairs
U.S. Department of the Interior
P.O. Box 37127
Washington, DC 20013-7127
202-208-6843
Fax: 202-219-0916
www.nps.gov

Along with other responsibilities, the Park Service administers 350 maintained areas in the National Park System, collects the National Register of Historic Places and a registry of natural sites, and manages the Urban Park and Recreation Recovery Program. It provides technical assistance in planning, acquisition and development of recreation resources, conducts surveys of historic buildings and engineering works, has available programs and resources for teachers, and administers a program in interagency archeological services. Information including brochures, maps, and a publications catalogue listing items ranging in price from $1 to $30 can be ordered from the Government Printing Office. The Office of Public Inquiries can refer you to other Park Service offices and can answer such questions as:

1) What archeological digs are currently in progress and where are they located?
2) What statistics are available on Park Service use, such as: total visits, visits by region and state, and overnight stays?
3) Where can I locate videos on historic people or national landmarks?
4) How do I find out whether or not my home is eligible for listing on the National Historic Register?
5) How can I receive a listing of the lesser known National Parks?

Performing Arts Division

Library of Congress
Thomas Jefferson Bldg.
Washington, DC 20540
202-707-5507
www.loc.gov/rr/perform

The Performing Arts Library is a joint project of the Library of Congress and the Kennedy Center, and offers information and reference assistance on dance, theater, opera, music, film, and broadcasting. The Performing Arts Library serves the research and information needs of the public, artists, and staff of the Center. The Library also identifies and locates the creative and resource materials necessary to develop new works and productions in the performing arts. Reference service is available by phone, in person, or by mail. They can answer such questions as:

1) How can an orchestral program of Irish composers be tailored for a young audience?
2) What information exists on different dance companies based in New York?
3) Is there information on what is required to start a record company?
4) Are there recordings of interviews or videotapes of famous actresses discussing their works?
5) Where can recordings of poetry readings be located?

Prints and Photographs Division

Library of Congress
James Madison Memorial Building, Room LM 337
First St. and Independence Ave., SW
Washington, DC 20540
202-707-6394

Fax: 202-707-6647

www.loc.gov/rr/print/

The visual collections of the Library of Congress provide a record of people, places, and events in the United States and throughout the world. The Prints and Photographs Division has custody of more than 10 million images in a variety of forms and media: Architecture, Design, and Engineering collections, Documentary Photographs, Fine Prints, Master Photographs, Popular and Applied Graphic Art, and Posters. Researchers may consult the collections in the Prints and Photographs Reading Room. The Reading Room houses the general and special card catalogues, files of photoprint reference copies, and a limited collection of reference books. Reference specialists are available for assistance. The division will accept limited requests by letter, but the staff cannot make lengthy searches. They can answer such questions as:

1) How can someone obtain a print of the Wright Brothers first flight?
2) What photos taken by Brady exist on the Civil War?
3) Where can someone locate photos of various housing projects undertaken by the Work Projects Administration under President Roosevelt?
4) What material is available to study the architecture of Frank Lloyd Wright?
5) What references are there chronicling the history of political cartooning?

Rare Books and Special Collections

Library of Congress

Thomas Jefferson Building

Washington, DC 20540

202-707-5434

www.loc.gov/rr/rarebook/

The Rare Book and Special Collections Division contains more than 650,000 volumes and broadsides, pamphlets, theater playbills, title pages, prints, manuscripts, posters, and photographs acquired with various collections. The materials the Division houses have come into its custody for a variety of reasons: monetary value, importance in the history of printing, binding, association interest, or fragility. Reference assistance is offered by telephone, in person, and by mail. They can answer such questions as:

1) What information exists on the history of ballooning?
2) What books do you have that contain the Confederate States imprint?
3) What references do you have on the history of print making?
4) Do you have information researchers can study regarding Columbus' discovery of America?
5) Do you have 15th century illuminated manuscripts for art history research?

Rural Information Center

National Agricultural Library

U.S. Department of Agriculture (USDA)

10301 Baltimore Blvd.

Beltsville, MD 20705

301-504-5547

800-633-7701

Fax: 301-504-5181

www.nal.usda.gov/ric

Email: ric@nal.usda.gov

The Rural Information Center is designed to provide information and referral services to local government officials, businesses, community organizations, and rural citizens working to maintain the vitality of America's rural areas. The Center provides customized information products to specific inquiries, refers users to organizations or experts in the field, performs database searches, furnishes bibliographies, identifies current USDA research and Cooperative Extension System programs, and assists users in accessing the National Agricultural Libraries' extensive collection. There is a cost recovery fee for photocopying articles and searches. They can answer such questions as:

1) Which organizations focus on rural health issues?
2) What resources for the historic preservation of farmland are available in rural areas?
3) How can tourism be promoted in small towns?
4) What are some examples of the more innovative economic development projects in rural communities?
5) What rural organizations focus specifically on research and development?

Science and Technology Division

Library of Congress
John Adams Building
Washington, DC 20540
202-707-5639
www.loc.gov/rr/scitech

The Science and Technology Division's collection contains 3.5 million books, nearly 60,000 journals, and 3.7 million technical reports. The collections include such treasures as first editions of Copernicus and Newton and the personal papers of the Wright Brothers and Alexander Graham Bell. The Division has primary responsibility for providing reference and bibliographic services and for recommending acquisitions in the broad areas of science and technology. Reference services are provided to users in person, by telephone, and by mail. Indirect reference service is provided through bibliographic guides (Tracer Bullets) and research reports prepared by Division subject specialists and reference librarians. Copies of reference guides are available at no charge. They can answer such questions as:

1) Where can one begin looking for information on lasers and their applications?
2) What are some good sources of information on volcanoes?
3) What resources exist on extraterrestrial life?
4) Where could someone find sources for information on medicinal plants?
5) How would one go about creating a hologram?

Women's Bureau Clearinghouse

U.S. Department of Labor
200 Constitution Ave., NW
Room S3002
Washington, DC 20210
800-827-5335
202-219-4486
Fax: 202-219-5529
www.dol.gov/dol/wb/
Email: wb_wwc@dol.gov

The Women's Bureau Clearinghouse was designed and established to assist employers in identifying the most appropriate policies for responding to the dependent care needs of employees seeking to balance their dual responsibilities. They can also provide information on women's issues, as well as work force issues that affect women. They can offer information and guidance in areas such as women-owned businesses, women workers, alternative work schedules, dependent care issues, and much more. They also have publications and other information available, much of which is free. They can answer such questions as:

1) What are some elder care program options?
2) What is the earning difference between men and women?
3) How does flex time work in companies similar to mine?
4) What are some alternate work schedules and how do they work?
5) What literature and other resources are available on employer-supported child care?

Statistics

National Agricultural Statistics Service

USDA South Building
Room 5805
U.S. Department of Agriculture (USDA)
Washington, DC 20250
800-727-9540
202-720-3896
Fax: 202-690-1311
www.usda.gov/nass/
Email: nass@nass.usda.gov

The National Agricultural Statistics Service collects data on crops, livestock, poultry, dairy, chemical use, prices, and labor, and publishes the official USDA state and national estimates through its Agricultural Statistics Board. There are nearly 400 reports annually covering domestic agriculture, such as estimates of production, stocks, inventories, prices, disposition, utilization, farm numbers and land, and other factors. They provide national profiles gathered from regular surveys of thousands of farmers, ranchers, and agribusinesses that voluntarily provide data on a confidential basis. Publications are available and range from free to $12. They can answer such questions as:

1) How has the use of a specific chemical for crop growth changed over the past five years?
2) Has the size of farms increased or decreased over the past ten years?
3) What statistics exist on wildlife damage to crops?
4) How has the weekly crop weather affected crop growth?
5) What data is there on livestock slaughter?

Federal Aviation Administration

Office of Public Affairs
800 Independence Ave., SW
Washington, DC 20591
202-366-4000
www.faa.gov
Email: gramick@postmaster2.dot.gov

The Federal Aviation Administration (FAA) is the starting place for any information on airlines, airports, and aircraft. The FAA regulates air commerce, develops civil aeronautics, installs and operates airports, conducts aeronautic research, and provides guidance and policy on accident prevention in general aviation. They keep statistics on air travel, accidents, and more. There are free publications on airline careers, aviation, and airplanes, as well as videos and curriculum guides. They can answer such questions as:

1) Which airlines had the worst on time rate for a given month?
2) What videos are available on aviation?
3) What is some historical information on women in aviation?
4) What are some statistics on air traffic accidents?
5) What methods are used to reduce the noise level of new aircraft?

National Clearinghouse for Census Data Services

Administrative Customer Service Division
Bureau of the Census
Washington, DC 20233
301-457-4100
Fax: 301-457-4714

www.census.gov

The National Clearinghouse for Census Data Services provides a referral service for persons who need assistance in obtaining Census Bureau data or in using Census Bureau products. This assistance ranges from market research using census data to tape copying or microcomputer services. The Clearinghouse includes organizations that provide services for accessing and using economic data and information from the Census Bureau's 2000 Census TIGER geographic database. They can answer such questions as:

1)   How can I update my business's mailing list using 2000 census statistics?
2)   How can the census help me trace my genealogical history?
3)   What is the TIGER geographic database, and how can I use it?
4)   Which products are available on CD-ROM?
5)   Does the Bureau have an online data service?

Census Information on Business

Bureau of the Census
U.S. Department of Commerce
Washington, DC 20233
301-457-4100
Fax: 301-457-4714
www.census.gov

The Bureau of the Census is a statistical agency that collects, tabulates, and publishes a wide variety of statistical data about the people and the economy of our nation. The Bureau makes available statistical results of its censuses, surveys, and other programs to the public through printed reports, computer tape, CD-ROMs, microfiche, and more. It also produces statistical compendia, catalogues, guides, and directories that are useful in locating information on specific subjects. A fee is charged for some of the information and searches. They can answer such questions as:

1)   What is the percentage of people who have a bachelor's degree in a particular state?
2)   What percent of women in the U.S. had a child last year?
3)   What is the total amount of water area in a given state?
4)   What are some statistics available on city government expenditures?
5)   What are the 10 fastest growing occupations?

Crime Statistics

Law Enforcement Support Section
Federal Bureau of Investigation
J. Edgar Hoover Bldg.
935 Pennsylvania Ave.
Washington, DC 20535
202-324-3000
www.fbi.gov

The Law Enforcement Support Section of the Federal Bureau of Investigation collects statistics for many towns with over 10,000 people, and can provide you with information such as the number of murders, robberies, assaults, burglaries, auto thefts, and more, although they do not rank cities. Many libraries carry their annual report, *Crime In The U.S.*, for which there is a cost. They can run a search on their database for specific information, although there is a fee assessed for this service. They can answer questions such as:

1)   When weapons are involved in a crime, which ones are most frequently used?
2)   How has the rate of auto theft in the U.S. changed over the past five years?
3)   Is Washington, DC still the murder capitol of the U.S.?
4)   Have the number of murders committed changed since the death penalty was reinstituted?
5)   What is the difference in the rate of burglaries from small towns to major metropolitan areas?

Economics: National and Regional

Bureau of Economic Analysis
U.S. Department of Commerce
Washington, DC 20230
202-606-9900
Fax: 202-606-5310
www.bea.doc.gov

The Bureau of Economic Analysis (BEA) provides information on national and regional economics. BEA collects basic information on such key issues as economic growth, inflation, regional development, and the nation's role in the world economy. It distributes a number of publications that measure, analyze, and forecast economic trends, which are available on recorded messages, online through the Economic Bulletin Board, and in BEA reports. They can answer such questions as:

1) What is the average per capita income in the United States?
2) Will the rate of inflation increase or decrease over the next five years, and by what percent?
3) What percentage of the Gross National Product (GNP) does the government spend on health care?
4) How does the United States' national unemployment rate compare to that of other industrialized countries?
5) What was the unemployment rate in Pennsylvania from 1989 to 1993?

Educational Research

U.S. Department of Education, OERI
555 New Jersey Ave., NW
Washington, DC 20208-5641
800-424-1616
202-219-1556
Fax: 202-219-1321
www.ed.gov/offices/OERI

The Education Information Branch staff specialists can provide information on topics such as early childhood education, elementary and secondary education, higher education, adult and vocational education, education finance, longitudinal statistical studies, and special education. They have publications and reports, many of which are free. They can answer such questions as:

1) What statistics are there on the number of students who receive loans, grants, and work/study assistance from state sources?
2) What are the statistics on private postsecondary education, such as enrollment, earned degrees conferred, and full and part-time faculty members and their salaries?
3) What information is available on how to choose a school for a child and what factors make a school a good one?
4) How can parents help their children become better readers?
5) What are the enrollment outcomes for recent master's and bachelor's degree recipients?

Fishery Statistics Division

NOAA Fisheries Headquarters
1335 East-West Highway, SSMC3
Silver Spring, MD 20910
301-713-2328
Fax: 301-713-4137
www.nmfs.noaa.gov

The Fisheries Statistics Division publishes statistical bulletins on marine recreational fishing and commercial fishing, and on the manufacture and commerce of fishery products. This Division has several annual and biannual reports available. They can answer such questions as:

1) How many fish were imported in a year, and what kind?

2) What is the most popular fish to export?
3) What kinds of fish are frozen?
4) What statistics exist on processed fish?
5) How many fish were caught by weekend fishermen?

Clearinghouse on Health Indexes

National Center for Health Statistics
U.S. Department of Health and Human Services
Public Health Service
6525 Belcrest Rd.
Hyattsville, MD 20782
301-436-8500
www.cdc.gov/nchs/

The National Center for Health Statistics provides information assistance in the development of health measures to health researchers, administrators, and planners. The Clearinghouse's definition of a health index is a measure that summarizes data from two or more components and purports to reflect the health status of an individual or defined group. Services provided to users include annotated bibliographies and reference and referral service. A publications catalogue is available, with items ranging in price from free to $20. They can answer such questions as:

1) What are the characteristics of persons with and without health care coverage?
2) What type of health care is generally provided to adolescents?
3) What method of contraception is used most frequently in the U.S.?
4) What data exists on the current living arrangements of women of childbearing ages in the U.S.?
5) What survey data exists on the firearm mortality rate among children?

United States International Trade Commission

Office of Industries
500 E St., SW
Washington, DC 20436
202-205-3296
Fax: 202-205-3161
www.usitc.gov/

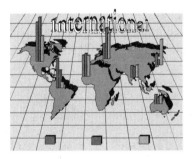

The Office of Industries at the U.S. International Trade Commission has experts assigned to every commodity imported into the U.S. These experts are responsible for investigation of the customs laws of the United States and foreign countries, the volume of imports in comparison with domestic production, the effects relating to competition of foreign industries, and all other factors affecting competition between articles of the U.S. and imported articles. They are knowledgeable about the domestic and foreign industry, and have statistical and factual information. They also have information regarding the tariff schedules. There is no charge for this information. They can answer such questions as:

1) What is the rate of duty for a product from a particular country?
2) What is the rate of import-export, the size of the market, and the major producers of women's sweaters?
3) How much of a product is exported and what is the size of the potential market for that product?
4) What happens if someone suspects an imported article is being subsidized or sold at less then fair value?
5) What can a company do if they feel they are being unfairly affected by import trade?

Justice Statistics Clearinghouse

Bureau of Justice Statistics
U.S. Department of Justice
Box 6000
Rockville, MD 20849
800-732-3277

Fax: 301-251-5212
www.ncjrs.org
Email: askncjrs@ncjrs.org
The Bureau of Justice Statistics (BJS) supports this Clearinghouse for those seeking crime and criminal justice data. In addition to distributing BJS publications, the Clearinghouse responds to statistics requests by offering document database searches, statistics information packages, referrals, and other related products and services. They can answer such questions as:
1)   What is the annual national estimate of crime against persons and households?
2)   What are the characteristics of victims?
3)   In what ways are juveniles handled differently from adults in the criminal justice system?
4)   How prevalent is organized crime?
5)   What is the recidivism rate, and when criminals are rearrested, with what crimes are they normally charged?

Labor Statistics Clearinghouse

Office of Publications
Bureau of Labor Statistics
U.S. Department of Labor
2 Massachusetts Ave., NE, Room 2863
Washington, DC 20212
202-606-7828
Fax: 202-606-7890
http://stats.bls.gov
Email: labstat.helpdesk@bls.gov
The Bureau of Labor Statistics (BLS) is the principal data-gathering agency of the federal government in the field of labor economics. The Bureau collects, processes, analyzes, and disseminates data relating to employment, unemployment, and other characteristics of the labor force; prices and consumer expenditures; wages, other worker compensation, and industrial relations; productivity; economic growth and employment projections; and occupational safety and health. This office can also provide you with a release schedule for BLS major economic indicators and the recorded message number. BLS can refer you to experts within the Bureau who can answer your specific question, provide you with historical information, and refer you to tables and charts for data. The BLS has publications, periodicals, magnetic tapes, diskettes, and more for sale. They can answer questions such as:
1)   What are the employment statistics and the outlook for a particular occupation?
2)   What is the unemployment rate for a state?
3)   What is the current wage for a word processor in Seattle, and what benefits are normally offered with such a position?
4)   What is the employment projection for a specific job?
5)   What is the consumer/producer price index, and how has it changed over time?

APPENDIX

Don't know who to call or where to turn for assistance? Try one of the offices listed below. Each listing should be able to either answer your question or direct you to an office near you.

The *Federal Information Center* can connect you with the appropriate federal government agency that handles your topic of interest. The *State Information Operator* can connect you to the correct state government office that can answer your question.

Federal Information Center
All locations
800-688-9889

State Information Offices

Alabama
334-242-8000
http://www.state.al.us

Alaska
907-465-2111
http://www.state.ak.us

Arizona
602-542-4900
http://www.state.az.us

Arkansas
501-682-3000
http://www.state.ar.us

California
916-322-9900
http://www.state.ca.us

Colorado
303-866-5000
http://www.state.co.us

Connecticut
860-240-0222
http://www.state.ct.us

Delaware
302-739-4000
http://www.state.de.us

District of Columbia
202-727-6161
http://www.ci.washington. dc.us

Florida
850-488-1234
http://www.state.fl.us

Georgia
404-656-2000
http://www.state.ga.us

Hawaii
808-548-6222
http://www.state.hi.us

Idaho
208-334-2411
http://www.state.id.us

Illinois
217-782-2000
http://www.state.il.us

Indiana
317-232-1000
http://www.state.in.us

Iowa
515-281-5011
http://www.state.ia.us

Kansas
913-296-0111
http://www.accesskansas.org

Kentucky
502-564-3130
http://www.kydirect.net

Louisiana
504-342-6600
http://www.state.la.us

Maine
207-582-9500
http://www.state.me.us

Maryland
800-449-4347
http://www.state.md.us

Massachusetts
617-722-2000
http://www.state.ma.us

Michigan
517-373-1837
http://www.state.mi.us

Minnesota
612-296-6013
http://www.state.mn.us

Mississippi
601-359-1000
http://www.state.ms.us

Missouri
573-751-2000
http://www.state.mo.us

Montana
406-444-2511
http://www.discoveringmontana.com

Nebraska
402-471-2311
http://www.state.ne.us

Nevada
702-687-5000
http://silver.state.nv.us

New Hampshire
603-271-1110
http://www.state.nh.us

New Jersey
609-292-2121
http://www.state.nj.us

New Mexico
505-827-4011
http://www.state.nm.us

New York
518-474-2121
http://www.state.ny.us

North Carolina
919-733-1110
http://www.ncgov.com

North Dakota
701-224-2000
http://www.discovernd.com

Ohio
614-466-2000
http://www.state.oh.us

Oklahoma
405-521-2011
http://www.state.ok.us

Oregon
503-378-3111
http://www.state.or.us

Pennsylvania
717-787-2121
http://www.state.pa.us

Rhode Island
401-222-2000
http://www.state.ri.us

South Carolina
803-734-1000
http://www.state.sc.us

South Dakota
605-773-3011
http://www.state.sd.us

Tennessee
615-741-3011
http://www.state.tn.us

Texas
512-463-4630
http://www.state.tx.us

Utah
801-538-3000
http://www.state.ut.us

Vermont
802-828-1110
http://www.state.vt.us

Virginia
804-786-0000
http://www.state.va.us

Washington
360-753-5000
http://access.wa.gov

West Virginia
304-558-3456
http://www.state.wv.us

Wisconsin
608-266-2211
http://www.wisconsin.gov

Wyoming
307-777-7011
http://www.state.wy.us

Index

Arms Control and Disarmament Agency, 1208
Arms control, 1208
Army, U.S., 741
Art contests, 803
Arthritis, 1190, 1191
Artists
  fellowships, 598
  grants, 597, 598, 599, 600
Arts
  grants, 555
  state and local grants, 559
Arts agencies
  regional, 559, 560, 561, 562
Arts organizations
  private, 597
Asbestos, 1171
Asbestos and Small Business Ombudsman Clearinghouse, 1171
Asian elephants
  grants, 176
Assault
  statistics, 1222
Assistance programs
  federal, 1214
Asthma camps, 529
Asthma Clearinghouse, 1191
Asthma, 1190, 1191, 1199
Atlases, 1216
Atmosphere, 1181
Attention Deficit Disorder, 522
Auto Safety Hotline, 507, 1147
Auto theft
  statistics, 1222
Automobiles. *See* cars
Automotive Consumer Action Program, 507
Avalanche, 1178
Aviation, 1221

B

BACT/LAER Clearinghouse, 1171
Ballooning
  history of, 1219
Banking, 551, 1135, 1148
  regulation, 1136
Banks
  community development, 1085
Battlefield preservation
  financial assistance, 1073
Battlefields
  location of, 1216
Bell, Alexander Graham, 1217, 1220
Bell's Palsy, 1203
Better Business Bureau Auto Line, 507
Better Chance, 866
Bid protests, 484
Bilingual education
  grants, 1094
Bilingual Education Clearinghouse, 1163

Bipolar disorder, 1203
Birth control, 1193
Birth marks, 1191
Black Student Fund, 864
Blindness, 1197
Blood diseases, 1199
Blood donations, 1192
Blood supply, 1191
Blood transfusions, 1192
Boating
  accidents, 1213
  navigational aids, 1213
  safety, 1172
  hotline, 1172
Boating Safety Hotline, 1213
Bone diseases, 1191
Bonsai, 1132, 1150
Books
  children, 1213
  rare, 1219
Boot camp programs, 1106
Botanic Garden, 1133
Botanic Garden, U.S., 1154
Botany, 1132, 1150
Branch of Geographic Names, 1216
Breakfast programs, 535
Breast Cancer Legal Project, 547
Breast cancer, 533, 534, 1192
Breast implants, 1197
Breastfeeding, 1201
Bridges
  replacement and rehabilitation, 1103
Broadcasting, 1168, 1218
Brownfields Economic Redevelopment Initiative, 1096
Buildings
  historic, 1218
Bureau of Alcohol, Tobacco, and Firearms, 1157
Bureau of Economic Analysis, 1138, 1223
Bureau of Health Professions, 754
Bureau of Indian Affairs, 1216, 764
Bureau of Justice Assistance Clearinghouse, 1159
Bureau of Justice Statistics, 1159, 1225
Bureau of Labor Statistics, 1141, 1225
Bureau of Land Management, 1180
Bureau of Primary Health Care, 1198
Bureau of the Census, 1222
Burglary
  statistics, 1222
Business
  assistance, 1136, 1145
  Eastern European countries, 1136
  environmental assistance, 1183
  exporting, 1139
  financial assistance, 1069
  freelance consultants, 495
  job training grants, 183
  marketing grants, 160
  networking, 168
  statistics, 1136

D

H_____

O____

Occupational Safety and Health Administration, 1140
Occupational safety, 1204
Oceanography, 1176, 1181
Oceans, 1181, 1183
Office for Victims of Crime Resource Center, 1160
Office of Business Liaison, 1136
Office of Community Planning and Development, 718
Office of Consumer Affairs, 510
Office of Educational Research and Improvement, 1223
Office of Federal Procurement Policy
  procurement, 498
Office of Indian Education Programs, 764
Office of Maritime Labor and Training, 765
Office of Migrant Education, 907
Office of Minority Health Resource Center, 1203
Office of Personnel Management, 742
  procurement, 498
Office of Postsecondary Education, 748
Office of Special Education and Rehabilitation Services, 749
Offices of Small and Disadvantaged Business Utilization, 495, 496
Ohio
  apprentice programs, 876
  arts agency, 574
  business assistance, 319
  business financing, 320
  corporation division, 135
  dislocated worker contacts, 880
  enterprise communities, 1082
  enterprise zone programs, 1122
  exports, 322
  federal procurement assistance, 491
  forestry commission, 1066
  Foundation Center collections, 146
  grants, 162
  historic preservation, 1076
  historic renovation, 708
  humanities council, 591
  Independent Living program, 905
  inventor's resources, 635
  Job Corps, 918
  job training programs, 1023
  JTPA contacts, 888
  migrant programs, 897
  nonprofit registration, 123
  school-to-work grantees, 893
  Small Business Development Centers, 425
  state housing programs, 686
  state procurement office, 502
  student aid, 785
  TAA-NAFTA contacts, 884
  tax incentives, 321
  urban supplemental zones, 1081
  venture capital clubs, 452
  venture capital, 474

  women and minorities, 322
  Youthbuild sites, 901
Oil spills, 1179
Oklahoma
  apprentice programs, 876
  arts agency, 574
  business assistance, 323
  business financing, 323
  corporation division, 135
  dislocated worker contacts, 880
  enterprise communities, 1082
  enterprise zone programs, 1122
  exports, 325
  federal procurement assistance, 491
  forestry commission, 1066
  Foundation Center collections, 147
  grants, 167
  historic preservation, 1076
  historic renovation, 708
  humanities council, 592
  Independent Living program, 905
  inventor's resources, 636
  Job Corps, 918
  job training programs, 1027
  JTPA contacts, 888
  migrant programs, 897
  nonprofit registration, 123
  school-to-work grantees, 893
  Small Business Development Centers, 428
  state housing programs, 686
  state procurement office, 502
  student aid, 786
  TAA-NAFTA contacts, 884
  tax incentives, 324
  venture capital clubs, 453
  venture capital, 475
  women and minorities, 326
  Youthbuild sites, 901
One-Stop Career Centers, 1095
Online Women's Business Center, 927
Opera, 1168, 1218
Oregon
  apprentice programs, 876
  arts agency, 574
  business assistance, 327
  business financing, 327
  corporation division, 135
  dislocated worker contacts, 880
  enterprise communities, 1082
  enterprise zone programs, 1122
  exports, 330
  federal procurement assistance, 491
  forestry commission, 1066
  Foundation Center collections, 147
  historic preservation, 1077
  historic renovation, 708
  humanities council, 592
  Independent Living program, 905
  inventor's resources, 637
  Job Corps, 918

Q____

R____

T_____

Matthew Lesko, Information USA, Inc., 12081 Nebel St., Rockville, MD 20852 • 1-800-955-7693 • www.lesko.com